NOT

IF

I

SAVE

YOU

FIRST

ALLY CARTER

NOT
IF
I
SAVE
YOU
FIRST

Scholastic Inc.

ISBN 978-1-338-28123-1

10 9 8 7 6 5 4 3 2 1   18 19 20 21 22

Printed in the U.S.A.   40
First printing, 2018

The text type was set in Perpetua.
Book design by Yaffa Jaskoll

**FOR MADELEINE ELISE BROCK,
THE ORIGINAL MAD DOG**

CHAPTER 1

SIX YEARS AGO

Dear Maddie,

    *There's a party at my house tomorrow night. Mom said
I can invite a friend if I want to.*

    So do you want to come?

    ____YES

    ____NO

    ____MAYBE

                              ——Logan

Madeleine Rose Manchester had absolutely no intention of invading the White House. But she knew seven different ways she could do it if she'd wanted to.

After all, Logan had lived there less than a year, and already he and Maddie had found four tunnels, two pseudo-secret passageways, and a cabinet near the kitchen that smelled faintly of cheese and only partially blocked an old service elevator that really wasn't as boarded up as everybody thought.

"Charlie?" Maddie asked the big man in the passenger seat of the dark SUV. He turned to look at where she sat, her seat belt snuggly around her, even though everyone knew silk wrinkled and Maddie had never had a silk dress before.

She'd already complained about it, but Charlie had told her that it was either wear a seat belt or walk, and her black leather shoes were new and they'd already started to pinch her feet, and Logan had told her there might be dancing later.

Maddie dearly, dearly hoped there would be dancing . . .

"Whatcha need, Mad?" Charlie asked while Walter kept driving.

"Did you know there's a place under the stairs in the East Wing that's full of spiders that died during the Nixon administration? Do you think that's true? I don't think that's true," she said without really waiting for Charlie to answer.

"I could ask Dad," Maddie went on. "But he didn't work here then. At least I don't *think* he worked here then. I mean, I know he's old. Like, really, really old. But is he that old?"

Charlie laughed, but Maddie wasn't exactly sure what was so funny. "I'm not sure, Mad, but you should say it exactly like that when you ask him."

This sounded like a very good idea to Maddie. "Thank you, Charlie. I'll do that." She thought for a moment, then went on.

"Did you know it's possible to crawl all the way from Logan's dad's office to the press room using the air ducts?"

"No." Charlie shook his head. "It's not."

"Sure it is," Maddie told him. "Logan bet me five dollars that I couldn't do it, so I did it, and then he gave me five ones instead of one five because Lincoln is his favorite."

"You can reach the Oval Office via the air ducts?" Charlie asked, spinning to look at her.

"Yes. But I ruined my favorite pink leggings."

"Then you should *definitely* tell your dad that."

"He doesn't care about my leggings," Maddie said, and Charlie shook his head.

"Not about that. About . . . Never mind, Mad. I'll tell him."

When they finally reached a pair of tall iron gates Maddie couldn't help but swing her legs and nervously kick at the back of Charlie's seat, but Charlie just rolled down his window and told the man with the clipboard, "We have a VIP guest for Rascal."

The guard looked in the back seat and smiled when he saw Maddie. Through the tinted windows she could see other guards circling the vehicle. Dogs sniffed around the bumpers, but the guard kept his gaze trained on her.

"Looks like a high-risk entrant to me, boys. I don't know if we should let her in."

"Hey, Felix," Maddie said, leaning forward. "Did you know you can fit two kids and three kittens in the little compartment underneath Logan's dad's desk? If the kittens are tame, that is. I wouldn't want to try it with mean kittens."

"Neither would I," Felix said, just as one of the men outside announced, "You're clear!"

Then Felix stepped back and waved them through the gates. "Have fun at the party!"

Logan never had fun at parties. In his experience, they very rarely meant pizza and bounce houses and ice cream. Not anymore. Sure, there was usually cake. But they were always fancy cakes that were tiny, and Logan's mom usually gave him *The Look* if he ate more than four. And ever since the time he asked the prime minister of Canada if she was going to eat *her* cake he hadn't been allowed to sit at the table with his parents.

Which, in Logan's opinion, was just as well.

"Is Maddie here yet?" he asked his mother.

"I don't know. Is she under the bed?" Logan's mom grinned and glanced through the bathroom door at the giant canopy bed upon which Logan lay.

"No. We don't fit."

"I am not going to ask how you know that," his mother said, then went back to fixing her makeup.

When the phone rang, she reached for it, and Logan heard her talking.

"Yes? Excellent. Send her up."

"Is Maddie—"

"She's on her way up," his mother told him, and Logan bounded off the bed, ran out into the hallway, then flew down the big stairs of the residence.

The farther he got from his mother, the more chaotic everything became. There were people with huge bunches of flowers, and staffers running up and down the stairs in high heels.

But all Logan really saw was Maddie.

"Mad Dog!" Logan screamed from the top of the stairs, racing to join her on the landing below. "You look . . ."

"Is my dress too wrinkled?" Maddie blurted as if the answer really, really mattered.

He shook his head. "It's . . . No. I don't think so. It's . . ."

But Logan trailed off as he followed Maddie's gaze through the bulletproof glass. The chaos of the building all but disappeared as, outside, a helicopter landed on the lawn. A group of men and women were running toward the house, crouching low beneath the helicopter's spinning blades.

Only the last two men off the chopper walked upright, laughing and talking as they strolled toward the doors.

Maddie turned to Logan. "Dad's home."

Maddie couldn't be sure if she was talking about Logan's father or her own. The statement was true in either case. But there was no denying that, as the two dads came into the house, the place went a little more—and a little less—crazy.

There was an energy that always surrounded Logan's father.

5

Some people stopped. Some people stared. But there was another group of people who seemed to constantly swirl and swarm around him, like a hive of bees caught inside a series of very tiny tornadoes, spinning in his orbit while everyone else hurried to get out of the way.

Everyone except Logan's mom. She didn't spin or rush or stare as she walked toward her husband, her red dress flowing behind her as she moved down the stairs.

"You're late," she said.

"Mr. President," one of his assistants cut in. "The speaker is waiting for you."

"He can wait until the president has kissed his wife and hugged his son and . . . changed into something decent," the first lady told the woman. And with that, the tiny tornadoes moved on to another part of the White House.

"Hello, darling," Logan's dad told the first lady as he leaned down to kiss her. When he pulled away she made a face and said, "You smell." Then she shifted her gaze onto Maddie. "What are we going to do with them, Mad?"

Maddie could only shake her head. "Boys always smell," she said truthfully.

"You get used to it, sweetheart," Logan's mom told her.

But Logan's dad didn't seem to mind. He just reached for his son and said, "Hey, kiddo." Then he turned to Maddie. "Kiddette."

Maddie dropped into a curtsy. "It's a pleasure to see you again, Logan's dad."

"And you, Manchester's daughter." The president bowed at the waist. "You are a far lovelier sight than your father, I can assure you."

"Thank you. My dress wasn't wrinkled when I put it on, you should know. The wrinkles are entirely Charlie's fault."

"I'll have a word with Charlie," the president said as Maddie's dad tried to pull her into a hug.

"Come here, Mad."

She pulled away and looked at the first lady. "You're right. They do stink."

"This is what I get for keeping the president safe?" Maddie's father asked.

"From treasonous deer? It's hard work, I'm sure." The first lady turned to her husband. "Now do I need to remind the pair of you that the Russian prime minister and his entire entourage, your entire cabinet, and all seven viewers of C-SPAN are expecting our very first state dinner to commence in forty-five minutes?"

Logan's dad cut a look at Maddie's. "Save me from her, Manchester."

But Maddie's father just shook his head. "Sorry, Mr. President. This time you're on your own."

It wasn't until the first lady dragged the president upstairs that Maddie felt Logan stir beside her. He'd been perfectly quiet—perfectly still—as if content to be a mere fly on the wall in the president's presence.

Then her father asked, "How you doing, Rascal?" and Logan's eyes got bigger.

"Did my dad really kill a deer?"

"No." Maddie's father crouched against the windowsill, bringing himself down closer to Logan's level. "Your father and a senator from Kentucky and I sat in a tree in the woods for seven hours, hoping to kill a deer."

"And you didn't see one?" Logan asked.

"No." Maddie's dad shook his head slowly. "We saw one."

Logan's eyes were wide. "And my dad didn't shoot it?"

"No." Maddie's dad sounded like he was carefully considering the answer. "Your dad was more interested in getting a vote out of the senator from Kentucky."

Logan still looked confused. "You had a gun. Why didn't you shoot it?"

Maddie's father seemed to think this was an excellent question. He leaned a little lower. "Because when I shoot, it isn't for fun."

"It's because you have to," Logan said.

Maddie's father nodded. "And what's more important than shooting, Rascal?"

Logan only had to think about the answer for a moment. "Making sure you don't have to?"

Maddie's dad tousled Logan's hair. "Good job."

When Maddie's father tried to pull her into another hug, Maddie pushed away even though her dress was already wrinkled. "You really do smell, Dad."

"Okay, Mad Dog. I give up. I'll go shower." He started down the stairs. "Now what are you two going to do in the next forty-one minutes?"

Maddie and Logan looked at each other and gave almost identical shrugs.

"Fine," her dad said. "Don't tell me. Just stay in the house and stay out of the way. It's kind of crazy around here."

He was almost out of sight before they said in unison, "We noticed."

Maddie was used to being pseudo invisible, but Logan had been in the spotlight so often in the past year or two that she could tell it was something of a new, but not entirely unwelcome, feeling as they walked through the chaos of the White House.

Doors slammed and phones rang, but no one noticed the first son and his friend, even when Logan said "In here" and punched numbers into a keypad beside a door that Maddie had never noticed before. When the door sprang open, he pulled Maddie into a hallway that was totally and completely silent.

"That's better," he said, then smiled at her.

"Are we supposed to be in here?"

Logan shrugged. "Probably not. But if they really wanted to keep us out, they shouldn't have let me see them punch in the code that one time."

Maddie thought he made a very excellent point. Everyone knew that Logan was really good at remembering things. All the things. Like phone numbers and access numbers and where the White House stored its chocolate.

It had been Maddie's experience that the White House maintained a supply of excellent chocolate. And that's what Maddie was thinking about when they found themselves in a long, empty hallway that ran from the loading docks to the kitchen. They walked in silence for a long time, until they reached a place where the hall branched, and Maddie knew they should turn around. Her dad and Logan's parents were going to be looking for them soon.

She was just about to drag him back to the crowds and the people and the noise when three men came rushing down the corridor, pushing a large rolling cart, almost oblivious to the two ten-year-olds who stood in their way.

Logan said, "Excuse me," because he was a good kid that way.

But Maddie's dad's job didn't depend on her being nice to strangers, so she said "How rude!" as they passed.

For a moment, she and Logan stood together in the corridor, a little bit stunned. Then something about the men and their location within the White House made her stop. Wonder. "Are they supposed to be here?" she asked.

Logan grimaced. "Russian security. The Russian delegation said they would only eat their own food prepared by their own chefs. They had to bring it in and keep it under armed guard and everything."

Maddie made a face. "I wouldn't like that. Eating cold food just because someone might want to kill me."

She was just starting to say something else when, suddenly, Logan reached into his pocket and blurted "Here!" as he thrust a small blue box toward her.

"What is it?" Maddie asked.

"A gift," Logan said. "For you."

"You got me a gift? Why?"

Logan looked like he wanted to roll his eyes, but he didn't. "Because you're my friend."

"Did you get something for all your friends?" she asked him.

Even in the too-bright fluorescent glare of the hallway, a shadow seemed to cross over Logan's face.

"You're my only friend," he said, and Maddie didn't ask any more questions.

She reached for the package slowly. Reverently. Then she pulled on the little white bow and opened the box. A moment later she was looking down at a piece of gold.

"It's so shiny," she said.

"It's a bracelet. Do you like it?"

"I love it."

Logan helped her put it on, and Maddie turned her wrist, letting the light reflect off the delicate chain and dangling charms.

"It's a little big," he told her. "But I wanted you to be able to wear it when you get older."

"I'll never take it off," Maddie said, and in that moment she had never meant anything more.

A silence stretched between them, and Logan had to look away, like staring at Maddie and her shiny gold bracelet was like staring at the sun. He blinked and said, "Well, I suppose we should get—"

"What are you two doing down here?" The first lady's voice echoed down the tile hall, cutting Logan off.

"We're staying out of the way," Maddie announced as she spun. She was very proud of that fact and thought it was high time some grown-up bragged about them for their discretion.

"That's a good plan," Logan's mother told her. "It's a zoo out there."

"Mom, do Maddie and I have to go? Couldn't we just watch TV in the residence or something?"

When the first lady looked at Logan her eyes were a little sad, like part of her wished that she could give him a normal night in a normal house. But Logan was never going to be normal ever again, and she couldn't bring herself to lie about it.

"You could watch TV," the first lady told him. "But I'm afraid tonight is very important for your father. Our relations with Russia are . . . strained. And he thinks that if you and I go, it might be more of a family thing than a political thing. Does that make sense?"

Logan nodded grimly. "Yeah. It does." Then he looked at his mother as if he were seeing her for the first time. "Why are you down here? Were you looking for us?"

"No." She smoothed the part of his hair that never did lie flat. "The kitchen called. There's some sort of problem, though why they need me I'll never know. I like your bracelet, Maddie."

Maddie hid her blush.

"I like your dress."

"Me too. Mainly because it does *this*." When the first lady started to spin, the wisps of red fabric floated around her like a cloud.

"It's a twirling dress!" Maddie wanted to clap.

"I know!" the first lady sounded like a ten-year-old herself.

Logan looked like he would never, ever understand girls, but he didn't bother to say so.

"Well, I'd better go see what they want so we can get this show on the road. You two should head that way. We'll be starting soon."

"Yes, ma'am," Maddie said as the first lady walked away, leaving Maddie and Logan alone.

They'd been alone about a thousand times over the past year, but when Maddie moved, her bracelet jingled and it felt like a different kind of *alone* than they had ever been before.

"So . . ." Logan said, looking at her.

"So . . ." Maddie said back, because what else could she do?

He held his arm out. "Shall we, my lady?"

Maddie dropped into a crooked curtsy, then took his arm. "Why yes, sir."

They didn't talk. They didn't laugh. They just walked toward the fanciest party in the country, arm in arm, like they weren't ten years old at all.

This time, they heard the three men before they saw them. The big cart made a squeaky, rattling noise as it rolled over the tile floor, and Maddie and Logan knew to move out of the way.

Russians, it seemed, liked to take their half out of the middle, so she and Logan pressed against the wall, and Maddie felt the cool tile through the mesh fabric on the back of her dress.

The men were shouting loud and fast in Russian, and Maddie didn't understand a word. She just pressed close to Logan for reasons she didn't know or understand.

Two of the Russians seemed really young, probably in their twenties. They had short dark hair and expensive suits with ugly ties. One of them pointed to the doors that seemed a mile away and Maddie caught the flash of a tattoo on his wrist—a weird two-headed bird being eaten by a wolf.

Her first thought was that she couldn't imagine why anyone would want something that ugly on their skin for forever.

Her second thought was that the muscles in Logan's arm had gone suddenly tight. Her hand hurt as he bent his arm, squeezing her fingers in the bend of his elbow. But Logan didn't even notice.

When the men passed, Maddie felt a rush of air, like a breeze in their wake. But one of the men—the one with the tattoo—paused for just a moment. He looked right at Logan, recognizing him. Considering something. When the other men shouted he kept his eyes trained on Logan.

Then he said something in Russian.

And winked.

But it wasn't playful. It wasn't teasing. And right then Maddie's head knew what her gut had suspected since she first saw their ugly ties: These men weren't Russian secret service. Maddie knew it in her bones, in her blood.

So who were they?

And why were they there?

Suddenly, Maddie's throat was tight; her heart was pounding.

"Logan . . ." she started, but Maddie trailed off when she followed Logan's gaze.

The Russians were ten feet away and moving fast toward the doors to the loading dock, pushing the heavy cart that seemed heavier than when they'd pushed it in.

If they were bringing in their delegation's meals, wouldn't the cart be lighter on the way out? Maddie wondered.

And then she saw it: the piece of gauzy red fabric that protruded from beneath the container's door, floating on the breeze.

"Logan?" The word was practically a gasp.

Maddie felt him moving, digging in his pocket as Maddie pulled away. She was starting to run toward them, to chase and follow . . .

And bite.

Maddie was an excellent biter.

But Logan was grabbing her arm with one hand. In the other, he held the tiny button that he had to keep on him at all times.

He pushed it, and for a second nothing happened. Then Maddie heard her father's voice.

"There you are!" Her dad was smiling, laughing. He was in his dark tux and his hair was still damp from his shower, and he was so handsome and tall and strong. And happy. Her father was happy.

Then he stopped and brought one hand to his earpiece and everything changed.

"What is it?" he asked Logan, who was trembling.

They could still hear the rattling of the cart's wheels as the Russians broke into a run.

"My mom. They have—"

Sirens were starting to blare and Maddie's dad was already breaking away and drawing his weapon. Maddie had seen his gun a million times, but she'd never seen it like that before—like it was an extension of him, a far colder and deadlier limb.

"You two. Hide!" her dad yelled as he started to run.

And the Russians started to fire.

CHAPTER 2

Maddie knew what her father's job was. In fact, it had been her grandfather's job even before that. Turns out, she came from a long line of people who were made to run *toward* the shots—to step in front of the bullets.

She'd just never really understood why.

But then Logan's mom was in a food cart and her dad was ducking behind a tall stack of water bottles wrapped in plastic, shooting the gun she'd never seen him fire.

It all happened in a second.

And it seemed to take a year.

"Daddy!" Maddie screamed even though she knew not to distract him, to get in the way.

"Maddie!" She felt Logan's hand on her arm. She heard her name screaming from his lips. But her father was still running *toward* the gunmen, and something about that seemed so fundamentally wrong that, for a moment, she could only stand there. Waiting.

All through the White House, sirens screamed. Logan's panic button had a GPS tracker, so the rest of the Secret Service would be there soon, Maddie knew. They were probably already blocking the exits and barricading the gates.

The president would be halfway to his underground bunker by now. But Maddie was still standing in that corridor, watching her father run. Fire. Fall.

One of the Russians was down. Maddie could see him sprawled at the end of the hallway.

Blood streaked across the floor, and Maddie couldn't help herself.

"Daddy!" she yelled again. She wanted to run to him, but Logan's grip on her arm was too tight.

Her new charm bracelet bit into her wrist as Logan pulled her into a doorway that offered a little cover, but not much. She should have been running, dragging the first son in the opposite direction—toward safety. But Maddie couldn't take her gaze off her father.

He was up again, limping forward and firing more. At the end of the corridor, a door opened. Bright light flooded the hall and there was shouting and running, more agents filing in from that direction.

Behind her, Maddie heard the heavy tread of running feet. The cavalry was coming. The Russians were surrounded.

But an animal is never more dangerous than when it's trapped. One lone Russian remained. For a moment, he was just a dark shape silhouetted against the glare of the bright lights. He stood perfectly still as he raised his gun and leveled it at Maddie's father.

Then the man smiled and, as if pulled by a magnet, the gun moved, to point directly at where Maddie and Logan huddled together.

The man shouted something in Russian—the words echoing off the hard floor and tile-covered walls. Maddie didn't know what he'd said, but she knew what he meant:

That it wasn't over.

That his cause was just.

That, someday, all of civilization was going to know—and fear—his name.

For a second, the world stood still, and then he pulled the trigger just as Maddie's father jumped between the man and Logan.

And fired.

At first the Russian stood, mouth gaping, as if he couldn't quite believe that someone would have the nerve to get in his way. To fire back. To go against whatever master plan had brought him to that place and time.

But then he looked down at his chest, at the place where blood was starting to ooze from beneath his ugly tie, and he dropped to his knees. Then to the floor.

He didn't move again.

"Rascal!" someone shouted, and Maddie could feel the

world change as the rest of the Secret Service swarmed around them.

"The first lady!"

Maddie's father's voice sounded faint, like he was half asleep, and yet he was still dragging himself toward the box. Blood trailed behind him, and Maddie couldn't be held back any longer.

She pulled away from Logan just in time to hear Charlie yell, "Maddie, you and Rascal stay right there!"

The agents were everywhere, a virtual wall between Maddie and Logan and the men who lay, not moving, on the floor, and Maddie knew Charlie wasn't keeping the two of them from danger. He was trying to keep them from the blood and the death and the things no ten-year-old should ever see, but Maddie was already crawling through the agents' legs, pushing toward the place where her father lay, too still on the floor.

There was so much blood.

She was going to ruin her dress.

But Maddie didn't care, so she crawled faster. When one of the agents gripped her around the waist and tried to pull her back, she kicked harder.

Two of the agents were pulling the first lady from the big steel box. She was limp and deathly pale, and everything was wrong.

Everything was so, so wrong, and Maddie had to fix it.

"Let me go!" she snapped at the men and women around her. "Let me—"

"Mad Dog?" Logan's voice was behind her, too soft and too faint—and that was why she turned.

"I got something on my tux," he said, looking down at the red spot that was on his white shirt and spreading quickly. "I promised I wouldn't get dirty," he said, then fell hard to the floor.

CHAPTER 3

FROM THE DESK OF MADELEINE
ROSE MANCHESTER

Dear Logan,

    This is called a letter. It's like an email but written on paper and sent through the regular mail (like bills). Your mom gave me this paper. Isn't it pretty? It's called stationery, and she said that I should use it to write to you since my dad says we have to leave.

    He doesn't ever talk about why we have to leave. But we're going just the same. Maybe it's because ever since he got out of the hospital our phone keeps ringing. I don't think he likes being a celebrity or whatever. The Man Who Saved the First Lady!

    Now he just wants to be the Man Who Doesn't Have a Telephone because we're not going to have one. Or a cell phone. Or Internet. Dad says he thinks it's going to be good for me.

    I think it's going to be lonely.

But you can write me back, he says! We can write all
the time.

    So . . . will you write me back?

Your (best) friend,
Maddie

ALASKA

SIX YEARS LATER

Turns out, the key to throwing a hatchet isn't in the wrist, like everyone always says. Sure, it's *a little bit* in the wrist. But it's also in the shoulders. And the hips. But, most of all, it's in the head, Madeleine Rose Manchester thought as she dug her second-favorite hatchet from the base of the big tree nearest to their cabin.

She no longer practiced with her favorite hatchet. No. The grip on that one hadn't been good for throwing ever since she'd bedazzled the handle last winter.

Her dad might have been angry at her if he had even noticed that she'd done it. Which he hadn't. For a man whose very survival had once depended upon noticing everything, he'd developed a nasty habit of not noticing anything in the past six years.

Or maybe, Maddie thought, he just no longer noticed her.

She dug the hatchet from the tree and moved back ten paces.

Twenty.

Thirty.

She took a deep breath, filling her lungs with cool, damp air. The shadows were long and the forest was still and Maddie knew that winter was coming fast.

She had wood to haul.

A chain saw to sharpen.

Someone needed to crawl on the roof and replace a couple of shingles, then reposition the solar panels that had been blown around by that big storm last week.

She also had a mountain of schoolwork she'd have to send with her father the next time he took the plane to Juneau.

Maybe she could get him to bring her thirty or forty more library books. They hadn't gotten much snow for the past year or two, but the sun was going to go behind a cloud soon, and it wouldn't come out again until Easter. When that happened, Maddie wanted to be ready.

Maddie was always ready.

She took a few more steps back, flipped the hatchet in her hand, drew back her arm.

And threw.

When the hatchet hit the tree, its blade sunk so deep into the wood that most girls couldn't have even pulled it free. But Maddie was never going to be most girls, she remembered as she jerked the hatchet from the tree and thought about maybe trying it from farther away. Maybe with her left hand.

But that was when she heard it—a hum in the distance, a mechanical whirling sound that broke through the stillness. Maddie turned and watched as the small red dot in the big blue sky grew larger and larger.

When the dot touched down in the middle of the lake and floated toward the cabin, Maddie couldn't help but remember another day. Another landing.

Another world.

"Dad's home," she said, but there was nothing but the wilderness to hear her.

"Mad Dog!" Michael Manchester shouted from the plane as soon as he killed the engine.

He was still a big man. Still strong. Even leaner somehow. In DC, Maddie's father had spent hours boxing and running and lifting weights. He'd taught courses on self-defense and used to spar with the president himself, who had once been an Olympic athlete.

But Maddie watched the man who leaped to the dock from the plane that sat on top of the water, bobbing on the rippling waves. He didn't move like that man used to move.

It could have had something to do with her father's bad leg. Many would have credited the shoulder injury or the three surgeries that had followed it.

But Maddie knew it was Alaska that had changed her father. In Maddie's not-so-uneducated opinion, Alaska could change anyone.

"Hey, kiddo! Did it rain while I was gone?"

"Yes, it rained," she told him. "It always rains."

"Good." He put an arm around her shoulder and pulled her tight against him. "I stink."

"I can tell." Maddie tried to pull away, but her father laughed and pulled her tighter.

"If the barrels are full, I'll heat some water and take a bath. How are you, kiddo?"

When they reached the porch of the small cabin, they both paused and pulled off their boots. It was a luxury, being able to do this outside. Soon it would be too cold, and Maddie wanted to keep the mud out of the house for as long as possible.

Even though *house* wasn't really the right word.

She followed her father into a room that held a wood-burning stove and a rickety table with four chairs. There was a shower rod over an open doorway that led to the kitchen, heavy curtains that could make the room private whenever one of them wanted to pull the tub in from the back porch and heat some water on the stove.

In DC, Maddie's bathroom had been entirely hers, with a pink shower curtain and towels so soft that Maddie would never, ever use them for something like drying her hands. Here, she had a tub and a curtain and, if she was lucky, four barrels full of rain

26

and not ice. It was like that other bathroom—that other life—was just a dream.

The main room held a recliner and a couch and three electric lights that worked as long as the sun was shining in summer or the wind was blowing in winter. And Maddie was grateful for the light. Light meant reading. It used to mean writing. But that was a long time ago. Back when Maddie had someone to write to. But Maddie didn't let herself think about that.

"So how are you, kiddo?" her father asked again. He was unloading his backpack, pulling out a few of the supplies he'd promised to bring back.

"Fine," she said.

It took a moment, but her father laughed.

"What is it?" she asked, and he shook his head.

"Nothing. It's just . . . I guess it finally happened," he said.

"What?"

When her father looked at her again, she couldn't tell if he was happy or sad. "You ran out of words." He started unloading library books, stacking them on their only table. "I knew you'd use them all up eventually, as fast as you went through them when you were a kid."

Maddie didn't know why exactly, but something in that sentiment stung. "I'm still a kid."

"What was that, sweetheart?" he asked, turning to her.

Maddie shook her head. "Nothing."

He looked like a man who knew better than to argue.

He pulled a half dozen newspapers from his backpack and those landed on top of the pile of books. On the cover of one, she saw a headline about the president, some trip he was taking overseas. She wondered briefly if her father was jealous of the men and women who'd be going with him. But, no; if her father had wanted that life, he could have had it.

Maddie was the only one who'd never been given a choice.

In the beginning, she used to ask her father why they'd left DC, when they'd return. At first the answers didn't make any sense. (For example, Maddie seriously doubted that they had to leave because Miss America had fallen in love with her father and wasn't going to rest until she became Maddie's stepmother.)

But then the answers stopped being crazy and started not coming at all, so Maddie didn't bother asking anymore. This was their home. This was their life. And any life that came before was nothing more than a very elaborate dream.

"Do you have any letters for me to take on my next run?" he asked. It was like he could read her mind sometimes, and when that happened Maddie was glad she lived in a small house in a huge forest. If the bears could read her mind, at least they had to keep their thoughts to themselves.

"Do you *bring* me any letters?" she asked.

Her father shook his head.

"Then that's your answer."

CHAPTER 4

Dear Logan,

   Dad said we'd have a house.

   Dad LIED.

   It's a cabin, he says, but it's more like a shack. I have
my own room, though. Well, technically, I have a little loft
that he built in the main room. It's just a mattress sitting on
a platform and a little lamp. But there's a curtain I can
draw if I want privacy, and I have it to myself. At least I do
when I'm not sharing it with the local wildlife. (Some people
will tell you that squirrels are cute and cuddly. They are
not. You can consider yourself warned!)

   I'm sorry I can't reply to anything you've said in your
letters, but they haven't gotten here yet. They're probably in
the mail.

   I really hope they're in the mail.

                                          Maddie

ALEXANDRIA, VIRGINIA

Logan couldn't hear the music. It simply pounded, beating in his skull until he wanted to scream. And maybe he would. It's not like anyone would hear it. He highly doubted anyone would care.

With so many bodies pressed so close he was almost anonymous here. Almost. But not quite.

He was a little taller than average, his hair a little darker. Only 2 percent of the population had green eyes. But Logan's most distinguishing feature was his shadow.

As he pushed through the crowd of bodies on the dance floor he could feel the big man following in his wake. And a little part of Logan wanted to crawl in some hole and hide. At least until the election was over and America had a new president. Maybe he or she would even have a screwup son, if Logan was lucky. But Logan hadn't been lucky in a really long time.

The noise level dropped a decibel or two when he pushed out of the living room and down a hall that led to the kitchen, where the game was already underway.

"Well, if it isn't the first son and his shadow!" Logan's least favorite person said two seconds after he walked through the swinging door.

The light was a little bit brighter in here, the music a little bit softer. For once, Logan could actually hear himself think.

"You should fold, Dempsey," he said.

"What?" Dempsey asked.

Logan looked down at the table covered with brightly colored chips and overturned cards.

"You should fold," he said again. "You know, quit while you're ahead."

Dempsey looked like he wanted to get out of his chair and fold Logan into a new shape, and he might have tried if not for Logan's shadow.

"What do you know about it?"

Logan didn't miss a beat. "I know you need a queen to make your straight, which means you've got an eight percent chance under the best of circumstances, which this isn't, considering Peterson there is holding one already."

Now Dempsey really did get up. "You cheating or something?"

"No." Logan shook his head. "I'm paying attention."

Logan always paid attention. To everything. Sometimes two inches of bright red fabric was all that stood between life and death, after all. Once you came to grips with that, cards were easy.

The whole table—the whole game—made sense to Logan with one glance. For a second, he wanted to join his friends. And he would have, if he hadn't noticed long ago that they weren't really his friends at all.

The music got louder for one brief moment as the door behind him opened and closed. Logan didn't turn around, though. Charlie had his back. So Logan wasn't expecting it when an arm slid around his neck and a soft cheek pressed against his.

"Logan!" the girl practically screamed. She slurred her words slightly and felt unsteady on her feet as she pulled Logan even closer. Then her phone was in her free hand and she was scream-ing, "Let's take a selfie!"

A bright flash filled the air and Logan's eyes burned while Charlie yelled, "No phones!"

"But my followers!" the girl complained as Charlie ripped the phone from her hands.

"You'll get this back at the end of the night," Charlie told her. He slid the phone into his pocket and glanced at Logan as he ques-tioned the girl, "How did you get this in here, anyway? We've got agents at the gate. They should have taken your phone."

The girl looked confused. "They did take my phone. That's my backup phone."

Charlie wanted to groan, Logan could tell. "I've got to go talk to someone," Charlie yelled over the still-pulsing music. He stepped toward the door but stopped himself.

"Something wrong?" Logan asked as if he didn't already know exactly what Charlie was thinking. "You can leave me alone for five minutes, you know."

"That's what you said in Paris."

"I apologized for Paris," Logan reminded him. "And Berlin. But I refuse to apologize for London because those scones I brought you were delicious."

"*Rascal.*" Charlie sounded like a man who couldn't decide whether to laugh or cry or just shake the boy he was paid to protect.

"What? Are you afraid I'm going to sneak out and go to a wild party? Charlie, I'm *at* a wild party. Besides, I need to go to the bathroom. Or are you going to follow me in there, too?"

"It was discussed after Buenos Aires."

At this, Logan shook his head. "Yeah. Well. We all have things we regret about Buenos Aires."

Logan eased closer to the bathroom, and Charlie eased toward the door.

"Charlie, go! Yell at the new guys."

"You've got your panic button?" Now Charlie sounded like a little old lady and not a former Navy SEAL.

"Of course," Logan said. It was the one Secret Service rule he never, ever broke. That button had saved his mother's life, and Charlie must have known it because he turned and pushed his way back through the crowded house.

He was gone before Logan did, in fact, go to the bathroom, where he removed two items from his pocket.

One was a small transmitter with state-of-the-art GPS and a button that, when pushed, could bring forth the hounds of war.

Another was a hot-pink cell phone with a not-too-terrible picture of a pretty girl and the president's son. Logan didn't stop to wonder how long it would take Charlie to realize Logan had picked his pocket. He just posted the picture to her account. The girl had followers to consider, after all.

Then he placed the panic button on the bathroom vanity, right where Charlie wouldn't have to look for it. Just because it was a rule he'd never broken before didn't mean there wasn't a first time for everything.

As he walked to the back door and across the dark, deep lawn, Logan never once looked back.

It was ten minutes before Charlie realized that he was no longer in the bathroom.

"Eight hours. You were gone for eight hours! *What were you thinking?*"

The Oval Office was one of the most intimidating rooms in the world—at least that's what the White House tour guides liked to say. But even though the room was powerful, Logan had figured out long ago that it had nothing on the man.

The president's suitcoat was draped over the back of his chair and his shirtsleeves were rolled up, his red power tie loosened. It was his working-man-stump-speech look—the one that went over well in midwestern mill towns. But in the Oval, it made him look like a man who had immense power at his disposal but would rather tear a person in two with his bare hands than bother calling in the marines.

"*Were* you thinking?" the president yelled again, and Logan forced a shrug.

"It wasn't a big deal."

"I'll tell you when it's a big deal and when it's not. That's my right as long as I'm—"

"President?" Logan guessed.

"Your father," the president finished.

"News flash: You already got reelected," Logan told him. "Unless you want to be Queen of England or something, you've run your last campaign."

"This isn't about my presidency—"

"I think the Secret Service would disagree," Logan cut in, but his father never slowed down.

"—this is about our family!"

Only then did Logan let himself glance at his mother, who muttered, "Joseph." His father spun on her.

"He posted a picture online and then took a walk. For eight hours. No detail. No panic button. Do you know what could have happened to him?"

"Yes, Joseph." Her voice was soft but strong. Her whisper echoed through the room like a roar. *"I know."*

They didn't talk about That Day. Not ever. Not in ages. But it was always there, simmering underneath the surface. In many ways, it was his father's legacy: the thing his two terms in office would be remembered for the most.

He was the president who had almost had his wife snatched out from under his nose.

His was the White House with blood on the floors.

"I'm sorry, sweetheart. I forgot," Logan's father said, but that was a lie. He didn't forget. None of them did. Maybe that's why the president spun on Logan and snapped, "Secret Service protocols exist for a reason. You of all people should know that."

35

"It was a selfie!" Logan couldn't help but shout. "If that were illegal, then every kid in America would be locked up."

"It wasn't just a selfie, and you know it! It was a beacon, transmitting your location to everyone in the world with a cell phone—a location from which you decided to wander off, unprotected. And you aren't just another kid in America. You are the president's son."

"Yeah." Logan bristled. "That's what they tell me."

Something in Logan's tone seemed to break through his father's armor, his rage began to fade into something closer to regret.

"I know you didn't choose this life. I know no teenager in their right mind ever would. But it *is* our life, and when I think about what could have happened . . . We all *know* what could happen!"

"But it didn't happen!"

As soon as the words left Logan's mouth, he knew he was going to lose. Worse, he knew he should.

He was being stupid. He was being careless. He was being selfish and stubborn and almost too cliché for words. But he hadn't been able to help himself. Not in London or Berlin or Buenos Aires. Logan really was his own worst enemy, which was saying something, he knew.

"I'll apologize to Charlie. I won't do it again."

"Oh, I know you won't do it again. But it's too late to apologize to Charlie."

"What do you mean?"

36

"I mean Charlie got hoodwinked by a sixteen-year-old. Again. So Charlie doesn't work here anymore."

"What? Did you transfer him to Treasury or—"

"Charlie has a nasty habit of losing the president's son, so now Charlie's got to find a new job."

"You can't do that!" Logan snapped. But the president smiled.

"I can do anything. I'm not just the president of the United States. I'm *your father*."

"Joseph," the first lady warned.

"Come on, Dad. You've got, what? A year left in office? What are you going to do, lock me up until CNN stops caring about us?"

For a moment, Logan's parents seemed to consider the idea, but then a smile passed between them. Which was worse.

"If the Secret Service can't keep you offline and out of trouble, then we're going to send you someplace where online and in trouble isn't an option."

Logan didn't even try to bite back his laugh. "Yeah, Mr. President. Good luck finding that."

Logan was already to the door, his hand on the knob, when his mother said, "Oh, we've already found it."

CHAPTER 5

Dear Logan,

    We've been here six months already. I can't believe it. Can you believe it? It feels like we just got here. And in other ways, it feels like I've never lived anywhere else. Like my old life was just a dream.

    Were you a dream?

    I told Dad that this has been a most excellent experience, but I'm ready to go back to our real life now.

    He just smiled and said this <u>is</u> our real life. I asked him when we were going back and he didn't answer. Which is an answer all its own, isn't it?

    Sometimes I think he doesn't want to go back. And sometimes I think he can't. We can't.

    I just don't know why.

                               Maddie

• • •

"Come here, kiddo. There's something we need to talk about."

The last time Maddie's dad had said those words she'd found herself on three planes (each progressively smaller than the last) within a week. So, needless to say, she wasn't the good kind of excited as he pulled up a chair at their old, battered table.

Maddie had never really understood why they had four chairs. It's not like they did a lot of entertaining. Not unless you counted the time Maddie had forgotten to lock up her cereal in an airtight container and a bear had tried to break through the cabin's front door. Which Maddie totally did not count. That bear hadn't been invited and would never be welcome again.

So she didn't really trust the look in her Dad's eyes when he glanced at the empty chair that wasn't stacked high with library books.

"Where are you going this time?" she asked because she knew him well. Too well.

It had been just the two of them since Maddie was three and her mom had died. And that was before they'd moved to the middle of nowhere. For six years it had been just the two of them. If Maddie didn't know her father, she didn't know anyone. There were no other options.

"I'm not going anywhere," he said quickly. Guiltily. "Or, well, I'm not going right now."

"Then what is it?" It took a lot to scare Madeleine Rose Manchester. She'd seen her father take a bullet. When she got up to go pee in the middle of the night she usually carried a revolver.

Fear and Maddie went way, way back, but she'd never seen her father look quite like he looked then.

"Nothing's wrong, kiddo. It's just that . . . I'm expecting . . . I mean . . . I heard from DC."

That, at last, stopped Maddie's heart from racing. At that point, Maddie's heart wasn't beating at all.

Maddie thought her father had burned that bridge, salted the earth, gone as far off the edge of the map as possible, and then dropped straight down and landed here, smack dab in the middle of nowhere.

"You're not going back," Maddie blurted because, it turned out, there *was* something worse than moving to a place where your best friends were either fictional or fur-covered. There was knowing your dad might take *another* bullet. "You quit," she reminded him.

"That's right, kiddo. I did quit. And they wouldn't have me anyway, even if I wanted to go back. Remember." He patted the leg that still ached sometimes and pulled aside the collar of his shirt just far enough for her to see his second-biggest scar.

"Yeah." Maddie laughed. But it wasn't funny. "Kind of hard to forget."

"I'm sorry, kiddo. What I'm trying to say is . . . the president and the first lady are sending us a surprise."

For a moment, Maddie couldn't help herself. She thought about the ice-cream sundaes that the White House chef used to make. She remembered one time when the first lady let her try on the shoes she'd worn to the inaugural ball. She could almost smell the new leather of her favorite chair in the White House screening room.

So when her dad got up and walked to the door she wasn't really following him, not consciously. She just couldn't stay behind.

Maddie could never stay behind.

"What's the surprise?"

As soon as they stepped off the porch, Maddie felt it. Or maybe she saw it. Heard it? She couldn't be sure. She just knew that something big was coming. Ripples spread across the water of the lake, and the trees started to toss and sway.

Glacier silt lined the banks of the lake, and it swirled like sand, stinging and blinding. A part of Maddie knew what she was going to see long before the helicopter appeared, hovering over the trees and then dropping softly to the ground.

"What kind of surprise, Dad?" Maddie asked again as his arm went around her, pulling her tight. Maybe she knew the answer. And that's why she pulled back, why she squeezed her eyes shut. It had nothing to do with the wind that swirled around her, full of silt and gravel and leaves.

Maddie knew that as soon as she opened her eyes, she was going to see a ghost.

But it turned out she didn't have to see him to know him. She just had to hear the words, "Hey, Mad Dog."

•   •   •

It's really her.

Logan shook his head for a moment. He couldn't be sure if he'd said the words out loud or not. Probably not. He glanced up at Mr. Manchester, studied his face. Definitely not. Maddie and her father weren't looking at him like he was stupid. They were looking at him like he was different.

And he was.

Some guys hit puberty and turn into football players or wrestlers or big, hairy creatures who look like science-lab experiments or something. Logan had just . . . grown. Everywhere. It felt like his fingers were a foot long. His feet seemed always at risk of bursting out of his shoes. His pants and his shirts, too. He was like the Incredible Hulk except not green and not quite so angry.

Oh, he was definitely angry. But he could also feel it fading a little. Like he was still in the helicopter, looking down on the lake and about a million acres of wilderness and the tiny dot that was his destination. Logan's anger looked smaller from there, like it was a long way off. And now there was only him and Mr. Manchester and a girl he used to know.

"It's you."

This time he for sure said it aloud because Maddie's dad glanced at her, then held out his hand for Logan.

"Good to see you, Rascal."

Mr. Manchester shook his hand like he was a man, but something about it made Logan feel more like a kid than ever. He'd been through probably twelve pairs of sneakers since he'd last seen the man, but in Mr. Manchester's presence Logan felt as if he might be ten until the end of time.

"You, too, sir," Logan said. He watched Maddie listen to the words. She didn't say a thing.

"How are your parents, Logan?" It was the first time Mr. Manchester had ever called him by his first name. It made Logan pull back for a moment, rethink things. Remember that Maddie's dad wasn't the head of the president's detail anymore. Now he was just Logan's dad's friend. And this wasn't supposed to be fun.

"My parents are well, sir. The president's blood pressure was a little high the last time I saw him, but that's to be expected."

"Yes. I imagine it is," Mr. Manchester said, then smiled.

"Is that why they're punishing you?" Maddie asked. "I mean they are punishing you, right? Why else would anyone come here?"

Logan watched her speak. Her voice was the same, but her mouth was different. Why had Logan never noticed her mouth before? Her bottom lip was fuller, but the top lip was shaped like a little bow, and he couldn't decide which lip he liked more. He knew he was going to have to do a lot more looking in order to choose. And it suddenly felt imperative that Logan choose very, very well.

He was aware, faintly, of Mr. Manchester shifting, saying "Maddie" like it was some kind of warning. "Logan's parents just asked if he could come here for a bit," her dad finished.

Logan wondered how much Maddie's dad knew. It was clear Maddie knew nothing. Not about Logan repeatedly slipping his detail or Charlie getting fired. Not about the poker club he'd been busted for running out of the Lincoln Bedroom last February, or how he'd gotten really good at forging his father's signature and had sold ten thousand dollars' worth of stuff on eBay before someone at the State Department figured out what he was doing and shut him down.

Logan had started six different social media accounts in the names of former presidential pets, and three were still operational. But if the sixteen followers of @SocksTheCat were wondering why Socks suddenly had so many . . . well . . . socks (and jackets, and an old copy of *The Call of the Wild*) no one was saying so.

No. Maddie didn't know about any of that. Maddie only knew that they used to be friends, and she looked like maybe that was a decision she might have come to regret.

Logan turned back to Mr. Manchester. "I'm glad to see you looking so well, sir."

Maddie's dad laughed and slapped him on the back. "Rumors of my death have been greatly exaggerated."

Logan smiled, but Maddie's voice was cold. "That's not funny."

And Logan remembered.

Blood. Cold tile and the way the shots were quieter than they should have been, and yet the sound seemed to reverberate forever.

"Mad, it's okay," her dad said, but Logan got the feeling that it wasn't—that it really wasn't okay at all.

"How have you been, Mad Dog?" Logan asked, but Maddie just glared at him.

"Awesome!" she said, but Logan was 98 percent certain she was being facetious. It quickly became 100 percent when Mr. Manchester said *"Mad"* and she spun on him.

"I'd ask if I could go to my room, but I don't have one."

Then she turned and headed toward the house.

But it wasn't a house. Not really. From where they stood, Logan could see a wooden porch and a steep roof over rough wooden walls made from logs that looked as big around as boulders.

Mr. Manchester's hand was firm as it landed on Logan's back. "Come on in. Let's get you settled."

Another helicopter was dropping to the ground just then and silt and gravel whirled, spinning in the air. Mr. Manchester had to shout over the noise.

"You go on!" Two agents were hopping out of the helicopter. "I'll get these guys set up."

Mr. Manchester shoved Logan's bags into his arms and pushed him toward the cabin. And Maddie.

Logan could hear men shouting. A crew was already unloading huge crates, and someone was setting up a tent. Soon there'd be cameras in the trees and a secure satellite signal trained on this location. But only two agents were staying behind. Logan's dad had been adamant about that.

There would be no chef. No housekeeper. No butler or driver

or even someone to wash his sheets. Logan wasn't on vacation. He would have a two-agent detail because that was the minimum, but other than that, his parents would have been just as happy to drop him off in the middle of nowhere and forget about him until the country had a new president.

A pair of small boots sat beside the door of the cabin, so Logan stopped on the porch and took his off as well. When he knocked, the door swung open, and he couldn't help but ease inside.

Logan wasn't really sure what he'd expected. Maybe a moose's head over a roaring fire, a bear-skin rug and steaming mugs of hot chocolate. But it wasn't like that.

There was something like a kitchen in what could have been a small hallway, with a stove and a curtain on a rod. Instead of a fireplace, he saw a black stove with a big pile of wood stacked not far away. There were shelves covered with books. A few small, dirty windows and floor lamps provided the only light. There were two doors. Through one, he saw a bed and a dresser. The other went out the back through the kitchen.

"It's not much, but it's home."

Maddie didn't sound ashamed. She just sounded . . . different. Angrier and more serious somehow. She was supposed to be rolling her eyes at him, teasing him about how big he'd gotten or how silly he was to have come all the way to Alaska and not have brought her a single piece of official White House chocolate.

Maddie was supposed to be smiling. But the girl in front of him looked like maybe she couldn't quite remember how.

"Where's your room?" he asked because he had no idea what else to say.

"Above you."

That's when Logan saw the little ladder beside the door, the loft that sat above the main room, a bright quilt over a small bed.

"That's cool," he said.

"Whatever."

"No. I mean it," Logan said. He'd been living at the most famous house in the world for seven years, and in its own way this small cabin was nicer and happier than 1600 Pennsylvania Avenue would ever be. "This is nice, Mad Dog. It's . . . warm."

"That's because Mad's got a good fire going!"

Only then did Logan realize they were no longer alone. Her father was pulling a stack of books from one of the chairs at the table. When Logan turned, he saw a cabinet with sparkly dresses that were two sizes too small for the girl he'd just met. There were old copies of teen magazines and a bottle of fingernail polish by the window. Right beside a hatchet that appeared to have sequins and rhinestones all around the handle.

"Maddie." Logan practically exhaled the word, finally seeing something of the girl he used to know in the angry young woman with the utterly fascinating mouth.

"What?" she asked.

"I—"

Logan knew he was supposed to say something. Pay her a compliment. Maybe grovel. His father always said that women expected a great deal of groveling, but Logan didn't know what to say. And, luckily, at that moment a totally different noise filled the air.

Ringing.

When you live in the White House, your whole world is one nonstop chorus of ringing phones, but something about the sound didn't belong in that small cabin.

There were no power lines. No phone lines. No water lines or gas lines. Maddie's world was pretty much line-free. Confused, Logan stole a glance at his best friend, but she wouldn't look at him.

Which meant she probably wasn't his best friend anymore.

The phone rang again, and all Logan could do was watch as something passed between Maddie and her father, a don't-pretend-you're-capable-of-ignoring-that look.

"I'll call them back," Mr. Manchester said. "Now, Logan. Are you hungry? I make a pretty mean pot of chili and Maddie's got some—"

"Base to Ridge Center. Ridge Center, do you read? Ridge Center, this is Base." The voice that filled the air was scratchy, and it took Logan a moment to see the old-fashioned radio that sat on a cluttered desk. "Ridge Center, do you read me?"

"Go ahead," Maddie told her father. "It must be important."

"Sorry, guys," Maddie's dad said as he sat on an old metal office chair and spun, reached for the microphone and answered. "Hello, Base, you've got Ridge Center. Go."

"Hey . . . Center. We've got a storm . . . in." The woman's words were spiked with static, coming in fits and starts.

48

Maddie's dad just laughed a little and pressed the button on the microphone. "It's Alaska, Base. Storms are always moving in."

It took a moment for the woman to answer. "This one's not so normal."

Maybe it was the tone of the woman's voice or the eerie, crackling static that filled the cabin, but Logan thought he could actually feel the air change when Maddie's father looked back at his daughter.

He pressed the button on the microphone. "How not normal?"

After a beat the woman answered, "We need you to . . . a run tomorrow morning before . . . hits."

Logan watched Maddie's face. It wasn't disappointment. She didn't roll her eyes. But it was like a string ran between her and her father, something pulled too tight for too long. He was afraid that it might snap.

"No can do, Base," her dad said. "I just got home."

Home. This place in the middle of nowhere, this building that was something between a cabin and a shack. This was home. And Logan wondered if Maddie felt the same.

"I'm sorry, Mike. I wouldn't ask if . . . emergency. We've got a group of scientists that were supposed to . . . resupplied in three days, but if this thing is half as bad as . . . won't make it then, and . . . needs medication. This thing might be bad enough that we can't make it in after, and—"

"I read you, Base." Maddie's dad's gaze never left his daughter's. "I'll leave at first light."

Logan heard a door close, but more than anything he felt Maddie's absence. In a way, he realized, he'd been feeling it for years.

"I'm sorry," Logan said, and he meant it. He really did. He was sorry that he'd ditched Charlie. Sorry Charlie had been fired. Sorry that he'd come here and upset whatever fragile ecosystem Maddie and her father had made for themselves.

But most of all Logan was sorry that Maddie no longer smiled when she looked at him. He was sorry that the girl he used to know was gone.

CHAPTER 6

Dear Logan,
    *I haven't been eaten by a bear yet. That's the good
news. But I think a bear might have eaten your letters.
That's the bad.*

                               Maddie

Maddie didn't turn the light on. Maybe because days were always short in winter, and even though she knew the solar panels would still get some sun and the wind never would stop blowing, she didn't want to drain their batteries just the same. Maybe it was because she knew she should be trying to sleep because at least eight hours was absolutely essential for good skin and clear eyes. All the beauty magazines said so.

Or maybe Maddie just didn't want anyone to see the light that she would shine beneath the curtain of her "room."

That's why she lay, unmoving, for what felt like hours in the little nest her father had built during their first winter in Alaska. It was always warmer up where she slept and safe away from any animals that might come calling in the middle of the night. But Maddie liked it mostly because she could pull the curtain and have some privacy, even if it was the kind of privacy one couldn't stand in fully upright and enjoy.

But that night Maddie stayed perfectly still, staring through the darkness until she couldn't take it anymore. Then she couldn't stop herself from reaching down between the mattress and the wall and wiggling her fingers until she found it.

The picture was folded into quarters, and thick lines creased the image. She knew each and every inch of it by heart . . . and still she reached for her emergency flashlight, risked a little light in order to look at it again.

Maddie still had that dress. Or parts of it. Their second winter in Alaska, Maddie had read every book the Juneau library had on learning how to sew, and over the years she'd turned all of her old clothes into new clothes. She'd saved the shiny white dress with the silver sequined sash for last. Now it was a jacket that might still fit, but Maddie had never, ever worn it except when she wanted to feel pretty sometimes in the darkest parts of winter.

It was hard to believe that it had once been such a pretty dress. Or that she'd been that happy girl. She wanted to believe that she'd forgotten Logan's face, but she hadn't. She knew him as soon as she saw him. Even though he now looked like a version of Logan that had been stretched and pulled and maybe dosed with some kind of magic potion to make him approximately three times his original size.

But in the picture—in her mind—they were the same height, and he had deep dimples and a mischievous grin and he kept his arm around her, the two of them ready for whatever adventures lay ahead.

As long as they could face them together.

Maddie's cheeks were wet then, and she reminded herself for the millionth time that she was never going to cry over Logan. Never, ever again. Then she took the photo and held it at the creases. It was time, she knew—time to tear it right down the center, rip it into a million pieces and throw them on the fire.

But she slipped it back between the wall and the mattress instead, back where it wouldn't hurt her anymore.

She closed her eyes and rolled over in her bed. She was going to sleep, she told herself. And when she woke up, maybe it would all just be a dream.

But that's when Maddie heard it.

There's a certain kind of noise that people make when they're trying not to make any noise at all, and right then the cabin was full of it.

Feet scraping and banging against chair legs, cabinet doors opening and closing in the dark. Maddie eased down her ladder and flipped on the floor lamp by the desk, but her father didn't whirl. He wasn't surprised. He'd made a career out of never, ever being surprised.

"How's the weather?" Maddie asked.

Her father shook the match in his hand, forcing it out, and Maddie saw the kindling in the stove catch. Soon the cabin would be filled with the smell of wood smoke and coffee.

"It's holding," her dad said with a glance out the window, as if it might have changed in the twenty seconds since he'd last looked. "Go back to bed, Mad."

It wasn't that early. Days are just short in Alaska at the beginning of winter. And the truth was, Maddie was the kind of tired that sleep couldn't really fix.

"When will you be back?" she asked.

"Tonight. If the weather holds."

She heard what he wasn't saying—that this was a big storm. It had to be to scare people who had lived in extreme weather most of their lives. But she also knew that nothing would keep her father from her. Absolutely nothing. And sometimes that was the scariest thing of all.

"I'm okay," she said. "I'll be okay. So don't take any chances. Please. If it's bad, don't risk it. I'll be fine. Don't worry about me."

"Sounds like you're the one who's worried."

"You're about to fly a plane the size of a large car over mountains and glaciers and through what might possibly be the storm of the year. *In Alaska.* So I'm allowed some trepidation."

"Well, I'm leaving my teenage daughter alone with a boy, so I'm allowed some, too."

Maddie couldn't help it—she glanced at the closed door to her father's room. Logan was in there on a small cot the Secret

54

Service guys must have brought with them when they set up their little base camp near the trees.

Logan.

"You going to be okay without me?" her father asked. Maddie forced herself to look away from the door.

"It's been six years, Dad. If I weren't okay without you here, I'd be dead by now."

"That's not what I mean, Mad. And I think you know it."

Maddie turned away from the door and the boy who had turned away from her. "Whatever."

"Mad—"

"I'm not going to kill the president's son." *No matter how much I might want to,* she silently added.

"That's not what I'm asking." Her father eased a little closer. Outside, the sun was coming up, and the cabin was the color of glowing coals. "Are you *okay?*" he tried again.

"I'm fine."

Her father filled a thermos with coffee, took it to his pack, then added his satellite phone and his wallet. "I thought you'd be happier to see him. You two were always so close."

"Yeah." Maddie filled a cup of coffee. "We *were.*"

The cabin was bright enough that her father could see her face, read her eyes.

"Maybe I shouldn't go."

"No. You have to go. You know you do. We're fine."

"There are two agents in the tents outside. They're in charge of security, but Logan . . . Logan's supposed to be roughing it."

55

"Oh, I'm sure he's in the lap of luxury."

"I mean it, Maddie. Make him haul wood. And tote water. And clean fish and fix the roof and whatever else you were going to do. His parents want him to carry his weight. I didn't mean to put this on you but . . ."

"I'm okay," she said. "We'll be okay."

"If you're sure," her dad said.

Maddie forced a smile. "Of course."

How many times had Maddie watched her father fly away? Too many to count, that was for sure. In the beginning, he took her with him. Her first taste of Alaska came at six thousand feet, soaring over glaciers, skirting above mountains, touching down on lakes so clear and cold that you could practically skip across them on bits of glacier ice, live like the seals that lay sunning themselves on the cold, wet land.

And then Maddie got older and was allowed to stay on her own for an hour. A day. A night. Her father was never, ever gone more than forty-eight hours, though. That was a rule that neither of them ever said aloud. He'd also never left her *Not Alone* before. And Maddie wasn't at all sure how to take it.

She crept to the closed door of her father's room. There was no light. No movement. It was almost like it was empty, just like always. But it wasn't, and that was a fact that Maddie could never, ever let herself forget.

She started the day's work by drawing the curtain over the kitchen door and heating the water. If the storm was bad, then this might be her last chance for a while, and she felt like she needed her armor for what was coming.

To Maddie, armor meant nail polish. And lip gloss. Really, lip gloss was essential to a girl's self-defense, she was certain. And clean hair. Oh, have mercy, did she ever need clean hair.

She worked as quickly and quietly as she could, and soon she was sinking into a tub full of hot sudsy bubbles, leaning her head back and letting the warm water wash over her.

She was never really warm in Alaska. Sure, sometimes she was hot. And sometimes she was freezing. But a nice, comfortable warm was something she only found in the bath, and so Maddie let herself close her eyes and sink lower and . . .

"Hey, Mad. I— Sorry!" the voice came from behind her, and Maddie found herself bolting upright and then sliding down beneath a thick blanket of bubbles.

She hadn't really fallen asleep. She'd just entered into a kind of *it's-early-and-I'm-still-sleepy-and-this-water-feels-really-really-good* kind of trance.

She'd forgotten she wasn't alone.

"Logan!" she yelled, and glanced behind her at where he stood with his back facing her, both hands over his eyes.

"I'm sorry! I— Why are you taking a bath in your kitchen?!"

"It's also the bathroom," Maddie was still yelling. "Stay turned around!"

"Right!"

"And put the curtain back!"

She watched Logan grope blindly behind him until one of his big hands found the curtain and pulled it closed again. Only then did she let herself relax. Which was the good news. But that also meant she had time to really think about what had just happened.

Which was the bad.

Hurriedly, Maddie stood and rinsed her hair and her body and wrapped herself in a big towel. She was halfway into her base layer when Logan's voice rang out from the other side of the curtain—too close—like he hadn't moved.

"Maddie, why were you taking a bath in the kitchen?"

"Because this is where we heat the water and take the baths. Bath. Room."

"Okay," Logan said in the manner of someone who didn't think it was okay at all. "So if this is the bathroom, then where do I—"

Maddie jerked her head through the curtain, then pointed. "It's about forty feet out that door."

Logan looked to the door outside, then back at Maddie. The look that crossed his face in that moment was almost worth having him there, listening to his stupid deep voice and staring at his stupid broad shoulders and putting up with the stupid little jerk that her heart made when he smiled.

"You've got to be kidding me," he muttered.

Maddie smirked. "Welcome to Alaska."

CHAPTER 7

Dear Logan,

I got all new clothes, which is NOT as exciting as it sounds. Turns out, they don't even make extreme-weather boots with sequins on them. If you ask me, they're missing out on a market. I mean, if you have to be stuck in the mud, shouldn't you at least have something pretty to look at?

Maddie

Going outside at this time of year meant four layers, in Maddie's considerable experience.

Wet layer (waterproof coat, boots).

Dry layer (jeans, flannel shirt).

Base layer (thermal top, leggings).

Under layer (tank top, control-top pantyhose—because in addition to making sure she had a smooth line under her jeans, they were crazy good at preventing friction and holding in body heat, and, in a pinch, Maddie knew she could totally use them to catch fish).

She was just starting to button her shirt when there was a knock on the door. An incredibly loud knock. If it weren't for the fact that their cabin had once held up while there was eight feet of snow on the roof, Maddie might have worried that Logan was getting ready to huff and puff and blow her house down.

But he just knocked again.

"Come in," Maddie said.

"Can I come in?" Logan yelled even though she was 99 percent sure he'd probably heard her.

"I said *come in*!" she shouted. Then, slowly, the doorknob turned.

She recognized the tuft of Logan's dark hair as he leaned inside.

"Well, I didn't want to take any chances."

It wasn't until he actually crossed the threshold that Maddie realized his hand was back over his eyes.

"I'm wearing clothes, Logan," Maddie said, because she absolutely was not going to smile. No. No way. She wasn't going to think that he looked adorable and that he was funny. Funny Logan was shot in a hallway six years ago. Adorable Logan was dead and Maddie would do well to never let herself forget it.

So she just stood there watching as Too-Tall, Too-Big, Too-Grown-Up Logan took his hand off of his eyes and studied her closely, looking from the top of her still-a-little-wet hair to the tips of her really thick socks.

That was when he cocked an eyebrow and asked, "Are you sure you're dressed?"

"What's that supposed to mean?"

One of Maddie's fears—one she had never shared with her father or wrote in her letters or ever, ever voiced aloud—was that she might forget people. How to be with them. How to talk to them. How to read them and make them laugh—that she might forget all the thousands of things that people do and don't say during every day of the world. And that's the fear that hit her right then: that Logan might be talking in a language that she'd forgotten how to speak.

Or maybe it was a language that she had never learned at all.

"I mean . . ." He looked at the green plaid of her flannel shirt. "Don't they make that in pink?"

She finished up the last of the buttons. "No. They don't."

Then Maddie reached for her favorite waterproof jacket, stepped outside, and started pulling on her boots.

"Mad Dog."

"My name is Maddie!" She didn't even realize she was shouting until he stepped back, like she'd slapped him. But Maddie consoled herself with the realization that he absolutely would have known it if she'd slapped him. "Or Madeleine. That's my name. I'd suggest you use it."

"Your dad calls you Mad Dog," Logan told her like it was the most foolproof argument in the world.

She stepped closer. She'd grown a lot in six years, but Logan had grown more. A lot more. She had to crane her neck to look up at him, but still, somehow, she could tell that she made him feel small. "I like my dad."

"So you don't like me?"

"You always were a smart kid, Logan."

With that, she jumped off the porch and stormed down the path toward the water. She saw two tents set up. A pair of Secret Service agents she didn't recognize practically smirked as she passed, like they'd been wanting to yell at Rascal for ages, like they were more than happy to sit aside and let a teenage girl take a stab at him. They looked like they'd even give her the knife.

Which wasn't necessary. Maddie always carried her own.

"I've got chores to do," she told them.

One of them nodded. "We'll be here if you need us."

Maddie turned and started through the woods. A few minutes later she heard heavy feet landing on the cold ground, someone yelling, "Maddie, wait up!"

But Maddie didn't wait up. She was through with waiting: for letters, for phone calls, for people and friends. Maddie was absolutely through with looking back.

"Maddie!" Logan wasn't breathing hard when he caught up with her, but he acted like he was. He'd thrown on his boots and a jacket, but he wasn't ready for Alaska. No one was ready for Alaska on their second day. Ever.

"Where's the fire?" Logan huffed.

"It's back there," Maddie snapped. "And it will go out if we don't get wood."

"There's wood," Logan said.

"There's *never* enough wood." Maddie shook her head like maybe he was the one who didn't understand what words meant.

"Mad Dog—Maddie. I'm sorry. Wait."

But Maddie didn't dare wait. "There's a storm coming, Logan."

"That's the rumor, yes."

"Dad won't be back until after dark—if then. And there's work to do. Lots of work."

"Okay, let's work."

She was supposed to make him do it, Maddie knew. And a part of her wanted to make him haul wood and use an ax and climb and claw and dig until his hands bled and his back ached and he would give anything to go back to his big, cushy bed in the most famous house in the world.

But another part of her wanted to turn her back and freeze him out. Freeze him dead.

He slapped his hands together, not to warm them, but to show he was ready for everything. Maddie wanted to laugh. He wasn't ready for anything.

"Just try to keep up."

She turned down a path and started walking. She could feel him on her heels as she shouted back, "Don't wander off by yourself. Especially at night. If you need to go out, tell Dad or take a pistol. Or . . . on second thought, don't go out at night."

"No nighttime wanderings. Check."

"And don't eat anything you see out here—berries and stuff. Some are delicious. Some will kill you dead."

"Poisonous berries. Check."

Maddie could feel Logan keeping pace just behind her. So she stopped. Spun.

"And whatever you do, don't drink the water. A guide once told Dad that some of the springs still have arsenic in them from the gold rush. I have no idea whether she was joking or not, but let's not risk it, okay?"

"Seriously?" Logan asked. He raised his eyebrows. "Alaska—where even the water will kill you. I'm surprised they don't have that on a T-shirt."

"*Logan*—" Maddie warned. Logan raised his hands in surrender.

"Poisonous water. Check."

She turned and started walking again, trusting him to follow like a shadow.

"And if you see a bear—"

"It's more afraid of me than I am of him," Logan filled in, but Maddie stopped short.

"No." She shook her head and looked at him like he might be a moron, which he probably was. "It's *not* afraid of you. It's a bear! So back away slowly and hope it doesn't want to kill you. Because it can without breaking a sweat."

Logan studied her face, then nodded slowly. "Killer bears. Check."

"And moose," Maddie added. "Moose are the meanest things in Alaska, which is saying something. We don't have a lot of moose around here, but that's just good to know. For the future."

Maddie knew the woods around her. She was aware of every step and rock as they climbed. She knew exactly how the sun would glisten off the lake and how small the cabin would seem when they crested the ridge.

Maddie knew this place, but the boy, she couldn't help thinking, was a stranger.

"Maddie . . ."

"What?" she didn't want to snap, but she really couldn't help herself.

When she looked up at Logan she had to squint against the sun. He was so tall now. So strong. In her memories, he was still a kid with freckles and hair that curled when it got too long. He was still a boy who could see anything and remember everything. But he'd forgotten all about her, and that made all the difference.

"What about you?" he asked. "Are *you* going to kill me?"

Maddie had to think about the answer.

"Why would I do that when I just have to get out of the way and let Alaska do it for me?"

She expected him to turn back after that, thought he might go lumbering down the trail to his Secret Service detail and the satellite phone they no doubt had. She thought he'd go find whatever gadget regular kids were obsessed with that month— or maybe, if he was desperate, a book or a graphic novel or something.

She truly, honestly did not expect him to follow.

She certainly never expected him to say, "You're different."

Maddie stopped and took her hatchet from its sheath, then pulled back her arm and hurled it at a tree thirty feet away. When its blade sunk into the bark with a satisfying *thunk* she looked at Logan. "What makes you say that?"

He backed away. "No reason."

There was a dead tree that was small and made good kindling. Maddie hurried to fill her arms with the wood she'd cut a few days before. She couldn't bring herself to face him when she said, "You're different, too."

"I know. I'm way better looking than I used to be."

She could hear the smile in his voice, so cocky but self-deprecating at the same time. It was a special brand of endearing, one you must learn after a lifetime spent in the spotlight, pleasing millions of people. The only person Maddie ever saw was her dad, and she couldn't even please herself most of the time.

So she scanned Logan, from his too-big feet to his still-messy hair. "There was only room for improvement."

Maddie's arms were full and she turned, starting back toward the path and the cabin and whatever she could find to make the day feel a little bit normal.

"My best friend left." Logan's voice sliced toward her on the wind, and something inside of Maddie snapped like the ice on the lake when summer is coming. It felt like she might fall through.

"Don't!" she shouted.

"Don't what?" Logan asked, all innocent.

"Don't act like I left you."

"You *did* leave!" Logan shouted, and Maddie couldn't help herself. She stalked toward him, closer to the edge of the cliff.

"I came here, Logan. This is my life. Look around. These are my friends. This is my school. This is my *life!*" The words echoed across the lake as if they bore repeating, and something in Logan must have known it, sensed it.

Because when he said "Mad . . ." his voice broke, but Maddie was the one who felt like crumbling.

And maybe she would have, except a person can't be weak in Alaska. A girl can't cry her way through the long, dark winter because her tears will just freeze on her face and ruin her skin and Maddie had learned that lesson the hard way ages ago.

"Did you even get them?" Maddie asked. "Did you even read them, Logan?"

"Read what?" he asked, and Maddie didn't know whether to scream or push him down the cliff. It would serve him right, she thought. The Secret Service agents probably wouldn't even blame her.

"I wrote you every week. Sometimes more than once a week. I wrote you every week for *two years*. I wrote you hundreds of letters, and every time my dad would fly home I'd run out to the lake to ask him if you'd written back yet. I'd lie to myself, make believe that I'd probably get all of your letters at once. I was gonna stay up all night reading them. I was going to read them all in order. I was going to make a big list of all the questions you'd ask me and then another list of questions I was going to ask you. I had highlighters. I had stickers. I wrote you every week and then I realized . . ."

"What?" Logan's voice was small, and Alaska was big. But Maddie heard it anyway.

"It didn't matter that my dad saved your mom that day. It didn't matter that the bullet only grazed you and . . . It didn't matter. My friend died that day. He died just the same."

"I never got any letters, Maddie."

"Nice try, Logan. You might try that on someone a lot more gullible than I am now."

"No. Seriously. I mean it. I never got any letters!"

"Don't lie to me, Logan. Abandon me. Ignore me—fine. But don't ever lie to me."

"I never got any letters! Maybe my parents—"

"Your mother gave me the stationery! She's the one who told me to write!"

"Maybe the White House thought they were spam or something."

"They weren't emails, Logan. They were *letters*."

"Yeah, but do you have any idea how much mail the White House gets? People write the first family all the time."

"You think I don't know that? You think the former head of your father's security detail didn't double-check the address?"

"I don't know, Mad. Don't hate me. Please. Don't hate me."

Something about the pleading, haunted look in his eyes made Maddie stumble back.

"I don't hate you, Logan. I don't even know you."

And that was so much worse.

"Mad Dog——"

He was reaching for her. He was going to take her hand, maybe smooth her hair. The wind was blowing hard and she hadn't bothered to pull it back. It was still a little damp from her bath, and it was going to be tangled now. It was mistake number eighty-seven for the day, Maddie was starting to realize.

She wasn't going to let number eighty-eight be believing him. Not ever again.

"Maddie, wait!"

Years of rage and pain came boiling up and spilling out. She was a volcano of hurt feelings, and Maddie hated herself for it. But not as much as she hated him.

"You don't get it, Logan. The best thing about my new life was that I never had to see you again."

The first thing you get good at in Alaska is first aid. There's no nurse's office, no urgent care—no ER just down the road and open twenty-four seven. Maddie could wrap an ankle and treat a burn, and she had never met a splinter she couldn't dig out.

But she'd never seen an injury like what those words did to Logan. And the truth was she had no desire to kiss it and make it better.

"Maddie, look——"

"No, Logan. I don't have to look. I don't have to see. I don't have to . . ."

But Maddie's voice trailed off and her anger faded away as she realized that Logan was actually pointing behind her, that he was backing away. Terror filled his face, and it took Maddie a moment to register the look—to remember that it was one she'd seen him wear once before.

Then she heard sounds that had no place in her forest: the snap of a twig beneath a boot; the scrape of a heel over a rock. The skidding of gravel as someone inched too close to the edge.

And Maddie spun just in time to see the butt of a gun slicing toward her. She actually felt the rush of air just before the sharp pain echoed through her face, reverberating down to her spine.

She heard yelling, screaming. And then the sky was too big and blue above her, the ground was rushing up too fast below.

"Maddie, no!" someone yelled, but it must have been a dream because it sounded just like Logan.

But Logan was gone. Logan was never coming back to her. Ever.

She huddled on the cold ground for a moment, then tried to turn over, maybe get a little more sleep, when she heard the voice in her dream again.

"Maddie, wake up. Maddie, please—"

She tried to rise. She wanted to get up—really, she did. She didn't want to be lazy and spoiled and too weak to survive on her own. But just when she got her hands under her, just when she was starting to push herself from the cold, hard ground a sharp pain slammed into her stomach—it was what Maddie always thought a steel-toed boot might feel like as it connected with a rib.

Yes. That was definitely what it felt like, she thought as she closed her eyes and turned over.

And over.

And over.

And when she finally stopped rolling Maddie didn't fight it anymore. She just let the lights go out.

CHAPTER 8

Dear Logan,

You know how my dad said he was going to leave the Secret Service because it was dangerous and he didn't want to risk getting killed and leaving me alone in the world and all that?

Well, he brought me to a place where he leaves me alone all the time and where pretty much even the AIR can kill you.

Seriously.

Things that can kill you in Alaska:

- *animals*
- *water*
- *snow*
- *ice*
- *falling trees*
- *more animals*
- *bacteria*

-the common cold

-hunger

-cliffs

-rocks

-poorly treated burns, cuts, and scrapes

-boredom

I may definitely die of boredom.

Maddie

For a long moment, Logan lay on the cold ground, looking at where Maddie was supposed to be. *She was just there,* he thought, even though the words didn't make any sense. Even though he should have been running, fighting, crawling, or shouting out for help instead of screaming the one word that mattered anymore: "Maddie!"

He was aware faintly of the cold ground beneath his knees, the feeling of rocks biting into his hands as he crawled toward the edge of the cliff.

Maddie was there. He knew it. In the movies, this was when you looked over the side to find a tiny ledge just a few feet down. Maybe she was clinging to a tree—a rock. Something. Anything.

Maddie was down there, and Logan had to get to her. She had to be hanging on.

But there was no ledge. No tree. Logan peered down at the small, twisted body tangled in the brush below. It was probably a fifty-foot fall to the place where she rested. Maybe farther.

It was so much farther.

But Logan wasn't going to think about that. He could reach her. He could dry all that blood that was over her face. There was so much blood. He could wipe it away and wake her up and they'd laugh about it.

He would tell her he was sorry.

He would. It wasn't too late to say it to her. It wasn't too late. Period.

Logan was so focused on Maddie and her blood and his guilt that he almost forgot about the man.

But when a huge boot landed in the dirt and the rocks in front of him, almost smashing one of Logan's fingers, Logan jerked back.

Slowly, he looked from Maddie's mangled body, up and up until he was squinting against the sun. Only when a head moved to block the light could Logan really see him.

"Shut up," the man said.

But he wasn't a man, really. He probably wasn't even that much older than Logan. In DC, he would have looked like a student at Georgetown, maybe an intern on the Hill. No way the man was older than twenty-five, and if anything he looked younger. He had dark hair a little too long and a dimple in his cheeks.

It was only the eyes. He had old eyes, like they had seen far too much danger and misery to be contained in fewer than twenty-five years.

"Do not move," the man said, and Logan tried to place his accent. Russian, he knew. But which part of Russia? It wasn't the accent of the gutter. No, whoever he was, he'd gone to decent schools. He was important to someone—somewhere. He wasn't some dumb thug with a gun and an ax to grind. No. He sounded like . . .

He sounded like the men in the corridor—like death itself—and it made Logan shutter and remind himself that this wasn't just another bad dream.

The man's hands were all over Logan then, patting him down and feeling in his pockets. Logan was too stunned to move, but when the man pulled out the small panic button that Logan had sworn to never abandon again, Logan shouted, "No!"

But the man was already pulling back his arm, and Logan watched the button fly over the edge of the cliff.

"Now get up. Slowly." The man climbed off of Logan and backed away, and a part of Logan knew that he was supposed to obey, follow directions. Be good and not make trouble because a grown-up had just given him an order.

But Logan had already forgotten his promise to be good. If anything, he was in the mood to be very, very bad, so as soon as he reached his knees, he put one foot underneath him and shot toward the man's legs, grabbing them in a death grip, twisting and plowing his shoulder into the man's thighs and knocking him to the ground.

Logan wasn't cold anymore. He wasn't hungry or tired or

jetlagged. He wasn't even angry. Anger has a beginning and an end. This was simply rage, like a fire had been burning inside of him since he saw his mother's dress sticking out of that rolling cart. This man was nothing but gasoline.

Logan didn't stop until he felt the man hit the ground with a satisfying *thunk*. The two of them rolled, kicking and tangled together. Logan managed to strike the man in the stomach, but it was like he didn't even feel it. The man just reversed their positions and brought the gun up, slamming it into Logan's gut in one fierce blow that made all the breath leave Logan's lungs. Logan turned, wanting to move, to strike. But they'd rolled close to the edge, and when the man pressed, Logan's head turned and there she was.

Maddie.

Not moving.

Face covered with blood.

Maddie was dead, and the realization made Logan's fire go out.

In a flash, the man was up and moving. He held Logan's arm behind his back as he dragged him to his knees, forcing a pair of handcuffs onto one wrist. Too tight.

But Logan couldn't find the words to complain.

All he could say was "You killed her."

The man didn't answer. He just dragged Logan to his feet, pulling his right hand in front of him and cuffing it to his left.

"I should really put your hands behind your back, but if you lose your balance and follow your friend down a ravine it will delay us. We cannot have delays."

"You killed her!" Logan yelled again, lunging forward and smashing his combined wrists against the man's chest, but the blows glanced off like they were nothing. When the gunman looked at Logan he seemed mostly annoyed.

"Yes, I did." The man's voice held no emotion. It was like Logan had asked him for the time, like maybe he was about to comment on the weather. This was just another day in this man's eyes.

Wake up.

Take a walk.

Kill a girl in cold blood.

"You killed her," Logan said again, and suddenly a calm, cold peace came over him. He turned from Maddie's mangled body, and when Logan spoke again, they were the most honest words he'd ever said: "So I'm going to kill you."

The man almost smiled.

"You are welcome to try."

Before Logan could lunge for him again, the man pulled a small silver key from his pocket and dangled it in front of Logan's eyes.

"This is your hope," he said, then brought the key to his lips, kissing it softly. "Good-bye," he said before tossing the key over the edge and into the deep ravine, just like Maddie.

"Maddie."

"Now walk," the man said. He poked Logan in the ribs with his gun and pushed him in the opposite direction from the cabin.

"You're not going to get it," Logan said. "Whatever you want, if you think kidnapping me is going to help you get it, you're wrong."

"Right now I want you to walk, and I'm going to get that," the Russian said with a shove in Logan's back, forcing his legs under him as gravity took over, pushing him farther and farther away from Maddie's body.

Maddie's head hurt. And her face felt funny. Like maybe she'd forgotten to take off one of her deep-conditioning masks. Or like maybe the batteries were low and she'd been burning a candle and wax had melted in her hair while she slept. It didn't burn, though. And her skin didn't hurt. But the sticky feeling made her feel like she'd never be clean again, like there wasn't enough water in Alaska to wash it all away.

It was stiff and itchy and . . .

She brought her hand to her face, then looked down at her fingers.

Red.

Maddie's hand started to shake. She was too cold, and when she looked at the blood that covered her fingers, she wanted to scream.

Logan.

Maddie remembered fighting with Logan.

She turned and looked up to where she had been—to where he was supposed to be. But the sun was too bright and she had to squint. Her head pounded and all she wanted to do was to lie back down, pillow her aching head on her arm, and go to sleep for an hour. A day. A lifetime.

Nothing would ever feel as good as sleep.

But there was something nagging at her, some thought that wouldn't let her rest.

As soon as she closed her eyes, she saw the gun coming too fast toward her; she felt the blow to her head, the ache of a kick to the gut. And she knew.

"Logan!" she tried, but she couldn't get enough air. All the sound had been kicked right out of her. "Logan!" she tried again, expecting him to peek over the side and tell her it was all some misunderstanding. One of his detail had gotten confused. Someone was going for help. He was going to climb down and get her, grab her in his suddenly-too-strong arms and carry her up the cliff.

She yelled one more time. "Logan!"

And when he didn't answer, she got a whole different kind of worried.

Her head still pounded and her side still ached, but those pains were fading as a new kind of terror took their place.

After all, it was one thing to fall and hit your head in the middle of nowhere. It was another to be knocked unconscious while standing beside the only child of the most powerful man in the world.

"Logan!" she shouted again.

Now wasn't the time to panic.

Now was the time to be smart. Be clever. If Logan was up there, he would have answered by now. Unless he couldn't answer. Unless he was hurt or dead.

But when she saw the red blood on her fingers she couldn't help but think about another piece of red—and instinctively she knew he was alive. After all, plenty of people might want to kill the president. But the president's family? No.

Logan wasn't a teenager. Logan was *leverage*. And leverage is only worth something when it's alive.

The thought should have been a comfort, but it wasn't. Maybe it was the pounding inside of Maddie's head. More likely, it was the flash she saw on the far side of the river, inching up another ridge, away from the lake and the cabin.

He was there: Logan was *there* and he was alive. But she couldn't tell if there was one gunman with him or two. Or twenty? Maddie cursed herself, utterly unsure. She felt sloppy and stupid and weak, so utterly weak that she could have laid there and wallowed in self-pity for the rest of her life, but she didn't have time for that.

She tried to climb to her feet, but her head swam and she might have been sick if there had been anything in her stomach besides a little coffee and last night's supper.

There was nothing inside of her but fear and regret.

On the far side of the river, Logan stumbled, and the big man hit him in the back, forcing him to climb higher. Faster.

Maddie put her hands to the ground, ready to push herself to her feet, but something cold and sharp bit into her palm. She jerked back, and there, imprinted on the soft flesh of her hand, was a key—a small metal key like to a set of handcuffs. She wanted to scream again because this key on the ground, more than the blood and the pain and the sight of Logan walking away, made it all seem real.

Maddie knew what she had to do. The Secret Service had sent two agents with Logan. Soon they'd be wondering why Rascal hadn't returned. They'd need to check in, touch base. They would be coming. Soon.

And they no doubt had satellite phones and maybe coms units. There was also her dad's old radio and the sat phone he left for emergencies. One way or another, help was waiting at the cabin. She just had to get there and then . . .

She felt a raindrop.

This happened in Alaska. Clouds could come from nowhere, filling the sky and turning a beautiful day into a deluge in a matter of minutes.

She felt another raindrop. And another. And another.

The soft earth where she'd landed was already starting to form puddles. Whatever trail Logan might be leaving would soon be washed away.

And right then, Maddie knew she had two options.

She could go for help, summon the cavalry and call the guards.

Or there was option two.

How many times had she questioned her father's sanity, wondering what kind of person ran *toward* gunshots?

But the rain was falling harder. So Maddie pulled up the hood of her jacket and watched Logan disappear into the trees and the brush on the opposite rise, and she thought about her father, running toward the gunmen, jumping in front of the bullets.

And Maddie did the only thing she could do: She followed.

CHAPTER 9

Dear Logan,

    When at last we meet again, you should probably know that I'm not the same girl I was when I got here; that's for sure. I've learned a lot. For example:

    Things I've learned in Alaska:

      1. It's cold.

      2. It's wet.

      3. Everything is slow.

      4. Especially the mail.

                     Maddie

The summer between eighth grade and Logan's freshman year of high school, he grew four inches and gained thirty-five pounds. Probably another twenty pounds turned from baby fat to muscle, and his feet grew so much his mother started buying his shoes two sizes too big. The president used to joke that it was going to impact the national debt just to feed him.

It wasn't fun. And it wasn't funny. Not for Logan, at least. It was like going to bed one night and waking up every morning in an entirely different body—one that didn't move the same, feel the same, work in the same way as the one he had always known. His fingers were clumsy and his feet were clunky and it felt like he was constantly at risk of moving too fast in the wrong direction and toppling over. It seemed to take months for his center of gravity to feel like his own again.

This is what that felt like.

Walking through the woods, still numb and angry, his hands bound in front of him as he plodded up a hill and over the rough ground, Logan's feet were heavier than they should have been. He stumbled and shuffled and dragged his new all-terrain boots over terrain that he never before could have dreamed of.

Logan was in good shape. He played sports in school and liked to swim and play pickup games with the off-duty Secret Service agents who always seemed to be hanging around the court at the White House.

But he was tired. He was winded. He wanted to sit down and stare forever.

He wanted Maddie back.

He'd just gotten Maddie back.

Logan didn't care when he ran into a tree limb and broke it, when he kicked a rock and sent it down the steep face of the hill, lost in the mud and muck.

It was starting to drizzle, but he barely felt it. Logan barely felt anything. At least he didn't until the man with the gun started to laugh.

"What's so funny?" Logan spat out the words, rainwater clinging to his mouth and spewing forth like he might be rabid.

But the kidnapper smiled. "You. Thinking you are going to leave a trail for someone to follow. You have seen too many movies, my friend."

"I'm not your friend."

"No. You are my hostage. Walk."

Logan turned and did as he was told, but he couldn't shut up. That was asking too much. His hands were starting to go numb, and he had to use his arms and lean at the waist to try to get enough momentum to drag his body upward.

"Do you really think no one is going to miss me? I thought you knew who I was. People tend to notice if the first kid goes AWOL."

"There is no one to miss you."

Now Logan wanted to laugh. "I'm the president's only child. When Maddie and I don't come back, they'll have an army in these woods. They'll have *the* Army."

He spun on the man, feeling triumphant, but the feeling turned to ice as a cold, cruel grin spread across the man's face.

"Are you thinking of the men in your camp or of your little

friend?" the man asked, then shook his head. "It does not matter. Like I said, there is *no one* to miss you."

Suddenly, the ground moved, the earth shifted. Logan blamed it on the wet, steep hillside, but it was more than that.

Charlie had gotten fired because of him, but in that moment, Logan knew that the two agents who'd been forced to follow him to Alaska had gotten much, much worse.

He could barely get the question out: "What did you do?"

"What I've only begun to do. Now walk." The Russian accent seemed thicker now, with this new, awful knowledge. "We cannot fall behind schedule."

He reached for Logan then, to grab him by the handcuffs and jerk him to his feet, toss him around as if he weighed nothing—were nothing.

But even as the clouds grew thicker, Logan's mind grew clearer. He could see it now: what had happened—what *was* happening. The Russian was right about one thing: Logan had watched a lot of movies, and he knew that there would be no negotiating for his freedom, no tearful, tense exchange. He'd seen this man's face; he'd heard his voice. Logan was a dead man. Just like the two agents who had brought him here.

Just like Maddie.

Maddie.

Logan heard a fierce roar that rumbled like thunder in the dense woods, but it wasn't a bear—it was his own mangled cry. He didn't think or feel or worry anymore. He just lunged at the man who was standing beneath him on the hillside.

Maddie was dead. And something inside of Logan was alive and fighting, and he didn't want it to stop until these woods were covered with blood.

He felt the man falling and grabbed hold tighter, and the two of them rolled over and over across the rocks. Tree limbs slashed against them. Logan tasted blood. His screams filled the air, a terrible piercing cry that he didn't even try to stop.

His hands were still cuffed, and he slammed them into the man's gut, pounding like a hammer with both fists. The man was dazed, but he wasn't stopped, and when Logan pulled back again, the Russian moved like a blur, reversing their positions and leaping to crouch over Logan, pressing his chest against the rocky ground.

Logan never even saw the knife.

Not until he felt it, cutting into the soft flesh between his pinkie finger and its neighbor. At first, his hands were too cold, too numb, and Logan was too high on adrenaline and anger to feel any pain. But then he saw the bright red drop of blood that bubbled up from his too-white skin.

He felt the kidnapper's warm breath on his cold cheek, heard the accented warning: "This is not the part of you I need," the man whispered near Logan's ear. "Now you must ask yourself: Do you want to lose more than just your girlfriend and your pride today?"

The man seemed to think he'd asked an excellent question, made an undeniable point. He didn't know that Logan had already lost everything that meant anything to him. A pinkie finger was the least of his problems.

No. The only thing Logan cared about was vengeance. And he wasn't going to get that—not right then; not right there. He wasn't going to get Maddie back with his bare fists. He had to . . .

I am never going to get Maddie back, Logan realized.

It was suddenly harder than it should have been to keep breathing.

The man dragged him to his feet, pushed him in the back. "Now walk."

Maddie knew her way across the river. Even cold and hungry and still a little too unsteady on her feet, she'd crossed the old fallen tree enough times to know that it could hold her.

The man hadn't known about it, though. Or maybe he hadn't wanted to risk climbing down the steep cliff face to reach it. In any case, by Maddie's estimation she'd gained at least an hour on them. But she'd probably been unconscious at least that long, so she didn't know how much good it did her. Besides, her head hurt too badly to think too much. So she just kept walking.

When she reached the place where riverbank gave way to trees, Maddie saw the broken branches. Even with the rain, someone had dug so deeply into the soft earth while searching for footing that it was almost impossible to miss the ruts. Now.

Maddie looked up at the sky, at the clouds that were growing thicker, darker. Maybe it was the drizzle that clung to her hair or the shock from her long, hard fall, but it was definitely getting colder. And it was going to get a whole lot worse before it got better. In a lot of ways.

Someone might miss Logan's tracks if they didn't know where to look for them—if the weather kept getting worse. So Maddie walked to the river and gathered the biggest rocks she could, then placed them like an arrow, pointing the way. She piled a few smaller stones on top, just high enough to be noticed in a few inches of snow and ice, but not so high that they might topple.

Then Maddie lowered her hood. She brought her hand to the side of her face and pressed her palm against the largest of the rocks until her bloody handprint shone like an eerie beacon, announcing to the world: *Trouble came this way.*

But trouble was Maddie's family's business, so she did the only thing that made sense: She followed it.

The footprints were easy to track for a while, but then the ground got rockier and the rain got harder. Luckily there were a lot of trampled bushes and broken branches. It looked like a bulldozer had passed that way, and a part of her wondered if Logan was doing it on purpose. She didn't know him well enough to say anymore, and that hurt almost as much as her head.

She could feel the swelling beneath her hair, but that was good, wasn't it? Better for it to swell out than in? Maybe her brain would be okay even if her hair would look terrible. Maddie consoled herself with the fact that there wouldn't be anyone around to see it. That and the whole life-and-death thing.

That's what made her bend at the waist and leverage herself higher. And higher. The rain was still falling, but she was making good time.

Her shoulder hurt, though, probably from the fall. And sometimes she'd find herself stopping, wincing, because it felt like a sword was going between her ribs, but she was pretty sure they weren't broken—just bruised.

It could be worse, she told herself.

She could have left home without a raincoat like a moron.

Was Logan wearing a raincoat? Maddie couldn't remember. She just knew he was a moron, and the thought should have worried her, but she just smiled a little. Logan was gone without a trace and she was calling him a moron in her mind.

Things were almost back to normal.

But then Maddie saw something on the hill—an overturned rock, like someone had struggled to make a step.

Not quite a moron, she told herself, and went to the rock, stacked a half dozen others around and on top of it with a small limb sticking straight up for good measure, and then she started up the hill again, certain that she was on the right path.

She wanted to run. She wanted to find him and make sure he was okay and just have the worrying part behind her.

But she also had to be careful, be quiet. If the man thought she was dead, then that could be her best weapon. She'd left her second-favorite hatchet stuck blade-deep in a tree at the top of the cliff, after all. So she stayed quiet, even though that came with its own set of problems.

As Maddie pushed through a piece of heavy brush, she heard a sound that sometimes haunted her nightmares.

Part grunt. Part growl.

Maddie froze on the path as the bear pivoted and saw her. It must have smelled her or heard her messing with the rocks and cursing Logan under her breath. Because, thankfully, it wasn't scared. It had known she was there, even if Maddie couldn't say the same.

It was covered in thick fur, fat and ready for winter as it rubbed up against a tree like it had an itch it couldn't quite scratch. But it didn't charge at her. If anything, it seemed annoyed that she'd intruded on its solitude. So Maddie did the only thing she could do—she put her hand on the hilt of her knife, then eased back, slowly slipping away.

When her heart returned to its chest, she veered off the beaten path but kept climbing.

She didn't stop to think about the truth of her situation: There were two predators in these woods, and Maddie wasn't sure which one scared her most.

CHAPTER 10

Dear Logan,

> *Alaska's really big.*
> *And really pretty.*
> *It's also really lonely.*
> *Sometimes I ask Dad why we're here, and he says it's for our health. Or because I'm almost old enough that he was going to have to "beat the boys off with sticks" if we'd stayed in DC. I don't think that's it, though. But if it is, he's found the place where the stick-to-boy ratio is probably the highest on earth.*

> > > > *Maddie*

Logan didn't know what time it was. Usually he was good about stuff like that: finding north, knowing how much daylight must be left. Maybe it was from spending so much of his life surrounded by the Secret Service. Logan had received more than a few lessons from well-meaning agents on knowing when someone looks out of place in a crowd or when a vehicle just doesn't quite fit in.

Someone had even told him once that if his father hadn't been president, he might have been a good candidate for the Blackthorne Institute (whatever that was—it didn't even have a website), so it felt weird not knowing where he was or where he was going.

When Logan remembered how far north they were and how close they were to the shortest day of the year, he had to wonder how much daylight even remained. He knew there were parts of Alaska that didn't get any sun at all in the middle of winter and some that got a few hours. Some got more. But Logan didn't know that much about this part of the state. Alaska was more than twice the size of Texas, after all. And then Logan had to hand it to the man at his back: There was no better place to get lost.

Maybe that was why it took him a moment to realize that someone was talking.

It took a moment more to realize that no one was talking to him.

Logan turned slowly. The storm had broken for a moment, and a rare bit of sunlight broke through the heavy canopy of the trees.

Some rainwater puddled on the ground, and Logan realized that it had started to freeze. Now that they weren't moving he could feel it: The air wasn't just chilly anymore; it was downright cold. He stomped his feet and wanted to put his hands in his pockets, but they were still cuffed in front of him and growing numb.

Logan had no idea if it was from the tight cuffs or the cold air. It didn't matter. It was the same person's fault either way.

"Nyet," the man said, and something about it made Logan want to laugh.

Then Logan saw the telephone.

And he actually wanted to laugh harder.

"There's no signal, dude!" he yelled. The words seemed to echo in the vast wilderness.

"Shut up!" the man spat in English, then turned his back to Logan.

He put the satellite phone to his ear and started talking fast and in Russian, and something in the sound of those guttural vowels and consonants made Logan shiver in a way that had nothing to do with the cold.

He remembered the feel of his shoulder hitting the wall as the men rushed down the center of the corridor. The flutter of a red dress. The piercing pain of the bullet slicing across his arm. The blood.

And the sounds of Maddie's screams.

Maddie.

Maddie was gone. She'd been gone for what felt like ages, it was true. But now she was the kind of gone he couldn't pretend away. He'd just gotten her back, and this man had taken her from him.

"I just got her back!"

Logan didn't even realize he was yelling until the man spun and stared at him. The phone was to his ear, and now that he was facing Logan, Logan could hear every word.

Logan's Russian wasn't perfect, but he recognized *"Yes, I have the boy"* when he heard it.

Logan wanted to smile at the words—not at what they were but that he'd understood them.

The morning after That Night, Logan's dad had pushed Logan's wheelchair down the hall to see Maddie's dad. Afterward, on the ride back, Logan had turned to his father and said, "I'm going to learn Russian."

His dad was still running a hand over the resignation letter that Mr. Manchester had given him, handwritten on hospital stationery. He must have understood what was happening—how much everything was going to change, even if Logan didn't yet realize that the president losing the head of his Secret Service detail meant the first son was also going to lose his best friend.

"Did you hear me?" Logan had said. "I'm going to learn Russian."

"Okay," his father had told him. "Go ahead."

So he had. It was perhaps the one good decision Logan had ever made in his life. At least it was the only one that seemed worthwhile in that moment.

"Yes. I am certain we will not be followed," the kidnapper said. He looked directly into Logan's eyes, and Logan tried to keep the same look of enraged indifference that he'd had before. He couldn't let on that he understood. It might be the only weapon he had, and he wasn't going to lose it too soon.

"Is the plane ready?" the kidnapper asked. *"We will be there. You just make sure we have a doctor."*

Only the last part surprised Logan, and he made a conscious effort to school his features, hide his reaction. Once he thought about it, it made a kind of sense. Logan wasn't really hurt yet, after all. But if he kept annoying this guy, he would be. And whoever this man was working for—whatever their motivation might be—no one drags the president's son through the wilderness in a storm if they don't need him alive.

They need me alive, Logan thought, but it didn't bring him any comfort. They thought he might be a pawn, a useful tool. They thought he had value. Logan would have laughed if it hadn't been so funny.

Instead, he just said, "He hates me."

The man took off his pack, slipped the satellite phone into a side pocket, and quickly drew the zipper shut—but not before Logan noted which pocket the phone was in.

It was like he hadn't spoken at all—like maybe he was the one speaking in another language, so he said again, louder, "He hates me!"

Finally the man looked up, and Logan couldn't help but cock an eyebrow, careful not to tip his hand.

"That was a ransom call, wasn't it?" Logan lied, and Maddie's killer seemed pleased to realize that the first son was as stupid as everyone said. It had always been in Logan's best interest to keep it that way. Now more than ever.

"If that was a ransom call, I hope you asked for a miracle, because the president of the United States *hates* me."

Maybe it sounded like fear, or anger, or moody teenage angst, but Logan wasn't really ready for the sight of the Russian dropping to a log and asking, "So are you saying I should just kill you now?"

"No." Logan shook his head. "I'm saying you should let me go. You see, he doesn't actually care what happens to me. But he would care a great deal if he were to be *embarrassed*. If someone took something that belongs to him, he'd need to make an example out of that somebody. So you'd be better off just letting me go."

The kidnapper studied Logan, as if maybe the intelligence he'd been given was off—like maybe the first son wasn't just sloppy and stupid, like maybe he might also be a little bit insane.

That was okay, Logan thought. There were times when insanity could be very beneficial.

"If you're right and there's no one looking for me, then that means no one knows I'm missing. *Yet.* If you let me go, it might stay that way for a while. You could be long gone, back to wherever you came from, before anyone even starts to care."

The man leaned closer, his accent heavier. "*I* will care."

Logan shook his head, like this man with the knife and the gun—this man who had hit Maddie in the head and kicked her in the gut, then pushed her off the edge of a cliff like she was a pebble and he wanted to see how far she would fly . . . Logan looked at him like *he* was the weak one, the one destined for disappointment.

When the words came, they were actually filled with pity. "You're not going to get what you want."

But the Russian stood slowly and leaned closer. "I already have what I want."

For a second, Logan actually believed him. It took a moment for him to remember.

"You don't seem to understand how this hostage business works. See . . . you take me. Then you trade me for something infinitely more valuable."

"Get up," the man said, as if Logan hadn't spoken at all. "We have lost too much light already."

That was when Logan realized that the sun wasn't where it should be. The days were so short; Logan had no idea what time it was. He only knew that when he started to stand, his head pounded. The earth tilted. And the meal he'd shared with Maddie and her father last night seemed forever ago.

"Move!" the man shouted.

Logan didn't want to do anything, but he knew he couldn't just sit there—he couldn't just die there. Because then he wouldn't be able to kill this man later.

So he swallowed his pride and asked, "Do you have anything to eat?"

"We eat when we rest. We rest when we lose the light."

"That's a great plan," Logan told him. "But I didn't have breakfast and we're not going to make any time until I get a little gas in the tank. I'm no good to you this way."

The thing that Logan hated the most was how much that was true. Maybe that's why the man believed him, because a moment later he was swinging off his pack and digging through a compartment, then tossing Logan something that looked like an energy bar. The writing was in Russian, some brand name Logan didn't know. But he ripped open the package and dug in, eating just the same.

"You eat while we walk," the man said, pushing Logan up the hill.

"What? No beverage? I was hoping for a nice latte."

The Russian threw him a canteen so quickly that Logan was actually surprised he caught it.

"Now walk," the man said.

Maddie was surprised when she finally heard the talking.

It had been so long since she'd been used to any kind of voices. That was the weirdest thing about her new life: It wasn't just the lack of people—it was the lack of sound. There was no radio in her world. No television. No YouTube or whatever Internet thing kids were into. A dozen different fads could have come and gone and Maddie wouldn't have even known they existed.

Sure, her dad brought her newspapers and magazines. Sometimes she watched movies that they had on DVD. She had her mom's old CD collection, and sometimes when Maddie was all alone she'd blast the soundtracks from nineties movies just as loud as she could and dance around the cabin like no one was watching. Because no one was.

But most days, Maddie's world was silent except for the sound of birds and running water, chain saws and the crack a tree makes just before it falls.

Voices didn't belong in that forest, but when Maddie heard them, they sounded like music.

Because the voices meant Logan was still alive.

Of course, if he kept talking to the man that way he wouldn't be for long. Maddie took some degree of comfort from the knowledge that she probably wasn't the only person in those woods who really, really wanted to kill him.

When Logan shouted, "I just got her back!" something inside of Maddie froze. She wondered for a moment if maybe she'd spent too long away from civilization. Maybe some words changed meaning while she was away because Logan sounded like someone who had just lost his very best friend.

Maddie might have felt sorry for him if she hadn't lost her own best friend years ago.

She made herself stay in the shelter of the trees, listening. Watching.

Logan is alive, Maddie thought again, and for the first time in hours she really let herself breathe.

He seemed more mad than afraid. She'd never seen him look like that before. But maybe he looked like that all the time now. Maybe this was how he did teenage angst. Maybe all boys did. It's not like she knew anyone to compare him to.

But no. It was more than that. Logan was going to kill the man who'd taken him.

Kill the man who'd hurt *her.*

And right then Maddie's biggest worry was making sure he didn't get himself killed first.

• • •

Logan ran his sleeve over his mouth. Or sleeves, rather. His hands were still cuffed, and he kept the energy bar in one, the canteen in the other. He had a feeling he should be savoring this, committing the feel of food and water to memory. He might not taste either one again for a very long time.

"So what's your name?" Logan wanted to sound casual, maybe crazy. A sane person would be terrified by now, he knew, ranting and rambling and promising to give the man with the gun anything he wanted.

But Logan had learned a long time ago that there was nothing you could give a man with a gun to make him happy. Men with guns were only satisfied when they *took*. And Logan was going to hang on to the last of his self-respect for as long as he possibly could.

So he took another bite and asked, "Is it Jimmy?" Logan plastered on a smile and looked back over his shoulder at the man who might have been his shadow if the sun hadn't gone back behind the clouds.

"Bob?" Logan guessed again. "Matthew, Mark, Luke? John? Larry? Steve?" He watched the man closely, and when the Russian's eye twitched Logan was so proud of himself for seeing it that he might have laughed. "It's Stefan, isn't it?"

Stefan didn't answer, but he didn't have to. Logan already knew he was right.

He took a big bite of his bar and turned to keep on walking. "I met some of your countrymen once. Well, I didn't so much meet them as I watched them try to kidnap my mother."

"Keep walking." The words were meant to be a jab in the back, but Logan didn't much care. Somewhere in that big wilderness there was a plane waiting on them. And a doctor just in case. Whatever his final destination, it probably wouldn't be as cozy as the middle of those trees and rocks, lost among the rain and the temperatures that were both falling too fast for comfort. Somehow, Logan knew that very shortly this place and time might feel like a vacation.

"These bars are good. You want a bite?"

"Shut up!" Now Stefan was the one who looked like he was stuck somewhere he didn't want to be, doing something he didn't want to do.

Logan shook his head. "Manners, Stefan."

But it was a mistake, because in an instant the knife was out. "Do you think you are cute? Funny? I need you, but I do not need your tongue. In fact, I see a great deal of benefit in relieving you of it right here. Right now."

A kind of wet-weather creek had sprung up during the storm as rainwater collected on the hillside, racing down toward the river below. When Stefan stepped forward, his foot landed in the water, but it was like he didn't even feel the chill. His rage was so hot that Logan half expected to see steam.

Logan held his hands up, stepped away. "Hey, I'm just making an honest offer."

Stefan glared. "I'm making an honest threat."

"I can see that," Logan said somberly. "You're obviously a man of your word."

"Walk," Stefan ordered, and Logan did as he was told.

It was only after a few steps that he exhaled, suddenly grateful that there wasn't a knife in his back.

"So just out of curiosity, what do you think I'm worth?" he asked when he just couldn't help himself. "I mean, it isn't often a person's put on the open market. What is the going rate for presidents' sons these days? Is it more or less than what you guys were going to get for my mother? Accounting for inflation, of course."

Logan didn't know what to expect: The knife? The gun? Maybe a nice hard shove into freezing water? He couldn't have been more surprised when the man said, "I did not take your mother."

"I know you didn't," Logan told him. "You were what? My age then?"

He wasn't much more than a kid now, Logan tried to remind himself. But kids are sent into war zones every day. Kids can be psychopaths. Kids can kill.

Stefan straightened. "If I had tried to take your mother, she would have been taken."

It wasn't a boast. It wasn't a threat. It was a simple fact of life, and Logan couldn't keep from saying, "I believe you."

"Good. Now walk."

The man stepped in front of Logan, as if to lead the way.

But with every step the echoing pulse that had been beating inside Logan's head for hours grew louder and louder.

Maddie is dead.

Maddie is dead.

Maddie is—

When Logan stumbled over one of the big rocks near the stream, his hands plunged into the freezing water, breaking his fall.

Maddie is dead, he thought one more time.

Before Logan even realized what he was doing, his cuffed hands were digging into the ground. He was kicking at the rock that was big, but not too big. It was jagged, and even with his cold hands Logan could feel the sharp, perfect edges.

With the sound of the rain hitting the leaves and the gurgling stream it was almost too easy to sneak up on the man. Logan knew he had one shot. If Stefan didn't go down immediately, there'd be a fight, and then the knife and the gun would come into play. Which was fine. Logan didn't care about getting stabbed, getting shot. Logan only cared about the weight of the stone and the timing of his step.

He raised his arms high overhead, said a prayer—

And saw it.

He had to blink, certain that it was a mirage—a sign. But it wasn't the kind of sign he was expecting, so he stepped a little closer, certain that there couldn't really be a piece of gold dangling from a tree limb, there in the middle of a storm in the middle of nowhere.

Had Stefan seen it? Maybe he thought it strange but insignificant.

After all, he hadn't chosen that charm bracelet six years ago, placed it on his best friend's wrist.

He didn't know to stand in the rain and whisper, "Maddie."

Logan told himself that she must have left it there, lost it ages ago.

But no. The bracelet was too clean and the forest was too large and the girl was too tough to die that easily. Logan should have known.

"What are you doing back there?" Stefan's voice came cutting through the mist, so Logan dropped the rock and grabbed the bracelet.

He held the canteen to the leaves that were dripping rainwater like a fountain.

"Refilling the canteen!" he shouted.

"Less water. More walking," the big Russian yelled.

Stefan didn't see the way Logan scanned the woods around them, looking for a girl who was far too careful to be seen.

He had no idea he was outnumbered.

CHAPTER 11

Dear Logan,

    I'm very sorry to hear that you are in a coma.

    Or maybe you have amnesia.

    Or you lost the use of your writing hand and are learning to write with your other hand, which we both know would be saying something since even with your good hand your penmanship is atrocious.

    Or, wait, maybe the White House is out of paper.

    Oh my gosh! Is the White House out of paper?! You'd think that would be in the newspapers that my dad brings, but I could see where it might be a national security risk. No wonder the press is keeping it hush-hush.

    Don't worry. Your secret is safe with me.

    Who am I going to tell?

                        Maddie

Logan's coat was red. Which was a good thing. For now. There's a reason the redcoats were pretty much doomed during the American Revolution. He stood out like a beacon among the huge trees and big rocks and leaf-covered ground that was getting slicker and slicker with every passing moment.

So Maddie didn't have to get too close to keep them in her sights. Plus, Logan must have made it his mission to kick every rock and break every branch he came across. Maddie was glad of it. As soon as the agents realized he was missing they should be able to track him down.

If the agents realized soon.

If the light held.

If the tracks didn't wash away.

If the whole forest didn't fall asleep beneath a blanket of snow and ice.

Someone has to come help, she wanted to scream.

Someone other than Maddie.

She heard the man yell something at Logan—"Less water. More walking."

And the air around Maddie got even colder. She knew the accent even if she didn't know the voice. It was one she still heard sometimes in her nightmares. On those nights, Maddie slept with her back to the wall and her hatchet by her bed. If her ghosts followed Maddie to Alaska, that was fine, she told herself. She was going to be ready.

But now she was hunching down behind a fallen log and watching as Logan and the kidnapper kept going.

But Logan had stopped. And turned. And Maddie knew he'd found the bracelet.

Which meant Phase One was working. If Logan knew she was alive and she was here, then maybe he would stop acting like an idiot who didn't care if he got himself killed.

It had taken all of Maddie's strength not to scream when Logan had picked up the rock and crept toward the gunman's back. Logan was ready to kill, and Maddie couldn't blame him. In Alaska, people hunted to survive all the time. But Alaska was also the kind of place where being stupid would kill *you*, and Maddie knew they might have only one chance. They had to make the most of it.

When Logan's red coat moved farther out of sight, Maddie left her hiding place and went to the deep tracks that Logan had left in the muddy ground. Then she picked up the end of the log she'd been hiding behind. It had been down for years, she could tell, rotting and decaying in the near constant moisture, and it was almost light as Maddie picked it up and swung it around. She dragged her knife through the bark, drawing an arrow and pointing the way.

Her dad would know that the log had been disturbed. Even if snow gathered on the top, any idiot would be able to see the arrow on the side, high enough that the snow and ice shouldn't cover it.

Someone had to see it.

Maddie told herself that her father would be landing soon. Logan's detail was probably out right then, searching and calling for reinforcements.

Soon. Someone would catch up with her soon.

Unless her dad's job had complications . . .

Unless his plane broke down or the storm came in faster than anyone was expecting . . .

Unless no one realized they should be looking in *this* direction . . .

Unless somehow, for some reason, she couldn't keep Logan in her sights . . .

Help has to come, Maddie told herself for what had to be the thousandth time.

But there are things you tell yourself. And there are things you *know*. And Maddie knew that the only person she could depend on was herself.

But that's okay, she thought. *I'm usually enough.*

Maddie took one last look at the marker she was leaving behind, then pulled her hood tighter around her face and started up the hill.

She had to keep up. Or, better, get ahead. The best hunting always happened when the prey came to you. Maddie could lie in wait. She could be prepared. She could have a plan and then hope and pray that Logan's stupid boy brain and stupid boy ego didn't get in the way of what she already knew would be a perfectly logical, smart-girl plan.

But first Maddie had to figure out *where*.

Not where Logan and the kidnapper were. But where Logan and the kidnapper were *going to be*.

That was Phase Two. And without Phase Two there could never, ever be a Phase Three. Which was important because Phases Four through Twenty were pretty much "hope" and "pray" and "try to get really, really lucky."

"Where are you . . . ?"

Maddie trailed off when she heard the sound of the water. The hill they were on was steep and rough, and one whole side was more like a cliff than a mountain. As Maddie crept toward it, she knew even before she pushed aside the thick green branches of the evergreens what she was going to see.

This part of Alaska was full of rivers and streams—massive ravines cut by glaciers centuries ago and dug deeper by the water that ran through them almost all year long.

The waterfall was proof of that.

The kidnapper could hide out in this forest for days if he wanted to. The Secret Service would have satellites trained on the cabin, but the mountains were covered with trees. As long as they kept walking—kept covered—then they were invisible from the sky. Which was smart. But the kidnapper had to know that someone would find them eventually. Logan was the president's son, after all. People would be looking. Lots of people. And soon.

So they had to be planning to get Logan out of there. Out of Alaska. Judging by the kidnapper's thick accent, probably even out of the country. After all, Russia was pretty close. Closer than the rest of the US.

But there were no roads in this part of Alaska. Which meant they had to take Logan out by boat or by plane, and they were moving away from the coast, which meant plane.

Which meant . . .

Maddie looked back at the waterfall, the deep, rough ravine that ran between the mountains, and just like that she knew where they were going—and what she had to do.

But *how*—how was another question entirely.

She was so busy thinking, running through options and possibilities, pros and cons, that she didn't pay attention to where she was stepping, not until it was totally too late.

Maddie heard the snap almost at the same moment that she felt the pain.

And then she found herself leaping, falling, and skidding across the uneven ground and rolling through the mud and the muck. Water was seeping through her jeans, and Maddie knew she needed to get her feet under her but her left leg felt like it was on fire.

It wasn't, though. It was just cut and bleeding. Her jeans were ripped and Maddie was almost afraid to pull back the denim and examine the deep stab wound in the side of her calf. But it wasn't as bad as it could have been. Maddie knew this like she knew her own name.

In a weird way, she'd been lucky, Maddie realized as she forced herself upright and hobbled to the old, rusty trap that had been set at some point in the past fifty years and then abandoned. The mechanism must have rusted through the decades. That's why Maddie had a flesh wound and not a leg that would never really work right again.

For a second, she just stood there, breathing too hard, feeling lucky to be alive.

Then her breath grew deeper and her heart started beating hard for an entirely different reason.

She might be bloody and hungry and covered with mud. She might not have friends, teachers, classes, cell coverage, adequate food (for the moment), or any prayer of finding help anytime soon.

But—Maddie smiled—she *did* have a plan.

CHAPTER 12

Dear Logan,

It's been two years. Seven hundred and thirty days since I sent my first letter. I'm not going to lie to myself anymore. You probably think you're too important to bother writing me back. I guess you lied, too, when you said we'd be friends forever.

I've learned a lot since I moved to Alaska, but the most important thing is this: Any friend who doesn't write back isn't your friend at all.

So good-bye from Alaska, where I am the most important person for twenty miles in any direction.

(I'm the only person for twenty miles in any direction.)

Maddie

• • •

Logan had thought he couldn't get any wetter or any colder, but he'd been wrong. So very, very wrong. Like the kind of wrong he was when he bet Maddie that he could eat all the ice cream in the White House deep freeze and then found out they were preparing for a state dinner and had a hundred gallons.

He made it through half of one huge tub before she took pity on him and made him stop.

He never wanted to feel that way again, but Logan was so cold, so sick. His feet hurt and his head hurt and that energy bar had turned to acid in his stomach. He might have thought Stefan had poisoned him except he knew for certain that Stefan's bosses were going to need him alive.

When the man pulled to a sudden stop, Logan almost knocked into him.

When Stefan said "We rest here," Logan almost wanted to cry with relief. It was only the weight of Maddie's bracelet in his pocket that kept him going.

He was walking as slowly as he could, but they'd been going for hours. More than once, he'd started to just sit down, stop walking. But Maddie was out there somewhere. Watching. Logan wasn't about to let her see him cry.

As soon as the kidnapper slid off his pack and sank onto a huge boulder, Logan dropped to a fallen tree.

On any other day, Logan might have walked from the clearing and looked out over the huge hills and narrow valleys, the massive wilderness that spread out before him like something from a movie. He was on an epic quest, he told himself. Any moment now, reinforcements were going to show up and he was going to save the maiden in distress.

But Logan had to laugh when he realized that *he* was the maiden in this scenario. And he didn't care one bit.

When the phone started ringing, it was a sound from another century—another world. *There are no phones in Mordor*, Logan wanted to snap before he realized: *It's the phone.*

"Da," the kidnapper said, answering it. He didn't bother to turn away from Logan, lower his voice.

"Get here!" the man shouted. Even if he hadn't understood every word, Logan would have known that Stefan was angry. Something wasn't going according to plan.

"No!" Stefan snapped. *"A boat will take too long. We cannot reach the coast now. There is no time. We must have the plane and the doctor."*

A beat passed while Stefan listened and Logan worried.

Whatever the person on the other end of the line was saying, it made Stefan stare at Logan, not just with hatred, but with fury. As if Logan had personally killed his dog, burned his house, and ruined his future. Logan was the thing that went bump in the night as far as Stefan was concerned, and Logan made a point of remembering that—of reminding himself that maybe not everyone wanted him taken alive.

"No. Everything is perfect on this end," Stefan said into the phone in Russian. Logan tried hard not to smile at the sarcasm he wasn't supposed to understand.

115

But he must have failed because Stefan snapped, "What?"

Logan shook his head. "It's rude to have conversations in front of people without including them. I'm kind of an expert, you see, because when I was seven my parents got me an etiquette tutor. And, you know, if there's one thing seven-year-old boys love, it's etiquette."

Logan smiled his too-bright smile, but Stefan only scowled.

"You should rest your mouth while you're resting your feet."

When the man hung up the phone and put it back in his pack, he pulled the zipper halfway.

But only half.

Logan could have sworn he'd done it on purpose, like eating in front of a starving man.

Then Stefan pulled a map from his pack and spread it on the nearest boulder. The map was laminated and unfolded into probably twenty squares.

"Can I have the canteen?" Logan asked as he stood and walked toward Stefan and his map.

"Here." Stefan shoved the canteen at him and Logan took it. He drained it in one long gulp, then handed it back, lingering a little too long over the map as he did so.

The map's creases gave it something of a grid-like pattern, which was great as far as Logan was concerned. He liked things tidy and straight and neat.

He liked things he could memorize.

He wasn't there more than ten seconds. Fifteen maybe. And Stefan never even got suspicious.

Maybe I'll join the CIA after this, Logan thought. *Or maybe I'll lock myself in my room and never leave again.*

He was turning, he was thinking, when a gust of wind blew through the trees. Rain hit him hard, and the temperature seemed to drop instantly to below freezing. It was like winter decided to wake up and blow out its birthday candles. The rain suddenly burst from the clouds, thicker and colder, and Logan squinted for a moment, as if maybe he could shake his head and open his eyes again and find it had all been a very bad dream.

But it wasn't a dream. It was a nightmare. When the wind blew again, it caught the map and whipped it off the rock and across the clearing.

They were in the middle of millions of acres of wilderness— no roads, no mile markers, and absolutely no cell signal. Google Maps would never get them to the airplane Stefan was so desperate to meet.

He needed that map.

So Stefan ran, chasing it like it was a butterfly flitting and floating on the freezing wind.

Logan didn't think about it. It wasn't a strategy or a plan. He only knew that Stefan was busy and his pack was sitting, abandoned, by the boulder.

The pack that had the satellite phone in it.

Logan didn't think at all, he just moved. Instinct taking over, the fight for survival warring with the fight for being smart.

But maybe *this* was smart. Maybe this was the right move at the right time. He didn't know. Didn't really care.

He just knew that he had to *do something*, and he was reaching into the half-zipped pocket of the pack—pulling the satellite phone free—before he could even blink. He almost had it in his own pocket when he felt something ram into his side like he'd just been hit by a bus.

He fell hard, but the ground was soft enough that the only thing that really hurt was his pride.

That was before Stefan managed to roll them again. Logan elbowed him in the ribs, but a moment later he was pinned against the ground, Stefan's heavy weight on top of him. Logan lashed out. He remembered everything every Secret Service agent had ever taught him during the long, boring nights in hotel suites and on campaign buses.

He managed to reverse their positions. He got in a good shot to Stefan's eye.

When the phone went skidding from Logan's hands, he lunged for it again—and that was his mistake.

Facedown in the mud, the cold seeped up from the ground and into Logan's bones. Stefan was on top of him and Logan couldn't breathe. Stefan was too heavy. And he had both hands on the back of Logan's head, pushing his face into the mud.

"This is what you are worth to me!"

Was Stefan yelling in Russian or in English? Logan didn't know. Didn't care. It was the last thing he was likely to ever hear in any case.

"This is what you are. I should kill you here. I should—"

"Why are boys so stupid?"

The voice was light and airy, like sunshine. And that's how Logan knew that he was dead—that even in death, Maddie Manchester was going to mock him, roll her eyes at him, taunt him until the end of time. It was the most comforting thought he'd had in ages.

But then Logan could breathe again—Stefan's weight was off his back, and Logan was able to roll over and look up into the freezing rain that struck his face like pinpricks, jolting him awake.

"You're alive," Stefan said, and Logan pushed away, gasping for air and grasping for balance as he pushed to his feet and turned to see the most beautiful sight he'd ever laid eyes on.

She must have washed the blood from her face, but a big bruise was growing at her temple. She was covered in mud and standing oddly, like she wanted to keep most of her weight on her right leg.

But Maddie was here. Maddie was alive.

"What are you doing?" Logan shouted.

"I couldn't let him kill you," she said, then smirked and looked at Stefan. "You see, I've been wanting to kill him for years. Couldn't let you steal my thunder."

"You lived," Stefan said, looking her up and down. Then Stefan actually smiled. "You must be very tough." Maddie looked like she wanted to smirk again, but Stefan went on. "And also very stupid."

Maddie shrugged at that. She actually looked like she might start chanting, *Sticks and stones may break my bones, but words from stupid Russian kidnappers can never hurt me.*

119

"I'm sure I am," she said. "But protecting *his* family happens to be my family business."

"Good." Stefan smiled. He reached down and pulled the satellite phone from the mud. He gathered up the map from where he'd dropped it. "This is very good."

Logan looked between the two of them as if maybe they had slipped into a language that he didn't speak.

"It's not good, Stefan," Logan told him. "If you haven't noticed, you're outnumbered."

Then Stefan turned on him, so fast it was like he wasn't frozen—wasn't tired, wasn't weary—at all. In the next moment, the knife was in his hand and at Logan's throat. When he spoke again, his mouth was an inch from Logan's ear.

"Oh, it is very good. Because now I have someone I can *kill*."

He pushed Logan toward Maddie and pulled the gun from the waistband of his jeans, pointed it in their direction while he went to retrieve his pack, sliding the phone inside.

Then he eased toward Maddie.

"Hands up."

Maddie complied, but not without saying, "Okay. Okay. But please . . . just don't judge me based on my cuticles, okay? When your primary heating source is a wood-burning stove, dry skin is your perpetual enemy."

For a moment, Stefan looked at her like maybe she wasn't entirely sane, like maybe kidnapping the president's son and dragging him across the wilderness in the freezing rain was okay but maybe he had no idea what to do with any teenage girl who might willingly come along for the ride.

But he was so happy with his new, highly disposable hostage that he was willing to compromise whatever questionable code of honor he happened to have, Logan realized as Stefan dug a length of slender rope from his pack and wrapped it around Maddie's wrists, tighter and tighter. And then the truth sank in: Maddie wasn't just Logan's ally. She was also Stefan's hostage.

Once her wrists were bound, Stefan ran a hand down her side, and Logan wanted to kill the man, but for an entirely new reason.

"Don't touch her!" Logan shouted, but it was like he'd never said a word.

The only difference was that now Stefan was smiling as he felt along Maddie's leg. Her backside.

"Leave her alone!" Logan shouted, but Stefan pulled back and held a small pocketknife between two of his fingers after he pulled it from the back pocket of Maddie's jeans.

"This isn't much of a knife." He slid it into his own pocket as he laughed. "You won't survive for long out here with this, little girl," he said—and for the first time Maddie actually looked like this wasn't the best plan she'd ever had.

Had she actually expected him not to search her? Had she thought she was going to sneak up on Stefan and stab him with a knife that had a blade three inches long? Was that what Maddie was playing at?

Well, the game was up, Logan realized, and Stefan had moved on to Maddie's jacket.

When he pulled out a small tube of Vaseline, she cocked an eyebrow. "In Alaska, bears will totally kill you, but chapped lips will make you wish you were dead, so . . ."

Stefan put the tube back in her pocket and didn't say a thing. He just ran his hands expertly down her arms and up her torso. When he reached the chain around her neck, Maddie looked affronted.

"Just because you're in the middle of nowhere doesn't mean a girl doesn't feel better when she's properly accessorized."

Which was more than Stefan could take. He looked more pained than when Logan had hit him as he pushed her away. "Enough!" Stefan shouted. "We walk now."

Stefan was readying the pack, taking one last look at the map. But Logan could only look at the face he'd thought he'd never see again.

"Why are you here? Why didn't you save yourself?" Logan asked. This time his voice actually broke. He was willing to die out here. He hadn't asked for this life, but he'd had seven years to get used to it—to accept the possibility.

But it should never have been Maddie's life, and the joy he'd felt when he found her bracelet was gone.

"Mad Dog, why didn't you run?" he asked again.

He honestly didn't expect an answer. He certainly wasn't expecting Maddie to raise her bound hands and throw them around his neck, to plaster her body against his and bring her lips to his mouth as if Logan might be holding her last breath.

He'd never kissed Maddie before. Until twenty-four hours ago, he'd never really thought about it. But he'd never cursed his handcuffs more than when he couldn't hold her, touch her, pull her close and keep her near and never, ever let her go.

Maddie hadn't run away—hadn't saved herself—because of this, Logan realized. This kiss.

He just didn't know how right he was until Maddie's lips parted and the kiss deepened . . . and Logan felt a small piece of metal pass from Maddie's mouth into his.

Then Maddie pulled back quickly.

She unwound her hands from around his neck, and when Stefan yelled, "Walk!" she did exactly as she was told.

Logan's legs weren't working right, though. Neither was his head.

Maddie had kissed him.

It was smart, he had to admit. How else could she be sure Stefan wouldn't find the key when he frisked her? What better way to pass Logan the key undetected?

She'd kissed him so that she could save him.

For the life of him, Logan had no idea why that made him feel so disappointed.

CHAPTER 13

Dear Logan,

    Okay, so I lied. I'm writing you another letter because, turns out, you're the only person I can really talk to. Even if you don't talk back. Maybe BECAUSE you don't talk back.

    If you were here, you'd tell me that I do all the talking anyway. Then I'd point out that you saying otherwise totally negates your own point.

    And then we'd probably argue about it for an hour. Maybe two. And then we'd go get ice cream.

    So I'm gonna keep writing these letters.

    I'm just never going to send them ever again.

                    Maddie

Maddie was real.

Maddie was alive.

Maddie was *here*.

And she was going to get them both killed.

"Oh my gosh! You guys walk so fast," she said, and for a moment she sounded almost like . . . Maddie. Or how Maddie used to sound when they were looking for ways to sneak into the Oval or trying to guess the middle names of all of the agents on his dad's detail. She sounded like Old Maddie. Not Older Maddie. Logan never realized how much he'd missed her.

He also never realized just how annoying she could be.

"I mean, it's no wonder you walk fast. Your legs are a lot longer than mine. How tall are you anyway?"

She turned around to look at Stefan, who had his gun out and pointed at her, but it didn't seem to faze Maddie. She just kept talking.

"You look tall. I'm only five four. I mean I pretend I'm five five, and I might be in boots. Do you think it counts if you're in boots?"

She stopped then and studied him. Stefan moved toward her and Logan jolted. He wanted to put himself between that gun and Maddie. And he wanted to put something between Maddie and the man.

"Who did you call?" Stefan snapped. "Who did you tell?"

Maddie actually scooted back, but she didn't look afraid.

"What are you talking about?"

"Who did you call for help?" Stefan shouted—and this time Maddie looked at *him* like maybe *he* was crazy.

"No one. *There is no one here!*" She threw out her arms and spun around. "There's never anyone here."

Stefan didn't know Maddie like Logan did. Or like Logan used to know her. He didn't hear the stress in her voice, didn't see the hurt in her eyes.

"No." Stefan shook his head. "You would not be so stupid as to get yourself captured."

"I don't know." Maddie shook her head. "I'm a teenage girl. People think we're pretty stupid."

Logan knew she was right. Logan also knew she didn't believe a word of it. Only a moron would, and Maddie was no moron. He'd seen enough in the barely twenty-four hours that he'd been here to know that Maddie had survived here—thrived here—for six years, almost entirely on her own. That Maddie was alive was proof enough that Stefan had absolutely no idea who he was dealing with.

That Maddie was smiling proved that she had every intention of keeping it that way.

"I thought I'd follow you, okay?" she went on. "I thought I might be useful."

Stefan looked at her for a long time, then let out a cold, clear laugh. "Useful how?"

Maddie shrugged. "I know things."

"I know things, too," Stefan said, all the laughter gone from his voice. "I know you're going to be very useful."

"I'm not going to let you kill him," Maddie said as if she had a choice in the matter—as if Stefan wasn't eight inches taller and sixty pounds heavier. As if he didn't have a gun and at least one knife and probably eight years of experience on her.

But the kind of experience Maddie had was different, and a part of Logan warmed at the thought.

"Where are my manners?" Logan tried to force as much sarcasm as possible into his voice. "Stefan, kidnapper extraordinaire, meet Maddie Manchester. Maddie, this is the man who tried to kill you."

"I *will* kill her if you get any ideas, Logan."

Logan gave a mocking smile. "You know my name. I'm touched."

"I can't touch you," Stefan stated. He sounded honestly disappointed, but then he turned to Maddie, pulled back his hand, and hit her hard across the face. Her head snapped and Logan actually heard the blow. He lunged for her, but halted, uncertain, as Maddie stumbled but managed to stay on her feet.

She didn't make a sound as Stefan finished, "But I *can* touch her."

"Leave her alone!" Logan yelled, but Stefan pulled Maddie close to him, a human shield.

His hand was around her throat, fingers not quite squeezing, but close. They could cut off her airway, crush her throat. They'd leave a bruise, Logan was certain, and it was just one more reason why he wanted his big, sharp rock back.

"I cannot hurt you, President's Son. But she has no value to me. Do we understand each other?" he asked, but Logan didn't answer. Words didn't come. *"Do we?"* Stefan shouted, the force of the words making his body shake and the hand at Maddie's throat tighten.

Maddie didn't make a single sound.

"Yes," Logan choked out.

"Good." Stefan took his arm away and pushed Maddie ahead of him. "Walk."

Maddie's throat didn't hurt. Not even a little bit. Her pride didn't either. Alaska never took it easy on her because she was a girl. Neither did her father. But ticked-off Russians probably didn't know that. By the look in Logan's eyes, neither did presidents' sons.

They both kept looking at her like she was just a . . . girl. Which was the best thing to happen to Maddie all day.

So she batted her eyelashes. She examined her nails. She didn't really talk again as they moved over the rough, wet ground.

Her hood was still up and pulled tight around her face. Maddie hated to lose her peripheral vision, but she wasn't going to be any help to anyone if she got sick. That was one lesson people in Alaska learned in a hurry.

"Are you okay?"

Maddie had to turn her head a little to look at Logan. She'd never seen him look like that—all stoic and broody and . . . hot.

She definitely wasn't going to think about how hot Logan looked because:

(A) It was Logan!

and

(B) She'd heard stories about girls who met cute boys and then lost their heads, and being that they were currently being held by a knife-wielding, ticked-off Russian, Maddie really didn't want to find out how literal that saying might be.

But Logan still looked worried—that much Maddie couldn't deny.

"It's going to be okay," she told him.

She kept her head down. She didn't turn again.

The rain was coming down more steadily, and it was possible that the man couldn't even hear her, so she risked a little more.

"They'll find us soon. Don't worry, Logan. Your team must have realized you were gone hours ago. You did a good job leaving a trail, and I left markers—really obvious markers. They'll find us soon."

Maddie was sure of it. She knew it in her gut. She'd lived her whole life with a man devoted to protecting others, and there were some things that all Secret Service agents had in common. They were all smart. And tough. And when they took a vow, they meant it. There was a reason that the Secret Service was the only arm of the US intelligence community that had never had a traitor.

Logan's detail was coming. And when they got there, Maddie only had to make sure she got Logan out of the way.

She turned her head. She smiled. She just wasn't expecting the look on Logan's face.

"They're not coming."

Logan's voice was low and he kept his head down, his gaze on the slick ground before them.

"Of course they're coming, Logan. They're good. I know those guys. Dad trained them."

"They're dead, Mad."

Maddie's steps actually faltered. There had been a little piece of her—a small sliver of light shining beneath the door of her mind, something telling her that hope was out there. Help was coming.

There had been a tiny voice whispering that she didn't have to do this alone.

She wasn't Logan's only chance.

She wasn't on her own—not really. She just had to keep Logan alive until the grown-ups came to take care of things.

But Maddie was the grown-up now, she knew, and she waited for the realization to hit her, for the panic to set in. But the panic didn't come, and Maddie didn't know whether to feel relief that she was prepared for this or sadness that being on her own was nothing new.

If Stefan had killed two Secret Service agents, then he wasn't just evil—he was also good at this. And Maddie didn't know which thought scared her more.

"Can your dad land in this?" Logan asked with a glance toward the sky that was growing darker, the rain that didn't feel like rain anymore. Maddie tipped her head up and felt the tiny stinging stabs that told her that sometime in the past five minutes the rain had turned to sleet.

Soon the ground would freeze, and the leaves and logs would be covered with ice and, eventually, snow.

"Mad, can your dad——" Logan started to repeat.

"I don't know," Maddie said. It was an honest answer. It also honestly scared her. "He won't take a chance. I made him promise that he wouldn't take any chances."

"Great." Logan kicked a rock, sent it tumbling down the hill.

Maddie knew exactly what it felt like.

"Help's gonna come, Logan," Maddie said. Maddie lied.

The weather was going to get worse and the night was going to be long, but the promise of help could be warmer than any fire, Maddie was certain.

"Okay," Logan said. "But even if he does land in this, what's he gonna do? Drag himself through the woods to . . . what? Find us?"

"Yes," Maddie said.

"He can't find us." Logan shook his head, but Maddie reached out and grabbed his arm.

They both had bound hands, but that just meant that both of her hands gripped both of his, like they were sharing some kind of solemn vow.

"*I* found you," she reminded him.

For a moment, Logan smiled. But then the smile faded. He shook his head and pulled away, started walking before Stefan could have an excuse or an opportunity to strike again.

"You should have run, Mad Dog."

"I did run. Right to you." She shrugged. "Someone has to keep you alive until help comes."

"Help's not coming."

Maddie knew better than to argue. So she tried a different angle. "Who is he?"

She didn't look back as she asked it. She just kept her head down, her face shielded against the sting of the falling ice.

"He's Russian," Logan said, as if that was all that mattered.

"You mean like . . ."

Maddie didn't say *six years ago*. She didn't have to. That incident was never far from her mind, and it couldn't have been far from Logan's either. It had changed both of their lives in so many ways. Logan might have been the one who'd been grazed by a bullet, but she knew they both had scars.

"Yeah," Logan said. "Just like that."

"What else?" Maddie asked. She needed details, data. Before the president went anywhere, an advance team spent weeks going over an area with a fine-tooth comb. Facts mattered. Information mattered. And Maddie needed every speck of it that she could get.

"He's got a sat phone," Logan told her. "He's been speaking to someone. He doesn't know I can speak Russian."

"You can speak Russian!"

"Keep your voice down."

This time, Maddie whispered. "You can speak Russian?"

"Yes. I learned a lot in six years."

132

Maddie wanted to scoff and roll her eyes and yell at him and at the world, but she just kept walking. "Yeah. So did I."

When they passed a low bush covered with berries, Maddie said a silent prayer of thanks that the weather had been so wacky.

She pulled a bunch of berries off as quickly as she could and pushed them in Logan's direction.

"Here. Eat these." She helped herself to some as Logan eyed her.

"They could be poisonous."

Well, the berries weren't going to kill him, but Maddie's look could have, so he did as he was told.

"I don't know who he's working for," Logan admitted. The berries must have hit his bloodstream, a fresh shot of sugar and adrenaline and hope that lasted until Logan admitted, "And I don't know where he's taking me."

This time, Maddie smiled. "That's okay." She plopped a berry in her mouth. "I do."

CHAPTER 14

Dear Logan,

> *Someday I'm going to write a book:* How Not to Die in Alaska—A Girl's Guide to Fashionable Survival.
>
> *I bet you don't know that a bobby pin can make an excellent fishing hook. You may think you can use just any kind of mud for mud masks, but trust me, you CAN'T! In a pinch, nothing starts a fire like nail polish remover.*
>
> *And don't even get me started on the lifesaving properties of a good pair of pantyhose.*
>
> *So I know a lot, in other words.*
>
> *I just don't know why I'm still writing you these letters.*

"I want you to get away."

At first, Maddie wasn't sure that Logan was talking to her. He could have been talking to himself, after all. He used to do that when they were kids. He'd mumble under his breath during tests at school or while they were eating snacks on the stairs or even while they huddled together in a tent on the lawn of the White House, pretending like they were on safari.

Maddie was used to the sound of Logan's voice, low and under his breath when he didn't think anyone was listening.

But Maddie was always listening.

"Maddie? Listen, I want you to get away."

"Shh," she warned, but she didn't look back at the man with the gun. And the knife. And the mysterious vendetta or cause.

"I'm going to undo the cuffs," Logan said. He gestured to the pocket where he'd placed the key. After the kiss.

Maddie absolutely did not let herself think about the kiss.

"He won't be expecting it. When I jump him, you can—"

"I'm not leaving you."

"You've got to leave me, Maddie." Logan risked a glance behind her. "He'll hurt you."

They couldn't stop.

It was getting too dark and the rain wasn't rain anymore. Ice was falling from the sky and collecting on the ground, covering fallen logs and the layer of leaves that blanketed the forest floor. Rocks were slick and sharp beneath their feet.

Maddie absolutely did not have time to stop and tell Logan he was an idiot.

But she really, really wanted to.

Mostly, she wanted him to feel as awful as she did.

"I've been hurt before, Logan. I'm getting pretty good at it."

But before she could turn and saunter off into the forest, point made, Logan took her hands in his. "They need me alive, Mad. They don't need you. They will hurt you."

"*You* need me," she said.

She watched the words wash over him, sink in. She saw how badly he wanted to shrug and argue, say that he didn't need a stupid girl to help him.

Which just showed how badly the opposite was true.

"You don't get it, Mad——" he said instead.

"No. *You* don't get it."

"Maddie——" Logan started, but Maddie was already turning around.

Shouting, "Mr. Kidnapper Man?"

She could practically hear Stefan's groan, but he still asked "What?"

"I need to go," she told him.

His gruff laugh cut through the air. "You're not going anywhere."

"No." Maddie crossed her legs. She bobbed up and down in the age-old way of two-year-olds everywhere. "I mean I need to *go* go."

Maddie never had the chance to learn Russian, but she knew a curse word when she heard one, no matter the language.

Loosely translated, it meant *girls are so annoying*.

On this, at least, he and Logan seemed to have found common ground.

"Fine," the man spat out after a moment. "We break."

They'd reached the side of the hill where the vegetation was thicker and the wind wasn't as strong. Maddie moved toward the thick bushes that were quickly turning white with ice.

"Stop!" the man yelled. Reluctantly, Maddie turned.

She actually rolled her eyes.

"Um . . . I'm mad at him"—she pointed at Logan—"and I don't know you, so I'm gonna need a little privacy."

The man looked at Logan again, as if he needed someone to explain stupid American females to him, but Logan only shrugged.

"Look," Maddie said, "I get it. You're a bad guy. You might not have any qualms about killing people, but I bet even you have the decency to let a sixteen-year-old girl pee in peace."

"Maddie . . ." Logan warned, but Maddie wasn't in the mood to listen.

Instead, she stepped closer to the man with the gun.

Stefan was strong. Athletic. Young. And he moved with such sure, easy grace that Maddie might have been impressed under any other circumstances. But these circumstances were far from normal.

In a flash, the knife was in his hand and he was moving toward her. Maddie saw Logan register the movement, but Stefan was too fast and too strong. When he grabbed her bound wrists and thrust the knife toward her, she didn't fight it. Even as Logan screamed "No!"

In the next moment Maddie's wrists were free. Blood was rushing back to her cold hands and they started to tingle and burn; she moved her fingers just to prove that she still could.

Logan, on the other hand, stood staring.

The man jerked his head toward the bushes and kept his knife on Logan.

"If you run, just remember: There are parts of him I do not need at all."

Pushing through the thick brush, Maddie heard her name. She spun back to look at Logan, who looked like maybe he'd never see her again.

"I'm not worth it," he told her.

She smiled. "I know."

Then she turned and pushed through the trees. Ice clung to branches, weighing them down and covering the forest in shiny, frosty sequins. It was like the whole world had been bedazzled, and Maddie could at least appreciate that aspect of it.

She was just starting to push aside a particularly shiny limb when something bolted out in front of her.

No.

Some*one*.

And Maddie didn't think about anything else.

She screamed.

When Logan heard the scream, he thought that it was over.

He just wasn't exactly sure what "it" was.

Maybe this long, terrible trek to an even more terrible fate. Maybe the fear that had been growing inside of him for hours.

But, no, Logan realized. What was over was the charade he was playing that Maddie wasn't the most important thing in the world to him right then—the idea that she hadn't been that for ages.

He didn't look at the man with the gun for permission. He didn't think about himself. He just burst through the dense trees and bushes, sliding over the slick ground, not caring about the ice.

It was a scream of shock and terror and it didn't matter to Logan what might happen to him. All he knew was that the bravest girl in the world sounded terrified.

And it was all his fault.

"Maddie!" he shouted, but he didn't hear anything back.

It was almost night, and the only light was that of a quickly fading dusk.

"Maddie!"

"It's okay."

When Logan heard her voice, he stopped and bent at the waist, hands on knees. He thought his heart might beat out of his chest.

"Maddie, where—"

"It's okay," a voice yelled. "It's just me."

The man who pushed through the brush wasn't as tall as the kidnapper, but he wore a thick coat and a wide-brimmed hat that kept the sleet at bay. He smiled at them, like maybe he'd been looking for them for hours.

But he hadn't. Logan could tell.

"Sorry to scare you folks. I just wasn't expecting to see any-one else out here. I can tell I'm not the only one."

Logan felt Stefan's eyes on him, saw the subtle shake of his head.

Then Logan noticed the firearm in a holster at the other man's waist.

"Which begs the question, what *are* you folks doing out here?" the man asked.

Logan saw Maddie standing just past the man's shoulder. He could actually see her thinking, planning.

"Nature hike," she said, and Logan felt Stefan coming up behind him. He felt the gun at his back.

"What are *you* doing here?" Stefan asked.

"Oh, just checking on things before the storm settles in and makes itself at home," the man said. He was dressed like a forest ranger. It made sense that some people would be posted in this vast wilderness, but Logan had never imagined they might cross paths with one.

"I think you folks are a long way from where you're sup-posed to be," the man said. "No one should be out here on a night like this."

There was some kind of war waging within Stefan—Logan could feel it.

Logan had pulled the sleeves of his jacket down to protect his freezing hands, and that, coupled with the dim and fading light, meant that the ranger probably had no idea that Logan's hands were bound. Maddie was running around, apparently free.

Did this man know that he'd just stumbled upon the kidnapping of the century? Had some kind of alarm been raised? Was every ranger within a hundred miles out looking for the first son right then?

Or was this simply sheer dumb luck?

"Are you lost?" The ranger looked right at Stefan. "Do you know what you're doing?"

"Yes," Stefan said. "I do."

But he wasn't talking about the route they were taking, the best tricks for staying warm and dry.

Stefan's voice had taken on an otherworldly quality as he said it, as if he'd been pulled back into some deep sleep.

Then he raised his gun.

He fired.

Once.

Twice.

And the ranger fell.

"No!" Maddie yelled, rushing toward the man. She clawed at his body, trying to turn him over, pull his face out of the ice and the mud. Trying to help him.

But he was too big and Maddie was too small, too cold. And Stefan was already there, ripping her away from the man and slinging her across the ice-covered floor of the woods.

She scampered back, crawling away. As if it were possible to escape, but whatever hope she might have had died when Stefan grabbed Maddie by the arm and jerked her to her feet.

When he pushed her toward Logan, she didn't say a

word. She just threw her arms around Logan's waist and held him tight.

They held each other as if it might possibly be the last thing they'd ever do.

He didn't think a thing about it when she slid her hands beneath his jacket except to register that her hands felt warmer than they should, that they felt right. That maybe it was all worth it just to have this moment.

"I was so scared," he told her. "When you screamed, I . . ."

But Logan trailed off when he felt her slide something beneath the waistband of his jeans at the small of his back, where the tail of his coat would hide it.

He pulled back and looked down into her eyes.

And he knew.

He risked a quick glance at the ranger's body on the ground.

The empty holster.

Logan wasn't sure whether he should be happy that they had a gun now or mad because this was almost as disappointing as the kiss.

CHAPTER 15

Dear Logan,

Remember when we were friends?

I do. But sometimes, honestly, I'd give anything to forget.

Maddie

The gun rubbed against the small of Logan's back with every step he took. It didn't scrape. It didn't hurt. It *burned*.

He'd never understood the phrase *burning a hole in your pocket* until then. He'd never known just how much self-restraint could hurt.

But his hands were bound in front of him, and he couldn't easily reach the gun without unclasping his cuffs. And Maddie had told him not to. In a way, she was far scarier than the very ticked-off Russian.

She wasn't even breathing hard as they climbed. Her footsteps never faltered, even once the ground was covered with sleet. Maddie knew that terrain.

But, most of all, Maddie had a plan.

If there was anything close to a home court advantage, she had it, and Logan tried to be smart. He tried to be patient.

He tried to forget the way Maddie had pressed against him, the feel of her hands at his back.

He tried to pretend like every single thing in his life wasn't changing. But Logan was smarter than anyone knew. Which meant that Logan knew that nothing in his life was ever going to be the same again.

"We have a gun," he whispered.

"Calm down, city boy. We have a *flare* gun, in case you didn't notice."

Logan hadn't noticed, but he wasn't as disappointed as he should have been. Right then, the *gun* part was the only part that mattered.

But Maddie wasn't so sure. "This means one shot. One shot means we have to be smart about it."

"Maddie——"

"Listen to me, Logan. Listen now. You have to do what I tell you. When I say something you can't ask *what*. You can't ask *why*. You can't argue. And for the love of all that is holy, you can*not* try some stupid macho move that is only going to get us both killed. Okay? You have to *listen* to me."

"Okay," he said, partly to make her stop talking. Stefan was close, and even though it was dark and the sleet was falling harder, it was so quiet out there that even a whisper seemed to echo for an hour.

"No. Logan, listen to me. You have to do *exactly* what I say *exactly* when I say it. Promise me."

"I promise," he said, and she nodded like maybe—just maybe—she might be in the mood to believe him.

She put her head down and kept trudging through the storm, and for a moment Logan thought that maybe everything was going to be okay, but then Maddie stumbled to a stop. When she spun, there was terror in her eyes.

"No!" she screamed.

Behind them, Stefan kept walking. He nudged her forward. "We do not stop here."

But Maddie was shaking her head, shouting, "I know where you're taking us."

"You know what I need you to know."

"I know that map is about twenty years out of date." She pointed at the folded pieces of plastic-covered paper sticking out from the pocket of his pack.

"Walk," he ordered.

"No."

"Mad—" Logan tried, but she pulled away from him and kept glaring up at Stefan, a look of rage—or maybe fear—in her eyes.

"If you think we're going to cross it, you're crazy. Or you have a death wish. Or both."

"Mad?" Logan had no idea what she was talking about, but Maddie was too frantic to fill him in.

145

"You're crazy!" she shouted. "We should go to Black Bear Bridge. I mean, it's not a bridge made of black bears, don't worry. But it's about twenty years newer and a hundred times safer— and if you haven't already noticed, we're not exactly dealing with ideal conditions here."

"What are you talking about?" Logan snapped. He was hungry and he was cold and frustration was coming off of him in waves.

But Maddie kept her gaze locked on Stefan. "Look, I know you don't care about me. And you probably don't even care about yourself. I get that. But you care about *him*." She pointed at Logan. "And he's not going to do you any good if he's at the bottom of a hundred-foot ravine, smashed into about a million little icy pieces." That part at least seemed to hit its mark. "I don't want to die. And you need him alive. So please. Let's just go to Black Bear Bridge."

Logan watched Stefan consider this. "How far is this Black Bear Bridge?" the Russian asked.

"It's not too far."

"How far?" Stefan snapped.

Maddie couldn't meet his gaze. "It's only a half day's walk."

"A half day's walk?" Stefan asked. "Under good conditions?"

Maddie had to nod.

"We go my way," Stefan said, and pushed forward.

"Let her go back," Logan was still pleading with Stefan ten minutes later. "It'll take her a day to walk back to her cabin, and you and I will be long gone by then, won't we? I mean, that's why we can't go to this other bridge, right? Because we're on a deadline here? Then let her go. You don't need her."

"Yes. I do."

Some faces just weren't supposed to smile. Stefan's was one of them, Maddie decided. Because when he grinned at Logan's words, it had an eerie effect, like he was ten moves away from checkmate and he was the only one who could see it. It made Maddie's heart pound harder, her hands want to shake. She wanted to reach for her own rock and take her chances, but that wasn't the smart play.

And they were currently in the middle of almost twenty million acres of wilderness with heavy precipitation and falling temperatures and absolutely no help on the way.

They didn't have time for stupid.

But that didn't wipe the smile from Stefan's face. It didn't dampen the fire that was burning inside of Logan.

"What's so funny?" Logan snapped. "Just let her go!"

It might have been sweet. Or heroic. Or even romantic—if Stefan hadn't taken a few more steps and then turned on them. The hill was tall and steep. Landslides and glaciers had scraped away huge chunks where no trees grew and the snow and the rain didn't stick. A river ran beneath them, curving through the forest like a snake. Freezing rain kept falling and the water down below was from the melting glaciers, which meant even in the middle of summer it was cold.

In good conditions, with the right gear, a person could climb down there. Maybe wade across if he had a death wish. But that would take time . . . and time was one of many things they didn't have.

And that's what brought them here—to a tenuous lifeline that ran between this hill and the next. Even in the darkness and the sleet it practically glowed, probably because it was covered with ice and looked like something that a Disney princess might have summoned and built with her two hands. In the remaining traces of light it practically glistened, shining like crystals. But Maddie knew what lay underneath.

Ropes ran across the gorge. Wooden planks had once been placed at regular intervals, spanning the two hundred feet of the bridge. But there had been too much rain, too much snow. Too many hot summer days and strong mountain winds in the twenty or so years since anyone stopped caring. No one ever came here. No one who did come here would forget that there was another, safer bridge not too terribly far away.

No one would be stupid enough to cross.

"I need your girlfriend, President's Son," Stefan said. "I need her to go across that bridge and show us how safe it is."

Safe wasn't a word that had been used to describe it in over a decade. Maybe longer. Long before she and her father had moved to Alaska. She had heard about this bridge, about how the parks department meant to come tear it down every summer, but with cutbacks and budget freezes it got delayed every year. Besides, it's not like anyone ever came here. It's not like anyone would ever be stupid enough—desperate enough—to try to cross it.

"She's not going across that," Logan said. He positioned his large body in between Maddie and Stefan.

"Logan?" Maddie's voice was smaller than it should have been.

"She's not doing it! She's not some kind of puppet. She's—"

"Logan?" Maddie tried again, but he was staring daggers into Stefan.

"We need you alive," Stefan reminded Logan. "So the girl can go or the girl can die here."

Stefan pulled his gun from his waistband and pointed it in Maddie's direction, but Logan was already shielding her.

Like he cared.

He just hadn't cared enough to write.

"Move," Stefan ordered.

"Logan?"

"You're not going to hurt her!" Logan shouted.

But Maddie just threw up her hands. "Boys!"

Logan seemed to remember exactly who was behind him. That she was a real person with a voice and opinions. She wasn't some ideal.

"Logan, listen to me." She grabbed him by the collar and pulled him close. Luckily Stefan had never retied her hands, so she was able to wrap her arms around him, feel him one more time.

"I'll be okay," she said.

"No, Mad. You can't do this."

But that was exactly the wrong thing to say because she pulled back. She actually cocked an eyebrow. "Watch me."

Logan wasn't willing to let her go. He took her arm. "No, Mad. I'm not going to let you."

"You're not *letting* me," she said, but when Logan dragged her closer she didn't fight. She didn't squirm or scream or push him away. No. That might have tipped Stefan off to exactly how formidable she was.

Yes. Exactly. That had to be why Maddie didn't resist at all when Logan pulled her body right up against his and said, "I'm not going to lose you again."

He even sounded like he meant it.

He looked into her eyes. "That's not a bridge, Mad Dog. It's suicide."

"Do you trust me?" Maddie asked.

"Hurry up!" Stefan yelled.

"Logan, do you trust me?" she asked again, urgent now. Time was running out. In a lot of ways.

And Logan nodded.

So Maddie went up on her tiptoes and pressed a warm kiss to Logan's cold cheek.

Then she whispered in his ear, "Step *exactly* where I step. And be *ready*."

She could see the question in his eyes: *Ready for what?* But he was at least smart enough not to say it aloud. Instead, he seemed to hold his breath.

And watch.

The ground at the mouth of the bridge was flat and wide and, by that point, covered with at least an inch of ice and snow. It actually crunched beneath Maddie's feet, tiny ice pellets grinding into almost nothing, pressing hard against the ground and getting slicker with every moment. Surely that was why she took a huge step, an awkward lunging jump that seemed to bypass as much of that space in front of the bridge as possible. But she was steady and sure on her feet as she eased toward the posts that stuck up from the ground. She reached out for them and pulled, relieved when they didn't wiggle. Then she gave one last look back.

"Logan?"

"You don't have to do it, Mad Dog," he said again, but she shook her head.

"Did you get my letters?" Maybe she was a fool for stepping out onto that bridge, but she couldn't do it without knowing. Once and for all.

He shook his head. "What letters?"

And then it was Maddie's turn to smile, but it was one without joy.

"I'll see you on the other side," she said.

When Maddie took a step, the first board was so slick that she actually skidded. There wasn't any traction, and Maddie had to grip the braces at the mouth of the bridge to steady herself. She almost fell to her knees.

"Maddie!" Logan yelled and lunged forward, but she looked back and shook him off.

"I'm fine," she said. "Just . . . *exactly*." She mouthed the last word and stared into his eyes, willing him to hear her, see her.

Believe her, knowing that for the first time in her life someone needed to follow in her footsteps.

When she was steady on her feet again, she tried the next board. And the next.

The third one creaked, but it seemed steady enough, so Maddie risked shifting her weight, only to have it splinter beneath her. But her hold on the rope handles held.

The old rope was freezing. As she moved her hand, ice slid off of the coarse bristles and bit into her cold skin. She was like a tiny, one-woman snowplow, clearing the way.

One step. Then another. Some of the boards were missing. Others hung at odd angles, and with the ice she didn't trust herself not to slip and fall. Only once did she have to jump, but Maddie was part goat, her father always said, and she landed lightly on the other side.

She risked a glance back at Logan.

"It's solid," she yelled. She might have even meant it.

But Logan was shaking his head. "Maddie, come back."

"Keep going!" Stefan shouted. His gun was out and pointed at Logan's back.

"Logan, come on," Maddie called to him.

"Mad—"

"Logan, you have to trust me. Please."

Maybe it was the *please* that did it. But he took one last look at Stefan, then moved toward the bridge.

CHAPTER 16

Dear Logan,

    Forgive me for not writing for several days. You see, I've been extremely busy with my new, oh-so-exciting life. See?

    Things to do in Alaska:

        -chop wood

        -catch fish

        -clean fish

        -haul wood

        -catch some more fish

        -try not to get eaten, smashed, burned, poisoned, or just, in general, die

    Seriously, trying not to die in Alaska is kind of a full-time job.

                                 Maddie

• • •

Logan stared at where Maddie stood, in the center of a bridge that looked like it should have already fallen based on the weight of the snow and the ice alone. Much less with Maddie's weight. Much less with his.

"Logan, it's okay!" she called to him. "Just do what I said."

He heard her words again: *From this moment on, step exactly where I step.*

There were things the Secret Service agents had to teach him, back when he was a kid and his dad was just a candidate—back when no one assumed they knew him. Back when Maddie really did.

The first lesson they teach a protectee is that, if an agent says duck, you duck. If an agent says run, you run. You don't stop for questions. You never, ever say *What?* Because in the time it takes you to stop and say that single word, a sniper can strike from a thousand yards away. It's the protectee's job to follow directions and then get out of the way and let the professionals do their jobs.

Maybe it was that training coming back to him. Or maybe it was the look in Maddie's eyes when she asked Logan to trust her. Logan swore right then that he never wanted to disappoint Maddie ever again. He owed her that much at least. He was going to mirror her movements exactly, even if he was at least fifty pounds heavier than she was. In the part of his brain that was always thinking, analyzing, calculating, Logan knew that just because a board was strong enough to hold her there was no guarantee that it would be strong enough to hold *him*. But it was as good a place as any to start.

He inched toward the bridge and paused to look down at the icy ground in front of him. It had been blowing and swirling all day and something like a drift covered the mouth of the bridge. But it wasn't so deep he had to wade.

"Remember! Be careful," she shouted. And something in Logan knew—just knew—that it was the *remember* that mattered.

Be ready, she'd said.

But ready for what?

There was only one way to find out.

Logan's footprints dwarfed Maddie's as he stepped into her tracks and moved slowly toward the bridge.

He could still feel Stefan behind him, on Logan's right, where he had an angle on both of his captives. He kept the gun trained on Logan as he matched Maddie's big step onto the mouth of the bridge, mirroring her in every way. But his hands were still cuffed in front of him, and he could only hang on to one side.

When he slipped on a slick board it was harder than it should have been to catch himself. His body kept twisting at the waist to grip the rope handles and he couldn't get centered.

When Logan slipped again, he risked a glance at Stefan, a smirk. "Bet you're wishing you hadn't thrown away that handcuff key about now, aren't you?" he asked.

"Walk!" Stefan ordered, and Logan forced himself to turn around.

Maddie was still inching closer to the other side, but she turned to him and nodded slowly, the universal signal for *it's time*.

So, slowly, Logan reached into his pocket for the key Stefan had thrown away that morning. In the darkness, Stefan couldn't see well enough to know what Logan was doing when he unhooked the left wrist cuff but kept his hands together.

With a glance back, he could see that Stefan had put away his gun and was approaching the bridge himself.

Maybe it was because he was coming from a slightly different angle. Maybe it was because he didn't think he had to listen to a teenage girl. Or maybe it was common sense for him to step right up to the edge, to the place where bridge met land. To the place where the snow was a little bit thicker.

To the place that Maddie—and then Logan—had jumped right over.

Stefan stepped into the deep snow and immediately his foot disappeared.

For a moment nothing happened.

And then Logan heard the snap.

The yell.

A moment later Stefan was falling over and digging at the snow and ice, pulling at his leg. But it wasn't just his leg.

Something clung to Stefan's dark jeans, like an animal that had locked its jaws around his calf and was hanging on for dear life. But it wasn't an animal, Logan realized.

No. In that moment *Stefan* was the animal, as he pried the metal jaws apart and pulled his leg free of the trap.

"Logan, run!" Maddie yelled, and Logan realized that she'd already made it to the far side of the bridge.

This was her plan.

This was their chance.

But Stefan had already pried the trap off his leg and tossed it into the abyss below. Hate and rage radiated from him.

They didn't have a moment to lose.

Stefan must have been so angry that he ignored Maddie's footsteps and started to run. As soon as his big foot landed on the first rung of the bridge, the board snapped. The bridge jerked beneath Logan's feet as Stefan grabbed at the ropes and lunged forward. The next board snapped, too, and Logan knew it was no accident.

He thought about the small knife that Stefan had taken from Maddie, and just like that he knew. Maddie had come here. Maddie had done this.

He had to get to Maddie.

Now.

Stefan's strong arm was wrapped around the icy ropes of the bridge. His good leg dangled down between the broken slats. There was too much pressure on the leg that had been in the trap. When he screamed, it sounded like a bear had been caught in Maddie's trap instead of a man.

And Logan didn't dare stick around to see if his bite was as bad as his growl.

"Logan, *exactly*!" Maddie yelled again, and Logan tried to match his steps to hers.

He tried to be fast.

He tried to be careful.

He needed so badly to be with Maddie again, both of them finally on the same side of the river after what felt like a lifetime apart.

Stefan grappled behind him, and the ropes swung. The bridge shifted, snow and ice crashing off the sides and disappearing into the vast darkness below.

But he was almost there. He could actually make out the look in her eyes—the little ring of blue that surrounded her irises. It was dark and he knew he couldn't actually see it—not really. But he could see *her* in a way he hadn't in years.

Somehow, it was a way he had *never* seen her.

So when the look of terror filled her eyes, he couldn't help but turn back.

Stefan had dragged himself free of the broken boards and was on his feet again, running toward them.

"Logan, now!" Maddie shouted, and Logan leaped toward her, bypassing the last six steps of the bridge. He landed hard on the ground and rolled as Maddie reached for him.

He tried to get to his feet. They had to run. They had to—

But Maddie's arms were around him then, pulling something from the small of his back.

She got free and rolled. Then, in one single, fluid motion she cocked the flare gun and aimed at the center of the old rope bridge.

There was still ice all over it, but Maddie had scraped away a lot as she walked, and when she took aim there was no indecision, no crisis of conscience or faith.

She was the image of her father as she fired.

Logan hadn't realized how dark it had gotten—it had happened little by little, bit by bit. But as soon as the flare left the gun it was instantly daylight—if sunlight were the color of fire.

Red streaked across the sky and soared across the dark ravine.

It reminded Logan vaguely of the Fourth of July. The first year he'd celebrated at the White House, Maddie had come over and her dad had made arrangements for them to go up on the roof with the snipers. It was the best view in DC, everyone said, and they'd lain together on an itchy blanket watching fireworks over the Washington Monument. Logan remembered the big, booming sounds, the streaking lights in reds and blues. But most of all, he remembered thinking that he should hold Maddie's hand but knowing that would be weird since she'd just started being his friend. His only friend. He couldn't run the risk of grossing her out by touching her with the hand he'd been using to eat popcorn with too much butter.

And that's what he thought about then.

Not Stefan.

Not Alaska.

Not even how cold and hungry and exhausted he was. How terrified.

Logan just wished he'd been brave enough to hold Maddie's hand.

When the flare hit the center of the bridge, nothing happened for a moment. It seemed as if maybe the fire was going to die there, smothered by the snow and the ice.

But then the old ropes and wood exploded in a wave of color and fire and heat, and Logan didn't doubt anymore. He swore to never put off anything ever again, and he reached for Maddie's hand, pulled it into his own.

It was so small, and not nearly as smooth as it should have been. It was a hand that had known work and hardship and . . .

Maddie pulled away, and Logan fought the hurt that was growing in his chest. Maybe she didn't want to touch him. Maybe she really did hate him, would hate him forever.

But Maddie walked to the side of the bridge, and then he saw a huge knife buried in the post, waiting.

"Stefan took your knife," he blurted like an idiot.

Maddie looked like she'd never been more insulted in her life. "I never leave the house with just one knife. Seriously. Do I look like a one-knife kind of girl?" She pulled it from the post and Logan could see the fire glistening off of a long blade that could have easily sliced through those old ropes. But they hadn't needed it. Yet.

She shoved the knife into a sheath in her boot. "Always have a backup," she said, and Logan heard a crack. He looked back to see the bridge breaking apart.

Stefan had rushed back to the other side, but he'd lost his pack. It was lying there, in the center of the bridge that was burning all around him.

The pack with the satellite phone.

Logan didn't think. He just started for the bridge. If he

could get the pack, he could get the phone, and then this would all be over.

The pack was between Logan and the fire and he could get there. He could—

But he never made it to the bridge, because Maddie's hand was back in his again, holding tight, yanking in the opposite direction.

"I can get it!" he yelled, but Maddie pulled back.

"Leave it!" she shouted.

Smoke filled the air as the fire spread. In the new light he could see her plainly, the worry in her eyes. The tension and the fear.

He tried to pull away again.

"We need it!" he shouted, but Maddie was stronger than she looked. So very strong as she pulled him back to her, wrapped her arms around his waist, and held him tight.

"I need you more."

The fire crackled and the bridge burned, and Logan knew without a shadow of a doubt that they could never, ever go back. This moment was going to change their lives forever.

He turned and looked at what lay on this side of the ravine. More trees. Another steep hill and ice-covered rocks.

And then he heard it, something like a pop. He risked a glance back, expecting to see the bridge finally breaking apart and falling into the abyss, but the bridge still stood. Barely.

He heard the sound again, the echo of the shot off the steep stone walls of the mountains that surrounded them. And through the smoke and the haze and the falling snow he saw the assassin on the opposite bank, arm raised and steady. Stefan's gun didn't even quiver as he shot again. And again.

"Run!" Logan and Maddie both shouted, and they started for the cover of the trees.

They never stopped holding hands.

CHAPTER 17

Dear Logan,

The next time you see me, you should call me Dr. Maddie. I basically have a medical degree in first aid. I mean, I know there is no such thing, but there totally should be. I can dig out a splinter using a safety pin or a pair of tweezers (which, really, what self-respecting girl DOESN'T have a pair of tweezers?). I can treat burns and scrapes and lots of stuff way too gross to put on paper.

So, yeah. Call me Dr. Maddie.

But who am I kidding?

You're never going to call me anything ever again.

Maddie

Logan could hear the shots still coming, long after he and Maddie were lost among the cover of the trees. The red glow of the fire was fading, but they took advantage of what light there was. Soon, there would be nothing but darkness and more snow. And probably bears.

Man, he really hoped there wouldn't be bears.

But then an even scarier thought occurred to him.

"Mad, is there really a Black Bear Bridge?"

She looked up at him. "Yes."

He wanted to curse but didn't. "I saw it on the map, I think. But it didn't look like a half day's walk."

"No. It's closer. But he doesn't know that. And I needed him to come this way. I needed . . ." She trailed off. She was breathing hard, Logan noticed. She'd been so strong for so long. He wanted to hug her, but the hand-holding was new enough. He didn't want to risk it.

"It worked, Mad. It was genius. It was evil. You're an evil genius, and I'm . . . I'm glad you're on my side."

"Don't act so surprised," she told him.

They walked on for a few minutes. The light of the fire was almost gone now. They couldn't even hear the Russian curse words piercing the too-cold, too-clear air.

With every step the snow and sleet fell harder, collecting on their hoods and their shoulders, and Logan didn't want to think about what would happen if they stopped moving, even for a minute.

"What's over here?" he asked.

"On this side of the river?"

"Yeah. There wasn't much detail on Stefan's map."

As Maddie shrugged, she lost her footing for a moment. She held tighter to Logan's hand to keep her feet.

"More of the same, I think," she said. "A few mining roads that have been out of commission for ages. An old ranger's station, but no one uses it, and I doubt it's stocked. Plus, it'd take all day to walk there."

Logan looked around the dark forest. "We're running out of day."

"Yes," Maddie said, and Logan could actually hear her teeth chattering.

"You're freezing," he said, trying to pull her closer.

Maddie winced and pulled away.

At first, he felt silly. He felt hurt. Maybe the hand-holding and the kissing and the superdramatic hugging were all for Stefan's benefit. Maddie was never going to have to slip a key from her mouth into his again, he realized. He was almost disappointed.

But then Maddie stumbled on the almost smooth ground. She was no longer the girl who had leaped across a decaying, ice-covered bridge. Instead, she was bending at the waist, and even in the darkness, Logan could tell that her face was too pale. Her hand had been too cold—even given the air and the snow and the terrible day they'd had.

"I'm fine. It's just a scratch," she said, but the words slurred and she swayed again.

"Maddie!" he snapped. He was almost mad at her. He was furious at himself as he went for the zipper of her outer jacket. She tried to push his hands away, but she was too weak.

His heart pounded in his chest and his hands started to shake for reasons that had nothing to do with the cold as he unzipped her jacket. Then he pulled aside a layer and felt it—something warm and sticky beneath the logo on her jacket.

Something that smelled like blood.

Maddie swayed a little. She tried to laugh as she looked up into his eyes and said, "Tag. I'm it."

And then she passed out cold.

Maddie was dreaming. She had to be. Why else would it feel like she was flying, floating through the air? Why else would she be hearing Logan's voice, talking to her through the dark?

"Stay with me, Mad Dog. I've got you. You're gonna be okay. Wake up, Maddie. Wake up. Wake up!" Logan shouted.

But it wasn't Logan. It couldn't be. Logan was back in DC and he wasn't her friend anymore. He'd never be her friend again.

Logan had died in that White House corridor. Her friend had died, gone away forever. But now he'd come back to her.

In her dream.

Maddie tried to roll over. She wanted to pull the covers up higher, wrap herself in them tighter. She wanted to stop shaking.

"No. Don't. Stop fighting, Mad Dog," Dream Logan told her, but Maddie wanted to laugh at him. Shows what he knew.

Maddie never could stop fighting.

But first she had to get warm.

She really should get up and put some more wood on the fire, but her eyelids were too heavy. And Dream Logan, as annoying as he might be, was better than No Logan. So Maddie let her eyes stay closed.

"Here," Dream Logan told her, and Maddie was suddenly warmer.

Maddie was so warm. She felt so safe. And so she slept.

And she had dreams of Real Logan, even though he was a lifetime away.

CHAPTER 18

Dear Logan,

I'm sorry that the stupid Russians shot you.

Mainly because I really want to shoot you, and I hate that they beat me to it.

Maddie

Maddie wasn't dying.

No. Logan wouldn't let her.

When he was little, Logan's mother used to tell him that he was the most stubborn child in the world. But that had been before they'd both met Maddie. She never gave up. She never gave in.

Maddie clung to life, so Logan clung to her. The farther he walked, the tighter he held her, and Logan didn't even feel the chill of the falling snow, even though he'd wrapped her in his jacket. He could still see the traces of blood on her face from her fall this morning. He knew the wound on her shoulder was probably still bleeding no matter how hard he had tried to stop it.

The little strip of red made him think about DC and *That Night*, about the fluttering fabric that trailed behind the rolling cart, about the realization that he might be about to lose his mother.

And then Logan realized that was no longer the scariest moment of his life.

This was the scariest moment of his life.

So Logan gripped her harder and kept moving.

Away from the burning bridge. Away from Stefan's only path over the ravine, assuming he made it there through the storm and the darkness.

Logan wasn't going to let Maddie go. Not now. Not ever again.

As soon as he stepped out of the helicopter—as soon as he'd seen her—he'd known she was different. Not just taller. Not just stronger. Not just significantly less sparkly.

No, the real change in Maddie had been in her eyes. They'd always shone like maybe they were bedazzled. But that light was gone, Logan had thought the day before.

Was it just a day?

He had to think. Of course it was. He'd been in Alaska a little over twenty-four hours.

He looked down at the girl who was sleeping in his arms. For twenty-four hours she had felt like a stranger, but with her eyes closed, in the shadowy darkness of the forest with only the palest hint of moonlight reflected off the snow, she looked like the

Maddie he used to know, like maybe she had fallen asleep watching a movie or maybe like she was just playing possum, wanting him to tickle her awake. For a minute, he could see his Maddie in the girl in his arms, as long as she was asleep.

So it was harder than it should have been to shake her one more time and say, "Maddie, wake up."

But she didn't even stir.

And Logan knew whatever he was doing, it wasn't enough.

He eased her to the ground and held his breath as he felt for her pulse. It was there, but faint. He leaned closer and felt her breath on his cheek—too light, though. He could see his own breath fogging in the cold air, but Maddie's was invisible. He had to check again, to make sure it was there.

And only then did Logan start to feel himself panic.

He'd read books on first aid. He'd gone through a documentary kick two summers before, and he knew that Maddie had lost a lot of blood today. She'd been shot. She'd been knocked down a cliff. And head wounds bled like crazy. Plus she was so little and it was so cold outside. No wonder she was shaking.

Except . . .

Logan went from scared to terrified when he realized she was no longer shaking.

"Maddie!" he yelled. He had to get her awake. He had to get her warm. He had to get her dry and hydrated and fed and . . . safe. He had to get Maddie safe.

But the snow was heavier. It landed on her face with thick

white flakes that melted on her smooth skin. It made it look like she was crying.

And now that Logan had stopped walking, he was starting to shiver, too. His skin was actually slick with sweat, but that was a lie. Logan wasn't hot. His body was lying to his mind, and soon the shock of it all was going to set in. Soon he was going to crash from this adrenaline and then . . .

Logan wasn't going to think about what happened then.

He rested for a moment, sitting on a log, but he kept Maddie on his lap. Maybe to consolidate their body heat. Maybe he didn't want to place her frail body on top of the snow and the ice. Or maybe Logan just wasn't going to let her go again. Ever. So he kept her on his lap as he thought.

"Hey, Mad Dog."

Somehow, Logan knew he had to keep talking. Not for her. But for him.

"You got big, you know. But I guess I got bigger. Mom told me to stop growing, but it's been a long time since I've done what they told me to do. You know that, don't you?"

Logan looked up at the sky that was so dark. He'd never seen anything so dark. He'd lived most of his life in cities, and even in the country—at places like Camp David—in Logan's world there were security lights and headlights and flashlights.

There was always light.

But Logan and Maddie were alone in the darkness. He knew that there were millions of acres around them, and Logan didn't see a single, solitary light——not on any of the distant hills. They were very much alone.

"I don't think your dad's going to be able to make it back in this, Mad Dog." He touched her forehead. It was still warm, but not too warm. If a fever was coming, it hadn't found her yet.

"I think you're stuck with me. I think we're alone. But that's okay. I promise not to tell anyone. I don't think they'll make us get married."

He looked down at her sleeping face.

Sleeping, Logan reminded himself. He absolutely refused to even think the word *unconscious*.

"That was a joke, Mad Dog. Wake up and laugh. Or, better yet, wake up and call me an idiot. Do it, I dare you."

Maddie never had been able to turn down a dare.

That must have been what did it, because Logan saw the snowflakes on her long, dark eyelashes start to flutter.

"Logan," she said, then tried to move. She tried to roll over in his arms, but Logan just held tighter.

"You're not here," she said, eyelids fluttering again, then going still, like she wanted to go back to sleep, but Logan couldn't let that happen.

"Maddie, stay with me."

"You're not here," she said again, but he shook her. Gently.

"Oh, I'm not?" He wanted to laugh he was so happy just to hear her groggy words.

She tried to twist in his arms again, but this time she was

twisting closer, snuggling into his warmth, and Logan didn't fight her in the least.

"No. You're gone," she said. "I'm just dreaming that you're here. And that you're hot now."

"You think I'm hot?"

Maddie made a little sound and nodded, something like *uh-huh*. "Dream You is. But he's not real."

She sounded sad. Disappointed. Lonely.

Logan looked out over the vast, empty darkness. Of course she was lonely. She'd been alone out here long before they were alone out here together.

"Maddie, I'm real," he whispered, and ran a finger across her forehead, tucking a stray hair underneath the shelter of her tightly drawn hood.

"No," she said. "You died."

Then Maddie drew a deep breath and shuddered, wincing in pain. When she closed her eyes, he could almost feel her start to slip away again.

"No! No, stay with me, Maddie. Mad Dog! Wake up!"

Logan was screaming, but he no longer cared who heard him.

"Stay with me, Mad Dog," he tried again. He shifted her in his arms like a baby who is trying to learn to sit up. "Maddie!"

"Logan?" she said, and she sounded a little more like herself. Which meant she sounded a little like she hated him. It was the sweetest sound that he had ever heard.

"Where's your coat?" she asked.

"You're wearing it," he told her. He didn't even try to hide his smile.

"You're an idiot," she said, trying to push herself upright, trying to take his coat off, he could tell, and give it back to him. But as soon as she moved, she winced. He could see the pain on her face, hear it in her voice as she cried out.

"No, Maddie. Don't move. You're hurt."

"Logan . . ." He could tell she wanted to argue. Even frozen and bleeding and half dead, Maddie wanted to argue. Then she remembered. "I was shot."

"Yes," he said, then tried to smile. "Your shoulder hurts, I know."

Maddie nodded as if remembering. He *did* know.

"How long was I out?"

"An hour? Maybe less. Probably less. But it felt like forever. I carried you away from the bridge and—Maddie, stay still. I've got you." He adjusted his grip on her, even though he knew he should get up. They had to keep moving. The sweat was drying on his body, and soon he would start shaking. He couldn't let that happen. He had to get her to safety or, at the very least, get her warm.

"We can't stay here, Logan," she said as if reading his mind. "We're sitting ducks here."

"He's on the other side of the river, remember?"

But Maddie had finally pushed herself upright. She had to face him. "That man's not the most dangerous thing in Alaska."

Five minutes before, Logan had been certain he'd never been

more afraid in his life, but something in Maddie's voice changed all that. She knew what she was talking about. She'd survived here for years. And the way she was pushing herself off his lap, the urgency with which she pulled off his coat and her own told him that this mattered. So he didn't argue.

"There were berries," she said.

"Yes. Do you want me to find some. I can . . ."

But Logan trailed off when Maddie started stripping. He knew he should have argued, but he'd lost the ability to speak at all.

It was well below freezing, but Maddie didn't stop. She just peeled off layer after layer until she could see the piece of Logan's T-shirt that he had shoved inside her clothes in hopes of stopping the bleeding.

She turned her back to him.

"Is there an exit wound?" she asked.

Numbly, Logan nodded.

"Is there?" she snapped, and he realized she couldn't see him well.

"Yes."

"Good."

"Get some snow. We have to wash the blood off."

"Maddie, I don't care about a little blood. I care that you're going to freeze to death."

"It smells," she said.

"I don't care that you stink, Mad."

"The bears are awake, Logan," she practically snapped. "There were berries today, remember? Which means they haven't run out of food yet. They should have started hibernating by now, but the climate is all screwed up and winters are so much shorter and . . . the bears are awake. Did you know bears have one of the best senses of smell of any predator on the planet? Polar bears can follow a scent for thirty miles. Grizzlies and black bears are almost as good, and we are surrounded by grizzly and black bears. Now help me wash the blood off."

"They could be hibernating," he told her.

It took a beat for her to answer. And it scared him.

"They're not" was all she said.

"But—"

"I saw one. Earlier today. When I was following you guys. I had to be quiet, which violates rule one of life in Alaska: You always want a bear to hear you coming. But I couldn't let you guys hear me coming, so . . . I saw one."

"Are you okay?" he asked.

She pushed his worry away. "I'm fine. He wasn't interested in me. But now that the weather's turned . . ."

"Oh," Logan said.

Maddie looked at him. "You think I stink?"

"No. I . . . Let's get you cleaned up."

Maddie reached down, pulled the knife from her boot, and started cutting away the pieces of her shirt that were the bloodiest.

Even in the moonlight, Logan could tell that Maddie's skin was as white as the snow. He might have called her Snow White. He might have joked or teased, but she was starting to shake again. He could tell she was struggling to stay upright.

But the bullet had passed right through her shoulder, and the wound was clotting well. They tore up her base layer and used it to scrub away the blood as best they could. When they were done, she handed him the pieces of her shirt and the part of his that he'd used to stanch the bleeding.

They'd been walking parallel to the river, but upstream. Logan just hadn't known where else to go.

So Maddie took the bloodiest of the rags and wrapped them around a rock, tying them over and over. She walked to the tree line and pulled back her arm to throw, but she winced and almost went to her knees. She would have if Logan hadn't caught her.

"I've got you," he said. She looked back at him, over her good shoulder. He could have sworn she let him take a little more of her weight, leaned into him with a little more softness.

He snaked his hand down her arm, then took the bundle from her hands.

"Let me."

He pulled back his strong right arm and threw as hard as he could.

In the center of the river, where the current was strongest, the water hadn't iced over. That was where the bundle landed. Logan knew it without seeing it, without hearing the telltale plop.

The bundle was gone. The rags were at the bottom of the river. But Maddie was still in his arms and she was still shaking.

They'd cut away the blood-covered portion of her clothing, and he helped her pull everything else back on. When he tried to zip her into his coat again, she shook her head.

"You need it," she said.

"You're in shock, Mad. You have to get warm." He tried again to wrap the coat around her, but Maddie was gaining her stubbornness even if not her strength.

"You're bigger than I am."

"Exactly." He shook the coat out again and reached for her.

"Which means if you go down, we're both in trouble. I need you, Logan." The words hurt her. But she said them anyway because there were too many things in those woods that could hurt them. Maddie wasn't the kind of girl who was willing to be killed by a secret. "I need you to be okay."

Slowly, Logan nodded. He pulled on his coat and zipped it up, placed the hood over his head.

"Now what?" he asked her.

She was finally bundled inside her own clothes and standing on her own feet, but they were both running on fumes.

"We walk," she said, then gave one last look across the river, to the place where some unknown man hunted them for some unknown reason. "We try to get as far away from here as possible."

CHAPTER 19

Dear Logan,

Did you know grizzly bears are always brown and black bears aren't always black, but black bears are never grizzlies?

I know a lot more than that, you know. But I'm not going to tell you because you never answer my letters.

Maddie

Maddie wasn't as cold as she should have been, and that was just one of the things that scared her.

The first sign of hypothermia was the shaking. The second was when the shaking stopped. Her first winter, her dad had sat her down and gone through it all. How important it was to stay warm. How staying warm didn't matter if you couldn't stay dry. She knew the most dangerous thing about the cold wasn't what it did to your body; it was what it did to your mind.

There were lots of cases of people getting so cold that they thought they were warm. They'd pull off their coats and shoes. They'd run out into the snow and the ice. Hypothermia made you stupid, and in Alaska, stupid would almost always get you killed.

That was why Maddie tried to pretend she was steadier on her feet than she was—why she kept talking, praying that her words wouldn't slur.

They had to keep walking. Keep moving. Because the rule of the wild is simple, and the order is not up for debate.

Shelter before fire.

Fire before water.

Water before food.

Food before pretty much anything else.

So step one was shelter. And the trees no longer counted.

"Keep an eye out for caves," she told Logan. "And sometimes you can crawl into the big trees, nest in around the roots. But we have to be careful."

"Because of bears?" Logan asked.

"And wolves," she said. "Wolves like places like that."

"Oh. There are wolves now. Yay," Logan said.

"If we find a big rock or something with shelter on one side, we can cut some brush and make a lean-to. We need cover. We have to get dry."

It felt like she was talking to herself—like when she was a little girl and she didn't want to go to sleep. She was always stubborn, her father told her. She'd chatter away for hours, and the heavier her eyelids got the louder she talked. She was doing it again, she knew, but this time she didn't care.

"Which way is the bridge?" Logan's voice was filled with concern as he stopped and surveyed their surroundings.

It was pitch-dark, of course. But a little moonlight filtered through the trees, and in a way the snow was a good thing. It covered their tracks and reflected what light there was, and their eyes had adjusted to the darkness. They could walk a little farther. But Logan didn't sound so sure.

"I'm turned around." He sounded panicked. He cursed. "Mad, I'm turned around."

"North is this way," she said. "The river's behind us, but it bends. We're okay."

"But where's the good bridge?"

"Behind us," she said. "He won't catch us. Not yet."

Maddie knew what Logan was thinking—fearing. She knew because she was thinking it, too. She stopped and looked up at him.

Which was a mistake.

Because he was even more handsome than he had been when he'd climbed out of the helicopter, all clean and styled and official.

Now it looked like he needed to shave, which was more than a little scary because

(A) *Logan shaved!*

And (B) it turned out, when pretty tall, pretty handsome boys needed to shave they became less "pretty" and more . . . handsome. Which was its own particular brand of terrifying.

His eyes seemed brighter in the darkness, his senses more alive. She tried not to remember how warm and safe she'd felt in his arms, but she kept looking up at him, trying to see her friend there. But her friend—her Logan—really was gone. And this boy—this almost-a-man—wasn't nearly as easy to hate as Maddie had been pretending.

Maybe that was why the trees started to swirl, why the sky began to spin.

She just knew that a moment later Logan's arms were around her again, and he was saying, "Whoa there."

"I'm not a horse," Maddie managed to mutter, but her heart wasn't in it. Even she could hear the words slur.

"Yeah. True. So maybe I need to give you a ride."

She wasn't exactly sure what that meant. After all, slang was constantly changing and Maddie had missed six whole years of teenage evolution. In Maddie's world, it was basically 1890, and that wasn't going to change anytime soon. So she had no idea what Logan was saying, but then her feet were off the ground and she was back in Logan's arms and he was walking.

"Put me down!" She hit him on the shoulder, but the blow just glanced off. Because he was so big. Or because she was so weak. Or both.

It was probably both, Maddie realized with something resembling indignation.

She was going to be really mad at herself as soon as she woke up. But that was later. Right now, sleep sounded so much better than fighting.

Sleep sounded like the most brilliant idea in the history of the world.

It had started snowing again—harder now—and Maddie let herself turn her face into the expanse of Logan's broad chest, burrow into his warmth.

She didn't want to close her eyes, but her eyelids had a different opinion on the subject.

She was floating again, drifting. Her shoulder didn't hurt. Her stomach didn't growl. But the forest kept swirling, faster and faster, and Maddie was perfectly willing to go swirling down the drain with the rest of the world.

But then she felt something jerk. Bounce. She started awake.

"Stay with me, Mad Dog."

Logan was there—that was right. It wasn't a dream. Was it?

Maybe it was.

"Maddie, stay with me!" he said again, and Maddie remembered she was in his arms and they were walking.

No. Logan was carrying her.

Logan, whom she hated. But then she thought about the bridge, the look in his eyes when he'd asked *What letters?* and Maddie's hate faded. It got covered by the blowing snow.

"Logan?"

"Yeah?'

"You're gonna wear yourself out," she told him.

"No, I'm not. And you're going into shock, Mad."

Maddie changed her mind again. The new worst part about their situation was that he was right. And he knew it.

"The bullet went straight through. I'm——"

"Stubborn," he finished for her. "When was the last time you ate anything?"

"There were the berries," she told him.

"That's what I thought," he said, and Maddie knew he didn't have a whole lot of room to talk. It's not like he and Stefan had hit a drive-through on their trek through the forest.

Maddie wanted to argue. But she decided to argue with her eyes closed.

There really was something inherently peaceful about being carried. No wonder babies seemed to like it.

"No. Not that easy," Logan said, and shook her again, like he wanted to toss her up in the air and catch her but he changed his mind at the last minute—just a jarring little bounce where she never even had to leave his arms. "Keep talking to me, Mad Dog. How else are the should-be-hibernating-by-now bears going to know to get out of our way?"

The stupid idiot boy with the sexy stubble had a point.

She turned her head to look up at him. He didn't even seem winded even though Maddie knew that she was heavy—she worked so hard and had so much muscle that she couldn't possibly be light.

"Logan?"

He glanced down at her. "Yeah, Mad Dog?"

"What did you mean? When you said that your dad hates you."

He walked on for a little while. There was nothing but the sound of his new boots crunching in the snow and the ice, the breaking of twigs and the wind in the trees. For a moment, she wasn't sure if she'd actually said the words aloud or not. Maybe she hadn't. Maybe this was the dream.

"Logan?" she said again, her voice softer than it should have been.

"I meant that the president hates me," Logan said at last, but it didn't make any sense. *Nothing* about anything made sense anymore to Maddie, not the least of which was why Logan was talking about his father like the man was a stranger.

"No, Logan. I know your dad, remember? He—"

"You don't know my dad, Mad Dog." Logan sounded like a man who wasn't in the mood to fight anymore.

Logan sounded like a man.

"But . . ." Maddie wanted to argue, but she didn't remember how. She just knew that sleep was the most wonderful thing in the world and the boy who was carrying her wouldn't let her do it.

"You know who he was when he was hanging around with your dad. You know who he is when the cameras are rolling. When the cameras aren't rolling . . ."

Maddie knew what he was saying then, even though the words didn't make any sense. Even though they might very well have been a part of this very cold, wet, and utterly surreal dream. She was going to wake up any moment and curse herself for letting the fire go out.

But the hurt in Logan's voice . . . She shifted and looked up. The pain in Logan's eyes was real.

"I'm smarter than he is. Did you know that? They had me tested. And my scores were . . . They were really high."

"You sound like that's a bad thing."

"Do you know what he said? When they got my scores? He said 'Now you don't have any excuses.'"

"Excuses for what?"

Logan shivered in a way that had nothing to do with the cold. "Imperfection. They had quantifiable proof that I could be perfect if I just wanted to be."

"Logan—"

"So I stopped wanting to be." He looked down at her, fat white snowflakes clinging to his dark lashes. "But there was one time I wish I had been."

"What does that mean?"

"It means that if I'd been just a little smarter, I could have stopped them before your dad got hurt. And if your dad hadn't gotten hurt, then maybe . . ."

He couldn't say the words, so Maddie said them for him. "Then maybe I wouldn't have left."

Logan walked faster then, with new purpose. As if the wolves were on their heels.

"It's not your fault, Logan. If it hadn't been for you, your mom would have been taken. She probably would have died. You're the one who saw her dress. You're the one who remembered to press your panic button and get help. You saved her."

He looked down at her. "I lost you."

Maddie didn't know what to say to that. He wasn't walking anymore. He was just standing in the snow and the cloudy streaks of moonlight, staring down into her eyes like maybe it wasn't too late to go back, do it all again.

But there were no second chances. Life didn't work that way, and Logan, genius that he was, was smart enough to know it. So he looked back to the trees and kept walking.

"I don't know why, you know?" Maddie's voice was faint, but she ran a hand across Logan's chest, like she was trying to feel his heartbeat through his coat. "One day he was in the hospital and the next he was coming home. But he wasn't home. Not really. He just told me to pack a bag and the next thing I knew we were here and we had other lives."

"Your dad loves you, Mad Dog."

There was awe in his voice. And envy.

Maddie hated every word.

"Logan, no. You're wrong. Your dad loves you, too."

Logan laughed then, and it was colder than the wind.

He started walking faster, away from the man who was chasing them, away from the risk that, in a way, had been on his trail for six long years and might never, ever stop.

"Rest, Mad," he told her.

"I thought I was supposed to keep talking."

"Yeah." Logan laughed a little. "I forgot who I was talking to."

"We're going to be okay."

Maddie was an excellent liar. When you talked as much as she did, you get good at saying all kinds of words. She could even convince herself most of the time. She'd gotten especially good at that in the past six years.

It's not that cold in here.

Elk meat is delicious and tastes like chicken.

It's almost impossible to get sick of salmon.

(Even though it is very, very possible to get sick of salmon.)

But the biggest lie was this: *I don't even need people anymore.*

Maddie needed her father. And Maddie needed Logan, even when he was just a memory or a name on a letter. Even when he was just someone to hate. Long before he was the boy who bound her wounds and kept her warm and carried her through the forest, she needed him.

Her darkest, deepest fear was that a part of her always would.

"You're not shaking anymore," Logan told her, looking down.

With the snow still falling and the ice in the trees, it was almost beautiful. It was almost like a dream. The good kind, for once.

"Mad?" He couldn't hide the worry in his voice or in his eyes. "You're not shaking anymore!"

"I feel fine," she told him.

"No. You don't feel anything. That's worse."

"It feels better," she said, even though she knew that he was right.

"We need to get you to a hospital."

"There is no hospital, Logan. There's no help."

"Then what is there?" he snapped. He didn't mean to. Maddie could see the remorse in his eyes as soon as he said it. He opened his mouth, as if to apologize, but then it felt like a movie again.

The snow stopped falling.

The clouds actually parted.

The moon sliced through the darkness, like a spotlight through the trees.

And there it was.

It was covered in ice, and snow had blown up against it, a drift that might have hidden its silhouette. But Maddie knew the shape of a roof when she saw one. Maddie knew miracles when she found them.

"There's that," she said, and Logan followed her gaze to the tiny cabin that sat a little higher on the hill.

CHAPTER 20

Dear Logan,

I really miss you. And I'm mad at you. But not as mad as I am at myself for continuing to write you these letters.

Maddie

It wasn't more than a shack, but the sight of it must have been enough to stun Logan, because he didn't complain when Maddie slid from his arms.

Then stumbled.

Her head spun a little, and she felt his arms around her again, but he didn't lift her. He just held her as they tried to climb the rise of the hill toward something that wasn't quite a cabin, wasn't quite a shack. But it was there. And it had a roof and walls and there was a stovepipe sticking out of the snow on top of the slanting roof.

"What is that?" Logan asked, and Maddie could see where he'd be confused.

"It's a trapper's shed," she said, then stopped. Every one of her senses seemed to go into overdrive as she looked around at the glowing white stillness, as she listened to the wind. Branches cracked under the weight of the snow and the ice, but not even the birds were moving out there.

They were alone.

For now.

"Logan, did you bring us here because you saw it on Stefan's map?"

The map and the bridge and the man seemed a million miles away. It seemed like it had happened last year. Six years ago. It was another lifetime. Everything had changed since waking up in Logan's arms.

Logan must have felt it, too, because he shook his head as if trying to shake off some foggy dream. "I . . . No."

"Think, Logan. If it was on the map, then he'll know it's here. We can't stay here." She looked at the snow-covered ground. Their footsteps stood out like neon in the moonlight. Now that Maddie was upright again—thinking again—she wanted to panic.

She looked up at the sky and prayed that the clouds would come back, that the snow would fall harder and cover their tracks.

It had been falling steadily for at least an hour. Maybe if they were lucky their steps near the bridge would be covered by the time Stefan made it there.

But Maddie felt like she hadn't been lucky in a very long time.

"Logan, think!" she snapped. "Was it on the map?"

Maddie knew him. Not the president's kid. Not the tabloid troublemaker. Maddie knew the boy who had been so freakishly smart and helplessly awkward that he had been willing to befriend the girl who never shut up. Just so he wouldn't have to do any talking.

Maddie knew Logan's secret. She didn't need to give him special tests to know the truth. Logan had seen that map. Which meant Logan would *remember* that map. He had to.

"Logan," she whispered. "Look."

So he closed his eyes. He shook his head. "It wasn't on there."

And Maddie felt herself sway again, falling into his arms.

Logan didn't want to cry. It wouldn't be manly, for starters. And for some reason, since seeing Maddie again, he felt the need to be as manly as possible. He didn't let himself think about why.

But mostly, Logan didn't want his tears to freeze. It would be the only part of him that wasn't frozen.

Like a guy who swears he isn't hungry until he actually smells food, Logan didn't know how cold he'd been. He didn't realize how hard it was to keep moving one foot in front of the other until he was moving toward a roof and four walls.

Going was one thing. But to go on and on, walking indefinitely toward nothing, was much worse.

It wasn't because he carried Maddie. No, just the opposite, in fact. Maddie's weight in his arms was what had kept him moving forward, what gave him his strength. Logan had no idea where they were going, but he knew what he was doing—he was getting Maddie to safety. It was the only thing worth doing. And he was going to do it if it killed him.

But now that the shack was in sight, Logan's legs wanted to falter. He wouldn't let them, though. Not now that Maddie was as white as the snow and teetering, unsteady as they climbed the hill.

Snow had drifted in front of the door, but there was no lock, and when Logan pushed against the wood it opened into the small, dark space that was just as frigid as the air outside. The drift collapsed, snow falling over the threshold and dusting the floor, but at least they were out of the wind here. They were at least a little safe from whatever predators might be filling the woods.

Or *some* of the predators, at least.

Logan hadn't lied to Maddie. The shack wasn't on Stefan's map. But he also knew that he'd left footprints. A day's worth of sleet had turned the ground to ice, and the snow was a fluffy blanket atop it. More had fallen, and the wind was blowing, but they could be tracked. It was possible. But there was nothing he could do about it, and he didn't dare mention his fears to Maddie, even though he knew she must be thinking the same thing. There are some worries that are just better if they're never said aloud.

"Oh, thank goodness," Maddie nearly doubled over in relief when she saw the small black cast-iron stove.

There was a matchbox sitting atop it and Logan bolted for it. "Empty," he said, tipping the box upside down to prove his point. Disappointment roiled within him, and he threw the empty box at the wall.

"We don't need it," Mad told him.

"But—"

"Not when we've got that."

He turned and saw the corner of the shack where wood was stacked and dry and waiting.

"Somebody up there loves us," Logan said. He actually bent down and kissed a log. It tasted like safety.

Maddie laughed at him, and that was the best thing in the shack, Logan decided. The sound of Maddie's laughter.

"That's a rule here," she told him. "There are cabins like this scattered all over, built by hunters or trappers or whatever. But if you use the wood, you replace it." She got a little somber. "You could be saving someone's life."

Then Logan remembered the matches. "Lot of good it does us without matches."

Maddie sounded insulted. "Bring me the box."

"Mad Dog, it's empty," he reminded her. Maybe the hypothermia was getting worse. Maybe she was starting to not think straight.

But she sounded just like Maddie—just like Old Maddie— when she said, "Will you bring me the box, *please?*"

So Logan did as she asked.

She eased open the door of the little stove. It was dusty and the hinges squeaked, but everything seemed okay. At least it did in the dark.

Logan watched as Maddie tried to tear at the cardboard of the box, but her hands shook. She was weaker than she'd ever admit, so he placed his hand over hers, took the box, and ripped.

"How small do you want the pieces?"

"Tear it into strips and make a little nest in the stove. Then go strip the bark off some of those birch logs."

"Okay," Logan said.

She was unzipping her coat, but it wasn't the hypothermia playing tricks on her, Logan was sure. He watched as she pulled on the chain that was around her neck, tugging something out from beneath her many layers.

The breath she drew was deep and shaky and almost reverent as she looked down at the small items in her hands.

"I was terrified he was going to take them," she said, but Logan couldn't imagine why. They were the most un-Maddie-like pieces of jewelry he had ever seen, but she held them like they were precious.

Like they were life itself.

"Here," he told her when he came back with the pieces of bark. "Is this enough?"

"Yes," she said, and took the biggest piece.

Logan knew a lot of things, not the least of which was when to get out of the way. That was the first thing he'd learned as a toddler in the governor's mansion. So he sat down and scooted back and watched Maddie make a small nest of the cardboard pieces inside the stove. Then she reached into her pocket and pulled out her little tube of Vaseline, but her hands were too cold and she could barely work the lid.

"Uh, Mad Dog, maybe your lips can wait?"

"You're more than welcome to wait outside," she said as she spread some on her lips. She smirked, then started spreading Vaseline all over one of the pieces of cardboard and wadding it up. By the time she placed it on the biggest piece of bark it was a tiny, greasy ball.

Her hands shook as she worked. She was so pale. He had to get her warm, but he knew better than to rush her.

"This is a firesteel," she explained, taking the necklace off and holding up a small metal rod. Then she held up the other piece. "And this is magnesium."

It wasn't big, maybe the size of a pack of gum. And Logan watched as Maddie carefully ran her knife along the magnesium block, shaving off little pieces that fell onto her oily piece of cardboard.

"Magnesium shavings are really flammable, and they burn super hot."

"Yeah. Four thousand degrees," Logan filled in.

"That's right." Maddie sounded shocked. And disappointed. Like maybe she couldn't call him an idiot anymore.

"That's why this works even when it's wet. It's better than matches," she explained.

"What about the Vaseline?"

"It's oil. The cardboard is a candle now, basically. Usually, you need the Vaseline. Or you need the magnesium. But tonight . . ."

"We need both?" Logan guessed.

She looked up at him. "I'm not taking any chances."

"What can I do?" he asked. He was feeling restless, desperate.

"Pray." She held the little rodlike piece of metal close to the ball, then brought the dull side of her knife to it and waited a moment, drew a deep breath before swiping her knife down the little rod.

Sparks flew, lighting the air. For one brief moment that frozen shack was full of fireflies. For one split second it was summer.

But then, just that quickly, it was gone and darkness filled the cabin. Logan could hear Maddie's breath rattle. Even in the shadows, he could see her hands shake.

Maddie didn't seem deterred, though. She acted like this happened all the time, being stranded in a blizzard a hundred miles from a hospital with nothing but a tiny, flickering spark standing between you and certain death.

Logan refused to think about the certain death part, so instead he looked at the girl.

A little blood was still in her hair, he could see it when the sparks flew again. He thought about the Maddie he used to know. She would have never been seen with her hair like that, with her face dirty and her nails broken. But that girl hadn't been silly. She hadn't been vain. She was just . . . bedazzled. And she was still before him, certain and strong and saving his life.

"You can do it," he reminded her. "You're Maddie Freaking Manchester. You used a bear trap on a really ticked-off Russian. You can start a fire."

So Maddie pulled her knife down the rod again. Sparks flew from the end and, in a flash, one of them caught.

Logan actually held his breath as Maddie blew on the tender flame, then transferred the little burning ball to the nest of cardboard inside the stove and surrounded it with more of the bark, careful not to smother the flames that were growing stronger and brighter and hotter with every moment.

As Maddie started adding bigger pieces of wood to the fire, Logan looked at her in the light. She still looked like his Maddie, but she was so much more now.

"It's a shame we didn't have any nail polish remover, huh?" he teased. He needed to hear her laugh again. Everything was okay when Maddie laughed.

But Maddie *didn't* laugh.

Instead, her head jerked up, almost like she'd heard a shot, seen a bear. Logan actually jolted, looking around. But Maddie was staring right at him.

"What did you just say?"

"I said it's a shame we don't have any nail polish remover. But I guess lip stuff will do." He looked down at the small flame that was slowly coming to life. An orangish glow washed over her face and she was maybe the most beautiful thing he'd ever seen. Or she would have been. If she hadn't looked like her best friend had just died. Again.

"Why did you say that?"

Logan wanted to laugh, tell her she was talking crazy, being so much of a girl.

"Why did you say that, Logan?" she practically shouted.

And Logan remembered the truth. The lie.

She'd been so mad, so . . . hurt. He hadn't thought . . . But that was the problem, wasn't it? Logan didn't think anymore.

"Logan, why—"

"I told you, Mad Dog," he said at last. He made himself meet her gaze. "I remember everything I read."

CHAPTER 21

Logan was thawing. Maybe it was the fire that was growing, throwing light around the cabin and putting off the sweetest heat that he had ever felt. But more likely it was the rage that was coming off of Maddie, burning like the sun.

She pushed herself across the cabin floor. Dust mixed with melting snow, and she didn't even care that they had come there to get dry. At that moment, she just had to get away from Logan.

"You read my letters? You got them. And you read them. And you never wrote me." The cold came again. *"You lied."*

"Maddie—"

"You . . . Why didn't you write me, Logan? Why?"

"Because you were gone!" Logan didn't know where the words came from or why he was shouting. He just knew that a hurt he thought was gone was pouring out of him and he couldn't stop it. Everything was too raw, too primitive. "You left. And you were better off."

"Do you think I *wanted* to go?" Maddie asked him. "If you really read my letters, you would have known . . . You would have known how it was." Her voice broke, and Logan knew how much that simple fact must have hurt her.

He pushed his hood back, ran a hand through his hair. "I didn't write to you, Mad, because I wanted you to stop writing to me."

"But why?" Maddie sounded like someone who had been waiting her entire life to ask that question. She looked like someone who would wait a lifetime more for an answer.

"Because you weren't just my best friend. You were my *only* friend. And I almost got you killed." He laughed a little, cold and dry. "Looks like that's a bad habit."

"I don't believe you," she told him.

"Fine. Don't believe me. But I know from personal experience that when your only friend leaves, sometimes the best thing you can do is try to convince yourself she never existed."

Logan hadn't thought that Maddie could go any paler, but she did. She swayed a little again, and he remembered her head and her shoulder. She was so small. She'd lost so much blood.

"I'm sorry if my letters were such a burden to you. I'm sorry I was anything to you."

Logan would have rather faced Stefan, the snow, a bear— anything but the look in Maddie's eyes before she turned from him. The bullet looked easy in comparison to the pain that he had caused. When she reached for a pan that had overturned and was lying on the dusty floor, she winced, and he bolted toward her.

"Let me," he said, but she climbed to her feet without help.

"We need snow," she said, and Logan knew she wasn't asking for help so much as she wanted to be alone.

"I'll do it," he said, then he took the pot and went outside. She needed a minute. He needed a minute. Those were the lies he told himself, but the truth was they both needed the past six years back. Only six years would do.

Logan filled the pot with snow, then pushed it around and dumped it out a few times to try to clean the dust away. Then he filled it with the cleanest, freshest-looking snow he could find, brought it back inside, and set it on the stove.

Maddie didn't face him.

Her coat and shirt were off and drying by the fire. She stood in her tank top, twisted at a strange angle, wincing.

"Maddie?"

"I'm fine," she snapped.

"You're not fine," he told her, and forced her to turn around. She'd found an old first aid kit and a bottle of booze and was trying to pour it on her wound, but the angle made it hard.

"Let me," he said, taking the bottle from her and pulling away the pieces of fabric they'd tried to use to stop the bleeding. He tossed the bloodiest of them in the fire, but when he opened the bottle and held it over the wound, he hesitated.

"This is going to hurt," he said.

And the look in her eyes almost killed him. "I've been hurt before."

When the alcohol hit the bullet wound, Maddie didn't even wince. She didn't say a word as he bandaged her up and put more wood on the fire. This was the same girl who'd once talked nonstop throughout the entire flight from DC to London, but now she acted like she'd never speak again.

"Maddie . . ."

She was moving then. There were some blankets on a shelf and Logan sighed with pleasure. When she found a pair of sweatpants and a flannel robe he almost wept with joy. But when Maddie started to undress, he panicked.

"What are you doing?"

"We've been in the freezing rain and snow all day, Logan. The fire isn't going to do us any good if we're both wet through. We'll chill. We will never get warm if we don't get dry, and we won't get dry if we don't . . ." She trailed off but gestured at her body. It was okay. Logan knew exactly what she was saying.

"Turn around," she told him.

"Mad, I don't know . . ."

"If you want to die, keep your clothes on. If you want to live long enough to get out of this mess, then turn around and strip. Put those on." She tossed him the sweatpants and a blanket. They were musty and cold, but they were also dry, unlike every layer of his clothing.

He risked a glance over his shoulder and saw a pale arm disappear into the robe.

He could hear Maddie moving a little, saw her laying out her clothes near the fire. Steam actually rose from her jeans and she leaned down to put another log in the stove. It was still far from hot in the cabin, but he wasn't shaking anymore and neither was she.

So he did as he was told, stripping off his wet things and then slipping into the sweatpants and wrapping the blanket around his shoulders.

"Come here," she told him.

The snow in the pan was melted, and Maddie found something like a cup and dipped it in, brought the warm water to Logan's lips.

"Tasty," he said.

Then he took the cup and got some water, held it out for her and she sipped. It felt like some kind of ritual. Like maybe now nothing could tear them asunder.

"We're not going to die here," Maddie told him. Logan held his hand over hers around the cup and took another sip.

He couldn't look away from her. "Of course not. That would be a terrible way to die. Your hair would be stuck like that. Probably forever."

She hit him on the shoulder, but she was smiling, and everything inside of Logan began to thaw.

He took another sip of water, then offered one to her. The water was starting to warm him from the inside, but Logan's stomach was still empty. It growled, the sound filling the little shack. Outside, the wind howled. There was a tiny window with grimy glass, and Logan could see that the snow had started to fall again.

"That's good," Maddie said, following his gaze. "It should cover our tracks and hide the smoke from the fire. We should be safe here."

Maddie looked around the tiny shack again, four walls barely thicker than cardboard, a hard wooden floor, raised a foot off of the frozen ground. But there was that black stove and a large stack of wood and a pot full of warm water, and that was enough to save their lives.

When she looked back at him, something in Logan broke in two because Maddie—his Maddie—was there, in that glance. Her full bottom lip started to tremble in a way that he knew had absolutely nothing to do with the cold.

"We're gonna—"

"Hey—"

They both spoke at exactly the same time. Logan smiled at her. "After you."

Maddie sank down to the hard floor, to the place where the fire was the hottest, right in front of the stove's open door. The wood was turning red and sparks flew occasionally, but Maddie didn't scoot away. She just wrapped her arms around her legs and brought an extra blanket around her like a cape. She looked like a superhero: Survival Girl. Logan had no doubt she'd save the day. In fact, she already had.

He sank down beside her. His raincoat wasn't far away, and

Logan could tell that it was already dry, so he pulled it close and draped it around both of their shoulders as they huddled closer to the fire.

There was nothing but the howling of the wind and the cracking and popping of the burning wood. And six long years of unanswered letters and even more unanswered questions.

"Mad—" Logan started just as Maddie said, "Remember those little cheese biscuits the White House chef used to make?"

Logan forgot what he was going to say. He laughed instead. "Remember them? I had one two days ago."

She turned to look up at him. "I miss those."

He looked down into her huge eyes. He pushed a curl away from her face. "I missed those, too. I missed them more than I can ever say."

And they both knew that they weren't talking about biscuits anymore.

When Logan put an arm around her, she didn't pull away. This time, she leaned into him. Maybe for warmth, but Logan didn't think so. He tried to wrap the jacket tighter around her, but then he bolted upright and moved away.

"I almost forgot."

He reached into the jacket pocket and pulled out a bunch of berries, held them toward Maddie like an offering. "Are these the good kind?"

"Yes!" Maddie said, then launched toward them. She put one in her mouth and chewed, then smiled. "These are a kind of cranberry, but be careful. There's a poisonous berry that looks a lot like them. So if we find more tomorrow, check with me before you eat anything, okay?"

"Okay," Logan said. He wanted to smile, watching Maddie talk. It was almost like old times.

"I'll catch something to cook in the morning. I don't think we're far from the river. There will be fish."

"You can do that?" Logan eyed her. Maddie eyed him back, a little offended.

"I caught a Russian killer."

Logan ate another berry. "Point taken."

They ate in silence for a while. When Maddie stopped to lick the juice from her fingers, Logan couldn't help himself.

He blurted, "I thought you were dead."

Maddie stopped eating and looked up at him. "I'm not."

She put a finger in her mouth again, and Logan told her, "Don't do that."

"Do what?" she asked, almost with a shrug.

"Don't die on me again. Ever."

Her hair was drying quickly in the heat of the fire, and it was turning into curls. He tugged one of the rings gently.

"Okay," she told him.

"And don't come back for me again. No matter what happens. I want you to run. To save yourself. Don't do something stupid just to get me a key. Even if your key delivery system was . . . unexpected."

"You don't mean that, Logan."

He laughed. "Oh, I wasn't expecting it. I promise."

"No." She pushed his hand away. "I mean . . . I'd do it again."

"So would I," Logan said, and then he couldn't help himself. He was leaning closer, drawn toward her like a magnet. Maddie was his true north, and he couldn't turn away from her then, not if his life depended on it.

Even if hers did.

He was growing closer and closer and then her lips were on his again, warmer now. She tasted like snow and berries and it was the sweetest thing that Logan had ever known.

When he pulled away he kissed her again on her forehead. Her blanket had fallen and the robe gaped a little, so he placed a quick kiss on the stretch of skin between her neck and the strap of her tank top—not far from the place where she'd been shot.

Maddie was shot, Logan reminded himself, then pulled away. But when she lay down before the fire, Logan could do nothing but spoon himself behind her, pull as many of the warm blankets around them as possible.

She put her head on his chest, and he put his arm around her shoulders and it was the single best moment of Logan's life.

Only one thought was able to ruin it.

"Mad, what happens tomorrow?" he asked.

The fire cracked again, and sparks flew.

"Tomorrow we make a phone call."

CHAPTER 22

For the third time in two days, Maddie woke up feeling like she was lost inside a dream.

She was too cold, but also too hot. An unfamiliar weight was draped across her waist, and she really, really needed to fluff her pillow. But then Maddie's eyes flew open, and she saw a stove that was full of hot coals and not much else. She shivered and realized that she was wearing her base layers and a threadbare robe and lying on a scratchy blanket. There was another blanket and some coats on top of her. But the most disturbing things were the arms. Two of them. One was beneath her head and one was wrapped around her waist, heavy and sure. And her hand was holding its hand and something inside of Maddie swore to never, ever let it go.

It wasn't a dream, Maddie realized. And she couldn't decide whether that should make her terrified or ecstatic.

Then there was a too-deep voice in her ear. "Good morning."

Maddie bolted away like maybe she'd been stung. "Yes. Um. Good morning."

Logan pushed upright. At some point in the night he must have gotten up to check his clothes, because he was wearing dry jeans and socks, a white T-shirt stretching across his broad chest.

Very broad.

Oh, so utterly broad that it didn't look at all like the chest that he'd had when they used to go swimming at the White House.

The sun was up, and light filled the little shack, filtering through holes in the walls and the roof and the small, grimy window. But they'd lived. And as soon as they were out of this mess Maddie was going to come back and fill this place with so much firewood and kindling that it might crumble under the weight of it all.

Then she realized Logan was eyeing her like maybe she looked as awful as she felt.

"What is it?" she blurted.

"I didn't know it was possible for hair to even point in that direction." He reached for her head, but she batted his hand away and he burst out laughing.

Maddie tried to run a hand through her hair, but her curls were too wild and windblown. It was all she could do to tuck it behind her ears.

"Better?" she asked.

"Oh, much," he said with so much sarcasm she hit him again. Just for good measure.

But then they both stopped smiling, stopped laughing, and Maddie realized they were still holding hands. It was like they had frozen that way, dried together in some kind of knot just like her hair.

"Did you sleep okay?" Maddie asked, even though she couldn't remember whether or not she'd asked it already.

"Yes. I slept perfectly."

"Oh. Okay. Uh . . ." She looked down at the place where she'd spent the night, wrapped up in him. "Your arm didn't fall asleep, did it?"

"No." Logan shook his head. The awkward was palpable. Maddie was practically drowning in it, but Logan seemed as cool as the wind. "My arm is perfect."

Then he pulled the blankets and the coats back over Maddie and went to put more wood on the fire. He froze in the act of putting a log on the coals and asked her, "Is this okay?"

Maddie glanced at the dirty window. "I think so. It looks overcast and it's still spitting sleet. No one's gonna see a little more smoke."

"Good." He tossed the log onto the fire, then hopped on the cold floor, jumping over Maddie's legs to land behind her. He sunk down and dragged her back into his arms and wrapped the blankets and coats around them both again. It was like a cocoon. Outside the blankets, the world was cold and scary and awkward.

Seriously, Maddie thought. A person could spontaneously combust from so much awkward. But inside the blankets the world was warm and safe and she didn't have to think about anything. Not about Russian kidnappers or unanswered letters. Not about the bullet or the fall or the lie that hurt more than anything else.

She wanted to close her eyes and sleep again, but when she moved, her shoulder felt like fire and a fresh wave of nausea ran through her body, and she knew that sleep wouldn't save them. For six years, mornings had started with chores, and Maddie knew that she could lay there in Logan's arms and make believe. Or she could get up and do something about it.

So Maddie got up.

"Logan, do you remember the map?" she asked before even really realizing that she'd been thinking about it. Even though some part of Maddie's brain had never *stopped* thinking about it.

"Yes," he said slowly. It was like he was wise to Maddie's cocoon analogy and he was very much Team Stay Inside Where It's Warm.

"Good," Maddie said.

At some point someone must have tried to make this little shack a home because one wall was covered with peeling, faded wallpaper. Maddie reached for her jeans and pulled them on. They were filthy and stiff but they were dry. She slipped off the robe and pulled on the second of her three shirts, then walked to the wallpaper and ripped. A piece came off in her hands.

There were pieces of old burnt wood around the base of the stove, and Maddie found one that turned her fingers black and handed it to Logan.

"I want you to draw it—as much of it as you can. I want to see what he sees."

She reached for her boots.

"Where are you going?" He acted almost hurt, like he didn't want to be left behind. Again.

"I'm going to go see what I can catch to eat."

"I'll go with you," Logan said, looking around and starting to pull on more of his own clothes.

"No." When Maddie realized she'd snapped she tried to soften her voice. "It's better if I go alone. I need the map. And we need food and we don't have enough time, so—"

"Mad Dog, it's okay." He nodded toward the door. "Go. Bring home the bacon."

There wasn't any bacon.

But there was a stream filled with fish, and Maddie had braved the cold long enough to pull off her pantyhose and catch some (a feat she *never* could have done in front of Logan).

An hour after she'd left she was warm again and in front of the fire. Logan was sitting beside her and they both looked at the fresh fillets that laid atop the big, flat rocks that Maddie had placed directly on the red-hot coals.

"No offense to the White House culinary team, but that's the best thing I've ever smelled," Logan said.

They would have both been perfectly willing to eat the fish raw and call it sushi, but the smell was doing Maddie almost as much good as the fire. It was warming her from the inside out. Or maybe it was just the way Logan sat closer to her now, their arms touching. Sometimes his hand was on her back. A time or two she caught herself leaning against his chest. When their hands touched neither moved away, and they just stayed like that.

Was that weird?

Or was it more weird to move her hand now for no apparent reason? Maddie knew the protocol for moving the president from the Oval Office to the Situation Room during a national security crisis, but she didn't know exactly how long one could—or should—touch the first son before one was at risk of offending the touchee or embarrassing the toucher. Or even really which one she was. She didn't remember touching him, after all. She just kind of was.

She just kind of couldn't stop it.

And, Maddie was starting to realize, neither could he.

"Tell me you forgive me, Maddie. Please. You don't even have to mean it. Just say it. For now."

"Logan . . ."

"I thought I was doing it for you."

And, with that, Maddie finally found it easy to move away.

"I needed you. I didn't have anyone."

"Which is better than having someone who's just going to get you hurt," Logan said, then looked around the cabin and laughed. "Lot of good that did you."

"Logan?" Maddie said, and slowly he turned to her.

"Tell me you forgive me, Mad Dog. Lie if you have to. I can't go out there thinking you don't know how much I . . . How much we . . . I need you to know that I'd do anything for you. Even give you up."

"Logan." Maddie looked up and found his eyes. The fire crackled and the snow fell, but all Maddie could ask was "What did he say? When he was on the phone?"

And just like that the spell was broken. Maddie missed the warmth of his fingers against hers, but she acted like it didn't matter.

She told herself it couldn't possibly matter.

The fish sizzled as Maddie took a long stick and moved the fillets around on the big rocks. She watched as Logan wrapped his hands around his knees.

"He was supposed to meet someone somewhere. Maybe last night? Maybe this morning or sometime today? I'm not sure. I don't think he ever said. It was a plane, I think. He said the boat wouldn't be fast enough. I don't know what he meant by that exactly. Seems to me like a plane would stand out."

Maddie turned on him. For a really smart boy, sometimes Logan could be really stupid.

"There are more people with pilot's licenses in Alaska than there are people with driver's licenses. No one's gonna notice one more small plane. And besides, the Secret Service will start looking for you today if they haven't already. The Russians are running out of time."

He shook his head and pulled his legs tighter. "You don't know that."

"Yes." Maddie forced herself to her feet. She'd already spent too long sitting, waiting. Leaning against someone who might not be there to catch her next time.

"Logan, you are the president's son. And you've been off the grid for almost twenty-four hours. And there's no reality where that goes unnoticed."

He was moving as she spoke, a subtle, rocking shift that he probably didn't even know he was doing. But when she finished he stopped and looked up at her. "And once they notice?"

Maddie pulled on her gloves and used the sleeve of her coat to pull the rocks from the coals. She sat them on the top of the stove and it was all she could do not to fall on the fish fillets and eat them in one gulp.

"Once they notice, they'll try to reach my dad, who is either back and going crazy or is on his way back and will begin going crazy anytime now."

She reached down and picked up a piece of flaky fish, put it in her mouth, and almost moaned with the taste of it. Logan stood and joined her.

"Then they'll pull up all the satellite footage from around the cabin to make sure no one flew you out. After that, they'll know you're on foot. And they'll start looking. We could start a signal fire—if we can find enough dry wood, which is doubtful. And even if we did, the bad guys would probably get here before the good guys, and we don't want to signal the wrong side."

After a few bites, he asked, "Do we head back for your house?"

Maddie thought about it for a long time before admitting, "I don't know. There are weapons there. And the radio. And maybe one of your agents survived? But Stefan could be expecting us to go there, so . . ."

All her life Maddie had heard stories of close calls and bad decisions, lucky breaks that made the difference between life and death. How would history judge this morning? She had to wonder. Would they be the idiots who turned back or the fools who didn't?

Maddie had no idea.

"I think if I were him, that's what I'd expect us to do. But I didn't spend as much time with him as you did."

Logan considered it while he ate another piece of fish and then took a sip of the fresh water that they'd melted on the stove that morning.

"Stefan found us there once," he said at last. Then he considered the tiny cabin. "Do we stay here?"

But there was something else in Logan's voice. Maddie felt it, too, as she glanced to the floor where they'd slept, wrapped up in each other, unaware of the world going totally to pieces all around them.

In the light of day, she could see it for what it was: a shack with peeling wallpaper and a soot-stained ceiling, but there were other things, too: a cracked vase on a shelf, a row of oddly shaped rocks, like some child's treasures.

This place had saved their lives, but life was going to be different outside the safety of its four walls. Maddie didn't want to think too hard about how or why.

"Once the clouds clear, someone's bound to see the smoke." She looked down at the last fish fillet, took a tiny piece, and then pushed the rest toward Logan. "I don't like the idea of . . . sitting. We wouldn't freeze to death here. Probably. But we could die here just the same. And I don't want to die waiting."

"Me either."

Logan's voice was sure and steady. He sounded like his dad, Maddie thought, but she didn't say so.

"You've got the map?" she asked. He pushed it toward her.

"I think we're somewhere about here." He pointed to a ridge that wasn't far from the river.

"Closer to here," she said, pointing to a spot nearer to the burned-out bridge.

"It felt like we walked longer last night."

She glanced up at him. "That's because you were walking for two."

"I'd do it again," he told her, but he was too serious. Too close. Maddie had to find a way to push him away without touching him, so she laughed.

"I hope I don't have to hold you to that," she said.

"Mad—"

"Dad didn't want me on this side of the river," she cut him off, pointing to the vast, empty places on the map—the nothingness that surrounded them.

"Why?" Logan asked, and Maddie shrugged.

"There was plenty of trouble on our side. I didn't need to go looking for more. What's this X?" Maddie asked, pointing to where Logan had marked the spot. "Was that on his map? Had he drawn it on there?"

"Yes and yes. Or, at least, someone had drawn it on there. But what he was hoping to find in the middle of a lake, I don't know."

Maddie knew. "That's where he was taking you. If they're flying you out, that's their rendezvous point. Land a small floatplane on that lake and load you up. You'd be in Russian airspace in just a few hours."

"Well, let's try to avoid that if at all possible," Logan teased.

"Good plan." Maddie pointed to the opposite edge of the map and thought about their options. "Canada is that way. We could be there in a couple of days. No one would expect us to walk to Canada."

"You were shot yesterday, Mad. You need a hospital. I'm not dragging you through the forest for two days just to get to Canada where who knows how many more days we'd have to walk to find some help."

"You could do it."

"That's true." Logan nodded, sounding sure. "I could carry you. That could—"

"No! *You* could walk to Canada. Logan, listen—I'll slow you down, but you're the one they want. If I could keep him distracted, then—"

"No! I am not leaving you out here with a madman."

"It was just an idea." Maddie shrugged.

"Well, it was a bad one. I'm never . . ." He trailed off, but there was something in his gaze. "I'm not leaving you alone."

"I didn't want you to be out there on your own either, you know."

"Good," Logan said, as if he didn't quite realize that they weren't arguing anymore.

For a long moment the cabin was silent except for the cracking of the tree limbs outside, the sparks from the dying fire.

"We're going to have to go back for it."

Neither of them said what *it* was. Neither of them had to.

Logan had almost run onto a burning bridge last night because that pack and the phone inside of it were so precious.

That phone was help. That phone was civilization. That phone was a helicopter and a complete squad of Army Rangers or Navy SEALS or whoever happened to be closest.

That phone was a warm bed and a hot meal and a shower. Oh have mercy—what Maddie wouldn't have done for a shower.

But that phone was also the second-most-obvious source of help, and if they were thinking about it, then Stefan might be as well.

Logan seemed to read Maddie's mind and her worries. "It's suicide."

But Maddie was shaking her head. Logan's fears were still rattling around in there, and despite her best efforts, some of them were even taking root.

"My dad has a sat phone. He's the one person we know we can trust."

"You're right," Logan told her. "And he's already on his way."

"Probably," Maddie said. "I mean, there's no way he risked flying in last night in all that weather. But when he does get back, he's going to come for us. I left markers, but who knows how many of them made it through the storm. They could be under three inches of ice and a foot of blowing snow by now. Dad might not find them. He may need backup. But if we can call him, he can fly to get us. The river will be frozen in places, and Dad can land there. Dad can land anywhere. He can get us and we can get out of here." Maddie studied him. The fire was cooling down, but neither of them went to get more wood. They wouldn't be there long enough to need it, they both seemed to know.

Then Logan shook his head. "I have to try for it."

And for the first time in her life Maddie didn't argue.

Maddie made Logan turn his red coat inside out so the light blue liner was what showed. They ate the last bites of fish. When Maddie opened the door, the sun was bright overhead, reflecting off the smooth, clear palate of white. It was almost too perfect to disturb, so for a moment they both stood on the threshold of the shack and looked back at the dying fire, the old stove, and the place on the floor where they'd slept.

"I live in the most famous house in the world, but . . ." Logan trailed off.

Maddie put her hand in his. "This is my favorite, too," she told him.

He squeezed, and they took a step out into a world that was too white—too clean, too new. There were animal tracks in the snow, but no footsteps. Maddie hated that they'd be leaving their own, but there was nothing they could do about that.

All of her senses were on high alert, but she could smell no other fires, see nothing but trees. There was nothing at all man-made for as far as the eye could see.

It felt to Maddie like they were all alone in the universe.

But they weren't.

And that was the scary part.

CHAPTER 23

The clouds stayed heavy and the sky stayed dim, but all around them the world shone like it was covered with crystals.

Maddie felt Logan at her back, following closely in her footsteps. Literally. As if maybe Stefan or his friends (if he had any) would be less likely to see one set of footprints than they would be to see two. Or maybe they might think it was someone else—someone on their own. But there were no other people for miles and miles around.

That was something it had taken Maddie a long time to get used to. For the first year or so it always felt like the trees had eyes, like someone was watching, listening. Like there was a whole silent, invisible city living up on the hill with a bird's-eye view of all she said or did.

But only the birds had that, Maddie knew now. And the birds, it seemed, weren't talking.

Then it was as if Maddie had summoned one with her

thoughts, because she heard a cry overhead and saw a bald eagle sweeping low, just above the snow-covered canopy of the trees.

"Was that . . . ?" Logan asked.

"We have a lot of eagles here. You can see their nests if you know where to look. They're huge sometimes. Like houses. They mate for life," she said without really realizing what she was saying.

Then she saw Logan's grin and looked back to the path, too quickly.

There was a bush covered with berries nearby, and Maddie pointed at it. "Yummy," she said as she pulled off as many berries as she could, passing a handful to Logan.

They walked a few yards more. Maddie could practically feel Logan's gaze burning into her back. "Yummy," she said, pointing to another bush. She pulled a few more berries and plopped them into her mouth. They were frozen, of course, but the cold, wet juice was a jolt to her system. She had a new bounce, a new purpose to her step when she saw yet another bush.

"Poison," she said, pointing to the third type of berry.

"They look just like all the others," Logan said.

Maddie glanced behind her. "Well, they're not. Trust me."

"So *not yummy*," Logan finished for her.

Maddie couldn't help but smile. "No. Not yummy."

They walked on for a few minutes more, every moment bringing them closer to where they'd started last night, their big head start dwindling with every step.

They moved slower the closer they got. It was like they both knew that any breaking twig or carelessly kicked rock could start an avalanche. Not of snow or of rocks. But of awful.

Yes, Maddie thought with a nod. An avalanche of awful was just one careless step away, so she stepped very carefully indeed.

Logan must have felt it, too, because when he spoke, he whispered. "What are the odds that our friend never found Black Bear Bridge?"

Maddie wasn't surprised at Logan's change of subject. Then again, did it even count as a change of subject if said subject was constantly on one's mind?

In the wintery stillness of the forest it was easy to believe that they were alone, locked together in some enchanted land. But they weren't alone. Eagles flew and tree limbs cracked in the distance, breaking under their icy weight. And forgetting that they weren't the only people in these woods was the most dangerous thing that either of them could do.

Maddie didn't even bother to answer Logan's question. It was an answer they both knew already. So instead she asked, "What would you do? If you were him, what would your play be?"

She could tell by the way he glanced around them that he wasn't going to have to think about his answer. He'd been asking himself that question for hours.

"I'd find Black Bear Bridge and get on this side of the river, and then I'd find some nice, cozy place to take cover and wait for us. That phone is the best way to get help. It might be the *only* way to get help. And you can bet Stefan knows it."

Maddie nodded. She kept pivoting, looking out across the

white horizon just like her father had taught her when she was a little girl and he made his living looking over crowds, scanning for danger. There was never a time in Maddie's life when she didn't know how to scan for danger. Sometimes she wondered what it would be like to *not* know that. Would she have preferred being a normal kind of girl who didn't know what was out there? But, no, Maddie realized. She was the kind of girl who always liked to see things coming.

Logan studied her, read her silence. "It's not too late, you know. We can still walk to Canada. Call it an adventure."

Maddie couldn't help but grin up at him. Logan had always had that effect on her. Spontaneous grinning usually ensued.

"I like Canada," she said. "They have really good donuts."

"They do have good donuts!" Logan exclaimed, as if he couldn't believe he had forgotten that incredibly important fact about one of America's closest allies and neighbors. "And I could learn to play hockey."

Maddie turned. "We could put maple syrup on everything," she said softly.

Then she felt Logan's hand take hers, and she turned to study him. "We would be really good Canadians."

"Right?"

Logan nodded. "Totally."

But Canada was a world away. They might as well have been talking about setting up camp on the moon.

The wind was colder, but the rain had stopped and they were both dry, for which Maddie was eternally grateful. Still, there was a nagging itch in the back of her mind, a little voice whispering that they weren't out of the woods yet.

They might never be out of the woods.

She looked up at the sky and knew that time was passing. Her father should have landed by now. The alarm should have sounded. Help was on its way, but Maddie had to keep Logan alive long enough for it to get there.

Time was ticking down, Maddie could tell. But toward what, she had no idea.

"How did they find me, Mad Dog?"

"Does it matter now?"

"Yes," Logan practically snapped. "Because there's no use risking our necks to get a sat phone if we have no idea who to call. What if there's a mole in the Secret Service or the White House? What if some secure communications channel got hacked?" Logan took a deep breath. "How are we going to keep from messing up again if we don't know where we messed up to begin with?"

To Maddie, it sounded like an excellent question. But it was one they didn't have time to answer.

"We'll figure that out, Logan. Later. After we call my dad and figure out a place for him to meet us. He can fly us out of here, and then we'll figure it out."

"I don't know." Logan's gaze was trained on the horizon. "Something's wrong." He gestured to the snow and the ice and the thousands of empty acres that surrounded them. "Out there. I can feel it."

Maddie wished she could argue, but she couldn't find the

words, so instead she said, "Tell me again, what he said on the phone."

She expected Logan to roll his eyes. The answer hadn't changed in the twenty minutes since she'd last asked.

But Logan was patient as he told her, "My Russian is pretty good, but it's not perfect. And I only heard half of the conversation, but he said that he had to get me somewhere by a certain time—today, I think. I'm not sure what time exactly, but I got the impression that time was of the essence. They were going to be there, waiting and ready."

"Who were *they*?" Maddie asked, but Logan just raised an eyebrow.

"The monster under the bed? The gunman on the grassy knoll?"

"Logan." Maddie wasn't losing patience. But maybe she was losing faith. "Was there a name? A group? An acronym? Anything?"

"A doctor," Logan said. "He said they'd have a doctor there."

"So they don't just want you taken alive," she said. "They're planning on keeping you that way."

"Yeah. Until they aren't."

Maddie could feel it then, the certain knowledge that Logan wasn't as strong as he acted, as cool or as sure as he looked. He was taller. And stronger. And his hands felt better when she held them, and his chest made a much larger pillow than it had when they were ten. She was sure about all that. But Logan was still the same boy he'd been when they were standing in that corridor. He was still terrified he was about to watch someone he cared about get taken away forever. And his deepest fear—the one Maddie

228

could see in his eyes—was that this time, he wouldn't be able to stop it.

"It's going to be okay, Logan. We're going to get the phone and call my dad. He'll tell us where he can land his plane, and then we'll all go to Canada."

"And get donuts," Logan said.

Maddie smiled. "Exactly." She turned and looked out at the frosty wilderness, eyes still scanning, mind still working. "But first we get a plan."

You could hardly tell there'd been a bridge there.

Between the fire and the snow, all the boards were gone, burned or crashed into the water below; the rope had turned to ash. It seemed so much farther down in the light of day, so much so that Maddie wondered if she would have even been able to summon the courage to do what she'd done the night before if she'd been able to see the rocks and the rapids and the ice that lived below.

"It's not that far down." Logan's words were strong, but his voice was significantly less steady.

"Yeah. Totally easy."

"Right?" Logan asked.

"Right," Maddie said.

But neither of them believed it. They stayed hunched behind an outcropping of rocks, higher on the hill. The river curved, and from their hiding place, with a light-colored blanket from the cabin draped over them, they had time to study the deep ravine and look for the pack and the phone and the man they knew had to be out there.

Hunting.

Maddie felt every bit her father's daughter as she scanned the trees and the rocks. She looked up into the icy branches and squinted her eyes, cursing the fact that she didn't have binoculars as she tried to see any footprints in the snow.

"What if he's down there?" she said.

Logan looked at her. "Then I guess we can stop worrying that he'll find us."

It seemed as good a point as any.

Maddie didn't want to wait too long. They didn't want to lose the light, and even with the berries they'd found, that morning's fish was a distant memory. And Maddie's shoulder was starting to burn. The wound needed more than a splash of old vodka and some bandages. She needed a big shot of antibiotics and a bath.

And a hairbrush.

But mostly she needed to get Logan out of there and far away from Stefan and whatever mysterious rendezvous was waiting in the woods.

She cut her eyes up at Logan. "Will it work?"

He grinned back. "There's one way to find out."

The heat that Maddie felt as they eased down the hill, closer to the ravine and the river, had nothing to do with Maddie's wound. It wasn't even the fault of the boy who stayed at her back, glancing over his shoulder periodically, their footsteps light and soft on the slick ground.

When they reached the place where the bridge used to be, Maddie could see that the two posts that had once held the ropes were still standing, but the rest of the bridge was a memory.

She crept closer to the edge and peered over.

"I should go," she said.

"No way," Logan said too loud.

"I've been living here for six years, Logan. I've climbed trees and cliffs and pretty much anything that can collect ice. I can do this. I can—"

Logan didn't argue. He just placed his hand on her shoulder and pressed his thumb against her bullet wound, and Maddie almost passed out from the pain. Stars swirled and her vision went black as she swayed. He hadn't even pressed very hard.

"You were saying?" he asked.

"You don't climb with your shoulder," she tried, but Logan knew better.

"Liar. You climb with your whole body, Mad Dog. And you know it. Even a body as little and adorable as yours."

Two things hit Maddie all at once:

First, the realization that Logan had called her little. And adorable. She wasn't at all sure what that was supposed to mean, but she couldn't possibly stop to figure it out because . . .

Second, Logan was taking off his coat and pushing up the sleeves of his shirt and she couldn't really stop looking at his forearms. At some point in the past six years Logan's forearms had become the most fascinating thing in the world, and Maddie had no idea how that had happened.

He placed his coat around her shoulders, tugged it tight. "Keep this warm for me, will you?"

Maddie didn't know what to say.

Then Logan was looking over the edge again. Stefan's pack peeked out from beneath the snow one-third of the way down. It wasn't a solid cliff face, but it was close.

"It's not that bad," he said.

"Logan . . ." She started to argue. A part of her knew she needed to argue, but the part of her brain that was ticking away the moments had stopped sounding like a clock.

It had started sounding like a bomb.

"I'm lighter," she told him.

He looked indignant. "I'm going," he said. And then he grabbed her. And he kissed her. And Maddie thought that maybe Logan's forearms were her second favorite thing.

When he paused and looked over the cliff one more time, he glanced back at her.

"It's a piece of cake," she lied.

But Logan just shook his head. "Man, I miss cake," he said, then eased himself over the edge.

Maddie didn't want to watch Logan's descent. They had discussed this. They knew the risks—Logan knew the risks. They had both accepted them grudgingly, and yet accepting a thing and liking that thing were two incredibly different things indeed.

She watched until he was out of sight and then eased a little way down the edge of the river. She kept an ear tuned to the sound of her father's plane. She kept one eye glued to the sky. Would he set out on foot, looking for them, or would he take the plane and search by air? Maddie couldn't be certain. But she was sure she wasn't alone.

She put the outcropping of rocks to her back.

And waited.

Alone.

Logan would be back soon.

If this plan worked, then they wouldn't have to worry about being chased anymore. They'd get the phone and call her dad and then he'd come get them and fly them far, far away. If this plan worked, then it would soon be over.

Maddie wrapped Logan's coat around her as she stood waiting. Listening.

The forest was full of sounds—rabbits and birds scavenging among the snow. Limbs falling and cracking under the weight of the first ice of the year.

But this was different. A crisp, clean snap.

Maddie spun to her left—looked back to the cliff—but it was too late. He was already there, standing in front of her. The gun was trained on the center of her chest, and the look on Stefan's face was pure, unadulterated loathing.

"You should have forgotten about the phone," he said.

CHAPTER 24

Maddie had seen evil up close; she'd witnessed terror and rage, and she knew better than most people the effect that pure hate can have on the human body.

First, in Maddie's experience, it was terrible for your skin. (If there was one thing a zit *loved*, it was stress.)

Second, it could do awful things to your eyes. They got glossy, but not with tears, with wild and untamed fury.

Finally, that much adrenaline might make you strong enough to lift a Toyota off a toddler or whatever, but it could also make your hands shake and your heart race.

That's how Stefan looked. His eyes were too wide, his lips were too dry, and his grip was too hard on the gun.

Maddie didn't scream. Or plead. Or cry. She just rolled her eyes and said, "But I'm a teenage girl. We're addicted to our phones, or haven't you heard?"

She could feel the boulder at her back, and as Stefan stepped closer, she knew there was nowhere to go. So she tensed.

"You think you are so smart." Stefan's accent was thicker. The words were cold.

"Well, not to brag, but I am number one in my class. Does it matter if you're the only one in your class?" she asked. "I don't know about—"

"Shut up!" he yelled, limping closer.

Maddie glanced down at the leg that wasn't moving quite right. The bear trap must have gotten him good, she realized. She tried not to smile. He'd wrapped rags around his hands, probably covering up some pretty nasty burns. Maddie thought about the pack that still rested on a ledge one-third of the way down the cliff and wanted to smile because Stefan no longer had his food or his phone or his map.

He didn't even have Logan, and Maddie wondered if he'd been able to make a fire the night before. Honestly, for a second she was simply impressed that he was still alive. He didn't just have a reason to kill, she realized. He had a reason to live. And that fact could prove very useful.

"Your boyfriend should not have left you here."

"He's *not* my boyfriend. I can tell because I don't have his name drawn inside a heart on a single notebook. I swear. And who says he left me? Maybe I left him? Maybe we found someplace safe and I stashed him there."

"I doubt that," Stefan said.

"I'd totally leave him, you know. Boys are annoying."

"True. But there is no safe place. And I am no fool. I knew you would come for the phone. I have been watching this spot since daybreak. I saw him go over the edge."

Stefan jerked Maddie against him, sliding the barrel of the gun along the smooth skin of her cheek like she needed a shave. "Now you are going to be very still and very quiet, and when he gets back with my phone I promise I will not kill you."

"You're a real sweetie, you know."

"Quiet," he snapped, and placed an arm around her from behind. His big bicep pressed against her neck, but Maddie could look back at him.

"So what's your story?"

Maddie didn't try to hide the singsong lilt of her voice as she spoke. She didn't want to. She'd learned at a very young age that nothing annoyed manly men more than girly girls, and if Maddie had one talent, it was truly exceptional girliness.

"Shut up and be quiet," Stefan snapped.

"That's just a tad redundant, FYI."

"Shut up!" he hissed near her ear.

Maddie couldn't help but shift her weight from foot to foot, almost pacing in place. She was careful of the ice and the snow, though. No use falling to the ground and having Stefan accidently pull the trigger.

"You really do give a lot of orders," she told him.

He tightened his grip. "I'm the one with the gun."

"Well, yeah. Sure. Technically. But I'm the one with the winning personality, and that should count for something."

"You should be scared," he said in the same tone a movie villain might use to say *You should be dead* when the hero materializes five years later, hungry for vengeance.

Stefan was confused, and Maddie couldn't blame him.

So she turned back and shrugged. "Maybe. But I don't think you're a bad guy."

He let her go and spun her around, grabbing Logan's unzipped coat and pulling her closer.

"I. Have. The. Gun," he reminded her.

Maddie smiled and pulled away. "And I have Taylor Swift's signature scent. Doesn't make me a pop star. It just makes me smell like Taylor Swift, which isn't as great as it sounds because, to a bear, Taylor Swift smells *delicious*."

Stefan stuttered for a moment, then fell silent. Maddie talked on.

"What makes you think he's gonna care?" she asked. "He's a smart kid. He'll probably see you here, realize you still have the gun, and run for the hills."

Maddie kept her gaze trained on the place where Logan was supposed to be. She only turned when she heard the laughter.

"What's so funny?"

"You are." Stefan actually smiled. It looked so foreign on his gruff face with its two days' growth of beard, his dirty clothes. He looked . . . handsome. And Maddie was almost entirely certain that she hated him just a little more for it.

"I'm not funny," she snapped. He'd knocked her down a cliff and held a knife to her throat and a gun to her back, but *this* was what Maddie found most offensive.

"Yes. You are. If you think he's not going to move heaven and earth to get you back, you are as crazy as you are stupid. He'll do whatever I say when he sees I have his woman."

For a moment, she couldn't reply. She was breathing too hard, like she'd just had to swim across the lake or climb a cliff or haul a whole elk carcass home by herself.

"If I mean so much to him, I would have gotten a letter at some point in the past six years, but thanks for the optimism. It's been a rough couple of hair days. I appreciate the vote of confidence."

She expected him to grunt something in Russian or threaten her with the gun again. But he just shook his head.

"You do not understand men."

At which point Maddie decided to go ahead and get angry. She jerked away and snapped, "Well, that's just silly, because clearly I've been around *so many of them*!"

She threw her arms out wide and spun, taking in the vast expanse of snow-covered trees and the ice-covered cliffs.

Down below, the river was running faster. The deepest portion hadn't frozen and she could actually hear the roar of one of the waterfalls that cascaded down the face of one of the mountains, a never-ending flow of ice-cold glacier water.

But there were no puffs of smoke, no lights from high school football stadiums or movie theaters or any of the hundreds of things that Maddie imagined must dominate the life of a teenage girl.

There certainly were no teenage boys.

"What?" she snapped when she faced him again. "Why are you smiling?" She wanted to slap that smile off his face for reasons that had nothing to do with kidnapping.

"You remind me of someone," he admitted.

This felt like progress to Maddie, proof that there might actually be a pulse beating beneath that too-broad, too-hard chest.

"Who?" she asked. "Is there a Mrs. Evil Assassin back in Mother Russia?"

"No," Stefan said, pulling her back toward him, turning her to make her a human shield. It was like she could actually feel him freeze. "I have no wife. But I do have . . . a sister."

She opened her mouth to speak, but the gun was pointed at her again, and Stefan was through talking.

But Maddie never quit talking, so she asked, "What's she like?"

"Alive" was Stefan's cold reply.

"She's why you're doing this, isn't she?"

Stefan didn't look scary, so much as he just looked scared. And something inside of Maddie actually hurt for him, in that moment. But she also hurt for herself and for Logan, because right then she knew there would be no stopping him. This wasn't about money or politics or even terror. This was personal. And personal was the most dangerous thing of all.

"The president always liked me, you know. You might not even need Logan. I'm enough. Just forget about Logan. You don't need him."

"They do need him," Stefan snapped. "Only him."

Maddie pulled back a little. "*They*, huh? Not *we?*"

Stefan was silent for a moment. Eagles circled overhead, their shadows dark on the snowy ground.

But the darkest part was the look on Stefan's face. "Maybe I will kill you after all."

He raised the gun.

He shook his head.

And a shadow fell across them both as Maddie said, "Now."

In the next moment, a haunting cry filled the air, and Stefan looked around like there must be a wounded bear or some other kind of animal, but there was just a shadow streaking across the sky.

Maddie was barely able to throw herself out of the way as Logan jumped from atop the outcropping of rocks, hurling himself toward Stefan and knocking him to the ground.

They hit the snow and started to roll, a tangle of limbs and ice and fury. Stefan was older and had some kind of training. But Logan was so terrified and so desperate that he didn't seem to feel the cold or the force of the blows. He didn't even notice how close they'd rolled to the edge of the steep ravine.

He just kept yelling, "Don't touch her! Don't you dare—"

"Logan, stop!" Maddie shouted. The snow was flying as they punched and kicked.

Stefan lashed out, trying to reverse their positions.

They were too close to the edge.

Logan was losing momentum.

So Maddie did the most obvious thing in the world: She ran toward the two of them and kicked Stefan's shin, right where the bear trap must have caught him, because he howled in pain, dropping the gun and bringing both hands to his leg.

And then Logan was on top of Stefan, pressing his head over the edge, like he might just pop it off his neck like the head of a dandelion, let it float away on the wind.

"Logan, stop. Please!" Maddie yelled, but it was like she was far, far away.

Like Logan still had to get her back.

Like he might never get her back.

"Don't you touch her," he growled, looking down at Stefan.

"Logan, stop," Maddie tried again.

But Logan didn't face her. He kept his knees on Stefan's arms and his hands around Stefan's throat. Squeezing.

"He would have killed you."

"Logan."

Stefan's face was turning red and he wasn't making a sound anymore. And Logan seemed to squeeze harder.

Maddie picked up the gun that lay, forgotten, in the snow.

And she fired.

The shot seemed to echo in the cold air, reverberating off the snow and the ice.

Overhead, birds flew away—eagles leaving their nests.

Logan dropped his hold on Stefan, pushed back, and stared up at Maddie.

"What the——"

"Get up." Maddie didn't point the gun at them, but she handled it like someone who would if she had to——like someone who knew how.

"Get up. Both of you," she said. "Before you make me angry."

Stefan actually cut his eyes at Logan. "I'm starting to understand why you didn't reply to those letters."

But it was a bad call because Logan was lunging for him again. "You don't get to talk to her. Or look at her. Or——"

Maddie fired again, the sound filling the air and cutting him off.

Logan jumped to his feet, but Stefan sank lower. He sat in the snow, and all Maddie could think was that his rear was going to get wet. Maddie knew how important a dry rear was to a person's well-being in Alaska, but this probably wasn't the time to say so.

"You might as well kill me," Stefan said.

"Okay," Logan said, reaching for the gun.

Maddie jerked it away. "Logan!"

From his place on the ground, Stefan laughed again. "Are you going to kill me, little girl?"

"No," Maddie snapped. "I'm going to tie you to a tree and make you smell like Taylor Swift and then wait for the bears to find you. They'll do it, you know. You'll be praying for a bullet."

Stefan actually shrugged. "Okay."

Logan was lunging toward Stefan again, shouting, "Do not tempt me."

Maddie could barely hold him back, but she did. Her arms

were around him, squeezing him tight. She tipped up her head and tried to look into his eyes. "Logan, let him tell us why."

"I think we know why," Logan said, but he wasn't fighting Maddie anymore. She kept one arm around him, though. Just in case.

"Logan, look at me. There are at least a half dozen perfectly good reasons why someone would want the president's son." She brought a hand to the stubble on his cheek. "I want to hear what *his* reason is."

When she turned back to Stefan the gun was in her hand, cold from the snow, but solid. She wanted to throw it off the edge of the cliff but knew that would be foolish. Weapons were important in Alaska, even under the best of circumstances. And these were far from ideal.

Stefan had turned his head to look out over the river. The waterfall must have been close, just around the bend, because Maddie could hear it like white noise in her head.

"Well?" Logan prodded.

Stefan turned back to them and looked up, like facing the sun. A shadow crossed his face when he studied Logan. Then he raised his gaze to the sky, to the real sun that was just starting to peak through the heavy clouds.

"Oh, are you running late?" Logan asked. "Please, don't let me stop you if there's someplace you need to be."

"It's too late now," Stefan said. "You win. Is that what you want me to say?"

Maddie shook her head and held Logan back again. "I want you to tell us who they are, Stefan. Do they have your sister? Is it supposed to be some kind of trade? Logan for her?"

But the Russian stayed silent.

"Why?" Maddie asked. "The United States doesn't negotiate with terrorists. Whatever they want Logan for, it won't work."

"This has *nothing* to do with your precious United States."

For the first time, Stefan's hands were shaking as he brought them to his face. Maddie had learned six years ago that any kind of animal can be dangerous if it's hurting or if its young is in danger.

Stefan was both. And even though Maddie had the gun, she was terrified.

"Stefan, she's okay. Wherever she is, wherever they have her, I'm sure she's just fine. I'm sure she's . . ."

It was the look in Stefan's eyes that made Maddie trail off, forced her to turn around. She felt Logan turning, too, but he froze just as she lurched toward the man who was bent and bloody and stumbling from the trees.

"Dad?"

CHAPTER 25

It wasn't Maddie's father. That much was obvious to Logan the moment the man stepped from the shade of the tall trees, out into the bright sunlight that reflected off the snow.

But Maddie wanted her father so badly, she was willing to believe in miracles. And it was a miracle, Logan had to remind himself. Just a different kind.

When Maddie slammed to a stop, Logan knew she must have realized who it really was.

"You. You're not dead," she blurted, even though Logan was pretty sure the forest ranger probably felt more dead than alive at that moment.

Maddie turned her back on Logan and Stefan and ran toward the ranger, who practically collapsed into her arms.

"Heard your shots," he said.

"It's okay. We've got you. You're safe now."

But the ranger's gaze was locked on Stefan. Rage and pure

hatred bloomed on his face, and Logan turned back to the man in the snow and saw a totally different expression: disbelief and also . . . fear.

"Step away from him, little girl," Stefan warned.

"No!" Maddie snapped. She pouted. She did everything but stomp her foot, but the gun was still firmly in her grip so no one dared to tell her that she sounded like a child. Probably because she was also a child who was an extremely good shot.

"It's okay. You're okay." Maddie spoke softly to the man. Like maybe he was an injured animal who might not realize she was there to help.

Blood covered his coat and he wasn't terribly steady on his feet, but he was alive and on this side of the river. And when he told Logan, "Step away from that man," his voice was strong and sure.

"It's okay." Maddie held up the gun. "We've disarmed him."

"Good work," the ranger said. "Now get over here," he told Logan, but he never took his gaze away from the man in the snow.

The man who had shot him for no apparent reason.

"Are you okay?" Logan asked, but the ranger shook the question off.

"I should be asking the same of you."

"I'm fine," Logan said. Then he looked at Maddie. "We're fine."

"Good. That makes things easier."

"Makes what easier?" Maddie asked.

Behind Logan, Stefan was yelling in Russian. *"You may be alive. But you will never be a wolf!"*

And just like that Logan was back in that long-ago corridor, listening to the echo of the very first words that Logan had translated from Russian into English: *A boy is no match for a wolf.*

Maybe it was Stefan's words or Logan's memory. Maybe it was the flash in the ranger's eyes, the sign he'd understood the Russian's threat. But more likely it was the tattoo that was peeking out from beneath the ranger's sleeve: a two-headed bird in the clutches of a wolf.

A tattoo that Logan had seen once before.

"Maddie!" Logan and Stefan shouted at the same time, but it was too late. She was too close, her guard too low, and the man pulled her back against him and squeezed her tight, his own gun suddenly pressed to her temple.

Logan's blood ran cold—but Maddie, being Maddie, groaned and said, *"Not again."*

"You folks need some help?" This time the ranger's words were too cheerful. He sounded borderline insane when he laughed. And when he spoke again, his too-friendly American voice was gone.

This time his accent was cold and hard and Russian.

"I knew you were a coward, Stefan, but you were a fool to try to save this girl as well. Now they'll both die."

Stefan was up, out of the snow and easing forward. "Let her go, Uri."

"Drop it!" the man snapped, squeezing Maddie tighter. "Drop your gun and kick it away." But Maddie just gripped and re-gripped the gun that was still in her hands.

Stefan inched slowly closer. "I have him, Uri. I have the president's son, and I'm taking him to the meeting place now."

"You must think me a fool!" Uri shouted.

"Let her go!" Logan roared.

"Logan," Maddie warned.

"Don't move, Mad Dog," Logan said, turning as Uri pulled Maddie backward, easing toward the shelter of the trees. He probably didn't even realize he was doing it. It was just natural instinct to seek cover.

"You will drop the gun," Uri growled into Maddie's ear.

"Do it, Mad Dog. It's okay."

"Logan . . ."

Was Maddie's voice breaking? Was it all finally too much? Logan would rather be shot again than watch her shed a single tear.

"It's okay, Mad Dog. Just drop the gun. It'll be okay."

But the two Russians probably didn't hear a word of it. Stefan was inching closer and Logan didn't know who to fear. Who to trust. Except for Maddie. He had always trusted Maddie.

But no matter how you counted it, this new Russian was out-numbered. It was just a matter of time.

"It's gonna be okay," Logan said, knowing that Maddie was more than capable of doing the math.

"I know it is," she said.

"I'm here," he told her, and watched her eyes go misty, because he *was* there. Logan was there and he was alive and he had carried her through a storm and bound her wounds.

He hadn't written her a single letter, but he hoped his actions would say so much more than words.

"You were careless, Stefan," Uri snapped. "You never should have let me live."

"I never meant to, I assure you," Stefan answered.

"What do you say, President's Son? Should I shoot the man who took you first? Or should I kill the girl he should have let me kill yesterday?"

"You don't need her!" Logan shouted, and Uri brought the gun to Maddie's temple.

"I know." Uri squeezed Maddie tighter. "Now drop your gun, little girl." There was no doubt he was out of patience. Especially when he shifted his aim and turned the barrel toward Logan. "Now."

"Logan?" Maddie said, the word a question: *Do you trust me? Will you forgive me? Will you still like me once you see who I really am?*

Logan shook his head, a warning. *DON'T TRY IT, MAD DOG.* But Maddie wasn't listening, so he shouted, "Take me!"

"Oh, I intend to." Then Uri spun. "Don't move, Stefan."

"I told you I was bringing them in," Stefan said.

Uri laughed. "If that was your intention, you would have let me kill the girl yesterday instead of shooting me like a coward. You still think you can save everyone, Stefan. But you can't save *anyone*."

Uri looked down at Maddie. "Isn't that right, sweetheart?"

"That's okay," Maddie said. "I'm kind of used to saving myself."

Maybe it was her words that knocked him off guard. Or maybe it was the way her skull crashed into his nose. But in any case Uri was pointing his gun in Maddie's direction in one moment and howling in pain the next.

Logan and Stefan watched, frozen, while she dropped to the icy ground and kicked at his legs, knocking him off balance.

The man was injured. Half starved and half frozen. But he was also half crazy with rage, and he came at her throat with both hands. Maddie didn't think. She just turned and rolled onto her back and pointed her gun straight up toward the canopy of trees.

And fired.

Logan and Maddie had been walking through the woods for hours, listening to the crack of trees under the weight of too much ice. The breaking limbs sounded like gunshots, Logan had thought at the time.

So it was almost surreal to hear the report of the pistol and then the sharp crack of the tree.

Uri was still over Maddie, strangling and screaming. He must have thought her a moron to waste a shot. But that would have been his last thought for a long time, because when the ice-covered tree limb landed atop him, he didn't move again.

"Maddie!" Logan screamed and ran toward her, but she was lost beneath the weight of the madman and the icy, heavy branch of the tree. Logan couldn't even see her. Nothing moved.

"Maddie, are you . . . ? Maddie!"

"I'm fine. Just smushed."

At her muffled shout Logan didn't know whether to laugh or to scream.

And then he remembered Stefan.

Uri's gun must have come loose in the struggle or the crash because when Logan turned he found Stefan stooping down into the snow. The gun was in his hands.

And Logan knew it was too late.

For a second he stood frozen in the snow and the ice and the sun that had finally decided to start shining. He looked at the man who had knocked Maddie down a hill and dragged Logan toward some unknown fate—the man who had left two Secret Service agents dead in Maddie's cabin—and Logan had the sinking feeling that they were right back where they'd started.

But before he could lunge or strike out, Stefan tucked the gun into the waist of his jeans and looked at Logan.

"Let's get her out of there," he said.

"Okay?" The word came out as a question, and Logan couldn't keep his gaze from slipping between Stefan and the gun.

"And then I'm going to tell you a story," Stefan said.

"A story about what?"

"A wolf."

CHAPTER 26

It had been a long time since Logan had had one of the night-mares. For years, though, they'd come to him in the dark: eyes better to see him with, teeth better to eat him with. The wolf had been there every time he'd closed his eyes. And whenever the world got too still or too quiet, he'd hear them again: the Russian words that he hadn't known the meaning to years ago, that he hadn't been able to forget ever since.

A boy is no match for a wolf.

He looked at Stefan. And a part of him wanted to growl.

But Maddie didn't have that problem.

"So . . ." she let the word draw out as she sat on a fallen log, legs crossed, like maybe she had just ordered a milk shake, like maybe this was the most ordinary thing in the world and she hadn't just hog-tied a rogue Russian to a tree. She actually took a moment to examine her nails. "Go ahead, Stefan. Tell us a story. Just make it a good one."

Behind her, Uri groaned, but Maddie must have had no doubts in her knot-tying ability because she didn't even turn around. She just kept staring up at the man who had tried to kill her, waiting as if they had all day.

"Six years ago, three men tried to take the first lady of the United States."

"We are aware," Maddie said. She gestured with her gun, a get-to-the-good-part gesture if Logan had ever seen one. But Stefan was deliberate as he talked on.

"You may think that is where the story begins, but in truth it started long before that day at the White House. Long before your father was the president. Long before any of us even existed. In a way, this all began more than eighty years ago, when a child was born in a Russian prison. Some say that he was kept there—in the prison, raised by two hundred mothers who were all criminally insane. But others swear that the guards did not want the responsibility of an infant, so they drew straws, and the loser took the baby to the woods—left him to be raised by the wolves."

"Stefan," Maddie said, "I really don't want to shoot you. But I will, you know. Right through the shoulder, make us nice and even."

But, to Stefan, it was like she hadn't spoken at all.

"My grandfather used to tell me stories from when he was a boy. In the coldest part of winter, he and his siblings would huddle in their beds, listen to the wolves howl, and wonder how one of the wolves could sound so human."

"The point, Stefan!" Maddie was up and stalking toward him.

She was no longer laughing, not teasing. They were all cold and hungry and ready for the ordeal to be over, and Logan wondered if it might finally be impatience that got the best of her.

"They named him Boris, this boy, because, of course Boris means—"

"*Wolf,*" Logan said.

"I know how it sounds. I know the stories are no doubt mostly myth, legend. But the man is real—of that much I am certain. And all legends are at least a little bit true. The people of my grandfather's village used to swear the child was feral, but he was also smart and ruthless. He was a boy when the war came. He was a young man as the Soviets rose, a man in his prime when they fell. He was born with nothing, but all it takes to rise to power is the willingness to do that which another will not."

Stefan paused and looked from Maddie to Logan, held his gaze.

"There was nothing the Wolf would not do. He had no family. No home. He was beholden only to his greed and his never-ending quest for power. Until . . . Until he had a son."

Logan blinked and shook his head. The chill that ran down his spine had nothing to do with the cold.

"But the son wanted to be more than his father. More powerful. More wealthy. But, most of all, more feared. So he hatched a plan. He became obsessed with walking into the White House and taking the wife of the most powerful man in the world."

Logan remembered the man who had winked at him in the corridor, his tattoo and his words.

A boy is no match for a wolf.

"*Da,*" Stefan said, and Logan realized he'd spoken aloud and in Russian.

"The plan was foolish, the risk not worth the reward. The Wolf knew that, and he forbade his son from taking such a stupid chance. But his son was full of bluster. And his son had a friend who was as arrogant and foolish as he was. So the two of them recruited another gun and . . . you know the rest."

"So this is revenge?" Maddie, of course, had to cut right to the heart of the matter. "The Wolf lost his son, so he's going to take the president's son and call it even? Are we in old-school eye-for-an-eye territory? Is that it?"

"Yes. And no." Stefan was shaking his head, as if there were too many secrets in there and they were warring with each other, trying to get out. "The Wolf is sick. Dying. And without a son— an heir—he needs to make sure his legacy lives on." Stefan pointed at where Uri sat bound to the tree. "That man hoped to be his successor."

"And what are you?" Logan asked. "What was *I*, some kind of pawn? Some kind of test? Whoever brings me back first wins, is that it?"

"No. I'm the brother of the man who talked his son into defying him. So I must be made to suffer, too."

"Your sister," Maddie said, filling in the blank.

"She needs medicine. Without it, she will die, too. I had one chance to save her. All I had to do was bring the boy to the Wolf and I could have my sister and my family's debt would be erased."

Stefan laughed the laugh of someone who doesn't find anything funny at all. "The best thugs in Russia, he has at his disposal, but he chooses me to do this thing because he wants to make as many people suffer as possible."

"You were supposed to take Logan to some meeting place, right? Will your sister be there? Or is she back in Russia?"

"She was supposed to be here. In Alaska. The Wolf is dying. He doesn't have much time. He will be there, too. He isn't going to wait for the boy to come to him. The Wolf will come to his prey."

A part of Logan wanted to laugh at Stefan, the words were so dramatic and surreal. But another part of Logan knew—a part had always known—that the Wolf was out there, howling in the night. And someday it was going to try to finish what was started six years ago.

"How?" Logan's voice was quiet as he turned back to Stefan. "How did Boris know I'd be in Alaska?"

Stefan almost smiled. "When you set up a secret social media account and post pictures about a big trip, you should remember that nothing in Russia stays a secret for long."

Logan looked at Maddie. He expected her to lecture him, yell at him—at least call him an idiot. But she was up and moving toward the cliff almost before Logan could reach her.

"We need the pack," Maddie said.

"Wait."

"No!" she shouted. "We need to call my dad and get you out of here. Now that we know there aren't any moles in the Secret Service . . . We need to get help, Logan. Now."

But Logan was looking from the steep cliff to Stefan and then to Maddie, who had been knocked unconscious and shot and dragged into a fight that wasn't her own.

"How much time does your sister have?" he asked the man who may or may not still be their enemy.

Slowly Stefan shook his head. "Not enough."

Maddie's shoulder hurt. Her head throbbed. That was how she knew it was almost over. If there'd been no help on the horizon—no hope—her body would have blocked out those aches and pains. She would have found a way to go on.

But as soon as Maddie saw Logan slip over the edge of the ravine, she actually staggered and dropped to a fallen log. She should have been afraid, she guessed. Technically she was outnumbered.

But Uri, the fake ranger, was tied to a tree and Maddie had a gun. But, most of all, Maddie had a new perspective on Stefan. He really wasn't a bad guy. But even good people can do bad things if given even just a little bit of a reason.

She saw him looking to the woods, to escape. So Maddie slipped the gun behind her back, tucking it into the waistband of her jeans. She saw him watch her do it.

"Don't run," she told him.

"Would you really shoot me?" He actually sounded like he might be teasing.

"Oh, I'd shoot you straight through the heart if I thought I had to. But I don't have to. And that's why you shouldn't run."

"They have my sister," he reminded her.

"And we're gonna call people who can get her back."

"Will they?" It wasn't a question. It was a dare. "Or will they take me to a place where I will never see the sun again? Maybe I will disappear forever."

"This isn't Russia," she reminded him, but Stefan's reply was a cold, hard laugh.

"Anywhere can be Russia. Besides, I took your prince."

"He's not *my* prince," Maddie snapped.

"He is American royalty. And I took him. I will never see freedom again. I will never see Natalia again. And I can live with that. *After* she is safe."

"If this Boris is as bad as you say he is—"

"He is worse," Stefan said, cutting her off.

"—then the Secret Service is going to want him. Trust me."

"She's very sick. Without her medicine . . ."

"They're already looking, I can promise you that. As soon as they realize their agents are dead, they'll—"

"They're not dead."

For a moment, Maddie was certain she'd misheard him. Maybe it was wishful thinking—hearing—on her part.

"What?"

"The men from the Secret Service . . . they are not dead. They were supposed to die, but I disabled them, tied them up inside your cabin. They are not dead."

Maddie hadn't realized how much that had weighed on her until the weight was lifted. She thought she might float away.

"They're alive."

"They were," Stefan said. "When I left them."

"Then help is coming," Maddie told him.

She got up and walked to the ledge, peered over. Logan looked so much bigger from that angle, all arms and legs, big strong hands that gripped the rocks. He'd reached the pack and he looked up, as if knowing that Maddie would be there. His smile was brighter than the sun.

"There's a rope!" he shouted.

"Throw it up!" she called back.

Five minutes later he was standing back at the top of the hill. He wasn't even breathing hard when he said, "We've got it."

Maddie thought she might cry. And maybe she would have if crying wasn't the world's leading cause of puffy eyes and skin blotchiness. For some reason, it seemed really, really important that Maddie's skin stay as blotch-free as possible in Logan's presence.

Logan dropped the pack to the ground and started digging through pockets.

"Food," he said with a sigh, tossing an energy bar in Maddie's direction. "Ibuprofen." He tossed the small bottle at her, too. "Take two of those. Now," he ordered. Maddie grinned, and for once in her life did as she was told.

"Where is it?" A hint of panic was seeping into Logan's voice. "Where is . . . ?"

But then his entire face changed. He took a deep breath, then pulled his hand from one of the pockets of the pack, the bright yellow phone gripped tightly in his hand.

"It's here."

Maddie thought she could kiss him.

She didn't, of course. But she could have. And it wasn't just out of relief or joy. It was because, in that moment, Logan just looked utterly kissable, and she didn't know what she thought about that.

"Give it," she ordered, and Logan handed it over. "Don't move!" she shouted as Stefan inched toward the trees.

Logan had already dropped the pack on a big, flat rock and was unloading it, carefully surveying exactly what they had.

There was the ibuprofen in a tiny white bottle. A canteen that was half full and three energy bars. A pack of Band-Aids, two empty plastic bags. A sleeping bag. A poncho. Two pairs of thick, tall socks, and something that looked like a solar phone charger.

Plus the map.

It was the most glorious collection of stuff that Maddie had ever seen. She ripped open the wrapper of the energy bar that Logan had handed her and then looked down at the satellite phone and dialed a number she knew by heart.

As it rang, she spread out the map and tried to locate their position, then pinpoint a place where her father could land.

They could meet up in an hour. Maybe significantly less. She was calling her father. Her father was coming. Maddie was so giddy she could practically hear the phone ringing on his end. She could practically . . .

She took another big bite of the energy bar, but then it suddenly turned to ashes in her mouth as she caught Logan's gaze.

"What's that noise?" he asked.

And Maddie realized that she wasn't imagining the sound of her father's phone ringing. She kept Stefan's sat phone to her ear, but she was no longer listening, not really.

She was looking at Logan, who was starting to rise, to turn, to look at the man who was now fully conscious, leaning against the tree, a cold, cruel smile across his face.

Maddie kept the phone to her ear, praying that she might hear her father say hello, or cuss, or cry. She wanted to hear her father's voice, but instead she heard his distinctive ringtone coming from the pocket of the ranger uniform.

She heard Uri ask, "Looking for someone?"

Maddie thought that maybe someone had knocked her off a cliff again. She felt like maybe, this time, she never would stop falling.

But Logan didn't have that problem.

"Where is it?" he shouted. He grabbed Uri by the lapels of his coat and pulled him as hard as he could with the man still tied to a tree. Logan started digging through pockets, ripping open the man's jacket until they both looked down at the ringing phone.

"Where did you get that?" Maddie's voice was cold and calm, but inside she was screaming. "Where did you get that?" she shouted this time, the words echoing out across the ice-cold river, maybe all the way to the sea.

But the man just smiled. "You didn't think the boy was all we wanted, did you?" He laughed like they were so silly. "The Wolf won't rest until he's hurt everyone who hurt his son. *Everyone.*"

Maddie couldn't help but remember all the times she'd asked her father why they'd had to leave DC, what was so special about Alaska. She'd begged to go to school somewhere. She'd wanted to make friends. Even in the most remote parts of the world people had satellite Internet, but not Maddie. She'd thought it was because of what happened in that corridor in DC. She'd thought it was because her father had almost died.

But that wasn't it.

It was because her father had *lived*, and he must have known that someday soon the Wolf would be there, trying to huff and puff and blow their cabin down.

"Where is he?" Logan shook the man again, but Maddie was spinning on Stefan.

"Did you know?"

"No," Stefan said, shaking his head slowly, like maybe he'd been a fool not to. "But that is the way of the Wolf."

"Is my father alive?" she asked the man tied to the tree. "Is he?" she shouted, pulling the gun from her waistband and taking aim.

"Mad," Logan warned, but Maddie wasn't listening.

"Where is my father?" she asked again, the words almost a growl.

"He's safe. For now." There was an eerie glow in the Russian's eyes, like maybe it was worth being captured and shot and knocked unconscious by an icy limb just to have such a good seat for her heartbreak.

"They'll keep him alive. He might even save himself, you know."

"How?" Logan asked.

The Russian smiled up at him. "By killing you, of course. The Wolf has always liked a trade. Maybe if he kills you, the Wolf will spare him. It's only a pity we did not know about the girl. We were told the daughter died in DC. The Wolf will be most distressed to learn he was mistaken."

"Don't look at her!" Logan shouted. His hands were around the man's throat. "You don't get to look at her or speak to her. You aren't good enough to breathe the same air as her, you—"

"Logan," Maddie tried.

"I will end you," Logan told the man.

"Logan," Maddie tried again, this time grabbing his hand. "They have my dad."

"I know, Mad Dog. We're going to get him back. We're—"

"Not we." She was shaking her head. She should have been screaming or crying, but her heart was numb, from the worry and the cold. For the first time in a long time she could see things plainly. It was like hunting, being all alone in the early hours of the day when everything is quiet and still and covered in freshly fallen snow. At times like that you can see farther, hear more. The world was crystal clear in that moment, and Maddie knew exactly what had to happen.

"You've got to call DC, Logan. You have to tell the Secret Service where you are. Tell them where my dad is. Tell them—"

"Okay, Mad Dog. We will. We'll tell them. And then—"

"No." Maddie was shaking her head. She eased farther away from the Russians, and Logan followed. It was as if both of them knew that this moment was too personal, too raw and too real to be shared with strangers.

Logan's arms went around her, sheltering her between his body and the low branch of a tree, gripping the cold wood despite the ice and the snow. Maddie laid her forehead against Logan's broad chest, resting for what felt like the first time. And the last.

"Mad Dog." Logan's voice was as soft as his touch as he lifted her chin, then gently tucked a piece of hair behind her ear. It said a lot about her situation that she no longer cared what her hair looked like. Or her skin. She only cared that she finally knew why her father had brought her to this big, empty world—why he'd kept her safe and taught her to survive here.

Because someday, she was going to have to return the favor.

"Tell me you know the phone number."

"Of course I know the phone number." Logan sounded more than a little bit offended.

"Tell me you'll call them."

"Mad Dog, of course I'm going to call them."

She put her hand over his. "Tell me you know where we are right now—that you know what to tell them. They have to send a chopper here. Now."

"Yes, Maddie. I know. But—"

There was a click, the sound faint but sharp in the cold air. For a moment Logan froze until Maddie went up on her toes and pressed her mouth to his for one split second.

"Tell me you forgive me."

But Maddie didn't wait for Logan's answer as he stared down at the shiny metal that hung around his wrist. He moved to reach for her, but the limb of the tree shook, showering them with falling snow. Logan tried again, then cursed, and Maddie had to mentally alter her list of supplies. They had:

Ibuprofen.

Socks.

Poncho.

Sleeping bag.

Solar charger.

Band-Aids.

And handcuffs. Maddie hadn't dared to forget about the handcuffs.

"Mad Dog," Logan started. "What did you—"

"Call them." She dropped Stefan's yellow phone a few feet away from Logan, where he could reach it with a little effort. "As soon as we're gone. Get them here. Save yourself."

"Maddie, wait!" Logan lunged for her but the cuff held tight.

"You're the president's son! If something happens to you, there could be war, Logan. Straight up war. The stock market could crash. There'd be congressional investigations and . . . I always really liked your mom. She's got to be worried sick. So call her. And let me do what I have to do."

"Not without me."

But something had happened inside of Maddie the moment she heard the sound of her father's phone. It was like she was above the Arctic Circle and the sun had gone down and she was standing on the front end of a long, dark winter.

"You seem to think this is a democracy, Logan. It's not. It's Alaska."

She knew that Logan kept shouting, cursing, but he might as well have been yelling at the snow because Maddie was already turning to Stefan.

"You know where they are?" she asked.

"I do."

"Will my father be where your sister is?"

"Probably."

"And the Wolf? Will he be there?"

"Definitely," Stefan said. "The Wolf has waited six long years for this moment. He will be where the blood is."

Maddie walked to the pack and gathered everything that she might need.

"Then let's go kill him."

CHAPTER 27

"What's she like?"

Maddie didn't turn back to look at Stefan, but she knew that he was back there. She could hear his heavy breath and his foot-steps crunching in the icy snow. But most of all, she knew that he had just as much reason to fight as she did. She was just glad that they were finally fighting on the same side.

"Natalia?" he said.

"Yes. How long have they had her?"

This time, it took a moment for Stefan to answer. Maybe because time didn't have any meaning anymore, with the short Alaskan days and gloomy, sunless sky. But more than likely because it felt like forever to Stefan. It was a feeling Maddie could relate to.

"Four days. The Wolf came for her four days ago."

Just four days. It wasn't much time, but it was forever in a lot of ways. Maddie knew better than anyone that it only took a moment for a life to change forever.

"What happens if she doesn't get her medicine?"

"It depends," Stefan said. "She is diabetic. She needs a daily shot of insulin. Depending on what she's been eating—*if* she's been eating . . . I do not know. She will likely need a doctor. The Wolf promised he would bring one. He was supposed to bring one. But the Wolf . . . he lies."

"She'll be fine," Maddie told him. "We're going to get her back."

The air was slightly warmer and the ground was covered with a slick sheen of water. Maddie hadn't known that there could be anything slicker than ice, but that was before she'd moved to Alaska. Now she knew that the ground could always be slicker, rougher, steeper. Things could always get worse. And they usually did before they got better.

She stopped for a moment when they reached the top of the ridge. Down below, there was an icy lake and a silt-covered beach. A familiar red plane floated in the distance, and it was all Maddie could do not to scream out for her father and run in its direction. She would have, too, if it hadn't been for the helicopter not far away. And the tents.

"That's it?" Maddie said—the words a question. Somehow, she'd expected something far bigger, darker, scarier. They'd been walking for more than a day, every step bringing them closer to this place. In a way, Maddie realized, this is where that White

House corridor led. Six years later, she was finally going to come out the other side.

"Binoculars," Maddie said, holding out her hands. Stefan gave her the pair they'd scavenged from the fake ranger's gear, and Maddie laid low on the ground. The snow and ice didn't melt through her raincoat, but she could feel it on her legs. It didn't matter. She trained the binoculars on the camp below, memorizing every possible detail.

"I count four guards," she said, handing the binoculars to Stefan. "Does that sound right to you?"

He looked into the binoculars and scanned the camp. "Yes. The Wolf would never leave home with fewer than two. Two extras make sense under the circumstances."

Smoke rose from a big fire that someone had built between the two tents. Three of the armed guards were positioned on the perimeter, scanning the trees. Waiting. For Stefan or Uri. For trouble.

Maddie looked up at the overcast sky.

"What is it?" Stefan asked her.

"There has to be a satellite looking for Logan. Drones, too. Someone's going to see that fire and come asking questions."

"Isn't that a good thing?"

"Yeah," Maddie admitted. "I think so. Logan will have called in the cavalry by now. Help could be just over that ridge."

Stefan looked at her. "Or not."

Maddie nodded. "Or not."

"So what do we do now?" Stefan was actually asking. She wasn't some tagalong, some annoying girl. She was the person with home court advantage, and he was smart enough to see it. She liked him for it. Even if she also still kind of hated him for trying to kill her and messing up her hair and all.

Maddie pushed up onto her knees in the snow. She started to stand.

It took her a moment to register that Stefan was standing behind her, and Uri's gun was in his hand. Maybe it was the way the sun was getting lower, the sky darker, but everything seemed to change as the ice bled through the denim of Maddie's jeans and the world got very dark and very cold.

"Uri was right, you know. You are the only child of the man who took the Wolf's only child." Stefan stared down the sight of the gun. "You would be more than enough to trade for my sister."

Logan was going to kill Maddie. As soon as he was certain she was safe, of course.

The metal cuff felt tighter, colder, when she was the one to put it on him, so he pulled against the limb again and growled and cursed under his breath.

Only the sound of the laughter made him stop.

"Your woman is either very smart. Or very stupid," the Russian said.

"Don't kid yourself, comrade," Logan told him. "She's both."

The yellow sat phone was lying in the snow. Waterproof, freeze-proof . . . idiot-proof. He just had to reach it. He just had to stretch. Sinking down, Logan stuck out one of his too-long legs, finally grateful for the extra inches as he eased the phone close enough to grab.

"They will kill him, you know," Uri said as if they were just making conversation. As if Logan actually cared about his opinion.

"Your new friend Stefan. The Wolf will shoot him dead." For some reason, when the silence came, Logan had to look at the man. He saw the look in Uri's eyes when he said, "The girl will not be so lucky."

Logan lunged for the man, but the cuff held and jerked him back, shaking snow and ice from the tree, raining down on top of him like fire.

"And you wonder why she left you," the man said with a laugh.

Logan turned back to the tree, looking at the icy branches, calculating the weight of the snow and the circumference of the limb. Then he started to climb, carefully, balancing himself on the icy length, edging farther and farther from the base of the tree until the limb snapped, crashing into the snow and taking Logan with it.

"Nicely done," the Russian mocked. "You're smarter than a tree. Your father must be so proud."

Logan's father was probably worried sick. For the first time, Logan let himself admit that much. The most powerful man in the world was probably frozen with grief. Logan couldn't even think about what his mother was probably feeling.

And Maddie . . .

Would they have reached the camp yet? Would she have seen her father?

How many rounds of ammo were there in the two guns? And did she get her other knife back—the little one that Stefan had taken? Maddie wasn't the kind of girl to be content with just one knife, after all.

But most of all, Logan wanted to know that she was going to be okay.

"They probably aren't dead yet," Uri told him. "If you leave now, you can catch them. Stop them."

"Stop them from what?"

"Walking into a trap."

"Those are big words for a man who got knocked unconscious and tied to a tree by a teenage girl," Logan reminded him.

"The girl's going to die, President's Son. And so is your new friend Stefan. If he thought the Wolf would honor his bargain, he is a fool. The Wolf lost everything six years ago. And before he dies, he is going to take all of his enemies down with him."

Logan was on his feet. He was reaching for the phone and wiping away the snow that covered the keys. It was cold in his hand, but it felt like life itself as he looked down at the screen and began to dial a number he knew by heart.

When he heard the beeping he thought it might have been the

phone finding a signal, maybe it was the White House switch-board, connecting him to a line.

But then Logan pulled the phone from his ear and looked down at the little flashing battery. When the screen went blank it felt like the part of him that had faith, that believed deep down that everything might be okay, turned off, too.

For a long time, he just stood, staring at the blank screen. The battery wasn't low. It was dead. The phone was a useless weight in his hands. And suddenly it was all too much.

He roared and almost threw it off the cliff, into the icy river below, before he remembered the charger.

Logan raced to the big, flat rock where the remnants of the packs were laid out. Maddie and Stefan must have taken Maddie's father's phone, so Logan grabbed Stefan's solar phone charger like it was a lifeline in a stormy sea. But the sky was so overcast that the phone didn't even register a charge. Not yet.

Logan looked around the big, flat rock at their collection of gear, but the map was gone, and Logan swore again to kill Maddie Manchester. Just as soon as he got her back.

"Having trouble?" Uri asked. Logan didn't think twice, lung-ing toward him.

"Where did they go?" he yelled.

But Uri shrugged, indifferent. "To their deaths, of course."

The map was still locked away in Logan's memory—locked inside his mind. But he didn't trust his bearings. There was too much at stake and the light was getting too low, and Logan knew that if he got turned around—if he missed a single landmark—he might never make it in time.

Logan grabbed the man and shook him, pounding his head into the tree. "Tell me where the camp is," he growled out.

"Why?" the Russian asked. "If I tell you where to find the girl, you're going to do what? Save the day? Let me go? Or maybe you will just kill me if I refuse."

"No." Logan let go and backed off. Angry as he was, he wasn't a killer. "You can either take me to the camp or stay here, tied to that tree, and wait for the bears to get hungry. It's your call."

CHAPTER 28

Maddie's hands were starting to tingle. Maybe it was nerves. Or the cold. Or maybe it was just what happened when you had to walk down a mountain and across a wide, snow-covered beach toward a wolf, all while keeping your hands on top of your head. All without trying to look back at the man who had the gun pointed directly at your spine.

She felt silly, really, in spite of everything. Sure, Stefan was taller and stronger and older. And he had a gun. But Maddie should have been able to take him. She would have been embarrassed if this ever got back to her friends.

But that was the upside to not having friends, Maddie realized. There wasn't a soul around to judge her, so Maddie walked on.

"Don't stop."

Stefan poked her in the back with the gun, pushing her slightly. She stumbled a little. Holding her hands that way made her shoulder ache and messed with her balance, but she absolutely refused to fall.

Stefan spoke again, but this time the words were in Russian and under his breath.

Logan could have interpreted, if he'd been there. But he wasn't. Logan was safe on the other side of the mountain. The Secret Service might have even found him already. She liked the thought of him in a helicopter with a heavy blanket over his shoulders, a hot drink in his hands.

Maddie would have given anything for a hot drink. But it was enough for her, the idea that maybe one of them might have already made it out of this ordeal alive.

Her arms dropped a little, fatigue settling in.

"Keep them up!" Stefan shouted with another push at her back. She took two large steps, stumbling forward and struggling to right herself.

And that was when she saw them.

The men appeared on the edges of her vision, assault rifles in their hands.

Stefan leveled his gun at her, but she stopped, looked back.

Something like pride glistened in his eyes as he said, "Tell the Wolf I've brought him something."

Not *someone*, Maddie realized. She was a *thing*, a piece of leverage.

One of the men laughed and the other joined in. When the second man spoke, it was in Russian, but Stefan sneered at the words. Then he answered, in English.

"She's better than the boy. Trust me. The Wolf will want to see this for himself."

The two guards must have been convinced because they gestured them toward the center of the camp.

"My sister?" Stefan asked.

One of the men nodded. "Alive" was his reply.

The two men fell into step on either side of Stefan. They kept their rifles pointed at the ground, but ready. Like one gunman might not be enough against a teenage girl. Maddie might have smiled, told herself that her reputation preceded her, but her shoulder hurt and her stomach growled. And she really had to go to the bathroom.

When they neared the tents, there was a rustling, and a moment later a man was standing before them, silhouetted by the smoke.

He was taller than she'd thought he'd be. Younger. Stronger. But when Maddie was finally close enough to see his eyes, she knew the mistake she'd just made.

"Where's the Wolf?" Stefan snapped at the man.

"Behind you," came a voice.

Slowly, Maddie turned. And she knew. It wasn't just that he was older. No. His eyes were cold and gray, but there was a fire inside of them. With one glance, Maddie feared she might get burned. They were the eyes of an animal, one dangerous and trapped. And right then Maddie understood the rumors and the nickname. She could believe that this man had been abandoned in a forest and raised by the wolves. He wasn't a man.

He was a feral beast, and Maddie shivered a little in spite of herself.

For a moment, she stood in the cold wind, hands fisted overhead, letting the man look his fill. Then he glanced at one of the guards. "Take his sister to the woods and shoot her."

The man turned for one of the tents, but Stefan was lunging forward.

"No! Wait!"

"We had a deal, Stefan," the Wolf told him. "Your sister for the boy. This is no boy."

"She's better," Stefan shouted, but the Wolf spun. It was like no one had dared to raise their voice to him in sixty years. And no one had, Maddie was certain.

"Kill him, too," the Wolf told the gunmen.

Stefan raised his gun, but he was too slow. The butt of an assault rifle was already slicing through the air, clipping him on the back of the head.

He went down hard and Maddie jerked free. She dropped her arms and started to run, but the second guard had already taken hold of her. He spat something in Russian, and the Wolf looked her over once again.

"Kill them all."

He turned and started toward the tent like he hadn't just ordered the deaths of three people. Like this was just another day, and nothing could surprise him—not anymore.

Well . . . nothing except the small, female voice behind him, saying, "Well, that would just be silly."

When the Wolf turned back to Maddie, it was like he was surprised she could speak. Or at the very least, like she'd have the good sense to sound terrified. But she didn't. If anything, she sounded . . . bored.

"You need better sources, Mr. Wolf Man," she told the most dangerous man in Russia.

"Why is that?" he asked her, honestly curious.

Maddie looked up at the cloudy sky then back to him, like she had all the time in the world.

"Well, because, (A) the Secret Service agent you've been obsessed with for six years doesn't have a *dead* daughter. He has an *awesome* daughter. And (B) I'm more than a little offended you didn't recognize the grade A hostage material that you have in front of you. I mean, if you're in the vengeance business I am a way better catch than Logan, who is an idiot, by the way."

"And C?" The Wolf almost smiled.

Behind him, Maddie could see a guard dragging a girl from one of the tents. She was weak and filthy, her face puffy with too many tears. But she was still alive and that was all that mattered.

"Stefan!" the girl shouted, but her voice was weak.

"C is easy, Boris." The Wolf turned back to Maddie, clearly confused by her smile. "You should have never let me get this close."

When Maddie pulled back her fist, the men didn't lunge, they didn't stop her. *How hard can she hit?* they all seemed to think in unison, but Maddie wasn't swinging at them. Instead, she was spinning, arm swirling through the air until she opened her fist and gray dust hurled toward the flames.

Stefan was diving toward his sister, tucking her into his arms and rolling away.

Maddie saw it, knew the girl was safe.

It was her last thought before the world caught fire.

CHAPTER 29

As soon as Logan heard the explosion, he stopped running and ducked instinctively as the flames formed a pillar that looked like it might be holding up the sky. For a split second, bright light overpowered the dusk. Dark smoke followed, billowing upward and blocking out the sun that was setting on the cloud-filled horizon.

The whole world turned black in that instant, and when it cleared, absolutely no one was still standing.

That was the bad news.

But the good news was that any disaster that large could only mean one thing: Maddie was still alive.

Maddie was an idiot. Or so she thought as she forced herself up and away from the fire that still roared behind her.

She'd shaved the entire block of magnesium, kept it clutched in her hands. Even though she knew it burned at four thousand degrees—even though that was exactly why she'd done it—she was still afraid her skin might blister, her hair might catch fire. She'd jumped as far from the flames as possible, and then all she had to do was roll and kick and claw her way over the body of the man who had fallen beside her.

One of the men with the assault rifles.

Maddie didn't think twice before picking up the weapon.

Through the smoke, Stefan stirred.

"The plane!" Maddie shouted. "Get to the plane. Now!"

Stefan didn't have to be told twice. He stood and swooped his frail little sister into his arms and started running to where her father's plane bobbed near the shore.

But Maddie couldn't leave yet. She would never leave without her father.

She crawled to the second gunman. Blood streamed from his head and he didn't move, so she grabbed his rifle and hurled it with all her might, sending it end over end into the icy water like she might be returning it to the Lady of the Lake.

Both of the men by the fire were unconscious, but Maddie knew there were two more guards out in the woods.

Two guards who would have no doubt heard the explosion.

Two guards who would be coming. Soon.

She forced herself to her feet. She was still wobbly, but there was no time to worry about a pesky little thing like balance, so she rushed toward the tent, hurled back the flap, and yelled "Dad?"

It was empty.

Maddie felt her legs start to give out. She was more tired, more hungry, more hopeless than she'd ever been in her life.

But then she turned and saw her father—

—on his knees in the snow, the Wolf's blade at his neck.

Maddie had left Logan the little knife. He thought he might have to thank her for that when this mess was over. Right after he killed her. Then kissed her. Then killed her again.

But the knife did come in handy. So did the rope.

Uri had struggled as Logan led him through the forest, but the man had stayed on his feet long enough to guide Logan to the camp. When the time came to tie Uri to another tree, the man's wound had started to fester and the fight was leaving him bit by bit. He didn't even try to struggle. He only smirked.

"Thanks for the tour," Logan said. He crammed one of Stefan's spare socks into the man's mouth. "I think I can find my way from here."

From that point, it was just a matter of waiting.

Of course, it didn't take long for Uri to spit out the gag. Of course, he started yelling. Even his grunts sounded Russian as they filled the woods.

And when the perimeter guard recognized Uri, the man rushed right toward him.

It was easier than Logan thought to pull back the tree branch he'd leveraged, send it hurling right toward the guard, and knock him off his feet. Then Logan pounced, pulling back his fist the way Maddie's dad had once taught him.

"You never know when you might meet a bully," Mr. Manchester had said.

It was a lesson Logan would never, ever forget.

The Wolf really was dying. It wasn't just the pallor of his skin, the way his clothes hung on his frame like he used to be a much larger man. It was also the desperation that seemed to be seeping from his pores. He was going to get his revenge. Even if it killed him.

Especially if it killed him. But that suited Maddie just fine.

"Drop the knife," she told him.

The assault rifle was heavy in her hands. She'd never touched one before. The only thing a gun like this hunted was people, and Maddie felt a little sick just holding it. But she didn't dare let it go.

The Wolf didn't care, though. He just laughed and brought the knife closer to her father's throat. A small drop of blood appeared on the edge of the blade, but her father didn't even wince.

His eyes were black and his lip was swollen, but he sounded exactly like himself when he ordered, "Get out of here, Mad."

"But, *Dad*—" Maddie drew out the word. "I just got here. You never let me have any fun."

"You were dead," the Wolf said. He almost sounded impressed. Then he tightened his grip on the knife. "And soon you will be again."

But before he could pierce her father's skin further, Maddie's dad threw back his head, catching Boris on the chin and knocking him off balance.

Her dad's hands were bound, but he moved like that was his preferred way of fighting as he threw himself at the old man, knocking him to the icy ground.

He was rising, leveraging himself over the Wolf when a shot rang out from the distance, and Maddie's father collapsed, blood spreading across his back.

"Maddie!" Logan's shout echoed across the lake, and Maddie spun. Froze. Because there he was, racing toward her.

He was supposed to be safe and warm and halfway through his sixth bowl of soup by now. He was supposed to have sent the Secret Service. He was supposed to have forgotten all about Maddie. Again. But he hadn't, and she honestly didn't know whether she should love him or hate him for it.

Boris was righting himself, pushing aside the limp form of Maddie's father, and Maddie saw the look in his eyes as he realized that the first son was walking willingly into camp, his hands over his head.

"Take me!" Logan shouted.

Another shot rang out, ricocheting off one of the big, flat rocks near the water. Then Boris shouted something in Russian and the firing stopped.

And Logan walked on, like this was the moment he'd been waiting for. Like this was the most important moment in his life. And maybe the last.

"I know who you are," Logan said. He kept his gaze locked on the old man. "You're the great Wolf. Your son came to start a war. He died a soldier's death. This man shot him." Logan pointed to where Maddie's father lay on the ground. "Because it was his *job* to protect *me*. It was always about me. My father. My mother. It was about my family then. It should be about my family now. So take me."

"I intend to," the Wolf said.

"But let the soldier and the girl go. One son for one son," Logan said, and for a moment it looked like the Wolf might laugh. Then Logan said, "Let them live to tell your story. Let them turn you into a legend—not just in Russia, but all over the world."

This, at last, seemed to make the old man wonder.

Maddie was aware of the guards pulling themselves upright, coming toward her. One of them gripped her too tight by the arm, shook her a little just to prove he was a big, tough guy as he ripped the rifle out of her hands.

But the Wolf said something in Russian and the man's grip loosened. Then he let go completely and forced her toward her father with a shove.

"Tell them," the Wolf said. "Go tell the world how the first son died."

Maddie looked at where her father lay on the ground, bleeding. Then to Logan, who had dropped to his knees. The Wolf strode toward him with purpose. It was almost ceremonial, almost sacred.

Logan wasn't the first son. He was a sacrificial lamb as he knelt at the old man's feet.

"Logan," Maddie warned, but he just smiled at her.

"Dear Mad Dog," he said softly. "I'm sorry I didn't write back sooner. But that doesn't mean I didn't miss you. I missed you every single day. Love, Logan."

"No!" Maddie's scream pierced the air, but the Wolf was already bringing his blade to Logan's throat.

"A son for a son," the Wolf said. He pulled back the blade.

Then stumbled. Staggered.

When he glanced down at his chest he seemed more confused than in pain. He looked from the knife in his own hand to the blade that was stuck hilt-deep in his chest, right where his heart would have been if he'd had one.

The old man seemed so confused as he dropped to the ground beside Logan.

Then he looked at the girl.

Her arm was still outstretched. Follow through was everything, after all. And even she hadn't been vain enough to bedazzle both her favorite hatchet *and* her favorite knife for throwing.

Her aim had been dead on.

For a moment, the only sound was the crackling fire. The hired guns didn't move, like they had no idea how to live in a world without the Wolf.

Then a soft voice said, "Mad Dog?" Her father stirred. The trance ended. And the Russians seemed to realize where they were and who they'd almost killed.

The two of them came then, rage and fear seeping out of them. The man with the rifle raised it, preparing to shoot. Just as the shot rang, Maddie dove, sliding across the snow and ice, reaching for her father.

She braced for the impact of the bullet, the stinging and the burn, but it was the Wolf's guard who was falling. His rifle dropped useless to the snowy ground, and Maddie looked back to see Stefan running from the woods, another rifle in his arms.

"Guess Stefan found the fourth guard," Logan said.

The other man had picked up the Wolf's knife, though, and he brandished it like a sword.

"Drop it," Maddie told him.

"You are unarmed. And a girl."

"She's the girl who killed the Wolf," Logan told the man. "And she's not alone."

Maddie smiled. It was sweet. She felt almost sorry for calling him an idiot. But then she realized what he'd said and that it was true. She *wasn't* alone. For the first time in six years she didn't have to rely almost entirely on herself. She had her father back, and Stefan. And Logan.

Maddie didn't let herself wonder how long it would last. It was enough that it was true for now.

Then Logan looked up at the overcast sky, and Maddie realized the full depth of his words. Helicopters filled the dim horizon like a flock of birds. The sun was almost down, and soon ice and snow and glacier silt would be swirling in the air, blinding them.

Maddie threw her body over her father, but he pushed her aside, smoothed her hair. "I'm okay, Mad Dog. I've had worse."

And those were the words that finally broke her.

Tears streamed down her face and she cried in awful, eye-puffing, skin-blotching, gut-wrenching sobs.

"I've got you, Mad Dog. You're okay."

But was she okay?

She couldn't help herself. She looked at Logan.

"Uri and another guard are tied up in the woods," he reported.

"I left a man unconscious on that ridge," Stefan said, pointing in the direction from which he'd appeared.

"Where's your sister?" she asked.

"In the plane," he said, then looked longingly at it.

"Can you fly?" she asked him.

"A bit," he said.

"Then go." Maddie didn't stop and think about the words, what they meant or how far the aftermath might follow them. She just knew that he'd been there for them in the end, and he was right. He'd taken the closest thing the US had to royalty. He might never see the sun.

"Get in the plane and leave. Now. Float it out around the bend and then take off as soon as you're out of sight of the choppers. Fly as low as you can, and we'll cover for you, but you have to get out of here. Now. Get your sister to a doctor and then go to ground and stay there. Both of you."

"Maddie . . ." Logan started, and she spun on him.

"Right?" she asked.

Logan put the yellow sat phone and its charger in Stefan's hand. "We'll call you when the coast is clear."

"Dad?" Maddie asked.

"Do it" was all her father said.

Then Stefan was running through the snow, and the plane was roaring to life and floating away while the helicopters looked like hornets on the horizon.

But Maddie stayed on the icy ground, holding tight to her father.

"The Wolf's dead, Dad. It's over. I think it's really over."

He looked up at her. "I'm sorry I never told you. I didn't want to scare you. You were just a kid and you'd been through too much. I'm sorry."

"Shh. Save your strength. Help's coming. We're going to get you well and then go home."

Home.

It wasn't until the helicopters landed and two dozen agents in full SWAT gear swarmed the beach that Maddie realized she actually wasn't sure where that was anymore.

CHAPTER 30

To whom it may concern,

I don't know what brought you to this little shed, but I hope you'll be happy here—for however long you need to stay. I've taken the liberty of restocking the woodpile and bringing some new blankets and a few dishes, some matches and a mirror (because even though you may be the only person for twenty miles in any direction, most people feel better when they know what their hair looks like).

Help yourself to the canned goods—that's what they're here for.

But, most of all, be careful and take care of this place. It's special to me.

Maddie

(and me, too—Logan)

• • •

It was the first week of January, which, in Maddie's experience, meant five layers. So no wonder she couldn't help but feel incredibly underdressed. Her skirt was too short. Her tights were too thin. Her shoes weren't even waterproof, and no matter how many strongly worded emails Maddie had written in protest, she had been strictly warned to leave her hatchet and both of her knives at home.

So Maddie was basically naked, in other words, as she stood outside the tall fence, looking at the wilderness that lay on the other side of the electric gates.

It was unknown terrain filled with potential predators, and Maddie didn't like the looks of it one bit.

"I can't do this," she said, pulling back. But she didn't go far before there was an arm around her waist, holding her firmly against a body that, if possible, had gotten even taller.

Logan looked down at her.

"Of course you can. You're Maddie Freaking Manchester. You caught a Russian kidnapper with a bear trap and a tree."

"Technically, I caught one Russian with a tree. I only wounded the second Russian with a bear trap."

"See? You're a natural. You're gonna fit right in."

"No." Maddie pulled back, tugging Logan's arm and trying her best to keep him in place when he started for the entry. "I can't do it. I don't belong here."

"Your dad needs surgery, Mad Dog. And physical therapy. And to sit through about a million debriefs. When that's all done, you can go back. I promise. But in the meantime you can't stay in Alaska by yourself. So please, stay here. With me? Please."

It all sounded so great in theory, but there was traffic on the street—cars and trucks whizzing by so fast that Maddie felt a little dizzy. The sidewalks were filled with people who never looked up from their phones, all of them seemingly in the middle of nowhere. But they weren't.

Maddie knew what the middle of nowhere looked like, felt like. It didn't smell like bus exhaust and it didn't taste like a breakfast that came from a bag.

Maddie's fingers itched and she wanted to run, but all she could say was "Logan, I don't go to school. I do worksheets and read library books and chop wood all winter. Seriously. If anyone in there needs some wood chopped or a generator repaired, then I'm their girl, but—"

"Mad Dog."

Logan cupped her cheeks with his big, warm hands, made her look up into his eyes.

"You're *my* girl," he said, and then he kissed her, right there in front of their school and his Secret Service detail—right in front of the world. So she kissed him back again.

And again.

And again.

Until he pulled back and looked into her eyes. "If anything goes wrong in there, I'll save you."

She took his hand. "Not if I save you first."

ACKNOWLEDGMENTS

In many ways, this is the most research-heavy book that I've ever written, because, in many ways, it's also the most realistic. Always before, I've written in worlds largely of my own making, but Alaska is a very real, very vast, very fascinating place, and I felt the need to get it as right as possible.

To that end, I went where people should always go for reliable answers: to librarians!

So I'd like to offer my most heartfelt thanks to Ida Olson, Elizabeth M. Nicolai, and Andrea Hirsh for their help in understanding life and survival in rural Alaska.

I'd also like to thank "Klondike Kevin," the guide who showed my family around Skagway and told us that the groundwater could kill us, thus making me desperate to set a book there.

Finally, I have to thank Kristin Nelson, David Levithan, and the wonderful team at Scholastic as well as all the amazing authors I harassed for a solid six months to try to get the title just right. I owe you, each and every one!

ABOUT THE AUTHOR

Ally Carter is the *New York Times* bestselling author of the Embassy Row series, as well as the Gallagher Girls and Heist Society series. Her books have been published all over the world, in over twenty languages. You can visit her online at www.allycarter.com.

W9-CCM-991

BRAZIL

4th Edition

**Where to Stay and Eat
for All Budgets**

**Must-See Sights
and Local Secrets**

Ratings You Can Trust

Fodor's Travel Publications   New York, Toronto, London, Sydney, Auckland
www.fodors.com

FODOR'S BRAZIL
Editor: Shannon Kelly

Editorial Production: Tom Holton
Editorial Contributors: Carolina Berard, Gabriela Dias, Rhan Flatin, Denise Oliveira, Mariane Oliveira, Jefferson Santos, Carlos Tornquist, Ana Lúcia do Vale
Maps: David Lindroth, Mark Stroud, *cartographers*; Rebecca Baer and Bob Blake, *map editors*
Design: Fabrizio La Rocca, *creative director*; Guido Caroti, *art director*; Moon Sun Kim, *cover designer*; Melanie Marin, *senior picture editor*
Production/Manufacturing: Angela L. McLean
Cover Photo (dancers at Carnival in Rio de Janeiro): ImageStates-Pictor/PictureQuest

Fourth Edition

ISBN: 1–4000–1647–9

ISBN-13: 978–1–4000–1647–1

ISSN: 0163–0628

SPECIAL SALES

This book is available for special discounts for bulk purchases for sales promotions or premiums. Special editions, including personalized covers, excerpts of existing books, and corporate imprints, can be created in large quantities for special needs. For more information, write to Special Markets/Premium Sales, 1745 Broadway, MD 6-2, New York, New York 10019, or e-mail special-markets@randomhouse.com.

AN IMPORTANT TIP & AN INVITATION

Although all prices, opening times, and other details in this book are based on information supplied to us at press time, changes occur all the time in the travel world, and Fodor's cannot accept responsibility for facts that become outdated or for inadvertent errors or omissions. So **always confirm information when it matters,** especially if you're making a detour to visit a specific place. Your experiences—positive and negative—matter to us. If we have missed or misstated something, **please write to us.** We follow up on all suggestions. Contact the Brazil editor at editors@fodors.com or c/o Fodor's at 1745 Broadway, New York, NY 10019.

PRINTED IN THE UNITED STATES OF AMERICA

10 9 8 7 6 5 4 3 2 1

Be a Fodor's Correspondent

Your opinion matters. It matters to us. It matters to your fellow Fodor's travelers, too. And we'd like to hear it. In fact, we *need* to hear it.

When you share your experiences and opinions, you become an active member of the Fodor's community. That means we'll not only use your feedback to make our books better, but we'll publish your names and comments whenever possible. Throughout our guides, look for "Word of Mouth," excerpts of your unvarnished feedback.

Here's how you can help improve Fodor's for all of us.

Tell us when we're right. We rely on local writers to give you an insider's perspective. But our writers and staff editors—who are the best in the business—depend on you. Your positive feedback is a vote to renew our recommendations for the next edition.

Tell us when we're wrong. We're proud that we update most of our guides every year. But we're not perfect. Things change. Hotels cut services. Museums change hours. Charming cafés lose charm. If our writer didn't quite capture the essence of a place, tell us how you'd do it differently. If any of our descriptions are inaccurate or inadequate, we'll incorporate your changes in the next edition and will correct factual errors at fodors.com *immediately.*

Tell us what to include. You probably have had fantastic travel experiences that aren't yet in Fodor's. Why not share them with a community of like-minded travelers? Maybe you chanced upon a beach or bistro or B&B that you don't want to keep to yourself. Tell us why we should include it. And share your discoveries and experiences with everyone directly at fodors.com. Your input may lead us to add a new listing or highlight a place we cover with a "Highly Recommended" star or with our highest rating, "Fodor's Choice."

Give us your opinion instantly at our feedback center at www.fodors.com/feedback. You may also e-mail editors@fodors.com with the subject line "Brazil Editor." Or send your nominations, comments, and complaints by mail to Brazil Editor, Fodor's, 1745 Broadway, New York, NY 10019.

You and travelers like you are the heart of the Fodor's community. Make our community richer by sharing your experiences. Be a Fodor's correspondent.

Boa Viagem!

Tim Jarrell, Publisher

CONTENTS

HOW TO USE THIS BOOK

Our Ratings

Sometimes you find terrific travel experiences and sometimes they just find you. But usually the burden is on you to select the right combination of experiences. That's where our ratings come in.

As travelers we've all discovered a place so wonderful that its worthiness is obvious. And sometimes that place is so experiential that superlatives don't do it justice: you just have to be there to know. These sights, properties, and experiences get our highest rating, **Fodor's Choice,** indicated by orange stars throughout this book.

Black stars highlight sights and properties we deem **Highly Recommended,** places that our writers, editors, and readers praise again and again for consistency and excellence.

By default, there's another category: any place we include in this book is by definition worth your time, unless we say otherwise. And we will.

Disagree with any of our choices? Care to nominate a place or suggest that we rate one more highly? Visit our feedback center at www.fodors.com/feedback.

Budget Well

Hotel and restaurant price categories from ¢ to $$$$ are defined in the opening pages of each chapter. For attractions, we always give standard adult admission fees; reductions are usually available for children, students, and senior citizens. Want to pay with plastic? **AE, D, DC, MC,** and **V** following restaurant and hotel listings indicate if American Express, Discover, Diners Club, MasterCard, and Visa are accepted.

Restaurants

Unless we state otherwise, restaurants are open for lunch and dinner daily. We mention dress only when there's a specific requirement and reservations only when they're essential or not accepted—it's always best to book ahead.

Hotels

Hotels have private bath, phone, TV, and air-conditioning and operate on the European Plan (aka EP, meaning without meals), unless we specify that they use the Continental Plan (CP, with a Continental breakfast), Breakfast Plan (BP, with a full breakfast), or Modified American Plan (MAP, with breakfast and dinner) or are all-inclusive (AI, including all meals and most activities). We always

list facilities but not whether you'll be charged an extra fee to use them, so when pricing accommodations, find out what's included.

Many Listings
* ★ Fodor's Choice
* ★ Highly recommended
* ✉ Physical address
* ✛ Directions
* ⌂ Mailing address
* ☎ Telephone
* 🖷 Fax
* ⊕ On the Web
* ✉ E-mail
* Admission fee
* ☉ Open/closed times
* ► Start of walk/itinerary
* Ⓜ Metro stations
* 🗖 Credit cards

Hotels & Restaurants
* 🔟 Hotel
* Number of rooms
* Facilities
* 🍴 Meal plans
* ✕ Restaurant
* Reservations
* Dress code
* Smoking
* BYOB
* ✕🔟 Hotel with restaurant that warrants a visit

Outdoors
* Golf
* Camping

Other
* Family-friendly
* Contact information
* ⇨ See also
* ✉ Branch address
* Take note

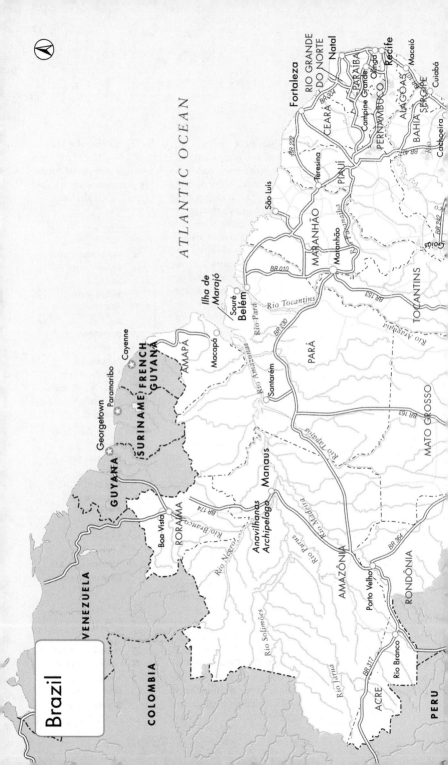

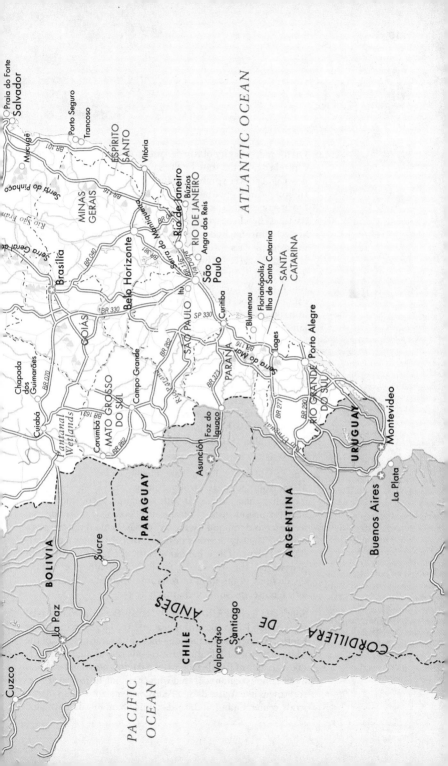

WHAT'S
WHERE

RIO DE JANEIRO	On the map, the city of Rio de Janeiro dangles from the south-central edge of the state by the same name. The city cascades down and between dramatic mountains and out to beaches that ribbon the metropolitan area. A national park since 1961 and the first one within an urban area, the Tijuca Forest, near Barra da Tijuca Beach, has more than 900 species of plants. The open-armed Christ the Redeemer statue atop Corcovado, often seen in postcards, lies within this park. On the west side of the city is White Rock (Pedra Branca) State Park, four times bigger than Tijuca park, with 30,888 acres of the original Mata Atlântica rain forest. When visiting Rio, make sure you take safety precautions 24 hours a day. Try to walk around accompanied and, in parks, do not stay by yourself. Bring cameras, because the landscape is wonderful, but take good care of them.
SIDE TRIPS FROM RIO	Rio de Janeiro State bulges from Brazil's southeast coast, just at the point where the country starts to narrow. Although the state is best known for its eponymous city, with famous beaches like Copacabana and Ipanema, inland you'll find several historical towns such as Petrópolis in refreshingly cool (relatively speaking) and lush mountainous settings; and along the coasts are quieter beach and water-sports destinations like Angra dos Reis, Ilha Grande, and Búzios; and the colonial town of Paraty.
SÃO PAULO	The capital of São Paulo State, this huge city is on a plateau 46 mi from the coast. Strolling along Avenida Paulista, once a country road, now lined with skyscrapers, you can almost hear the urgent buzz of business. Indeed, if you are looking for peace and tranquillity, the city of São Paulo is not the place for you. The city breathes business, rush, pollution, and traffic. And many of its inhabitants enjoy the fast pace. To compensate for the stress, São Paulo has seemingly countless distractions in the form of restaurants, cinema, theater, galleries, museums, and much, much more.
SIDE TRIPS FROM SÃO PAULO	South and west of Rio de Janeiro State is the industrial coastal state of São Paulo. Beautiful beaches, the large ocean port of Santos, ecological sanctuaries—including some patches of the Mata Atlântica (Atlantic Forest)—all run along its shores. Like the state of Rio de Janeiro, São Paulo's heartland includes mountainous regions covered with charming historical and resort towns like Águas de São Pedro, with its hot springs; handicraft center Embu; and 16th-century Santana de Parnaíba.

Ilhabela is São Paulo's destination of choice for beach bums and water-sports fanatics.

THE SOUTH

The three southernmost states—Paraná, just below São Paulo, Santa Catarina, and Rio Grande do Sul—run along the coast and stretch inland to the borders of Uruguay, Argentina, and Paraguay. Together they compose the narrowest section of Brazil's territory, covering 220,000 square mi, an area about the size of France. Curitiba, the capital of Paraná, is on a plateau 50 mi from the sea. Santa Catarina's capital, Florianópolis, literally straddles the Atlantic, its coastal mainland portion connected by a bridge to its offshore island portion. Rio Grande do Sul's capital, Porto Alegre, is halfway between São Paulo and Buenos Aires (about a 1½-hour flight from either city). Far to the west is the mighty Foz de Iguaçu (Iguaçu Falls).

If you visit the south in June or July (Brazil's winter), bring jackets and coats, as temperatures can drop as low as in Europe or the U.S. (about 32° F). Snow is rare, but not completely unheard-of in Santa Catarina and Rio Grande do Sul. Bring umbrellas, especially for Curitiba. If people in the south don't seem as friendly as those from Rio or Bahia, don't be offended. People tend to be more reserved, but are open to making friends or giving a helping hand when asked.

MINAS GERAIS

Roughly the size of Spain, the inland state of Minas Gerais is northwest of Rio de Janeiro and São Paulo. Near the center of the state is the capital, Belo Horizonte. Just southeast of Belo is the Serra do Espinhaço, where most of the state's gold towns lie a short drive from one another. Diamantina, land of diamonds, is north of Belo Horizonte, and Mariana, founded in 1696, is to the southwest. The state's southern region is dominated by spas, such as those in Poços de Caldas and Caxambú. Ouro Preto, known for its baroque architecture, is embedded 3,500 feet high in mountains that rise well above 6,200 feet in the Serra do Espinhaço. Tiradentes, with its waterfalls and breathtaking views of the São José Sierra, is 130 mi southwest of Belo Horizonte.

WHAT'S WHERE

BRASÍLIA & THE WEST	Built in five years and inaugurated in 1960, Brasília became a global model of urbanism and modern architecture. The nation's capital lies in the geographical center of the country in a vast, flat region dominated by the *cerrado*, or Brazilian savanna. The cerrado extends west through the sparsely populated "frontier" states of Goiás, Tocantins, Mato Grosso, and Mato Grosso do Sul. The massive Pantanal—an untamable mosaic of swamp and forest teeming with wildlife, including vultures in all hues of the rainbow—is the dominant feature of the far west both in geography and in tourist appeal. Despite its beauty, Brasília has one major drawback: it is not a "pedestrian-friendly" city. Be prepared to either take taxis often or rent a car. Between June and September, it doesn't rain at all and you must drink a lot of water. It is a good time of the year for swimming or sports on the lake (Lago Paranoá).
SALVADOR & BAHIA	On a huge bay, the city of Salvador, the capital of Bahia State, is divided between valley and hill. The enormous Lacerda Elevator connects the two parts, the Cidade Baixa (Lower City) and the Cidade Alta (Upper City). In the nearby waters of All Saints' Bay, with island settlements dating from colonial times (Frades and Itaparica), all is full of life and history. Salvador has plenty to do and see, from beaches to craftsmanship. The city's cuisine is quite unique within Brazil, thanks to its African influence. Eating at a restaurant with local specialties is an experience that should not be missed. To the west of Salvador in the state's heartland is Lençois, a village lying in the splendor of the Chapada Diamantina, a plateau covered with rare flowers and orchids. In the state's southern region are some of Brazil's most beautiful beaches, near Porto Seguro.
RECIFE, NATAL & FORTALEZA	On Brazil's most curvaceous bit of coast, nearly 600 mi north of Salvador, are two colonial cities, Olinda and Recife, with beaches lapped by warm waters and caressed by cooling breezes. The capital of Pernambuco State, Recife is affectionately called the Venice of Brazil because it is bathed by the sea and crisscrossed by rivers and bridges dating from the 1640s. Recife can be seen from the hills of Olinda 3½ mi away. About 130 mi to the north is Natal, the capital city of Rio Grande do Norte, where the sun shines an average of 300 days a year. Appropriately dubbed the "Cidade do Sol" (City of the Sun), Natal is geographically the closest Brazilian city to Europe and Africa. The state's coastline of dunes, beaches, and fishing vil-

lages unfolds 50 mi to the south and 180 mi to the north. In the southern part of the state are some of Brazil's most spectacular beaches: Ponta Negra, Pirangi, and Búzios. In Fortaleza, capital of Ceará, 340 mi north of Natal, you can revel in miles of urban beaches with warm ocean waters and cool breezes. Thirty miles east of Fortaleza is Iguapé, where dunes are so high and smooth you can ski down their slopes. These cities are very touristy, even among Brazilians. Many people from São Paulo vacation here.

THE AMAZON

Through the centuries many have tried in vain to conquer Brazil's vast northwest, a mythical land of a thousand rivers dominated by one giant, the Amazon River. Flowing for more than 4,000 mi, this gargantuan waterway is so wide in places you can't see the shore from a riverboat's deck. It is banked by a rain forest that houses the greatest variety of life on earth. Manaus, the capital city of Amazonas State, is a free-trade zone with electronic gadgets buzzing around magnificent 19th-century buildings, and lies almost exactly at the longitudinal center of the continent. Santarém is a bit less than 500 mi downriver and halfway between Manaus and the Atlantic. Before reaching the ocean, the river splits in two, leading northeast to Macapá and east to Belém. In the 200 mi between the river's opposite banks lies the Ilha do Marajó, the world's largest river island, roughly the size of the U.S. state of Indiana.

QUINTESSENTIAL BRAZIL

Historic places

Many of Brazil's cultural distinctions can be explained by its past. To understand modern Brazil, it is essential that one know something about Portugal's colonization of the country and Brazil's slave trade with Africa. Salvador is undoubtedly one of the best places to learn about the Africans' influence on Brazilian way of life, because it was the major port during the slave trade. Ouro Preto, a UNESCO World Heritage Site in Minas Gerais State, and other Gold Towns are important for their historic and distinctive Brazilian baroque architecture. Rio de Janeiro was the seat of power for the Portuguese and then the Brazilian monarchy from the 16th to the 19th centuries, and the seat of Brazil's government until 1960. Rio's Centro neighborhood holds well-preserved vestiges of those days. The current capital, Brasília, is worth a few days of your time for its modern architecture and its importance in Brazil's modern political history.

Carnival

In the heat of the South American summer (February or March, depending on the date of Easter), the country explodes in gaiety. Brazil comes alive, from such cities as Rio de Janeiro, Salvador, and Recife—where hundreds of thousands dance in formal parades as well as spontaneous street parties fueled by *trio elétricos,* which are flatbed trucks that carry bands from neighborhood to neighborhood—to the small towns of Pará or Goiás. Carnival season involves not only the days right before Lent (Friday through Ash Wednesday), but also months of rehearsal beforehand. And the sparks of passion flow over into other events throughout the year: religious festivals, ball games, weekend dances. Some of the best Carnivals are in Rio de Janeiro, Salvador, and Olinda.

A good place to start learning about Brazil and Brazilians is with the country's so-called "national passions"—music, soccer, and Carnaval. Brazil's past can also help you understand its present, and some cultural activities will undoubtedly enrich your trip.

Music

You will inevitably be exposed to Brazilian music while you are here, whether on your taxi driver's radio or in live-music bars in every town. Go to Rio for live bossa nova and samba, northeastern cities for *axé* and *pagode,* Brasília for rock, and the southeast for pop. Bossa nova, which is sort of the equivalent of classic rock in Brazil, is seeing somewhat of a comeback among younger generations, thanks to Maria Rita, daughter of bossa-nova icon Elis Regina, and a handful of other singers. Samba is undoubtedly the most popular music *du jour.* If you want to get a handle on Brazilian music, you'll have to do your homework: there are as many varieties of samba as there are of rock music; add to that the many variations of axé, bossa nova, *forró, frevo, lundu, maxixe,* and *tropicalismo,* and you'll be thoroughly overwhelmed . . . and exhilarated.

Soccer

Fûtebol (soccer) is called *o jogo bonito* (the beautiful game) in Brazil, and is considered an art form. Matches can be a blast: expect to see fans at their passionate best and sometimes at their worst. To avoid getting caught in a skirmish among fans, buy the best reserved seats (despite the cost) and ask about which matches are calmer. For example, in Rio, avoid matches between Flamengo and Fluminense—the "Fla-Flu" rivalry is notoriously heated. Simply watching matches on TV with Brazilians can be more fun than you ever had in your life. And when Brazil wins the World Cup . . . well, to say the celebrations are unique is an understatement. Top soccer players in Brazil are treated like deities. Pelé retired in the 1980s and is still revered as a national hero. The biggest stars today are Ronaldo, or "O Fenômeno" ("The Phenomenon"); Ronaldinho Gaúcho; and Robinho.

IF YOU LIKE

Beaches

Brazil has thousands of gorgeous beaches, so you're bound to find a little slice of heaven wherever you are. In the northeast you find sweeping, isolated expanses of dunes; warm aquamarine waters; and constant breezes. Rio's famous beaches are vibrant, social, and beautiful. The south has glorious sands and cooler climes. A short list doesn't do them justice, but these are some of our favorite beach destinations:

- **Rio de Janeiro.** Barra da Tijuca, Prainha, and Grumari are the most naturally beautiful beaches in the city of Rio. Copacabana and Ipanema are the best beach "scenes." Out of the city, Búzios has some of the country's most gorgeous beaches.

- **Ceará.** Canoa Quebrada, near Fortaleza, and Jericoacoara are our two favorite northeastern beaches for sheer beauty and relaxation.

- **Paraná.** Ilha do Mel is known as the Paradise of the South Atlantic, and is one of the best ecotourism destinations in Brazil.

- **Santa Catarina.** It's difficult to choose one beach to recommend on Ilha de Santa Catarina and Florianópolis. Garopaba, Praia dos Ingleses, and Praia Mole are the most famous, and Jurerê Internacional is the favorite among the well-to-do.

- **São Paulo.** Ilhabela is a paradise of more than 25 beaches.

- **Bahia.** Praia do Forte has plenty of leisure activities, 12 km (7 mi) of beaches, and is the number-one place to see sea turtles in Brazil.

Nature

This is one of the best places on earth for nature-lovers. There are so many things to see that you will need to prioritize your itinerary. The Amazon and the Pantanal, Brazil's two ecological wonderlands, are givens, but some lesser-known gems are waiting to be discovered by tourists, like Curitiba, known as the "ecological city" because of its many parks and green areas. Our favorite nature destinations follow.

- **Pantanal Wetlands.** This vast floodplain is the best place to see wildlife outside sub-Saharan Africa. Its savannas, forests, and swamps are home to more than 600 bird species as well as anacondas, jaguars, monkeys, and other creatures.

- **The Amazon Rain Forest.** A visit to the world-famous Amazon is one of those "life-list" experiences. Its scope and natural wealth are truly awe-inspiring.

- **Parque Nacional da Chapada Diamantina, west of Salvador.** One of Brazil's most spectacular parks, Chapada Diamantina was a former diamond mining center. Today it is a center for hard and soft adventure.

- **Parque Nacional do Iguaçu.** This amazing preserve has one of the world's most fantastic waterfalls.

- **Parque da Pedreira, Curitiba.** Impressive landscaping and unique structures have given an abandoned quarry new life.

- **Projeto Tamar, Praia do Forte.** Each year, September through March, more than 400,000 baby turtles are hatched along this beach northeast of Salvador.

Partying

Brazilians are famous for their Carnival, the biggest party of the year, but any time of year is occasion for revelry in Brazil. Even small towns have multitudes of festivals that may start out with a mass but end with dancing in the streets. Nearly every town has live-music venues playing samba, axé, forró, and MPB (Brazilian pop music) year-round—most with dancing. Brazilians—men and women alike—seem to have been born shaking their groove thing. If you can't dance the samba, don't worry, a lot of Brazilians can't either—they just know how to fake it.

- **Rio de Janeiro.** Music and dance clubs stay open all night long here, especially in Lapa. This is one of the top places in Brazil to hear great samba and jazz. Carnival is the biggest party of the year, but New Year's Eve in Rio is also a fabulous celebration.

- **Salvador.** The center of axé (Brazilian pop) music in Brazil and of Afro-Brazilian culture, Salvador has an easygoing party scene, bit its Carnival is considered Brazil's biggest and craziest party, where you can dance in the streets for eight days straight.

- **Belo Horizonte.** With more bars per capita than any other city in Brazil, it's obvious that BH knows how to party. The music scene is quite lively here—especially for MPB.

- **São Paulo.** If you crave elite clubs and rubbing elbows with Brazilian stars and millionaires, and sipping martinis at rooftop skyscraper bars, head to São Paulo, Brazil's poshest place to party.

Food

Trying cuisines unique to Brazil can be a highlight of your trip. Each region has its own specialties: exotic fish dishes in the Amazon; African spiced casseroles in Bahia; and the seasoned bean paste *tutu* in Minas Gerais. Much was inherited from the Portuguese, including the popular fish stews, *caldeiradas,* and beef stews, *cozidos,* boiled with vegetables.

- **feijoada.** The national dish, feijoada, is a thick stew with a base of black beans, combined with sausage, bacon, pork loin, and other meats that originated in Bahia. Traditional versions may include pig's feet, ears, and other "choice" meats that some say add the best flavor. Feijoada is usually accompanied by *farofa* (toasted manioc flour), rice, and collard greens.

- **churrasco.** Served at *churrascarias,* churrasco is meat, poultry, or fish roasted on spits over an open fire. In a *rodízio*-style churrascaria, you get all the meat and side dishes you can eat, prix-fixe. Rodízio means "going around," which explains the waiters who constantly circle the restaurant, only resting their skewers to slice another piece of meat onto your plate.

- **caipirinha.** The national drink is *caipirinha,* crushed lime, ice, sugar, and *cachaça,* a liquor distilled from sugarcane.

- **guaraná.** Be sure to try this carbonated soft drink made with the Amazonian fruit of the same name. It has a unique but subtle flavor.

- **cafezinhos** These thimble-size cups of coffee with tons of sugar keep Brazilians going between meals.

WHEN TO GO

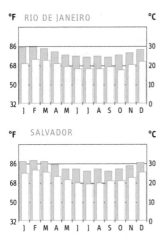

Prices in beach resorts are invariably higher during the Brazilian summer season (December–February) and in July (school-break month). If you're looking for a bargain, stick to May–June and August–October. Rio and beach resorts along the coast, especially in the northeast, suffer from oppressive heat November through April, but in Rio the temperature can drop to uncomfortable levels for swimming June through August. If you want sun and hot weather and want to enjoy beaches and cities in the south, come in the high season, as temperatures can be very low from May to December.

Climate

Seasons below the equator are the reverse of the north—summer in Brazil runs from December to March and winter from June to September. The rainy season in Brazil occurs during the summer months. Showers can be torrential but usually last no more than an hour or two. The Amazon and the Pantanal have the most pronounced rainy seasons, running roughly from November to May and marked by heavy, twice-daily downpours.

Rio de Janeiro is on the tropic of Capricorn, and its climate is just that—tropical. Summers are hot and humid. The same pattern holds true for the entire Brazilian coastline north of Rio, although temperatures are slightly higher year-round in Salvador and the northeastern coastal cities. In the Amazon, where the equator crosses the country, temperatures in the high 80s to the 90s (30s C) are common all year. In the south, São Paulo, and parts of Minas Gerais, winter temperatures can fall to the low 40s (5° C–8° C). In the southern states of Santa Catarina and Rio Grande do Sul, snowfalls occur in winter, although they're seldom more than dustings.

☎ Forecasts **Weather Channel Connection** ☎ 900/932-8437, 95¢ per minute ⊕ www.weather.com ⊕ www.weather.com.br.

SMART TRAVEL TIPS

The organizations in this section can provide information to supplement this guide; contact them for up-to-the-minute details, and consult the A to Z sections that end each chapter for facts on the various topics as they relate to Brazil's many regions.

ADDRESSES

Finding addresses in Brazil can be frustrating, as streets often have more than one name and numbers are sometimes assigned haphazardly. In some places street numbering doesn't enjoy the wide popularity it has achieved elsewhere; hence, you may find the notation "s/n," meaning *sem número* (without number). In rural areas and small towns there may only be directions to a place rather than to a formal address (i.e., street and number). Often such areas do not have official addresses and/or don't need them.

In Portuguese *avenida* (avenue), *rua,* (street) and *travessa* (lane) are abbreviated (as *Av., R.,* and *Trv.* or *Tr.*), while *estrada* (highway) often isn't abbreviated. Street numbers follow street names. Eight-digit postal codes (CEP) are widely used.

In some written addresses you might see other abbreviations. For example, an address might read, "R. Presidente Faria 221-4°, s. 413, 90160-091 Porto Alegre, RS" which translates as 221 Rua Presidente Faria, 4th floor, Room 413 ("s." is short for *sala*), postal code 90160-091, in the city of Porto Alegre, in the state of Rio Grande do Sul. You might also see *andar* (floor) or *edifício* (building).

The abbreviations for Brazilian states covered in this book are: Amazonas (AM); Bahia (BA); Ceará (CE); Distrito Federal (Federal District, aka Brasília; DF); Goiás (GO); Minas Gerais (MG); Mato Grosso do Sul (MS); Mato Grosso (MT); Pará (PA); Paraíba (PB); Paran (PR); Pernambuco (PE); Rio de Janeiro (RJ); Rio Grande do Sul (RS); Santa Catarina (SC); São Paulo (SP).

AIR TRAVEL

Within a country as big as Brazil, it's especially important to plan your itinerary with care. Book as far in advance as possible, particularly for weekend travel. Planes tend to fill up on Friday, especially to or from Brasília or Manaus. For more booking tips and to check prices and make online flight reservations, log on to www.fodors.com.

ARRIVING & DEPARTING

Miami, Newark, New York, and Toronto are the major gateways for flights to Brazil from North America. Several airlines fly directly from London, but there's no direct service from Australia or New Zealand. At this writing, most flights to Brazil from North America and the United Kingdom connect through São Paulo. For airport information, *see* São Paulo A to Z *in* Chapter 2.

The flying time from New York is 12 hours to Rio (with a stop in SP) and 10 hours to São Paulo. From Miami it's 8½ hours to Rio and 8 hours to São Paulo. Bear in mind that most flights to Rio or other Brazilian cities have stops, either in São Paulo or in Miami. If flying with a Brazilian airline, you might stop in Florianópolis, Brasília, or Porto Alegre before reaching Rio de Janeiro. Usually the connect time in São Paulo is 1 hour, 15 minutes. Most flights from Los Angeles go through Miami, and flight times are about 13 hours, not including layover in Miami (which can be 4–5 hours). From London it's 11 hours to São Paulo.

From the U.S.: Varig, Brazil's largest airline and a partner with United Airlines, flies nonstop from New York, Los Angeles, and Miami to/from São Paulo. Varig also has nonstop service to Manaus from Miami. TAM, another Brazil-based international carrier and a partner with American Airlines, flies nonstop from New York and Miami to São Paulo, with continuing service to Rio and connections to other cities. TAM also offers nonstop service between Miami and Manaus. Continental Airlines flies nonstop from Newark to São Paulo. Delta offers nonstop service from Atlanta to São Paulo and Rio.

From Canada: Air Canada, a Varig partner, has nonstop service between Toronto and São Paulo.

From the U.K.: British Airways has nonstop service from London to Rio and São Paulo. Varig has nonstop service to São Paulo. Continental flies from London to Newark and Houston, with connecting flights to Rio and São Paulo.

From Australia & New Zealand: From Sydney, Australia, you can fly to Los Angeles, then continue to Brazil on Varig. Another option is to fly Qantas to Buenos Aires, where you connect to Varig and fly on to São Paulo, Rio, Porto Alegre, Florianópolis, Salvador, and Brasília. Air New Zealand has flights to major Brazilian cities through its partnership with Varig.

🛧 International Airlines Air Canada ☎ 888/712-7786 in North America, 11/3254-6600 in Brazil ⊕ www.aircanada.com. Air New Zealand ☎ 0800/737-000 in New Zealand, 11/3214-5588 in Brazil ⊕ www.airnz.co.nz. American Airlines ☎ 800/433-7300 in North America, 8457/789-789 in the U.K., 11/4502-4000 in Brazil ⊕ www.aa.com. British Airways ☎ 0870/850-9850 in the U.K., 11/3145-9700 in Brazil ⊕ www.britishairways.com. Continental Airlines ☎ 800/231-0856 in North America, 0845/607-6760 in the U.K., 0800/702-7500 in Brazil ⊕ www.continental.com. Delta Airlines ☎ 800/241-4141 in North America, 0800/221-121 in Brazil ⊕ www.delta.com. Qantas ☎ 13/13-13 in Australia, 9/357-8900 in Auckland, 0800/808-767 elsewhere in New Zealand, 11/3145-5090 in Brazil ⊕ www.qantas.com.au. TAM ☎ 888/235-9826 in the U.S., 118/903-4003 in the U.K., 0800/570-5700 and 4002-5700 in Brazil ⊕ www.tamairlines.com. United Airlines ☎ 800/864-8331 in the U.S., 845/8444-777 in the U.K., 0800/16-2323 in Brazil ⊕ www.united.com. Varig ☎ 800/468-2744 in the U.S., 870/120-3020 in the U.K., 11/4003-7000 in Brazil ⊕ www.varig.com.

GETTING AROUND

There's regular jet service within the country between all major cities and most medium-size cities. Remote areas are also accessible—as long as you don't mind small planes. Flights can be long, lasting several hours for trips to the Amazon, with stops en route. The most widely used service is the Varig Ponte Aérea (Air Bridge), the Rio–São Paulo shuttle, which departs every half hour from 6 AM to 10:30 PM (service switches to every 15 minutes during morning and evening rush hours). Fares (one-way) for the Rio–São Paulo shuttle service vary from $40 (with BRA) to $170 (with TAM); reservations aren't necessary.

Gol is a low-cost airline whose tickets can be purchased either in person at an agency or through their Web site. You can pay with cash or an American Express credit card (or any Brazilian credit card). BRA Airlines and WebJet have fares that are competitive with Gol. WebJet flies only to São Paulo, Rio, Porto Alegre, Florianópolis, Belo Horizonte, and Brasília. Trip Linhas Aéreas flies from Recife and Natal to Fernando de Noronha, and also has some flights in far western Brazil.

The flight from Rio to São Paulo or Belo Horizonte is 1 hour; Rio to Brasília is 1½ hours; Rio to Salvador is 2 hours; Rio to Belém or Curitiba is 2½ hours. From São Paulo it's 4 hours to Manaus and 1½ hours to Iguaçu Falls.

🛦 **Domestic Airlines BRA** ☎ 11/5090–9006 in Brazil ⊕ www.voebra.com.br. **Gol** ☎ 0300/789–2121 in Brazil ⊕ www.voegol.com.br. **TAM** ☎ 888/235–9826 in the U.S., 305/406–2826 in Miami, 118/903–4003 in the U.K., 0800/570–5700 in Brazil ⊕ www.tamairlines.com. **Varig** ☎ 800/468–2744 in the U.S., 870/120–3020 in the U.K., 11/4003–7000 in Brazil ⊕ www.varig.com. **Trip Linhas Aéreas** ☎ 084/3644–1129 in Natal, 081/3464–4610 in Recife ⊕ www.airtrip.com.br. **WebJet Linhas Aéreas** ☎ 0800/722–1212 in Brazil ⊕ www.webjet.com.br.

AIR PASSES

Air passes from TAM or Varig can save you hundreds of dollars if you plan to travel a lot within Brazil. These can only be purchased outside Brazil. Varig's Brazil AirPass costs $560 for five coupons, which are valid for 21 days on flights to more than 100 cities within Brazil on Varig or its affiliates, Rio-Sul or Nordeste. You can buy up to four additional coupons (a total of nine) for $100 each. TAM's 21-day Brazilian AirPass costs $399 for four coupons, with additional coupons at $100 each.

If you plan to visit more than one of the Mercosur (Southern Common Market) countries—Argentina, Brazil, Paraguay, and Uruguay—the Mercosur Pass presents the greatest savings. It's valid on Aerolineas Argentinas, Varig, and several other carriers. You must visit at least two countries within a minimum of seven days and a maximum of 30 days. Pricing is based on mileage, ranging from $225 for flights totaling between 1,900 and 3,000 km (1,200 and 1,900 mi) to $870 for flights totaling more than 11,300 km (7,000 mi). Contact participating airlines or tour operators and travel agents who specialize in South American travel for information and purchase.

RECONFIRMING

Reconfirm flights within Brazil, even if you have a ticket and a reservation, as flights tend to operate at full capacity.

AIRPORT TRANSFERS

To ensure that your city destination is understood, write it down on a piece of paper and present it to bus or taxi drivers, most of whom don't speak English.

DEPARTURE TAXES

Be prepared to pay a hefty departure tax when you leave Brazil, which runs about R$78 ($33) for international flights. A departure tax also applies to flights within Brazil; amounts vary roughly between R$11 and R$22 ($4 and $10). Although some airports accept credit cards in payment of departure taxes, it's wise to have the appropriate amount in reais.

HOW TO COMPLAIN

If your baggage goes astray or your flight goes awry, complain right away. Most carriers require that you **file a claim immediately.** The Aviation Consumer Protection Division of the Department of Transportation publishes *Fly-Rights,* which discusses airlines and consumer issues and is available online. You can also find articles and information on mytravelrights.com, the Web site of the nonprofit Consumer Travel Rights Center.

🛦 **Airline Complaints Aviation Consumer Protection Division** ✉ U.S. Department of Transportation, Office of Aviation Enforcement and Proceedings, C-75, Room 4107, 400 7th St. SW, Washington, DC 20590 ☎ 202/366–2220 ⊕ airconsumer.ost.dot.gov. **Federal Aviation Administration Consumer Hotline** ✉ for inquiries: FAA, 800 Independence Ave. SW, Washington, DC 20591 ☎ 800/322–7873

⊕ www.faa.gov. **Transportation Security Administration** ☏ 1-866/289-9673 ⊕ www.tsa.gov.

BUS TRAVEL

The nation's *ônibus* (bus) network is affordable, comprehensive, and efficient—compensating for the lack of trains and the high cost of air travel. Every major city can be reached by bus, as can most small to medium-size communities.

The quality of buses in Brazil is quite good; in many cases better than in the U.S., depending on the type of bus (⇨ Classes, *below*). The number of stops at roadside cafés depends on the length of the trip. A trip from São Paulo to Curitiba, for example, which takes about 6 hours, has only one 20-minute stop; overnight buses may not stop at all. Usually buses stop at large and nice outlets with food, souvenirs, and magazines.

Lengthy bus trips will involve travel over some bad highways, a fact of life in Brazil. Trips to northern, northeastern, and central Brazil tend to be especially trying; the best paved highways are in the southeast and in the south. When traveling by bus, **bring water, toilet paper or tissues, and an additional top layer of clothing** (the latter will come in handy if it gets cold, or it can serve as a pillow). Travel light, dress comfortably, and **keep a close watch on your belongings**—especially in bus stations. If your bus stops at a roadside café, take your belongings with you.

CLASSES

When buying a ticket, you will be asked whether you want the *ônibus convencional,* the simplest option; the *ônibus executive,* with air-conditioning, coffee and water, more space between seats, and a pillow and blanket; or the *leito,* where you have all facilities of an executive bus plus a seat that reclines completely. If you're over 5'10", buy the most expensive ticket available and try for front-row seats, where you will have more space.

Most buses used for long trips are modern and comfortable, usually with bathrooms and air-conditioning. Note that regular buses used for shorter hauls may be labeled AR CONDICIONADO (AIR-CONDITIONED) but often are not.

CUTTING COSTS

Bus fares are substantially cheaper than in North America or Europe. Between Rio and São Paulo (6½–7 hours), for example, a bus departs every half hour and costs about $22–$34; a night sleeper will run about $34–$43. Sometimes competing companies serve the same routes, so it can pay to shop around.

PAYING & RESERVATIONS

Tickets are sold at bus-company offices, at city bus terminals, and in some travel agencies. Larger cities may have different terminals for buses to different destinations, and some small towns may not have a terminal at all (you're usually picked up and dropped off at the line's office, invariably in a central location). **Expect to pay with cash,** as credit cards aren't accepted everywhere. Reservations or advance-ticket purchases generally aren't necessary except for trips to resort areas during high season—particularly on weekends—or during major holidays (Christmas, Carnival, etc.) and school-break periods (July and December/January). In general, **arrive at bus stations early, particularly for peak-season travel.**

BUSINESS TRAVEL

You may need a business visa (valid for 90 days) to enter Brazil. It has all the same requirements as a tourist visa, but you'll also need a letter on company letterhead addressed to the embassy or consulate and signed by an authorized representative (other than you), stating the nature of your business in Brazil, itinerary, business contacts, dates of arrival and departure, and that the company assumes all financial and moral responsibility while you're in Brazil. For fees and other information, *see* Passports & Visas.

CLOTHING

If you're doing business in Brazil, you'll need the same attire you would wear in U.S. and European cities: for men, suits and ties; for women, suits for day wear and cocktail dresses or the like for an evening out.

COMPUTERS ON THE ROAD

If you're traveling with a laptop, carry a spare battery, a universal adapter plug, and a converter if your computer isn't dual voltage. Ask about electrical surges before plugging in your computer. Keep your disks out of the sun and avoid excessive heat for both your computer and disks. In Brazil carrying a laptop computer signals wealth and could make you a target for thieves; conceal your laptop in a generic bag and keep it close to you at all times.

Internet access is widespread. In addition to business centers in luxury hotels and full-fledged cyber cafés, look for computers set up in telephone offices. Rates range from $4 to $7 an hour. Dial-up speeds are variable, though they tend toward the sluggish.

ETIQUETTE

Brazilians tend to be punctual for business meetings, but not for more informal occasions—be prepared to wait for 15 minutes to have dinner, for example. There are no set rules about who pays for dinners or drinks in a business situation. If your spouse is in the country with you, ask whether your Brazilian colleagues are taking their spouses before arriving as a couple. In a business environment, a simple handshake is the norm. Kissing on the cheek or giving hugs is common among friends and family members. However, in a formal dinner situation women generally get a kiss on the cheek. When in doubt, go with the handshake.

CAMERAS & FILM

Brazil, with its majestic landscapes and varied cityscapes, is a photographer's dream. Brazilians are usually amenable to having picture-taking visitors in their midst, but you should always **ask permission before taking pictures in churches or of individuals.**

If you plan to take photos on some of the country's many beaches, bring a skylight (81B or 81C) or polarizing filter to minimize haze and light problems. If you're visiting the Amazon or Pantanal, bring high-speed film to compensate for low light under the tree canopy and invest in a telephoto lens to photograph wildlife;

standard zoom lenses in the 35 mm–88 mm range won't capture enough detail.

Casual photographers should consider using inexpensive cameras to reduce the risks inherent in traveling with sophisticated equipment. Single-use cameras with panoramic or underwater functions are also nice supplements to a standard camera and its gear.

⚑ Photo Help **Kodak Information Center** ☎ 800/ 242-2424 ⊕ www.kodak.com.

EQUIPMENT PRECAUTIONS

Don't pack unprocessed film, single-use cameras, or cameras with film inside in checked luggage. High-intensity x-ray machines used to view checked luggage will fog your film. Lower-intensity x-rays for carry-on luggage usually will not harm your film, but play it safe and ask for hand inspection. U.S. airports are required to honor this request, but non-U.S. airports may refuse it. Lead-lined bags can protect film from x-ray scans to some extent. Pack your film in a small bag that is easily removed from your larger luggage in case an inspector requires that your bag go through more than one scan or in case you are forced to check your carry-on luggage. Motion picture film should not pass through even low-intensity x-rays. Process it before traveling or call the airport in advance to arrange for a hand inspection. Digital cameras are not affected by airport x-ray machines.

Keep videotapes and computer disks away from metal detectors. Assume that you will have to remove your laptop from its case. Carry an extra supply of batteries, and be prepared to turn on your camera, camcorder, or laptop to prove to airport security personnel that the device is real.

Always keep film, tape, and computer disks out of the sun, and on jungle trips **keep your equipment in resealable plastic bags** to protect it from dampness. Petty crime is a problem throughout Brazil, particularly in the cities, so keep a close eye on your gear.

FILM & DEVELOPING

Major brands of film and digital memory cards for common camera types are easy to find in almost any city or town in Brazil. Memory cards are sold in most photography stores and electronics shops, especially in malls. Good-quality film developing is available all over Brazil, even in small towns.

VIDEOS

The system used in Brazil is PAL-M. The average price of a blank VHS tape is about $4 for 60 minutes and $5 for 120 minutes. A DV tape (60 minutes) costs about $13. Tapes, batteries, cables, and other equipment are readily available in electronics shops, convenience stores, gas stations, newsstands, and even some street-side stalls.

CAR TRAVEL

Driving is chaotic in cities like São Paulo, but much easier in cities like Curitiba and Brasília. In the countryside the usually rough roads, lack of clearly marked signs, and language difference are discouraging for driving. Further, the cost of renting can be steep. All that said, certain areas are most enjoyable when explored on your own in a car: the beach areas of Búzios and the Costa Verde (near Rio) and the Belo Horizonte region; the North Shore beaches outside São Paulo; and many of the inland and coastal towns of the south, a region with many good roads.

Brazil has more than 1.65 million km (1.02 million mi) of highway, about 10% of it paved. The country's highway department estimates that 40% of the federal highways (those with either the designation *BR* or a state abbreviation such as *RJ* or *SP*), which constitute 70% of Brazil's total road system, are in a dangerous state of disrepair. Evidence of this is everywhere: potholes, lack of signage, inadequate shoulders. Landslides and flooding after heavy rains are frequent and at times shut down entire stretches of key highways. Recent construction has improved the situation, but independent land travel in Brazil definitely has its liabilities.

Increasing traffic adds to the system's woes, but fortunately in large cities like Curitiba and Brasília there are now cameras to detect and fine abusive drivers.

This has decreased traffic accidents significantly, but you should be careful anyway. Some drivers slow down only when close to these cameras. The worst offenders are bus and truck drivers. For these reasons, we recommend that you rely on taxis and buses for short distances and on planes for longer journeys.

Some common-sense tips: before you set out, establish an itinerary and ask about gas stations. Be sure to **plan your daily driving distance conservatively** and **don't drive after dark.** Always obey speed limits and traffic regulations.

Always give the rental car a once-over to make sure the headlights, jack, and tires (including the spare) are in working condition.

CUTTING COSTS

Although international car-rental agencies have better service and maintenance track records than local firms (they also provide better breakdown assistance), your best bet at getting a good rate is to rent on arrival, particularly from local companies. But reserve ahead if you plan to rent during a holiday period, and check that a confirmed reservation guarantees you a car. You can contact local agencies through their Web sites in advance. (For details on local agencies, *see* A to Z sections *in* each chapter.)

Consider hiring a car and driver through your hotel concierge, or make a deal with a taxi driver for extended sightseeing at a long-term rate. Often drivers charge a set hourly rate, regardless of the distance traveled. You'll have to pay cash, but you may actually spend less than you would for a rental car.

Before you pick up a car in one city and leave it in another, ask about drop-off charges or one-way service fees, which can be substantial. Also inquire about early-return policies; some rental agencies charge extra if you return the car before the time specified in your contract while others give you a refund for the days not used. Most agencies note the tank's fuel level on your contract; to avoid a hefty refueling fee, return the car with the same tank level. If the tank was full, refill it just before you turn in the car, but be aware that gas stations near the rental outlet may overcharge. It's almost never a deal to buy a tank of gas with the car when you rent it; the understanding is that you'll return it empty, but some fuel usually remains.

EMERGENCIES

The Automóvel Clube do Brasil (Automobile Club of Brazil) provides emergency assistance to foreign motorists in cities and on highways but only if they're members of an automobile club in their own nation. 🚩 Emergency Service **Automóvel Clube do Brasil** ✉ Viaduto Dona Paulina, 34 conjunto 125, Centro, São Paulo ☎ 11/3107–5764 ⊕ www. automovelclubdobrasil.com.br.

GASOLINE

Gasoline in Brazil costs around R\$2.15 (74¢) a liter, which is about \$2.75 per gallon. Unleaded gas, called *especial,* costs about the same. Brazil also has an extensive fleet of ethanol-powered cars, and you might end up with one from a rental agency. Ethanol fuel is sold at all gas stations and is a little cheaper than gasoline. However, these cars get lower mileage, so they offer little advantage over gas-powered cars. Stations are plentiful both within cities and on major highways, and many are open 24 hours a day, 7 days a week. In smaller towns few stations take credit cards, and their hours are more limited.

DRIVING PERMITS

You need an international driver's license if you plan to drive in Brazil. International driving permits (IDPs) are available from the American, Canadian, and New Zealand automobile associations; in the United Kingdom from the Automobile Association and Royal Automobile Club; and in Australia from the Royal Automobile Club or state-run automobile associations. These international permits, valid only in conjunction with your regular driver's license, are universally recognized.

INSURANCE

When driving a rented car you are generally responsible for any damage to or loss of the vehicle. You also may be liable for any property damage or personal injury that you may cause while driving. Before

you rent, see what coverage you already have under the terms of your personal auto-insurance policy and credit cards.

PARKING

Finding a space in most cities—particularly Rio, São Paulo, Belo Horizonte, and Salvador—is a major task. It's best to **head for a garage or a lot** and leave your car with the attendant. There are no meters; instead, there's a system involving coupons that you must post in your car's window, which allows you to park for a certain time period (one or two hours). You can buy them from uniformed street-parking attendants or at newsstands. Should you find a space on the street, you'll probably have to pay a fee for parking services. Or you might run into unauthorized street parking offered by the so-called *flanelinhas* (literally, "flannel wearers"), who may charge from R\$2 (85¢) to R\$5 (\$2) in advance. This is more common in São Paulo.

No-parking zones are marked by a crossed-out capital letter *E* (which means *estacionamento,* Portuguese for "parking"). These zones, more often than not, are filled with cars that rarely are bothered by the police.

ROAD MAPS

Quatro Rodas is the most famous map and guide publisher in Brazil and you can find it in bookshops or newsstands. It has atlases, books, and maps of different sizes for states, regions, and cities. If you're a beach aficionado, look for this company's four-color book of topographical maps of all the nation's beaches. If you speak Portuguese, take a look at ⊕ www.estradas. com.br; choose MAPAS from the pull-down menu to get highway maps and distances between major cities. The site also has links to and telephone numbers for organizations that provide road conditions information.

RULES OF THE ROAD

Brazilians drive on the right, and in general traffic laws are the same as those in the United States. The use of seat belts is mandatory. The national speed limit ranges from 60 to 80 kph (36–48 mph). In Brazil the minimum driving age is 18.

SAFETY

If you get a ticket for some sort of violation, be polite with the policemen and try to solve the issue either by accepting the ticket (if you committed the violation) or by explaining your position (if you did not commit a violation). Even though it is common to see scams in cases like this, the best option is to solve the problem as honestly as possible, especially if you are a foreigner. It is true that there are corrupt policemen, but they cannot force you to pay something you should not and, even if this would happen, you can make a complaint, though you may spend a good deal of time settling it.

⨕ Major Agencies Avis ☎ 800/331–1084 in the U.S., 800/879–2847 in Canada, 0870/606–0100 in the U.K., 02/9353–9000 in Australia, 09/526–2847 in New Zealand, 0800/19–8456 in Brazil ⊕ www.avis. com. **Budget** ☎ 800/472–3325 in the U.S., 800/268–8900 in Canada, 0870/156–5656 in the U.K, 1300/794–344 in Australia, 0800/283–438 in New Zealand, 11/2117–2000 in São Paulo, 0800/725–2000 elsewhere in Brazil ⊕ www.budget.com. **Hertz** ☎ 800/654–3001 in the U.S., 800/263–0600 in Canada, 0870/844–8844 in the U.K., 02/9669–2444 in Australia, 09/256–8690 in New Zealand, 0800/701–7300 in Brazil ⊕ www.hertz.com. **National Car Rental** ☎ 800/227–7368 in the U.S. and Canada, 0870/400–4581 in the U.K., 07/3854–1499 in Australia, 0800/800–115 in New Zealand, 0800/227–3876 in Brazil ⊕ www.nationalcar.com.

CHILDREN IN BRAZIL

Brazil is a country of great cultural diversity, so try to attend one of the many festivals held all over the country throughout the year. These often feature music and dance performances that transcend language barriers and acquaint children with Brazilian folklore. Older kids and teenagers may be captivated by Brazil's plants and animals. Take a guided tour of an urban park or a trek into a national preserve. Such expeditions are a safe, easy way to experience nature. Brazilians welcome kids in almost all places.

If you are renting a car, don't forget to arrange for a car seat when you reserve. For general advice about traveling with children, consult *Fodor's FYI: Travel with Your Baby* (available in bookstores everywhere).

ATTRACTIONS

Guia da Semana, a Portuguese-language Web site, lists events for kids in São Paulo, Rio, Belo Horizonte, Porto Alegre, Brasília, Salvador, Curitiba, and Florianópolis.

Consider hiring a bilingual guide specifically for your kids so that they can feel free to ask their questions and have fun. EMBRATUR (the national tourism agency) has bilingual guides that can provide this service.

Sights and attractions that are especially appealing to children are indicated by a rubber-duckie icon (🐤) in the margin.

⨕ Resources EMBRATUR ☎ 020/7385–9975 in the U.K., 212/997–3360 in the U.S. ⊕ www.embratur. gov.br. **Guia da Semana** ⊕ www.guiadasemana. com.br.

FOOD & DRINK

In Brazil you will be able to find many restaurants, snack bars, and fast-food outlets that are family friendly. In malls you can eat with kids in the *praças de alimentação*, but it won't be hard, especially in large cities, to find fast-food chains such as McDonald's, Habib's, and Giraffas. Habib's has hamburgers, pizza, and some Arab specialties like *kibes* (fried lamb croquettes). Giraffas has hamburgers and typical Brazilian foods like rice, beans, meat, and salad.

Water from the faucet is not safe to drink in Brazil. For more information about Food & Drink, *see* Eating Out *and* Health, *below.*

LODGING

Large hotels often offer a range of supervised activities—picnics, movies, classes, contests—for children of all ages. Most hotels in Brazil allow children under a certain age to stay in their parents' room at no extra charge, but others charge for them as extra adults; be sure to find out the cutoff age for children's discounts.

PASSPORTS & VISAS

Remember that even small children and infants need passports, and children with U.S., Canadian, or Australian citizenship need visas as well. Bring documents that prove you are the parent or legal guardian. A single parent traveling with children must bring a letter from the other parent to prove both parents are aware of the trip.

Any person under the age of 18 who isn't traveling with both parents or legal guardian(s) must provide a notarized letter of consent signed by the nonaccompanying parent or guardian. The notarized letter must be authenticated by the Brazilian embassy or consulate and translated into Portuguese.

Children must have all their inoculations up to date (those between the ages of three months and six years must have an international polio vaccination certificate) before leaving home.

PACKING & SUPPLIES

Literature for kids in English is hard to find in Brazil, except in large bookstores such as Fnac. Inexpensive art supplies such as crayons (*giz de cera*), paint (*tinta*), and coloring books (*livros de pintar*) are sold in stationery stores, bookstores, newsstands, and some supermarkets and street stalls.

You can find international brands of baby formula (*leite nan*) and diapers (*fraldas*) in drugstores, supermarkets, and convenience shops. The average cost of a 450-gram (16-ounce) container of formula is $6. The average price for a package of diapers is $3.

For more information on what to pack, *see* Packing, *below.*

SAFETY & PRECAUTIONS

- Arrange for a car seat in advance if you are renting a car.

- Riptides are a force to be reckoned with. Ask locals to point out safe places to swim and never let a child swim unattended in the ocean or go deeper than his or her waist.

- Sunburn and dehydration can be serious in Brazil. Slather on the sunscreen and make sure kids swim in T-shirts and wear hats. (Even waterproof sunscreen can wear off quickly.) Give kids lots of water or juice.

- Kids are more prone to stomach problems from contaminated water, so avoid tap water and ice.

- Wild animals aren't pets; explain how harmful it is to feed the monkeys, no matter how cute and tame they seem.

- Use insect repellent in areas with mosquitoes and ticks, and keep in mind that some of the more "natural" repellents are not strong enough for Brazilian bugs.

- In case of emergencies, have your child's blood type and allergy status in Portuguese.

- Have your children carry their own copies of their legal documents and contact information (hotel name and address).

- Extravagant or very expensive clothing and sneakers call thieves' attention.

CONSUMER PROTECTION

Whether you're shopping for gifts or purchasing travel services, **pay with a major credit card** whenever possible, so you can cancel payment or get reimbursed if there's a problem (and you can provide documentation). If you're doing business with a particular company for the first time, contact your local Better Business Bureau and the attorney general's offices in your state and (for U.S. businesses) the company's home state as well. Have any complaints been filed? Finally, if you're buying a package or tour, always consider travel insurance that includes default coverage (⇨ Insurance). ▣ BBBs **Council of Better Business Bureaus** ✉ 4200 Wilson Blvd., Suite 800, Arlington, VA 22203 ☎ 703/276-0100 🖷 703/525-8277 ⊕ www.bbb.org.

CRUISE TRAVEL

Cruise itineraries to Brazil change frequently, so contact a travel agent or a cruise company to get the most recent information. Popular Brazilian ports of call include Belém, Fortaleza, Manaus, Recife, Rio, Salvador, and Vitória (in Espínito Santo State).

If time and money are no object, consider a 69-day voyage with Fred. Olsen Cruises, which might include Europe, Argentina, and the Caribbean.

To learn how to plan, choose, and book a cruise-ship voyage, consult *Fodor's FYI: Plan & Enjoy Your Cruise* (available in bookstores everywhere).

⚓ Cruise Lines Abercrombie & Kent ☎ 800/554–7016 ⊕ www.abercrombiekent.com. **Clipper Cruise Line** ☎ 800/325–0010 or 314/655–6700 ⊕ www.clippercruise.com. **Celebrity Cruises** ☎ 800/647–2251 in the U.S. and Canada, 800/018–2525 in the U.K. ⊕ www.celebritycruises.com. **Crystal Cruises** ☎ 866/446–6625 ⊕ www.crystalcruises.com. **Cunard** ☎ 800/728–6273 ⊕ www.cunard.com. **Fred. Olsen Cruises** ☎ 147/374–2424 in the U.K. ⊕ www.fredolsencruises.co.uk. **G.A.P. Adventures** ☎ 416/260–0999 or 800/708–7761 ⊕ www.gapadventures.com. **Holland America Line** ☎ 877/932–4259 ⊕ www.hollandamerica.com. **Lindblad Expeditions** ☎ 800/397–3348 or 212/765–7740 ⊕ www.lindblad.com. **Orient Lines** ☎ 800/333–7300 ⊕ www.orientlines.com. **Radisson Seven Seas Cruises** ☎ 877/505–5370 ⊕ www.rssc.com. **Royal Olympic Cruises** ☎ 800/801–6086 ⊕ www.royalolympiccruises.com **Seabourn Cruise Lines** ☎ 800/929–9391 ⊕ www.seabourn.com. **Silversea Cruises** ☎ 877/760–9052 in the U.S. and Canada, 870/333–7030 in the U.K. ⊕ www.silversea.com.

CUSTOMS & DUTIES

Traveling home with articles made from animal parts, certain types of wood, or plant fibers can result in big fines and even jail time, so beware. When shopping abroad, keep receipts for all purchases. Upon reentering the country, **be ready to show customs officials what you've bought.** Pack purchases together in an easily accessible place. If you think a duty is incorrect, appeal the assessment. If you object to the way your clearance was handled, note the inspector's badge number. In either case, first ask to see a supervisor. If the problem isn't resolved, write to the appropriate authorities, beginning with the port director at your point of entry.

IN AUSTRALIA

Australian residents who are 18 or older may bring home A$900 worth of souvenirs and gifts (including jewelry), 250 cigarettes or 250 grams of cigars or other tobacco products, and 2.25 liters of alcohol (including wine, beer, and spirits). Residents under 18 may bring back A$450 worth of goods. If any of these individual allowances are exceeded, you must pay duty for the entire amount (of the group of products in which the allowance was exceeded). Members of the same family traveling together may pool their allowances. Prohibited items include meat products. Seeds, plants, and fruits need to be declared upon arrival.

⚓ Australian Customs Service ⌂ Customs House, 10 Cooks River Dr., Sydney International Airport, Sydney, NSW 2020 ☎ 02/6275–6666 or 1300/363263, 02/8334–7444 or 1800/020–504 quarantine-inquiry line 🖷 02/8339–6714 ⊕ www.customs.gov.au.

IN BRAZIL

In addition to personal items, you're permitted to bring in, duty-free, up to R$1,175 ($500) worth of gifts purchased abroad, including up to 2 liters of liquor. If you plan to bring in plants, you may do so only with documentation authenticated by the consular service.

IN CANADA

Canadian residents who have been out of Canada for at least seven days may bring in C$750 worth of goods duty-free. If you've been away fewer than seven days but more than 48 hours, the duty-free allowance drops to C$200. If your trip lasts 24 to 48 hours, the allowance is C$50; if the goods are worth more than C$50, you must pay full duty on all of the goods. You may not pool allowances with family members. Goods claimed under the C$750 exemption may follow you by mail; those claimed under the lesser exemptions must accompany you. Alcohol and tobacco products may be included in the seven-day and 48-hour exemptions but not in the 24-hour exemption. If you meet the age requirements of the province or territory through which you reenter Canada, you may bring in, duty-free, 1.5 liters of wine *or* 1.14 liters (40 imperial ounces) of liquor *or* 24 12-ounce cans or bottles of beer or ale. Also, if you meet the local age requirement for tobacco products, you may bring in, duty-free, 200 cigarettes, 50 cigars or cigarillos, and 200 grams of tobacco. You may have to pay a minimum duty on tobacco products, regardless of whether or not you exceed your personal exemption. Check ahead of time with the Canada Border Services Agency or the Department of Agriculture for policies regarding meat products, seeds, plants, and fruits.

You may send an unlimited number of gifts (only one gift per recipient, however) worth up to C$60 each duty-free to Canada. Label the package UNSOLICITED GIFT—VALUE UNDER $60. Alcohol and tobacco are excluded.

📋 **Canada Border Services Agency** ✉ Customs Information Services, 191 Laurier Ave. W, 15th floor, Ottawa, Ontario K1A 0L5 ☎ 800/461-9999 in Canada, 204/983-3500, 506/636-5064 ⊕ www.cbsa.gc.ca.

IN NEW ZEALAND

All homeward-bound residents may bring back NZ$700 worth of souvenirs and gifts; passengers may not pool their allowances, and children can claim only the concession on goods intended for their own use. For those 17 or older, the duty-free allowance also includes 4.5 liters of wine or beer; one 1,125-ml bottle of spirits; and either 200 cigarettes, 250 grams of tobacco, 50 cigars, *or* a combination of the three up to 250 grams. Meat products, seeds, plants, and fruits must be declared upon arrival to the Agricultural Services Department.

📋 **New Zealand Customs** ✉ Head office: The Customhouse, 17-21 Whitmore St., Box 2218, Wellington ☎ 09/300-5399 or 0800/428-786 ⊕ www.customs.govt.nz.

IN THE U.K.

From Brazil, you may bring home, duty-free, 200 cigarettes, 50 cigars, 100 cigarillos, or 250 grams of tobacco; 1 liter of spirits or 2 liters of fortified or sparkling wine or liqueurs; 2 liters of still table wine; 60 ml of perfume; 250 ml of toilet water; plus £145 worth of other goods, including gifts and souvenirs. Prohibited items include meat and dairy products, seeds, plants, and fruits.

📋 **HM Customs and Excise** ✉ Portcullis House, 21 Cowbridge Rd. E, Cardiff CF11 9SS ☎ 0845/010-9000 or 0208/929-0152 advice service, 0208/929-6731 or 0208/910-3602 complaints ⊕ www.hmce.gov.uk.

IN THE U.S.

U.S. residents who have been out of the country for at least 48 hours may bring home, for personal use, $800 worth of foreign goods duty-free, as long as they haven't used the $800 allowance or any part of it in the past 30 days. This exemption may include 1 liter of alcohol (for travelers 21 and older), 200 cigarettes, and 100 non-Cuban cigars. Family members from the same household who are traveling together may pool their $800 personal exemptions. For fewer than 48 hours, the duty-free allowance drops to $200, which may include 50 cigarettes, 10 non-Cuban cigars, and 150 ml of alcohol (or 150 ml of perfume containing alcohol). The $200 allowance cannot be combined with other individuals' exemptions, and if you exceed it, the full value of all the goods will be taxed. Antiques, which U.S. Customs and Border Protection defines as objects more than 100 years old, enter duty-free, as do original works of art done entirely by hand, including paintings, drawings, and sculptures. This doesn't apply to folk art or handicrafts, which are in general dutiable.

You may also send packages home duty-free, with a limit of one parcel per addressee per day (except alcohol or tobacco products or perfume worth more than $5). You can mail up to $200 worth of goods for personal use; label the package PERSONAL USE and attach a list of its contents and their retail value. If the package contains your used personal belongings, mark it AMERICAN GOODS RETURNED to avoid paying duties. You may send up to $100 worth of goods as a gift; mark the package UNSOLICITED GIFT. Mailed items do not affect your duty-free allowance on your return.

To avoid paying duty on foreign-made high-ticket items you already own and will take on your trip, register them with a local customs office before you leave the country. Consider filing a Certificate of Registration for laptops, cameras, watches, and other digital devices identified with serial numbers or other permanent markings; you can keep the certificate for other trips. Otherwise, bring a sales receipt or insurance form to show that you owned the item before you left the United States.

For more about duties, restricted items, and other information about international travel, check out U.S. Customs and Border Protection's online brochure, *Know Before You Go.* You can also file complaints on the U.S. Customs and Border Protection Web site, listed below.

📑 **U.S. Customs and Border Protection** ✉ for inquiries and complaints, 1300 Pennsylvania Ave. NW, Washington, DC 20229 ⊕ www.cbp.gov ☎ 877/227–5551, 202/354–1000.

DISABILITIES & ACCESSIBILITY

Although international chain hotels in large cities have some suitable rooms and facilities for people in wheelchairs, and it's easy to hire private cars and drivers for excursions, Brazil isn't very well equipped to handle travelers with disabilities. There are few ramps and curb cuts, and it takes effort and planning to negotiate cobbled city streets, get around museums and other buildings, and explore the countryside. City centers such as Rio de Janeiro are the most accessible places to visit; indeed, some areas on the south side of Rio *do* have ramps and wide sidewalks with even surfaces. Legislation concerning people with disabilities has been approved but has yet to be enforced. There's no central clearinghouse for information on this topic, so the best local resource is the staff at your hotel.

SIGHTS & ATTRACTIONS

Don't expect top visitor destinations to be fully equipped for people using wheelchairs. In some places you will find elevators and other facilities, but unfortunately Brazil still lacks the appropriate infrastructure for people with disabilities, especially those using wheelchairs. However, talking to the staff at your hotel might help in that they can contact specialized agencies or adapt their facilities to the disabled guest. If you speak Portuguese, the Web site of Aventura Especial, an NGO, is an excellent resource for informa-

tion on the accessibility of various destinations in Brazil (in the "Destinos" section). Places identified with the logo of Aventura Especial have infrastructure and trained staff for people with disabilities.

📑 Resource. **Aventura Especial.** ⊕ www.aventuraespecial.com.br.

TRANSPORTATION

Buses in most cities are not adapted to serve people with disabilities. One of the few exceptions is the city of Curitiba, in the state of Paraná. In airports it is not hard to move around, as there are escalators and elevators. With regard to car-rental agencies, Hertz (São Paulo only) and Unidas are two of the very few companies that have cars with hand controls.

The U.S. Department of Transportation Aviation Consumer Protection Division's online publication *New Horizons: Information for the Air Traveler with a Disability* offers advice for travelers with a disability, and outlines basic rights. Visit DisabilityInfo.gov for general information.

📑 Car Rental. **Hertz.** ☎ 0800/701-7300 ⊕ www.hertz.com.br. **Unidas.** ☎ 0800/122-288 ⊕ www.unidas.com.br.

📑 Information and Complaints **Aviation Consumer Protection Division** (⇨ Air Travel) for airline-related problems; ⊕ airconsumer.ost.dot.gov/publications/horizons.htm for airline travel advice and rights. **Departmental Office of Civil Rights** ✉ for general inquiries, U.S. Department of Transportation, S-30, 400 7th St. SW, Room 10215, Washington, DC 20590 ☎ 202/366-4648, 202/366-8538 TTY ⊟ 202/366-9371 ⊕ www.dotcr.ost.dot.gov. **Disability Rights Section** ✉ NYAV, U.S. Department of Justice, Civil Rights Division, 950 Pennsylvania Ave. NW, Washington, DC 20530 ☎ ADA information line 202/514–0301, 800/514–0301, 202/514–0383 TTY, 800/514–0383 TTY ⊕ www.ada.gov. **U.S. Department of Transportation Hotline** ☎ for disability-related air-travel problems, 800/778-4838 or 800/455-9880 TTY.

TOUR COMPANIES & TRAVEL AGENCIES

One of the few Brazilian package-tour operators with staff trained to assist people with disabilities is EcoAção Turismo de Aventura, in Brotas (São Paulo State). The company has only adventure tourism packages. Access Adventures, CareVacations, and Flying Wheels Travel are U.S.-based companies specializing in travelers with mobility problems.

F Access Adventures/B. Roberts Travel ⊠ 1876 East Ave., Rochester, NY 14610 ☎ 800/444–6540 ⊕ www.brobertstravel.com, run by a former physical-rehabilitation counselor. **CareVacations** ⊠ No. 5, 5110–50 Ave., Leduc, Alberta, Canada, T9E 6V4 ☎ 780/986–6404 or 877/478–7827 ⊟ 780/986–8332 ⊕ www.carevacations.com, for group tours and cruise vacations. **EcoAção Turismo de Aventura.** ⊠ Rua Mário Pinotti 205, 17380–000 Brotas, SP ☎ 014/3653–8040 ⊕ www.ecoacaotour.com.br. **Flying Wheels Travel** ⊠ 143 W. Bridge St., Box 382, Owatonna, MN 55060 ☎ 507/451–5005 ⊟ 507/451–1685 ⊕ www.flyingwheelstravel.com, for custom itineraries.

EATING & DRINKING

Eating is a national passion in Brazil, and portions are huge. In many restaurants plates are prepared for two people; when you order, ask if one plate will suffice—or even better, glance around to see the size of portions at other tables.

In major cities the variety of eateries is staggering: restaurants of all sizes and categories, snack bars, and fast-food outlets line downtown streets and fight for space in shopping malls. Pricing systems vary from open menus to buffets where you weigh your plate. In São Paulo, for example, Italian eateries—whose risottos rival those of Bologna—sit beside pan-Asian restaurants, which, like the chicest spots in North America and Europe, serve everything from Thai *satay* to sushi. In addition, there are excellent Portuguese, Chinese, Japanese, Arab, and Spanish restaurants.

Outside the cities you find primarily typical, low-cost Brazilian meals that consist simply of *feijão preto* (black beans) and *arroz* (rice) served with beef, chicken, or fish. Manioc, a root vegetable that's used in a variety of ways, and beef are adored everywhere. Note that Brazilians eat few vegetables, and these often must be ordered separately.

The restaurants we list are the cream of the crop in each price category. Properties indicated by a ✕⊡ are lodging establishments whose restaurant warrants a special trip. Price categories are as follows:

CATEGORY	AT DINNER
$$$$	over R$60
$$$	R$45–R$60
$$	R$30–R$45
$	R$15–R$30
¢	under R$15

Prices are for a main course at dinner.

MEALS & SPECIALTIES

Between the extremes of sophistication and austere simplicity, each region has its own cuisine. You find exotic fish dishes in the Amazon, African-spiced dishes in Bahia, and well-seasoned bean mashes in Minas Gerais (⇨ For more information on regional cuisine, *see* CloseUp boxes *in* regional chapters.)

Many Brazilian dishes are adaptations of Portuguese specialties. Fish stews called *caldeiradas* and beef stews called *cozidos* (a wide variety of vegetables boiled with different cuts of beef and pork) are popular, as is *bacalhau,* salt cod cooked in sauce or grilled. *Salgados* (literally, "salteds") are appetizers or snacks served in sit-down restaurants as well as at stand-up *lanchonetes* (luncheonettes). Dried salted meats form the basis of many dishes from the interior and northeast of Brazil, and pork is used heavily in dishes from Minas Gerais. Brazil's national dish is *feijoada* (a stew of black beans, sausage, pork, and beef), which is often served with rice, shredded kale, orange slices, and manioc flour or meal—called *farofa* if it's coarsely ground, *farinha* if finely ground—that has been fried with onions, oil, and egg.

One of the most avid national passions is the *churrascaria*, where meats are roasted on spits over an open fire, usually *rodízio* style. Rodízio means "going around," and waiters circulate nonstop carrying skewers laden with charbroiled hunks of beef, pork, and chicken, which are sliced onto your plate with ritualistic ardor. For a set price you get all the meat and side dishes you can eat.

Brazilian *doces* (desserts), particularly those of Bahia, are very sweet, and many are descendants of the egg-based custards and puddings of Portugal and France. *Cocada* is shredded coconut caked with sugar; *quindim* is a small tart made from egg yolks and coconut; *doce de banana* (or any other fruit) is banana cooked in sugar; *ambrosia* is a lumpy milk-and-sugar pudding.

Coffee is served black and strong with sugar in demitasse cups and is called *cafezinho*. (Requests for *descafeinado* [decaf] are met with a firm shake of the head "no," a blank stare, or outright amusement.) Coffee is taken with milk—called *café com leite*—only at breakfast. Bottled mineral water is sold in two forms: carbonated or plain (*com gás* and *sem gás*, respectively).

MEALTIMES
It's hard to find breakfast outside a hotel restaurant. At lunch and dinner portions are large. Often a single dish will easily feed two people; no one will be the least bit surprised if you order one entrée and ask for two plates. In addition, some restaurants automatically bring a *couvert* (an appetizer course of such items as bread, cheese or pâté, olives, quail eggs, and the like). You'll be charged extra for this, and you're perfectly within your rights to send it back if you don't want it.

Mealtimes vary according to locale. In Rio and São Paulo, lunch and dinner are served later than in the United States. In restaurants lunch usually starts around 12 and can last until 3. Dinner is always eaten after 7 and in many cases not until 10. In Minas Gerais, the northeast, and smaller towns in general, dinner and lunch are taken at roughly the same time as in the States.

Unless otherwise noted, the restaurants listed in this guide are open daily for lunch and dinner.

PAYING
Credit cards are widely accepted at restaurants in the major cities. In the countryside all but the smallest establishments generally accept credit cards as well. Gratuity is 10% of the total sum, and it is sometimes included in the bill; when it is not, it is optional to give the waiter a tip.

RESERVATIONS & DRESS
Appropriate dress for dinner in Brazil can vary dramatically. As a general rule, dress more formally for expensive restaurants. In most restaurants dress is casual, but even moderately priced places might frown upon shorts.

Reservations are always a good idea; we mention them only when they're essential or not accepted. Book as far ahead as you can, and reconfirm as soon as you arrive. (Large parties should always call ahead to check the reservations policy.) We mention dress only when men are required to wear a jacket or a jacket and tie.

WINE, BEER & SPIRITS
The national drink is the *caipirinha*, made of crushed lime, sugar, and *pinga* or *cachaça* (sugarcane liquor). When whipped with crushed ice, fruit juices, and condensed milk, the pinga/cachaça becomes a *batida*. A *caipivodka*, or *caipiroska*, is the same cocktail with vodka instead of cachaça. Some bars make both drinks using a fruit other than lime, such as kiwi and *maracujá* (passion fruit). Brazil has many brands of bottled beer. In general, though, Brazilians prefer tap beer, called *chopp*, which is sold in bars and restaurants. Be sure to try the carbonated soft drink *guaraná*, made using the Amazonian fruit of the same name. It is extremely popular in Brazil.

ECOTOURISM
Ecotourism is an ever more popular form of travel. Some ecotour operators are more trustworthy than others, however. ⇨ For our recommendations, *see* the Adventure & Learning Vacations chapter, *at* the end of this book.

GUIDELINES FOR SUSTAINABLE TRAVEL
- Use local guides or services, eat in local restaurants, and buy local crafts or produce to make your visit beneficial to those who live near protected areas.

- Do some research to find out whether or not your prospective tour company actually has "eco-friendly" policies, such as: hiring and training locals as guides, drivers, managers, and office workers; making a serious commitment to educate visitors about plant and animal life, geography, and history; controlling the numbers of people allowed daily onto a given site; restoring watersheds and anything else damaged by trail building, foot traffic, or overuse; and discouraging wildlife feeding or any other disruptive behavior (such as making loud noises that scare birds into flight).

- Donate to local conservation groups that aid ecological efforts in Brazil.

- Don't remove plants, rocks, shells, or animals from their natural environment. **It's illegal to take anything, alive or dead, out of a national park or any other protected area.**

ELECTRICITY

The current in Brazil isn't regulated: in São Paulo and Rio it's 110 or 120 volts (the same as in the United States and Canada); in Recife and Brasília it's 220 volts (the same as in Europe); and in Manaus and Salvador it's 127 volts. Electricity is AC (alternating current) at 60 Hz, similar to that in Europe. To use electric-powered equipment purchased in the U.S. or Canada, **bring a converter and adapter.** Wall outlets take Continental-type plugs, with two round prongs. Consider buying a universal adapter, which has several types of plugs in one handy unit.

If your appliances are dual-voltage, you'll need only an adapter. Don't use 110-volt outlets marked FOR SHAVERS ONLY for high-wattage appliances such as blow-dryers. Most laptops operate equally well on 110 and 220 volts and so require only an adapter.

Some hotels are equipped to handle various types of plugs and electrical devices. Check with your hotel before packing converters and adapters.

EMBASSIES & CONSULATES

Australia **Australian Embassy** ✉ SES Quadra 801 Conjunto K, Lote 7, 70200-010 Brasília, DF

☎ 061/3226-3111 🖷 61/3226-1112 ⊕ www.brazil.embassy.gov.au. **Australian Consulates** ✉ Veirano e Advogados Associados, Av. Presidente Wilson 231, 23rd floor, 20030-021 Rio de Janeiro RJ ☎ 021/3824-4624 🖷 021/262-4247 ✉ Alameda Ministro Rocha Azevedo 456, 2nd floor, Jardim Paulista, 01410-000 São Paulo, SP ☎ 011/3085-6247 Ext. 204 🖷 011/3082-4140.

Canada **Canadian Embassy** ✉ SES, Av. das Nações, Quadra 803, Lote 16, 70410-900 Brasília, DF ☎ 061/3424-5400 ⊕ www.dfait-maeci.gc.ca/brazil. **Canadian Consulates** ✉ Atlântica Business Center, Av. Atlântica 1130, 5th floor, Copacabana, 22021-000 Rio de Janeiro, RJ ☎ 021/2543-3004 🖷 021/2275-2195 ✉ Brooklin Centro Empresarial Nações Unidas, Av. das Nações Unidas 12901, 16th floor, 04578-000 São Paulo, SP ☎ 011/5509-4321 🖷 011/5509-4050.

New Zealand **New Zealand Embassy** ✉ SHIS QI-9, Conjunto 16, casa 01, Lago Sul 71625-160 Brasília, DF ☎ 061/248-9900 🖷 061/248-9916. **New Zealand Consulate** ✉ Alameda Campinas 579, 15th floor, Cerqueira Cesar, 01404-000 São Paulo, SP ☎ 011/3148-0616 🖷 011/3148-2521 ✉ consuladonz@nzte.govt.nz.

United Kingdom **British Embassy** ✉ SES, Av. das Nações, Quadra 801, Conjunto K, Lote 8, 70200-010 Brasília, DF ☎ 061/3329-2300 🖷 061/3329-2369 ⊕ www.reinounido.org.br. **British Consulate** ✉ Rua dos Inconfidentes 1075, sala 1302, Savassi, 30140-120 Belo Horizonte, MG ☎ 031/3261-2072 🖷 031/3261-0226 ✉ Rua Presidente Faria 51, 2nd floor, Conjunto 203, 80020-918 Curitiba, PR ☎ 041/3322-1202 🖷 041/3322-3537 ✉ Edifício Galleria, Av. Conselheiro Aguiar 2941, 3rd floor, Boa Viagem, 51020-020 Recife, PE ☎ 081/3465-0230 🖷 081/3465-0247 ✉ Praia do Flamengo 284, 2nd floor, Flamengo, 22210-030 Rio de Janeiro, RJ ☎ 021/2555-9600 🖷 021/2555-9672 ✉ Rua Ferreira de Araújo 741, 2nd floor, Pinheiros, 05428-002 São Paulo, SP ☎ 011/ 3094-2700 🖷 011/3094-2717. **Honorary British Consulate** ✉ Ed. Palladium Center, Av. Governador J. Malcher 815, Conjunto 410/411, 66060-230 Belém, PA ☎ 091/222-5074 🖷 091/212-0274 ✉ Grupo Edson Queiroz, Leonardo Mota, 501, Meireles, 60170-040 Fortaleza, CE ☎ 085/242-0888 🖷 085/ 242-9222 ✉ Swedish Match da Amazônia S.A., Rua Poraquê 240, Distrito Industrial, 69075-180 Manaus, AM ☎ 092/613-1819 🖷 092/613-1420 ✉ Edifício Montreal, Rua Itapeva 110, Conjunto 505 Passo D'Areia, 91350-080 Porto Alegre, RS ☎ 051/3341-0720 🖷 051/3341-0720 ✉ CEPARH, 4th floor, Rua Caetano Moura, 35, Fed-

eração, 40210-341 Salvador, BA ☎ 071/3247-8216.
🔢 United States **American Embassy** ⌗ SES, Av.
das Nações, Quadra 801, Lote 3, 70403-900 Brasília,
DF ☎ 61/ 3312-7000 📠 61/3225-9136 ⊕ www.
embaixada-americana.org.br. **American Consular
Agency** ⌗ Av. Santos Dumont 2828, sala 708,
Aldeota, 60150-161 Fortaleza, CE ☎ 085/3486-1306
📠 085/3486-1308. **American Consulate** ⌗ Av.
Presidente Wilson 147, 20030-020 Rio de Janeiro, RJ
☎ 021/ 3823-2000 📠 021/3823-2003 ⌗ Henry
Dunant, 700, Chácara Santo Antônio, 04709-110 São
Paulo, SP ☎ 011/5186-7000 📠 011/5186-7199. **U.S.
Commercial Service** ⌗ Rua Timbiras 1200, 7th
floor, Funcionários, Belo Horizonte ☎ 031/
3213-1571.

ETIQUETTE & BEHAVIOR

Although Brazil is a predominately
Catholic country, in many places there's
an anything-goes outlook. As a rule,
coastal areas (particularly Rio and parts of
the northeast) are considerably less conservative than inland areas and cities
throughout the south. People dress nicely
to enter churches (no shorts or tiny shirts),
and hats are frowned upon during mass.

On beaches everybody wears swimming
suits. Despite the impossibly small size of
Brazilian bikinis, going topless is not only
severely frowned upon, but considered a
serious violation that may involve the police. Never go topless unless you are on a
nudist beach.

Whether they tend toward the conservative
or the risqué, Brazilians tend to be a very
friendly lot. Don't be afraid to smile in the
streets, ask for directions, or strike up a
conversation with a local. The slower pace
of life in much of the country reflects an un-
wavering appreciation of family and friendship (as well as a respect for the heat);
knowing this will help you understand why
things may take a little longer to get done.

Your conversations in Brazil will probably
be about your stay here. Brazilians are
often curious about what foreigners think
about their country, whether they liked
what they have seen so far, etc. Talking
too much about clichés such as beautiful
women and Carnival might be insensitive,
as some Brazilians consider these offensive
stereotypes.

Throughout the country use the thumbs-
up gesture to indicate that something is
OK. The gesture created by making a circle with your thumb and index finger and
holding your other fingers up in the air has
a very rude meaning.

GAY & LESBIAN TRAVEL

Brazil is South America's most popular
destination for gay and lesbian travelers,
and major cities such as Rio de Janeiro,
São Paulo, and Salvador have numerous
gay bars, organizations, and publications.
In 2005, São Paulo hosted the largest gay-
pride parade in history: the police reported
that nearly 2 million people attended (including 700,000 tourists). The city hosts
the parade annually. The great Carnaval
celebrations include many gay parades. At
the end of the year, Mix Brasil International Festival of Sexual Diversity takes
place in São Paulo, Rio de Janeiro, and
Porto Alegre.

Still, the acceptance of same-sex couples in
the major cities is often limited to more
touristy areas. Hotels are little by little trying to adapt to the increasing number of
same-sex couples, which means you may
or may not have difficulties getting a
room. Public displays of affection between
same-sex couples are severely frowned
upon and usually cause problems in public
places, especially around senior citizens or
families with kids. Cities like Rio are more
tolerant in this regard, but, just to be on
the safe side, be discreet if you do not
want to cause problems.

GAY-FRIENDLY DESTINATIONS

Rio is much like New York City or any
other large metropolitan center with regard to acceptance of gays and lesbians.
Rio's gay beach scene is at Bolsa, on Copacabana Beach in front of the Copacabana Palace, and at Ipanema, by Posts 8
and 9, east of Rua Farme de Amoedo (also
called "Farme Gay"). Locals on these
sandy stretches are usually open to questions about what's happening in the gay
and lesbian community.

In São Paulo, gay and lesbian bars and services are concentrated in Largo do
Arouche and Jardins.

GAY & LESBIAN RESOURCES IN BRAZIL

Disque Defesa Homossexual is a number set up by the Rio police to aid lesbians and gays who have suffered violence or discrimination. Grupo Arco-Íris is a nonprofit association founded in 1993 that organizes meetings and debates in Rio about themes related to gays and lesbians. In Salvador you can get gay and lesbian information and purchase the guide *Guia para Gays* (R$10) from the Grupo Gay da Bahia. Style Travel, an offshoot of the established Brasil Plus travel agency, is a great source of information on gay and lesbian lodgings, tours, and nightlife options in Rio. It can supply knowledgeable, English-speaking gay and lesbian guides and arrange trips to outlying areas. Style Travel is a member of the International Gay and Lesbian Travel Association (IGLTA). Riogayguide.com is a great soup-to-nuts resource for bars, clubs, cafés, hotels, and events in Rio.

▶ **Disque Defesa Homossexual** ☎ 021/3399-1111 ⊙ weekdays 10-5. **Grupo Arco-Íris de Conscientização Homossexual** ☎ 021/2552-5995. **Grupo Gay da Bahia** ⊠ Rua Frei Vicente, 24, Pelourinho, Salvador, BA ☎ 071/ 321-1848. **Style Travel** ⊠ Av. da Américas, 4200, Bloco 9 - Sala 119A ☎ 021/ 3150-3150 ⊕ www.styletravel.com.br. **Riogayguide. com** ⊕ www.riogayguide.com.

▶ Gay- & Lesbian-Friendly Travel Agencies **Different Roads Travel** ⊠ 1017 N. LaCienega Blvd., Suite 308, West Hollywood, CA 90069 ☎ 310/289-6000 or 800/429-8747 (Ext. 14 for both) 🖷 310/855-0323 ✉ lgernert@tzell.com. **Kennedy Travel** ⊠ 130 W. 42nd St., Suite 401, New York, NY 10036 ☎ 800/237-7433 or 212/840-8659 🖷 212/730-2269 ⊕ www.kennedytravel.com. **Now, Voyager** ⊠ 4406 18th St., San Francisco, CA 94114 ☎ 415/626-1169 or 800/255-6951 🖷 415/626-8626 ⊕ www.nowvoyager.com. **Skylink Travel and Tour/Flying Dutchmen Travel** ⊠ 1455 N. Dutton Ave., Suite A, Santa Rosa, CA 95401 ☎ 707/546-9888 or 800/225-5759 🖷 707/636-0951; serving lesbian travelers.

HEALTH

The best recommendation to avoid health problems is to seek a doctor before and after traveling, just to be on the safe side. Some vaccines must be applied long before traveling so that their protective effect is guaranteed, and some prophylactic medicines must be taken also in advance so that the doctor and the patient are aware of possible side effects.

English-speaking medical assistance in Brazil is quite rare. It's best to contact your consulate or embassy if you need medical assistance. Seek private clinics or hospitals—getting an appointment in the government's healthcare system is a slow process.

AMAZON-SPECIFIC HEALTH

Several months before you go to the Amazon, visit a tropical medicine specialist to find out what vaccinations you need. Describe your planned adventure, and get tips on how to prepare. Read about tropical diseases in the Amazon so you know the symptoms and how to treat them should you fall ill.

Bites & Stings: Tropical forests are home to lots of ants, bees, spiders, scorpions, centipedes, and caterpillars, many of which bite or sting. Their unpleasant attacks largely can be avoided by wearing protective clothing and by not playing with them. If you are allergic to bites and stings, you should carry an adrenaline kit. Remember to check you shoes in the morning for small guests. Many plants have spines and thorns that may also result in wounds, so beware of where you place your hands and feet. Mosquitoes and gnats are abundant in some places. Mosquitoes can carry both malaria and dengue, so it's important to protect yourself. Only stronger versions of repellents with picaridin or DEET (diethyl toluamide) keep them away. A *mosquiteiro* (netting for hammock or bed) helps tremendously at night. Ticks live in forests, too. If you find one on you, remove it and treat the site with disinfectant. Chiggers inhabit grassy areas and are nearly invisible. Repellent sprayed on shoes, socks, and pants helps, as does powdered sulfur. Escaping without a few bites is nearly impossible, however, and some anti-itch ointment will help you sleep at night.

Pirhanas are rarely a problem, except as supporting actors in B movies, but ask locals or your guide before you swim. Freshwater stingrays hide in shallow water, and they're difficult to see, but if you step on one, you'll feel it. A sting from its barbed tail can be excruciating and long in healing. This bad memory can usually be avoided by dragging your feet as you move slowly through shallow water, where the rays can avoid you. Another unlikely, thought possible, encounter is with venemous snakes. Bushmasters, fer-de-lance relatives, and several others are present though rarely seen. Shoes or boots and long pants are excellent preventative measures. When in the forest, watch cloesly where you step.

Food & Water: Throughout the region, avoid drinking tap water and using ice made from it. In the cities most restaurants buy ice made from purified water. Bottled water is generally easy to find. Beware of where you eat. Many of the street-side stands are not very clean. Over-the-counter remedies can ease discomfort. For loose bowels, Floratil can be purchased woutout a doctor's prescription. Estomazil and Sorrisal (which may contain asprin) are two remedies for upset stomach.

Infections & Diseases: In a remote area the likeliest health issues are often infection and dehydration. Infections are common from insect bites and cuts. Treat them quickly, so they don't worsen. Dehydration can result from gastrointestinal problems or inadequate water. Be sure to keep yourself hydrated with clean water, and learn what to do about gastrointestinal issues. Most visitors to the Amazon depart with nothing more than a bit of *turista* (traveler's diarrhea), but some common infections and diseases about which you should inform yourself are rabies, Chagas' disease, malaria, yellow fever, meningitis, hepatitis, and dengue fever.

Brazil has the highest number of cases of malaria in the Americas. The most problematic area is the Amazon region. Transmission is more common in rural and semi-rural areas, but also occurs in the periphery of urban areas. Malaria-carrying mosquitoes usually bite at night (beginning at dusk) and indoors.

Dengue is carried by mosquitoes that bite during the day, but you should not have

problems if you are staying in a hotel and take the precautions listed below, valid for all diseases aforementioned:

- Use mosquito repellents and screens on windows and doors, and sleep in rooms with air-conditioning, if possible.

- Apply insect repellents with DEET or picaridin when hiking in rural or forested areas.

- Wear long-sleeved shirts and long pants at night.

- Do not leave water in sinks, tubs, or discarded bottles. Dengue mosquitoes thrive in urban areas and lay their eggs in clean water.

- If you suspect you contracted dengue fever, *do not* take asprin, because it can impair blood clotting.

- Avoid bathing in lakes or rivers without prior knowledge about the quality of water and the risks involved.

Shots & Medications: Vaccinations agaist hepatitis A and B, menengitis, typhoid, and yellow fever are highly recommended. Consult your doctor about whether to get a rabies vaccination. **Check with the CDC's International Travelers' Hotline** (Health Warnings, below) if you plan to visit remote regions or stay for more than six weeks.

Discuss the option of taking antimalarial drugs with your doctor. Note that in parts of nothern Brazil, a particularly aggressive strain of malaria has become resistant to one antimalarial drug—chloroquine®). Some antimalarial drugs have rather unpleasant side effects—from headaches, nausea, and dizziness to psychosis, convulsions, and hallucinations.

DIVERS' ALERT
Do not fly within 24 hours of scuba diving.

Neophyte divers should have a complete physical exam before undertaking a dive. If you have travel insurance that covers evacuations, **make sure your policy applies to scuba-related injuries,** as not all companies provide this coverage.

FOOD & DRINK

The major health risk in Brazil is traveler's diarrhea, caused by eating contaminated fruit or vegetables or drinking contaminated water. So watch what you eat—on and off the beaten path. Avoid ice, uncooked food, and unpasteurized milk and milk products, and **drink only bottled water** or water that has been boiled for at least 20 minutes, even when brushing your teeth. The use of bottled water for brushing your teeth is not necessary in large cities, where water is treated. Don't use ice unless you know it's made from purified water. (Ice in city restaurants is usually safe.) Peel or thoroughly wash fresh fruits and vegetables. Avoid eating food from street vendors.

Choose industrially packaged beverages when you can. Order tropical juices from places that appear clean and reliable. Avoid eating egg-based foods such as mayonnaise in restaurants to prevent stomach indisposition.

INFECTIOUS DISEASES & VIRUSES

The Amazon and other remote areas (Amazon-Specific Health, above) are the only places in Brazil where you really need worry about infectious diseases. Most travelers to Brazil return home unscathed apart from a bit of traveler's diarrhea. However, you should visit a doctor at least six weeks prior to traveling to discuss recommended vaccinations, some of which require multiple shots over a period of weeks. If you get sick weeks, months, or in rare cases, years after your trip, make sure your doctor administers blood tests for tropical diseases.

Meningococcal meningitis and typhoid fever are common in certain areas of Brazil—and not only in remote areas like the Amazon. Meningitis has been a problem around São Paulo in recent years. Dengue fever and malaria—both caused by mosquito bites—are common in Brazil or in certain areas of Brazil. Both are usually only a problem in the Amazon, but dengue can affect urban areas and malaria is sometimes found in urban peripheries. Talk with your doctor about what precautions to take.

MEDICAL INSURANCE

For information on medical insurance, *see* Trip Insurance.

OVER-THE-COUNTER REMEDIES

Mild cases of diarrhea may respond to Imodium (known generically as loperamide) or Pepto-Bismol (not as strong), both of which can be purchased over the counter at a *farmácia* (pharmacy). Drink plenty of purified water or *chá* (tea)—*camomila* (chamomile) is a good folk remedy. In severe cases rehydrate yourself with a salt–sugar solution: ½ teaspoon *sal* (salt) and 4 tablespoons *açúcar* (sugar) per quart of *agua* (water).

Pharmacies also sell antidiarrheal medicines, but an effective home remedy is the same as the rehydrating concoction: a teaspoon of sugar plus a quarter teaspoon of salt in a liter of water.

Aspirin is *aspirina*; Tylenol is pronounced *tee-luh-nawl*.

PESTS & OTHER HAZARDS

You'll likely encounter more insects than you're used to in Brazil, but they generally only present health problems in the Amazon.

Heatstroke and heat prostration are common though easily preventable maladies throughout Brazil. The symptoms for either can vary but always start with headaches, nausea, and dizziness. If ignored, these symptoms can worsen until you require medical attention. In hot weather be sure to rehydrate regularly, wear loose lightweight clothing, and avoid overexerting yourself.

SHOTS & MEDICATIONS

For travel anywhere in Brazil, it is recommended that you have updated vaccines for diphtheria, tetanus, and polio. Children must additionally have current inoculations against measles, mumps, and rubella.

Yellow fever immunization is compulsory to enter Brazil if you are traveling directly from one of the following countries in South America (or from one of several African countries): Bolivia; Colombia; Ecuador; French Guiana; Peru; or

Venezuela. You must have an International Certificate of Immunization proving that you've been vaccinated.

🗒 Health Warnings **National Centers for Disease Control and Prevention** (CDC) ✉ Office of Health Communication, National Center for Infectious Diseases, Division of Quarantine, Travelers' Health, 1600 Clifton Rd. NE, Atlanta, GA 30333 ☎ 877/394–8747 international travelers' health line, 800/311–3435 other inquiries, 404/498–1600 Division of Quarantine and international health information ☎ 888/232–3299 ⊕ www.cdc.gov/travel. **Travel Health Online** ⊕ tripprep.com. **World Health Organization** (WHO) ⊕ www.who.int.

HOLIDAYS

Major national holidays include: New Year's Day (January 1, but sometimes December 31 is also taken a holiday); Carnaval (the week preceding Ash Wednesday); Good Friday (the Friday before Easter Sunday); Easter Sunday; Tiradentes Day (Apr. 21); Labor Day (May 1); Corpus Christi (60 days after Easter Sunday); Independence Day (Sept. 7); Our Lady of Aparecida Day (Oct. 12); All Souls' Day (Nov. 1); Declaration of the Republic Day (Nov. 15); and Christmas.

LANGUAGE

Brazil is surrounded by Spanish-speaking countries, but the national language here is Portuguese, not Spanish. Curiously enough, most Brazilians will understand you if you speak only Spanish, but do it slowly. Don't expect Brazilians to speak perfect Spanish, however, as it is easier for them to understand it than to speak it. If you speak Spanish, there's no guarantee you'll understand Portuguese—although the written languages are similar, pronunciation is much different.

Those used to traveling in Europe are often shocked by how little English is spoken or understood in Brazil. That said, educated Brazilians and, in general, at least some of the staff at hotels, tour operators, and travel agencies will speak English. Store clerks and waiters may speak a smattering of English; taxi and bus drivers won't. You're more likely to find English-speaking locals in major cities than in

small towns or the countryside. In the northeast and the Amazon you may have difficulty even in cities. Learning some basic sentences in Portuguese will come in handy.

LODGING

Unlike lodging in European countries, all hotels in Brazil have bathrooms in their rooms. In fact, Brazilians find it strange to not have such facility in hotels abroad. The simplest type of accommodation usually consists of a bed, TV, table, bathroom, a little fridge, a telephone, and a bathroom with a shower. (Budget hotels in the Amazon or northeast will not always have hot water, however.) In luxury hotels you will also generally have Internet access, cable TV, and a bathroom with a bathtub and shower.

Hotels listed with EMBRATUR, Brazil's national tourism board, are rated using stars. Staff training is a big part of the rating, but it's not a perfect system since stars are awarded based on the number of amenities rather than their quality.

The lodgings we list are the cream of the crop in each price category. We always list the facilities that are available, but we don't specify whether they cost extra; when pricing accommodations, always ask what's included and what costs extra. **All rooms have private bathrooms, air-conditioning, telephones, and televisions unless we indicate otherwise.**

Properties are assigned price categories based on the range between their least and most expensive standard double rooms at high season (excluding holidays). **Properties marked** ✕⊡ are lodging establishments whose restaurants warrant a special trip. Price categories are as follows:

CATEGORY	FOR TWO PEOPLE
$$$$	over R$500
$$$	R$375–R$500
$$	R$250–R$375
$	R$125–R$250
¢	under R$125

Prices are for a standard double room in high season, excluding taxes.

BOOKING

When you book a room, you pay, in addition to the base fee, tourism fees equaling 10% of the room price plus (sometimes) R$1.50. Hotels accept credit cards for payment, but first ask if there's a discount for cash. Try to bargain hard for a cash-on-the-barrel discount, then pay in local currency.

If you ask for a double room, you'll get a room for two people, but you're not guaranteed a double mattress. If you'd like to avoid twin beds, ask for a *cama de casal* ("couple's bed").

Carnival, the year's principal festival, takes place during the four days preceding Ash Wednesday. For top hotels in Rio, Salvador, and Recife—the three leading Carnaval cities—you must make reservations a year in advance. Hotel rates rise by 20% on average for Carnival. Not as well known outside Brazil but equally impressive is Rio's New Year's Eve celebration. More than a million people gather along Copacabana Beach for a massive fireworks display and to honor the sea goddess Iemanjá. To ensure a room, book at least six months in advance.

In the hinterlands it's good to look at any room before accepting it; expense is no guarantee of charm or cleanliness, and accommodations can vary dramatically within a single hotel. Also, be sure to check the shower: some hotels have electric-powered showerheads rather than central water heaters. In theory, you can adjust both the water's heat and its pressure. In practice, if you want hot water you have to turn the water pressure down; if you want pressure, expect a brisk rinse. Careful! Don't adjust the power when you're under the water—you can get a little shock. Note that in the Amazon and other remote areas, what's billed as "hot" water may be lukewarm at best—even in higher-end hotels.

CUTTING COSTS

- When buying from an online consolidator like Hotels.com, carefully read the fine print detailing penalties for changes and cancellations. Also, be sure to confirm your reservation.

- Start looking as early as possible.

- Sign up for free membership programs with chain hotels; you may getting a "signing bonus" of a room upgrade.

- If you're not sure of your dates but you want to book anyway, make sure you're aware of the hotel's cancellation policy so you don't get nailed with a fat fee.

- Don't dismiss nature lodges as overly expensive; they often include three meals and guided tours and can be some of the best deals.

- If you speak Portuguese, www.hoteldesconto.com.br is a good site for discounts.

- Try booking directly with mid-range hotels; you may be able to get a better deal.

MEALPLANS

In every hotel review we specify whether a meal plan is included in the base price of a room by using the following acronyms:

EP: European Plan (no meals)

CP: Continental Plan (Continental breakfast)

BP: Breakfast Plan (full breakfast)

MAP: Modified American Plan (breakfast and dinner)

FAP: Full American Plan (breakfast, lunch, and dinner)

AI: All Inclusive (all meals, drinks, and most activities)

APARTMENTS & VILLAS

If you want a home base that's roomy enough for a family and comes with cooking facilities, consider a furnished rental. These can save you money, especially if you're traveling with a group. Home-exchange directories sometimes list rentals as well as exchanges. Also *see* "'Flat' Hotels," *below.*

In most Brazilian cities you will have hot water in showers. In hot cities like Rio and Salvador you will find electric showers and, in the south, where temperatures can get down to freezing in the winter, make sure both your room and bathroom have heat. Ask for instructions on how to turn the heat on, as it may vary. In the far north, hot water might not be available. In other cities an air-conditioner and/or a fan will undoubtedly be more useful than heat.

⚐ International Agents **Hideaways International** ⊠ 767 Islington St., Portsmouth, NH 03801 ☎ 603/430-4433 or 800/843-4433 ⊟ 603/430-4444 ⊕ www.hideaways.com, annual membership $185. **Villas International** ⊠ 4340 Redwood Hwy., Suite D309, San Rafael, CA 94903 ☎ 415/499-9490 or 800/221-2260 ⊟ 415/499-9491 ⊕ www.villasintl.com.

CHAIN HOTELS

⚐ Chain Hotels **Best Western** ☎ 800/528-1234 ⊕ www.bestwestern.com. **Comfort Inn** ☎ 800/424-6423 ⊕ www.choicehotels.com. **Hilton** ☎ 800/445-8667 ⊕ www.hilton.com. **Holiday Inn** ☎ 800/465-4329 ⊕ www.ichotelsgroup.com. **Hyatt Hotels & Resorts** ☎ 800/233-1234 ⊕ www.hyatt.com. **Inter-Continental** ☎ 800/327-0200 ⊕ www.ichotelsgroup.com. **Marriott** ☎ 800/228-9290 ⊕ www.marriott.com. **Le Meridien** ☎ 800/543-4300 ⊕ www.lemeridien.com. **Quality Inn** ☎ 800/424-6423 ⊕ www.choicehotels.com. **Radisson** ☎ 800/333-3333 ⊕ www.radisson.com. **Renaissance Hotels & Resorts** ☎ 800/468-3571 ⊕ www.marriott.com. **Sheraton** ☎ 800/325-3535 ⊕ www.starwood.com/sheraton.

FAZENDAS

Another accommodation option is to stay on a *fazenda* (farm), or *hotel fazenda,* where you can experience a rural environment. They are ideal for families with kids, as most have adventure sports and programs for children. Some farms in the state of São Paulo date back to colonial times, when they were famous Brazilian coffee farms. Prices range from around $50 to $125 per day for adults, but the actual cost depends a lot which facilities and activities you choose. The prices we give usually include all meals (but be sure to check this beforehand) and are valid for the months of January, February, July, and December (high season). You can get discounts of up to 30% during the low season.

"FLAT" HOTELS

Popular with large groups, and frequented more often by Brazilians than foreigners, flat hotels (also called block hotels or apartment-hotels) have kitchen facilities and more space than typical hotels. Some have amenities such as pools.

HOME EXCHANGES

If you would like to exchange your home for someone else's, join a home-exchange organization, which will send you its updated listings of available exchanges for a year and will include your own listing in at least one of them. It's up to you to make specific arrangements.

⚐ Exchange Clubs **HomeLink USA** ⊠ 2937 N.W. 9th Terrace, Wilton Manors, FL 33311 ☎ 954/566-2687 or 800/638-3841 ⊟ 954/566-2783 ⊕ www.homelink.org; $75 yearly for a listing and online access; $45 additional to receive directories. **Intervac U.S.** ⊠ 30 Corte San Fernando, Tiburon, CA 94920 ☎ 800/756-4663 ⊟ 415/435-7440 ⊕ www.intervacus.com; $128 yearly for a listing, online access, and a catalog; $68 without catalog.

POUSADAS

If you want the facilities of a hotel plus the family environment of an apartment, but at a lower cost, a *pousada* is a good option. Cheaper than hotels and farms, pousadas are simple inns, often in historic houses. They usually have swimming pools, parking lots, air-conditioning and/or fans, TVs, refrigerators, and common areas such as bars, laundry, and living rooms. Some have a common kitchen for guests who prefer to cook their own meals.

MAIL & SHIPPING

Post offices are called *correios,* and branches are marked by name and by a logo that looks something like two interlocked fingers; most are open weekdays 9–5 and Saturday until noon. Mailboxes are small yellow boxes marked CORREIOS that sit atop metal pedestals on street corners. Airmail from Brazil takes 10 or more days to reach the United States, possibly longer to Canada and the United Kingdom, and definitely longer to Australia and New Zealand.

EXPRESS SERVICES

Brazil has both national and international express mail service, the price of which varies according to the weight of the package and the destination. FedEx is available in São Paulo, Campinas, Rio, and Porto Alegre. In other areas international express mail can be sent with DHL, or Sedex Mundo, available in post offices.

🖪 Express Services **DHL** ☎ 11/3618-3200in Brazil ⊕ www.dhl.com.br. **FedEx** ☎ 011/5641-7788 in São Paulo, 0800/90-3333 elsewhere in Brazil ⊕ www.fedex.com/br_english.
🖪 Post Office **Correios** ☎ 0800/570-0100 in Brazil ⊕ www.correios.com.br.

POSTAL RATES
A simple airmail letter from Brazil to the United States and most parts of Europe, including the United Kingdom, costs about R$2.16 (91¢). Aerograms and postcards cost the same.

RECEIVING MAIL
Mail can be addressed to **poste restante** and sent to any major post office. The address must include the code for that particular branch. American Express will hold mail for its cardholders.

MONEY MATTERS
Brazil's unit of currency is the *real* (R$; plural: *reais*). One real is 100 *centavos* (cents). There are notes worth 1, 5, 10, 20, 50, and 100 reais, together with coins worth 1, 5, 10, 25, and 50 centavos and 1 real.

When in Brazil, pay for everything with credit cards or with reais.

Prices throughout this guide are given for adults. Substantially reduced fees are almost always available for children, students, and senior citizens. For information on taxes, *see* Taxes *in* Money.

WHAT IT COSTS
Brasília, Rio, and São Paulo tend to be the most expensive cities. In Curitiba things tend to be much cheaper than in other large cities. You are also likely to find things cheaper in the countryside. The average price of a cup of coffee, for example, is R$2 (85¢) in Brazil. However, depending on where you are, it can cost between R$1.5 and R$3.

Top hotels in Rio and São Paulo go for more than $180 a night, and meals can—but do not have to—cost as much. Outside Brazil's two largest cities and Brasília,

prices for food and lodging tend to drop considerably. Self-service restaurants where you pay by weight (per kilo, about 2.2 pounds) are inexpensive alternatives everywhere, though be sure to choose carefully among them. A considerable advantage of self-service restaurants is that you don't need to know the names of the foods, which is especially helpful for those who don't speak Portuguese.

Taxis can be pricey, and prices vary enormously from one city to another—not only because price tables may be different, but also (and mainly) because of traffic. In São Paulo, for example, expect to pay more, as you are going to spend more time inside the taxi, due to traffic. City buses, subways, and long-distance buses are all inexpensive; plane fares aren't. If you are price-conscious and want to travel by plane within Brazil, cheaper alternatives are Gol airlines, BRA, or WebJet.

ATMS & BANKS
Nearly all the nation's major banks have ATMs, known in Brazil as *caixas eletrônicos,* for which you must use a card with a credit-card logo. MasterCard/Cirrus holders can withdraw at Banco Itau, Banco do Brasil, HSBC, and Banco24horas ATMs; Visa holders can use Bradesco ATMs and those at Banco do Brasil. American Express cardholders can make withdrawals at most Bradesco ATMs marked 24 HORAS. To be on the safe side, carry a variety of cards. Note also that if your PIN is more than four digits long and/or uses letters instead of numbers, it might not work. **If you don't have one, get a four-digit PIN before your trip.** For your card to function in some ATMs, you may need to hit a screen command (perhaps, *estrangeiro*) if you are a foreign client.

Banks are, with a few exceptions, open weekdays 10–4.

CREDIT CARDS
In Brazil's largest cities and leading tourist centers, restaurants, hotels, and shops accept major international credit cards. Off the beaten track, you may have more difficulty using them. Many gas stations in rural Brazil don't take credit cards.

For costly items use your credit card whenever possible—you'll come out ahead, whether the exchange rate at which your purchase is calculated is the one in effect the day the vendor's bank abroad processes the charge or the one prevailing on the day the charge company's service center processes it at home.

Throughout this guide, the following abbreviations are used: **AE,** American Express; **DC,** Diners Club; **MC,** MasterCard; and **V,** Visa.

🔳 Reporting Lost Cards **MasterCard/Cirrus** ☎ 0800/891-3294 in Brazil. **Visa/Plus** ☎ 0800/ 99-0001 in Brazil.

CURRENCY EXCHANGE

At this writing, the real is at 2.99 to the euro, 4.25 to the pound sterling, 2.35 to the U.S. dollar, 1.96 to the Canadian dollar, 1.83 to the Australia dollar, and 1.65 to the New Zealand dollar.

For the most favorable rates, **change money through banks.** Although ATM transaction fees may be higher abroad than at home, ATM rates are excellent because they're based on wholesale rates offered only by major banks. You won't do as well at *casas de câmbio* (exchange houses), in airports or rail and bus stations, in hotels, in restaurants, or in stores.

To avoid lines at airport exchange booths, get a bit of local currency before you leave home. Don't wait until the last minute to do this as many banks—even the international ones—don't have reais on hand and must order them for you. This can take a couple of days. Outside larger cities, changing money in Brazil becomes more of a challenge. When leaving a large city for a smaller town, bring enough cash for your trip. For an average week in a Brazilian city, a good strategy is to convert $500 into reais. This provides sufficient cash for most expenses, such as taxis and small purchases and snacks.

🔳 Exchange Services **International Currency Express** ✉ 427 N. Camden Dr., Suite F, Beverly Hills, CA 90210 ☎ 888/278-6628 orders 🖷 310/278-6410 ⊕ www.foreignmoney.com. **Travel Ex Currency Services** ☎ 800/287-7362 orders and retail locations ⊕ www.travelex.com.

TAXES

Sales tax is included in the prices shown on goods in stores. Hotel, meal, and car rental taxes are usually tacked on in addition to the costs shown on menus and brochures. At this writing, hotel taxes are roughly 5%, meal taxes 10%, and car-rental taxes 12%.

Departure taxes on international flights from Brazil aren't always included in your ticket and can run as high as R$86 ($36); domestic flights may incur a R$22 ($9.30) tax. Although U.S. dollars are accepted in some airports, **be prepared to pay departure taxes in reais.**

TIPPING

Wages can be paltry in Brazil, so a little generosity in tipping can go a long way. Tipping in dollars is not recommended— at best it's insulting; at worst, you might be targeted for a robbery. Large hotels that receive lots of international guests are the exception. Some restaurants add a 10% service charge onto the check. If there's no service charge, you can leave as much as you want, but 15% is a good amount. In deluxe hotels tip porters R$2 per bag, chambermaids R$2 per day, and bellhops R$4–R$6 for room and valet service. Tips for doormen and concierges vary, depending on the services provided. A good tip would be at least R$22, with an average of R$11. For moderate and inexpensive hotels, tips tend to be minimal (salaries are so low that virtually anything is well received). If a taxi driver helps you with your luggage, a per-bag charge of about R$1 is levied in addition to the fare. In general, tip taxi drivers 10% of the fare.

If a service station attendant does anything beyond filling up the gas tank, leave him a small tip of some spare change. Tipping in bars and cafés follows the rules of restaurants, although at outdoor bars Brazilians rarely leave a gratuity if they have had only a soft drink or a beer. At airports and at train and bus stations, tip the last porter who puts your bags into the cab (R$1 a bag at airports, 50 centavos a bag at bus and train stations).

TRAVELER'S CHECKS

Do you need traveler's checks? It depends on where you're headed. If you're going to rural areas and small towns, go with cash; traveler's checks are best used in cities. Traveler's checks can be exchanged at hotels, banks, *casas de câmbio* (exchange services), travel agencies, and shops in malls or stores that cater to tourists. Many small tradesmen are at a total loss when faced with traveler's checks. Note, however, that the rate for traveler's checks is lower than that for cash, and hotels often change them at a rate that's lower than that available at banks or casas de câmbio.

Lost or stolen checks can usually be replaced within 24 hours. To ensure a speedy refund, buy your own traveler's checks—don't let someone else pay for them: irregularities like this can cause delays. The person who bought the checks should make the call to request a refund.

Traveler's checks should be in U.S. dollars. Some casas de câmbio accept only American Express traveler's checks, but you should be able to cash checks from other major banks in larger Brazilian cities.

PACKING

For sightseeing, casual clothing and good walking shoes are appropriate; most restaurants don't require formal attire. For beach vacations bring lightweight sportswear, a bathing suit, a beach cover-up, a sun hat, and waterproof sunscreen that is at least SPF 15. A sarong or a light cotton blanket makes a handy beach towel, picnic blanket, and cushion for hard seats, among other things.

Dress will depend on the season and on your destination. If you are going to coastal cities such as Rio, Florianópolis, and Salvador in the summer, dress more informally and feel free to wear flip-flops (thongs) all day. Southeastern cities like São Paulo, Curitiba, and Porto Alegre, which have lower temperatures, tend to be more formal and more conservative when it comes to dressing. This has also to do with culture, as sometimes Brazilians from the south are shocked by the way people in Rio dress. You will, however, encounter plenty of fashionistas in Rio, and it's a good idea to have some nicer clothing and shoes for going out at night.

Travel in rain-forest areas requires long-sleeve shirts, long pants, socks, waterproof hiking boots (sneakers are less desirable, but work in a pinch), a hat, a light waterproof jacket, a bathing suit, and plenty of strong insect repellent. (Amazonian bugs tend to be oblivious to non-DEET or non-picaridin repellents.) Other useful items include a screw-top water container that you can fill with bottled water, a money pouch, a travel flashlight and extra batteries, a Swiss Army knife with a bottle opener, a medical kit, binoculars, a pocket calculator, and lots of extra film.

Check *Fodor's How to Pack* (available at on-line retailers and bookstores everywhere) for more tips.

To avoid customs and security delays, carry medications in their original packaging. **Never pack prescription drugs, valuables, or undeveloped film in luggage to be checked.**

To avoid having your checked luggage chosen for hand inspection, don't cram bags full. The U.S. Transportation Security Administration suggests packing shoes on top and placing personal items you don't want touched in clear plastic bags.

PASSPORTS & VISAS

At this writing, passports and visas are required for citizens—even infants—of the U.S., Canada, and Australia for entry to Brazil. U.K. and New Zealand citizens need only a passport. Business travelers may need a special business visa (⇨ Business Travel).

PASSPORTS

The best time to apply for a passport or to renew is in fall and winter. Before any trip, check your passport's expiration date, and, if necessary, renew it as soon as possible.

U.S. passport applications for children under age 14 require consent from both parents or legal guardians; both parents must appear together to sign the application. If only one parent appears, he or she must submit a written statement from the other parent authorizing passport issuance for the child. A parent with sole authority must present evidence of it when applying; acceptable documentation includes the child's certified birth certificate listing only the applying parent, a court order specifically permitting this parent's travel with the child, or a death certificate for the nonapplying parent. Application forms and instructions are available on the Web site of the U.S. State Department's Bureau of Consular Affairs (⊕ travel.state.gov).

When in Brazil, carry your passport or a copy with you at all times. **Make two photocopies of the data page** (one for someone at home and another for you, carried separately from your passport). If you lose your passport, promptly call the nearest embassy or consulate and the local police.

If your passport is lost or stolen, first call the police—having the police report can make replacement easier—and then call your embassy (⇨ Embassies & Consulates, *above*). You'll get a temporary Emergency Travel Document that will need to be replaced once you return home. Fees vary according to how fast you need the passport; in some cases the fee covers your permanent replacement as well. The new document will not have your entry stamps; ask if your embassy takes care of this, or whether it's your responsibility to get the necessary immigration authorization.

🛂 Australia **Passports Australia** Australian Department of Foreign Affairs and Trade ☎ 131-232 ⊕ www.passports.gov.au.

🛂 Canada **Passport Office** ✉ to mail in applications: 70 Cremazie St., Gatineau, Québec J8Y 3P2 ☎ 819/994-3500 or 800/567-6868 ⊕ www.ppt.gc.ca.

🛂 New Zealand **New Zealand Passports Office** ☎ 0800/22-5050 or 04/474-8100 ⊕ www.passports.govt.nz.

🛂 U.K. **U.K. Passport Service** ☎ 0870/521-0410 ⊕ www.passport.gov.uk.

🛂 U.S. **National Passport Information Center** ☎ 877/487-2778, 888/874-7793 TDD/TTY ⊕ travel.state.gov.

VISAS

Visas are required for U.S., Canadian, and Australian citizens. **Go to the Web site for the Brazilian embassy or consulate nearest you for the most up to date information.**

At this writing, tourist visa fees are US$100 for Americans, C$72 for Canadians, and A$90 for Australians. Additional fees may be levied if you apply by mail. Obtaining a visa can be a slow process, and you must have every bit of paperwork in order when you visit the consulate, so read instructions carefully. (For example, in the U.S., the fee can only be paid by a U.S. Postal Service money order.)

To get the location of the Brazilian consulate to which you must apply, contact the Brazilian embassy. Note that some consulates don't allow you to apply for a visa by mail. If you don't live near a city with a consulate, consider hiring a concierge-type service to do your legwork. Many cities have these companies, which not only help with the paperwork, but also send someone to wait in line for you.

🛂 Australia **Brazilian Embassy** ☏ 19 Forster Crescent, Yarralumla, Canberra, ACT 2600 ☎ 612/6273-2372 🖷 612/6273-2375 ⊕ www.brazil.org.au.
🛂 Canada **Brazilian Embassy** ✉ 450 Wilbrod St., Ottawa, ON, K1N 6M8 ☎ 613/237-1090 🖷 613/237-6144 ⊕ www.brasembottawa.org.
🛂 New Zealand **Brazilian Embassy** ✉ Box 5432, 10 Brandon St., level 9, Wellington ☎ 04/473-3516 🖷 04/473-3517 ⊕ www.brazil.org.nz.
🛂 U.K. **Brazilian Embassy** ✉ 32 Green St., London, W1K 7AT ☎ 020/7499-0877 ⊕ www.brazil.org.uk.
🛂 U.S. **Brazilian Embassy** ✉ 3006 Massachusetts Ave. NW, Washington, DC 20008 ☎ 202/238-2700 ⊕ www.brasilemb.org.

RESTROOMS

The word for "bathroom" is *banheiro*, though the term *sanitários* (toilets) is also used. *Homens* means "men" and *mulheres* means "women." Around major tourist attractions and along the main beaches in big cities, you'll find public restrooms. In other areas you may have to rely on the kindness of local restaurant and shop owners. If a smile and polite request (*"Por favor, posso usar o banheiro?"*) doesn't work, become a customer—the purchase of a drink or a knickknack might just buy you a trip to the bathroom. Rest areas with relatively clean, well-equipped bathrooms are plentiful along major highways. Still, carry a pocket-size package of tissues in case there's no toilet paper. Tip bathroom attendants with a few spare centavos.

SAFETY

Although there has been a real effort to crack down on tourist-related crime, particularly in Rio, petty street thievery is still prevalent in urban areas, especially in places around tourist hotels, restaurants, and discos. By day the countryside is safe.

Note that Brazilian law requires everyone to have official identification with them at all times. Carry a copy of your passport's data page and of the Brazilian visa stamp (leave the actual passport in the hotel safe).

For many English-speaking tourists in Brazil, standing out like a sore thumb is unavoidable. But there are some precautions you should take, even in churches:

• Don't bring anything you can't stand to lose.

• Don't wear expensive jewelry or watches—stories of thieves yanking chains or earrings off travelers aren't uncommon.

• In cities, don't carry expensive cameras or lots of cash.

• Don't let a camera hang around your neck while you wander around. Keep it in a secure camera bag, preferably one with a chain or wire embedded in the strap.

• Carry backpacks on your front; thieves can slit your backpack and run away with its contents before you notice. Be attentive while walking around and when riding on buses.

• Don't wear a waist pack—thieves can cut the strap.

• Distribute your cash and any valuables (including credit cards and passport) among a deep front pocket, an inside jacket or vest pocket, and a hidden money belt. (If you use a money belt, carry some cash in your purse or wallet so you don't have to reach for the hidden pouch in public.)

• Keep your hand on your wallet if you are in a crowd or on a crowded bus or boat. Do not keep it in your back pocket.

• Don't let your purse just dangle from your shoulder; always hold on to it with your hand for added security. If you cross the strap over your body, you run the risk of being dragged with your bag if you're mugged.

• Keep car windows rolled up and car doors locked at all times in cities; elsewhere, roll up windows and lock doors whenever you leave your car.

• Park in designated parking lots if possible.

• Never leave valuables visible in a car, even in an attended parking lot: take them inside with you whenever possible, or lock them in the trunk.

• Padlock your luggage.

• Talk with locals or your hotel staff about crime in the area. They will be able to tell you if it's safe to walk around after dark and what to avoid.

• Never walk in a narrow space between a building and a car parked on the street close to it; a prime hiding spot for thieves.

• Do not walk in parks or on the beach at night.

• Never leave a drink unattended in a club or bar: scams involving date-rape drugs have been reported in the past few years, targeting both men and women.

• Never leave your belongings unattended anywhere, especially at the beach.

• If you're traveling by bus or boat, or just walking in crowded areas, carabiners come in handy for clipping your bag or other items to a luggage rack, your belt loops, or any other ingenious place to provide extra security.

- If your hotel room has a safe, use it, even if it's an extra charge. If your room doesn't have one, ask the manager to put your valuables in the hotel safe and ask him or her to sign a list of what you are storing there.

- If you are involved in an altercation with a mugger, immediately surrender your possessions and walk away quickly.

If the worst happens and you want to make a police report, be prepared to wait hours for an English-speaking officer and to see justice done. Many people prefer not to make a police report unless their passport is stolen, but this will depend on the area and on the police officer you talk to. If your credit card is stolen, call your credit-card company using the numbers we provide (⇨ Credit Cards *in* Money Matters, *above*).

For tips that pertain especially to women, *see* Women Travelers, *below*.

LOCAL SCAMS

Most tourist-related crimes occur in busy public areas: beaches, sidewalks or plazas, bus stations (and on buses, too). In these settings pickpockets, usually young children, work in groups. One or more will try to distract you while another grabs a wallet, bag, or camera. **Beware of children who suddenly thrust themselves in front of you** to ask for money or who offer to shine your shoes. Another member of the gang may strike from behind, grab whatever valuable is available, and disappear in the crowd. It's best not to protest while being mugged. Those on the take are sometimes armed or will tell you that their backup is, and although they're often quite young, they can be dangerous.

On the other hand, some of these children *are* only looking for handouts; 50 centavos is an average amount to give. Usually these kids will show up when you park your car on a street and will ask to "take care of your car" so that nothing happens to it;

that's why they expect to be paid. We strongly recommend that you give a few cents to these kids, especially in São Paulo, otherwise they might damage your car. Depending on the neighborhood, however, these so-called *guardadores de carros* (car guardians) charge much more, from R$1 to R$10. An alternative to this is to park in paid parking lots, which can be more expensive, but much safer.

SENIOR-CITIZEN TRAVEL

There's no reason why active, well-traveled senior citizens shouldn't visit Brazil, whether on an independent (but prebooked) vacation, an escorted tour, or an adventure vacation. The country is full of good hotels and competent ground operators to meet your flights and organize your sightseeing. Before you leave home, however, determine what medical services your health insurance will cover outside the United States; note that Medicare doesn't provide for payment of hospital and medical services outside the United States. If you need additional travel insurance, buy it.

To qualify for age-related discounts, mention your senior-citizen status up front when booking hotel reservations (not when checking out) and before you're seated in restaurants (not when paying the bill). Be sure to have identification on hand. When renting a car, ask about promotional car-rental discounts, which can be cheaper than senior-citizen rates.

COMPANIES SPECIALIZING IN TRAVEL FOR SENIOR CITIZENS

The American Association of Retired Persons offers its members discounts on travel packages, hotels, airfares, and car rentals in exchange for a $12.50 annual fee. Elderhostel is a not-for-profit organization that organizes study programs for people 55 and over.

🖪 Educational Programs **The American Association of Retired Persons** (AARP) ☎ 888/687-2277 in the U.S. ⊕ www.aarp.org. **Elderhostel** ☎ 877/426-8056, 978/323-4141 international callers, 877/426-2167 TTY 🖷 877/426-2166 ⊕ www.elderhostel.org. **Interhostel** ☎ 603/862-1147, 800/733-9753 in the U.S. ⊕ www.learn.unh.edu.

SHOPPING

Most Brazilian cities have a wide selection of small shops and malls. In general, choose the former if you want local items and lower prices. Malls are the place for famous national and international stores. In both cases you will find lots of interesting things to buy, including the famous Brazilian bikinis. São Paulo and Rio have the best shopping in Brazil.

Generally, small shops are open weekdays from 9 to 6 and on Saturday from 9 to 1 or 2. Centers and malls are often open from 10 to 10. Some centers and malls are open on Sunday.

For Information on Taxes *see* Money Matters, *above.*

SMART SOUVENIRS

If you like souvenirs that reflect the regions you visit, consider the following:

- Embroidered towels from the Northeast.

- Dehydrated flowers from the central region of Brazil. You can find them in Brasília's street fairs.

- *Cuias de chimarrão* (teapots): gauchos from Rio Grande do Sul drink their typical tea in these pots.

- Local food and beverages such as *cachaça,* Minas Gerais's candies made of cheese and fruit, and chocolates with Amazonian fruits from the north.

- Winter clothes in the state of Paraná: Curitiba is known for its high-quality and reasonably priced winterwear.

- In Recife you can buy fine pieces of workmanship made of wood, such as small carvings of animals, bowls, etc.

- *Berimbau,* an instrument used in *capoeira,* can be found in Rio and Salvador. The berimbau, and capoeira in general, is closely associated with Brazil's black slave culture.

BARGAINING

Bargaining is acceptable in Brazil, but don't go overboard. Usually when Brazilian bargain, they ask for a discount but are not insistent if the request is refused. It's common to ask for 5% or 10% off the sticker price. Bargaining is mostly done in street fairs, but it is sometimes acceptable in regular stores. Don't try it in malls or fancy outlets.

WATCH OUT

Be careful when buying souvenirs to bring home. Items you can purchase in Brazil, but which might not be permissible to import into other countries, especially the U.S., include *cachaça* (sugarcane liquor), plants and fresh fruits, souvenirs made with animal products, and some medicines. Bringing firearms, pirated goods, or animals across borders will undoubtedly cause you problems.

For more information, consult the Web sites below.

Australian Customs Service ⊕ www.customs.gov.au. **Canada Border Services Agency** ⊕ www.cbsa-asfc.gc.ca. **HM Revenue & Customs** ⊕ www.hmrc.gov.uk. **New Zealand Customs Service** ⊕ www.customs.gov.nz. **U.S. State Department** ⊕ http://travel.state.gov. **U.S. Customs & Border Protection** ⊕ www.customs.gov.

STUDENTS IN BRAZIL

Although airfares to and within Brazil are high, you can take buses to most destinations for mere dollars, and you can usually find safe, comfortable (if sparse) accommodations for a fraction of what it might cost back home. Most Brazilian cities also have vibrant student populations. In stalwart university towns like Ouro Preto in Minas Gerais State, you may find inexpensive lodging at fraternity houses (*repúblicas*). Students are supposed to be given a 50% discount at movie theaters and concert halls, although some places don't observe this practice. Foreign visitors may also qualify for discounts at some sporting events. Contact a travel agency for full details on discounts and how to qualify for them.

IDs & Services STA Travel ✉ 10 Downing St., New York, NY 10014 ☎ 212/627-3111, 800/777-0112 24-hr service center 🖷 212/627-3387 ⊕ www.sta.com. **Travel Cuts** ✉ 187 College St., Toronto, Ontario M5T 1P7, Canada ☎ 800/592-2887 in the U.S., 416/979-2406 or 866/246-9762 in Canada 🖷 416/979-8167 ⊕ www.travelcuts.com.

HOSTELS

There are about 100 hostels scattered across Brazil, all of them affiliated with Hostelling International (HI). Many Brazilian hostels' names are preceded by the letters *AJ* (Albergues de Juventude). The Federação Brasileira dos Albergues de Juventude (FBJA; Brazilian Federation of Youth Hostels) is based in Rio.

Membership in any HI national hostel association, open to travelers of all ages, allows you to stay in HI-affiliated hostels at member rates; one-year membership is about $28 for adults (C$35 for a two-year minimum membership in Canada, £15 in the U.K., A$52 in Australia, and NZ$40 in New Zealand); hostels charge about $10–$30 per night. Members have priority if the hostel is full; they're also eligible for discounts around the world, even on rail and bus travel in some countries.

For information about youth hostels in Brazil, contact the Associação Paulista de Albergues da Juventude. The association sells a book ($2.50) that lists hostels throughout the country.

🗐 Organizations **Associação Paulista de Albergues da Juventude** ✉ Rua 7 de Abril 386, 2nd floor, República, São Paulo 01320-040 ☎ 011/3258-0388. **Federação Brasileira dos Albergues de Juventude** ✉ Rua General Dionísio 63, Botafogo, Rio de Janeiro, RJ 22271-050 ☎ 021/2286-0303. **Hostelling International–USA** ✉ 8401 Colesville Rd., Suite 600, Silver Spring, MD 20910 ☎ 301/495-1240 🖷 301/495-6697 🌐 www.hiusa.org. **Hostelling International–Canada** ✉ 205 Catherine St., Suite 400, Ottawa, Ontario K2P 1C3 ☎ 613/237-7884 or 800/663-5777 🖷 613/237-7868 🌐 www.hihostels.ca. **YHA England and Wales** ✉ Trevelyan House, Dimple Rd., Matlock, Derbyshire DE4 3YH, U.K. ☎ 0870/870-8808, 0870/770-8868, 0162/959-2600 🖷 0870/770-6127 🌐 www.yha.org.uk. **YHA Australia** ✉ 422 Kent St., Sydney, NSW 2001 ☎ 02/9261-1111 🖷 02/9261-1969 🌐 www.yha.com.au. **YHA New Zealand** ✉ Level 1, Moorhouse City, 166 Moorhouse Ave., Box 436, Christchurch ☎ 03/379-9970 or 0800/278-299 🖷 03/365-4476 🌐 www.yha.org.nz.

TELEPHONES

The number of digits in Brazilian telephone numbers varies widely. The country code for Brazil is 55. When dialing a Brazilian number from abroad, drop the initial zero from the local area code.

Public phones are everywhere and are called *orelhões* (big ears) because of their shape. The phones take phone cards only.

CALLING WITHIN BRAZIL

Local calls can be made most easily from pay phones, which take phone cards only. A bar or restaurant may allow you to use its private phone for a local call if you're a customer.

If you want to call from your hotel, remember long-distance calls within Brazil are expensive, and hotels add a surcharge.

With the privatization of the Brazilian telecommunications network, there's a wide choice of long-distance companies. Hence, to make direct-dial long-distance calls, you must find out which companies serve the area from which you're calling and then get their access codes—the staff at your hotel can help. (Some hotels have already made the choice for you, so you may not need an access code when calling from the hotel itself.) For long-distance calls within Brazil, dial 0 + the access code + the area code and number. To call Rio, for example, dial 0, then 21 (for Embratel, a major long-distance and international provider), then 21 (Rio's area code), and then the number.

Some commonly used area codes in Brazil:

Brasília	61
Florianópolis	48
Fortaleza	85
Foz do Iguaçú	45
Manaus	92
Recife	81
Rio de Janeiro (city)	21
Salvador	71
São Paulo (city)	11

For local directory assistance, dial 102. For directory assistance in another Brazilian city, dial 0 + the access code + the area code of that city + 121. English-speaking operators are not available, but you can ask to talk to the supervising team, who may speak English. Another suggestion is to ask a Portuguese-speaking friend to make this call for you or even visit ⊕ www.brasiltelecom.com.br and click "102 Online."

CALLING INTERNATIONALLY FROM BRAZIL

International calls from Brazil are extremely expensive. Hotels also add a surcharge, increasing this cost even more. Calls can be made from public phone booths with a prepaid phone card. You can also go to phone offices. Ask your hotel staff about the closest office, as they are less common in Brazil than pay phones.

For international calls, dial 00 + 23 (for Intelig, a long-distance company) or 21 (for Embratel, another long-distance company) + the country code + the area code and number. For operator-assisted international calls, dial 00–0111. For international information, dial 00–0333. To make a collect long-distance call (which will cost 40% more than a normal call), dial 9 + the area code and the number.

The country code is 1 for the United States and Canada, 61 for Australia, 64 for New Zealand, and 44 for the United Kingdom.

AT&T, MCI, and Sprint operators are also accessible from Brazil; **get the local access codes before you leave home** for your destinations. You may find the local access number for AT&T, MCI, or Sprint blocked in many hotel rooms. First ask the hotel operator to connect you. If the hotel operator balks, ask for an international operator, or dial the international operator yourself. One way to improve your odds of getting connected to your long-distance carrier is to travel with more than one company's calling card (a hotel may block Sprint, for example, but not MCI). If all else fails, call from a pay phone. If you are traveling for a longer period of time, consider renting a cell-phone from a local company.

⚡ Access Codes AT&T Direct ☎ 0800/890−0288 or 0800/888−8288. **MCI WorldPhone** ☎ 000−8012. **Sprint International Access** ☎ 0800/888−7800, 0800/890−8000, or 0800/888−8000.

CELL PHONES

Average prices for cell-phone rental are $4 per day, $22 per week, $51 per month. Phone rental companies include PressCell and ConnectCom. You might also be able to rent a cell phone through your hotel. Depending on the length of your stay and the rental fees, it might make more sense to buy a cell phone here than to rent one. A simple phone costs around $45, and cell-phone stores are abundant in every city.

If you prefer bringing your own phone, make sure you check the international fees while in Brazil. When you get back home, you will have to pay for them in dollars, but if you buy/rent a phone here, the fees are all in reais. Rates for cell phone calls are usually about 64¢ per minute.

⚡ Cell Rental Companies. ConnectCom ☎ 21/2275−8461 or 21/2541−1122 in Brazil ⊕ www.connectcomrj.com.br. **PressCell** ☎ 21/3322−2692 in Brazil ⊕ www.presscell.com.

PHONE CARDS

All pay phones in Brazil take phone cards only. Buy a phone card, a *cartão telefônico* at a *posto telefônico* (phone office), newsstand, or post office. Cards come with a varying number of units (each unit is usually worth a couple of minutes), which will determine the price. Buy a couple of cards if you don't think you'll have the chance again soon. These phone cards can be used for international, local, and long-distance calls within Brazil. Be aware that calling internationally using these cards is extremely expensive and your units will expire pretty quickly. If you do want to do this, buy many cards with the maximum units (50). A 20-minute card costs about $1.25; a 50-minute card costs around $2.50.

TIME

Brazil covers four time zones. Most of the country, including Rio, São Paulo, Porto Alegre, Salvador, Brasília, Belo Horizonte, Recife, and Belém, is three hours behind GMT (Greenwich mean time), which is the same time zone as New York. Manaus and the Pantanal are an hour behind those cities, and the far western Amazon is an hour behind Manaus. Fernando de Noronha, an archipelago off Brazil's northeast coast, is two hours behind GMT.

TOURS & PACKAGES

Because everything is prearranged on a prepackaged tour or independent vacation, you spend less time planning—and often get it all at a good price. Don't confuse packages and guided tours. When you buy a package, you travel on your own, just as though you had planned the trip yourself.

For information on specific packages and tours, *see* the Adventure & Learning Vacations chapter *at* the end of this book.

Tour-Operator Recommendations American Society of Travel Agents (⇨ Travel Agencies). **CrossSphere—The Global Association for Packaged Travel** ⊠ 546 E. Main St., Lexington, KY 40508 ☎ 859/226–4444 or 800/682–8886 🖷 859/226–4414 ⊕ www.CrossSphere.com. **United States Tour Operators Association** (USTOA) ⊠ 275 Madison Ave., Suite 2014, New York, NY 10016 ☎ 212/599–6599 🖷 212/599–6744 ⊕ www.ustoa.com.

BUYER BEWARE

Each year consumers are stranded or lose their money when tour operators—even large ones with excellent reputations—go out of business. So check out the operator. Ask several travel agents about its reputation, and try to **book with a company that has a consumer-protection program.** (Look for information in the company's brochure.) In the United States, members of the United States Tour Operators Association are required to set aside funds (up to $1 million) to help eligible customers cover payments and travel arrangements in the event that the company defaults. It's also a good idea to choose a company that participates in the American Society of Travel Agents' Tour Operator Program; ASTA will act as mediator in any disputes between you and your tour operator.

Remember that the more your package or tour includes, the better you can predict the ultimate cost of your vacation. Make sure you know exactly what is covered, and beware of hidden costs. Are taxes, tips, and transfers included? Entertainment and excursions? These can add up.

TRAIN TRAVEL

Brazil has an outdated and insufficient rail network, the smallest of any of the world's large nations. Although there are com-

muter rails to destinations around major cities, don't plan on taking passenger trains between major cities. There's one exception: the Serra Verde Express from Curitiba to Paranaguá—in the southern state of Paraná—is a fabulous ride with spectacular vistas of ravines, mountains, and waterfalls from bridges and viaducts (⇨ Train Travel *in* The South Essentials, chapter 5).

TRAVEL AGENCIES

A good travel agent puts your needs first. Look for an agency that has been in business at least five years, emphasizes customer service, and has someone on staff who specializes in your destination. In addition, **make sure the agency belongs to a professional trade organization.** The American Society of Travel Agents (ASTA) has more than 10,000 members in some 140 countries, enforces a strict code of ethics, and will step in to mediate agent-client disputes involving ASTA members. ASTA also maintains a directory of agents on its Web site; ASTA's ⊕ TravelSense. org, a trip planning and travel advice site, can also help to locate a travel agent who caters to your needs. (If a travel agency is also acting as your tour operator, *see* Buyer Beware *in* Tours & Packages.)

Make sure your travel agent knows the accommodations and other services of the place being recommended. Ask about the hotel's location, room size, beds, and whether it has a pool, room service, or programs for children, if you care about these. Has your agent been there in person or sent others whom you can contact?

Local Agent Referrals American Society of Travel Agents (ASTA) ⊠ 1101 King St., Suite 200, Alexandria, VA 22314 ☎ 703/739–2782 or 800/965–2782 24-hr hotline 🖷 703/684–8319 ⊕ www.astanet.com and www.travelsense.org. **Association of British Travel Agents** ⊠ 68–71 Newman St., London W1T 3AH ☎ 020/7637–2444 🖷 020/7637–0713 ⊕ www.abta.com. **Association of Canadian Travel Agencies** ⊠ 130 Albert St., Suite 1705, Ottawa, Ontario K1P 5G4 ☎ 613/237–3657 🖷 613/237–7052 ⊕ www.acta.ca. **Australian Federation of Travel Agents** ⊠ Level 3, 309 Pitt St., Sydney, NSW 2000 ☎ 02/9264–3299 or 1300/363–416 🖷 02/9264–1085 ⊕ www.afta.com.au. **Travel Agents' As-**

sociation of New Zealand ✉ Level 5, Tourism and Travel House, 79 Boulcott St., Box 1888, Wellington 6001 ☎ 04/499-0104 🖷 04/499-0786 🌐 www.taanz.org.nz.

TRIP INSURANCE

The most useful travel-insurance plan is a comprehensive policy that includes coverage for trip cancellation and interruption, default, trip delay, and medical expenses (with a waiver for preexisting conditions).

Without insurance you'll lose all or most of your money if you cancel your trip, regardless of the reason. Default insurance covers you if your tour operator, airline, or cruise line goes out of business—the chances of which have been increasing. Trip-delay covers expenses that arise because of bad weather or mechanical delays. Study the fine print when comparing policies.

When you're traveling internationally, a key component of travel insurance is coverage for medical bills incurred if you get sick on the road. Such expenses aren't generally covered by Medicare or private policies. U.K. residents can buy a travel-insurance policy valid for most vacations taken during the year in which it's purchased (but check preexisting-condition coverage). British and Australian citizens need extra medical coverage when traveling overseas.

Always **buy travel policies directly from the insurance company**; if you buy them from a cruise line, airline, or tour operator that goes out of business you probably won't be covered for the agency or operator's default, a major risk. Before making any purchase, review your existing health and home-owner's policies to find what they cover away from home.

🔳 Travel Insurers In the U.S.: **Access America** ✉ 2805 N. Parham Rd., Richmond, VA 23294 ☎ 800/284-8300 🖷 804/673-1469 or 800/346-9265 🌐 www.accessamerica.com. **Travel Guard International** ✉ 1145 Clark St., Stevens Point, WI 54481 ☎ 800/826-1300 or 715/345-1041 🖷 800/955-8785 or 715/345-1990 🌐 www.travelguard.com. 🔳 In the U.K.: **Association of British Insurers** ✉ 51 Gresham St., London EC2V 7HQ ☎ 020/7600-3333 🖷 020/7696-8999 🌐 www.abi.org.uk.

In Canada: **RBC Insurance** ✉ 6880 Financial Dr., Mississauga, Ontario L5N 7Y5 ☎ 800/387-4357 or 905/816-2559 🖷 888/298-6458 🌐 www.rbcinsurance.com. In Australia: **Insurance Council of Australia** ✉ Level 3, 56 Pitt St., Sydney, NSW 2000 ☎ 02/9253-5100 🖷 02/9253-5111 🌐 www.ica.com.au. In New Zealand: **Insurance Council of New Zealand** ✉ Level 7, 111-115 Customhouse Quay, Box 474, Wellington ☎ 04/472-5230 🖷 04/473-3011 🌐 www.icnz.org.nz.

VISITOR INFORMATION

EMBRATUR, Brazil's national tourism organization, doesn't have offices overseas, though its Web site (⇨ *below*) is helpful. For information in your home country, contact the Brazilian embassy or the closest consulate (⇨ Visas, *in* Passports & Visas, *above*)—some of which have Web sites and staff dedicated to promoting tourism. Cities and towns throughout Brazil have local tourist boards, and some state capitals also have state tourism offices.

WEB SITES WE LIKE

We wouldn't be doing our job if we didn't recommend Fodors.com (🌐 www.fodors.com), a complete travel-planning site. You can research prices and book plane tickets, hotel rooms, rental cars, vacation packages, and more. In addition, you can post your pressing questions in the Travel Talk section. Other planning tools include a currency converter and weather reports, and there are loads of links to travel resources.

For good information you may have to search by region, state, or city—and hope that at least one of them has a comprehensive official site of its own. **Don't rule out foreign-language sites**; some have links to sites that present information in more than one language, including English. On Portuguese-language sites, watch for the name of the region, state, or city in which you have an interest. The search terms in Portuguese for "look," "find," and "get" are *olhar* or *achar, buscar,* and *pegar*; "next" and "last" (as in "next/last 10") are *próximo* or *seguinte* and *último* or *anterior.* Keep an eye out for such words as: *turismo* (tourism), *turístico* (tourist-related), *hotéis* (hotels), *restaurantes* (restaurants), *governo* (government), *estado* (state), and *cidade* (city).

The following sites should get you started: ⊕ www.embratur.gov.br (the official Brazilian tourist board site, with information in English provided by the Brazilian embassy in London), ⊕ www.varig.com (Varig Airlines' site, with English information), ⊕ www.brazilny.org (the official consular Web site in New York, with details about other consulates and the embassy as well as travel information and links to other sites), ⊕ www.brazilinfocenter.org (a Washington, D.C.–based organization that promotes political and business issues rather than tourism, but whose Web site has an incredible number of helpful links), ⊕ www.vivabrazil.com (a site with background and travel info on Brazil's different regions as well as links that will help you arrange your trip). The online magazine *Brazzil,* ⊕ www.brazzil.com, has interesting articles on culture and politics in English.

🚹 Government Advisories **U.S. Department of State** ✉ Bureau of Consular Affairs, Overseas Citizens Services Office, 2201 C St. NW Washington, DC 20520 ☎ 202/647–5225, 888/407–4747 or 317/472–2328 for interactive hotline ⊕ www.travel.state.gov. **Consular Affairs Bureau of Canada** ☎ 800/267–6788 or 613/944–6788 ⊕ www.voyage.gc.ca. **U.K. Foreign and Commonwealth Office** ✉ Travel Advice Unit, Consular Directorate, Old Admiralty Building, London SW1A 2PA ☎ 0870/606–0290 or 020/7008–1500 ⊕ www.fco.gov.uk/travel. **Australian Department of Foreign Affairs and Trade** ☎ 300/139–281 travel advisories, 02/6261–1299 Consular Travel Advice ⊕ www.smartraveller.gov.au or www.dfat.gov.au. **New Zealand Ministry of Foreign Affairs and Trade** ☎ 04/439–8000 ⊕ www.mft.govt.nz.

WOMEN TRAVELERS

Although women are gradually assuming a more important role in the nation's job force, machismo is still a strong part of Brazilian culture. You should have no fear of traveling unaccompanied, but you should still take a few precautions. Ask your hotel staff to recommend a reliable cab company, and **call for a taxi instead of hailing one on the street,** especially at night. **Dress to avoid unwanted attention.** For example, always wear a cover-up when heading to or from the beach. When visiting churches, temples, or other sacred places, locals will appreciate it if you dress conservatively.

Depending on the place and the time of the day, it might be dangerous for a woman to be by herself (in a bar late at night, for example). Brazilian men are said to have an insurmountable urge to flirt, and that has been our personal experience. This can be either fun or inconvenient, and it is up to you to decide whether you give them attention or not.

Shaking hands with men, talking to them by yourself, and even kissing cheeks lightly as a greeting are not considered taboos. However, when you greet men for the first time, be on your guard, as some Brazilian men take advantage of the "kissing greeting" to be closer to you (this doesn't mean, however, that they will attack you). Avoid eye contact with unsavory individuals. If such a person approaches you, discourage him by politely but firmly saying, "*Por favor, me dê licença*" (pohr fah-**vohr,** meh day lee-**sehn**-see-ah), which means "Excuse me, please," and then walk away with resolve.

Hermail and Journeywoman are two Web sites specifically for women traveling alone or with other women. Ela Brasil is a U.S.-based sustainable-travel tour company owned and operated by Brazilian women.

🚹 Resources **Ela Brasil Tours** ☎ 203/840–9010 in the U.S. ⊕ www.elabrasil.com. **Hermail.net** ⊕ www.hermail.net. **Journeywoman** ⊕ www.journeywoman.com.

Rio de Janeiro

WORD OF MOUTH

"For those of you considering Rio...don't hold back...GO NOW before it becomes too popular. We travel extensively and it's not often that we go back to the same place twice but we are definitely going back next year from Xmas to New Year's. It's a real GEM!!"

—George

"What a fantastic city—I can't rave enough. . . . One of the highlights was the Vasco da Gama game against São Paulo–based upstarts Porto Preto as part of the Brazilian Futebol Championships."

—ptorr

Updated by
Denise Oliveira

WELCOME TO THE CIDADE MARAVILHOSA, or the Marvelous City, as Rio is known in Brazil. Synonymous with the girl from Ipanema, the dramatic view from the Pão de Açúcar (Sugar Loaf), and famous Carnival celebrations, Rio is also a city of stunning architecture, good museums, and marvelous food. Rio is also home to 23 beaches, an almost continuous 73-km (45-mi) ribbon of sand.

As you leave the airport and head towards Ipanema or Copacabana, you'll drive for about half an hour on a highway from where you'll begin to get a sense of the city's dramatic contrast between beautiful landscape and devastating poverty. In this teeming metropolis, the very rich and the very poor live in uneasy proximity. But by the time you reach breezy, sunny Avenida Atlântica—flanked on one side by white beach and azure sea and on the other by condominiums and hotels—your heart will leap with expectation as you begin to recognize the postcard-famous sights. Now you're truly in Rio, where the 10 million *cariocas* (residents of the city of Rio) dwell and live life to its fullest.

Enthusiasm is boundless and contagious in Rio. Prepare to have your senses engaged and your inhibitions untied. Rio seduces with a host of images: the joyous bustle of vendors at Sunday's Feira Hippie (Hippie Fair); the tipsy babble at sidewalk cafés as patrons sip their last glass of icy beer under the stars; the blanket of lights beneath Pão de Açúcar; the bikers, joggers, strollers, and power walkers who parade along the beach each morning. Borrow the carioca spirit for your stay; you may find yourself reluctant to give it back.

History

Before a Portuguese ship arrived in Rio on January 1, 1502, the region was populated by various indigenous groups, such as the Tupinambás and the Tamoios. The crew of that Portuguese ship thought they had arrived at the mouth of a river, so they named the city Rio de Janeiro (January River). It later became clear that it was not a river at all, but a bay, now called the Baía de Guanabara (Guanabara Bay), but the name stuck.

The Portuguese began to establish a presence in Rio de Janeiro between 1502 and the 1550s. But the potential wealth of the country (particularly from pau-brasil, a very valuable type of wood) attracted other colonizers as well, and in 1555 the French began to occupy Rio. Struggles between the Portuguese and the French ensued, and in 1567 the Portuguese expelled the French. By then, the Portuguese had renamed the city São Sebastião do Rio de Janeiro. At the end of the century, in 1599, the Dutch also tried to occupy Rio, but they were blocked by the Portuguese.

For almost three hundred years the Portuguese ruled Brazil. At first the colonial capital was Salvador, in the state of Bahia. In 1736 the capital was transferred to Rio. The Portuguese met with resistance from various indigenous groups in the Rio region. Violent fighting followed, and many of the indigenous tribes were completely destroyed.

In 1808, the Portuguese royal family fled Napoleon's army and moved from Portugal to Rio. While the government headquarters remained in

1

Numbers in the text correspond to numbers in the margin and on the Rio Centro & Environs map and the Rio de Janeiro City map.

If you have
3 days

Spend Day 1 at **Copacabana Beach** and/or **Ipanema Beach** for an introduction to Rio's "beautiful people" and beautiful coastline. For lunch, get an introduction to Brazilian "barbecue" at Porção in Flamengo. Catch the phenomenal sunsets from the **Pão de Açúcar** ㉕ toward the end of the day. Do the **Theatro Municipal** ❽ in the morning on Day 2, and then wander around Centro, stopping at the Confeitaria Colombo for lunch and peeking into some of the churches, like the **Catedral de São Sebastião do Rio de Janeiro** ⑪. On weekdays, swing by the little **Museu Carmen Miranda** ㉔ to see the Brazilian bombshell's costumes, jewelry, and wild headdresses.In the evening join the fun at a samba show.

On your third day, trek out to **Corcovado** ㉑ for a sweeping view of the city. It's best to visit early in the morning before the haze and the tour buses have set in.Then hit the shops. If it's raining or you prefer indoor shops, go to Shopping Rio Sul mall. If you prefer the fresh air, stroll along Rua Visconde de Pirajá and its side streets in Ipanema. In the afternoon, go back to the beach, perhaps trying the more far-flung sands of breezy **Barra da Tijuca,** west of Leblon. If you're in the city on Sunday, wander through Ipanema's **Feira Hippie.** In the evening try the national dish, *feijoada* (a hearty stew of black beans and pork) at Ipanema's Casa da Feijoada.

If you have
5 days

On your first day take the cable car to **Pão de Açúcar** ▶ ㉕, and explore Centro. Catch some live music in the evening in one of the city's many bars and clubs. The next day jump on the cogwheel train to **Corcovado** ㉑ and set aside time for the captivating **Theatro Municipal** ❽ before indulging in a Brazilian barbecue at Marius or Porção. Bike or walk off lunch at **Lagoa Rodrigo de Freitas,** then slide into a shopping center. On your third day stroll from Copacabana to Ipanema, stopping en route to order a tropical pizza at Bar Garota de Ipanema.

Take an organized favela (shantytown) tour in the afternoon (never wander into a favela alone) and in the evening dine on feijoada. On the fourth day head for **Petrópolis** (⇨ chapter 2) to see the imperial palace, or make the 40-minute drive to **Sítio Roberto Burle Marx** to see the country house and gardens of Brazil's most famous landscaper. If you prefer to stay in town, wander through Centro and head for the **Palácio do Catete** ⑲. Try to also work in the **Museu de Arte Moderna** ⑬ . Weekdays wind up the day at the kitschy **Museu Carmen Miranda** ㉔. Have your concierge check the evening schedule at the Banco do Brasil Cultural Center. On your last day take the Santa Teresa trolley to the **Museu Chácara do Céu** ⑮ , then do some shopping, or head back to the Zona Sul to relax at the beach.

If you have
7–10
days

If you've got at least a week to spend in Rio, we recommend you *leave* the city for a few days. Follow the three- or five-day itineraries above, and then slide out of town to Petrópolis, Angra dos Reis, Parati, or Búzios (⇨ chapter 2). If you've got extra time in Rio, roam through the **Jardim Botânico** ㉖, bike around **Lagoa Rodrigo de Freitas,** and consider an escape to **Prainha** and **Grumari** beaches and the **Sítio Roberto Burle Marx.**

Rio de Janeiro, the royal family built elaborate vacation mansions in the nearby town of Petrópolis.

In 1889, when Brazil gained its independence, Rio was declared the capital of the Republic of Brazil. It held this title until 1960, when the federal government was moved from Rio to Brasília.

Even though Rio is no longer the political capital of Brazil, it retains its place as the cultural heartbeat of the country. Throughout the twentieth century Rio attracted tourists from all over the world and it continues to be Brazil's number-one tourist destination.

Navigating

Cariocas divide their city into three sections: Zona Norte (North Zone), Zona Sul (South Zone), and Centro, the downtown area that separates the other two. Aside from museums, churches, and historic sights, most tourist activity is in beach- and hotel-laden Zona Sul, primarily in Copacabana and Ipanema. Centro is filled with the remnants of the old Portuguese colony, including some impressive neoclassical architecture. The Zona Norte is primarily a residential area, but the international airport and the soccer stadium are here.

The metro extends from the Zona Norte to Copacabana, with a shuttle to Ipanema and Leblon. Within Ipanema and Copacabana, it's quite easy to get around on foot, but some attractions (e.g., Copacabana Palace to the Hippie Fair) are a bit far apart, so a taxi might be the way to go. After dark, you should always take a taxi, and it's very easy to hail taxis on every main street. Public buses are cheap and cover every inch of the city, but are difficult to figure out if you don't speak Portuguese. Never take the bus at night.

For more information about public transport, *see* Rio de Janeiro Essentials, *at* the end of this chapter.

The Neighborhoods

Centro
Architectural gems left behind from the days of Portuguese colonialism share space with modern high-rises in Rio's financial district. Ornately decorated churches, museums, and palaces are just some of the highlights. The neighborhood is a virtual ghost town from Saturday afternoon until Monday morning, when the work week begins.

Copacabana
The longest stretch of beach in Rio is the main attraction in the city's most touristed neighborhood. It's the perfect place to stroll, people-watch, soak up the sun, or gaze in awe at the giant old apartment buildings and hotels (including the Copacabana Palace) that line the Avenida Atlântica.

Ipanema
Famous for being the place where the "Girl from Ipanema" was spied and then written into lyrical history by Tom Jobim and Vinicius de Moraes

Beaches Rio's beaches define its culture: vibrant, joyful, beautiful. From infants to senior citizens, and from women in barely-there string bikinis to Speedo-wearing men—and the tourists goggling at it all (yes, that man *is* wearing a thong!)—the beach culture seduces everyone who visits. Because the beaches are intertwined with the city's urban core, the cleanliness of the ocean can vary from day to day; your hotel concierge can help you decide which beach to hit for swimming.

1

Carnival Rio's Carnival is right up there with Mardi Gras in New Orleans, and carnivals in Venice and Trinidad and Tobago. Carnival celebrations unfold all over Brazil, and there's a lively debate as to whether Rio or Salvador has the best, but no other city can match Rio in terms of glitter, glitz, or downright decadence.

Music Rio is the music capital of Brazil. It witnessed the birth of bossa nova and *choro*, and it is here that samba became established as Brazil's national style. A seemingly endless stream of first-class concerts of all styles of Brazilian music takes place here: classical music at the Theatro Municipal, samba at Lapa's nightclubs, and bossa nova at Ipanema's bars, to name just a few.

Eating Out Be prepared to indulge in some of the finest dining you've experienced. The cuisine in Rio is a true reflection of the ethnic diversity within Brazil. There are wonderful Portuguese and Brazilian options, but Rio is also home to fantastic Italian and Japanese restaurants.

Enjoying the Landscape The unique juxtaposition of sea and mountains makes Rio the beautiful city that it is. You can experience the view from the ocean by taking a boat cruise, or a more adventurous kayaking trip, or you can climb one of the many mountains of the Floresta da Tijuca by trolley or by foot to take in the view.

---

back in the '60s, this posh neighborhood today is a collection of tree-lined streets harboring upscale condos, fabulous restaurants, and trendy shopping. The beach is beautiful and attracts not only tourists but cariocas from all over the city.

Lapa
Adjacent to Centro, this historic neighborhood has some of the best music halls and dance clubs in the city. If you're looking to explore Rio's nightlife, you'll become intimately familiar with Lapa.

Leblon
Extending west from Ipanema, this affluent, intimate community borrows some of its neighbor's trendy charms, but is slightly funkier. The narrow streets are flush with small restaurants and bars. Sadly, the beach here is not great for swimming since the water is often polluted.

Santa Teresa

One of the first residential neighborhoods in Rio, Santa Teresa is worth a visit to explore its narrow, cobblestone streets lined with beautiful, Portuguese-style homes. It also has some traditional Brazilian restaurants, excellent local craft stores, and art galleries.

São Conrado & Barra da Tijuca

West of Leblon, these low-key Zona Sul neighborhoods have long stretches of unspoiled beach. Residential condos and malls crowd the streets, which are not suitable for walking around. It's best to take a cab straight to the beaches, which are quieter than Copacabana and Ipanema and are especially recommended for kids. Hang gliders land just behind São Conrado Beach.

Safety

City Safety

Despite Rio's reputation, crime is no more likely than in any large city, and many cariocas feel that the city's safety is unfairly portrayed by the media. Most crimes involving visitors occur in crowded public areas: beaches, busy sidewalks, intersections, and city buses. Pickpockets, usually children, work in groups. One will distract you while another grabs a wallet, bag, or camera. Be particularly wary of children who thrust themselves in front of you and ask for money or offer to shine your shoes. Another member of the gang may strike from behind, grabbing your valuables and disappearing into the crowd. Another tactic is for criminals to approach your car at intersections. Always keep doors locked and windows partially closed. Leave valuables in your hotel safe, don't wear expensive jewelry or watches, and keep cameras out of sight.

Beach Safety

Don't shun the beaches because of reports of crime, but *do* take precautions. Leave jewelry, passports, and large sums of cash at your hotel; don't wander alone and at night; and be alert when groups of friendly youths engage you in conversation (sometimes they're trying to distract you while one of their cohorts snatches your belongings). A big danger is actually the sun. From 10 AM to 3 PM the rays are merciless, making heavy-duty sunscreen, hats, cover-ups, and plenty of liquids essential; you can also rent a beach umbrella from vendors on the beach or your hotel. Hawkers stroll the beaches with beverages, food, and trinkets. Unlike in other beach destinations you may have experienced, these guys are no-nonsense salespeople, and quickly move on if you shake your head no. Most beach-goers take advantage of their services. Beach vendors aren't supposed to charge more than R$5.50 for a bottle of beer or other alcoholic beverage, R$3 for a coconut water. Lifeguard stations, including bathrooms and showers, are found every kilometer.

When to Go

Rio is a year-round destination, but Carnival (usually in February) is the best time to soak up the city's energy. Arrive a few days before the celebrations begin, or stay a few days after they end in order to enjoy the museums and other sights that close for the four days of revelry. Last-minute Louies need not apply: you'll have to book your hotel and flight at least one year in advance for Carnival.

The hottest months in Rio tend to be January through March, when temperatures often soar above 100 degrees. The city generally sees the most rain during December, when it might rain for days at a time. To tour the city at a quieter time with gentler temperatures and at lower prices, come in the off-season, from May to October (Brazil's winter). The temperature in the winter tends to be in the upper 70s during the day and rarely falls below 50 degrees at night.

EXPLORING

Centro & Environs

Rio's settlement dates back to 1555, and much of the city's rich history is captured in traditional churches, government buildings, and villas, which are tucked in and around Centro. You can use the metro to get downtown, but wear comfortable shoes and be ready to walk multiple blocks as you explore this city's historic center. If you're not up for a long walk, consider taking an organized bus tour.

What locals generally refer to as Centro is a sprawling collection of several districts that contain the city's oldest neighborhoods, churches, and most enchanting cafés. Rio's beaches, broad boulevards, and modern architecture may be impressive; but its colonial structures, old narrow streets, and alleyways in leafy inland neighborhoods are no less so. The metro stations that serve Centro are Cinelândia, Carioca, Uruguaiana, Presidente Vargas, Central, and Praça Onze.

a good walk

Start at the **Mosteiro de São Bento** ❶ ► for your first taste of Brazilian baroque architecture. From here move south into the heart of Centro. At the beginning of Avenida Presidente Vargas you'll find the solid **Igreja de Nossa Senhora da Candelária** ❷. From this church, walk south along Avenida 1° de Março, crossing it and heading west to a network of narrow lanes and alleys highlighted by the **Beco do Comércio** ❸, a pedestrian street. After wandering this area, return to Avenida 1° de Março and walk southeast to the Praça 15 de Novembro, a square that's dominated by the **Paço Imperial** ❹. A few blocks away is the large **Museu Histórico Nacional** ❺.

From the Museu Histórico Nacional, follow Rua Santa Luzia southeast to Avenida Rio Branco, Centro's main thoroughfare. North one block is the Victorian **Biblioteca Nacional** ❻, and one block up from it is the French neoclassical **Museu Nacional de Belas Artes** ❼. In the middle of the next block up and across Rio Branco are the **Theatro Municipal** ❽ and its elegant café. Continue north on Rio Branco and turn left on Avenida Almirante Barroso. A short walk northwest brings you to the Largo da Carioca, a large square near the Carioca metro stop. Atop a low hill overlooking it are the **Igreja de São Francisco da Penitência** ❾ and the **Con-**

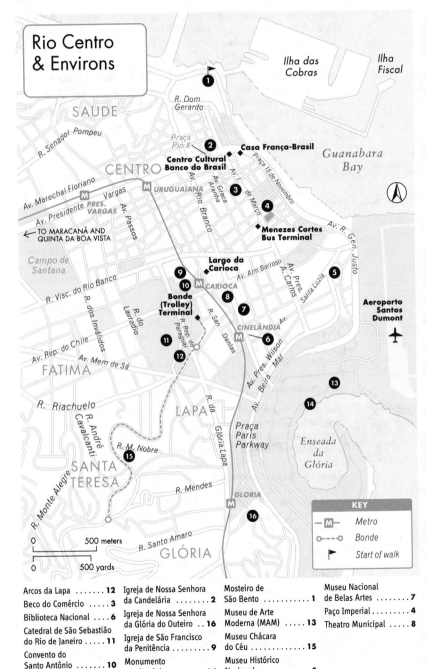

Rio Centro & Environs

SAUDE

R. Senador Pompeu

R. Dom Gerardo

Praça Pio X

Casa França-Brasil

Centro Cultural Banco do Brasil

CENTRO

Av. Marechal Floriano

Av. Presidente PRES. Vargas
Av. Presidente VARGAS

Av. Graça Aranha

Av. 1 de Março

Praça 15 de Novembro

Guanabara Bay

Ilha das Cobras

Ilha Fiscal

← TO MARACANÃ AND QUINTA DA BOA VISTA

Campo de Santana

R. Visc. do Rio Branco

R. dos Inválidos

R. do Lavradio

Av. Rio Branco

Av. Passos

Menezes Cortes Bus Terminal

Largo da Carioca

Av. Alm Barroso

CARIOCA

Bonde (Trolley) Terminal

R. Rep. do Paraguai

R. São Dantas

Av. A. Carlos

Av. Pres. Santa Luzia

CINELÂNDIA

Av. Pres. Wilson

Av. Beira - Mar

Av. R. Gen. Justo

Aeroporto Santos Dumont

Av. Rep. do Chile

Av. Mem de Sá

FATIMA

R. Riachuelo

R. André Cavalcanti

R. M. Nobre

LAPA

R. da Glória Lapa

Praça Paris Parkway

Enseada da Glória

SANTA TERESA

R. Monte Alegre

R. Mendes

GLORIA

R. Santo Amaro

GLÓRIA

0   500 meters

0   500 yards

vento do Santo Antônio ⑩. The architecturally striking (or absurd, depending on your viewpoint) **Catedral de São Sebastião do Rio de Janeiro** ⑪ is just south, off Avenida República do Chile.

TIMING &
PRECAUTIONS This walk takes two to three hours. It is safest to explore Centro on weekdays, when the streets are populated by office workers—it can feel like a ghost town on weekends. Pickpockets are ubiquitous here, so carry only what you need, don't wear flashy jewelry, and keep an extra stash of cash or a credit card in a hidden pocket or money belt.

Numbers in the text correspond to numbers in the margin and on the Rio Centro and Environs map.

What to See

⑫ **Arcos da Lapa.** Formerly the Aqueduto da Carioca (Carioca Aqueduct), this structure with 42 massive stone arches was built between 1744 and 1750 to carry water from the Carioca River in the hillside neighborhood of Santa Teresa to Centro. In 1896 the city transportation company converted the then-abandoned aqueduct to a viaduct, laying trolley tracks along it. Since then Rio's distinctive trolley cars (called "*bondes*" because they were financed by foreign bonds) have carried people between Santa Teresa and Centro. Guard your belongings particularly closely when you ride the open-sided bondes. ✉ *Estação Carioca, Rua Professor Lélio Gama, Centro* ☏ *021/2240–5709 or 021/2240–5709* ✇ *R$1* ☉ *Bondes leave every 20 minutes 6 AM–10 PM* Ⓜ *Carioca or Cinelândia.*

❸ **Beco do Comércio.** A network of narrow streets and alleys centers on this pedestrian thoroughfare. The area is flanked by restored 18th-century homes, now converted to offices. The best known is the Edifício Teles de Menezes. Once a functional aqueduct and the source of water for downtown Rio, the **Arco do Teles,** links this area with Praça 15 de Novembro. ✉ *Praça 15 de Novembro 34, Centro* Ⓜ *Uruguaiana.*

❻ **Biblioteca Nacional.** Corinthian columns adorn the neoclassical National Library (built between 1905 and 1908), the first such establishment in Latin America. Its original archives were brought to Brazil by King João VI in 1808. Today it contains roughly 13 million books, including two 15th-century printed Bibles, and manuscript New Testaments from the 11th and 12th centuries; first-edition Mozart scores as well as scores by Carlos Gomes (who adapted the José de Alencar novel about Brazil's Indians, *O Guarani,* into an opera of the same name); books that belonged to Empress Teresa Christina; and many other manuscripts, prints, and drawings. Tours are available in English. ✉ *Av. Rio Branco 219, Centro* ☏ *021/2262–8255 or 021/2220–9484* ⊕ *www.bn.br* ✇ *Tours R$2* ☉ *By guided tour only, weekdays at 11, 1, and 3* Ⓜ *Cinelândia.*

⑪ **Catedral de São Sebastião do Rio de Janeiro** (Catedral Metropolitana.) The exterior of this circa-1960 metropolitan cathedral, which looks like a concrete beehive, can be off-putting. The daring modern design stands in sharp contrast to the baroque style of other churches. But don't judge until you've stepped inside. Outstanding stained-glass windows transform the interior—which is 80 meters (263 feet) high and 96 meters (315 feet) in diameter—into a warm yet serious place of worship that accommodates up to 20,000 people. An 8½-ton granite rock lends considerable weight to the concept of an altar. ☒ *Av. República do Chile 245, Centro* ☎ *021/2240–2869* 🖃 *Free* ☉ *Daily 7:30–5:30* Ⓜ *Carioca or Cinelândia.*

🔟 **Convento do Santo Antônio.** The Convent of St. Anthony was completed in 1780, but some parts date from 1615, making it one of Rio's oldest structures. Its baroque interior contains priceless colonial art—including wood carvings and wall paintings. The sacristy is covered with azulejos (Portuguese tiles). Note that the church has no bell tower: its bells hang from a double arch on the monastery ceiling. An exterior mausoleum contains the tombs of the offspring of Dom Pedro I and Dom Pedro II. ☒ *Largo da Carioca 5, Centro* ☎ *021/2262–0129* 🖃 *Free* ☉ *By appointment only, call ahead to set up a visit* Ⓜ *Carioca.*

❷ **Igreja de Nossa Senhora da Candelária.** The classic symmetry of Candelária's white dome and bell towers casts an unexpected air of sanity over the chaos of downtown traffic. The church was built on the site of a chapel founded in 1610 by Antônio de Palma after he survived a shipwreck; paintings in the present dome tell his tale. Construction on the present church began in 1775, and although it was formally dedicated by the emperor in 1811, work on the dome wasn't completed until 1877. The sculpted bronze doors were exhibited at the 1889 world's fair in Paris. ☒ *Praça Pio X, Centro* ☎ *021/2233–2324* 🖃 *Free* ☉ *Weekdays 7:30–4, Sat. 8–noon, Sun. 9–1* Ⓜ *Uruguaiana.*

❾ **Igreja de São Francisco da Penitência.** The church was completed in 1737, nearly four decades after it was started. Today it's famed for its wooden sculptures and rich gold-leaf interior. The nave contains a painting of St. Francis, the patron of the church—reportedly the first painting in Brazil done in perspective. ☒ *Largo da Carioca 5, Centro* ☎ *021/2262–0197* 🖃 *R$2* ☉ *Tues.–Fri. 9–noon and 1–4* Ⓜ *Carioca.*

⓮ **Monumento aos Pracinhas.** The Monument to the Brazilian Dead of World War II (the nation sided with the Allies during the conflict) is actually a museum and monument combined. It houses military uniforms, medals, stamps, and documents belonging to soldiers. Two soaring columns flank the tomb of an unknown soldier. The first Sunday of each month Brazil's armed forces perform a colorful changing of the guard. ☒ *Parque Brigadeiro Eduardo Gomes, Flamengo* ☎ *021/2240–1283* 🖃 *Free* ☉ *Tues.–Sun. 10–4* Ⓜ *Cinelândia.*

▶ ❶ **Mosteiro de São Bento.** Just a glimpse of this church's main altar can fill you with awe. Layer upon layer of curvaceous wood carvings coated in gold create a sense of movement. Spiral columns whirl upward to capitals topped by cherubs so chubby and angels so purposeful they seem almost animated. Although the Benedictines arrived in 1586, they didn't begin work on this church and monastery until 1617. It was completed in 1641, but such artisans as Mestre Valentim (who designed the silver chandeliers) continued to add details almost through to the 19th century. Every Sunday at 10, mass is accompanied by Gregorian chants. ☒ *Rua Dom Gerardo 68, Centro* ☎ *021/2291–7122* 🖃 *Free* ☉ *Weekdays 7–11 and 2:30–5:30.*

❸ Museu de Arte Moderna (MAM). In a striking concrete-and-glass building, the Modern Art Museum has a collection of some 1,700 works by artists from Brazil and elsewhere. It also hosts significant special exhibitions and has a movie theater that plays art films. ✉ *Av. Infante Dom Henrique 85, Flamengo* ☎ *021/2240–4944* ⊕ *www.mamrio.org.br* ⊙ *Tues.–Fri. noon–6, weekends noon–7* 💲 *R$5* Ⓜ *Cinelândia.*

❺ Museu Histórico Nacional. The building that houses the National History Museum dates from 1762, though some sections—such as the battlements—were erected as early as 1603. It seems appropriate that this colonial structure should exhibit relics that document Brazil's history. Among its treasures are rare papers, Latin American coins, carriages, cannons, and religious art. ✉ *Praça Marechal Ancora, Centro* ☎ *021/2550–9224 or 021/2220–2328* 💲 *Tues.–Sat. R$6, Sun. free* ⊙ *Tues.–Fri. 10–5:30, weekends 2–6* Ⓜ *Carioca or Cinelândia.*

❼ Museu Nacional de Belas Artes. Works by Brazil's leading 19th- and 20th-century artists fill the space at the National Museum of Fine Arts. The most notable canvases are those by the country's best-known modernist, Cândido Portinari, but be on the lookout for such gems as Leandro Joaquim's heartwarming 18th-century painting of Rio (a window to a time when fishermen still cast nets in the waters below the landmark Igreja de Nossa Senhora da Glória do Outeiro). After wandering the picture galleries, tour the extensive collections of folk and African art. ✉ *Av. Rio Branco 199, Centro* ☎ *021/2240–0068* ⊕ *www.iphan. gov.br* 💲 *R$4, free Sun.* ⊙ *Tues.–Fri. 10–6, weekends 2–6* Ⓜ *Carioca or Cinelândia.*

❹ Paço Imperial. This two-story colonial building with thick stone walls and an ornate entrance was built in 1743 and for the next 60 years was the headquarters for Brazil's captains (viceroys), appointed by the Portuguese court in Lisbon. When King João VI arrived, he made it his royal palace. After Brazil's declaration of independence, emperors Dom Pedro I and II called the palace home. When the monarchy was overthrown, the building became Rio's central post office. Restoration work in the 1980s transformed it into a cultural center and concert hall. The building houses a restaurant, a coffee shop, a stationery-and-CD shop, and a movie theater. The square on which the palace sits, Praça 15 de Novembro, known in colonial days as Largo do Paço, has witnessed some of Brazil's most significant historic moments: it is where two emperors were crowned, slavery was abolished, and Emperor Pedro II was deposed. The square's modern name is a reference to the date of the declaration of the Republic of Brazil: November 15, 1889. ✉ *Praça 15 de Novembro 48, Centro* ☎ *021/2533–4407* ⊕ *www.pacoimperial.com.br* 💲 *Free* ⊙ *Tues.–Sun. noon–6.*

❽ Theatro Municipal. If you visit one place in Centro, make it this theater, modeled after the Paris Opera House and opened in 1909. Carrara marble, stunning mosaics, glittering chandeliers, bronze and onyx statues, gilded mirrors, German stained-glass windows, brazilwood inlay floors, and murals by Brazilian artists Eliseu Visconti and Rodolfo Amoedo make the Municipal Theater opulent indeed. The main entrance and first two galleries are particularly ornate. As you climb to the upper floors, the decor becomes simpler, a reflection of a time when different classes entered through different doors and sat in separate sections—but also due in part to the exhaustion of funds toward the end of the project. The theater seats 2,357—with outstanding sight lines—for its dance performances and classical music concerts. English-speaking guides are available. ⊠ *Praça Floriano 210, Centro* ☎ *021/2299–1717* ✉ *Tours R$4* ⊙ *Tours begin every 30 minutes weekdays 10–5* ⊕ *www. theatromunicipal.rj.gov.br* Ⓜ *Cinelândia or Carioca.*

need a break? Elegance joins good but simple food at **Café do Odeon BR** (⊠ Praça Floriano 7, Centro ☎ 021/2240-2573), close to the Theatro Municipal. Appetizers and sandwiches can revitalize after walking downtown. The Odeon BR is one of Rio's most traditional movie theaters and was renovated in 2000. The café's veranda has a view to Praça Cinelândia. To taste a little of the carioca life, try the bar **Carlitos** (⊠ Rua Álvaro Alvim 36, Loja E, Centro ☎ 021/ 2262–6567), on a street parallel to Theatro Municipal. Don't expect a fashionable place but a spot where the *chopp* (draft beer) is good and *batidas* (sweet alcoholic drinks mixed in a blender) come in many flavors—from tropical fruits to gingerbread.

Zona Sul

Zona Sul is the heartbeat of Rio—a mix of residential areas, office buildings, shops, restaurants, bars, and beaches. It's the most affluent part of the city, with beautiful condos housing Rio's middle and upper class. It's also the most culturally diverse part of the city, home to dozens of theaters and music halls. The best-known neighborhoods of the Zona Sul are Copacabana, Ipanema, and Leblon.

Copacabana is Rio's most famous tourist neighborhood thanks to its fabulous beach and grand-dame hotels like the Copacabana Palace. The main thoroughfare is Avenida Nossa Senhora de Copacabana, two blocks inland from the beach. The commercial street is filled with shops, restaurants, and sidewalks crowded with colorful characters. Despite having some of the best hotels in Rio, Copacabana's heyday is over, and the neighborhood is quite a bit grittier than Ipanema or Leblon. It's no secret to thieves that tourists congregate here, so walking around after dark should be avoided.

Ipanema, Leblon, and the blocks surrounding Lagoa Rodrigo de Freitas are part of Rio's money belt. For an up-close look at the posh apartment buildings, stroll down beachfront Avenida Vieira Souto and its extension, Avenida Delfim Moreira, or drive around the lagoon on Avenida Epitácio Pessoa. The tree-lined streets between Ipanema Beach and the lagoon are as peaceful as they are attractive. The boutiques along Rua Garcia D'Ávila make window-shopping a sophisticated endeavor. Other chic areas near the beach include Praça Nossa Senhora da Paz, which is lined with wonderful restaurants and bars; Rua Vinicius de Moraes; and Rua Farme de Amoedo.

a good walk

The best way to get to know Ipanema and Copacabana is to walk these neighborhoods. In the morning, take the time to walk the boardwalk in Copacabana and sit at one of the kiosks and sip fresh coconut water straight out of the coconut. Head to Ipanema for lunch—try Casa da Feijoada for an introduction to Brazil's national dish—and then take a stroll down Rua Visconde de Pirajá, beginning at the Praça General Osório, just next to the restaurant. On Sundays, stop at the **Feira Hippie (Hippie Fair)** at this square, to browse through jewelry, leather bags and shoes, and artwork. Continue along Visconde de Pirajá, passing many of Ipanema's finest restaurant and shops. Window shopping can easily take up an entire day, but you might also want to stop in for a free tour at **H. Stern** (make reservations in advance). Bakeries and juice bars are found on most street corners. This street is most populated during the week, which is also when most stores will be open. End up at Gula Gula for a bite to eat or Mil Frutas for a sweet treat.

TIMING & PRECAUTIONS

Sunday is the best day for this walk: the street near Copacabana is closed to automobiles, and the Hippie Fair is open in Ipanema. Explore the streets of the Zona Sul during the day, when the sun and the crowds are out.

Copacabana & Leme

Fodor'sChoice
★

Praia de Copacabana. Maddening traffic, noise, packed apartment blocks, and a world-famous beach—this is Copacabana, or Manhattan with bikinis. Walk along the neighborhood's classic crescent to dive headfirst into Rio's beach culture, a cradle-to-grave lifestyle that begins with toddlers accompanying their parents to the water and ends with silver-haired seniors walking hand in hand along the sidewalk. Copacabana hums with activity: you're likely to see athletic men playing volleyball using only their feet and heads, not their hands—a sport Brazilians have dubbed *futevôlei*. As you can tell by all the goal nets, soccer is also popular, and Copacabana frequently hosts the annual world beach soccer championships. You can swim here, although pollution levels and a strong undertow can sometimes be discouraging. Pollution levels change daily and are well publicized; someone at your hotel should be able to get you the information.

Copacabana's privileged live on beachfront Avenida Atlântica, famed for its wide mosaic sidewalks designed by Burle Marx, and for its grand hotels—including the Copacabana Palace Hotel—and cafés with sidewalk seating. On Sunday two of the avenue's lanes are closed to traffic and are taken over by joggers, rollerbladers, cyclists, and pedestrians. ⊠ *Av. Princesa Isabel to Rua Francisco Otaviano, Copacabana.*

need a break?

Stop in for a drink at one of Avenida Atlântica's few air-conditioned cafés. The windows of **Manoel & Juaquim** (⊠ Av. Atlântica 1936, Copacabana ☎ 021/2236–6768) face the sands, so you can settle in with a cold draft beer or a light meal (the garlic potatoes are unbeatable) while watching carioca life unfold.

Praia do Leme. A natural extension of Copacabana Beach to the northeast, toward the Pão de Açúcar, is Leme Beach. A rock formation juts into the water here, forming a quiet cove that's less crowded than the

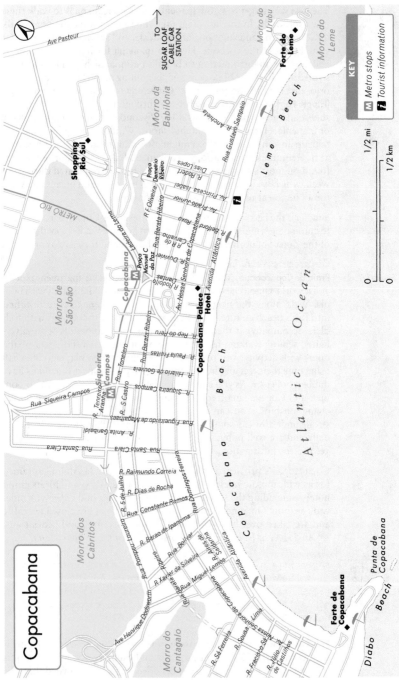

Copacabana

Ave Pasteur

Morro do
Urubu

Morro do
Leme

TO →
SUGAR LOAF
CABLE CAR
STATION

**Forte do
Leme**

L e m e   B e a c h

Rua Gustavo Sampaio

R. Anchieta

Morro da
Babilônia

Shopping
Rio Sul

Praça
Demétrio
Ribeiro

R.F. Oliveira

Dias Lopes

R. Rodolfo

Laranjeiras e Leme

Rua Baratta Ribeiro

Av. Princesa Isabel

Av. Prado Júnior

R. Belford Roxo

R. de Carvalho

R. Duvivier

KEY

METRO RIO

Praça
Manuel C
da Paz

Copacabana

R. Nossa Senhora de Copacabana

Avenida Atlântica

Morro de
São João

R. Rodolfo
Dantas

**Copacabana Palace
Hotel**

R. Rep. do Perú

Rua Tonelero

Rua Baratta Ribeiro

R. Paula Freitas

C o p a c a b a n a   B e a c h

A t l a n t i c   O c e a n

**Siqueira
Campos**

R. Hilário de Gouveia

R. Siqueira Campos

Rua Siqueira Campos

R. Teneiro
Aranha

R. S. Castro

Rua Figueiredo de Magalhães

R. Anita Garibaldi

Rua Santa Clara

Rua Santa Clara

R. Raimundo Correia

R. Dias de Rocha

R. 5 de Julho

Rua Constante Ramos

Rua Domingos Ferreira

Rua Barão de Ipanema

R. Pompeu Loureiro

R. Tonelero

R. Barão de Ipanema

Rua Bolívar

R. Xavier da Silveira

R. Santa Clara

Av. N. Sra. de Copacabana

Rua Miguel Lemos

Av. Atlântica de
Salgado

R. Alves de

Avenida Atlântica

Morro dos
Cabritos

Morro do
Cantagalo

Ave Henrique Dodsworth

R. Sá Ferreira

R. Sousa Lima

R. Francisco Sá

R. Júlio
de Castilhos

Av. Nossa Senhora de Copacabana

**Forte de
Copacabana**

Punta de
Copacabana

D i a b o   B e a c h

KEY

M Metro stops

🛈 Tourist information

1/2 mi

1/2 km

0

0

rest of the beach. Along a sidewalk, at the side of the mountain over-looking Leme, anglers stand elbow to elbow with their lines dangling into the sea. ☒ *Av. Princesa Isabel to Morro do Leme, Leme.*

Ipanema & Arpoador

Museu H. Stern. The world headquarters of H. Stern has a small museum where you can see rare gems. A self-guided audio tour explains the entire process of cutting, polishing, and setting stones. Afterward, you get a personal consultation with a salesperson and a gift box with five small stones. The museum can arrange transport back to your hotel. ☒ *Rua Visconde de Pirajá 490, Ipanema* ☎ *021/2106–0000* 🎫 *Free* ⊙ *Tours by appointment only.*

Praia do Arpoador. This beach, at the east end of Ipanema, has great waves for surfing. Non-surfers tend to avoid the water for fear of getting hit by boards. But it's popular for sunbathing. A short climb up the big rock formation gets you an amazingly gorgeous view of Ipanema. ☒ *Rua Joaquim Nabubo to Rua Francisco Otaviano, Arpoador.*

FodorŚChoice
★   **Praia de Ipanema.** As you stroll along this beach, you catch a cross section of the city's residents, each favoring a particular stretch. One area is dominated by families (near Posto [Post] 10), another is favored by the gay community (near Posto 8). Throughout the day you'll see groups playing beach volleyball and soccer, and if you're lucky you'll even get to see Brazilian Olympic volleyball champions practicing on the beach. There are kiosks all along the boardwalk, where you can get anything from the typical coconut water to fried shrimp and turnovers. ☒ *Rua Joaquim Nabuco to Av. Epitácio Pessoa, Ipanema.*

> **need a break?**
>
> Have you ever wondered if there really *was* a girl from Ipanema? The song was inspired by schoolgirl Heloisa Pinheiro, who caught the fancy of songwriter Antônio Carlos (aka Tom) Jobim and his pal lyricist Vinicius de Moraes as she walked past the two bohemians sitting in their favorite bar. They then penned one of last century's classics. That was in 1962, and today the bar has been renamed **Bar Garota de Ipanema** (☒ Rua Vinicius de Moraes 49-A, Ipanema ☎ 021/2523–3787).

West of Leblon

Museu Casa do Pontal. If you're heading toward Prainha or beyond to Grumari, consider taking a detour to Brazil's largest folk-art museum. One room houses a wonderful mechanical sculpture that represents all of the *escolas de samba* (samba schools) that march in the Carnival parades. Another mechanical "scene" depicts a circus in action. This private collection is owned by a French expatriate, Jacques Van de Beuque, who has been collecting Brazilian treasures—including religious pieces—since he arrived in the country in 1946. ☒ *Estrada do Pontal 3295, Grumari* ☎ *021/2490–3278* 🎫 *R$10* ⊙ *Tues.–Sun. 9:30–5.*

Praia Barra da Tijuca. Some cariocas consider the beach at Barra da Tijuca to be Rio's best, and the 18-km-long (11-mi-long) sweep of sand and jostling waves certainly is dramatic. Pollution isn't generally a problem, and in many places neither are crowds. Barra's water is cooler and

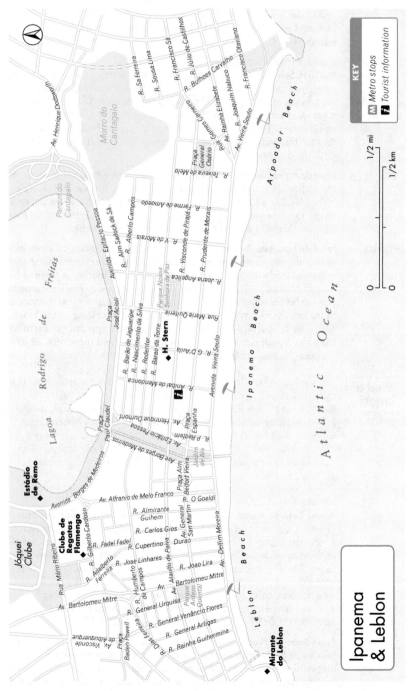

Ipanema & Leblon

NEW YEAR'S EVE IN RIO

ALTHOUGH RIO'S ANNUAL CARNIVAL is an amazing spectacle, there is perhaps no stranger sight than that which takes place on the beaches in many of Brazil's cities each New Year's Eve. Under the warm tropical sky and with the backdrop of the modern city, thousands of adherents of the Candomblé religion—vulgarly known as macumba—honor Iemanjá, the goddess of the sea.

The advent of the new year is a time for renewal and to ask for blessings. The faithful of all ages, colors, and classes pour onto the beaches at around 10 PM, mostly at Copacabana. Some draw mystic signs in the sand. Others lay out white tablecloths with gifts befitting the proud, beautiful goddess: combs, mirrors, lipsticks, hair ribbons, perfumes, wines. Still others bring flowers with notes asking for favors tucked amid the blossoms. Worshippers chant and sing over their offerings and set candles around them.

By 11:30 PM the beaches are a mass of white-clad believers with flickering candles—the shore looks as if it has been invaded by millions of fireflies. At midnight the singing, shrieking, and sobbing is accompanied by fireworks, sirens, and bells. After that the faithful rush to the water for the moment of truth: if the goddess is satisfied with an offering, it's carried out to sea, and the gift giver's wish will come true. If, however, Iemanjá is displeased with an offering, the ocean throws it back; the gift giver must try again another year.

---

its breezes more refreshing than those at other beaches. The waves can be strong in spots; this attracts surfers, windsurfers, and jet skiers, but you should swim with caution. The beach is set slightly below a sidewalk, where cafés and restaurants beckon. Condos have also sprung up here, and the city's largest shopping centers and supermarkets have made inland Barra their home.

At the far end of Sernambetiba, Barra's beachfront avenue (the name of the street was recently changed to Avenida Lúcio Costa, but most people still know it as Sernambetiba) is **Recreio dos Bandeirantes,** a 1-km (½-mi) stretch of sand anchored by a huge rock, which creates a small protected cove. Its quiet seclusion makes it popular with families. The calm, pollution-free water, with no waves or currents, is good for bathing, but don't try to swim around the rock—it's bigger than it looks.

At this writing, hotels, restaurants, and other tourist attractions are opening in the Barra da Tijuca neighborhood in preparation for the Pan-American Games, which are to be held in Rio in July 2007.

Praia de Grumari. About five minutes beyond Prainha, off Estrada de Guaratiba, is Grumari, a beach that seems a preview of paradise. What it lacks in amenities—it has only a couple of groupings of thatch-roof huts selling drinks and snacks—it makes up for in natural beauty: the glorious red sands of its quiet cove are backed by low, lush hills. Weekends are extremely crowded. Take a lunch break at Restaurante Point de Grumari (⇨ Where to Eat, *below*), which serves excellent fish dishes. If you've ventured this far, you might as well take a slight detour to the **Museu Casa do Pontal,** Brazil's largest folk-art museum, and the **Sítio Roberto Burle Marx** for an in-depth look at one of Brazil's greatest artists.

Prainha. The length of two football fields, Prainha is a vest-pocket beach favored by surfers, who take charge of it on weekends. The swimming is good, but watch out for surfboards. On weekdays, especially in the off-season, the beach is almost empty; on weekends, particularly in peak season, the road to and from Prainha and nearby Grumari is so crowded it almost becomes a parking lot. ⊠ *35 km (22 mi) west of Ipanema on the coast road; accessible only by car from Av. Lúcio Costa (Av. Sernambetiba).*

São Conrado. Blocked by the imposing Dois Irmãos Mountain, Avenida Niemeyer snakes along rugged cliffs that offer spectacular sea views on the left. The road returns to sea level again in São Conrado, a natural amphitheater surrounded by forested mountains and the ocean. Development of what is now a mostly residential area began in the late '60s with an eye on Rio's high society. A short stretch along its beach includes the condominiums of a former president, the ex-wife of another former president, an ex-governor of Rio de Janeiro State, and a one-time Central Bank president. The far end of São Conrado is marked by the towering Pedra da Gávea, a huge flattop granite boulder. Next to it is Pedra Bonita, the mountain from which gliders depart. (Although this beach was the city's most popular a few years ago, contaminated water has discouraged swimmers.)

Ironically, the neighborhood is surrounded by favelas (shantytowns). Much of the high ground has been taken over by Rio's largest favela, Rocinha, where an estimated 200,000 people live. This precarious city within a city seems poised to slide down the hill. It and others like it are the result of Rio's chronic housing problem coupled with the refusal by many of the city's poor to live in distant working-class neighborhoods. Though the favelas are dangerous for the uninitiated, they have their own internal order, and their tremendous expansion has even upper-class cariocas referring to them not as slums but as neighborhoods. The favelas enjoy prime vistas, and most are constructed of brick. It is not advisable to enter a favela unless you are with an organized tour that has assured you of its safety. ⊠ *Just west of Leblon.*

Fodor'sChoice   **Sítio Roberto Burle Marx** (Roberto Burle Marx Farm). Beyond Grumari,
★   the road winds through mangrove swamps and tropical forest. It's an apt setting for the plantation-turned-museum where Brazil's famous landscape designer Roberto Burle Marx is memorialized. Marx, the mind behind Rio's swirling mosaic beachfront walkways and the Atêrro do Flamengo, was said to have "painted with plants" and was the first designer to use Brazilian flora in his projects. More than 3,500 species—including some discovered by and named for Marx as well as many on

WHAT'S YOUR BEACH STYLE?

RIO'S CIRCUIT OF PRAIAS *(beaches) begins with Flamengo, on Guanabara Bay, but the best strands are in the Zona Sul. Beaches are the city's pulse points: exercise centers, gathering places, lovers' lanes. Although cariocas wander into the water to cool off, most spend their time sunning and socializing, not swimming. Copacabana and Ipanema are nerve centers. Beaches west of São Conrado are increasingly isolated and undeveloped.*

Praia do Flamengo. *Power-walkers, volleyballers, and yoga enthusiasts come to Flamengo Beach to work up a sweat. It isn't a tourist destination, and you rarely see people swimming (pollution can be a problem) or sunbathing.*

Praia do Botafogo. *The view of the bay and the Sugar Loaf from this beach is breathtaking, but it isn't a popular beach with tourists or even locals, due to pollution in the bay waters.*

Praia do Vermelha. *This tiny beach neighboring the Pão de Açucar has beautiful scenery but polluted waters. It's generally populated only by cariocas who live nearby.*

Praia do Leme. *A continuation of Copacabana Beach, Leme has a similar feel. Lined with kiosks and volleyball nets, it's a popular with locals and tourists.*

Praia do Diabo. *Between Ipanema and Copacabana, this small strip attracts surfers. The view is beautiful, and if you're at Ipanema, it's worth the walk to Praia do Diabo.*

Praia de Copacabana. *The city's grande dame, Copacabana is a 3-km (2-mi) stretch packed to the gills on sunny days with sunbathers, vendors, and athletes. Kiosks along its busy promenade have snacks and drinks. Cafés and high-rise hotels line the waterfront avenue.*

Praia de Ipanema. *Always-crowded Ipanema is smaller than Copacabana, but equally famous. It's a perfect place to sunbathe and people-watch. At the east end is the dramatic rock formation Pedra do Arpoador; visible to the west, past Leblon, is the Morro Dois Irmaos (Two Brothers Mountain) and the hillside Vidigal favela.*

Praia do Leblon. *Ipanema Beach extends west to meet Leblon Beach, which has the same feel. It's very popular for exercising on the sand or boardwalk. Water pollution is a problem.*

Praia do São Conrado. *Hang gliders land here after leaping from a nearby peak. The proximity to the Rocinha favela keeps many people away. Tourists are rare.*

Praia Barra da Tijuca. *Rio's longest beach (18 km/11 mi) has clean and cool waters. Its far end, called Recreio dos Bandeirantes, was a fishing village until the late 1960s. The neighborhood of Barra da Tijuca feels like a suburb, and the beach reflects that. It attracts families with young children and older folks out for a stroll.*

Prainha. *Just beyond Barra da Tijuca, Prainha has rough seas that make it popular with surfers. It's nearly empty on weekdays.*

Praia de Grumari. *The copper sands of this lovely beach are packed on weekends. It has little infrastructure but clean sand and water, and is backed by green hills.*

GETTING THERE

For beaches not accessible by metro, consider taking a taxi. City buses and chartered minivans drop you off along the shore, but safety is an issue. Most beaches have parking lots—look for attendants in green-and-yellow vests. Turismo Clássico (⇨ By Car in Rio de Janeiro Essentials) can arrange for drivers and guides.

the endangered list—flourish at this 100-acre estate. He grouped his plants not only according to their soil and light needs but also according to their shape and texture. Marx also liked to mix the modern with the traditional—a recurring theme throughout the property. The results are both whimsical and elegant. In 1985 he bequeathed the farm to the Brazilian government, though he remained here until his death in 1994. His house is now a cultural center full of his belongings, including collections of folk art. The grounds also contain his large ultramodern studio (he was a painter, too) and a small, restored colonial chapel dedicated to St. Anthony. ⊠ *Estrada Roberto Burle Marx 2019, Pedra da Guaratiba* ☎ *021/2410–1412* ✉ *R$5* ☉ *Tues.–Sun. by appointment only; Tours at 9:30 AM and 1:30 PM.*

The Lush Inland

In the western portion of the city north of Leblon, trees and hills dominate the landscape in the neighborhoods of Jardim Botânico, Lagoa, Cosme Velho, and Tijuca. In addition their parks and gardens, these primarily residential neighborhoods have marvelous museums, seductive architecture, and tantalizing restaurants. The architecture is a mix of modern condominiums and colonial houses. They tend to be quieter neighborhoods during the day because they are not on the beachfront, but also have some of the hippest nightclubs in Rio. You can't say you've seen Rio until you've taken in the view from Corcovado and then strolled through its forested areas or beside its inland Lagoa (Lagoon) Rodrigo de Freitas—hanging out just like a true carioca.

Public transportation doesn't conveniently reach the sights here; take a taxi or a tour.

Numbers in the margin correspond to numbers on the Rio de Janeiro City map.

Jardim Botânico

㉖ **Jardim Botânico.** The 340-acre Botanical Garden contains more than 5,000 species of tropical and subtropical plants and trees, including 900 varieties of palms (some more than a century old) and more than 140 species of birds. The temperature is usually a good 12°C (22°F) cooler in the shady garden that was created in 1808 by Portuguese king João VI during his exile in Brazil. In 1842 the garden gained its most impressive adornment, the Avenue of the Royal Palms, a 720-meter (800-yard) double row of 134 soaring royal palms. Elsewhere in the gardens, the Casa dos Pilões, an old gunpowder factory, has been restored and displays objects that pertained to both the nobility and their slaves. Also on the grounds are a library, a small café, and a gift shop that sells souvenirs with ecological themes. ⊠ *Rua Jardim Botânico 1008, Jardim Botânico* ☎ *021/2294–9349* ⊕ *www.jbrj.gov.br* ✉ *R$4* ☉ *Daily 8–5. Guided tours by appointment.*

Cosme Velho

㉑ **Corcovado.** There's an eternal argument about which view is better, from Pão de Açúcar (Sugar Loaf) or from here. In our opinion, it is best to visit Sugar Loaf *before* you visit Corcovado, or you will remember

FodorśChoice
★

Sugar Loaf only as an anticlimax. Corcovado has two advantages: at 690 meters (2,300 feet), it's nearly twice as high and offers an excellent view of Pão de Açúcar itself. The sheer 300-meter (1,000-foot) granite face of Corcovado (the name means "hunchback" and refers to the mountain's shape) has always been a difficult undertaking for climbers.

It wasn't until 1921, the centennial of Brazil's independence from Portugal, that someone had the idea of placing a statue atop Corcovado. A team of French artisans headed by sculptor Paul Landowski was assigned the task of erecting a statue of Christ with his arms apart as if embracing the city. (Nowadays, mischievous cariocas say Christ is getting ready to clap for his favorite escola de samba.) It took 10 years, but on October 12, 1931, the *Cristo Redentor* (Christ the Redeemer) was unveiled. The sleek, modern figure rises more than 30 meters (100 feet) from a 6-meter (20-foot) pedestal and weighs 700 tons. In the evening a powerful lighting system transforms it into a dramatic icon.

There are two ways to reach the top: by cogwheel train (R$30, which includes R$5 entrance fee) or by taxi (R$10 per person, plus R$5 entrance fee per person). The train, built in 1885, provides delightful views of Ipanema and Leblon from an absurd angle of ascent, as well as a close look at thick vegetation and butterflies. (You may wonder what those oblong medicine balls hanging from the trees are, the ones that look like spiked watermelons tied to ropes—they're *jaca,* or jackfruit.) Trains leave the **Cosme Velho station** (⊠ Rua Cosme Velho 513, Cosme Velho ☎ 021/2558–1329 ⊕ www.corcovado.com.br) for the steep, 5-km (3-mi), 17-minute ascent. Trains run from 9 AM to 6 PM and depart every 30 minutes. Late-afternoon trains are the most popular; on weekends be prepared for a long wait. To get to the summit, you can climb up 220 steep, zigzagging steps (which was the only option available prior to 2003), or take an escalator or a panoramic elevator. If you choose the stairs, you pass little cafés and shops selling film and souvenirs along the way. Once at the top, all of Rio stretches out before you.

Visit Corcovado on a clear day; clouds often obscure the Christ statue and the view of the city. Go as early in the morning as possible, before people start pouring out of the tour buses, and before the haze sets in. ⊠ *Estrada da Redentor, Cosme Velho* ⊕ *www.corcovado.org.br* ⊞ *R$5* ⊙ *Daily 9–6.*

㉒ Museu de Arte Naïf do Brasil. More than 8,000 art naïf works by Brazil's best (as well as works by other self-taught painters from around the world) grace the walls of this colonial mansion that was once the studio of painter Eliseu Visconti. The pieces, in what is reputedly the world's largest and most complete collection of primitive paintings, date from the 15th century through contemporary times. Don't miss the colorful, colossal 7×4–meter (22×13–foot) canvas that depicts the city of Rio; it reportedly took five years to complete. This museum sprang from a collection started decades ago by a jewelry designer who later created a foundation to oversee the art. ⊠ *Rua Cosme Velho 561, Cosme Velho* ☎ *021/2205–8612 or 021/2205–8547* ⊞ *R$8* ⊙ *Tues.–Fri. 10–6, weekends noon–6.*

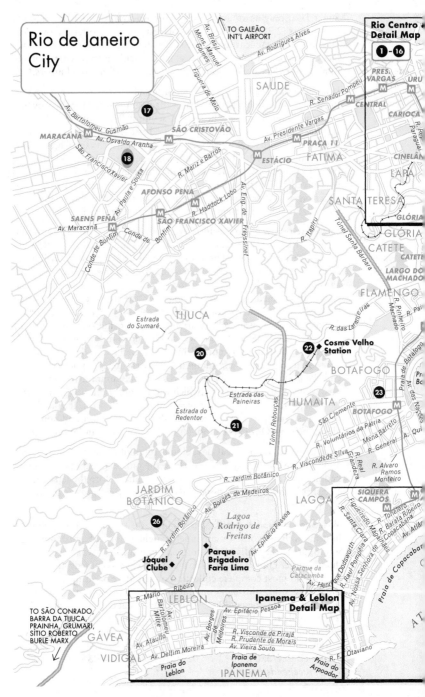

Rio de Janeiro City

TO GALEÃO INT'L AIRPORT

Av. Brasil
Mons. Gomes
Figueira de Melo
Av. Rodrigues Alves
SAUDE
R. Senador Pompeu

Rio Centro
Detail Map
1-**16**

PRES. VARGAS
URU
Ⓜ

CENTRAL
CARIOCA

Av. Bartolomeu Gusmão
SÃO CRISTOVÃO
MARACANÃ Ⓜ Av. Osvaldo Aranha

17

Av. Presidente Vargas
CINELÂN

LAPA

São Francisco Xavier
R. Mariz e Barros
18
ESTÁCIO
PRAÇA 11
FATIMA

AFONSO PENA
R. Haddock Lobo
Av. Eng. de Freyssinet
SANTA TERESA

SAENS PEÑA Ⓜ
Av. Maracanã
Conde de Bonfim
Conde de Bonfim
SÃO FRANCISCO XAVIER
Av. Paula e Sousa

GLÓRIA

Túnel Santa Bárbara
GLÓRIA
CATETE
CATETE

R. Itapiru

LARGO DO
MACHADO

FLAMENGO

Estrada do Sumaré
TIJUCA
R. das Laranjeiras
R. Pinheiro Machado
R. Pai

20
Cosme Velho Station
22 ◆ Cosme Velho

BOTAFOGO

Praia de Botafogo
Pr
Bo

Estrada das Paineiras
HUMAITA
23
Ⓜ
BOTAFOGO
Av. das Nações

Estrada do Redentor
21
São Clemente
R. Voluntários da Pátria
Mena Barreto
A. Qui

Túnel Rebouças
R. Visconde de Sílva
R. Real Grandeza
R. General A.
R. Alvaro Ramos Monteiro

R. Jardim Botânico
LAGOA
SIQUERA CAMPOS
Ⓜ

JARDIM BOTÂNICO
Av. Borges de Medeiros
R. Figueiredo Magalhães
R. Santa Clara
R. Toneleros
R. Barata Ribeiro
Av. N. Sra. de Copacabana
Av. Atlân

26
Lagoa Rodrigo de Freitas
Av. Epitácio Pessoa
R. Raul Pompéia
R. Nossa Senhora de Copacabana

R. Jardim Botânico
Jóquei Clube ◆
◆ Parque Brigadeiro Faria Lima
Parque da Catacumba
Praia de Copacaba

Av. Henr

Ribeiro
R. Mário
LEBLON
Av. Epitácio Pessoa
Ipanema & Leblon
Detail Map

TO SÃO CONRADO, BARRA DA TIJUCA, PRAINHA, GRUMARI, SÍTIO ROBERTO BURLE MARX
GÁVEA
Av. Bartolomeu Mitre
Av. Ataulfo
Av. Delfim Moreira
Av. Borges de Medeiros
R. Visconde de Pirajá
R. Prudente de Morais
Av. Vieira Souto
Otaviano
R. F.

VIDIGAL
Praia do Leblon
Praia de Ipanema
IPANEMA
Praia do Arpoador

AT

Ilha das
Cobras

*Baía de
Guanabara*

**enezes Cortes
us Terminal**

**Aeroporto
Santos
Dumont**

arque do
lamengo

Praia do Flamengo

URCA

Av. João
Luis Alves

Praia de
Fora

Praia da Urca

Av. São Sebastião

Av. Portugal

VERMELHA

R. Gustavo
Sampaio

Praia do
Leme

LEME

OCEAN

ABANA

**Copacabana
Detail Map**

```
0                          1 mile
0           1 km
```

KEY
▶ *Start of walk*
Ⓜ *Metro*
┝━━━┥ *Street Car*
•••••• *Cable Car*

Tijuca

20 **Floresta da Tijuca** (Quagmire Forest). Surrounding Corcovado is the dense, tropical Tijuca Forest. Once part of a Brazilian nobleman's estate, it's studded with exotic trees and thick jungle vines and has a delightful waterfall, the Cascatinha de Taunay. About 180 meters (200 yards) beyond the waterfall is the small pink-and-purple Capela Mayrink (Mayrink Chapel), with painted panels by the 20th-century Brazilian artist Cândido Portinari.

From several points along this national park's 96 km (60 mi) of narrow winding roads the views are breathtaking. Some of the most spectacular are from Dona Marta, on the way up Corcovado; the Emperor's Table, supposedly where Brazil's last emperor, Pedro II, took his court for picnics; and, farther down the road, the Chinese View, the area where Portuguese king João VI allegedly settled the first Chinese immigrants to Brazil, who came in the early 19th century to develop tea plantations. A great way to see the forest is by jeep; you can arrange tours through a number of agencies, such as **Trilhas do Rio Ecoturismo & Aventura** (☎ 021/ 2425–8441 or 021/2424–5455 ⊕ www.trilhasdorio.com.br), a highly professional tour company with fun programs and well-trained guides. Request an English-speaking guide when you book. **Jeep Tour** (☎ 21/ 2589–0883 ⊕ www.jeeptour.com.br) is another option. ⊠ *Entrance at Praça Afonso Viseu 561, Tijuca* ☎ *021/2492–2253* ⊠ *Free* ☉ *Daily 8–5.*

Flamengo & Botafogo

These largely residential neighborhoods connect the southern beach districts and Centro via a series of highways that intersect here. It's very easy to reach these neighborhoods by metro. Apartment buildings dominate, but Rio Sul—one of the city's most popular shopping centers—is here, as are some of the city's best museums and public spaces.

The eponymous beach at Flamengo no longer draws swimmers (its gentle waters look appealing but are polluted; the people you see are sunning, not swimming). A marina sits on a bay at one end of the beach, which is connected via a busy boulevard to the smaller beach (also polluted), at Botafogo. The city's yacht club is here, and when Rio was Brazil's capital, it was also the site of the city's glittering embassy row. The embassies were long ago transferred to Brasília, but the mansions that housed them remain. Among Botafogo's more interesting mansion- and tree-lined streets are Mariana, Sorocaba, Matriz, and Visconde e Silva.

23 **Casa Rui Barbosa.** Slightly inland from the Atêrro is a museum in what was once the house of 19th-century Brazilian statesmen and scholar Rui Barbosa (a liberal from Bahia State who drafted one of Brazil's early constitutions). The pink mansion dates from 1849 and contains memorabilia of Barbosa's life, including his 1913 car and an extensive library that's often consulted by scholars from around the world. ⊠ *Rua São Clemente 134, Botafogo* ☎ *021/2537–0036* ⊠ *Free* ☉ *Tues.–Sun. 9–5* Ⓜ *Botafogo.*

18 **Museu Carmen Miranda.** This tribute to the Brazilian bombshell is in a circular building that resembles a concrete spaceship (its door even opens upward rather than out). On display are some of the elaborate costumes and incredibly high platform shoes worn by the actress, who was viewed as a national icon by some and as a traitor to true Brazilian culture by others. Hollywood photos of Miranda, who was only 46 when she died of a heart attack in 1955, show her in her trademark turban and jewelry. Also here are her records and movie posters and such memorabilia as the silver hand mirror she was clutching when she died. Guided tours are given by appointment, but guides do not speak English. ✉ *Atêrro do Flamengo park, Av. Rui Barbosa s/n, across from Av. Rui Barbosa 560, Flamengo* ☎ *021/2299–5586* ⊕ *www.sec.rj.gov. br* 🎫 *Free* ☉ *Tues.–Fri. 10–5, weekends noon–5* Ⓜ *Flamengo.*

> **need a break?**   Flamengo has some of Rio's better small restaurants. For authentic Brazilian fare, the bohemian community heads to **Lamas** (✉ Rua Marquês de Abrantes 18 ☎ 021/2556–0799), which is a quick taxi ride from the Carmen Miranda Museum.

Parque do Flamengo. Flanking the Baía de Guanabara from the Glória neighborhood to Flamengo is this waterfront park. It gets its name from its location atop an *atêrro* (landfill), and was designed by landscape architect Roberto Burle Marx. Paths used for jogging, walking, and biking wind through it. There are also playgrounds and public tennis and basketball courts. On weekends the freeway beside the park is closed to traffic, and the entire area becomes one enormous public space. ✉ *Inland of the beach, from Glória to Botafogo* 🎫 *Free* ☉ *Daily 24 hours* Ⓜ *Glória or Flamengo.*

Urca

Tiny sheltered Urca faces Botafogo. The quiet neighborhood with single-family homes and tree-lined streets is separated by the Pão de Açúcar from a small underwhelming patch of yellow sand called Praia Vermelha. This beach is, in turn, blocked by the Urubu and Leme mountains from the 1-km (½-mi) Leme Beach at the start of the Zona Sul. Besides having one of the city's most famous attractions, the Pão de Açúcar, Urca has our favorite branch of the world-famous churrascaria Porcão (⇨ Where to Eat).

★ ㉕ **Pão de Açúcar** (Sugar Loaf). This soaring 1,300-meter (approximately 4,290-foot) granite block at the mouth of Baía de Guanabara was originally called *pau-nh-acugua* (high, pointed peak) by the indigenous Tupi people. To the Portuguese the phrase seemed similar to *pão de açúcar*; the rock's shape reminded them of the conical loaves in which refined sugar was sold. Italian-made bubble cars holding 75 passengers each move up the mountain in two stages. The first stop is at Morro da Urca, a smaller, 212-meter (705-foot) mountain; the second is at the summit of Pão de Açúcar itself. The trip to each level takes three minutes. In high season long lines form for the cable car; the rest of the year the wait is seldom more than 30 minutes. ✉ *Av. Pasteur 520, Praia Vermelha, Urca* ☎ *021/2546–8400* ⊕ *www.bondinho.com.br* 🎫 *R$30* ☉ *Daily 8 AM–10 PM.*

Catete, Glória & Lapa

These three neighborhoods surround the city center. Catete formerly housed the national government and still has beautiful buildings (such as the Palácio do Catete) that are worth visiting. Gloria is famous for its beautiful churches, which are cariocas' favorite churches to get married in. Lapa also has beautiful architecture that can be explored on foot during the day, but at night it's best to get around in taxis. Lapa is also home to some of the best music halls in the city and attracts music lovers every night of the week.

Numbers in the margin correspond to numbers on the Rio Centro and Environs map and the Rio de Janeiro City map

⑯ Igreja de Nossa Senhora da Glória do Outeiro. Atop a hill, this baroque church is visible from many spots in the city, making it a landmark that's truly cherished by the cariocas. Its location was a strategic point in the city's early days. Estácio da Sá took this hill from the French in the 1560s and then went on to expand the first settlement and found a city for the Portuguese. The church, which wasn't built until 1739, is notable for its octagonal floor plan, large dome, ornamental stonework, and vivid tile work. The church has a small museum inside with baroque art. Tours are given by appointment only. ⊠ *Praça Nossa Senhora da Glória 135, Glória* ☎ *021/2557–4600* ⊠ *Church free, museum R$2* ☉ *Weekdays 9–noon and 1–5, weekends 9–noon. Museum closed Mon.* Ⓜ *Glória.*

⑲ Palácio do Catete. Once the villa of a German baron, the elegant, 19th-century granite-and-marble palace became the presidential residence after the 1889 coup overthrew the monarchy and established the Republic of Brazil. Eighteen presidents lived here. Gaze at the palace's gleaming parquet floors and intricate bas relief ceilings as you wander through its **Museu da República** (Museum of the Republic). The permanent exhibits include a shroud-draped view of the bedroom where President Getúlio Vargas committed suicide in 1954 after the military threatened to overthrow his government. Presidential memorabilia, furniture, and paintings that date from the proclamation of the republic to the end of Brazil's military regime in 1985 are also displayed. A small contemporary art gallery, a movie theater, a restaurant, and a theater operate within the museum. ⊠ *Rua do Catete 153, Catete* ☎ *021/2558–6350* ⊠ *Tues. and Thurs.–Sat., R$6. Wed. and Sun., free* ☉ *Tues., Thurs., and Fri. noon–5, Wed. 2–5, Sat. and Sun. 2–6* Ⓜ *Catete.*

FodorśChoice
★

Santa Teresa

With its cobblestone streets and bohemian atmosphere, Santa Teresa is a delightfully eccentric neighborhood. Gabled Victorian mansions sit beside alpine-style chalets as well as more prosaic dwellings—many hanging at unbelievable angles from the flower-encrusted hills. Cafés, galleries, and antiques shops have nudged their way into nooks and crannies between the colorful homes, many of which house artists and their studios.

Every Saturday at 10 AM the city gives a guided **bonde tour** (trolley tour) through Santa Teresa for R$4. The tour lasts two hours and can accommodate up to 40 people. Meet at the Bonde Station, behind the Petrobras building near the Cinelândia metro station; get there a little early to guarantee a spot.

Numbers in the text correspond to numbers on the Rio Centro and Environs map.

★ ⑮ **Museu Chácara do Céu.** The collection of mostly modern works at the Museum of the Small Farm of the Sky was left—along with the hilltop house that contains it—by one of Rio's greatest arts patrons, Raymundo de Castro Maya. Included are originals by 20th-century masters Picasso, Braque, Dalí, Degas, Matisse, Modigliani, and Monet. The Brazilian holdings include priceless 17th- and 18th-century maps and works by leading modernists. From the grounds you have great views of the aqueduct, Centro, and the bay. ⊠ *Rua Murtinho Nobre 93, Santa Teresa* ☎ *021/2507–1932* 💲 *R\$2* ☉ *Mon. and Wed.–Sun. noon–5.*

 need a break?

Santa Teresa attracts artists, musicians, and intellectuals to its eclectic slopes. One of their favorite hangouts is **Bar do Arnaudo** (⊠ Rua Almirante Alexandrino 316-B, Santa Teresa ☎ 021/2252–7246), which is always full.

West of Downtown

Neighborhoods west of downtown are mainly residential. Some are middle-class and some are poor. Unless you're a local, it's hard to know which areas are safe and which are not, so you should avoid wandering around. (Though wandering around Quinta da Boa Vista is fine.) You can easily get to Maracanã and Quinta da Boa Vista by metro, but avoid coming here after dark.

⑱ **Maracanã.** From the Igreja de Nossa Senhora da Candelária, walk 3½ blocks to the Uruguaiana station and take the metro to the world's largest soccer stadium. Officially called Estádio Mário Filho after a famous journalist, it's best known as Maracanã, which is the name of the surrounding neighborhood and a nearby river. The 178,000-seat stadium (with standing room for another 42,000) was built in record time to host the 1950 World Cup. Brazil lost its chance at the cup by losing a match 2–1 to Uruguay—a game that's still analyzed a half-century later. Soccer star Pelé made his 1,000th goal here in 1969. The smaller, 17,000-seat arena in the same complex has hosted Madonna, Paul McCartney, and Pope John Paul II. Guided stadium tours are available. ⊠ *Rua Professor Eurico Rabelo, Gate 16* ☎ 021/2568–9962 or 021/2569–4916 💲 *Tours R\$3* ☉ *Tours daily 9–5, except on match days* Ⓜ *Maracanã.*

⑰ **Quinta da Boa Vista.** West of downtown, on the landscaped grounds of a former royal estate, are pools and marble statues, as well as the **Museu Nacional** and the **Jardim Zoológico.** Housed in what was once the imperial palace (built in 1803), the museum has exhibits on Brazil's past and on its flora, fauna, and minerals—including the biggest meteorite (5 tons) found in the southern hemisphere. At the zoo you can see animals from Brazil's wilds in re-created natural habitats. Glimpse bats and sloths at the Nocturnal House. ⊠ *Av. Paulo e Silva and Av. Bartolomeu de Gusmão* ☎ *021/2568–8262 for museum, 021/2569–2024 for zoo* 🖼 *Museum R$3; zoo R$5 weekends, R$4 Tues.–Fri.* ⊗ *Museum Tues.–Sun. 10–4; zoo Tues.–Sun. 9–4:30* Ⓜ *São Cristóvão.*

WHERE TO EAT

With more than 900 restaurants, Rio's dining choices are broad, from low-key Middle Eastern cafés to elegant contemporary eateries with award-winning kitchens and first-class service. The succulent offerings in the *churrascarias* (restaurants specializing in grilled meats) can be mesmerizing for meat lovers—especially the places that serve *rodízio* style (grilled meat on skewers is continuously brought to your table—until you can eat no more). Hotel restaurants often serve the national dish, feijoada, on Saturday—sometimes Friday, too. Wash it down with a *chopp* (the local draft beer; pronounced "shop") or a *caipirinha* (crushed lime, crushed ice, and a potent sugarcane liquor called *cachaça*).

For vegetarians there is an abundance of salad bars, where you pay for your greens by the kilo. And seafood restaurants are everywhere. Note that it's perfectly safe to eat fresh produce in clean, upscale places; avoid shellfish in all but the best restaurants.

Cariocas do not take a siesta and *almoço* (lunch) is small—often just a *lanche* (literally "snack," but includes sandwiches). Dinner is a late affair; if you arrive at 7, you may be the only one in the restaurant. Popular places seat customers until well after midnight on weekends, when the normal closing hour is 2 AM. Cariocas love to linger in *botecos,* plain but pleasant bars that may also serve food, and such establishments abound. Most serve dishes in the $–$$ range, and portions are large enough for two people to share.

Many restaurants have a fixed-price menu as well as à la carte fare. Many also include what is referred to as a *couvert* (cover charge) for the bread and other appetizers placed on the table. Leaving a 10% tip is enough, but check your bill: it may already have been added. Some restaurants don't accept credit cards, and dress is almost always casual.

	WHAT IT COSTS In Reais				
	$$$$	$$$	$$	$	¢
AT DINNER	over R$60	R$45–R$60	R$30–R$45	R$15–R$30	under R$15

Prices are for a main course at dinner.

Centro

Cafés

¢ ✕ **Confeitaria Colombo.** At the turn of the 20th century this belle epoque
Fodor'sChoice structure was Rio's preeminent café, the site of elaborate balls, after-
★ noon teas for upper-class *senhoras,* and a center of political intrigue and

gossip. Enormous Jacaranda-framed mirrors from Belgium, stained glass from France, and tiles from Portugal add to the art-nouveau decor. Meals are buffet-style, with classic Brazilian dishes. The best way to absorb the opulence is as Rio's high society did a century ago: with *chá da tarde,* or afternoon tea (R$32). But you can also just stop by for a pastry and coffee. ⊠ *Rua Gonçalves Dias 32, Centro* ☎ *021/2232–2300* ⊕ *www.confeitariacolombo.com.br* ⊟ *AE, DC, MC, V* ⊗ *Closed Sun. No dinner* Ⓜ *Carioca.*

Seafood

$$–$$$ ✕ **Albamar.** Opened in 1933, Albamar faces Guanabara Bay. The restaurant is owned by the waitstaff, assuring efficient service. The circular green building serves fine seafood and fish. The chef's-style *à moda* dishes are good choices. The menu lists a fish fillet with white-wine sauce, sour cream, shrimp, and mussels, served with mashed potatoes; Spanish-style octopus with potatoes; and six codfish balls. Albamar closes at 6 PM. ⊠ *Praça Marechal Âncora 186, Centro* ☎ *021/2240–8428* ⊟ *AE, DC, MC, V* ⊗ *No dinner. Closed Mon.* Ⓜ *Carioca.*

Vegetarian

¢–$ ✕ **Bistrô do Paço.** A good option for a light lunch, the daily buffet of salads (R$14 per person) includes carrot salad with oranges, potatoes, and apples. You also can try an onion, cheese, or spinach quiche. ⊠ *Praça Quinze 48, Centro* ☎ *021/2262–3613* ⊟ *AE, D, MC, V* ⊗ *Closes at 7:30 during the week and at 7 on weekends* Ⓜ *Uruguaiana.*

Copacabana & Leme

Brazilian

$$$$ ✕ **Marius.** This well-regarded churrascaria serves more than a dozen types of sizzling meats rodízio style. Marius is famed for taking the usual meat cuts to a higher level of sophistication. The variety of side dishes is good, and includes Japanese food and fish. ⊠ *Av. Atlântica 290A, Leme* ☎ *021/2104–9000* ⊟ *AE, DC, MC, V.*

$$$–$$$$ ✕ **Siri Mole.** For typical food from the northeast of Brazil, this is the place. It's a small but absolutely comfortable restaurant that makes exotic dishes such as *acarajé,* a mix of fried smashed white beans and shrimp. Don't miss the *moqueca de siri,* a crab stew with *dendê* oil (spicy orange palm oil), and coconut milk. ⊠ *Rua Francisco Otaviano 50, Copacabana* ☎ *021/2267–0894* ⊟ *AE, DC, MC, V* Ⓜ *Siqueira Campos, then shuttle bus to Praça General Osório, get off at last stop in Copacabana.*

Eclectic

$–$$ ✕ **Aipo & Aipim.** There are more than 20 salads and hot dishes at this self-serve eatery with live music. After walking through the hot-dish and salad buffet, take your plate up to the grill and pick steaks, chicken, and pork cuts. Waiters take orders for drinks at your table. There are multiple branches in Copacabana and one in Ipanema. The Ipanema branch is only open until 6. ⊠ *Nossa Senhora de Copacabana 391, Loja B, Copacabana* ☎ *021/2255–6285* ⊟ *AE, DC, MC, V* Ⓜ *Cardeal Arcoverde* ⊠ *Rua Visconde de Pirajá 145, Ipanema* ☎ *021/2522–7300* ⊟ *AE, DC, MC, V* Ⓜ *Siqueira Campos then shuttle bus to Praça General Osório.*

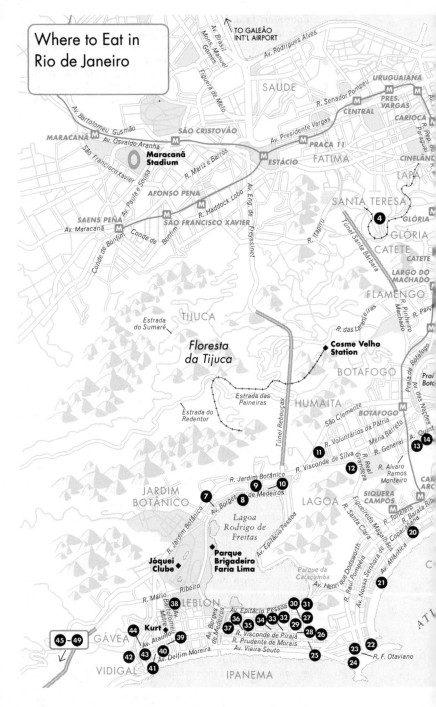

Where to Eat in Rio de Janeiro

TO GALEÃO INT'L AIRPORT

French

$$$$ ✕ **Le Pré-Catalan.** Considered the best French cuisine in Rio, this is the *carioca* version of the charming Parisian restaurant of the same name in the Bois du Boulogne. This highly reputed establishment has a prix-fixe menu (R$110) with four choices for appetizers, main dish, and dessert that changes periodically. À la carte options average around R$45, and include such specialties as a lamb dish that is cooked for seven hours. ⊠ *Sofitel Rio Palace, Av. Atlântica 4240, Level E, Copacabana* ☎ *021/ 2525–1160* ⌂ *Reservations essential* ▭ *AE, DC, MC, V* ☉ *No lunch* Ⓜ *No metro.*

★ **$$$$** ✕ **Le Saint Honoré.** An extraordinary view of Copacabana Beach from the 37th floor of Le Meridien hotel accompanies fine French–Brazilian fusion cuisine at Le Saint Honoré, which has prix-fixe and à la carte options. Typical French dishes are combined with Brazilian specialties in popular dishes like smoked *surubim* (an Amazonian fish) served in a shrimp sauce and marinated in three different types of local olive oils, and lamb fillet with *farofa* (fried yucca flour) and a corn beignet. The esteemed magazine *Veja Rio* rated this the number-one French restaurant in Rio for 2005. ⊠ *Av. Atlântica 1020, 37th floor, Copacabana* ☎ *021/3873–8880* ⌂ *Reservations essential* ⛨ *Jacket and tie* ▭ *AE, DC, MC, V.*

Italian

★ **$$$–$$$$** ✕ **D'Amici.** This place has the largest wine list in Rio, with 300 labels, ranging from R$26 to R$10,000—for the Romanée Conti—and also serves 30 types of wine by the glass (R$7–R$26). The restaurant is consistently a favorite in Rio for its food and atmosphere. The lamb with arugula risotto is a specialty, and the pasta in general is their best choice. ⊠ *Rua Antônio Vieira 18, Leme* ☎ *021/2541–4477* ▭ *AE, DC, MC, V* ⌂ *Reservations essential.*

★ **$$$–$$$$** ✕ **Cipriani.** For a superb dining experience, start with a Cipriani, champagne with fresh peach juice (really a Bellini), and move on to an appetizer of snook carpaccio with eggplant and capers or a salad of endive marinated in red wine. The pasta dishes are prepared with great care, and the meat and fish entrées are appropriate to their lavish surroundings—with a view to the hotel's beautiful pool. The degustation menu is R$180, or R$295 with wine. ⊠ *Copacabana Palace hotel, Av. Atlântica 1702, Copacabana* ☎ *021/2545–8747* ⌂ *Reservations essential* ▭ *AE, DC, MC, V* Ⓜ *Cardeal Arcoverde.*

Seafood

$$–$$$$ ✕ **Azul Marinho.** Sophisticated is the first word that comes to mind when you enter this quiet restaurant with formal service and a giant panoramic window looking out onto a barely trafficked street across from Arpoador Beach. *Moqueca* is the specialty, made with shrimp, cod, lobster, crab, or octopus—or a mix of them all. Meals are elegant and the seafood is fresh, but our favorite reason to go to Azul Marinho is to sit at its outdoor tables near the beach, enjoying early-evening appetizers, drinks, and sunset. ⊠ *Av. Francisco Bhering s/n, Arpoador* ☎ *021/3813–4228* ⊕ *www.cozinhatipica.com.br* ▭ *AE, D, DC, MC, V.*

$–$$$$ ✕ **Shirley.** Homemade Spanish seafood casseroles and soups are the draw at this traditional Leme restaurant tucked onto a shady street. Try the *zarzuela,* a seafood soup, or *cazuela,* a fish fillet with white-wine sauce. Don't be turned off by the simple decor (a few paintings hung on wood-paneled walls): the food is terrific. ⊠ *Rua Gustavo Sampaio 610, Leme* ☎ *021/2275–1398* ⌂ *Reservations not accepted* ▭ *No credit cards.*

¢–$$ ✕ **Don Camillo.** There's always something new on the menu at this Copacabana beachfront restaurant. Try the baked mix of lobster, shrimp, squid, mussels, tomato, potato, and fresh fish of the day, or stick to their delicious thin crust pizza. The Italian atmosphere is completed by a musical group that sings traditional Italian songs. ⊠ *Av. Atlântica 3056, Copacabana* ☎ *021/2549–9958* ⊕ *www.tempero.com.br/doncamillo/index.htm* ▭ *AE, D, DC, MC, V* Ⓜ *Cardeal Arcoverde.*

Flamengo & Botafogo

Brazilian

$$–$$$$ ✕ **Yorubá.** Exotic and delicious dishes are served at this restaurant, one of the few places that go beyond traditional African–Brazilian cuisine. Try the Afro menu, a selection of contemporary West African dishes. Service can be slow, but you are well rewarded for the wait. The *piripiri* (a spicy rice with ginger, coconut milk, and shrimp) is worth the price of R$65 for two. ⊠ *Rua Arnaldo Quintela 94, Botafogo* ☎ *021/2541–9387* ▭ *AE, V* Ⓜ *Botafogo.*

$$$ ✕ **Porcão.** The ultimate in Brazilian churrascaria experiences, Porcão has
FodorsChoice bow-tied waiters who flit between linen-draped tables, wielding giant
★ skewers, and slicing you portions of sizzling barbecued beef, pork, and chicken until you say uncle. The buffet is huge, with salads, sushi, and, on Saturdays, more than 15 types of feijoada. (Hats off if you can do churrasco *and* feijoada in one sitting!) Porcão is a chain, with four restaurants in Rio—including the one in Ipanema (⇨ *below*)—and another in the suburb of Niterói, but the nearly floor-to-ceiling windows with a view over Guanabara Bay to the Sugar Loaf make the Flamengo branch our top choice. ⊠ *Av. Infante Dom Henrique, Parque do Flamengo* ☎ *021/2554–8535* ▭ *AE, DC, MC, V* Ⓜ *Siqueira Campos, then shuttle bus to Praça General Osório* Ⓜ *Flamengo.*

Eclectic

$$–$$$$ ✕ **Alho & Óleo.** Home-made pasta is the hallmark of this place of vivid European inspiration. There are many options, including *picatina alcapone* (beef fillet with lime sauce), and sage-and-ricotta tortellini. Finish with a pear dessert cooked in white wine with vanilla ice cream and chocolate topping. ⊠ *Rua Buarque de Macedo 13, Flamengo* ☎ *021/2225–3418* ▭ *AE, V, MC, DC* Ⓜ *Catete.*

French

$$$$ ✕ **Carême.** This charming bistro, decorated in a romantic style, offers several fine prix-fixe menus (R$138 each) as well as an extensive à la carte menu (a fish dish, for instance, would average around R$50). The restaurant prides itself in using lots of organic ingredients, and serves delicious desserts. ⊠ *Rua Visconde de Caravelas 113, Botafogo* ☎ *021/2537–2274* ⌂ *Reservations essential* ☉ *No lunch* ▭ *AE, DC, MC, V* Ⓜ *Botafogo.*

SWEET TEMPTATIONS

RIO HAS A FINE SELECTION of irresistible dessert parlors perfect for a day-time outing or a post-dinner stop.

The Bakers (✉ Rua Visconde de Pirajá 330 Ipanema ☎ 21/3201–5050 ✉ Rua do Ouvidor 140 Centro ☎ 021/2232–3226 ✉ Rua Santa Clara 86 Copacabana ☎ 021/3209–1212 ⊕ www.thebakers.com.br) is a great choice for delicious cookies and cakes, including a cheesecake make with Brazilian fruits.

The mouthwatering cakes and pies at **Chaika** (✉ Rua Visconde de Pirajá 321 Ipanema ☎ 021/2287–8776 ⊕ www.chaika.com.br) come in flavors as simple as chocolate and as exotic as coconut with pineapple. They are complemented by a great selection of homemade ice creams.

Just two blocks from the beach, quaint hangout **Colher de Pau** (✉ Rua Farme de Amoedo 39 Ipanema ☎ 021/2523–3018) serves delicious desserts, including a famous coconut pie.

Inside a beautiful, historic ballroom, dessert and teahouse **Confeitaria Colombo** (✉ Rua Gonçalves Dias 32 Centro ☎ 021/2232–2300 ⊕ www.confeitariacolombo.com.br) is a perfect place to rest during your tour of Centro. Here you can get the cookie or pastry of your choice, including delicious French profiteroles, as well as traditional Brazilian desserts made with local fruits.

Buffet-style restaurant **Da Silva** (✉ Rua Barão da Torre 600 Ipanema ☎ 021/2521–1289) specializes in typical Portuguese desserts.

The dozens of dessert selections at **Doce Delicia** (✉ Rua Anibal de Mendonça 55 Ipanema ☎ 021/2259–0239) ranges from international favorites like a traditional chocolate cake to local specialities, such as a delicious guava paste.

Still operated by the same Austrian family that opened it in the 1970s, **Kurt** (✉ Rua General Urquiza 117 Leblon ☎ 021/2294–0599 ⊕ www.confeitariakurt.com.br) specializes in traditional European desserts like Austrian Sacher torte, German strudel, and Black Forest cake, with a few Brazil-inspired choices, like passion-fruit mousse cake.

For ice cream, you can't do better than **Mil Frutas** (✉ Rua Garcia d'Avila Ipanema ☎ 021/2521–1384 ✉ Rua J. J. Seabra, across from no. 6 Jardim Botânico ☎ 021/2511–2550). You could go for plain old chocolate, by why not chocolate with maracujá (passion fruit) instead? The canela com gengibre (cinnamon with ginger) is highly recommended, as are some of the more exotic fruit flavors unique to Brazil, like acerola and açaí.

Italian

$ ╳ **Pizza Park.** This enormous pizzeria is part of the hip Cobal Humaitá complex, which houses about a dozen bars and restaurants, whose mostly outdoor tables and chairs abut one another to create a lively scene that extends late into the night. It's a great place to hang out with friends, and the waitstaff will let you linger over your pizza and beer for as long as you like. More than 30 varieties of pizza are on the menu. ✉ *Rua Voluntários da Pátria 446, Botafogo* ☎ *021/2537–5383 or 021/2537–2602* ▤ *AE, DC, MC, V.*

Portuguese

$–$$$$ ╳ **Adega do Valentim.** Generous portions of cod, goat, and stews easily serve two or three people. The appetizers, especially the *bolinho de bacalhau* (fried cod dumplings), are popular. The restaurant is near Rio Sul Shopping Center, on the way from Copacabana Beach to Guanabara Bay. ✉ *Rua da Passagem 178, Botafogo* ☎ *021/2541–1166* ▤ *AE, D, DC, MC, V.*

Ipanema & Leblon

Brazilian

$$$–$$$$ ╳ **Esplanada Grill.** This churrascaria serves high-quality meat like T-bone steak or *picanha*, a tasty Brazilian cut of beef marbled with some fat. All the grilled dishes come with fried palm hearts, baked potatoes, and rice. An average meal is R$90. ✉ *Rua Barão da Torre 600, Ipanema* ☎ *021/2512–2970* ▤ *AE, DC, MC, V* Ⓜ *Siqueira Campos, then shuttle bus to Praça General Osório.*

★ $$$ ╳ **Porcão.** A convenient location makes this branch of Rio's famous churrascaria the most popular one with tourists, but we prefer the Flamengo branch (⇨ above) for its fabulous view. You'll get the same excellent service and quality of food here, but in a smaller space with no view. ✉ *Rua Barão da Torre 218, Ipanema* ☎ *021/2522–0999* ▤ *AE, DC, MC, V* Ⓜ *Siqueira Campos, then shuttle bus to Praça General Osório.*

★ $$ ╳ **Casa da Feijoada.** Many restaurants serve Brazil's savory national dish on Saturdays, but here the huge pots of the stew simmer every day. You can choose which of the nine types of meat you want in your stew, but if it's your first time, waiters will bring you a "safe" version with sausage, beef, and pork—and sans feet and ears. The feijoada comes with the traditional side dishes of rice, collard greens, *farofa* (toasted and seasoned manioc flour), *aipim* (fried yucca), *torresminho* (pork rinds), and orange slices (to lower your cholesterol!). Not feeling like the feijoada? The menu has entrées as well, like baked chicken, shrimp in coconut milk, grilled trout, and filet mignon. Desserts include *quindim* (a yolk-and-sugar pudding with coconut crust) and Romeo and Juliet (guava compote with fresh cheese). The caipirinhas are made not only with lime but also with tangerine, passion fruit, pineapple, strawberry, or kiwi. Be careful—they're strong. ✉ *Rua Prudente de Morais 10, Ipanema* ☎ *021/2247–2776* ⊕ *www.cozinhatipica.com.br* ▤ *AE, DC, MC, V* Ⓜ *Siqueira Campos, then shuttle bus to Praça General Osório.*

¢–$$ ╳ **Jobi.** Not to be missed, Jobi is a Leblon institution—and since it's open daily from 9 AM to 4 AM, you should be able to squeeze it in. It's the sort of place you can go to in your bikini straight from the beach. Basic sandwiches and salads are on the menu, but the reason to go is the fabulous seafood. Order a full meal or just try various appetizers. The bolinho de bacalhau (mini cod cakes) may be the best in town. ⊠ *Rua Ataulfo de Paiva 1166, Leblon* ☎ *021/2274–0547* ▭ *AE* ☺ *Breakfast served.*

¢–$ ✕ **Colher de Pau.** Just two blocks from Ipanema Beach, this chilled-out place is a great place for a bite during or after a day in the sun. It's open from breakfast through dinner, and serves good sandwiches and salads plus healthy grilled fish or steak, and great desserts. ⊠ *Rua Farme de Amoedo 39, Ipanema* ☎ *021/2523–3018* ▭ *AE, DC, MC, V* ☺ *Breakfast served.*

¢–$ ✕ **New Natural.** One of many restaurants in Rio where you pay per kilo, this one stands out for its use of natural and organic products. You'll have multiple vegetarian options and lots of soy-based dishes. They also serve delicious fruit juices. On hot days, choose the somewhat hidden upstairs dining room, which is air-conditioned. ⊠ *Rua Barão da Torre, Ipanema* ☎ *021/2247–1335* ▭ *AE, DC, MC, V.*

Cafés

★ ¢–$$ ✕ **Garcia & Rodrigues.** Cariocas breakfast at this cozy combination café, delicatessen, liquor shop, and trendy restaurant. At lunchtime choose from a selection of sandwiches, such as marinated salmon, pastrami, or buffalo-milk cheese. Dinner, based on French cuisine, is served until 12:30 AM Monday–Thursday and until 1 AM Friday and Saturday. On Sunday nights the café is open until midnight, but à la carte meals are not served. ⊠ *Av. Ataulfo de Paiva 1251, Leblon* ☎ *021/2512–8188* ▭ *AE, DC, MC, V.*

¢–$$ ✕ **Gula Gula.** Salads at upscale café Gula Gula are anything but boring. Beyond classics like Caesar and chicken pesto, fresh local fruits and veggies are mixed into salads like eggplant with tomatoes, herbs, *queijo Minas* (a mild, white cheese), and mint dressing, or organic palm-heart salad with tomatoes, watercress, and raisins. Grilled fish or steak, baked potatoes, and soups are good non-salad options. ⊠ *Rua Anibal de Mendonça 132, Ipanema* ☎ *021/2259–3084* ⊕ *www.gulagula.com.br* ▭ *AE, DC, MC, V.*

Eclectic

¢–$ ✕ **Doce Delícia.** Make your own dish by choosing from 5 to 15 of the 42 combinations of vegetables, side dishes, hot dishes, and fruit. Quiche, salmon, grilled tenderloin, chicken, and cold pasta are some of the choices. Dressings range from the light and yogurt based to innovative creations combining mustard and lemon. There are plenty of vegetarian options. The slick decor and fresh ingredients make this a popular choice for a regular clientele in the trendy area of Ipanema. For a reasonable price you can also pick main dishes from the menu—for example, the chicken breast with honey and rosemary sauce for R$17. ⊠ *Rua Aníbal de Mendonça 55, Ipanema* ☎ *021/2259–0239* ▭ *AE, MC, V.*

¢–$ ✕ **Fazendola.** The name means "small farm," and this restaurant is reminiscent of a Brazilian farm with its wooden furniture and dim lighting. Homemade dishes prepared with very fresh ingredients are sold by the kilo. The other option is to try their delicious pizza, which you can order either à la carte or "all you can eat." ⊠ *Rua Jangadeiros 14B, Ipanema* ☎ *021/2247–9600* ⊟ *AE, DC, MC, V* Ⓜ *Siqueira Campos, then shuttle bus to Praça General Osório.*

Indian

$–$$ ✕ **Natraj.** One block from Leblon's beachfront, this traditional Indian restaurant has a tasting menu for two, with eight portions of different dishes, a good option for a reasonable price. It can be ordered in vegetarian or nonvegetarian versions. Other suggestions are the many *pulau* (rice) and *dhal* (bean or pea) dishes, which may come with vegetables, coconut, fresh white cheese, or *panir,* and spices, or masala. You can also order à la carte. Good options for starters, the *samosas* are fine pastries with chicken, beef, mixed-vegetable, or potato-and-pea fillings. ⊠ *Av. General San Martin 1219, Leblon* ☎ *021/2239–4745* ⊟ *D, MC, V.*

Italian

$$–$$$ ✕ **Gero.** This high-end restaurant serves homemade pastas and risottos, and fish and meat dishes. Vegetarian options are plentiful. Typical Italian desserts served include gelato and profiteroles. ⊠ *Rua Anibal de Mendonca 157 Ipanema* ☎ *21/2239–8158* ⊟ *AE, D, DC, MC, V.*

$–$$$$ ✕ **Margutta.** Just a block from Ipanema Beach, Margutta has a reputation for outstanding Mediterranean-style seafood, such as broiled fish in tomato sauce and fresh herbs or lobster cooked in aluminum foil with butter and saffron rice. Polenta is made with fancy funghi and olive oil flavored with white truffles. ⊠ *Av. Henrique Dumont 62, Ipanema* ☎ *021/2511–0878* ⊟ *AE, DC, MC, V* ☯ *No lunch weekdays.*

$–$$ ✕ **Cappriciosa.** There are lots of pizza places in Rio, but this one emerges at the top of the list. Delicious thin-crust pizzas are served with every topping imaginable, from the standard margheritta to fancy prosciuttos and interesting spices. Its tall glass windows and location in the heart of Ipanema make for perfect people-watching. ⊠ *Rua Vinicius de Moraes 175, Ipanema* ☎ *021/2523–3394* ⊟ *AE, DC, MC* ☯ *No lunch.*

Japanese

$$–$$$$ ✕ **Madame Butterfly.** At this fine Japanese restaurant, start with pumpkin *gyoza* (dumplings) with shrimp, a platter with six rolls, or the Beijing duck salad, a mix of greens and shredded duck with tangerine sauce. Main dishes include grilled salmon with honey and miso, and the best sukiyaki in Rio. ⊠ *Rua Barão da Torre 472, Ipanema* ☎ *021/2267–4347* ⊟ *AE, V.*

Mexican

$–$$ ✕ **Guapo Loco.** Bustling crowds feast on tamales, enchiladas, and other Mexican favorites until the last customer leaves. Tequila has garnered quite a following in Rio, making Guapo Loco one of the favorite Mexican places thanks to its good margaritas. ⊠ *Rua Rainha Guilhermina 48, Leblon* ☎ *021/2294–2915* ⊟ *MC, V* ☯ *No lunch weekdays.*

Portuguese

$$$–$$$$ ✕ **Antiquarius.** This much-loved establishment is famous for its flawless rendering of Portuguese classics. A recommended dish is the *cozido,* a stew with onions, yams, carrots, pumpkin, cabbage, bananas,
Fodor'sChoice ★

and more. The *cataplana,* a seafood stew with rice, is also marvelous, and the *perna de cordeiro* (leg of lamb) is the most requested dish on the menu. The wine list impresses even Portuguese gourmands. ⊠ *Rua Aristides Espínola 19, Leblon* ☎ *021/2294–1049* ⌫ *Reservations essential* ▭ *DC, MC.*

Seafood

$$$–$$$$
FodorsChoice
★
✕ **Satyricon.** Some of the best seafood in town is served at this eclectic Italian seafood restaurant, which has impressed the likes of Madonna and Sting. The *pargo* (fish baked in a thick layer of rock salt) is a specialty, and the sushi and sashimi are well loved. ⊠ *Rua Barão da Torre 192, Ipanema* ☎ *021/2521–0627* ▭ *DC, MC, V* Ⓜ *Siqueira Campos, then shuttle bus to Praça General Osório.*

Vegetarian
Also see New Natural *in* Brazilian, *above.*

$$
✕ **Celeiro.** One of Rio's few organic restaurants, Celeiro is always full. There are approximately 20 salads on the buffet, as well as a wide selection of pastas. ⊠ *Rua Dias Ferreira 199, Leblon* ☎ *021/2274–7843* ▭ *D, MC, V* ☺ *No dinner. Closed Sun.*

$–$$
✕ **Vegetariano Social Clube.** Vegan restaurants are rare in Rio, and this is by far the most sophisticated. The small eatery has carefully prepared dishes free of any animal products that go much beyond brown rice or burdock. ⊠ *Rua Conde de Bernadotte 26, Loja L, Leblon* ☎ *021/2294–5200* ⊕ *www.vegetarianosocialclube.com.br* ▭ *D, MC, V.*

Jardim Botanico

French

$$$$
FodorsChoice
★
✕ **Olympe.** The menu's all-Brazilian ingredients are a unique trait of this innovative restaurant that blends native flavors with nouvelle techniques. Every dish—from the crab or lobster flan to chicken, fish, and duck prepared with exotic herbs and sauces—is exceptionally light. The passion-fruit crepe soufflé is a favorite dessert. ⊠ *Rua Custódio Serrão 62, Jardim Botânico* ☎ *021/2537–8582* ⌫ *Reservations essential* ▭ *AE, MC, V.*

Italian

$$–$$$
FodorsChoice
★
✕ **Quadrifoglio.** Considered by most locals to be the best Italian restaurant in the city, cozy Quadrifoglio is tucked away on a quiet street. The food and the service are impeccable; the restaurant has been around since 1991 and much of the original waitstaff still works there. Some favorite entrée choices are spinach ravioli and the fabulous salads. Leave room for desserts, which are what the place is most famous for. ⊠ *Rua J. J. Seabra 19, Jardim Botanico* ☎ *021/2294–1433* ☺ *No dinner Sun., no lunch Sat.* ▭ *AE, DC, MC, V.*

Lagoa

Eclectic

$$–$$$
✕ **Mistura Fina.** A combination of traditional Portuguese and Brazilian dishes is combined with elegant design here, making this an excellent

choice for a romantic dinner out. Above the restaurant there is live music and an outdoor balcony, so you can enjoy dinner and then spend the rest of your evening just upstairs. The service can be slow, but the food is well worth the wait. ✉ *Av. Borges de Medeiros 3207, Lagoa* ☎ *021/2537-2844* ⊕ *www.misturafina.com.br* ⊟ *AE, DC, MC.*

Santa Teresa

Brazilian

$-$$ ✕ **Bar do Arnaudo.** A neighborhood favorite for 30-plus years, this informal tavern serves generous portions of unusual Brazilian food. Case in point: goat and broccoli with *pirão* (cassava mush) and rice. Portions are large enough to serve two or even three. For dessert, sweetened condensed milk is cooked to a creamy caramel-like paste and served atop slices of *coalho* (a semihard cow cheese). Arnaudo has nice views of the city and Guanabara Bay. ✉ *Rua Almirante Alexandrino 316-B, Santa Teresa* ☎ *021/2252-7246* ⊟ *MC.*

São Conrado, Barra da Tijuca & Beyond

Brazilian

$$-$$$ ✕ **Barra Grill.** A favorite stop after a long day at Praia Barra, this informal and popular steak house serves some of the best meat in town. Prices for the rodízio-style meals are slightly higher on weekends than during the week. Reservations are essential on weekends. ✉ *Av. Ministro Ivan Lins 314, Barra da Tijuca* ☎ *021/2493-6060* ⊟ *AE, DC, MC, V.*

Italian

$$-$$$ ✕ **Alfredo.** The pasta here is excellent, especially the fettuccine Alfredo and the spaghetti carbonara. They also serve a delicious lamb dish. The restaurant has a view of the hotel pool. ✉ *Inter-Continental Rio hotel, Av. Prefeito Mendes de Morais 222, São Conrado* ☎ *021/3323-2200* ⊟ *AE, DC, MC, V* ✆ *No lunch.*

Seafood

$$-$$$ ✕ **Restaurante Point de Grumari.** From Grumari, Estrada de Guaratiba climbs up through dense forest, emerging atop a hill above the vast Guaratiba flatlands. Here you find this eatery famed for grilling fish to perfection. With its shady setting, glorious vistas, and live music performances (samba, bossa nova, jazz), it's the perfect spot for lunch (it's open daily noon-6:30) after a morning on the beach and before an afternoon at the Sítio Roberto Burle Marx or the Museu Casa do Pontal. ✉ *Estrada do Grumari 710, Grumari* ☎ *021/2410-1434* ✆ *No dinner* ⊟ *AE, DC, MC, V.*

$-$$$ ✕ **476.** At the end of a road with stunning coastal views, 476 is all about
Fodor's Choice simplicity, with just seven delicious entrées that include *moquecas*
★ (seafood stews), grilled seafood, and curries. It has only 20 tables, some in a lovely garden at water's edge. The quiet fishing village 13 km (8 mi) west of Barra da Tijuca is a nice respite from the bustling Zona Sul. Tell the taxi driver to take you to "Quatro Sete Meia." ✉ *Rua Barros de Alarcão 476, Pedra da Guaratiba* ☎ *021/2417-1716* ⚷ *Reservations essential* ⊟ *AE, MC, V.*

WHERE TO STAY

Most hotels are in Copacabana and Ipanema. Copacabana hotels are close to the action (and the metro), but the neighborhood is noisier than Ipanema (which is itself noisier than São Conrado and Barra da Tijuca). If you plan to spend lots of time at the beach, stay at a hotel along Copacabana, Ipanema, or Barra da Tijuca (Copacabana has the advantage of being accessible by metro.) Note that "motels" aren't aimed at tourists. They attract couples looking for privacy and usually rent by the hour.

In the days just prior to and during Carnival, already peak-season rates can double, even triple. Expect to pay a premium for a room with a view. Many hotels include breakfast in the rate, but the quality varies from a full buffet to a hard roll with butter. If you're traveling during peak periods, make reservations as far in advance as possible.

		WHAT IT COSTS In Reais			
	$$$$	**$$$**	**$$**	**$**	**¢**
FOR 2 PEOPLE	over R$500	R$375–R$500	R$250–R$375	R$125–R$250	under R$125

Prices are for a standard double room in high season, excluding taxes.

Centro

$–$$ ⊡ **Guanabara Palace Hotel.** A member of the Windsor chain that was remodeled in 2001, the Guanabara is one of the few solid hotel choices right in Centro. Rooms are reasonably sized and tastefully done in brown and beige. The restaurant serves elaborate buffet meals. The contemporary rooftop pool area, with its stunning views of Guanabara Bay, absolutely gleams thanks to its pristine white tiles, white trellises, and white patio furnishings. ⊠ *Av. Presidente Vargas 392, Centro 20071-000* ☎ *021/2216–1313* 🖷 *021/2516–1582* ⊕ *www.windsorhoteis. com/en-us/gu_loca.asp* ↪ *510 rooms, 3 suites* ⌂ *Restaurant, room service, in-room safes, minibars, cable TV, in-room broadband, Wi-Fi, pool, health club, sauna, bar, dry cleaning, laundry service, business services, meeting rooms, parking (fee), no-smoking rooms* ▤ *AE, DC, MC, V* ⦿*| BP* Ⓜ *Uruguaiana.*

Copacabana & Leme

These neighborhoods can be dangerous at night, so it's wise to get around by taxi after dark.

$$$$ ⊡ **Copacabana Palace.** Built in 1923 for the visiting king of Belgium and inspired by Nice's Negresco and Cannes's Carlton, the Copacabana was the first luxury hotel in South America, and it is still one of the top hotels on the continent. Marlene Dietrich, Robert De Niro, and Princess Di have stayed here. It has a neoclassical facade and one of the city's largest and most attractive swimming pools. One of its two restaurants, the Cipriani, is rated among the city's best for its northern Italian cui-

FodorśChoice
★

sine. The Saturday feijoada is extraordinary. ⊠ *Av. Atlântica 1702, Copacabana 22021-001* ☎ *021/2548–7070, 0800/21–1533, 800/237–1236 in the U.S.* 🖷 *021/2235–7330* ⊕ *www.copacabanapalace.orient-express.com* ➴ *122 rooms, 111 suites* ♨ *2 restaurants, room service, in-room safes, cable TV, in-room VCRs, in-room DVD in most rooms, in-room broadband, Wi-Fi, tennis court, pool, health club, hair salon, spa, 2 bars, dry cleaning, laundry service, concierge, business services, meeting room, parking (fee), no-smoking rooms* ▭ *AE, DC, MC, V* Ⓜ *Cardeal Arcoverde.*

$$$$ ✕🖾 **Le Meridien.** Of the leading Copacabana hotels, the 37-story French-owned Meridien is the closest to Centro, making it a favorite of business travelers. Rooms are soundproof and have dark-wood furniture; at this writing, standard rooms could benefit from an update. The hotel has a complete executive center. The restaurant, Le Saint Honoré (⇨ above) is one of the city's best; the piano bar is lively at night. ⊠ *Av. Atlântica 1020, Copacabana 22010-000* ☎ *021/3873–8888 or 0800/25–7171* 🖷 *021/3873–8788* ⊕ *www.meridien-br.com/rio* ➴ *496 rooms, 53 suites* ♨ *2 restaurants, piano bar, room service, in-room safes, cable TV, in-room data ports, high-speed Internet in some rooms, pool, hair salon, sauna, bar, dry cleaning, laundry service, concierge, business services, parking (fee), no-smoking floors* ▭ *AE, DC, MC, V.*

$$$$ 🖾 **Marriott Rio de Janeiro.** You could be walking into a Marriott in any part of the world, which is a comfort for some and a curse for others. Expect spotlessly clean rooms and public areas, an efficient English-speaking staff, and the most modern (and expensive) services and facilities available. Despite the enormous lobby, rooms here are smaller than at most Marriott hotels. Some have views of Avenida Atlântica and Copacabana, others look onto the interior atrium. Business travelers are the Marriott's bread and butter, but thanks to its location—the front door spits you out onto Copacabana Beach—it attracts quite a few tourists as well. The sushi bar ($$$) gets rave reviews. ⊠ *Av. Atlântica 2600, Copacabana 22041-001* ☎ *021/2545–6500* 🖷 *021/2545–6555* ⊕ *www.marriottbrasil.com* ➴ *229 rooms, 16 suites* ♨ *Restaurant, room service, in-room safes, cable TV, in-room broadband, Wi-Fi, pool, health club, sauna, massage, dry cleaning, laundry service, concierge, business services, meeting rooms, parking (fee), no-smoking rooms* ▭ *AE, DC, MC, V.*

$$$$ 🖾 **Rio Othon Palace.** The flagship of the Brazilian Othon chain, this 30-story hotel is not new, but it does have a prime view of Copacabana's distinctive black-and-white sidewalk mosaic from the rooftop pool, bar, and sundeck. The executive floor has secretarial support, fax machines, and computer hookups. Only the master-floor suites have been recently renovated (in 2002). ⊠ *Av. Atlântica 3264, Copacabana 22070-001* ☎ *021/2522–1522* 🖷 *021/2522–1697* ⊕ *www.hoteis-othon.com.br* ➴ *554 rooms, 30 suites* ♨ *2 restaurants, room service, in-room safes, minibars, cable TV, in-room data ports, pool, health club, sauna, 2 bars, nightclub, dry cleaning, laundry service, concierge, business services, free parking, no-smoking rooms* ▭ *AE, DC, MC, V.*

$$$–$$$$ 🖾 **Excelsior.** This hotel, part of the Windsor chain, may have been built in the 1950s, but its look is sleek and contemporary—from the sparkling

Where to Stay in Rio de Janeiro

Ilha das Cobras

Baía de Guanabara

Menezes Cortes
us Terminal

Aeroporto
Santos
Dumont

Av. Gen. Justo

Av. Carlos

arque do
lamengo

etrô) Dom Henrique

Praia do Flamengo

GO

osa

Av. João
Luis Alves

URCA

Praia de
Fora

Av. São Sebastião

Praia da Urca

Av. Portugal

VERMELHA

R. Gustavo
Sampaio

LEME

Praia do
Leme

OCEAN

ABANA

0 —————————— 1 mile
0 —————————— 1 km

KEY

⚑ *Start of walk*

Ⓜ *Metro*

⊷⊶⊷ *Street Car*

·⊶·⊶· *Cable Car*

marble lobby to the guest-room closets paneled in gleaming jacaranda (Brazilian redwood). Service is top-rate. The expansive breakfast buffet is served in the hotel's window-banked restaurant facing the avenue and beach. The equally elaborate lunch and dinner buffets cost roughly R$35. The rooftop bar–pool area offers an escape from the hustle and bustle. Ask for a room with a view over Copacabana Beach. ⊠ *Av. Atlântica 1800, Copacabana 22021-001* ☎ *021/2545–6000, 0800/704–2827, 800/444–885 in the U.S.* ⊟ *021/2257–1850* ⊕ *www.windsorhoteis.com.br* ⇥ *233 rooms, 12 suites* ⌂ *Restaurant, room service, in-room safes, minibars, cable TV, in-room broadband, Wi-Fi, pool, sauna, health club, 2 bars, dry cleaning, laundry service, concierge, meeting room, free parking, no-smoking rooms* ⊟ *AE, DC, MC, V* ⊠⊟ *BP* Ⓜ *Cardeal Arcoverde.*

$$$–$$$$ 🏨 **Rio Atlântica.** Renovated in 2004, the Atlântica allows rooftop sunbathing and swimming and has a bar with a view of Copacabana Beach. The service is superb. Excellent restaurants, shopping, and nightlife in Copacabana are all within walking distance. Bathrooms are large and very clean. Standard rooms do not have a view. Oceanfront suites have an oversize balcony. ⊠ *Av. Atlântica 2964, Copacabana 22070-000* ☎ *021/2548–6332 or 0800/26–6332* ⊟ *021/2255–6410* ⊕ *www.pestana.com* ⇥ *109 rooms, 105 suites* ⌂ *2 restaurants, bar, room service, in-room safes, cable TV, in-room data ports, in-room broadband in some rooms, Wi-Fi, pool, health club, sauna, massage, dry cleaning, laundry service, concierge, business services, meeting room, free parking, no-smoking rooms* ⊟ *AE, DC, MC, V.*

★ $$$–$$$$ 🏨 **Sofitel Rio Palace.** Anchoring one end of Copacabana Beach, this hotel was given a top-to-bottom face-lift in 2000 and is once again one of the best on the strip. The building's H shape gives breathtaking views of the sea, the mountains, or both from the balconies of all rooms. The most reasonably priced rooms face one of the pools opposite the beach. All other units have an ocean view. The first floors are home to Shopping Casino Atlântico, an upscale mall with home accessories, decorative art, and antiques stores. One pool gets the morning sun; the other, afternoon rays. The restaurant Le Pré-Catalan is as good as its Parisian original. Chef Roland Villard, from the French Culinary Academy, is welcoming and creates new dishes every two weeks. ⊠ *Av. Atlântica 4240, Copacabana 22070-002* ☎ *021/2525–1232, 0800/703–7003, 800/7763–4835 in the U.S.* ⊕ *www.accorhotels.com.br* ⇥ *372 rooms, 16 suites* ⌂ *2 restaurants, bar, in-room safes, cable TV, in-room broadband, Wi-Fi, 2 pools, health club, sauna, shops, dry cleaning, laundry service, concierge, business services, convention center, free parking, no-smoking rooms* ⊟ *AE, DC, MC, V.*

$$–$$$ 🏨 **Atlântico Copacabana.** Just three blocks from Copacabana Beach and close to the Siqueira Campos metro station, this hotel has a great location for the price. Rooms are simple and slightly larger than average. Choose a room on one of the top floors to avoid the street noise of this residential area. Rooms have tile floors and are simply and plainly furnished. ⊠ *Rua Siqueira Campos 90, Copacabana 22031-070* ☎ *021/2548–0011* ⊟ *021/2235–7941* ⊕ *www.atlanticocopacabana.com.br* ⇥ *114 rooms, 13 suites* ⌂ *Restaurant, room service, in-room safes, cable TV, in-room broadband, pool, health club, sauna, bar, dry cleaning, laun-*

dry service, concierge, business services, parking (fee) ☐ *AE, DC, MC, V* ⃒◉⃒ *BP* Ⓜ *Siqueira Campos.*

$$–$$$ 🏨 **Luxor Regente Hotel.** The best of the Luxor hotels in Rio, the Regente was renovated in 2004. The restaurant Forno e Fogão has a good feijoada, though it's not as well known as that of the Copacabana Palace. The suites have whirlpool baths. The gym area is small, but the hotel is committed to continually updating its equipment. If you choose a standard room, be sure that it's not one that faces south; those rooms have an unfortunate view of a trash-can-filled alley. Other rooms look out over Avenida Atlântica and Copacabana Beach. ⊠ *Av. Atlântica 3716, Copacabana 22070-001* ☎ *021/2525–2070 or 0800/16–5322* 🖷 *021/2267–7693* ⊕ *www.luxor-hotels.com/regente* 📞 *228 rooms, 2 suites* ⚭ *Restaurant, room service, in-room safes, cable TV, some in-room broadband, pool, health club, sauna, dry cleaning, laundry service, concierge, business services, parking (fee), no-smoking rooms* ☐ *AE, DC, MC, V* ⃒◉⃒ *BP.*

$$–$$$ 🏨 **Miramar Palace.** A mix of old and new, this beachfront hotel has some of the largest rooms in Rio with some of the best views. Classic accents like the Carrara marble floor of the lobby and the spectacular glass chandeliers that light the restaurant are contrasted with modern amenities like wireless Internet and the contemporary 16th-floor bar with an unobstructed view of the entire sweep of Copacabana. ⊠ *Av. Atlântica 3668, Copacabana 22070-001* ☎ *021/2525–0303 or 0800/23–2211* 🖷 *021/2521–3294* ⊕ *www.windsorhoteis.com* 📞 *147 rooms, 9 suites* ⚭ *Restaurant, coffee shop, tea shop, room service, in-room safes, cable TV, in-room data ports, Internet room, Wi-Fi, bar, dry cleaning, laundry service, concierge, free parking, no-smoking rooms* ☐ *AE, DC, MC, V* ⃒◉⃒ *BP.*

$$–$$$ 🏨 **Plaza Copacabana Hotel.** At the east entrance of Copacabana and in the shadow of the Sugar Loaf, this hotel is close to the beach but also near the large Rio Sul shopping center, with restaurants and movie theaters. The metro is just a few blocks away. The hotel still looks new (it opened in 1999) but the decor is nothing special. The real reason to stay here is the staff, which is extremely accommodating and welcoming. The rooftop gym and pool have nice views of Copacabana Beach. ⊠ *Av. Princesa Isabel 263, Copacabana 22011-010* ☎ *021/2195–5500 or 0800/90–2090* 🖷 *021/2543–8071* ⊕ *www.windsorhoteis.com* 📞 *233 rooms, 4 suites* ⚭ *Restaurant, room service, in-room safes, cable TV, in-room broadband, Wi-Fi, pool, health club, sauna, bar, dry cleaning, laundry service, concierge, business services, free parking, no-smoking floors, airport shuttle, travel services* ☐ *AE, DC, MC, V* ⃒◉⃒ *BP.*

★ **$$–$$$** 🏨 **Rio Internacional.** All rooms at this Copacabana landmark hotel have balconies with sea views, a rarity on Avenida Atlântica. The hotel is Swiss owned, and the tidy and modern Scandinavian design is one of its best assets. The pool area and gym are both perched above the beach, with great views. All guests are welcomed with a glass of champagne. ⊠ *Av. Atlântica 1500, Copacabana 22021-000* ☎ *021/2543–1555 or 0800/21–1559* 🖷 *021/2542–5443* ⊕ *www.riointernacional.com.br* 📞 *117 rooms, 11 suites* ⚭ *Restaurant, room service, in-room safes, cable TV, in-room broadband, Wi-Fi, pool, health club, sauna, massage, 2 bars, dry cleaning, laundry service, concierge, business services, parking (fee), no-smoking floors* ☐ *AE, DC, MC, V* Ⓜ *Cardeal Arco Verde.*

$–$$$ ⊡ **Parthenon Arpoador.** The flexibility of an apartment is combined with the services of a hotel in this luxurious building just steps from Copacabana Beach. All units are apartment-style, each with a bedroom, living room, bathroom, and small kitchen. Though a bit smaller than you might expect, apartments are modern, almost futuristic, with bright-white furniture, and everything is sparkling clean. The building is new and extremely well maintained. Each room has a balcony, but only some have an ocean view. ⊠ *Rua Francisco Otaviano 61, Copacabana 22070-010* ☎ *021/3222–9600* ✆ *parthenonarpoador@accorhotels.com* ⬐ *48 apartments* ⌂ *Copacabana, coffee shop, high-speed Internet access in all rooms, business center, concierge, free parking, no-smoking rooms, cable TV, DVD, microwave, gym, pool* ▤ *AE, DC, MC, V* ⍾ *EP.*

$$ ⊡ **Windsor Palace Hotel.** Close to the shopping area of Copacabana, the Windsor Palace has standard, unexciting hotel rooms. From the fifth floor up, rooms have balconies, but only those from the 12th floor up have ocean views. Overall, this is a solid mid-range option with decent services. The rooftop pool has a view of Copacabana beach, and it's just two blocks from the Siqueira Campos metro station. ⊠ *Rua Domingos Ferreira 6, Copacabana 22050-010* ☎ *021/2545–9000* ⎙ *021/2549–9373* ⊕ *www.windsorhoteis.com* ⬐ *73 rooms, 1 suite* ⌂ *Restaurant, room service, in-room safes, cable TV, pool, sauna, bar, dry cleaning, laundry service, concierge, meeting room, Internet room, free parking, no-smoking floors* ▤ *AE, DC, MC, V* ⍾ *BP* Ⓜ *Siqueira Campos.*

$–$$ ⊡ **Leme Othon Palace.** Unexciting but adequate, this hotel has large rooms and a quiet beachfront location. Built in 1964, it has a subdued, conservative air and lacks some modern amenities, although many rooms were renovated in 2004. Its location near Leme Beach and many transportation choices is the reason to stay here, despite slightly run-down accommodations. The metro station is six blocks away. ⊠ *Av. Atlântica 656, Leme 22010-000* ☎ *021/3873–5900* ⎙ *021/3873–5904* ⊕ *www.hoteis-othon.com.br* ⬐ *163 rooms, 27 suites* ⌂ *Restaurant, room service, in-room safes, cable TV, some in-room data ports, Internet room, bar, dry cleaning, laundry service, concierge, business services* ▤ *AE, DC, MC, V* Ⓜ *Cardeal Arco Verde.*

$–$$ ⊡ **Ouro Verde Hotel.** Since the 1950s this hotel has been favored for its efficient, personalized service. The tasteful art-deco style, with some French twists, is in step with the emphasis on quality and graciousness. However, some visitors note that the carpets and other furnishings are looking a bit worse for wear. All front rooms face the beach; those in the back on the 6th through 12th floors have a view of Corcovado. ⊠ *Av. Atlântica 1456, Copacabana 22021-000* ☎ *021/2543–4123* ⎙ *021/ 2542–4597* ⊕ *www.dayrell.com.br* ⬐ *60 rooms, 2 suites* ⌂ *Restaurant, room service, in-room safes, cable TV, in-room data ports, Internet room, bar, library, dry cleaning, laundry service, no-smoking rooms* ▤ *AE, DC, MC, V* Ⓜ *Cardeal Arco Verde.*

$ ⊡ **Copacabana Rio Hotel.** Brightly decorated in blues, yellows, and reds, the rooms here are nicer than those you find at many more-expensive places. A few rooms have wonderful views of Pedra da Gávea (Gávea Rock). From the heated rooftop pool you can see Copacabana Beach and Sugar Loaf. You're practically in Ipanema here, so the metro station is a bit of a hike (10 blocks away). ✉ *Av. Nossa Senhora de Copacabana 1256, Copacabana 22070-010* ☏ *021/2267–9900* 📠 *021/2267–2271* ⊕ *www.copacabanariohotel.com.br* ⇗ *90 rooms, 8 suites* ⟁ *Restaurant, in-room safes, cable TV, pool, sauna, laundry service, health club, concierge, meeting room, parking (fee)* ▤ *AE, DC, MC, V* ⟠ *BP* Ⓜ *Siqueira Campos.*

$ ⊡ **Hotel Debret.** This former apartment building scores points for keeping its prices moderate despite a beachfront location. The decor honors Brazil's past: the lobby has baroque statues and prints depicting colonial scenes, and the rooms are furnished in dark, heavy wood. The hotel has a loyal following among diplomats and businesspeople that are more interested in functionality and low prices than elegance. The buffet breakfast with a view of the beach is one of the hotel's best assets. Corner rooms tend to be the largest. ✉ *Av. Atlântica 3564, Copacabana 22060-040* ☏ *021/2522–0132* 📠 *021/2521–0899* ⊕ *www.debret.com* ⇗ *95 rooms, 11 suites* ⟁ *Restaurant, in-room safes, cable TV, some in-room data ports, Internet room, business services, bar, dry cleaning, laundry service* ▤ *AE, DC, MC, V* ⟠ *BP.*

$ ⊡ **Royalty Copacabana.** Just three blocks from the beach, this hotel is still removed enough to provide peace and quiet. The back rooms from the third floor up are the quietest and have mountain views; front rooms face the sea. ✉ *Rua Tonelero 154, Copacabana 22030-000* ☏ *021/2548–5699* 📠 *021/2255–1999* ⊕ *www.royaltyhotel.com.br* ⇗ *123 rooms, 13 suites* ⟁ *Restaurant, in-room safes, cable TV, in-room broadband, Wi-Fi, business services, pool, gym, sauna, bar, parking (fee), no-smoking rooms* ▤ *AE, DC, MC, V* ⟠ *BP* Ⓜ *Siqueira Campos.*

$ ⊡ **Toledo.** Although it has few amenities, the Toledo goes the extra mile to make the best of what it does have. The staff is friendly, the service is efficient, and the location—on a quiet backstreet of Copacabana, a block from the beach—isn't bad either. Back rooms from the 9th to the 14th floors have sea views and sliding floor-to-ceiling windows. Some rooms are much larger than others, so specify if you have a preference. ✉ *Rua Domingos Ferreira 71, Copacabana 22050-010* ☏ *021/2257–1990* 📠 *021/2257–1931* ⊕ *www.hoteltoledo.com.br* ⇗ *92 rooms* ⟁ *Coffee shop, in-room safes, TV, Internet room* ▤ *AE, DC, MC, V* ⟠ *BP* Ⓜ *Siqueira Campos.*

$ ⊡ **Vilamar Copacabana.** A small hotel by Rio's standards, Vilamar has petite rooms. The pool is small, too, but since you're only 200 meters (about 660 feet) from the beach, the size of the pool shouldn't be a problem. Rooms on the lower level get some street noise. ✉ *Rua Bolívar 75, Copacabana 22061-020* ☏ *021/3461–5601* 📠 *021/2547–7528* ⊕ *www.hotelvilamarcopacabana.com.br* ⇗ *56 rooms, 14 suites* ⟁ *Restaurant, in-room safes, refrigerators, cable TV, in-room broadband, pool, sauna, exercise room, bar, business services, parking (fee), no-smoking rooms* ▤ *AE, DC, MC, V* ⟠ *BP.*

Flamengo

$–$$ ⊡ **Novo Mundo.** A short walk from the Catete metro station and just five minutes by car from Santos Dumont Airport, this traditional hotel is on Guanabara Bay in Flamengo, near Glória. Convention rooms are popular with the business crowd. Deluxe rooms have a view of the bay and also of the Pão de Açúcar. The traditional restaurant, Flamboyant, has buffet service during the week and feijoada every Saturday. ⊠ *Praia do Flamengo 20, Flamengo 22210-030* ☎ *021/2105–7000 or 0800/ 25–3355* ⊕ *www.hotelnovomundo-rio.com.br* ↦ *209 rooms, 22 suites* ⌂ *Restaurant, in-room safes, refrigerators, cable TV, in-room broadband in some rooms, hair salon, bar, dry cleaning, laundry service, meeting room, parking (fee), no-smoking floor* ▭ *AE, D, MC, V* ⏉ *BP* Ⓜ *Catete.*

Ipanema & Leblon

$$$$ 🏨 **Caesar Park.** In the heart of Ipanema, close to high-class shops and
Fodor'sChoice gourmet restaurants, this beachfront hotel has established itself as a fa-
★ vorite of business travelers, celebrities, and heads of state, who appreciate its impeccable service. The hotel has a business center including
secretarial services and fax machines. Among other comforts, the hotel
has a bar and pool with a breathtaking view on the top floor, with an
excellent Italian restaurant, Galani, which serves a fabulous Sunday brunch
and an impeccable executive lunch, with buffet starters and desserts and
à la carte main courses. Another restaurant serves feijoada every Saturday. ⊠ *Av. Vieira Souto 460, Ipanema 22420-000* ☎ *021/2525–2525,
0800/21–0789, 877/223–7272 in the U.S.* ⊕ *www.caesarpark-rio.com*
↦ *190 rooms, 32 suites* ⌂ *3 restaurants, room service, in-room safes,
cable TV, in-room broadband, Wi-Fi, pool, gym, massage, sauna, bar,
babysitting, dry cleaning, laundry service, concierge, business services,
meeting room, free parking, no-smoking floors* ▭ *AE, DC, MC, V.*

$$$$ 🏨 **Everest Rio Hotel.** With standard service but one of Rio's finest rooftop
views—a postcard shot of Corcovado and the lagoon—this hotel is in
the heart of Ipanema's shopping and dining district, a block from the
beach. Back rooms have sea views. It lacks any compelling decor but
has many amenities for business travelers. The restaurant 360°, on the
top floor close to the swimming pool, has seafood and some specialties
from the south of Brazil. There's a sushi bar on the ground floor. ⊠ *Rua
Prudente de Morais 1117, Ipanema 22420-041* ☎ *021/2525–2200 or
0800/24–4485* 🖷 *021/2521–3198* ⊕ *www.everest.com.br* ↦ *148
rooms, 8 suites* ⌂ *Restaurant, room service, in-room safes, cable TV,
in-room broadband, Wi-Fi, pool, sauna, bar, dry cleaning, laundry service, concierge, business services, parking (fee), no-smoking floors*
▭ *AE, DC, MC, V.*

$$$–$$$$ 🏨 **Praia Ipanema.** This hotel isn't deluxe, but it has a great location across
from the beach and between Ipanema and Leblon. You can see the sea
from all its rooms. Choose the higher floors to enjoy the view and avoid
the traffic noise. Take in the dramatic beach view from the pool area
on the roof of the 15-story building. You can also catch a breeze from
your private balcony (every room has one) or enjoy live music at the
hotel bar every Friday night. ⊠ *Av. Vieira Souto 706, Ipanema 22440-
000* ☎ *021/2540–4949* 🖷 *021/2239–6889* ⊕ *www.praiaipanema.com*
↦ *103 rooms* ⌂ *Restaurant with ocean view, room service, in-room
safes, cable TV, in-room broadband, Wi-Fi, pool, health club, sauna, 2*

bars, dry cleaning, laundry service, concierge, business services, free parking ☰ *AE, DC, MC, V* ⍰ *BP.*

$$$–$$$$ ⊡ **Best Western Sol Ipanema.** Another of Rio's crop of tall, slender hotels, this one has a great location between Rua Vinicius de Moraes and Farme de Amoedo, where there are several bars, anchoring the eastern end of Ipanema Beach. While it isn't luxurious, the hotel has comfortable accommodations. Deluxe front rooms have panoramic beach views, although back rooms from the eighth floor up, which are the same size, have views of the lagoon and Corcovado. ⊠ *Av. Vieira Souto 320, Ipanema 22420-000* ☎ *021/2525–2020* 🖶 *021/2247–8484* ⊕ *www.solipanema. com.br* ⤳ *90 rooms* ⌂ *Restaurant, pool, 2 bars, room service, in-room broadband, refrigerator, cable TV, laundry services, dry cleaning, meeting rooms, free parking, no-smoking rooms* ☰ *AE, DC, MC, V* ⍰ *BP.*

$$–$$$$ ⊡ **Golden Tulip Ipanema Plaza.** European standards and solid service are the hallmarks of this hotel. The rooms are large, with white-tile floors and modern facilities. Decor is tastefully tropical. In the center of Ipanema, very close to the beach, the hotel is on a street with multiple restaurants and bars. From the rooftop pool it's possible to see not only the ocean, but also the lagoon and the statue of Christ the Redeemer. A brand new floor was recently opened, featuring very elegant Italian fixtures and fine linens. ⊠ *Rua Farme de Amoedo 34, Ipanema 22420-020* ☎ *021/3687–2000* 🖶 *021/3687–2001* ⊕ *www.ipanemaplazahotel. com* ⤳ *124 rooms, 16 suites* ⌂ *Restaurant, room service, in-room safes, cable TV, in-room broadband, Wi-Fi, pool, health club, sauna, dry cleaning, laundry service, concierge, business services, meeting room, parking (fee), no-smoking floors* ☰ *AE, DC, MC, V* ⍰ *BP.*

$$ ⊡ **Leblon Flat Service.** Small, decorated, and furnished apartments have one or two bedrooms and balconies at this hotel-like apartment complex. Leblon beach is only three blocks away. This is a good option for those who want to save money by cooking at home. ⊠ *Rua Professor Antônio Maria Teixeira 33, Leblon 22430-050* ☎ *021/2529–8332 for information, 021/2239–4598 for reservations* 🖶 *021/2259–2191* ⌂ *Restaurant, coffee shop, in-room safes, kitchens, cable TV, pool, gym, sauna, bar, laundry facilities, meeting room* ⤳ *120 apartments* ☰ *AE, DC, MC, V.*

$–$$ ⊡ **Arpoador Inn.** This simple pocket-size hotel occupies the stretch of sand known as Arpoador. Surfers ride the waves, and pedestrians rule the roadway—a traffic-free street allows direct beach access. At sunset the view from the rocks that mark the end of the beach is considered one of Rio's most beautiful. The spectacle is visible from the hotel's back rooms (deluxe rooms) that face Arpoador Beach; avoid the front rooms, which are noisy. Built in the '70s, the hotel has since been renovated and has a well-known seafood restaurant on the ground floor overlooking the beach. Some rooms are much larger than others, so specify if you have a preference. ⊠ *Rua Francisco Otaviano 177, Ipanema 22080-040* ☎ *021/2523–0060* 🖶 *021/2511–5094* ⤳ *50 rooms* ⌂ *Restaurant, room service, in-room safes, cable TV, Internet room, bar, dry cleaning, laundry service* ☰ *AE, DC, MC, V* ⍰ *BP.*

$ ⊡ **Ipanema Inn.** If you want to stay in Ipanema and avoid the high prices of beachfront accommodations, this no-frills hotel with great service fits the bill. Just a half block from the beach, close to Praça Nossa Senhora da Paz, it's convenient not only for sun worshipers but also for those seeking to explore Ipanema's varied nightlife. ✉ *Rua Maria Quitéria 27, Ipanema 22410-040* ☎ *021/2523–6092 or 021/2274–6995* ◁ *56 rooms* ⌂ *Dining room, in-room safes, cable TV, Internet room, bar, dry cleaning, laundry service* ☰ *AE, DC, MC, V* ⍟ *BP.*

★ ¢–$ ⌧ **Adventure Hostel.** In the heart of Ipanema, this hostel, opened in 2005, has double and quadruple rooms and is on a par, in terms of quality of rooms and service, with many more-expensive hotels. You must rent bath and beach towels. The bedrooms, shared bathrooms and public areas are all sparkling clean, and there is security on site all night. It's just a few blocks from the beach and Ipanema's best restaurants and shopping. The hostel organizes many city tours and ecological tours for its guests (not included in nightly rate). ✉ *Rua Vinicius de Morais 174, Ipanema 22411-010* ☎ *021/3813–2726* ⊕ *www.adventurehostel.com. br* ◁ *10 rooms with shared bath* ⌂ *Internet room, laundry facilities; no room TVs, no room phones* ☰ *MC* ⍟ *BP.*

¢–$ ⌧ **Ipanema Sweet.** In this residential building in the heart of Ipanema, owners rent out their units by the night, week, or month. Just two blocks from the beach and steps away from Ipanema's best bars, restaurants, and shopping, the location cannot be beat. All units have their own bathroom, kitchen, and living room, and some are also equipped with television, DVD player, and Internet connection. If you like the idea of experiencing Rio like a local, this might be the place for you. A good grocery store across the street makes preparing meals easy. The building has a small swimming pool and small exercise room. The bus connecting Ipanema to the metro in Copacabana is one block from the building. ✉ *Rua Visconde de Pirajá 161, Ipanema 22420-010* ☎ *Sonia Maria Cordeiro: 021/2551–0488 or 021/9241–8139* ✍ *sonia-cordeiro@globo.com* ☰ *No credit cards* ⍟ *EP.*

São Conrado, Barra da Tijuca & Beyond

$$$$ ⌧ **InterContinental Rio.** One of the city's few resorts is in São Conrado, on its own slice of beachfront next to the Gávea Golf and Country Club. Attractions include a cocktail lounge, an Italian restaurant (the Alfredo), and a buffet with feijoada every Saturday. Every room has an original tapestry done by a Brazilian artist and a balcony overlooking the ocean. The nearby mall is much less crowded than those with more central locations. The club floor, on the higher levels, has extra facilities like daily newspapers and a tearoom. ✉ *Av. Prefeito Mendes de Morais 222, São Conrado 22610-090* ☎ *021/3323–2200, 800/327–0200 in the U.S.* ⎙ *021/3323–5500* ⊕ *www.interconti.com* ◁ *429 rooms, 58 suites, 20 cabanas* ⌂ *2 restaurants, room service, in-room safes, cable TV, in-room broadband in some rooms, golf privileges, 3 tennis courts, 3 pools, health club, hair salon, spa, sauna, 2 bars, shops, dry cleaning, laundry service, concierge, business services, convention center, car rental, travel services, free parking, no-smoking rooms* ☰ *AE, DC, MC, V.*

$$$–$$$$ ⌧ **Sheraton Barra Hotel e Suites.** Opened in 2003, this mammoth gleaming-white hotel has balconies in each room that overlook Barra Beach. The decor is futuristic, with white walls, brushed nickel and mahogany

accents, skillful lighting, and clean lines. Be prepared to rent a car or spend a good deal of money on taxis when staying in this neighborhood, as there's no metro station and unreliable bus service. ✉ *Av. Lúcio Costa 3150, Barra da Tijuca 22630-010* ☎ *021/3139–8000* 🖷 *021/3139–8025* ⊕ *www.sheraton.com/barra* ☕ *264 rooms, 28 suites* ⏦ *Restaurant, room service, cable TV, in-room broadband, pool, wading pool, gym, 2 hot tubs, sauna, spa, squash, bar, concierge, business services, meeting rooms, parking (fee)* ⊟ *AE, DC, MC, V.*

$$$–$$$$ 🖥 **Sheraton Rio Hotel & Towers.** Built so that it dominates Vidigal, between Leblon and São Conrado, this is the only hotel in Rio with a "private" beach. (It's open to the public, but so closed off to anything but the hotel that usually only Sheraton guests use it.) Guest rooms are tastefully decorated, and all have balconies with sea views, although some are very limited. Floors in the Towers section are reserved for business travelers. Be prepared for numerous taxi rides because of the hotel's isolated location. ✉ *Av. Niemeyer 121, Vidigal 22450-220* ☎ *021/ 2274–1122, 0800/21–0750, 800/325–3589 in the U.S.* 🖷 *021/2239–5643* ⊕ *www.sheraton-rio.com* ☕ *500 rooms, 59 suites* ⏦ *3 restaurants, in-room safes, cable TV, in-room broadband in some rooms, Wi-Fi, 3 tennis courts, 3 pools, gym, sauna, hair salon, private beach, 2 bars, shops, dry cleaning, laundry service, concierge, business services, meeting room, car rental, travel services, parking (fee), no-smoking rooms* ⊟ *AE, DC, MC, V* ⎆ *BP.*

NIGHTLIFE & THE ARTS

Rio's nightlife is as hard to resist as its beaches. Options range from samba shows shamelessly aimed at visitors to sultry dance halls that play *forró,* a music style that originated in Brazil's northeast during World War II. (American GIs stationed at refueling stops opened up their clubs "for all," which, when pronounced with a Brazilian accent, became "forró.") Seek out the sounds of big band, rock, and everything in between. One of the happiest mediums is *música popular brasileira* (MPB), the generic term for popular Brazilian music, which ranges from pop to jazz. Note that establishments in this carefree city often have carefree hours; call ahead to confirm opening times.

For opera, theater, music, dance, film, and other performing arts listings, pick up the Portuguese-language *Rio Prá Você,* published by Riotur, the city's tourist board. *Este Mês no Rio* (This Month in Rio) and similar publications are available at most hotels, and your hotel concierge is also a good source of information. The Portuguese-language newspapers *Jornal do Brasil* and *O Globo* publish schedules of events in the entertainment sections of their Friday editions, which are found online at ⊕ www.jb.com.br and ⊕ www.oglobo.com.br.

Nightlife

Cariocas love to chat while drinking until late hours in bars and restaurants all around town. Brazilian rhythms like samba and forró fill the night with excitement, most notably in Lapa, Copacabana, Ipanema, and Leblon.

The strip along Avenida Princesa Isabel at the end of Copacabana—near Le Meridien hotel—is known for its numerous burlesque, striptease, and sex shows. Be warned: some of the female patrons may be prostitutes.

Bars

Bars and lounges often ask for a nominal cover in the form of either a drink minimum or a music charge. *Choperias* (pubs) and *botecos* (bars specializing in draft beer and appetizers) are casual places you can go wearing a swimsuit.

COPACABANA At **Cervantes** (⌧ Av. Prado Júnior 335, Copacabana ☏ 021/2275–6147) the beer goes well with the house special, French-bread sandwiches filled with beef, pork, and cheese. You may add sauces, onions, or even fruits—a specialty is pork and pineapple. Steaks with rice or french fries are also on the menu. It's closed Mondays.

COSME VELHO Hidden behind a small entryway in the Cosme Velho neighborhood, the **Clan Café** (⌧ Rua Cosme Velho 564, Cosme Velho ☏ 021/ 2558–2322) is a great place to catch some live music in an outdoor courtyard. Right across the street from the Corcovado train station, it is open Tuesday–Saturday starting at 6 PM.

IPANEMA The area around the intersection of Rua Visconde de Pirajá and Vinicius de Moraes is a good place to bar-hop.

Back in the '60s, regulars Tom Jobim and Vinicius de Moraes, who wrote the song "The Girl from Ipanema," sat at tables at **Bar Garota de Ipanema** (⌧ Rua Vinicius de Moraes 39, Ipanema ☏ 021/2523–3787 Ⓜ Siqueira Campos, then shuttle bus to Praça General Osório), then called Bar Veloso, and longingly watched the song's heroine head for the beach. They sat at the table for two near the door. The unpretentious beachfront choperia **Barril 1800** (⌧ Av. Vieira Souto 110, Ipanema ☏ 021/2523–0085 Ⓜ Siqueira Campos, then shuttle bus to Praça General Osório) is an Ipanema landmark and is usually jammed with people grabbing an icy beer or cocktail and a snack.

LAGOA The collection of bar and restaurant kiosks along a western portion of the lagoon are collectively called, simply, the **Lagoa** (⌧ Parque Brigadeiro Faria Lima, turnoff near the BR gas station). The food itself—a mix of Italian, burgers, and other non-traditional Brazilian—is not spectacular, but the view of the lagoon and the lighted Christ statue in the distance is. Kiosks close down at around 1 AM.

LAPA Many bars line the Avenida Mede Sá beginning near the Arcos da Lapa, so you can easily stroll down the street to find what appeals to you.

Second-floor bar and pizzeria **Encontro Carioca** feeds the late-night Lapa crowd until 5 AM Thursday through Saturday. It shares owners with downstairs neighbor Carioca da Gema (⇨ Music Clubs, *below*). Pizzas have toppings like shiitake mushrooms, calabresa, and shrimp. Need a sugar rush? Try a banana-and-chocolate pizza. **Nova Capela** (⌧ Av. Mem de Sá 96, Lapa ☏ 021/2252–6228 Ⓜ No metro) is a 100-year-old restaurant-bar in Rio's traditional downtown nightlife area. Beer, cachaça, and Brazilian meals and appetizers are served in generous portions.

WHY RIO'S CARNIVAL RULES

MANY PEOPLE TOUT THE VIRTUES of Carnival in Salvador and other cities in Brazil, but Rio's Carnival is the real deal. After all, it was here that the whole thing started. The first samba schools appeared in Rio in the 19th century and it was here that the parades happened for the first time. It is no accident that for every Carnival (in February or early March, depending on where Lent falls on the calendar), Brazil comes to a halt to see the parades in Rio de Janeiro. In those four days (Saturday, Sunday, Monday, and Tuesday) it's said that Brazilians think only of samba, women and beer—Rio's Carnival triad. Without the three, the party is not complete, Brazilians say.

The mulatas, women fantasically dressed in barely-there sequin-and-feather-adorned costumes, are at the head of the parades. They are what one generally thinks of when Brazilian Carnival comes to mind— so again, what is considered a quintessential part of Carnival was born in Rio. Right behind them comes the rousing percussion wing. Then come the floats, full of color, over three meters high. Beautiful women with the tiniest of golden bikinis ride them, sensually dancing the samba, accompanied on the street level by the various alas (wings, or sections), of the escola de samba (samba school). Each of the 14 schools creates an overall theme with its floats, costumes, music, and dancers; each wing of the school wears a different type of costume, all of them breathtaking. In some cases, more than $1 million is spent on the extravagant displays. Rehearsals for the better part of a year lead to one hour-and-twenty-minute performance for each samba school. At the end of Carnival, the best samba school is elected the champion of the year's parade by a group of jurors, in a dispute closely followed by millions of Brazilians throughout the country.

Though past Carnivals took place in Centro, today the parades are in the Sambódromo, a huge stadium, open only for Carnival, that was designed by the renowned architect Oscar Niemeyer and built in the heart of the city in 1984. It can be reached by subway or by taxi, and admittance tickets cost US$30—but if you want a seat, you'll pay between US$200 and $1,000. The Brazilian Tourism Office has links to a Sambódromo map on its Web site (www.braziltourism.org/sambodromo.shtml) and great tips about which seats to choose.

The carioca (resident of Rio) makes no distinction between Brazilians and foreigners at Carnival, and even those who have no familiarity whatsoever with samba are welcome to participate in the event. To join a samba school all you have to do is attend one of the rehearsals in the school's headquarters and pay about US$200 for a costume (this includes the admittance ticket). Then just join the party!

— by Carla Aranha

For a flip-side opinion, see "Carnival in Salvador: Brazil's Wildest Party" in Chapter 8.

LEBLON & GÁVEA Famed for having the best cachaça in Rio, the **Academia da Cachaça** (✉Rua Conde de Bernadotte 26G, Leblon ☎ 021/2239–1542) is a trendy spot to grab some delicious appetizers and linger over traditional drinks. True to its name, **Bar do Hotel** (✉ Marina All Suites, Av. Delfim Moreira 696, Leblon ☎ 021/2540–4990) is a hotel bar that serves drinks and dinner. It gets extremely crowded for drinks on Friday and Saturday nights. Don't expect anything fancy at **Bracarense** (✉ Rua José Linhares 85B, Leblon ☎ 021/2294–3549), a small informal place where cariocas linger with their beers on the sidewalk in front of the bar. It's perfect for after a soccer game in Maracanã; many come just to talk about sports.

Near the Jóquei Clube, **Hipódromo** (✉ Praça Santos Dumont 108, Gávea ☎ 021/2294–0095) has good chopp, simple food, and crowds of young people living it up. Pizza and draft beer are the mainstays of **Pizzaria Guanabara** (✉ Av. Ataulfo de Paiva 1228, Leblon ☎ 021/2294–0797 🖻 AE, D, DC, V), which has had a loyal after-midnight crowd for more ★ than 40 years. Artists tend to hang out here. At **Seu Martin** (✉ Av. General San Martin 1.196, Leblon ☎ 021/2274–0800 ☉ Closed for lunch on Mon.) cocktails, cheesecake, light food, sandwiches, and salad are served to the sound of jazz.

Dance Clubs

Rio's *danceterias* (discos) pulse with loud music and flashing lights. At a number of places, including samba clubs, you can dance to live Brazilian music. *Gafieiras* are old-fashioned ballroom dance halls, usually patronized by an equally old-fashioned clientele. Upon entry to some clubs you're given a card to carry—each successive drink is marked on it. You pay on departure for what you've consumed.

CENTRO A great place to listen to live music and eat typical Brazilian food, **Cachaçaria Mangue Seco** (✉ Rua do Lavradio 23, Centro ☎ 021/ 3852–1947) is a laid-back music hall in the popular Rua do Lavradio. It's closed Sundays. **Estudantina** (✉ Praça Tiradentes 79, Centro ☎ 021/ 2232–1149) is an extremely popular nightclub that packs in as many as 1,500 people on weekends to dance to the sound of samba.

COPACABANA **Bunker** (✉ Rua Raul Pompéia 94, Copacabana ☎ 021/3813–0300) is a dance hall with three lounges. Most of the time two of them are playing different styles of electronic music, with the third blaring rock and roll. Open Thursday–Sunday, plan to arrive around midnight. There's a small stage for the occasional local bands. Call for schedules.

LARANJEIRAS If you're up for a late night of dancing with local cariocas, try the famous **Casa Rosa** (✉ Rua Alice 550, Laranjeiras ☎ 021/9363–4645). It was once a well-known brothel, but has now been converted into a popular nightclub.

LAPA & GÁVEA If you prefer to be where the trends are, try **00** (✉ Av. Padre Leonel Franca 240, Gávea ☎ 021/2540–8041), a restaurant–café–sushi bar with a variety of DJs playing sets of house music, drum and bass, and trance, depending on the DJ. Call to get the program. It's open Tuesday through Sunday; DJ gets going at midnight. Saturday is "gay night." At the large nightclub **Asa Branca** (✉ Av. Mem de Sá 17, Lapa ☎ 021/2224–9358

✉ DC, MC, V ⊗ Closed Mon.), modern geometric designs are combined with old-fashioned fixtures. Big bands and popular Brazilian musicians keep the crowd busy from 10 PM until dawn. Even if you don't want to dance, it's worth checking out the **Democraticus** (✉ Rua do Riachuela 91, Lapa ☎ No phone) dance hall. Founded in 1867 as a political club, it was recently converted into a dance club, and attracts all age groups from around the city. The hall is impressive and the live music is great. Open Wednesday through Saturday.

LEBLON   You're likely to spot celebrities at **Melt** (✉ Rua Rita Ludolf 47, Leblon ☎ 021/2249–9309), a hip nightclub in a hip neighborhood. Dancing gets going around 11 PM.

Gay & Lesbian Bars & Clubs

Rio is a relatively gay-friendly city; the community even has its own gala during Carnival. Style Travel Agency offers tours targeted to gay and lesbian travelers and has information on local happenings. The hippest cariocas—both gay and straight—hang out in Ipanema and Leblon.

COPACABANA   **La Girl** (✉ Rua Raul Pompeia 102, Copacabana ☎ 021/2513–4993 ⊕ www.lagirl.com.br) disco catering to lesbians. Next to La Girl, **Le Boy** (✉ Rua Paul Pompéia 102, Copacabana ☎ 021/2513–4993 ⊕ www.leboy.com.br) is a gay disco that draws an upscale clientele.

IPANEMA   The young energetic crowd at **Bar Bofetada** (✉ Rua Farme de Amoedo 87–87A, Ipanema ☎ 021/2227–1675) downs chopp and caipirinhas and delicious seafood (the owners are Portuguese) or meat platters large enough to share. On weekends the tables flow out onto the street. The **Galeria Café** (✉ Rua Teixeira de Mello 31E–F, Ipanema ☎ 021/2523–8250 ⊕ www.galeriacafe.com.br) is a bar with house–techno music for a sophisticated crowd. From Thursday to Saturday it's packed not only inside but has patrons overflowing out onto the sidewalk.

Music Clubs

Although nightclubs often serve food, their main attraction is live music; it's best to eat elsewhere earlier.

COPACABANA   **Bip Bip** (✉ Rua Almirante Gonçalves 50, Copacabana ☎ 021/2267–9696) is a one-of-a-kind hole in the wall where some of the best local musicians have gathered for decades. It's a real gem in Copacabana and not to be missed.

IPANEMA   You may rightly associate sultry bossa nova with Brazil, but it's increasingly hard to find venues that offer it. **Vinicius** (✉ Rua Vinicius de Moraes 39, Ipanema ☎ 021/2287–1497 Ⓜ Siqueira Campos, then shuttle bus to Praça General Osório) is one of the few that do. Along with nightly live samba, jazz, popular music, or bossa nova, it has a good kitchen.

LAGOA   At **Mistura Fina** (✉ Av. Borges de Medeiros 3207, Lagoa Rodrigo de Freitas, Lagoa ☎ 021/2537–2844 ⊕ www.misturafina.com.br) fine jazz combines with excellent food. Call for a schedule.

LAPA   Rio institution **Carioca da Gema** (✉ Rua Mem de Sá 79, Lapa ☎ 021/
★   2221–0043 ⊕ www.barcariocadagema.com.br) attracts some of the best samba talent around, including up-and-comers. By 11 PM it can be

hard to find a place to stand—but regulars still find a way to samba. **Dama da Noite** (✉ Av. Gomes Freire 773, Lapa ☎ 021/3380–6100 ⊕ www.damadanoite.com.br) is a cozy place to listen to great live music and indulge in fabulous crepes. Opened in 2005, **Estrela da Lapa** (✉ Rua Mem de Sá, Lapa ☎ 021/2507–6686 ⊕ www.estreladalapa.com. br) has live bossa nova and samba in an classy, open space with tall pine ceilings and low lighting. Shows (R$18) start at around 8:30, and later on Saturdays. Appetizers and a few entrées are served.

★ Most places cease to be cool once they achieve the renown of **Rio Scenarium** (✉ Rua do Lavradio 20, Lapa ☎ 021/2233–3239 ⊕ www. rioscenarium.com.br), but locals still have a deep fondness for this eclectic and kooky lounge. It's also unusual in that it attracts 22-year-old hipsters, 80-year-old grandparents, and everyone in between. The three-story city-block-sized townhouse is decorated with yard-sale antiques like old bicycles, suitcases, and blenders. If you want to snag a table near the dance floor and music—some of the best samba and *choro* (instrumental music with improvisational classical guitar) bands around— arrive before 8 PM or make a reservation. **Semente** (✉ Rua Joaquim Silva 138, Lapa ☎ 021/2509–3591) is a small but popular samba club on a street in Lapa famous for its quality music.

LEBLON **Plataforma** (✉ Rua Adalberto Ferreira 32, Leblon ☎ 021/2274–4022), the most spectacular of Rio's samba shows, has elaborate costumes and a variety of musical numbers including samba and rumba. A two-hour show costs about R$100, drinks not included. Downstairs is a hangout for many local luminaries and entertainers. Upstairs you can eat at Plataforma's famed barbecue restaurant.

The Arts

Although MPB (Brazilian popular music) may have overshadowed *música erudita* (classical music), Rio has a number of orchestras. The Orquestra Sinfônica Brasileira and the Orquestra do Theatro Municipal are the most prominent. Tickets to performing arts events are inexpensive by international standards and may be purchased at the theater or concert hall box offices. Dress is generally smart-casual, although the conservative upper crust still likes to dress elegantly for the Theatro Municipal. Don't wear valuable jewelry or carry lots of cash.

Rio has an avid filmgoing public and a well-regarded film industry (you may catch a flick that later hits the international movie circuit). Films are screened in small *cineclubes,* or state-of-the-art movie theaters (many in shopping malls). Foreign movies are shown in their original language with Portuguese subtitles (only children's films are dubbed). After dark, exercise caution in Cinelândia, where there's a large concentration of theaters.

In addition to its many museums, Rio has several privately funded cultural centers. These host changing, often exceptional art and photography exhibits as well as film series, lectures, and children's programs. All the big newspapers have daily cultural sections that tell what's going on in the city—in Portuguese.

Classical Music

Opened in 1922, the **Escola de Música da UFRJ** (✉ Rua do Passeio 98, Lapa ☎ 021/2240–1391 ⊕ www.musica.ufrj.br Ⓜ Cinelândia), the Music School auditorium, called Salao Leopoldo Miguez, inspired by the Gauveau Hall in Paris, has 1,100 seats where you can listen to chamber music, symphony orchestras, and opera, all free of charge. **Instituto Moreira Salles** (✉ Rua Marquês de São Vicente 476, Gávea ☎ 021/3284–7400 ⊕ www.ims.com.br), surrounded by beautiful gardens, has just the right atmosphere for listening to classical music. *Projeto Villa-Lobinhos,* whose performances are dedicated to children, is one of their projects. Listen to musicians performing pieces from Bach, Chopin, Debussy, and other classical composers. **Sala Cecília Meireles** (✉ Largo da Lapa 47, Centro ☎ 021/2224–4291 Ⓜ Cinelândia) is a traditional midsize concert room that hosts classical music performances.

Concert Halls

Circo Voador (✉ Next to Arcos da Lapa, Lapa ☎ 021/2533–5873 ⊕ www.circovoador.com.br) is an outdoor concert venue in downtown Rio that hosts big celebrities as well as local bands and theater. The 4,500-seat **Claro Hall** (✉ Av. Ayrton Senna 3000, Barra da Tijuca ☎ 021/2156–7300 ⊕ www.clarohall.com.br) hosts music concerts, theater, and dance events. Many pop stars have performed here. **Canecão** (✉ Av. Venceslau Brâs 215, Botafogo ☎ 021/2543–1241 ⊕ www.canecao.com.br) is the most traditional venue for the biggest names on the national music scene. It seats up to 5,000 people; reserve a table up front.

Samba-School Shows

Open rehearsals attract crowds of samba enthusiasts to the *escolas de samba* (samba schools) from August to Carnival (February or March) as fans gather to practice the year's rhythms and lyrics in preparation for the parade. Ticket prices range from R$5 to R$15.

Acadêmicos do Salgueiro (✉ Rua Silva Teles 104, Andaraí ☎ 021/2288–3065 ⊕ www.salgueiro.com.br) rehearses Saturday at 11 PM. **Beija-Flor** (✉ Pracinha Wallace Paes Leme 1025, Nilópolis ☎ 021/2791–2866 ⊕ www.beija-flor.com.br) rehearses Thursday at 9 PM. **Estação Primeira de Mangueira** (✉ Rua Visconde de Niterói 1072 Mangueira ☎ 021/3872–6787 ⊕ www.mangueira.com.br) rehearses Saturday at 11 PM. **Imperatriz Leopoldinense** (✉ Rua Professor Lacê 235, Ramos ☎ 021/2560–8037 ⊕ www.imperatrizleopoldinense.com.br) rehearses Sunday at 4 PM.

Império Serrano (✉ Av. Ministro Edgard Romero 114, Madureira ☎ 021/2489–8722 ⊕ www.imperioserrano.com) rehearses Saturday at 11 PM. **Mocidade Independente de Padre Miguel** (✉ Rua Coronel Tamarindo 38, Padre Miguel ☎ 021/3332–5823 ⊕ www.mocidadeindependente.com.br) rehearses Saturday at 11 PM. **Portela** (✉ Rua Clara Nunes 81, Madureira ☎ 021/2489–6440 ⊕ www.gresportela.com.br) rehearses Wednesday at 8 PM, Friday at 10 PM, and Sunday at 5 PM. **Caprichosos de Pilares** (✉ Rua Faleiros 1, Pilares ☎ 021/2592–5620) rehearses Saturdays at 10 PM. **Unidos de Vila Isabel** (✉ Boulevard 28 de Setembro 382, Vila Isabel ☎ 021/3181–4869) rehearses Saturday at 10 PM.

Film

Part of the Grupo Estação, an art-house chain, the **Estação Ipanema** (⊠ Av. Visconde de Pirajá 605, Ipanema ☎ 021/2279–4603) is a charming theater with two auditoriums and a coffee shop in a lively area of small restaurants and bookstores, perfect for hanging out before or after the films. Once the only movie theater in Rio with a smoking room, **Espaço Paissandu** still exists, although smoking is now forbidden. (⊠ Rua Senador Vergueiro 35, Flamengo ☎ 021/2285–7314 Ⓜ Flamengo) seats over 400 people. **Espaço Unibanco de Cinema** (⊠ Rua Voluntários da Pátria 35, Botafogo ☎ 021/2226–1986 Ⓜ Botafogo), with three auditoriums, shares space with a coffee shop and a secondhand shop selling books, records, and magazines. Members of the Brazilian film industry hang out here, hosting frequent premieres and events.

In one of the very few remaining houses on the Ipanema beachfront, **Laura Alvim** (⊠ Av. Vieira Souto 176, Ipanema ☎ 021/2267–1647 Ⓜ Siqueira Campos, then shuttle bus to Praça General Osório) is a small theater presenting several second-run films. Check the program on your way back from the beach. **Odeon BR** (⊠ Praça Floriano 7, Cinelândia ☎ 021/2240–1093 Ⓜ Cinelândia) is one of the most beautiful, charming, and important movie theaters in Brazil. In Cinelândia (movieland), a traditional neighborhood in downtown with a concentration of movie theaters, Odeon BR hosts international and Brazilian film exhibits, festivals, and art films. Opened in 1926, the theater has been restored to preserve its original neoclassic architecture. Arrive early to enjoy the coffee shop. **Roxy** (⊠ Av. Nossa Senhora de Copacabana 945A, Copacabana ☎ 021/2547–4576), in the heart of Copacabana two blocks from the beach, groups three midsize auditoriums that show American blockbusters as well as Brazilian films.

Opera

FodorśChoice ★   **Theatro Municipal** (⊠ Praça Floriano, Centro ☎ 021/2262–3501 or 021/2299–1717 ⊕ www.theatromunicipal.rj.gov.br) is the city's main performing arts venue, hosting dance, opera (often with international stars as guest artists), symphony concerts, and theater events year-round—although the season officially runs from April to December. The theater also has its own ballet company.

Theater

Centro Cultural Banco do Brasil (⊠ Rua 1° de Março 66, Centro ☎ 021/3808–2020 ⊕ www.cultura-e.com.br Ⓜ Uruguaiana), constructed in 1880, was once the headquarters of the Banco do Brasil. In the late 1980s the six-story domed building with marble floors was transformed into a cultural center for plays, art exhibitions, and music recitals. It has a bookstore, three theaters, a video hall, four individual video booths, a movie theater, two auditoriums, a restaurant, a coffee shop, and a tearoom. Guided tours in English may be scheduled. It's open Tuesday–Sunday 10–9.

The traditional **Teatro João Caetano** (⊠ Praça Tiradentes, Centro ☎ 021/2221–0305 Ⓜ Presidente Vargas) holds 1,200 seats and offers a large choice of programs, from drama to dance, inexpensively. **Teatro Villa-Lobos** (⊠ Av. Princesa Isabel 440, Copacabana ☎ 021/2275–6695 or

021/2541–6799), a 463-seat theater, has drama productions and occasional dance performances.

SPORTS & THE OUTDOORS

Auto Racing

Brazilian race-car drivers rank among the world's best, and frequently compete in international events. At the **Autódromo Internacional Nelson Piquet** (Nelson Piquet International Racetrack; ⊠ Av. Embaixador Abelardo Bueno, Jacarepaguá ☎ 021/2421–4949), you get a taste of the speed as you watch the checkered flag drop on competitions in the Formula I Grand Prix circuit named after one of the country's most famous racers, Emerson Fittipaldi.

Boating & Sailing

Saveiro's Tour (⊠ Rua Conde de Lages 44, Glória ☎ 021/2225–6064 ⊕ www.saveiros.com.br Ⓜ Glória) charters all types of crewed vessels for any length of time. You can arrange an afternoon of waterskiing with a speedboat or a weekend aboard a yacht.

Golf

The 18-hole **Gávea Golf Club** (⊠ Estrada da Gávea 800, São Conrado ☎ 021/3322–4141) has a greens fee of R$350. If you're staying at the Sheraton, Inter-Continental, or Copacabana Palace, you get a R$70 discount. Ask your hotel concierge to make a reservation for the next day. **Golden Green Golf Club** (⊠ Av. Canal de Marapendi 2901, Barra da Tijuca ☎ 021/2434–0429 ⊕ www.fgerj.com.br/conheca_golfe/clubes/golden.asp) was the first public golf club in Brazil. You can rent equipment for the six-hole course. The greens fee is R$50 Tuesday–Friday and R$60 weekends and holidays. The club is open 7 AM–10 PM.

Hang Gliding

A 30-minute hang-glider flight at **Just Fly** (☎ 021/2268–0565 or 021/9985–7540), during which you jump from Pedra Bonita in the Parque Nacional da Tijuca and land at Praia do Pepino in São Conrado, costs R$240 including transportation to and from your hotel. For a little more you can have 12 pictures taken. **HiltonFlyRio Hand Gliding Center** (⊠ Rua Jose Higino 254, Tijuca ☎ 021/2278–3779 or 021/9964–2607 ⊕ www.hiltonflyrio.com) has guided flights overlooking Rio's amazing scenery. The cost is R$280 and includes transportation to and from your hotel and a set of 12 photographs of your flight. **São Conrado Eco-Aventura** (☎ 021/2522–5586, 021/7893–7211, or 021/9966–7010 ⊕ www.guia4ventos.com.br) is another company that can give you a hang-gliding view of Rio.

Hiking

Centro Excursionista Brasileiro (⊠ Av. Almirante Barroso 2, Centro ☎ 021/2252–9844) provides guides, maps, and gear for hiking expeditions they lead throughout the metropolitan area.

FodorsChoice **Trilhas do Rio Ecoturismo & Aventura** (⊠ Rua Francisca Sales 645,
★ Jacarepagua ☎ 021/2425–8441 or 021/2424–5455 ⊕ www.trilhasdorio.

CloseUp

THE BEAUTIFUL GAME

BRAZILIANS ARE MAD ABOUT *FUTEBOL* (soccer), and players here are fast and skillful. The best possess jinga (literally, "sway"), a quality that translates roughly as a feline, almost swaggering grace. Some of their ball-handling moves are so fluid they seem more akin to ballet—or samba—than to sport.

Futebol is believed to have been introduced in the late 19th century by British immigrants. By the early 20th century upper-class Brazilians had formed their own leagues, as had the nation's European immigrants, who were already familiar with the game. Because it requires little equipment, the sport also found a following in Brazil's poor communities.

Today you see young brasileiros everywhere practicing—any of these boys could be a future futebol hero. Brazil has turned out many international stars: the most famous, Pelé, retired more than 20

years ago and is still revered as a national hero. The country's team is a repeat World-Cup titleholder. Nothing inspires more pride in Brazilians than their fifth World Cup win in 2002.

Fans come to games with musical instruments, flags, banners, streamers, and firecrackers. There's no better way to witness the spectacle than to join 91,999 other fans at the world's largest soccer stadium, Rio's Estádio Maracanã. Even if you don't have a great view of the field, you'll certainly be a part of the event. The main carioca teams are Flamengo, Vasco da Gama, Fluminense, and Botafogo. A match between any of these teams (especially a legendary "Fla-Flu" game) is a great spectacle.

com.br) leads hikes and other outdoor activities within the city and surrounding areas. An inexpensive way to explore nature with very knowledgeable guides.

Horse Racing

Races are held year-round in the **Jóquei Clube** (✉ Praça Santos Dumont 31, Gávea ☎ 021/2512–9988) from Friday to Monday. On Friday the race starts at 3:45, and on weekends races start at 1:45 PM; on Monday the first race is at 6:15 PM. The big event of the year, the Brazilian Derby, is held the first Sunday of August.

Soccer

You can watch a game at the **Estádio Maracanã** (✉ Rua Prof. Eurico Rabelo, Maracanã ☎ 021/2568–9962 ⊕ www.suderj.rj.gov.br/maracana/main.asp Ⓜ Maracanã), where the fans are part of the spectacle. During the season the top game is played each Sunday at around 5. The four most popular teams are Botafogo, Flamengo, Fluminense, and Vasco da Gama. A game with any of them is soccer at its finest. Tickets are available at the door. Arrive 30 minutes early to get the best seats.

SHOPPING

Stroll down streets lined with fashionable boutiques, barter with vendors at street fairs, or wander through one of more than two-dozen air-conditioned malls. Good bets are leather, suede, jewelry, and cool summer clothing in natural fibers. Also look for coffee, art, and samba and bossa nova CDs.

Ipanema is Rio's most fashionable shopping district. Its many exclusive boutiques are in arcades, with the majority along Rua Visconde de Pirajá. Copacabana has souvenir shops, bookstores, and branches of some of Rio's better shops along Avenida Nossa Senhora de Copacabana and connecting streets. For upscale jewelry, head to Avenida Atlântica. Brazil is one of the world's largest producers of gold and the largest supplier of colored gemstones, with deposits of aquamarines, amethysts, diamonds, emeralds, rubellites, topazes, and tourmalines. If you're planning to go to Minas Gerais, do your jewelry shopping there; otherwise, stick with shops that have certificates of authenticity and quality.

Centers & Malls

Although **Barra Shopping** (⊠ Av. das Américas 4666, Barra da Tijuca ☎ 021/3089–1100 ⊕ www.barrashopping.com.br) is about 30 km (19 mi) from the city center, shoppers from all over town head to this mall, one of South America's largest. It has a medical center and a bowling alley as well as shops. **Rio Sul** (⊠ Av. Lauro Müller 116, Botafogo ☎ 021/2545–7200 ⊕ www.riosul.com.br) is one of the city's most popular retail complexes, with four movie screens and a giant food court. Domestic and international fashions are sold at **São Conrado Fashion Mall** (⊠ Estrada da Gávea 899, São Conrado ☎ 021/2111–4444 ⊕ www.scfashionmall.com.br), Rio's least crowded mall, has an abundance of natural light. Emporio Armani, Ermenegildo Zegna, Kenzo, Petit Lippe, and a four-screen movie theater are here.

Shopping Center Cassino Atlântico (⊠ Av. Nossa Senhora de Copacabana, Copacabana ☎ 021/2523–8709), adjoining the Rio Palace hotel, is dominated by antiques shops, jewelry stores, art galleries, and souvenir outlets. At **Shopping Center da Gávea** (⊠ Rua Marquês de São Vicente 52, Gávea ☎ 021/2274–9896) several top art galleries—of which the best are Ana Maria Niemeyer, Borghese, and Toulouse—join a small but select mix of fashionable clothing and leather-goods stores. Four theaters show the best plays in town.

Department Store

Rio's largest chain department store, **Lojas Americanas** (⊠ Rua do Passeio 42–56, Centro ☎ 021/2524–0284 ⊕ www.lojasamericanas.com.br Ⓜ Cinelândia ⊠ Rua Visconde de Pirajá 526, Ipanema ☎ 021/2274–0590) has casual clothing, toys, records, candy, cosmetics, and sporting goods.

Markets

In the evening and on weekends along the median of **Avenida Atlântica,** artisans spread out their wares. You can find paintings, carvings, handicrafts, sequined dresses, and hammocks from the northeast. **Babilônia Feira Hype** (✉ Jockey Club Brasileiro, Rua Jardim Botânico, Jardim Botânico ☎ 021/2253–9800 ⊕ www.babiloniahype.com.br) takes place every other weekend (although occasionally they skip a weekend, call ahead to confirm) from 2 PM to 10 PM. This fair combines fashion, design, art, and gastronomy. It's good not only for shopping but for watching the beautiful people go by. Admission is R$5.

★ The **Feira Hippie** (✉ Praça General Osório, Ipanema) is a colorful handicrafts street fair held every Sunday 9–6. Shop for high-quality jewelry, hand-painted dresses, paintings, wood carvings, leather bags and sandals, rag dolls, knickknacks, furniture, and samba percussion instruments.

★ The crowded, lively Feira de São Cristovão, better known as the **Feira Nordestina** (Northeastern Fair; ✉ Campo de São Cristóvão, São Cristóvão ☎ 021/3860–9862 or 021/386–9976 ⊕ www.feiradesaocristovao.com. br) is a social event for Brazilians from the northeast living in Rio. They gather to hear their own distinctive music, eat regional foods, and buy tools and cheap clothing. If you can't get to that part of the country, come here for a very unique experience. It's opens Tuesday–Thursday 10–4 and from Friday at 10 AM until Sunday at 11 PM (continuously).

Open-air **Feira de Antiquários da Praça 15 de Novembro,** near the Praça 15 de Novembro, has china and silver sets, watches, Asian rugs, and chandeliers Saturdays 9–5. On Sunday (9–5) the same fair goes to Praça Santos Dumont, in Jardim Botânico. Vendors at **Feira do Rio Antigo** (Rio Antique Fair; ✉ Rua do Lavradio, Centro ☎ 021/2252–2669) sell antiques, rare books, records, and all types of objets d'art on every first Saturday afternoon of the month. They move to the Casa Shopping Center in Barra da Tijuca on Sunday. A street fair, **Feirarte** (✉ Praça do Lido, Copacabana), similar to the Feira Hippie, takes place weekends 8–6. Cardeal Arcoverde is the closest metro station.

Specialty Shops

Art

Contorno (✉ Shopping Center da Gávea, Rua Marquês de São Vicente 52, Loja 261, Gávea ☎ 021/2274–3832) shows an eclectic selection of Brazilian art. **No Meio do Caminho Art & Home Furnishings** (✉ Av. General San Martin 1247, Leblon ☎ 021/2294–1330) is very popular with local artists and architects from Rio, who visit the store to keep up with the latest trends. It specializes in contemporary art, and features only the work of Brazilian artists. The store will ship abroad.

Several shops and some art galleries at **Rio Design Center** (✉ Av. Ataulfo de Paiva 270, Leblon ☎ 021/3206–9100 ⊕ www.riodesign.com.br), like Anita Schwartz Galeria, have contemporary art.

Beachwear

A bikini shop with many mall locations in addition to the Rio Sul branch, **Blueman** (✉ Rio Sul, Av. Lauro Müller 116, Loja B01, Botafogo

☎ 021/2541–6896 ⊕ www.bluemanbrazil.com.br) carries *tangas* (string bikinis) that virtually define Brazil in much of North America's imagination. Tangas are said to have been invented in Ipanema—and they don't take up much room in your luggage. The market leader in beachwear, **Bum Bum** (✉ Rua Visconde de Pirajá 351, Loja B, Ipanema ☎ 021/2287–9951 ⊕ www.bumbum.com.br ✉ Shopping Rio Sul, Rua Lauro Müller 116, Loja 401, Botafogo ☎ 021/2542–9614 ✉ Barra Shopping, Av. das Américas 4666, Loja 134B, Barra da Tijuca ☎ 021/2431–8323) opened in 1979, when the stylist Alcindo Silva Filho, known as Cidinho, decided to create the smallest (and by some accounts, the sexiest) bikinis in town. Two decades later Bum Bum remains a solid beachwear brand. At **Lenny** (✉ Fórum Ipanema, Rua Visconde de Pirajá 351, Loja 114, Ipanema ☎ 021/2287–7912 ⊕ www.lenny.com.br) expect sophistication, comfortable sizes, and lots of fashionable beach accessories. Lenny is quite expensive, but the bikinis are particularly creative. A *très* chic bikini designer, **Salinas** (✉ Rio Sul, Rua Lauro Müller 116, Loja C, Botafogo ☎ 021/2275–0793) is the label de rigueur with the fashionable set in Búzios and other resort areas. For bikinis larger than a postage stamp, try **Track & Field** (✉ Rio Sul, Rua Lauro Müller 116, Loja 401 B09, Botafogo ☎ 021/2295–5996 ⊕ www.tf.com.br), a sportswear shop.

Beauty

O Boticario (✉ Rua Visconde de Pirajá 244, Ipanema ☎ 021/2267–4104 ⊕ www.oboticario.com.br) is Brazil's answer to Origins. It carries soaps, lotions, perfumes, shampoos, and cosmetics made from typical local plants and seeds. **Daya Zen** (✉ Rua Visconde de Pirajá 161, 3rd floor, Ipanema ☎ 021/2247–0489 or 2247–9093 ⊕ www.dayaterapias.com.br) sells beauty products and is also a day spa. Stop by the store to buy a few of the wonderful soaps or incense, and treat yourself to a relaxing and transformational massage.

The drugstore **Farma Life** (✉ Av. Ataulfo de Paiva 644, Loja B, Leblon ☎ 021/2511–4937 or 021/2239–1178 ⊕ www.farmalife.com.br) has a wide selection of beauty products. If after a day or shopping your feet are moaning, stop by **Spa do Pé** (✉ Av. Nossa Senhora de Copacabana 1066, Loja C, Copacabana ☎ 021/2523–8430 or 021/2523–2556 ⊕ www.spadope.com.br Ⓜ Siqueira Campos) for a massage, manicure, or a foot treatment.

Books

All you could need to entertain and guide yourself in Rio is inside **Livraria Letras & Expressõs** (✉ Rua Visconde de Pirajá 276, Ipanema ☎ 021/2521–6110 ⊕ www.letraseexpressoes.com.br ✉ Av. Ataulfo de Paiva 1292, Loja C, Leblon ☎ 021/2511–5085). Maps and magazines fill the store; the Ipanema location has a cozy coffee shop (with Internet access) on the second floor. **Livraria Saraiva** (✉ Rio Sul Shopping Center, Rua Lauro Müller 16, 3nd floor, Botafogo ☎ 021/2543–7002 ⊕ www.livrariasaraiva.com.br) is an enormous bookstore that carries books in both Portuguese and English. This Rio Sul location also sells a large selection of CDs and travel guides, and has a cozy coffee shop. **Livraria Leonardo da Vinci** (✉ Av. Rio Branco 185, Centro ☎ 021/2533–2237 ⊕ www.leonardodavinci.com.br Ⓜ Carioca), one of Rio's best bookstores for foreign-language titles, this shop has a wide selection of books in English, Spanish, and French.

Cachaça

Academia da Cachaça (⊠ Rua Conde Bernadote 26, Loja G, Leblon ☎ 021/ 2239–1542) is not only *the* place in Rio to try caipirinhas—made with dozens kinds of tropical fruits—but is a temple of cachaça. The small bar with extraordinary appetizers from northeast Brazil sells 50 brands of cachaça by the glass or bottle. At **Garapa Doida** (⊠ Rua Carlos Góis 234, Loja F, Leblon ☎ 021/2274–8186) learn how to prepare a good caipirinha and to buy everything you need to make it, including glasses, straws, barrels to conserve the alcohol, and cachaça brands from all over the country.

Garrafeira (⊠ Rua Dias Ferreira 259, Loja A, Leblon ☎ 021/2512–3336) is a charming liquor store that sells more than 10 kinds of cachaça, including some brands from Piauí and Parati, a state and a city well known for producing good ones. Thirty types of cachaça and imported olives, nuts, apricots, salmon, and more are sold at **Lidador** (⊠ Rua da Assembléia 65, Centro ☎ 021/2533–4896 Ⓜ Carioca ⊠ Rua Barata Ribeiro 505, Copacabana ☎ 021/2549–0091 Ⓜ Siqueira Campos ⊠ Botafogo Praia Shopping, Praia de Botafogo 400, Loja 201, Botafogo ☎ 021/2237–9057 Ⓜ Botafogo).

Clothing

Animale (⊠ Rua Joana Angelica 116, Ipanema ☎ 021/2227–3318 ⊕ www.animale.com.br) sets the trend in women's fashion in Rio. Unlike that of any other store, Animale's clothing is original and uniquely Brazilian, ranging from Brazilian blue jeans to elaborate and sensual tops and jackets. **Aviator** (⊠ Rua Visconde de Pirajá 444, Ipanema ☎ 021/ 2523–8908 ⊕ www.aviator.com.br) carries trendy clothing for men. A good to place some new T-shirts or pants, or you can go all out and buy yourself a new suit that follows the latest in Brazilian fashion.

Casa Futurista (⊠ Rua Visconde de Pirajá 253, Ipanema ☎ 021/ 2522–7103) carries an enormous selection of Brazilian lingerie. Also a great place to buy swimwear in larger sizes, for those who don't want to wear the tiny bikinis sold at most other stores. At **Krishna** (⊠ Rio Sul, Av. Lauro Müller 116, Loja B30, Botafogo ☎ 021/2542–2443 ⊠ São Conrado Fashion Mall, Estrada da Gávea 899, São Conrado ☎ 021/ 3322–0437) the specialty is classic feminine dresses and separates—many in fine linens, cottons, and silks.

Osklen (⊠ Rua Maria Quitéria 85, Ipanema ☎ 021/2227–2911 ⊠ São Conrado Fashion Mall, Estrada da Gávea 899, São Conrado ☎ 021/ 3083–0000 ⊠ Barra Shopping, Av. das Américas 4666, Barra da Tijuca ☎ 021/3089–1100 ⊕ www.barrashopping.com.br) is a synonym for sporty casual clothing with a fashionable flair. The clothes—from trousers to coats to tennis shoes—are designed for outdoor use.

Richards (⊠ Rua Maria Quiteria 95, Ipanema ☎ 021/2294–7996 ⊕ www.richards.com.br) has an English name, but it is actually one of the most traditional clothing stores in Brazil. Originally just for men, Richards now also carries women's clothing. They sell classic but uniquely Brazilian styles.

Coffee

Armazém do Café (✉ Rua Visconde de Pirajá 547, Ipanema ☎ 021/ 2259–0209 ✉ Rua Rita Ludolf 87, Loja B, Leblon ☎ 021/2259–0170) is a complete coffee shop with several brands of tasteful and high-quality *ouro negro* (black gold), as coffee was once called in the country because of its economic value. The shop also sells coffee machines. The supermarket **Pão de Açúcar** (✉ Av. Nossa Senhora Copacabana 493, Copacabana ☎ 021/2548–0483 Ⓜ Siqueira Campos) is a good bet for coffee and is cheaper than buying it at a coffee shop. Open 24 hours, **Zona Sul** (✉ Prudente de Morais 49, Ipanema ☎ 021/2267–3936) has a wide selection of coffee, and other goods at reasonable prices.

Handicrafts

Inside the Museu do Índio (Museum of the Indian), **Artíndia** (✉ Rua das Palmeiras 55, Botafogo ☎ 021/2286–8899 ⊕ www.museudoindio.org. br Ⓜ Botafogo) has handcrafted items made by several Brazilian tribes: toys, necklaces made of seeds and feathers, musical instruments, and traditional Brazilian cooking pans made of iron. The shop is open weekdays 9–5:30 and weekends 1–5. **Chamma da Amazônia** (✉ Rio Sul Shopping Center, Rua Lauro Müller 16, 2nd floor kiosk, Botafogo ☎ 021/2542–4866 ⊕ www.chammadamazonia.com.br) has jewelry made from seeds from the Amazon and other parts of Brazil. The store also sells beauty products and fragrances made with uniquely Brazilian ingredients.

Curio L Folclore (✉ Rua Visconde de Pirajá 490, Ipanema ☎ 021/ 2106–0000), owned by H. Stern jewelry, bursts with primitive paintings, costume jewelry, leather and ceramic crafts, and birds and flowers carved from stone. Quality is high, but some items have been imported from other South American nations. Close to the train station to Corcovado, **Jeito Brasileiro** (✉ Rua Erere 11 A, Cosme Velho ☎ 021/ 2205–7636) has a great variety of paintings; handcrafted wood, leather, and ceramic items; and also some pieces from the Camurim tribe. The shop is open weekdays 9–6, Saturday 9–4, and Sunday 9–1.

La Vereda (✉ Rua Almirante Alexandrino 428, Santa Teresa ☎ 021/ 2507–0317 Ⓜ Carioca) is an art and souvenir store that sells beautiful local crafts, and you'll find items that you probably wouldn't find anywhere else in the city. From the metro station, you take the *bonde* (streetcar) to Santa Teresa, getting off at Largo dos Guimaraes.

Jewelry

Amsterdam Sauer (✉ Rua Visconde de Pirajá 484, Ipanema ☎ 021/ 2512–9878, 021/2239–8045 for the museum), one of Rio's top names in jewelry, has top prices. Jules Roger Sauer, the founder of these stores (with branches in Brazil, the United States, and the Caribbean), is particularly known for his fascination with emeralds. The on-site gemstone museum is open weekdays 10–6 and Saturday 9–2 (tour reservations are a good idea). For nearly 30 years **Antônio Bernardo** (✉ Fórum Ipanema, Rua Visconde de Pirajá 351, Loja 104, Ipanema ☎ 021/2523–3192 ⊕ www.antoniobernardo.com.br ✉ São Conrado Fashion Mall, Estrada da Gávea 899, São Conrado ☎ 021/3322–3113 ✉ Shopping Center da

Gávea, Rua Marquês de São Vicente 52, Gávea ☎ 021/2274–7796) has been making gorgeous jewelry with contemporary designs.

Hans Stern started his empire in 1945 with an initial investment of about $200. Today his interests include mining and production operations as well as 170 stores in Europe, the Americas, and the Middle East. His award-winning designers create truly distinctive contemporary pieces (the inventory runs to about 300,000 items). At the world headquarters of **H. Stern** (⊠ Rua Visconde de Pirajá 490, Ipanema ☎ 021/2106–0000), you can see exhibits of rare stones and watch craftspeople transform rough stones into sparkling jewels. There's also a museum you can tour. The shops downstairs sell more affordable pieces and folkloric items.

Leather Goods

Constança Basto (⊠ Rua Visconde de Pirajá 371, Loja 206, Ipanema ☎ 021/2247–9932) has women's shoes made of crocodile and snake leather in original styles. Most pairs cost upwards of R$200. Traditional carioca boutique **Mariazinha** (⊠ Rio Sul, Av. Lauro Müller 116, Loja C34A, Botafogo ☎ 021/2541–6695 ⊠ Rio Visconde de Pirajá 365, Ipanema ☎ 021/2523–2340), almost 40 years old, carries fashionable and modern footwear for women and is one of the city's finest clothing brands that follows international trends.

Mr. Cat (⊠ Botafogo Praia Shopping, Praia de Botafogo 400, Botafogo ☎ 021/2237–9087 ⊕ www.mrcat.com.br Ⓜ Botafogo) carries some of Rio's best handbags and leather shoes for men and women. **Pano Profano** (⊠ Rua Visconde de Pirajá 228, Ipanema ☎ 021/2247–6028) specializes in leather goods and is a great place to shop for top-quality leather shoes, belts, and handbags. **Victor Hugo** (⊠Rio Sul, Av. Lauro Müller 116, Loja B19, Botafogo ☎ 021/2543–9290), a Uruguayan who began making handbags when he came to Brazil in the 1970s, has become famous nationally for his quality leather handbags. The bags are similar in quality to more expensive brands like Louis Vuitton, Gucci, and Prada.

Music

Modern Sound (⊠ Rua Barata Ribeiro 502 D, Copacabana ☎ 021/2548–5005 ⊕ www.modernsound.com.br Ⓜ Siqueira Campos) was a traditional shop that turned into a self-designated megamusic store. Aside from the 50,000 CD titles—which include lots of rarities—the store carries music equipment and accessories and has a charming bistro, where live music, from jazz to bossa nova, is played by the finest carioca musicians. **Musical Carioca** (⊠Rua da Carioca 89, Centro ☎021/2524–6029 or 021/2524–6991 ⊕www.musicalcarioca.com.br) is a paradise for music lovers, and shares a street with many other music stores. Brazilian percussion instruments are sold here, too.

Toca do Vinicius (⊠ Rua Vinicius de Moraes 129, Loja C, Ipanema ☎ 021/2247–5227) bills itself as a "cultural space and bossa nova salon." The shop, though tiny, does indeed seem like a gathering place for bossa nova aficionados from around the world, and if you're one of them, there's a good chance you'll leave the shop with an e-mail address for at least one new pal. Amid the friendly atmosphere, you can find books (a few in English), sheet music, and T-shirts as well as CDs.

Shoes

Arezzo (✉ Rua Visconde de Pirajá 295, Loja B, Ipanema ☎ 021/ 2521–4737) is one of the best places in town to buy women's shoes. Always on top of the latest fashion, Arezzo's prices are reasonable and their selection is huge.

Surf Gear

Invicta Boardshop (✉ Rua Francisco Otaviano 67, Loja L, Copacabana ☎ 021/2523–0499 Ⓜ Siqueira Campos) sells all the clothing and equipment you might need for your surfing vacation. It is one of several surf shops on this block. From the metro stop take the shuttle bus towards Praça General Osório, get off at last stop in Copacabana.

RIO DE JANEIRO ESSENTIALS

Transportation

For more information about transportation, *see* Smart Travel Tips A to Z, *at* the front of this book.

BY AIR

Nearly three dozen airlines regularly serve Rio. Several of the international carriers also offer Rio–São Paulo flights.

AIRPORTS All international flights and most domestic flights arrive and depart from the Aeroporto Internacional Antônio Carlos Jobim, also known as Galeão. The airport is about 45 minutes northwest of the beach area and most of Rio's hotels. Aeroporto Santos Dumont, 20 minutes from the beaches and within walking distance of Centro, serves the Rio–São Paulo air shuttle and a few air-taxi firms.

🔃 Airports **Aeroporto Internacional Antônio Carlos Jobim** (Galeão) ☎ 021/3398–4526. **Aeroporto Santos Dumont** ☎ 021/3814–7070.

AIRPORT TRANSFERS Special airport taxis have booths in the arrival areas of both airports. Fares to all parts of Rio are posted at the booths, and you pay in advance (about R$41–R$56). Also trustworthy are the white radio taxis parked in the same areas; these charge an average of 20% less. Three reliable special taxi firms are Transcoopass, Cootramo, and Coopertramo.

Buses run by Empresa Real park curbside outside customs at Galeão and outside the main door at Santos Dumont; for R$5 they make the hour-long trip from Galeão into the city, following the beachfront drives and stopping at all hotels along the way. If your hotel is inland, the driver will let you off at the nearest corner. Buses leave from the airport every half hour from 5:20 AM to 11 PM. Two of the taxi firms have vans at the international airport: Cootramo has a van (with 11 seats) to downtown for R$57 and to Copacabana for R$78. Coopertramo does the same for R$70 and R$80, but the van has a capacity to transport 15.

🔃 **Cootramo** ☎ 021/2560–5442, 021/3976–9944, or 021/3976–9945. **Coopertramo** ☎ 021/2560–2022. **Empresa Real** ☎ 021/2560–7041 or 0800/24–0850. **Transcoopass** ☎ 021/2560–4888.

BY BUS

ARRIVING &
DEPARTING Regular service is available to and from Rio. Long-distance and international buses leave from the Rodoviária Novo Rio. Any local bus marked RODOVIÁRIA will take you to the station. You can buy tickets at the depot or, for some destinations, from travel agents. Buses also leave from the more conveniently located Menezes Cortes Terminal, near Praça 15 de Novembro. These buses travel to different neighborhoods of Rio (Barra da Tijuca, Santa Cruz, Campo Grande, and Recreio) and to nearby cities Nieterói, Petrópolis, and Nova Friburgo, among others.

🚌 **Rodoviária Novo Rio** ⊠ Av. Francisco Bicalho 1, São Cristóvão ☎ 021/2291-5151. **Menezes Cortes Terminal** ⊠ Rua São José 35, Centro ☎ 021/2299-1380.

GETTING
AROUND
Don't attempt using the bus unless you know which line to take and you speak enough Portuguese to ask directions (drivers don't speak English). Never take the bus at night. Much has been made of the threat of being robbed on Rio's city buses, and many local residents no longer ride public buses. If you are going to use a public bus, don't wear expensive watches or jewelry, carry a camera or a map in hand, or talk loudly in English. It's also wise to avoid buses during rush hour.

That said, local buses are inexpensive (about R$1–R$2.50) and can take you anywhere you want to go. (Route maps aren't available, but the tourist office has lists of routes to the most popular sights.) You enter buses at the front, where you pay the attendant and pass through a turnstile, then exit at the rear. Have your fare in hand when you board to avoid flashing bills or wallets.

The upscale, privately run, and air-conditioned **Frescão** buses run between the beaches, downtown, and Rio's two airports. These vehicles, which look like highway buses, stop at regular bus stops but also may be flagged down wherever you see them. Minivans run back and forth along beachfront avenues. Fares start at about R$1.40.

BY CAR

ARRIVING &
DEPARTING
Arriving from São Paulo (429 km/266 mi on BR 116) or Brasília (1,150 km/714 mi on BR 040), you enter Rio via Avenida Brasil, which runs into Centro's beachside drive, the Avenida Infante Dom Henrique. This runs along Rio's Baía de Guanabara and passes through the Copacabana Tunnel to Copacabana Beach. The beachside Avenida Atlântica continues into Ipanema and Leblon along Avenidas Antônio Carlos Jobim (Ipanema) and Delfim Moreira (Leblon). From Galeão take the Airport Expressway (known as the Linha Vermelha, or Red Line) to the beach area. This expressway takes you through two tunnels and into Lagoa. Exit on Avenida Epitácio Pessoa, the winding street encircling the lagoon. To reach Copacabana, exit at Avenida Henrique Dodsworth (known as the Corte do Cantagalo). For Ipanema and Leblon there are several exits, beginning with Rua Maria Quitéria.

GETTING
AROUND
The carioca style of driving is passionate to the point of abandon: traffic jams are common, the streets aren't well marked, and red lights are often more decorative than functional. Although there are parking areas along the beachfront boulevards, finding a spot can still be a problem.

If you do choose to drive, exercise extreme caution, wear seat belts at all times, and keep the doors locked.

There's a gas station on every main street in Rio: for example, on Avenida Atlântica in Copacabana, around the Lagoa Rodrigo de Freitas, and at Avenida Vieira Souto in Ipanema. International companies, such as Shell and Esso, are represented. The gas stations run by Brazilian oil company Petrobras are called BR. Ipiranga is another local option. Half the gas stations are open from 6 AM until 10 PM, and half are open 24 hours and have convenience stores. Gas stations don't have emergency service, so ask when you rent whether your car-rental insurance includes it.

Car rentals can be arranged through hotels or agencies and at this writing cost about R$110–R$250 a day for standard models. Major agencies include Avis, Hertz, and Unidas. Localiza is a local agency. Hertz and Unidas have desks at the international and domestic airports.

Turismo Clássico Travel, one of the country's most reliable travel and transport agencies, can arrange for a driver to get you around within the city, with or without an English-speaking guide (US$30 per hour). Classico's owners, Liliana and Vera, speak English, and each has 20 years of experience in organizing transportation. They also lead sightseeing tours.

🖪 Rental Agencies **Avis** ✉ Av. Princesa Isabel 350, Copacabana ☎ 021/2543-8579. **Hertz** ✉ Av. Princesa Isabel 334, Copacabana ☎ 021/2275-7440 or 0800/701-7300 ✉ Aeroporto Internacional Antônio Carlos Jobim ☎ 021/3398-4339 ✉ Aeroporto Santos Dumont ☎ 021/2262-0612. **Localiza Rent a Car** ✉ Av. Princesa Isabel 214, Copacabana ☎ 021/2275-3340 ✉ Aeroporto Internacional Antônio Carlos Jobim ☎ 021/3398-5445 ✉ Aeroporto Santos Dumont ☎ 021/2533-2677. **Unidas** ☎ 021/4001-2222 for main reservations line ✉ Aeroporto Santos Dumont, Av. Senador Salgado Filho s/n, Centro ☎ 021/2240-9181 ✉ Av. Princesa Isabel 166, Copacabana ☎ 021/3685-1212 ✉ Aeroporto Internacional do Galeão, Estrada do Galeão s/n, Ilha do Governador ☎ 021/3398-2286.

🖪 Transport Agency **Turismo Clássico Travel** ✉ Av. Nossa Senhora de Copacabana 1059, Sala 805, Copacabana ☎ 021/2523-3390.

BY SUBWAY

Rio's subway system, the metro, is clean, relatively safe, and efficient—a delight to use—but it's not comprehensive and has only two lines. It's great option to get from Copacabana to Centro, but not for Ipanema or Leblon, since the southernmost metro stop (called Siqueira Campos) is in Copacabana. The metro shuttle can get you to and from Siqueira Campos to Ipanema. Reaching sights distant from metro stations can be a challenge, especially in summer when the infamous carioca traffic fans what is already 90-degree exasperation. Plan your tours accordingly; tourism offices and some metro stations have maps.

Trains run daily 5 AM–midnight Monday–Saturday, and 7 AM–11 PM Sundays and holidays. A single metro ticket at this writing costs R$2.25. Combination metro-bus tickets allow you to take special buses to and from the Siqueira Campos station: one runs to Leblon via Jardim Botânico and Jóckey; the other goes to Leblon by way of Túnel Velho, Copacabana, and Ipanema.

🖪 **Metrô Rio Information Line** ☎ 021/3211-6300 ⊕ www.metrorio.com.br.

BY TAXI

Taxis are plentiful in Rio, and in most parts of the city you can easily flag one down on the street.

Yellow taxis have meters that start at a set price and have two rates. The "1" rate applies to fares before 8 PM, and the "2" rate applies to fares after 8 PM, on Sunday, on holidays, throughout December, in the neighborhoods of São Conrado and Barra da Tijuca, and when climbing steep hills. Drivers are required to post a chart noting the current fares on the inside of the left rear window.

Radio taxis and several companies that routinely serve hotels (and whose drivers often speak English) are also options. They charge 30% more than other taxis but are reliable and usually air-conditioned. Other cabs working with the hotels also charge more, normally a fixed fee that you should agree on before you leave. Reliable radio-cab companies include Centro de Taxis, Coopacarioca, and Coopatur.

Most carioca cabbies are pleasant, but there are exceptions. Remain alert and trust your instincts. Unless you've negotiated a flat fee with the driver, be sure the meter is turned on. Few cab drivers speak English.

🚩 **Centro de Taxis** ☎ 021/2195-1000. **Coopacarioca** ☎ 021/2518-1818. **Coopatur** ☎ 021/2573-1009.

BY TRAIN

ARRIVING & DEPARTING   Intercity trains leave from the central station that starred in the Oscar-nominated movie of the same name, Estação Dom Pedro II Central do Brasil. Trains, including a daily overnight train to São Paulo, also leave from the Estação Leopoldina Barao de Maria, near Praça 15 de Novembro.

🚩 **Estação Dom Pedro II Central do Brasil** ✉ Praça Cristiano Otoni on Av. President Vargas, Centro ☎ 021/2588-9494.

Contacts & Resources

BANKS & EXCHANGE SERVICES

Generally, exchange rates are better in the city than at the airport, and cash gets better rates than traveler's checks. Most Brazilian banks don't exchange money. One that does is Banco do Brasil. The branch at Galeão offers good exchange rates, but it won't provide credit-card advances.

Casas de câmbio (exchange houses) are found all over the city, especially along the beaches and on Avenida Nossa Senhora de Copacabana and Rua Visconde de Pirajá in Ipanema. Many change money without charging a service fee. Sometimes, depending on the amount of money you wish to exchange, exchange houses have a better rate than the banks. American Express is another option.

Some hotels, such as the Caesar Park and the Copacabana Palace, offer competitive rates but charge a commission if you're not a guest. On weekends hotels may be your best bet, because few other places are open. Or try the Banco 24 Horas automatic teller machines (ATMs) throughout town, which dispense reais.

🚩 **American Express** ✉ Av. Atlântica 1702 B, Copacabana ☎ 021/2548-2148 or 0800/702-0777. **Banco do Brasil** ✉ Rua Bartolomeu Mitre 438 A, Leblon ☎ 021/2512-9992

Rua Senador Dantas 105, Centro 021/3808-2689 Aeroporto Internacional Antônio Carlos Jobim, 3rd floor 021/3398-3652. **Banco 24 Horas ATM** Av. Nossa Senhora de Copacabana 202 Av. Nossa Senhora de Copacabana 599 Av. Nossa Senhora de Copacabana 1366 Rua Visconde de Pirajá 174, Ipanema. **Casa Universal** Av. Nossa Senhora de Copacabana 371 E, Copacabana 021/2548-6696.

EMERGENCIES

The Tourism Police station is open 24 hours.

Ambulance and Fire 193. **Police** 190 www.novapolicia.rj.gov.br. **Tourism Police** Rua Humberto de Campos 315, Leblon 021/3399-7170.

Medical Clinics Cardio Plus Rua Visconde de Pirajá 330, Ipanema 021/2521-4899. **Galdino Campos Cardio Copa Medical Clinic** Av. Nossa Senhora de Copacabana 492, Copacabana 021/2548-9966. **Medtur** Av. Nossa Senhora de Copacabana 647, Copacabana 021/2235-3339. **Copa D'Or** Rua Figueiredo Magalhães 875, Copacabana 021/2545-3600.

24-Hour Pharmacies Drogaria Pacheco Av. Nossa Senhora de Copacabana 534, Copacabana 021/2548-1525. **Farmácia do Leme** Av. Prado Júnior 237, Leme 021/2275-3847.

INTERNET

Brazilians are joining the Internet community in increasing numbers, and the staff at many hotels can arrange Internet access for guests. In addition, you can head to several cybercafés around town for coffee while you check your e-mail. Web access tends to be around R$10 per hour. Café do Ubaldo is in a bookstore; Geographic Café is in a clothing store.

Internet Cafés Café do Ubaldo Livraria Letras e Expressões, Rua Visconde de Pirajá 276, Ipanema 021/2521-6110 M Siqueira Campos, then shuttle bus to Praça General Osório. **Cyber Coffee** Rio Sul Shopping Center, Rua Lauro Müller 16, 3rd floor, Botafogo 021/2543-6886. **Geographic Café** Wollner, Rua Visconde de Pirajá 511, Ipanema 021/2512-3608. **Tudo É Fácil** Rua Xavier da Silveira 19, loja B, Copacabana 021/2543-7229 M Cardeal Arcoverde.

MAIL & SHIPPING

The main post office is in Centro, but there are branches all over the city, including one at Galeão, several on Avenida Nossa Senhora de Copacabana in Copacabana, and one on Rua Visconde de Pirajá in Ipanema. Most are open weekdays 8–5 and Saturday 8–noon. Federal Express and DHL have offices open weekdays, but shipping usually takes longer than just overnight. You can call a day ahead to schedule pickup.

Express Services DHL Rua Barao de Tefé 7, Centro 021/2516-0828 or 0800/701-0833. **Federal Express** Av. Calógeras 23, Centro 0800/903-333.

Post Office Agência Central Av. Presidente Vargas 3077 021/2503-8467.

TOUR OPTIONS

CITY TOURS English-speaking guides at Gray Line are superb. In addition to a variety of city tours, the company also offers trips outside town, whether you'd like to go white-water rafting on the Rio Paraíbuna, tour a coffee plantation, or spend time in Petrópolis. Helicopter tours are also an option.

Private Tours take you around old Rio, the favelas, Corcovado, Floresta da Tijuca, Prainha, and Grumari in a jeep. Guides are available who speak English, Hungarian, French, and German. Hang-glide or paraglide over

Pedra da Gávea and Pedra Bonita under the supervision of São Conrado Eco-Aventura.

Carlos Roquette is a history teacher who runs Cultural Rio, an agency that hosts trips to 8,000 destinations. Most are historic sites. A guided visit costs around US$110 for four hours, depending on the size of the group. Favela Tour offers a fascinating half-day tour of two favelas. For anyone with an interest in Brazil beyond the beaches, such tours are highly recommended. The company's English-speaking guides can also be contracted for other outings.

Rio Hiking takes small groups on nightlife tours to clubs and bars beyond the regular tourist circuit.

🇮🇹 **Cultural Rio** ☎ 021/9911-3829 ⊕ www.culturalrio.com.br. **Favela Tour** ☎ 021/3322-2727 ⊕ www.favelatour.com.br. **Gray Line** ☎ 021/2512-9919. **Private Tours** ☎☎ 021/2232-9710 ⊕ www.privatetours.com.br. **Rio Hiking** ☎ 021/2552-9204 or 021/9721-0594 ⊕ www.riohiking.com.br.

ECOLOGY & THE OUTDOORS You can ride around the Floresta da Tijuca and Corcovado or take a tour to Angra dos Reis and Teresópolis in renovated World War II jeeps (1942 Dodge Commanders, Willys F-75s, and others) with the well-organized Ecology and Culture Jeep Tours. Guides speak English, French, German, and Spanish. The company also has a range of ecological tours, including some on horseback.

Trilhas do Rio organizes frequent outdoor trips so you can get to know the Floresta da Tijuca and other ecological treasures in and around Rio. Rio Hiking tours combine city sightseeing with nature hikes to the Floresta da Tijuca and other areas, plus overnight trips to Paraty and Ilha Grande.

🇮🇹 **Ecology and Culture Jeep Tours** ☎ 021/2108-5800 ⊕ www.jeeptour.com.br. **Rio Hiking** ☎ 021/2552-9204 or 021/9721-0594 ⊕ www.riohiking.com.br. **Trilhas do Rio** ☎ 021/2425-8441 or 021/2424-5455 ⊕ www.trilhasdorio.com.br.

HELICOPTER TOURS Helisight gives a number of helicopter tours whose flights may pass over the *Cristo Redentor,* Copacabana, Ipanema, and/or Maracanã stadium. There are night flights as well; reserve ahead for these daily 9–6.

🇮🇹 **Helisight** ✉ Conde de Bernadote 26, Leblon ☎ 021/2511-2141, 021/2542-7895, or 021/2259-6995 ⊕ www.helisight.com.br.

VISITOR INFORMATION

The Rio de Janeiro city tourism department, Riotur, has an information booth, which is open 8–5 daily. There are also city tourism desks at the airports and the Novo Rio bus terminal. The Rio de Janeiro state tourism board, Turisrio, is open weekdays 9–6. You can also try contacting Brazil's national tourism board, Embratur.

🇮🇹 **Embratur** ✉ Rua Uruguaiana 174, Centro ☎ 021/2509-6292 ⊕ www.embratur.gov.br. **Riotur** ✉ Rua da Assembléia 10, near Praça 15 de Novembro, Centro ☎ 021/2217-7575 or 0800/707-1808 ⊕www.rio.rj.gov.br/riotur. **Riotur information booth** ✉Av. Princesa Isabel 183, Copacabana ☎ 021/2541-7522. **Turisrio** ✉ Rua da Ajuda 5, Centro ☎ 021/2215-0011 ⊕ www.turisrio.rj.gov.br.

Side Trips from Rio

WORD OF MOUTH

"Petropolis is a beautiful city, looks just like Switzerland, lots of chalet-type houses. Wonderful old mansions that you can visit. It is much, much cooler than Rio since it's up in the mountains. . . . This was a GREAT day trip."

—Sandy

"I was in Brazil for two weeks and my three days in Paraty were my favorite. Great restaurants, great art, beautiful town, beautiful harbor, etc. I would NOT miss going to this place."

—Scott

Updated by
Ana Lúcia do
Vale

THE STATE OF RIO DE JANEIRO HOLDS JUST AS MUCH ALLURE as the eponymous city. Just across Guanabara Bay is Niterói, a city whose ancient forts provide a window on history and a great view of Rio. Niterói mixes the past with the ultramodern spaceshiplike Museu de Arte Contemporânea. A scenic road leads northeast to Petrópolis and the opulent imperial palace that was the summer home of Brazil's emperor. Swiss-settled Nova Friburgo peeks from a lush valley speckled with waterfalls farther north. East of Rio, on the Costa Azul (Blue Coast), sailboat-jammed Cabo Frio is a popular eastern coastal resort, and although Brigitte Bardot in a bikini may have put nearby Búzios on the map, its 23 beaches, temperate weather, and sophisticated ambience have kept it there.

West of Rio, on Brazil's Costa Verde (Green Coast), Angra dos Reis is the jumping-off point for 365 islands that pepper a picturesque bay, with unforgettable spots for diving. One of the loveliest, Ilha Grande, is lapped by emerald waters and retains an unspoiled flavor despite its popularity. The most amazing gem, however, is the southwestern coastal town of Paraty, with its 18th-century Portuguese architecture; the lovely cays sprinkled along its bay have attracted American, European, and Brazilian celebrities.

About the Restaurants

Along the Green Coast and the Blue Coast (west and east of Rio), seafood restaurants are especially good. Paraty and Búzios, in particular, have some excellent restaurants. Mealtimes tend to be later in resort towns, especially during high season (December–April), where it's not uncommon to eat at 10 PM.

About the Hotels

Beachfront pousadas line the beachfronts on the coasts east and west of Rio. Historic towns like Paraty and Petrópolis have some gorgeous 18th-century inns, some of which can be a bit drafty. Búzios has some of the best small-scale accommodations in Brazil. Large, multistory resort-type hotels are unusual.

WHAT IT COSTS In Reais					
	$$$$	**$$$**	**$$**	**$**	**¢**
RESTAURANTS	over R$60	R$45–R$60	R$30–R$45	R$15–R$30	under R$15
HOTELS	over R$500	R$375–R$500	R$250–R$375	R$125–R$250	under $R125

Restaurant prices are for a dinner entrée. Hotel prices are for two people in a standard double room in high season, excluding taxes.

THE BLUE COAST

Niterói is a bedroom community of the nearby city of Rio de Janeiro, just across the bay. Some of the best views of Rio are from here. For beautiful beaches and relaxation by the sea, head to Cabo Frio and Búzios. Less than two hours from Rio by car or bus, Cabo Frio is a family resort known for its bikini shops and blue transparent water. Búzios is a

Beaches

The state of Rio de Janeiro has a wide variety of astonishing beaches. Some, like João Fernandes in Búzios, are über-fashionable and chic, crowded with tables and umbrellas, and have beach services and a calm relaxing sea. Other Búzios beaches are a contrast—more hidden, without anything but sand and water. And beaches on islands in the emerald sea of Angra Bay, including Ilha Grande, are ripe for snorkeling, diving, and other water sports. In fact, the area around Angra is considered one of the best places for diving on Brazil's southeast coast.

History

History is everywhere in the coastal cities of the state. Most of them, like Cabo Frio, were founded by the Portuguese when they built forts to protect the coast from French invasion. Churches were some of the first buildings erected in these cities, leaving us with lots of 18th-century churches to explore today. Paraty has particularly interesting churches built separately for freed slaves and the white community. Petrópolis, in the mountains, was once the summer home of the imperial family and now holds the Museu Imperial, a very well organized museum with restored rooms, and an excellent collection of antiques and paintings.

Seafood

Many of the coastal cities in Rio were once fishing villages (local fisherman still work in most), so it's no surprise that the seafood is superb. Those who try the *camarão casadinho* (colossal shrimp) in Paraty never forget the experience. In Cabo Frio, even at the food kiosks at the beach, it's easy to find unforgettable anchovies, prepared simply in the oven, with tomatoes and oil, or fried. A special gray shrimp populates the Itajuru channel in Cabo Frio; they're very small at first sight, but absolutely delicious, especially when pan-fried with a touch of garlic and lemon.

Natural Beauty

If you have a good pair of tennis shoes and a bottle of water you are prepared to experience Rio's great outdoors. Petrópolis is part of the Parque Nacional da Serra dos Órgãos, with several waterfalls, like Cachoeira do Véu da Noiva, and natural pools. Lush Ilha Grande is car-free, leaving you two choices to go from one beach to another: by boat or on foot. The reward for an hour's walk on Ilha Grande is wonderful views of the beaches around the island.

---

small, charming town with 23 beaches on an 8-km (5-mi) peninsula. A car or dune-buggy (easy to rent in Búzios) is essential for beach-hopping—which is recommended.

Niterói

27 *14 km (9 mi) east of Rio.*

Ranked as having the highest quality of life in Rio de Janeiro State, Niterói, literally, "hidden waters," was founded in 1573. Old and new come together in this city of almost 460,000 inhabitants, where both a modern naval industry and traditional fishing help support the economy. Ocean beaches and the Fortaleza de Santa Cruz—an ancient fortress built in 1555 to protect the bay—draw visitors, but so does the ultramodern Museu de Arte Contemporânea. From Praia de Icaraí you can see the entire Guanabara Bay, with the sunset behind Sugar Loaf and Corcovado.

Ferries from Rio's Praça 15 de Novembro cross the bay in just 20 minutes, arriving at Praça Araribóia or at the Terminal Hidroviário de Charitas, designed by the well-known architect Oscar Niemeyer (he designed most of Brasília).

Every Sunday at 10 AM a **tourist ferry** (☎ 021/2533–7524 or 021/2532–6274) departs from Praça 15 de Novembro, and circles Guanabara Bay, taking in the Botafogo Inlet, Niterói beaches, Charitas, Icaraí, and the Rio-Niterói bridge, all for R$10.

The modern-art **Museu de Arte Contemporânea** is an Oscar Niemeyer creation opened in the 1990's that looks a bit like a spaceship. The collection itself is underwhelming; the exterior is the reason to visit. The museum is just five minutes from Praça Araribóia (in downtown Niterói, where the ferries stop), a nice walk along the coastline. ⊠ *Estrada de Boa Viagem, Boa Viagem* ☎ *021/2620–2400* ⊕ *www.macniteroi.com* ☞ *R$4, free Weds.* ☉ *Tues.–Sun. 10–6.*

The **Fortaleza de Santa Cruz** was the first fort built on Guanabara Bay, in 1555. Distributed on two floors are cannons, a sun clock, and the Santa Barbara Chapel, dating from the 17th century. It's best to visit in the cool morning hours. Fifteen minutes from downtown Niterói, it's an easy taxi ride (R$26), or there's a bus that goes straight to Jurujuba (No. 33) from the ferry dock. ⊠ *Estrada General Eurico Gaspar Dutra, Jurujuba* ☎ *021/2711–0462 or 021/2710–7840* ☞ *R$4* ☉ *Tues.–Sun. 9–5.*

Built as a lookout point, **Forte Barão do Rio Branco** was armed and turned into a battery in 1567. Inside is the Forte do Imbuí, another fortress, which is a wonderful place to walk, with a great view of Guanabara Bay and Rio. ⊠ *Av. Marechal Pessoa Leal 265, Jurujuba* ☎ *021/2711–0366 or 021/2711–0566* ☞ *R$6* ☉ *Weekends 9–5.*

Cabo Frio

28 *155 km (101 mi) east of Rio.*

Set up as a defensive port from which to ship wood to Portugal nearly four centuries ago, Cabo Frio has evolved into a resort town renowned for its fresh seafood. It's also a prime jumping-off point for the endless number of white-sand beaches that crisscross the area around town and the offshore islands. A favorite sailing destination, its turquoise waters are crowded with sailboats and yachts on holidays and weekends. The town itself combines attractive baroque architecture in its historic area and modern buildings along the coastline. The city of almost 130,000 people can grow to 10 times the population in summer (December–March).

Praia do Forte is popular thanks to its calm, clear waters and long stretch of sand. On weekends it's jammed with colorful beach umbrellas, swim-

mers, sun lovers, and food kiosks that extend their services to tables at the sand. Be prepared to deal with all kinds of vendors on the sand, some obnoxiously insistent, some selling unique souvenirs. Some distance away, **Praia Brava and Praia do Foguete** lure surfers to their crashing waves. Just 10 km (6 mi) south of Cabo Frio is cozy **Arraial do Cabo,** with transparent beaches and the Gruta Azul—a 15-meter-tall cave over the blue sea—and Pontal do Atalaia, an extraordinary viewing point.

Cabo Frio hotels are not as nice as those in nearby Búzios, so you're better off staying there and making the short trip to Cabo Frio by car or via a 50-minute bus trip (R$2.10). Restaurants in Cabo Frio tend to be of the by-the-kilo, cheap variety and change frequently. Head to Boulevard Canal for restaurants and nightlife. To find the finest Brazilian bikinis—from the sexiest and tiniest *fio dental* (dental floss) styles to more modest sizes—go to Rua dos Biquínis, with dozens of high-quality beachwear shops with good prices. In summer shops close at around midnight.

Where to Stay

$–$$ **Caribe Park Hotel.** Rooms are simple, with wood furniture and ceramic floors, but Caribe Park is very well located, close to Praia do Forte and downtown. ⊠ *Av. do Contorno 186, Praia do Forte, 28906-030* ☎ *022/ 2645–5050 or 022/2643–2235* ⊕ *www.hotelcaribe.com.br* ⊅ *130* *rooms* ☆ *Restaurant, room service, in-room safes, refrigerators, cable TV, in-room data ports, 2 pools, sauna, laundry service, tennis court, playground* ☰ *AE, DC, MC, V* ◉ *MAP.*

$–$$ 🏨 **Hotel Joalpa.** Three blocks from Praia do Forte, but in front of not-as-crowded Praia das Dunas, Joalpa has rooms that can accommodate five people. ✉ *Rua dos Cravos 2, Balneário das Dunas, 28908-280* ☎ *022/2645–4848* ⊕ *www.joalpa.com.br* 📞 *68 rooms* ☆ *Restaurant, room service, refrigerators, cable TV, pool, sauna, laundry service* ☰ *AE, DC, MC, V* ◉ *BP.*

$–$$ 🏨 **Malibu Palace Hotel.** One of the most traditional hotels in Cabo Frio, the Malibu Palace is simply decorated but has the advantage of being just in front of Praia do Forte, with its blue transparent waters, and in the center of the city just blocks from shops and restaurants. The hotel has beach service, like umbrellas. ✉ *Av. do Contorno 900, at Praia do Forte, 28907-250* ☎ *022/2643–1955 or 022/2645–5131* ⊕ *www. malibupalace.com.br* 📞 *110 rooms* ☆ *Restaurant, room service, in-room safes, refrigerators, cable TV, in-room data ports, 2 pools, gym, sauna, dry cleaning, laundry service, no-smoking rooms, beach service* ☰ *AE, DC, MC, V* ◉ *MAP.*

Búzios

㉙ FodorsChoice ★ *24 km (15 mi) northeast of Cabo Frio; 176 km (126 mi) northeast of Rio.*

Búzios, a little more than two hours from Rio, is a string of gorgeous beaches on an 8-km-long (5-mi-long) peninsula. Europeans and South Americans (especially Argentineans and Chileans) flock here year-round to do absolutely nothing. It was little more than a fishing village until the 1960's, when Brigitte Bardot escaped from the paparazzi here, but was eventually found, and fame for little Búzios followed. A bronze statue on the Orla Bardot, along the water near downtown, was crafted in her honor. Since Bardot's time, some of Búzios's old fishing shacks have given way to *pousadas*, or inns (some of them luxurious, a few inexpensive), restaurants, and bars run by people who came on vacation and never left. Despite the growth, Búzios retains some of the charm of a small fishing village, and the balance of the cosmopolitan and the primitive is seductive.

March through June is low season, when temperatures range from about 27°C (80°F) to 32°C (90°F), and prices often drop 30%–40%. The water is still warm, but the beaches are not overcrowded; the area seems much more intimate than in the spring and summer months of October through February. Not much English is spoken here outside of a few select hotels, but a little Spanish or French will get you a long way.

Each of the beaches has something different: the lovely, intimate Azeda and Azedinha are local favorites (and the spots where you may find top-less bathing); Ferradura is known for jet skiing and excellent food kiosks; Lagoinha is referred to as a magic beach and has a natural amphitheater where world-class musicians hold concerts; João Fernandes is a popular beach for its warm waters and many good food kiosks; Geribá is a big and beautiful white-sand half-moon crescent; Brava is the surfers' beach; and Manguinhos is popular with windsurfers.

The **Tour Shop** has a mini-golf field (with 21 greens), a zip line (R$20), and trolleys that take you from your hotel to 12 beaches (R$40), with three departures a day. A three-hour catamaran trip around Búzios goes to 17 beaches (R$40), and a day trip by boat to Gruta Azul in nearby Arraial do Cabo (⇨ Cabo Frio, *above*) is R$100 per person, lunch included. ⊠ *Orla Bardot 550, Armação dos Búzios* ☎ *022/2623–4733 or 022/2623–0292* ⊕ *www.tourshop.com.br.*

Where to Stay & Eat

★ **$$$–$$$$** ✕ **Satyricon.** The Italian fish restaurant famous in Rio has opened up shop here as well. The seafood is expensive but excellent, and includes the famous rock salt–baked whole fish. ⊠ *Av. José Bento Ribeiro Dantas (Orla Bardot) 500* ☎ *022/2623–1595* ⊟ *AE, DC, MC, V.*

★ **$–$$$$** ✕ **Cigalon.** Widely considered the best restaurant in Búzios, Cigalon is an elegant place with a veranda overlooking the beach. Though the waiters are bow-tied and the tables white-clothed and candlelit, this is still Búzios, and casual but clean dress is just fine. The food is French-inspired, and includes lamb steak, braised duck breast, and lobster with rice and almonds. A departure from the French fare is the full menu of homemade pastas. If you're having trouble making up your mind among the tempting options, the tasting menu for R$33 might be your best bet. ⊠ *Rua das Pedras 199, Centro* ☎ *022/2623–6284* ⊟ *AE, DC, MC, V.*

$$–$$$$ ✕ **Estância Don Juan.** Argentineans love Búzios and expertly grilled beef, which is the specialty this typical Argentinean restaurant with traditional decor. Make a reservation for the Tuesday-night tango show. ⊠ *Rua das Pedras 178* ☎ *22/2623–2169* ⊟ *AE, DC, MC, V* ⊕ *www.estanciadonjuan.com.br.*

$$ ✕ **Buzin.** Behind fashionable Rua das Pedras, Rua Turíbio de Farias is a buffet per-kilo restaurant with churrasco, many varieties of seafood—including sushi—and salads. The reasonable prices, many choices, and casual atmosphere make it a great post-beach stop. Try the shrimp fried in oil and garlic or the *picanha* beef, a very tender cut of beef found in every churrascaria. ⊠ *Rua Turíbio de Farias 273* ☎ *022/2633–7051* ⊟ *AE, DC, MC, V* ⊕ *www.buzin.com.br.*

$–$$ ✕ **Capricciosa.** Well-known in Rio, the Búzios branch of this pizzeria has the same high-quality pies. The Margarita (Margherita) Gourmet is a must, with a thin crust topped with tomatoes and buffalo mozzarella. ⊠ *Av. José Bento Ribeiro Dantas 500, Praia da Armação* ☎ *022/ 2623–1595* ⊟ *AE, DC, MC, V.*

¢–$$ ✕ **Chez Michou.** This Belgian-owned *crêperie* and nighttime meeting spot for 20-somethings on the main drag in the center of town is the best place to eat if you want something quick, light, and inexpensive. You can choose from among about 50 crepe fillings. At night the street-side tables buzz with locals and visitors congregating to drink and people-watch. ⊠ *Rua da Pedras 90* ☎ *022/2623–2169* ⊕ *www.chezmichou.com.br* ⊟ *No credit cards.*

CloseUp

COCONUT WATER: THE ULTIMATE REHYDRATOR

BRAZILIANS HAVE LONG KNOWN that green coconut water is one of the best ways to keep hydrated in the intense heat, but now Americans and Brits are catching on, as coconut water is being bottled and sold as a sports drink in the U.S. and U.K. The same electrolytic balance found in our blood is also found in coconut water, which makes it ideal for rehydration. It's much lower in sugar than most sports drinks and is full of potassium and manganese. Another interesting fact: coconut water and blood plasma have so much in common that the former has been used successfully for blood transfusions in times of need.

Green coconuts are essentially young coconuts. They have a bit of soft meat inside, and quite a bit of water; coconuts that are six to nine months old contain about 3 cups (750 mL) of water. The brown coconuts that tend to appear on grocery shelves in the U.S. are mature coconuts whose green husk has been removed and whose water has been absorbed into the meat, which is usually quite dry.

You can't get far in Brazil without encountering a coconut-water stand: they're on the Copacabana boardwalk, on rural roadsides, and on the beaches from Florianópolis to Fortaleza. The vendor will usually cut a small opening in the top of the coconut with a machete, and give you a straw to drink the water. Afterward, ask him to open the coconut so you can eat the tasty, slippery flesh as well.

$$$$ **Casas Brancas.** If you're looking for complete relaxation, and you've
Fodor'sChoice got the wallet for it, this is the place to stay in Búzios. The quirky build-
★ ing was constructed on several levels facing the beach, which makes for interestingly shaped rooms. Each is decorated with care, but simple cottage style and zenlike peace and quiet are the hallmarks here. Get an ocean-view room, and one with a private balcony if you can swing it. The spa is one of the best in town. ⊠ Alto do Humaitá 10, off Orla Bardot, Centro 28950–000 ☎ 022/2623–1458 ⊕ www.casasbrancas. com.br ⇝ 29 rooms, 3 suites ⚹ Restaurant, cable TV, in-room safes, pool, spa, Internet room, laundry service ⊟ AE, V ¹⁰¹ BP.

$$$–$$$$ **Hotel le Relais de la Borie.** Imagine a country farmhouse with a tropical bent and steps right down to the beach, and you've got La Borie. An inviting warmth pervades the property, especially in the "living room" with a fireplace. (Evenings do get chilly here.) The pool area overlooks beautiful Geribá Beach. All-white rooms have tile floors; some have ocean views, others have views of the interior courtyard and garden. ⊠ Rua dos Gravatás 1374, Geribá 28950–000 ☎ 022/2620-8504 ⊕ www.laborie.com.br ⇝ 38 rooms, 1 suite ⚹ Restaurant, cable TV, in-room safes, pool, hot tub, sauna, spa, exercise equipment, Internet room, laundry service ⊟ AE, DC, MC, V ¹⁰¹ BP.

$$$–$$$$ 🏨 **Rio Búzios Beach Hotel.** Opened in 2004, this hotel is just a few steps from João Fernandes Beach. Rooms are decorated with wicker furniture and it has a special old style panoramic elevator (in fact a replica of Corcovado's in Rio) with a view of the beach. At night the hotel has a free shuttle service to downtown. ✉ *Rua João Fernandes 2, João Fernandes 28950–000* 📞 *022/2623–6073* 🌐 *www.riobuzios.com.br* 🛏 *64 rooms ⟋ Restaurant, room service, refrigerators, in-room safes, cable TV, pool, gym, sauna, bar* 🖃 *AE, DC, MC, V* ⏐◯⏐ *BP.*

$$$ 🏨 **Brava Hotel.** Simply decorated and of Mediterranean inspiration, Brava has small suites, each with a balcony and sea view. It's practically on Brava Beach and has a wonderful ocean view from the pool and the restaurant. ✉ *Rua 17, lote 14, quadra O, Praia Brava, 28950–000* 📞📠 *022/2623–5943* 🌐 *www.buziosonline.com.br/bravahotel* 🛏 *29 suites ⟋ Restaurant, room service, in-room safes, refrigerators, cable TV, pool, spa, dry cleaning, laundry service, no-smoking rooms* 🖃 *AE, DC, MC, V.*

★ **$$$** 🏨 **Galápagos Inn.** Overlooking the charming Orla Bardot—the continuation of Rua das Pedras, where people congregate at night—this hotel also has a view of the sea and, best of all, a view of the sunset. Rooms are comfortable, with decoration inspired by the sea. Verandas have views to João Fernandinho Beach, and there's bar service at the beach. The hotel is included in Brazil's esteemed Roteiros de Charme club, a highly exclusive association of the nation's best places to stay. ✉ *Praia João Fernandinho 3, 28925-000* 📞 *022/2620–8800 or 022/2623–6161* 🌐 *www.galapagos.com.br* 🛏 *37 rooms ⟋ Restaurant, room service, in-room safes, refrigerators, cable TV, in-room data ports, pool, sauna, bar, dry cleaning, laundry service, no-smoking rooms* 🖃 *AE, DC, MC, V* ⏐◯⏐ *BP.*

$$–$$$ 🏨 **Maravista Pousada.** This health-conscious hotel doubles as one of the best spas in Brazil one week per month. (The spa is closed the other three weeks.) Ligia Azevedo, well known for her spa in Rio, operates Búzios's Spa Ligia Azevedo (www.ligiazevedo.com.br), which has group activities like aquatic gymnastics and yoga classes, plus personalized fitness programs, physician-prescribed diets, massage, and beauty treatments. Ligia recommends a full week in the spa to feel the results. It's not hard to take her advice, as the pousada is built right on 4-km Geriba Beach. Rooms have modern decoration with pastel colors, and some have verandas with a sea view. All meals are included during the spa week. ✉ *Rua dos Gravatás 1058, Praia de Geribá, 28950–000* 📞 *022/2623–2130 hotel, 021/2438–0149 spa* 🌐 *www.maravista.com.br* 🛏 *16 ⟋ Refrigerators, in-room safes, pool, sauna, bar* 🖃 *AE, DC, MC, V* ⏐◯⏐ *EP.*

$$ 🏨 **Ilha Branca Inn.** Just 100 meters from the sands of João Fernandes Beach, Ilha has charming and colorful rooms. The hotel was remodeled in 2003 with a new gym and sauna, and a pool with panoramic ocean view. Rooms are individually decorated, with tile floors and wrought-iron, dark-wood, and wicker furnishings. Some face the beach and have verandas. ✉ *Rua João Fernandes 1, Praia de João Fernandes , 28950–000* 📞 *22/2623–2525 or 22/2623–6664* 🌐 *www.ilhabranca.com* 🛏 *67 rooms ⟋ Restaurant, in-room safes, refrigerator, cable tv, bar, sauna, 2 pools, gym* 🖃 *AE, MC, V* ⏐◯⏐ *BP.*

$$ ⌂ **Pousada dos Gravatás.** Its location right on long Praia de Geribá makes this pousada the best budget option in Búzios. Suites have pool and ocean views. Standard apartments are at the back of the pousada, facing an internal patio. Rooms aren't big, but they are comfortable, with decor inspired by the sea. There's bar service on the beach. ⌂ *Rua dos Gravatás 67, Praia de Geribá, 28950-000* ☎ *022/2623–1218* ⊕ *www.pousadagravatas.com.br* ⌁ *55 rooms* ⌂ *Room service, refrigerators, cable TV, 2 pools, gym, sauna, bar, beach service* ⊟ *AE, DC, MC, V* ⏐⊘⏐ *BP.*

$$ ⌂ **Pousada Pedra da Laguna.** Next to Ferradura Beach and in front of Ponta da Lagoinha—a place close to the rocks where the sea forms natural pools—is this Roteiros de Charme hotel. Apartments are spacious and have balconies. Only the suite has a sea view; rooms overlook the pool. It's a 15-minute walk from Rua das Pedras (or five minutes by car). ⌂ *Rua 6, lote 6, quadra F, Praia da Ferradura, 28950-000* ☎☎ *022/2623–1965 or 022/2623–2569* ⊕ *www.pedradalaguna.cjb.net* ⌁ *24 rooms, 1 suite* ⌂ *Restaurant, room service, in-room safes, refrigerators, cable TV, tennis court, pool, sauna, laundry service* ⊟ *AE, V* ⏐⊘⏐ *BP.*

NORTH OF RIO

The Swiss colonization of Nova Friburgo is apparent in its architecture and the delicious fondues served in several restaurants. Known as the lingerie capital, because of its industry, Friburgo is surrounded by small districts, like São Pedro da Serra and Lumiar, with waterfalls and natural pools. Nearby Petrópolis is a charming village that was once the summer home of the imperial family. Temperatures in these north-of-Rio towns are low by Brazilian standards—an average of 55°F (13°C) in winter.

Nova Friburgo

㉚ *122 km (79 mi) northeast of Petrópolis; 137 km (121 mi) northeast of Rio.*

This summer resort town was settled by Swiss immigrants in the early 1800s, when Brazil was actively encouraging European immigration and when the economic situation in Switzerland was bad. Woods, rivers, and waterfalls encircle the city. Homemade liquors, jams, and cheeses pack the shelves of the town's small markets. The lingerie industry supports the city nowadays, with some companies exporting to Europe and elsewhere internationally. Shops in downtown Friburgo and close to Ponte da Saudade (near the bus terminal) sell high-quality lingerie for reasonable prices. Cariocas also come here to unwind in the cool mountain climate.

A cable car rises more than 4,750 feet (1,450 meters) to **Morro da Cruz,** where you get a spectacular view of Friburgo. ⌂ *Praça Teleférica* ☎ *022/2522–4834* ⌺ *R$12* ⊙ *Weekdays 9–noon and 1–5, weekends 9–6.*

Where to Stay

★ $$ ⌂ **Akaskay.** Situated in the district of Mury, 6 mi (9 km) from Nova Friburgo, this hotel is the place to relax in a natural mountain environment.

The rooms have cedarwood walls and electric fireplaces, and the only noise you can hear is from a nearby streamlet. Outdoors, there's a spring-water swimming pool (unheated) and a hot tub. The place is surrounded by forest, and Saturday-morning yoga classes in the garden's meditation temple help you relax even further, as do shiatsu massages and beauty treatments. Transportation to nearby restaurants is free. ⊠ *Estrada Norge Hamburgo, Mury, access at Km 71 off RJ 116, 28615-615* ☎ *22/2542–1163* ⊕ *www.akaskay.com.br* ⤶ *14 rooms, 1 chalet* ⏶ *Cable TV, refrigerator, in-room safes, sauna, pool, bar* ▤ *AE, DC, MC, V* ¶◎¶ *BP.*

$$ ⊡ **Hotel Bucsky.** Long walks through the forest that surrounds the hotel are among the draws at this country-house inn. Opened in 1940 by members of a Hungarian family that first established themselves as restaurant owners in Rio, the hotel has a rustic style, with some rooms in pine. Rooms aren't large. The buffet-style restaurant is not luxurious, but it serves good, simple food. The hotel holds gastronomic festivals that center around German and Hungarian cuisines. ⊠ *Estrada Rio-Friburgo, Km 76.5, Ponte da Saudade 28615-160* ☎ *022/2522–5052 or 022/ 2522–5500* ⊟ *022/2522–9769* ⊕ *www.hotelbucsky.com.br* ⤶ *60 rooms, 10 suites* ⏶ *Room service, refrigerators, cable TV, miniature golf, tennis court, pool, sauna, laundry service* ▤ *AE, DC, MC, V* ¶◎¶ *FAP.*

Petrópolis

⑤ *68 km (42 mi) northeast of Rio.*

The hilly highway northeast of the city rumbles past forests and waterfalls en route to a mountain town so refreshing and picturesque that Dom Pedro II, Brazil's second emperor, spent his summers in it. From 1889 to 1899 it was also the country's year-round seat of government. Horse-drawn carriages shuttle between the sights (available in front of the Museu Imperial), passing flowering gardens, shady parks, and imposing pink mansions. The city holds also the Encantada (Enchanted), the peculiar house created by Santos Dumont. A variety of shops along Rua Teresa sell winter clothes; shops are open Tuesday–Sunday 9–6 and Monday 2–6.

★ The **Museu Imperial** is the magnificent 44-room palace that was the summer home of Dom Pedro II, emperor of Brazil, and his family in the 19th century. The colossal structure is filled with polished wooden floors, artwork, and grand chandeliers. You can also see the diamond-encrusted gold crown and scepter of Brazil's last emperor, as well as other royal jewels. ⊠ *Rua da Imperatriz 220, Centro* ☎ *024/2237–8000* ⊕ *www. museuimperial.gov.br* ⛟ *R$8* ⊙ *Tues.–Sun. 11–6.*

From the Museu Imperial you can walk three long blocks or take a horse-drawn carriage to **São Pedro de Alcântara,** the Gothic cathedral containing the tombs of Dom Pedro II; his wife, Dona Teresa Cristina; and their daughter, Princesa Isabel. ⊠ *Rua São Pedro de Alcântara 60, Centro* ☎ *024/2242–4300* ⛟ *Free* ⊙ *Tues.–Sun. 8–noon and 2–6.*

The **Palácio de Cristal** (Crystal Palace), a stained-glass and iron building made in France and assembled in Brazil, was a wedding present to

Princesa Isabel. During the imperial years it was used as a ballroom: it was here the princess held a celebration dance after she abolished slavery in Brazil in 1888. ⊠ *Praça da Confluência, Rua Alfredo Pachá* ☎ *024/2247–3721* ⌨ *Free* ☉ *Tues.–Sun. 9–5.*

The **Casa de Santos Dumont** (Santos Dumont House) was built in 1918 by one of the world's first aviators. Dumont invented the 14-bis airplane and was the first person to achieve flight in Europe in 1906. (Some argue that he flew before the Wright Brothers—an argument that strangely endures despite historic accounts of the Wrights flying in 1903). Dumont's strange inventions fill the house and permeate its architecture in the stairs that force you to begin climbing with your right foot, a (heated!) shower he invented before most homes had showers, and a bed that transformed into a desk. The home doesn't have a kitchen because Dumont ordered his food from a nearby hotel—the first documented restaurant delivery service in Brazil. ⊠ *Rua do Encantado 22* ☎ *024/2247–3158* ⌨ *R$3* ☉ *Tue–Sun 9:30–5.*

The **Circuito Caminhos do Brejal** is a tour in a jeep to visit small farms around the city that produce milk and cheese, cachaça, and trout, plus crafts shops. Choose from the 20- or 30-km route with Miira's Tours. ☎ *024/2242–2875* ⊕ *www.miirastours.com.br* ⌨ *R$68.*

Where to Stay & Eat

$ ✕**Bauernstube.** German food is the backbone of this log cabin–style eatery. The bratwurst and sauerkraut are properly seasoned, and the strudel is an excellent choice for polishing off a meal. ⊠ *Av. Dr. Nelson de Sá Earp 297* ☎ *024/2242–1097* ⊟ *DC, MC, V* ☉ *Closed Mon.*

$ ✕**Trutas do Rocio.** Trout, trout, and more trout is served at this restaurant next to river teeming with—you guessed it—trout. The fish is prepared as appetizers in patê or in a cassava dough pastry. Entrées include grilled trout or trout cooked in almond sauce, mustard sauce, or orange sauce. The small, rustic restaurant has only a 22-person capacity. ⊠ *Estrada da Vargem Grande 6333, Rocio* ☎ *024/2242–7053* ⊕ *www.trutas.com.br* ⊟ *AE, DC, MC, V* ⌗ *Reservations essential* ☉ *No dinner.*

★ $$$ ✕☐ **Locanda Della Mimosa.** This cozy pousada has only a few suites, but the service is first-class. It's in a valley filled with bougainvillea trees, with trails for long walks. The suites are decorated in a classical style with imperial influences. Tea is served in the afternoon. The Italian restaurant, run by the talented Danio Braga, who is always cooking up novelties, is open Thursday through Sunday and has a degustation menu ($$$$) of specialties from different regions of Italy. ⊠ *Km 71.5, BR 040, Alameda das Mimosas 30, Vale Florido, 25725-490* ☎ *024/2233–5405* ⊕ *www.locanda.com.br* ⌁ *6 suites* ⌂ *Restaurant, room service, cable TV, pool, sauna, bar* ⊟ *AE, DC, MC, V* ⫶⊙⫶ *BP* ☉ *Closed Mon.–Wed.*

$$ ✕☐ **Pousada de Alcobaça.** Just north of Petrópolis, this is considered by many to be the loveliest inn in the area. The grounds have beautiful gardens and a swimming pool. The kitchen turns out exceptional breakfasts, lunches, and high teas with an emphasis on fresh ingredients. Meals ($–$$$), which include savory pastas, are served in the garden. A pot roast is a must and is prepared in a charming farm kitchen. The hotel grows its own vegetables and herbs. All rooms in the early-20th-cen-

tury house are cozy and decorated in a rustic style. ⊠ *Agostinho Goulão 298, Corrêas, 25730-050* ☎ *024/2221–1240* 🖷 *024/2222–3162* 🛏 *11 rooms* ⊕ *www.pousadadaalcobaca.com.br* ♨ *Restaurant, room service, cable TV, tennis court, pool, sauna, laundry service* ▤ *AE, DC, MC, V* ⦿ *BP.*

$ 🏨 **Hotel Casablanca Imperial.** Just 50 meters from the Museu Imperial downtown, the hotel is in a colonial-style house built in 1952. The rooms are simply and warmly decorated with mahogany furniture and have hardwood floors. The charming bistro serves French fare. ⊠ *Rua da Imperatriz 286, Centro 25610-320* ☎ *024/2242–6662* ⊕ *www. casablancahotel.com.br/imperial* 🛏 *32 rooms* ♨ *Restaurant, room service, able TV, pool, bar, sauna, laundry service, game room* ▤ *AE, D, MC, V* ⦿ *BP.*

$ ✕🏨 **Pousada Monte Imperial.** A few kilometers from downtown, this Euro-style inn has a lobby with a fireplace and a restaurant–bar. Rooms are cozy and rustic, in an old European style, and have a view of the historic center of the city. Drinks and meals can be taken in the lovely garden. ⊠ *Rua José de Alencar 27, Centro 25610-050* ☎ *024/2237–1664* ⊕ *www.pousadamonteimperial.com.br* 🛏 *14 rooms* ♨ *Restaurant, fans, cable TV, pool, bar, laundry service; no a/c* ▤ *AE, DC, MC, V* ⦿ *BP.*

THE GREEN COAST

Italy has the charming Costa Azurra, Brazil has the Costa Verde (Green Coast). The emerald sea of Angra's bay is one of the best places in the southeast of Rio de Janeiro for diving. The abundant sealife and transparent waters with nearly year-round visibility make the experience unique. But you don't have to be a diver to enjoy yourself in the several boat tours in the region. Beautiful Ilha Grande, the biggest island on the bay, requires some adventurous spirit as no cars are allowed on the island. Paraty combines historic beauty with underexplored spots, like the district of Trindade with some lovely beaches. Areas around Paraty produce some of the best Brazilian cachaça, and visiting a distillery can be compared to taking a tour in a vineyard. During Carnival, normally quiet Paraty holds the Bloco da Lama, a parade where participants smear mud from local Praia do Jabaquara on one another—it's meant to represent the rituals of driving away evil spirits practiced by prehistoric tribes.

Angra dos Reis

❸❷ *168 km (91 mi) west of Rio.*

Angra dos Reis (Bay of Kings) anchors the rugged Costa Verde in an area of beautiful beaches, colonial architecture, and clear green waters. Schooners, yachts, sailboats, and fishing skiffs thread among the 365 offshore islands, one for every day of the year. Indeed, Angra dos Reis's popularity lies in its strategic location—ideal for exploring those islands, many of which are deserted patches of sand and green great for swimming and snorkeling. Organized boat tours from shore can take you to favored island haunts.

The **Associação dos Barqueiros** (☎ 024/3365–3165) runs tours to Ilha da Gipóia, which has several paradisial beaches like Jurubaíba, excellent for diving.

Where to Stay & Eat

★ **$$$$** ✕▦ **Hotel do Frade & Golf Resort.** Guest-room balconies overlook the sea and a private beach at this modern resort hotel. The many sports options include boat rentals (sailboats, motorboats, catamarans) and scuba diving. It's no surprise that seafood is good at the buffet restaurant, Scuna ($$). Other restaurants, serving a variety of international cuisines, open in summer. ⊠ *Km 513, BR 101, Praia do Frade, 32 km (20 mi) west of Angra do Reis, 23900-000 ☎ 024/3369–9500 or 0800–8881234 ⊕ www.hoteldofrade.com.br 🖷 024/3369–2254 ⇲ 160 rooms ⚐ 5 restaurants, room service, in-room safes, refrigerators, cable TV, in-room data ports, 18-hole golf course, 7 tennis courts, pool, boating, jet skiing, bar, cinema, babysitting, dry cleaning, laundry service, no-smoking rooms ⊟ AE, D, DC, MC, V* ⍰ *FAP.*

$$$$ ▦ **Pestana Angra Hotel.** Electric cars shuttle you from the door of your chalet to the sand of the hotel's private beach. Water activities abound. The 55-square-meter (590-square-foot) chalets have balconies and separate guest rooms. Suites have whirlpool baths, saunas, and beach views. ⊠ *Estrada do Contorno 3700, Retiro, 23900-000 ☎ 024/ 3364–2005 🖷 024/3365–1909 ⊕ www.pestana.com ⇲ 27 chalets ⚐ In-room safes, refrigerators, cable TV, in-room data ports, pool, gym, massage, sauna, beach, boating, jet skiing, bar, dry cleaning, laundry service, concierge, convention center ⊟ AE, D, DC, MC, V.*

$$ ▦ **Hotel do Bosque.** Inside the Parque Perequê and close to the river of the same name, this hotel has boat service to its private beach across the river. Apartments look out onto an internal garden. Only the suites face the river. There's bar service at the beach. ⊠ *Km 533, BR 101, Praia de Mambucaba, 23908-000 ☎0800/704–3130, 024/3362–3130 for hotel, 21/2286–9711 for reservations in Rio ⊕ www.hoteldobosque.com.br ⇲ 52 rooms, 4 suites ⚐ Room service, refrigerators, cable TV, in-room data ports, tennis court, pool, sauna, beach, boating, bar, laundry service ⊟ AE, DC, MC, V.*

$$ ▦ **Portogalo Suíte.** Perched on a hill with a wonderful view of the bay, the exposed-brick buildings at this hotel have a rustic appeal. Rooms have balconies with sea view. Although starkly white and cool, with tile floors, the rooms are clean and right by the beach. A cable car takes guests down the hillside to the beach and the marina. ⊠ *Km 71, BR 101, Praia de Itapinhoacanga, 25 km (16 mi) south of town, 23900-000 ☎ 024/3361–4343 or 0800/282–4343 🖷 024/3361–4361 ⊕www. portogalosuite.com.br ⇲ 86 rooms ⚐ Room service, in-room safes, refrigerators, cable TV, in-room data ports, 2 tennis courts, pool, sauna, jet skiing, bar, dry cleaning, laundry service ⊟ AE, D, DC, MC, V.*

Ilha Grande

❸ One of the most popular islands in Brazil is the lush, mountainous Ilha Grande. Just 2 km (1 mi) and a 90-minute ferry ride from Angra dos Reis or Mangaratiba, it has more than 100 idyllic beaches—sandy ribbons that stretch on and on with a backdrop of tropical foliage. Ferries arrive at Vila do Abraão, and from there you can roam paths that lead from one slip of sand to the next or negotiate with local boatmen for jaunts to the beaches or more remote islets.

A 10-minute walk from Vila do Abraão takes you to the hot waters off Praia da Júlia and Praia Comprida. The transparent sea at Abraãozinho Beach is another 25-minute walk from Vila do Abraão. If you choose to go by boat, don't miss the big waves of Lopes Mendes Beach or the astonishingly blue Mediterranean-like water of Lagoa Azul. Scuba-diving fans should head to Gruta do Acaiá to see turtles and colorful South American fish.

It's smart to take to the island only what you can carry, as you have to walk to your hotel. But men at the pier make a living helping tourists carry luggage (about R$5 per bag).

Where to Stay & Eat

$–$$ ✕ **Lua e Mar.** Expect fresh and well prepared seafood at this casual place, where you can stroll in after sunbathing, still wearing your Havaianas. ⊠ *Rua da Praia, Vila do Abraão* ☎ *024/3361–5113* ▭ *D, MC, V* ✆ *Closed Apr.–Nov.*

$–$$ ✕ **O Pescador.** Inside the pousada of the same name, this rustic but cozy restaurant mixes seafood with Italian. The specialties are grilled fish (types of fish vary according to the season), bought from local fishermen. Grilled dourado and grouper are served most of the year. ⊠ *Rua da Praia, Vila do Abraão* ☎ *024/3361–5114* ▭ *V.*

★ **$$** ▦ **Pousada Sankay.** The colorful rooms with sea view have names inspired by sea creatures, like Lagosta (lobster) or Golfinho (dolphin). Kayaks, canoes, and other boats are available to rent, as is diving equipment. A boat from the pousada can pick you up at Angra dos Reis. ⊠ *Enseada do Bananal, 23990-000* ☎ *024/3365–4065* ⊕ *www.pousadasankay. com.br* ⬎ *12 rooms* ♨ *Restaurant, cable TV, refrigerator, bar, sauna, pool, gym, playground* ▭ *AE, DC, MC, V* ⍾ *MAP* ✆ *Closed June.*

$ ▦ **Farol dos Borbas.** Like all lodging options on the island, Farol dos Borbas has simple rooms, but its advantage is its location about 150 feet (50 meters) from the pier where the ferry from Angra dos Reis stops. The hotel has boat service, with tours around the island. ⊠ *Rua da Praia 881, Vila do Abraão, 23960-970* ☎ *024/3361–5260, 024/3361–5261, or 024/3361–5866* ⊕ *www.ilhagrandetur.com.br* ⬎ *14 rooms* ♨ *Room service, cable TV, refrigerators,* ▭ *D, MC, V* ⍾ *BP.*

$ ▦ **Pousada do Canto.** Freshly decorated with wicker furniture in a colonial-style house, this pousada is just in front of Praia do Canto. The place has a summery, tropical atmosphere, with a palapa-roof bar by the pool, and a knotty log fence around the property. Some rooms face the ocean and have verandas. ⊠ *Rua da Praia 121, Vila do Abraão, 23990-000* ☎ *024/3361–5115* ⊕ *www.viladoabraao.com.br/docanto.htm* ⬎ *11 rooms* ♨ *Cable TV, refrigerators, pool* ▭ *AE, D, MC, V* ⍾ *BP.*

¢ ▦ **Recreio da Praia.** A three-minute walk from the pier, this pousada has simply decorated rooms with sofa beds. ⊠ *Rua da Praia, Vila do Abraão, 23960-000* ☎ *024/3361–5266 or 024/3361–5375* ⬎ *10 rooms* ♨ *Restaurant, room service, refrigerators, cable TV, laundry service* ▭ *MC, V* ⍾ *BP.*

Paraty

34 *99 km (60 mi) southwest of Angra dos Reis; 261 km (140 mi) southwest of Rio.*

This stunning colonial city—also spelled Parati—is one of the oldest in Brazil, and one of South America's gems. Giant iron chains hang from posts at the beginning of the mazelike grid of cobblestone streets, closing them to all but pedestrians, horses, and bicycles. Until the 18th century this was an important transit point for gold plucked from the Minas Gerais—a safe harbor protected from pirates by a fort. (The cobblestones are the rock ballast brought from Lisbon, then unloaded to make room in the ships for their gold cargoes.) In 1720, however, the colonial powers cut a new trail from the gold mines straight to Rio de Janeiro, bypassing the town and leaving it isolated. It remained that way until contemporary times, when artists, writers, and others "discovered" the community and UNESCO placed it on its World Heritage Site list.

Paraty isn't a city peppered with lavish mansions and opulent palaces; rather, it has a simple beauty. By the time the sun breaks over the bay each morning—illuminating the whitewashed, colorfully trimmed buildings—the fishermen have begun spreading out their catch at the outdoor market. The best way to explore is simply to begin walking winding streets banked with centuries-old buildings that hide quaint inns, tony restaurants, shops, and art galleries. As cars are forbidden in the historic center, take comfortable, sensible shoes to navigate the uneven cobblestones.

Paraty is jammed with churches, but the most intriguing are the trio whose congregations were segregated by race during the colonial era: the Igreja de Nossa Senhora do Rosário, Igreja de Santa Rita, and Igreja de Nossa Senhora das Dores. Once you've finished your in-town exploration, you can begin investigating what makes this a weekend escape for cariocas: the lush, tropical offshore islands and not-so-distant coastal beaches.

The town feels safer than most places in Brazil, and you'll notice a distinct lack of panhandlers here. This is a true small town, where offenses tend to be relegated to the occasional crimes of passion rather than violence committed against tourists or petty theft. Walking around at night is generally safe in the center of town.

Casa da Cultura. The museum in the Casa da Cultura is a good place to get acquainted with the town's history and culture. Downstairs is one of the best gift shops in town, with crafts made by local artisans. (✉ Rua Dona Geralda 177, at Rua Dr. Samuel Costa ☎ 24/3371–2325 ⊕ www. paraty.com.br/casadacultura 🎟 Museum R$5 ⊘ Sun.–Mon. and Wed.–Thurs. 10–6:30, Fri.–Sat. 1–9:30).

The town's slaves built the **Igreja de Nossa Senhora do Rosário** for themselves around 1725 because the other churches in town were reserved for the white population. ✉ *Rua do Comércio* ☎ *024/3371–1467* 🎟 *R$1, R$2 combination ticket with other Paraty churches and Forte Defensor* ⊘ *Tues.–Sun. 9–5.*

The Green Coast > **89**

The neoclassical **Igreja de Nossa Senhora dos Remédios** was built in 1787. It holds the small art gallery Pinacoteca Antônio Marino Gouveia, with paintings of modern artists such as Djanira, Di Cavalcanti, and Anita Malfatti. ⊠ *Rua da Matriz* ☎ *024/3371–2946* ✉ *R$1, R$2 combination ticket with other Paraty churches and Forte Defensor* ☉ *Tues.–Sun. 9–noon and 2–5.*

The oldest church in Paraty, the simple and clean-lined **Igreja de Santa Rita** was built in 1722 by and for freed slaves. Today it houses a small religious art museum (Museu de Arte Sacra). It's a typical Jesuit church with a tower and three front windows. Religious art objects inside the church are constantly being restored. ⊠ *Rua Santa Rita* ☎ *024/ 3371–1620* ✉ *R$1, R$2 combination ticket with other Paraty churches and Forte Defensor* ☉ *Wed.–Sun. 9–noon and 2–5.*

The **Igreja de Nossa Senhora das Dores,** built in 1800, was the church of the community's small but elite white population. ⊠ *Rua Dr. Pereira* ☎ *024/3371–2946* ✉ *R$1, R$2 combination ticket with other Paraty churches and Forte Defensor* ☉ *Tues.–Sun. 9–5.*

The **Forte Defensor Perpétuo** was built in the early 1700s (and rebuilt in 1822) as a defense against pirates and is now home to a folk-arts center. It sits north of town. ⊠ *Morro da Vila Velha* ☎ *No phone* ✉ *R$1, R$2 combination ticket with Paraty churches* ☉ *Wed.–Sun. 9–5.*

Beyond its colonial downtown, Paraty has natural beauty worth exploring. **Paraty Tours** (⊠ Av. Roberto Silveira 11, Centro, Paraty 23970-000 ☎ 24/3371–2651 or 24/3371–1428 ⊕ www.paratytours.com.br) has a six-hour jeep tour that goes to the Serra da Bocaina National Park, crossing rivers and visiting fantastic waterfalls, stops at a cachaça distillery, and provides for lunch in a restaurant close to a river with a natural pool. Other tours include hiking the Caminho do Ouro, a visit to the breathtaking Praia do Sono or to the untouched little fishing village of Trindade (25 km/16 mi from Paraty), which has places to snorkel and swim in crystal-clear water. Transfers from Rio or elsewhere, horse and bike tours, and diving are also available.

The **Caminho de Ouro** (Gold Trail) was originally forged by indigenous tribes and later used by the Portuguese to cart gold, coffee, and sugarcane to Paraty, where it was shipped to Portugal. Nearly 3½ km (2 mi) of the original 610-km (380-mi) trail have been restored. A guide certified by the tourism board is required, which makes sense, since it's the history behind the trail that really makes it worthwhile. Show up for the guided tours (in Portuguese), or make arrangements with Paraty Tours. A natural pool with waterfalls near the trailhead is ideal for a dip on hot days. ⊠ *Estrada Paraty–Cunha (RJ 165), across Ponte Branca bridge, 20 km (12 mi) north of town* ☎ *024/3371–1897* ✉ *R$15* ☉ *Guided walks Mon. and Weds.–Sat. at 11:30 and 2:30, Sun. at 10* ⊕ *www.eco-paraty.com/caminhodoouro.*

Where to Stay & Eat

$$–$$$$ ✕ **Merlin o Mago.** The German chef and owner, Hado Steinbrecher, was a former photojournalist and gastronomic critic who studied in France,

but travelled through Asia, mainly in Thailand and India. The cuisine here is an interesting mixture of Brazilian, French, and Thai traditions. Entrées include grilled shrimp flambéed in cognac or snook wrapped in a crepe with yogurt and green pepper, topped with caviar. ⊠ *Rua do Comércio 376, Centro* ⊕ *www.paraty.com.br/merlin* ☎ *024/3371–2157* ▤ *D, MC, V.*

$$–$$$$ **Refúgio.** Near the water in a quiet part of town, this seafood restaurant with excelled codfish cakes is a great place for a romantic dinner. Cafe tables out front sit under heat lamps. Moquecas are excellent. ⊠ *Praça do Porto, loja 4, in front of the wharf, Centro Histórico* ☎ *024/3371–2447* ⊕ *www.eco-paraty.com/refugio* ▤ *DC, MC, V.*

$$–$$$ ✕ **Banana da Terra.** This is one of the best places in town for colossal shrimp. It's hard to find this dish from February to May, during the shrimp spawning season. The restaurant is in a colonial house, decorated with 19th century pictures of the city and cachaça labels. The name of the place comes from another of its specialties: *banana da terra* (plantain), which is part of many dishes, like grilled fish with garlic butter, herbs, plantains, and rice. ⊠ *Rua Doutor Samuel Costa 198, Centro* ☎ *024/3371–1725* ▤ *AE, D, DC, MC, V.*

$–$$$ ✕ **Restaurante do Hiltinho.** This is one of the most elegant restaurants in Paraty. Its specialty is *camarão casadinho,* fried colossal shrimp stuffed with hot *farofa* (toasted cassava flour) made with small shrimp. Even if you're familiar with jumbo shrimp, you might be astonished at the size of these. Seafood outnumbers other dishes two to one, but the filet mignon is very good. The service borders on perfection, as does the elegant decor, with French doors opening onto the street. ⊠ *Rua Marechal Deodoro 233, Centro Histórico de Paraty* ☎ *024/3371–1432* ▤ *AE, DC, MC, V.*

$$–$$$$ ⌂ **Pousada do Sandi.** The most upscale hotel in Paraty still feels like a small, personalized inn, and oozes nautical-themed 18th-century charm. Luxurious by Paraty standard, rooms are tasteful, and some have terraces overlooking the city's cobblestoned streets, but furnishings are simple, and walls are a bit bare. The lobby, pool area, and restaurant are some of the nicest, homiest parts of the hotel. ⊠ *Largo do Rosário 1, Centro Histórico, 23970-000* ☎ *24/3371–2100 hotel, 11/3864–9111 reservations* ⊕ *www. pousadadosandi.com.br* ↝ *25 rooms, 1 suite* ⌂ *Restaurant, cable TV, in-room safes, pool, Internet room* ▤ *AE, DC, MC, V* ⦿ *BP.*

★ $$ ⌂ **Pousada Porto Imperial.** In the oldest part of town just behind the Igreja da Matriz de Nossa Senhora dos Remédios, this historic building has rooms that ring a series of courtyards and a swimming pool. The pousada is decorated with a collection of typical Brazilian artwork—ceramics, tapestries, and colonial furniture—and also has a tropical garden filled with bromeliads. Noise from the square across the street can be a problem during festival times. ⊠ *Rua Tenente Francisco Antônio (Rua do Comércio) s/n, Centro Histórico, 23970-000* ☎ *024/3371–2323* 🖶 *024/ 3371–2111* ⊕ *www.pousadaportoimperial.com.br* ↝ *48 rooms, 3 suites* ⌂ *Restaurant, room service, in-room safes, refrigerators, cable TV, pool, sauna, bar, laundry service* ▤ *AE, MC, V.*

$ ⌂ **Pousada do Ouro.** Inside an 18th-century building with a garden courtyard, this inn is a block from the Igreja da Matriz de Nossa Senhora dos

Remédios. Although it's on the beach, only one suite has a sea view. The decor is colonial style; rooms face an internal garden. ⊠ *Rua Dr. Pereira 145, old Rua da Praia, Centro Histórico, 23970-000* ☎ *024/3371–2033 or 024/3371–1378* 🖷 *024/3371–1311* ⊕ *www.pousadaouro.com.br* ⤴ *18 rooms, 8 suites* ♺ *Restaurant, room service, in-room safes, refrigerators, cable TV, pool, sauna, bar, laundry service* ▭ *AE, DC, MC, V* ⏶ *BP.*

★ $ 🏨 **Pousada Pardieiro.** The houses that make up this property are decorated in a 19th-century Brazilian-colonial style. Rooms have dark-wood-carved beds and antique bureaus. There are no TVs in the rooms, but there's a special living room with a home theater. A beautiful patio has birds and orchids. ⊠ *Rua do Comércio 74, Centro Histórico, 23970-000* ☎ *024/3371–1370* 🖷 *024/3371–1139* ⊕ *www. pousadapardieiro.com.br* ⤴ *27 rooms* ♺ *Restaurant, room service, in-room safes, refrigerators, pool, sauna, bar, laundry service* ▭ *AE, V.*

¢ 🏨 **Pousada do Príncipe.** A prince (the great-grandson of Emperor Pedro

FodorsChoice II) owns this aptly named inn at the edge of the colonial city. The hotel

★ is painted in the yellow and green of the imperial flag, and its quiet, colorful public areas are graced by photos of the royal family. Rooms are small, decorated in a colonial style, and face either the internal garden or the swimming pool, which is in the plant-filled patio. The kitchen is impressive, too; its chef turns out an exceptional feijoada. ⊠ *Av. Roberto Silveira 289, 23970-000* ☎ *024/3371–2266* ⊕ *www. pousadadoprincipe.com.br* 🖷 *024/3371–2120* ⤴ *31 rooms, 3 suites* ♺ *Restaurant, room service, fans, some in-room safes, refrigerators, cable TV, 2 tennis courts, pool, sauna, laundry service; no a/c in some rooms* ▭ *AE, DC, MC, V.*

Shopping

Paraty is known countrywide for its fine cachaça brands, including Coqueiro, Corisco, Vamos Nessa, Itatinga, Murycana, Paratyana e Maré Alta. **Empório da Cachaça** (⊠ Rua Doutor Samuel Costa 22, Centro ☎ 024/3371–6329) has more than 300 brands of the sugarcane liquor—both local and national brands. **Porto da Pinga** (⊠ Rua da Matriz 12, Centro ☎ 024/9907–4370) is a good choice for cachaças.

SIDE TRIPS FROM RIO ESSENTIALS

Transportation

Renting a car or taking a bus or shuttle are generally the best ways to get around Rio de Janeiro State. Most destinations are within a few hours of the city of Rio.

For more information about transportation, *see* Smart Travel Tips A to Z, *at* the front of this book.

BY AIR

TEAM has charter flights (about R$575) to Búzios from Rio that run infrequently, depending on demand (eight people are required for a flight).

🛈 **TEAM Transportes Aéreos** ☎ *021/3328-1616* ⊕ *www.voeteam.com.br.*

BY BOAT

Passenger ferries for Niterói leave from Praça 15 de Novembro in Rio. In 20 minutes you arrive at Praça Araribóia, in downtown Niterói, or at the Terminal Hidroviário de Charitas. Barcas S/A boats (R$2) are bigger and slower than the newer Catamaran Jumbo Cat fleet (R$4).

The two ferries to Ilha Grande are run by Barcas S/A. The ferry for Vila do Abraão on Ilha Grande leaves Angra dos Reis, from Cais da Lapa at Avenida dos Reis Magos, daily at 3:30 PM and returns weekdays at 10 AM and weekends at 11 AM; the price is R$4.90 one way. Another ferry leaves Mangaratiba (80 km/50 mi west of Rio) weekdays at 8 AM and weekends at 9 AM and returns daily at 5:30 PM; the price is R$4.90 (R$12 weekends). The trip takes an hour and a half.

Call Barcas S/A in Rio for information about Angra dos Reis and Ilha Grande ferries. TELEBARCAS is a telephone hotline for information about all the ferries, and is open weekdays 8–7 and weekends 8–noon.
🚹 **Barcas S/A** ✉ Praça Araribóia 6–8, Niterói ☎ 021/2719-1892 or 021/2620-6766, 021/2533-6661 for Ilha Grande information ⊕ www.barcas-sa.com.br. **Catamaran Jumbo Cat** ✉ Praça Araribóia s/n, Niterói ☎ 021/2620-8589 or 021/2620-8670. **TELEBARCAS** ✉ Rio de Janeiro ☎ 021/2533-7524 or 021/2532-6274.

BY BUS

Several bus companies, including Auto Viação 1001, depart for Niterói (R$4) from Avenida Princesa Isabel in Copacabana; from Botafogo at the beach; and from the Menezes Cortes Terminal (⇨ Rio de Janeiro Essentials, *in* chapter 1). Niterói-bound buses continue on to Nova Friburgo. The price from Rio to Nova Friburgo is about R$20. Única buses leave hourly from Rio's Rodoviária Novo Rio (⇨ Rio de Janeiro Essentials, *in* chapter 1) and travel to Petrópolis (about R$13). Costa Verde buses leave Rio daily every hour for Angra dos Reis (R$20), and every two hours for Paraty (R$35). Cabo Frio buses depart from the Novo Rio station. Regional bus service connects Petrópolis with Nova Friburgo (Rodoviária Norte) and Paraty with Angra dos Reis. For these buses, just show up at the terminal and buy a ticket for the next departing bus. Reunidas buses have daily trips from São Paulo to Paraty (R$34), departing from the Terminal Tietê in São Paulo (⇨ São Paulo Essentials, *in* chapter 3).

The prices we list are for air-conditioned buses. Fares for buses without air-conditioning are slightly less (usually just a few reais difference). Make sure you request an air-conditioned bus when you buy your ticket.

Buses, a shuttle service, and airplanes regularly travel between Búzios and Rio. The best option is the shuttle service, which picks you up in Rio in the morning and drops you at your pousada before noon. Contact Turismo Clássico Travel in Rio for reservations. Municipal buses connect Cabo Frio and Búzios. All buses from Búzios depart from the Terminal Auto Viação 1001.
🚹 Bus Terminals **Rodoviária Angra dos Reis** ✉ Av. Toscano Brito 110, Balneário ☎ 024/3365-2041. **Rodoviária Niterói** ✉ Av. Feliciano Sodré s/n, Centro ☎ 021/2620-8847.

Rodoviária Nova Friburgo Norte ⊠ Praça Feliciano Costa, 2.5 km (1.5 mi) north of town ☎ 022/2522-06095. **Rodoviária Nova Friburgo Sul** ⊠ Ponte da Saudade, 4 km (2.5 mi) south of town ☎ 022/2522-0400. **Rodoviária Paraty** ⊠ Rua Jango Pádua west of old town ☎ 024/3371-1224. **Rodoviária Petrópolis** ⊠ Rua Doutor Porciúncula 75 ☎ 024/2237-6262. **Terminal Auto Viação 1001** ⊠ Estrada da Usina Velha 444 ☎ 022/2623-2050.

🚍 Bus Companies **Auto Viação 1001** ☎ 021/0300-3131001. **Costa Verde** ☎ 021/2516-2437 or 021/2233-3809. **Reunidas** ☎ 011/3619-0910 or 0800/709-9020. **Turismo Clássico Travel** ☎ 021/2523-3390. **Única** ☎ 021/2263-8792.

BY CAR

To reach Niterói by car, take the 14-km-long (9-mi-long) Presidente Costa e Silva Bridge, also known as Rio-Niterói. The toll is R$3.20. BR 101 connects the city to the Costa Verde and Paraty. Head north and along BR 040 to reach the mountain towns of Petrópolis and Novo Friburgo. Coastal communities Cabo Frio and Búzios are east of Rio along or off RJ 106.

Contacts & Resources

BANKS & EXCHANGING SERVICES

There are banks and ATMs in each community, but it's best to get reais before leaving Rio. Check in advance with your hotel to make sure credit cards are accepted.

Some banks accept only cards with Visa/Plus logos and others accept only cards with MasterCard/Cirrus logos. Banco24horas ATMs usually accept all cards, including American Express. *See* "Money Matters" *in* Smart Travel Tips A to Z for more information.

🚍 **Banco 24 Horas ATMs** ⊠ Rua Júlio Maria 235, Centro, Angra dos Reis ⊕ www.banco24horas.com.br ⊠ Praça Santos Dumont, Centro, Búzios ⊠ Rua Itajuru, Cabo Frio ⊠ Rua Miguel de Frias 180, Icaraí, Niterói ⊠ Praça Dermerval Barbosa Moreira, Nova Friburgo ⊠ Rua Roberto Silveira, Praça Chafariz, Paraty ⊠ Rua Tereza 231, Petrópolis.

EMERGENCIES

🚍 Hospitals & Clinics **Hospital Municipal Nelson de Sá Earp** ⊠ Rua Paulino Afonso 45, Centro, Petrópolis ☎ 024/2237-4062. **Hospital Universitário Antônio Pedro** ⊠ Rua Marquês do Paraná 303, Centro, Niterói ☎ 021/2620-2828. **Santa Casa de Misericórdia** ⊠ Rua Doutor Coutinho 84, Centro, Angra dos Reis ☎ 024/3365-0131. **Santa Casa de Misericórdia** ⊠ Av. São Pedro de Alcântara, Pontal, Paraty ☎ 024/3371-1623. **Hospital Municipal São José Operário** ⊠ Rua Governador Valadares 22, São Cristóvão, Cabo Frio ☎ 022/2643-2732.

🚍 Late-Night & 24-Hour Pharmacies **Drogaria Pacheco** ⊠ Av. José Elias Rabha, inside Angra Shopping center, Parque das Palmeiras, Angra dos Reis ☎ 024/3365-4908. **Drogaria Pacheco** ⊠ Rua Gavião Peixoto 115, Niterói ☎ 021/2610-7713. **Drogaria Pacheco** ⊠ Rua do Imperador 271, Centro, Petrópolis ☎ 024/2237-3133 or 024/2237-5367. **Drogaria do Povo** ⊠ Rua Ezio Cardoso da Fonseca 14, Loja 2, Jardim Esperança, Cabo Frio ☎ 022/2629-9282. **Droga Tudo** ⊠ Av. Roberto Silveira, Centro, Paraty ☎ 024/3371-2965.

INTERNET

Almost every town has a cybercafé, with prices ranging from R$3 to R$6 per hour.

🖥 Internet Cafés **Arena Jogos** ⊠ Rua Presidente Backer 148, Icaraí, Niterói ☎ 021/2722-6144. **Compuland Internet** ⊠ Rua 16 de Março 326, Centro, Petrópolis ☎ 24/2237-2747. **Cyber Mar** ⊠ Av. Teixeira e Souza 30, lj. 4, Shopping Victor Nunes da Rocha, Cabo Frio ☎ 22/2645-5754. **Ilhagrande.com** ⊠ Rua Getúlio Vargas s/n, Vila do Abraão, Ilha Grande ☎ 24/3361-5630. **Paraty Cyber Café** ⊠ Av. Roberto Silveira 17, Centro, Paraty ☎ 24/3371-6249. **Sysweb Cybercafé** ⊠ Rua Moisés Amélio 17, lj. 129, Cadima Shopping, Centro, Nova Friburgo ☎ 22/2523-3744. **Versus Lan House** ⊠ Rua Coronel Carvalho 215, lj. 2, Centro, Angra dos Reis.

MAIL & SHIPPING

The Correios (Brazilian post office) has a branch in every city, some with express overseas services and pickup on demand. Post offices are open weekdays 8–5 and Saturdays 8–noon.

🖥 Post Offices **Correios** ☎ 0800/570-0100 ⊕ www.correios.com.br ⊠ Praça Lopes Trovão 142, Centro, Angra dos Reis ⊠ Av. Beira Mar 7, Vila do Abraão, Angra dos Reis ⊠ Rua Manoel de Carvalho 70, lj 3, Centro, Búzios ⊠ Largo Santo Antônio 55, Centro, Cabo Frio ⊠ Rua Visconde do Rio Branco 481, Centro, Niterói ⊠ Rua Gavião Peixoto 262, Niterói ⊠ Praça Presidente Getúlio Vargas 85, Nova Friburgo ⊠ Rua José Milton de Oliveira, Centro, Paraty ⊠ Rua do Imperador 350, Petrópolis.

TOUR OPTIONS

South America Experience has weeklong tours to Paraty and Ilha Grande (US$280–US$380). Participants tend to be young (20s and 30s) and adventurous, as accommodations are 3 stars or fewer, and there are lots of activities—like hiking, rapelling, biking—involved.

🖥 **South America Experience** ☎ 021/2513-4091 ⊕ www.southamericaexperience.com.

VISITOR INFORMATION

Tourist offices are generally open weekdays from 8 or 8:30 to 6 and Saturday from 8 or 9 to 4; some have limited Sunday hours, too. The Niterói Tourism Office is open daily 9–6. The Tourism Information hotline is an English-language information source about Rio de Janeiro State.

🖥 Tourist Information **Angra dos Reis Tourism Office** ⊠ Across from bus station on Rua Largo da Lapa, Angra dos Reis ☎ 024/3365-1175 Ext. 2186 ⊕ www.angra.rj.gov.br. **Búzios Tourism Office** ⊠ Praça Santos Dumont 111, Búzios ☎ 022/2623-2099 ⊕ www.buziosonline.com.br. **Cabo Frio Tourism Office** ⊠ Av. de Contorno, Praia do Forte, Cabo Frio ☎ 024/2647-1689 ⊕ www.cabofrioturismo.rj.gov.br. **IlhaGrande.com** ⊕ www.ilhagrande.com. br. **Niterói Tourism Office** ⊠ Estrada Leopoldo Fróes 773, São Francisco ☎ 021/2710-2727 or 0800/282-8835 ⊕ www.niteroi.rj.gov.br or www.neltur.com.br/niteroi. **Nova Friburgo Tourism Office** ⊠ Praça Dr. Demervel B. Moreira, Nova Friburgo ☎ 022/2523-8000 ⊕ www.friweb.com.br. **Paraty Tourism Office** ⊠ Av. Roberto da Silveira 6 ☎ 024/3371-1897 ⊕ www.paraty.com.br. **Petrópolis Tourism Office** ⊠ Praça da Confluência 3, Petrópolis ☎ 0800/24-1516 ⊕ www.petropolis.rj.gov.br. **Tourism Information** ☎ 0800/282-2007.

São Paulo

WORD OF MOUTH

"Since we like to visit large cities, São Paulo didn't disappoint. . . . The Japanese population here is second only to Japan itself, so there's a variety of restaurants and temples in the Japan Town if you're interested. . . . We were fascinated by the diversity of the people."

—Tran

"If you like arts don't miss the MASP (Museu de Arte de São Paulo). Take some fresh air at the Ibirapuera Park, go shopping at the Iguatemi Mall and have fun in thousands of bars, clubs, and restaurants from all over the world."

—Nino

Updated by
Gabriela Dias
and Eduardo
Acquarone

SÃO PAULO IS A MEGALOPOLIS OF 17 MILLION PEOPLE, with endless stands of skyscrapers defining the horizon from every angle. The largest city in South America, São Paulo even makes New York City, with its population of about 8 million, seem small in comparison. And this nearly 500-year-old capital of São Paulo State gets bigger every year: it now sprawls across some 8,000 square km (3,089 square mi), of which 1,525 square km (589 square mi) make up the city proper.

The main financial hub in the country, São Paulo is also Brazil's most cosmopolitan city, with top-rate nightlife and restaurants and impressive cultural and arts scenes. Most of the wealthiest people in Brazil live here—and the rest of them drop by at least once a year to shop for clothes, shoes, accessories, luxury items, and anything else that money can buy. *Paulistanos* (São Paulo inhabitants) work hard and spend a lot, and there's no escaping the many shopping and eating temptations.

Despite—or because of—these qualities, many tourists, Brazilian and foreigners, avoid visiting the city. Too noisy, too polluted, too crowded, they say—and they have a point. São Paulo is hardly a beautiful city; it's fast-paced and there's lots to do, but it's also a concrete jungle, with nothing as attractive as Rio's hills and beaches. Yet, even as the smog reddens your eyes, you'll see that there's much to explore here. When you get tired of laid-back beaches, São Paulo is just the right place to go.

History

São Paulo wasn't big and important right from the start. It was founded in 1554 by Jesuit priests who began converting native Indians to Catholicism. The town was built strategically on a plateau, protected from attack and served by many rivers. It remained unimportant to the Portuguese crown until the 1600s, when it became the departure point for the *bandeira* (literally, "flag") expeditions, whose members set out to look for gemstones and gold, to enslave Indians, and, later, to capture escaped African slaves. In the process, these adventurers established roads into vast portions of previously unexplored territory. São Paulo also saw Emperor Dom Pedro I declare independence from Portugal in 1822, by the Rio Ipiranga (Ipiranga River), near the city.

It was only in the late 19th century that São Paulo became a driving force in the country. As the state established itself as one of Brazil's main coffee producers, the city attracted laborers and investors from many countries. Italians, Portuguese, Spanish, Germans, and Japanese put their talents and energies to work. By 1895, 70,000 of the 130,000 residents were immigrants. Their efforts transformed the place from a sleepy mission post into a dynamic financial and cultural hub, with people of all colors and religions living and working together peacefully.

Avenida Paulista was once the site of many a coffee baron's mansion. Money flowed from these private domains into civic and cultural institutions. The arts began to flourish, and by the 1920s São Paulo was promoting such great artists as Mário and Oswald de Andrade, who introduced modern elements into Brazilian art.

If you have
3 days

On the first day, plan a walk along Avenida Paulista and visit its many cultural attractions, such as **Museu de Arte de São Paulo (MASP)** 🔵 and **Instituto Itaú Cultural** 🔵. In the evening, you could see a movie at the nearby Espaço Unibanco, or try one of the Italian restaurants in Bixiga, the Italian neighborhood, near the start of Avenida Paulista. Head to Centro on the second day to see such landmarks as **Edifício Martinelli** 🔵 and **Teatro Municipal** 🔵. Don't miss the Latin crafts exhibit at the **Memorial da América Latina,** northwest of Centro. On the third day, head for **Parque Ibirapuera** to visit one of its museums or just relax under the trees. After that, you can try one of the bars in nearby Itaim or Vila Olímpia to see how paulistas enjoy their happy hour.

If you have
5 days

In addition to the attractions outlined in the three-day itinerary, take a day to visit the snake museum at Instituto Butantã at the **Universidade de São Paulo** and/or the **Fundação Maria Luisa e Oscar Americano** 🔵. These sights are far from one another; it's best to get a cab. You can go by bus, but it's slow going. In the evening, get a drink at one of Vila Madalena's bars; here you can see a part of the city's exciting nightlife. On your last day, tour **Museu do Ipiranga** 🔵 and its environs, where Brazil's independence was declared. Afterward, walk by Liberdade neighborhood to see the Japanese shops and have dinner at one of the local restaurants.

In the 1950s the auto industry began to develop and contributed greatly to São Paulo's contemporary wealth—and problems. Over the next 30 years, people from throughout Brazil, especially the northeast, came seeking jobs, which transformed the city's landscape by increasing slums and poverty. Between the 1950s and today, the city's main revenue moved from industry to banking and commerce.

Today, like many major European or American hubs, São Paulo struggles to meet its citizens' transportation and housing needs, and goods and services are expensive. Like most of its counterparts elsewhere in the world, it hasn't yet found an answer to these problems.

Navigating

Each neighborhood seems a testament to a different period of the city's history. São Paulo's first inhabitants, Jesuit missionaries and treasure-hunting pioneers, lived in the largely pedestrians-only hilltop and valley areas, particularly Vale do Anhangabaú. Later these areas became Centro (downtown district), a financial and cultural center that's still home to the stock exchange and many banks. It's now the focus of revitalization efforts.

The Bela Vista and Bixiga (the city's little Italy) neighborhoods, near Centro, are home to many theaters and bars. In the 19th century many families who made fortunes from coffee built whimsical mansions in the ridge-top Avenida Paulista neighborhood. Beginning with the post–World War II industrial boom, these homes gave way to skyscrapers. Many of the best hotels are also on or near this avenue.

During the economic growth of the 1970s, many businesses moved west and downhill to a former swamp. You'll find the tall buildings of Avenida Brigadeiro Faria Lima, the stylish homes of the Jardins neighborhood, and the Shopping Center Iguatemi (Brazil's first mall) just off the banks of the Rio Pinheiros.

Nowadays, large-scale construction of corporate headquarters continues south, between the Marginal Pinheiros Beltway and Avenida Engenheiro Luís Carlos Berrini, not far from the luxurious Daslu.

The Neighborhoods

Centro
This downtown area has the city's most interesting historic architecture and some of its most famous sights.

Liberdade:
Southeast of Centro, Liberdade is the center of São Paulo's vibrant Japanese, Korean, and Chinese communities. It's also a popular tourist attraction, with lots of culturally motivated markets and restaurants.

Avenida Paulista:
Some of the city's best hotels, biggest financial companies and banks, and most of its cultural institutions center around this massive (eight-lane-wide) main drag that spans several neighborhoods south and west of Centro.

Bixiga:
Officially called Bela Vista, this is São Paulo's Little Italy, with plenty of restaurants, theaters, and nightlife. It's an old, working-class neighborhood where everybody knows everybody.

Jardins:
A trendy neighborhood that's ideal for shopping buffs, Jardins is one of the few parts of São Paulo that's ideal for walking around. It's one of the safest neighborhoods at night, too.

Itaim Bibi:
Like Jardins, its neighbor just to the north, Itaim, has fashionable bars, restaurants, and shops. Some of the most expensive and exclusive nightlife in the city is here.

Pinheiros:
Nightlife-central Pinheiros, northwest of Jardins and Avenida Paulista, is chock full of bars, clubs, and late-night restaurants.

Vila Madalena:
If Pinheiros doesn't have what you crave for nightlife, Vila Madalena, to the north, probably will. Bohemian artists started moving to this 'hood in the '70s, and today it's a well-established artsy enclave, with high-end galleries and bars.

Shopping People come from all over Brazil and South America to shop in São Paulo. Go to Jardins or Itaim if you want to stroll on the streets among the rich and famous, or find a shopping mall to buy leather items, jewelry, gifts, antiques, or art.

Eating Out More than 12,000 restaurants fill this melting pot of cultures, including the country's best Japanese, Italian, pizzerias, and cafés. Also excellent are Portuguese, German, French, Spanish, and traditional Brazilian restaurants. Don't miss the extravaganza of restaurants, food stands, and grocery items at historic Mercado Municipal.

Dance Clubs & Live Music The city's eclectic heritage is reflected in its nightlife. São Paulo is one of the few places in Brazil where you can dance to throbbing techno music even after the sun comes up, lose yourself into one of the many rock joints around town and hear live MPB (Brazilian popular music), jazz, and blues acts, all on the same night. The entertainment is 24/7—guaranteed.

Bars Bars in Brazil are much more than a place to grab a drink. People go to barzinhos (little bars), as locals call them, to spend the whole night talking, people-watching, discussing politics or soccer and, of course, having a caipirinha. In São Paulo, you can choose between the upscale bars of Jardins and the young-oriented (and always crowded) of Vila Madalena.

Soccer If you love the beautiful game, why not spend some time in São Paulo watching the best soccer in Brazil? Games are played year-round in the major stadiums of the city. Choose your home team from the popular Corinthians, the elitist São Paulo, and the Italian-based Palmeiras. If you like the underdogs, go to Móoca and cheer for Juventus while eating a cannoli on their home turf.

Health & Safety

City Safety

Stay alert and guard your belongings at all times. Avoid wearing expensive sneakers or watches and flashy jewelry, or carrying cameras—all of which attract attention. Of all the tourist sights, Centro and Liberdade are the most targeted by muggers. Other places where crimes often occur are at ATMs and at the airports, particularly if you're carrying a laptop.

If you're driving, stay alert during traffic jams and at stop signs, mainly at night, and don't deviate from the main streets and beltways. Watch out for motorcycle drivers—there are many who are express couriers, but some are robbers, and you should be suspect when there are two people on one bike.

Health

The air pollution might irritate your eyes, especially in July and August (dirty air is held in the city by thermal inversions), so pack eye drops.

When to Go

Cultural events—film and music festivals and fashion and art exhibits—happen mostly between April and December. During the South American summer (January–March) the weather is rainy, and floods can disrupt traffic. In summer, make reservations for beach resorts as far in advance as possible, particularly for weekend stays. In winter (June–July), follow the same rule for visits to Campos do Jordão. In the summer months temperatures can easily go up to 35 degrees Celsius (95 degrees Fahrenheit). In winter they rarely get lower than 10°C (50°F).

EXPLORING

Centro

Even though the downtown district has its share of petty crime, it's one of the few places with a significant amount of pre-20th-century history. Explore the areas where the city began and see examples of architecture, some of it beautifully restored, from the 19th century. The best way to get here is by metro.

Numbers in the text correspond to numbers in the margin and on the São Paulo Centro map.

a good walk

Begin at the **Edifício Copan ❶ ▶**, designed by Brazilian architect Oscar Niemeyer. Farther up Avenida Ipiranga is **Edifício Itália ❷**, once the city's tallest building. Continue north along the avenue and turn right on the pedestrians-only Rua Barão de Itapetininga, with its many shops and street vendors. Follow it to the neobaroque **Teatro Municipal ❸**, in the Praça Ramos de Azevedo. Head east across the square to the Viaduto do Chá, a monumental overpass above the Vale do Anhangabaú—the heart of São Paulo. At the end of this viaduct, walk left down Rua Líbero Badaró until you reach Avenida São João, then turn right to see the gothic **Edifício Martinelli ⓫**. A bit farther along São João, between Rua 15 de Novembro and Rua João Brícola, is the 36-floor **Edifício BANESPA ❿**. Continue right on 15 de Novembro and you will reach Praça da Sé, the city's true center and the site of the **Catedral da Sé ❺**.

Head north out of Praça da Sé and right onto Rua Roberto Simonsen, home of the **Solar da Marquesa de Santos ❼**, the city's only surviving late-18th-century residence. Nearby is the **Pátio do Colégio ❽**, which marks the spot where the city was founded, and has a nice café. Walk north along Rua Boa Vista, then right down Ladeira Porto Geral and Rua Basílio Jafet until the corner of Rua da Cantareira, where you can see the fully restored **Mercado Municipal ⓭**. Go back to Rua Boa Vista and follow it right onto Largo de São Bento to the must-see **Mosteiro de São Bento ⓬**.

TIMING & PRECAUTIONS This route requires two to three hours on foot, depending on where you choose to stop. Start early so you can linger at your leisure. Streets are

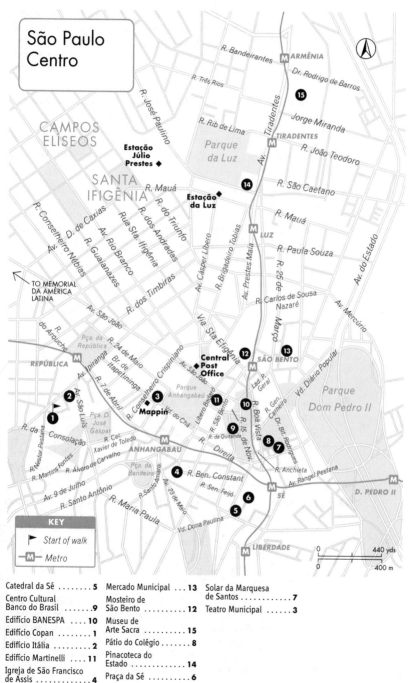

São Paulo Centro

CAMPOS ELÍSEOS

SANTA IFIGÊNIA

R. Bandeirantes

ARMÊNIA

Dr. Rodrigo de Barros

R. Três Rios

Jorge Miranda

15

R. José Paulino

R. Rib de Lima

Parque da Luz

TIRADENTES

R. João Teodoro

Estação Júlio Prestes ◆

14

R. São Caetano

R. Mauá

Estação da Luz ◆

LUZ

R. Mauá

R. D. de Caxias

R. do Triunfo

R. dos Andradas

R. Conselheiro Nébias

Av. Rio Branco

Rua Sta. Ifigênia

R. Guaianazes

Av. Cásper Líbero

R. Brigadeiro Tobias

R. Paula Souza

Av. Prestes Maia

R. 25 de Março

R. Carlos de Sousa Nazaré

Av. do Estado

TO MEMORIAL DA AMÉRICA LATINA

R. dos Timbiras

Av. São João

Av. Mercúrio

R. do Arouche

Pça. da República

R. 24 de Maio

Br. de Itapetininga

Via Sta Efigênia

Central Post Office ◆

12

SÃO BENTO

13

Parque Dom Pedro II

REPÚBLICA

Av. Ipiranga

R. 7 de Abril

R. Conselheiro Crispiniano

Av. São João

Parque Anhangabaú

11

R. São Bento

10

Lad. P. Geral

R. Gen. Carneiro

Vd. Diário Popular

2

Av. São Luís

Pça. D. José Gaspar

3

Mappin

R. do Chá

Libero Badaró

R. Boa Vista

Dr. Br.t Rodrigues

1

R. da Consolação

R. Cel. Xavier de Toledo

9

R. de Quitanda

8

7

R. Nestor Pestana

R. Martins Fontes

R. Álvaro de Carvalho

ANHANGABAÚ

R. Direita

R. 15 de Nov.

4

R. Ben. Constant

R. Anchieta

Pça. da Bandeira

Av. Rangel Pestana

Av. 9 de Julho

R. Santo Antônio

R. Santo Amaro

Av. 25 de Maio

R. Sen. Feijó

6

SÉ

D. PEDRO II

R. Maria Paula

Vd. Dona Paulina

5

LIBERDADE

0 ——— 440 yds

0 ——— 400 m

KEY

▶ Start of walk

Ⓜ Metro

less crowded on weekends, but some buildings are closed. On Sundays and holidays you can do a carriage tour (⇨ Tour Options *in* São Paulo Essentials). Pickpocketing can be a problem, so keep a low profile, don't wear expensive jewelry or watches, and bring only what money you absolutely need. Touring with a guide usually provides some extra security.

What to See

❺ Catedral da Sé. The imposing 14-tower neogothic church, renovated in 2002, has tours through the crypt that contains the remains of Tibiriçá, a native Brazilian who helped the Portuguese back in 1554. ⊠ *Praça da Sé s/n, Centro* ☎ *011/3106–2709, tour 011/3107–6832* 🎫 *Tour R$3* ⊗ *Mon. and Wed.–Sat. 8–5, Sun. 8:30–6; tour Mon. and Wed.–Sat. 9:30–4:30* Ⓜ *Sé.*

❾ Centro Cultural Banco do Brasil. In a neoclassic 1901 building, this cultural center has become a popular space in town for modern and contemporary art. It has three floors of exhibition rooms, a theater, an auditorium, a movie theater, and a video room. ⊠ *Rua Álvares Penteado 112, Centro* ☎ *011/3113–3600* 🎫 *Free* ⊗ *Tues.–Sun. 10–9* Ⓜ *Sé.*

> **need a break?**
>
> **Café Girondino** (⊠ Rua Boa Vista 365, Centro ☎ 011/3229–4574 ⊕ www.cafegirondino.com.br Ⓜ São Bento) is crowded with finance types on weekdays, from happy hour until 11 PM. The bar serves good draft beer and sandwiches. Pictures on the wall depict Centro in its early days. **Café do Pateo** (⊠ Praça Pátio do Colégio 2, Centro ☎ 011/3106–4303 Ⓜ São Bento) is great for a quick break before or after appreciating the museum. On a large balcony overlooking the east side of town, it serves cold and hot drinks along with typical snacks, such as *pão de queijo* (cheese bread).

❿ Edifício BANESPA. If you can't fit tea or drinks at the top of the Edifício Itália into your Centro tour, get your panoramic view of the city atop the 36-floor BANESPA Building. It was constructed in 1947 and modeled after New York's Empire State Building. A radio traffic reporter squints through the smog every morning from here. ⊠ *Rua João Brícola 24, Centro* ☎ *011/3249–7180* 🎫 *Free* ⊗ *Weekdays 10–5* Ⓜ *São Bento.*

▶ **❶ Edifício Copan.** The architect of this serpentine apartment and office block, Oscar Niemeyer, went on to design much of Brasília, the nation's capital. The building has the clean, white, undulating curves characteristic of his work. The Copan was constructed in 1950, and its 1,160 apartments house about 5,600 people. At night the area is overrun by prostitutes and transvestites. ⊠ *Av. Ipiranga 200, Centro* ☎ *011/3257–6169* ⊕ *www.copansp.com.br* Ⓜ *Anhangabaú.*

❷ Edifício Itália. To see the astounding view from atop the Itália Building, you'll have to patronize the Terraço Itália restaurant, on the 41st floor. As the restaurant is expensive and not one of the city's best, afternoon tea or a drink is the best way to get the view. Tea is served 3–5:30, and the bar opens at 6. ⊠ *Av. Ipiranga 344, Centro* ☎ *011/3257–6566 restaurant* ⊕ *www.terracoitalia.com.br* Ⓜ *República.*

★ ⓫ **Edifício Martinelli.** Amid São Paulo's modern 1950s-era skyscrapers, the gothic Martinelli Building is a welcome anomaly. Built in 1929 by Italian immigrant–turned-count Giuseppe Martinelli, it was the city's first skyscraper. The whimsical penthouse is worth checking out. The rooftop has a great view; to go there, you need to get permission from the building manager on the ground floor and leave your ID at the front desk. Then take the elevator to the 34th floor and walk up two more flights. ⊠ *Av. São João 35, Centro* ☎ *011/3104–2477* 🎫 *Free* ⊘ *Mon.–Wed. and Fri. 9–11 and 2–3:30, Thurs. 9–11, Sat. 9–11:30* Ⓜ *São Bento.*

❹ **Igreja de São Francisco de Assis.** The baroque St. Francis of Assisi Church is actually two churches with a common name, one run by Catholic clergy and the other by lay brothers. One of the city's best-preserved Portuguese colonial buildings, it was built between 1647 and 1790, and restored in 1997. ⊠ *Largo São Francisco 133, Centro* ☎ *011/3106–0081* ⊕ *www.franciscanos.org.br* 🎫 *Free* ⊘ *Daily 7:30 AM–7 PM* Ⓜ *Sé or Anhangabaú.*

off the beaten path

MEMORIAL DA AMÉRICA LATINA – A group of buildings designed by Oscar Niemeyer, the Latin American Memorial includes the Pavilhão da Criatividade Popular (Popular Creativity Pavilion), which has a permanent exhibition of handicrafts from all over Latin America. The Salão de Atos Building shows the panel *Tiradentes*, about an independence hero from Minas Gerais, painted by Cândido Portinari in 1949. Regular activities include shows, videos, and films. Ask for an English-speaking guide. ⊠ *Av. Auro Soares de Moura Andrade 664 Barra Funda* ☎ *011/3823–4600* ⊕ *www.memorial.sp.gov.br* 🎫 *Free* ⊘ *Tues.–Sun. 9–6* Ⓜ *Barra Funda.*

⓭ **Mercado Municipal.** The city's first grocery market, this huge, 1928 neobaroque-style building got a major renovation in 2004, and is now the quintessential hot spot for gourmets and food lovers. The building, nicknamed Mercadão (Big Market) by locals, houses 318 stands that sell just about everything edible, including meat, vegetables, cheese, spices, and fish from all over Brazil. It also has restaurants and traditional snack places—don't miss the salt cod *pastel* at Hocca Bar. ⊠ *Rua da Cantareira 306, Centro* ☎ *011/3228–0673* ⊕ *www.mercadomunicipal. com.br* 🎫 *Free* ⊘ *Mon.–Sat. 5 AM–6 PM, Sun. 7–4* Ⓜ *São Bento.*

Fodor'sChoice
★

★ ⓬ **Mosteiro de São Bento.** This unique, Norman–Byzantine church constructed between 1910 and 1922 was designed by German architect Richard Berndl. Its enormous organ has some 6,000 pipes, and its Russian image of the Kasperovo Virgin is covered with 6,000 pearls from the Black Sea. If you go on Sunday, don't miss the 10 AM mass and the monks' Gregorian chants. ⊠ *Largo de São Bento, Centro* ☎ *011/3328–8799* ⊕ *www.mosteiro.org.br* 🎫 *Free* ⊘ *Weekdays 6 AM–6:30 PM, weekends 6–12 and 4–6* Ⓜ *São Bento.*

★ ⓯ **Museu de Arte Sacra.** If you can't get to Bahia or Minas Gerais during your stay in Brazil, you can get a taste of the fabulous baroque and rococo art found there at the Museum of Sacred Art. On display is a collection of 4,000 wooden and terra-cotta masks, jewelry, and liturgical objects from all over the country (but primarily Minas Gerais and Bahia), dating from the 17th century to the present. The on-site convent was founded in 1774. ⊠ *Av. Tiradentes 676, Centro* ☎ *011/3326–1373* ⊠ *R\$4* ☉ *Tues.–Sun. 11–6* Ⓜ *Luz.*

❽ Pátio do Colégio/Museu Padre Anchieta. São Paulo was founded by the Jesuits José de Anchieta and Manoel da Nóbrega in the College Courtyard in 1554. The church was constructed in 1896 in the same style as the chapel built by the Jesuits. In the small museum you can see some paintings from the colonization period and an exhibition of early sacred art and relics. ⊠ *Pátio do Colégio 2, Centro* ☎ *011/3105–6899* ⊕ *www.pateocollegio.com.br* ⊠ *Museum R\$5* ☉ *Museum Tues.–Sun. 9–5; church Mon.–Sat. 8:15–7, Sun. mass at 10* AM Ⓜ *Sé.*

⓮ Pinacoteca do Estado. The building that houses the State Art Gallery was constructed in 1905 and renovated in 1998. The permanent collection has more than 5,000 works of art, including more than 10 Rodin sculptures and several pieces by famous Brazilian artists like Tarsila do Amaral (whose work consists of colorful, somewhat abstract portraits) and Cândido Portinari (whose oil paintings have social and historical themes). The building has a restaurant. ⊠ *Praça da Luz 2, Centro* ☎ *011/3229–9844* ⊕ *www.uol.com.br/pinasp* ⊠ *R\$4, Sat. free* ☉ *Tues.–Sun. 10–6* Ⓜ *Luz.*

❻ Praça da Sé. Two major metro lines cross under the large, busy Praça da Sé, which marks the city's geographical center and houses its main cathedral (⇨ Catedral da Sé, *above*). Here migrants from Brazil's poor northeast often gather to enjoy their music and to sell and buy regional items such as medicinal herbs, while street children hang out trying to avoid the periodic (and controversial) police sweeps to get them off the street. ⊠ *Praça da Sé s/n, Centro* Ⓜ *Sé.*

❼ Solar da Marquesa de Santos. This 18th-century manor house was bought by Marquesa de Santos in 1843, and became famous for housing the emperor's mistress. Now it contains a museum that hosts temporary painting, photo, and sculpture exhibits that usually focus on a São Paulo theme. ⊠ *Rua Roberto Simonsen 136, Centro* ☎ *011/3105–2030* ⊠ *Free* ☉ *Tues.–Sun. 9–5* Ⓜ *Sé.*

❸ Teatro Municipal. Inspired by the Paris Opéra, the Municipal Theater was built between 1903 and 1911 with art-nouveau elements. *Hamlet* was the first play presented, and the house went on to host such luminaries as Isadora Duncan in 1916 and Anna Pavlova in 1919. Plays and operas are still staged here; local newspapers have schedules and information on how to get tickets. The fully restored auditorium, resplendent with gold leaf, moss-green velvet, marble, and mirrors, has 1,500 seats and is usually open only to those attending cultural events; if you are not, reserve a guided tour at least a month in advance. ⊠ *Praça Ramos de Azevedo, Centro* ☎ *011/3222–8698* ⊕ *www.prefeitura.sp.gov.br/ theatromunicipal* ⊠ *Tours R\$10* ☉ *Tours by appointment Tues. and Thurs. at 1* PM Ⓜ *Anhangabaú.*

Liberdade

In 1908 a group of Japanese arrived to work as contract farm laborers in São Paulo State. In the next five decades, roughly a quarter of a million of their countrymen followed, forming what is now the largest Japanese colony outside Japan. Distinguished today by a large number of successful businesspeople, professionals, and politicians, the community also made important contributions to Brazilian agriculture during the last century. The Japanese are credited with introducing the persimmon, the azalea, the tangerine, and the kiwi to Brazil.

The red-porticoed entryway to Liberdade (which means "Freedom") is south of Praça da Sé, behind the cathedral. The neighborhood is home to many first-, second-, and third-generation Nippo-Brazilians, as well as to more recent Chinese and Korean immigrants. Clustered around Avenida Liberdade are shops with everything from imported bubble gum to miniature robots and Kabuki face paint.

The best time to visit Liberdade is on Sunday during the street fair at Praça Liberdade, where Asian food, crafts, and souvenirs are sold. The fair will very likely be crowded, so keep your wits about you and do not wander around at night.

Numbers in the text correspond to numbers in the margin and on the São Paulo City map.

What to See

⑰ Museu da Imigração Japonesa. The Museum of Japanese Immigration has two floors of exhibits about Nippo-Brazilian culture and farm life, and about Japanese contributions to Brazilian horticulture, along with World War II memorials. Call ahead to arrange for an English-language tour. ⊠ *Rua São Joaquim 381, Liberdade* ☎ *011/3209–5465* ☞ *R$3* ☉ *Tues.–Sun. 1:30–5:30* Ⓜ *São Joaquim.*

★ **⑯ Praça Liberdade.** Every weekend 10–7, this plaza hosts a sprawling Asian food and crafts fair that exhibits São Paulo's eclectic cultural mix. You may see, for example, Afro-Brazilians dressed in colorful kimonos hawking grilled shrimp on a stick. Several religious celebrations are held here, like April's Hanamatsuri, commemorating the birth of the Buddha. Apart from the fair and special events, the only other reason to visit this square is to stop by at the nearby Japanese shops and restaurants. ⊠ *Av. da Liberdade and Rua dos Estudantes, Liberdade* Ⓜ *Liberdade.*

Avenida Paulista & Bixiga

Money once poured into and out of the coffee barons' mansions that lined Avenida Paulista, making it, in a sense, the financial hub. And so it is today, though the money is now centered in the major banks. Like the barons before them, many of these financial institutions generously support the arts. Numerous places have changing exhibitions—often free—in the Paulista neighborhood. Nearby Bixiga, São Paulo's Little Italy, is full of restaurants.

Numbers in the text correspond to numbers in the margin and on the São Paulo City map.

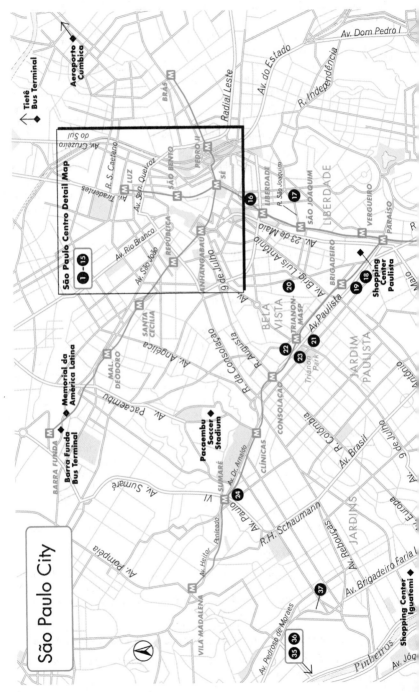

São Paulo City

São Paulo Centro Detail Map
1 - 15

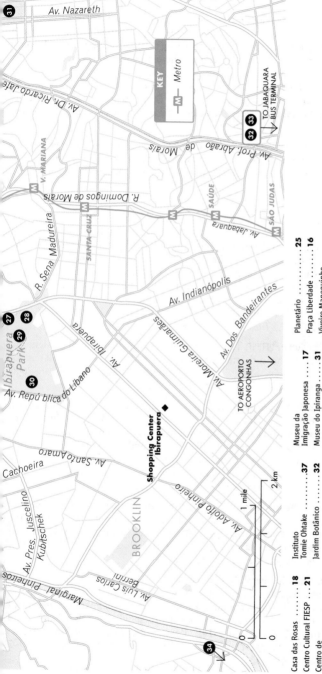

Av. Nazareth

KEY

Ⓜ — *Metro*

TO JABAQUARA
BUS TERMINAL

Av. Dr. Ricardo Jafet

Av. Prof. Abrahão de Morais

V. MARIANA

R. Domingos de Morais

R. Sena Madureira

SANTA CRUZ

SAÚDE

SÃO JUDAS

Av. Jabaquara

Av. Indianópolis

Ibirapuera Park

Av. Ibirapuera

Av. Moreira Guimarães

Av. Dos Bandeirantes

Av. República do Líbano

Av. Santo Amaro

Cachoeira

Av. Pres. Juscelino Kubitschek

Marginal Pinheiros

Av. Luis Carlos Berrini

Av. Adolfo Pinheiro

BROOKLIN

Shopping Center
Ibirapuera

TO AEROPORTO
CONGONHAS →

0   1 mile
0   2 km

Casa das Rosas **18**

Centro Cultural FIESP . . . **21**

Centro de
Cultural Judaica **24**

Fiera do Bixiga **20**

Fundação Maria Luisa e
Oscar Americano **34**

Instituto Butantã **36**

Instituto Itaú Cultural . . . **19**

Instituto
Tomie Ohtake **37**

Jardim Botânico **32**

Museu de
Arte Contemporânea
(MAC) **35**

Museu de Arte
Moderna (MAM) **29**

Museu de Arte de
São Paulo (MASP) **22**

Museu da
Imigração Japonesa **17**

Museu do Ipiranga **31**

Oca **27**

Parque Trianon **23**

Parque Zoológico
de São Paulo **33**

Pavilhão da Bienal **28**

Pavilhão Japonês **26**

Planetário **25**

Praça Liberdade **16**

Viveiro Manequinho
Lopes **30**

A Good Tour

Begin at the **Museu de Arte de São Paulo (MASP)** ㉒, which has one of Brazil's best collections of fine art. Across the street is **Parque Trianon** ㉓, where many businesspeople eat lunch. Leaving the park, veer right onto Avenida Paulista and head for the **Centro Cultural FIESP** ㉑, which frequently has art and theatrical presentations. Continue a few more blocks along Avenida Paulista or take the subway to the **Instituto Itaú Cultural** ⑲, a great place to see digital and contemporary Brazilian art. In the next block is **Casa das Rosas** ⑱, where you can rest your feet at a beautiful Versailles-inspired garden.

TIMING & PRECAUTIONS

This tour takes about two to three hours, including a brief visit to MASP. Busy, well-lighted Avenida Paulista may well be the safest place in the city. Even so, stay alert and hold onto your bags, particularly in Parque Trianon.

What to See

⑱ **Casa das Rosas.** The House of the Roses, a French-style mansion with gardens inspired by those at Versailles, seems out of place next to the skyscrapers of Paulista. It was built in 1935 by famous *paulistano* architect Ramos de Azevedo for one of his daughters. The building was home to the same family until 1986, when it was made an official municipal landmark. It was later opened as a cultural center, and it's one of the avenue's few remaining early-20th-century buildings. ⊠ *Av. Paulista 37, Paraíso* ☎ *011/3251–5271* ⊕ *www.casadasrosas.sp.gov. br* ⊠ *Free* ☉ *Tues.–Sun. 10–6* Ⓜ *Brigadeiro.*

㉑ **Centro Cultural FIESP.** The cultural center of São Paulo State's Federation of Industry has a theater, a library of art and comic books, and temporary art exhibits. ⊠ *Av. Paulista 1313, Jardim Paulista* ☎ *011/3146–7000* ⊠ *Free* ⊕ *www.fiesp.org.br* ☉ *Tues.–Sun. 9–7* Ⓜ *Trianon.*

㉔ **Centro da Cultura Judaica.** This Torah-shaped concrete building is one of the newest architectural hot spots in town. Inaugurated in 2003 to display Jewish history and culture in Brazil, it houses a theater and an art gallery and promotes exhibits, lectures, and book fairs. The café serves local Jewish cuisine. ⊠ *Rua Oscar Freire 2500, Pinheiros* ☎ *011/ 3065–4333* ⊕ *www.culturajudaica.org.br* ⊠ *Free* ☉ *Weekdays 10–9, weekends 2–7* Ⓜ *Sumaré.*

⑳ **Feira do Bixiga.** Strolling through this flea market is a favorite Sunday activity for paulistanos. Crafts, antiques, and furniture are among the wares. Walk up the São José staircase to see **Rua dos Ingleses**, a typical and well-preserved turn-of-the-century Bixiga street. ⊠ *Praça Dom Orione s/n, Bixiga* ⊠ *Free* ☉ *Sun. 8–5.*

⑲ **Instituto Itaú Cultural.** Maintained by Itaú, one of Brazil's largest private banks, this cultural institute has art shows as well as lectures, workshops, and films. It also maintains an archive with the photographic history of São Paulo and a library which specializes in works on Brazilian art and culture. ⊠ *Av. Paulista 149, Paraíso* ☎ *011/2168–1700* ⊕ *www. itaucultural.org.br* ⊠ *Free* ☉ *Tues.–Fri. 10–9, weekends 10–7* Ⓜ *Brigadeiro.*

need a break?

A recommended snack is the delicious *bauru*—a sandwich with roast beef, tomato, cucumber, and a mix of melted cheeses—at **Ponto Chic** (⌧ Praça Osvaldo Cruz 26, Bixiga ☎ 011/3289–1480 ⊕ www. pontochic.com.br ⊙ Daily 11 AM–2 AM), a block east of Instituto Itaú Cultural, across Avenida Paulista. The restaurant claims to have invented the sandwich.

㉒ Museu de Arte de São Paulo (MASP). One of the city's premier fine-arts collections, with more than 7,000 pieces, is in this striking low-rise, elevated on two massive concrete pillars 256 feet apart. Highlights of the collection are works by Van Gogh, Renoir, Delacroix, Cézanne, Monet, Rembrandt, Picasso, and Degas. Baroque sculptor Aleijadinho, expressionist painter Lasar Segall, and expressionist/surrealist painter Cândido Portinari are three of the many Brazilian artists represented. The huge open area beneath the museum is often used for cultural events and is the site of a charming Sunday antiques fair. ⌧ *Av. Paulista 1578, Bela Vista* ☎ *011/3251–5644* ⊕ *www.masp.art.br* ⌧ *R$10* ⊙ *Tues.–Sun. 11–6* Ⓜ *Trianon.*

FodorśChoice ★

㉓ Parque Trianon. Originally created in 1892 as a showcase for local vegetation, in 1968 the park was renovated by Roberto Burle Marx, the Brazilian landscaper famed for Rio's mosaic-tile beachfront sidewalks. You can escape the noise of the street and admire the flora and the 300-year-old trees while seated on one of the benches sculpted to look like chairs. ⌧ *Rua Peixoto Gomide 949, Jardim Paulista* ☎ *011/3289–2160* ⌧ *Free* ⊙ *Daily 6–6* Ⓜ *Trianon.*

Parque Ibirapuera

Ibirapuera is São Paulo's Central Park, though it is slightly less than half the size of and is often more crowded on sunny weekends than its NYC counterpart. In the 1950s the land, which originally contained the municipal nurseries, was chosen as the site of a public park to commemorate the city's 400th anniversary. Oscar Niemeyer and Roberto Burle Marx were called in to join the team of professionals assigned to the project. The park was inaugurated in 1954, and some pavilions used for the opening festivities still sit amid its 160 hectares (395 acres). It has jogging and biking paths, a lake, and rolling lawns. You can rent bicycles at a number of places near park entrances for about R$5 an hour.

A Good Walk

Enter at Gate 9A, walk around the lake and turn right to the **Pavilhão Japonês** ㉖. Then follow the path to the Marquise do Ibirapuera, a structure that connects several buildings, including the **Museu de Arte Moderna (MAM)** ㉙ and the **Pavilhão da Bienal** ㉘, which houses a small branch of the Museu de Arte Contemporânea (MAC). Across from the Marquise, appreciate the spacecraft-looking **Oca** ㉗, where special exhibits are often held. When you exit the compound, walk toward Gate 7 and the **Viveiro Manequinho Lopes** ㉚, with its many species of Brazilian trees.

TIMING & PRECAUTIONS

The park can take up a whole day, though you can probably do this tour in one afternoon. On Sundays, thousands of *paulistanos* seek refuge from the surrounding concrete, which can make the park hard to navigate, but fun for people-watching.

What to See

29 Museu de Arte Moderna (MAM). More than 4,500 paintings, installations, sculptures, and other works from modern and contemporary artists such as Alfredo Volpi and Ligia Clark are part of the Modern Art Museum's permanent collection. Temporary exhibits feature works by new local artists. The giant wall of glass, designed by Brazilian architect Lina Bo Bardi, serves as a window beckoning you to peek inside. ⊠ *Av. Pedro Álvares Cabral s/n, Gate 3, Parque Ibirapuera* ☎ *011/5549–9688* ⊕ *www.mam.org.br* ⊠ *R$5.50 (free Sun.)* ◷ *Tues.–Sun. 10–6.*

 need a break? The **Bar do MAM** (⊠ Gate 3, Parque Ibirapuera ☎ 011/5549–9688 Ext. 1143), inside the Museu de Arte Moderna, serves lunch and snacks, plus sandwiches, pies, soda, coffee, and tea. It's the only place to buy food in the park, apart from hot-dog stands.

27 Oca. This spacecraft-looking building that hosts art exhibits is pure Oscar Niemeyer. Its temporary traditional- and pop-art exhibits usually break attendance records. When exhibits aren't on, the building is usually not open to the public. Admission varies; check local newspapers for exhibits. ⊠ *Gate 3, Parque Ibirapuera* ☎ *011/5574–5505 or 5579–9912 exhibit information.*

28 Pavilhão da Bienal. In every even-numbered year this pavilion hosts the Bienal (Biennial) art exhibition, which draws hundreds of artists from more than 60 countries. The first such event was held in 1951 in Parque Trianon and drew artists from 21 countries. It was moved to this Oscar Niemeyer–designed building—with its large open spaces and floors connected by circular slopes—after Ibirapuera Park's 1954 inauguration. Odd-numbered years bring an architecture exhibition. The pavilion also houses a branch of the **Museu de Arte Contemporânea** (MAC; ⊠ 3rd floor, Parque Ibirapuera ☎ 011/5573–9974 direct line, 011/5574–5922 automated English line ⊕ www.macvirtual.usp.br ⊠ Free ◷ Tues.–Sun. 10–7). There's much more to see at the main branch of the museum, at the University of São Paulo, but this park branch has some temporary exhibits. ⊠ *Gate 3, Parque Ibirapuera* ☎ *011/5573–9974 or 011/5574–5922* ⊕ *www.bienalsaopaulo.org.br.*

26 Pavilhão Japonês. An exact replica of the Katsura Imperial Palace in Kyoto, Japan, the Japanese Pavilion is also one of the structures built for the park's inauguration. It was designed by University of Tokyo professor Sutemi Horiguti and built in Japan. It took four months to reassemble beside the man-made lake in the Japanese-style garden with a goldfish-filled lake. The main building displays samurai clothes and pottery and sculpture from several dynasties. Rooms upstairs are used for traditional tea ceremonies. ⊠ *Gate 10, Parque Ibirapuera* ☎ *011/5573–6453* ⊠ *R$3* ◷ *Weds. and weekends 10–noon and 1–5.*

⟳ 25 Planetário. Paulistanos love the planetarium and, until it was closed for renovation in 1999, frequently filled the 350 seats under its 48-foot-high

THE HARDEST WORD TO TRANSLATE

FEW WORDS EXPLAIN THE *Brazilian character as well as saudade. Deriving from the word solitate ("loneliness," in Latin), its meaning is close to nostalgia, and defines a feeling of loss of something very dear. When a Brazilian doesn't see a friend for a long time, for example, when they meet again one will say that she felt saudade—a mixture of sadness at not having seen the friend in a long time and a feeling of affection and nostalgia. Considered one of the most difficult words to translate, saudade received a definition from the famous linguist, A.F.G Bell, who wrote that "The famous word saudade is a vague and constant desire for something other than the present, a turning towards the past or the future, an indolent dreaming wistfulness." The word appears in the lyrics of famous Brazilian songs like "Chega de Saudade" (No More Saudade), the first bossa nova song and a milestone in Brazilian culture.*

dome. At this writing, it is scheduled to reopen, completely renovated, in 2006. Check the Web site for updates. ✉ *Gate 10, Av. Pedro Álvares Cabral, Parque Ibirapuera* ☎ *011/5575–5206* ⊕ *www.planetario.s2w.com.br.*

30 **Viveiro Manequinho Lopes.** The Manequinho Lopes Nursery is where most plants and trees used by the city are grown. The original was built in the 1920s; the current version was designed by Roberto Burle Marx. Specimens are of such Brazilian trees as *ipê, pau-jacaré,* and *pau-brasil,* the tree for which the country was named (the red dye it produces was greatly valued by the Europeans). ✉ *Gate 7A, Av. República do Líbano, Parque Ibirapuera* ☎ *011/3887–7723* ⊙ *Weekdays 7–5.*

Elsewhere in São Paulo

Several far-flung sights are worth a taxi ride to see. West of Centro is the Universidade de São Paulo (USP), which has two very interesting museums: a branch of the Museu de Arte Contemporânea and the Instituto Butantã, with its collection of creatures that slither and crawl. Head southwest of Centro to the Fundação Maria Luisa e Oscar Americano, a museum with a forest and garden in the residential neighborhood of Morumbi. In the Parque do Estado, southeast of Centro, are the Jardim Botânico and the Parque Zoológico de São Paulo.

What to See

★ **34** **Fundação Maria Luisa e Oscar Americano.** A beautiful, quiet private wooded estate is the setting for the Maria Luisa and Oscar Americano Foundation. Paintings, furniture, sacred art, silver, porcelain, engravings, personal possessions of the Brazilian royal family, tapestries, and sculpture are among the 1,500 objects from the Portuguese colonial and imperial periods. There are some modern pieces as well, along with an exclusive tea room and an auditorium that hosts concerts on Sundays. ✉ *Av. Morumbi 4077,*

Morumbi ☎ 011/3742–0077 ⊕ *www.fundacaooscaramericano.org.br* ⊡ *R$8* ⏱ *Tues.–Fri. 11–5, weekends 10–5.*

🖐 ㊱ **Instituto Butantã.** In 1888 a Brazilian scientist, with the aid of the state government, turned a farmhouse into a center for the production of snake serum. Today the Instituto Butantã has more than 70,000 snakes, spiders, scorpions, and lizards in its five museums. It still extracts venom and processes it into serum that's made available to victims of poisonous bites throughout Latin America. ⊠ *Av. Vital Brasil 1500, Cidade Universitária* ☎ *011/3726–7222* ⊕ *www.butantan.gov.br* ⊡ *R$5* ⏱ *Tues.–Sun. 9–4:30.*

㊲ **Instituto Tomie Ohtake.** Designed by the architect Ruy Ohtake, this futuristic institute shows modern and contemporary art. It has eight exhibition rooms, a video room, a theater, an auditorium, a bookstore, a café, and a restaurant with a well-reputed Sunday brunch. ⊠ *Av. Brigadeiro Faria Lima 201, Pinheiros* ☎ *011/6844–1900* ⊕ *www. institutotomieohtake.org.br* ⊡ *Free* ⏱ *Tues.–Sun. 11–8.*

🖐 ㉜ **Jardim Botânico.** The Botanical Gardens contain about 3,000 plants belonging to more than 340 native species. The greenhouse has Atlantic rain-forest species, an orchid house, and a collection of aquatic plants. ⊠ *Av. Miguel Stéfano 3031, Parque do Estado, Água Funda* ☎ *011/ 5073–6300* ⊕ *www.ibot.sp.gov.br* ⊡ *R$3* ⏱ *Wed.–Sun. 9–5.*

㉟ **Museu de Arte Contemporânea** (MAC). On the grounds of the country's largest university, Universidade de São Paulo, the main branch of the MAC displays the work of world-renowned European artists Pablo Picasso, Amedeo Modigliani, Wassily Kandinsky, Joan Miró, and Henri Matisse. Also look for the works of well-known Brazilian artists Anita Malfatti, Tarsila do Amaral, Cândido Portinari, and Emiliano Di Cavalcanti. The smaller branch of the MAC is at the Parque Ibirapuera. ⊠ *Rua da Reitoria 160, Cidade Universitária* ☎ *011/3091–3018* ⊕ *www.mac. usp.br* ⊡ *Free* ⏱ *Tues.–Fri. 10–5, weekends 10–4.*

㉛ **Museu do Ipiranga.** The oldest and most visited museum in town, Museu Paulista, or do Ipiranga, occupies an 1890 building constructed to honor Brazil's independence from Portugal, declared in the Ipiranga area in 1822 by then-emperor Dom Pedro I. The huge Pedro Américo oil painting depicting this very moment lies in the main room of this French-inspired eclectic palace, whose famous gardens were patterned after those of Versailles. Dom Pedro's tomb lies under one of the museum's monuments. ⊠ *Parque da Independência, s/n, Ipiranga* ☎ *011/6165–8026* ⊕ *www.mp.usp.br* ⊡ *R$2* ⏱ *Tues.–Sun. 9–4:45.*

★ 🖐 ㉝ **Parque Zoológico de São Paulo.** The 200-acre São Paulo Zoo has more than 3,000 animals, and many of its 410 species—such as the *mico-leão-dourado* (golden lion tamarin monkey)—are endangered. See the monkey houses, built on small islands in the park's lake, and the Casa do Sangue Frio (Cold-Blooded House), with reptilian and amphibious creatures. ⊠ *Av. Miguel Stéfano 4241, Parque do Estado, Água Funda* ☎ *011/5073–0811* ⊕ *www.zoologico.com.br* ⊡ *R$10* ⏱ *Tues.–Sun. 9–5.*

A LAND OF CONTRASTS

IN THIS GIGANTIC TERRITORY, *larger than the continental United States, contrasts are overwhelming. Brazil is a fabulously rich land, but it's full of inequalities. You're as apt to see five-star hotels and resorts as you are shantytowns. Shopping malls, McDonald's restaurants, and international banks stand side by side with street vendors peddling homemade foods and herbal medicines. Brazil's GNP is nearly US$795 billion (more than half that of Latin America as a whole), yet it also has a relatively high infant mortality rate (out of 1,000 babies born, 34 don't make it to their first birthday) and one of the world's worst distributions of wealth. The nation has more than 100 million acres of arable land; unequaled reserves of iron, bauxite, manganese, and other minerals; and mammoth hydroelectric power plants. Yet reckless mining and agricultural procedures—particularly in the Amazon— have poisoned rivers, created deserts, and dislodged entire Indian tribes. Further, the racial democracy for which Brazil is often praised is more evident in the bustling downtown markets than in the plush salons of suburban socialites.*

If you examine Brazil's demographics, you'll find other stark contrasts. You can drive through vast regions in the central cerrados (savannas), the southern pampas, or the northeastern sertão (arid interior) without seeing a soul and then, paradoxically, spend hours stuck in traffic in a major city. The bloated urban areas harbor nearly 80% of the population. They're like cauldrons that contain a stew of many races seasoned by regional customs and accents. Although Brazil is considered a Latin country—and the Portuguese language does, indeed, help to unify it—any type of person fits the Brazilian "mold." The country's racial composition reflects the historical contact among native peoples, Portuguese

colonizers, African slaves, and immigrants from Germany, Italy, Japan, and even the United States.

In diversity, religion runs a close second to ethnicity. Although the almanac will tell you that Brazil is 70% Catholic, the people's spiritual lives are much more eclectic. Some estimates put the number of spiritualists—many of whom are followers of the 19th-century Belgian medium Alan Kardec—at 40 million. Candomblé, Macumba, Umbanda, and other cults inspired by African religions and deities abound. And, recently, Pentecostal sects have opened one church after another, performing exorcisms and miraculous "cures" in front of packed auditoriums. Most of these churches and cults welcome visitors of any creed or culture. Brazilians, it seems, are anything but sectarian.

Brazil is truly a land of contrasts, and any visit here is likely to be a sensuous adventure. A variety of cultures, beliefs, and topographies makes this warm nation a showcase of diversity. An array of nature's bounty—from passion fruit and papaya to giant river fish and coastal crabs—has inspired chefs from all over the world to come and try their hands at Brazilian restaurants (adding lightness and zest to the country's already exquisite cuisine). All over the land, spas with bubbling mineral water and soothing hot springs offer the best of both nature and technology. Whether you travel to the Amazon rain forest, the mountain towns of Minas Gerais, the urban jungle of São Paulo, or the immense central plateau surrounding Brasília, you'll plunge into an exotic mix of colors, rhythms, and pastimes.

— *José Fonseca*

WHERE TO EAT

São Paulo's social scene centers on dining out, and there are many establishments from which to choose (new ones seem to open as often as the sun rises). You can find German, Japanese, Spanish, Italian, and Portuguese restaurants as well as top-quality French and Indian spots. And when it comes to pizza, São Paulo is to Brazil what New York is to the U.S. Be sure to also try *beirute,* a Lebanese sandwich served hot on toasted Syrian bread and filled with roast beef, cheese, lettuce, and tomato.

Of the domestic restaurants, the innumerable *churrascarias* (places that serve a nonstop stream of barbecued meat) are beloved by paulistanos. Many restaurants serve *feijoada* (the national dish of black beans and a variety of meats) on Wednesday and Saturday; top restaurants do it up in fancy buffets. It's also easy to find restaurants that specialize in other traditional Brazilian dishes, such as *moqueca* (fish stew made with coconut milk and *dendê,* a palm oil), along with other regional dishes from Bahia and Minas Gerais states, and from the far northeast.

Virado à paulista (beans, eggs, and collard greens) is a typical São Paulo dish. In the nearby countryside, traditional farm cooking reigns, with rich stews and roasts and freshwater fish dishes. *Pintado na brasa* (charcoal-broiled catfish) is one of these regional classics that you can taste even in city restaurants.

When you finish the meal, don't forget to ask for a *cafezinho* ("little coffee," usually very strong). From authentic Italian espressos to regular Brazilian Santos, São Paulo serves the best coffees in the country.

Most places don't require jacket and tie, but people tend to dress up; establishments in the $$$ to $$$$ categories expect you to look neat and elegant—a step above what's expected at the best restaurants elsewhere in Brazil.

WHAT IT COSTS In Reais				
$$$$	**$$$**	**$$**	**$**	**¢**
AT DINNER	over R$60	R$45–R$60	R$30–R$45	R$15–R$30	under R$15

Prices are for a main course at dinner.

Brazilian

$$$–$$$$ ✕ **Baby Beef Rubaiyat.** The family that owns and runs this restaurant serves meat from their ranch in Mato Grosso do Sul State. Charcoal-grilled fare—baby boar (on request at least two hours in advance), steak, chicken, salmon, and more—is served at the buffet. A salad bar has all sorts of options. Wednesday and Saturday are feijoada nights, and on Friday the emphasis is on seafood. ⊠ *Alameda Santos 86, Paraíso* ☎ *011/3141–1188* ⊕ *www.rubayat.com.br* ☐ V Ⓜ *Paraíso* ⊠ *Avenida Brigadeiro Faria Lima 2954, Itaim Bibi* ☎ *011/3078–9486* ☐ V Ⓜ *Paraíso.*

\$–\$\$\$ ✕ **Esplanada Grill.** The beautiful people hang out in the bar of this highly regarded churrascaria. The thinly sliced *picanha* steak (similar to rump steak) is excellent; it goes well with a house salad (hearts of palm and shredded, fried potatoes), onion rings, and creamed spinach. The restaurant's version of the traditional *pão de queijo* (cheese bread) is widely viewed as one of the best. ✉ *Morumbi Shopping Center, 1st floor, Av. Roque Petroni Jr. 1089, Morumbi* ☎ *011/5181–8156* 🖃 *AE, DC, MC, V.*

\$\$ ✕ **Bargaço.** The original Bargaço, in Salvador, has long been considered the best Bahian restaurant in that city. If you can't make it to the northeast, be sure to have a meal in the São Paulo branch. Seafood is the calling card. ✉ *Rua Oscar Freire 1189, Cerqueira César* ☎ *011/3085–5058* 🖃 *DC, MC* Ⓜ *Consolação.*

★ \$–\$\$ ✕ **Consulado Mineiro.** During and after the Saturday crafts and antiques fair in Praça Benedito Calixto, it may take an hour to get a table at this homey restaurant. Among the traditional *mineiro* (from Minas Gerais State) dishes are the *mandioca com carne de sol* (cassava with salted meat) appetizer and the *tutu* (pork loin with beans, pasta, cabbage, and rice) entrée. The cachaça menu is extensive, with rare, premium, and homemade brands. Several types of *batidas* (fruit-and-alcohol mixtures) and caipirinhas are served. ✉ *Rua Praça Benedito Calixto 74, Pinheiros* ☎ *011/3064–3882* ⊕ *www.consuladomineiro.com.br* 🖃 *AE, DC, MC, V* ☾ *Closed Mon.* ✉ *Rua Cônego Eugenio Leite 504, Pinheiros* ☎ *011/ 3898–3241* 🖃 *AE, DC, MC, V.*

¢–\$\$ ✕ **Sujinho–Bisteca d'Ouro.** The modest Sujinho serves churrasco without any frills. It's the perfect place for those who simply want to eat a gorgeous piece of meat. The portions are so large that one dish can usually feed two. A few options on the menu creep into the \$\$\$ price range. ✉ *Rua da Consolação 2078, Cerqueira César* ☎ *011/3231–5207* ⊕ *www.sujinho.com.br* 🖃 *No credit cards* Ⓜ *Consolação.*

\$ ✕ **Dona Lucinha.** Mineiro dishes are the specialties at this modest eatery with plain wooden tables. The classic cuisine is served as a buffet only: more than 50 stone pots hold dishes like *feijão tropeiro* (beans with manioc flour). Save room for a dessert of ambrosia. ✉ *Av. Chibarás 399, Moema* ☎ *011/5051–2050* 🖃 *AE, DC, MC, V* ✉ *Rua Bela Cintra 2325, Jardins* ☎ *011/3082–3797* ⊕ *www.donalucinha.com.br* 🖃 *AE, DC, MC, V* ☾ *Closed Mon.*

★ ¢–\$ ✕ **Frevo.** Paulistanos of all types and ages flock to this Jardins luncheonette for its beirute sandwiches, filled with ham and cheese, tuna, or chicken, and for its draft beer and fruit juices in flavors such as *acerola* (Antilles cherry), passion fruit, and papaya. ✉ *Rua Oscar Freire 603, Jardins* ☎ *011/3082–3434* 🖃 *AE, DC, MC, V.*

Continental

\$–\$\$\$ ✕ **Cantaloup.** That paulistanos take food seriously has not been lost on the folks at Cantaloup. The converted warehouse houses two dining areas: Oversize photos decorate the walls of the slightly formal room, and a fountain and plants make the second area feel more casual. Try the filet mignon with risotto or the beef tenderloin with almonds and spinach.

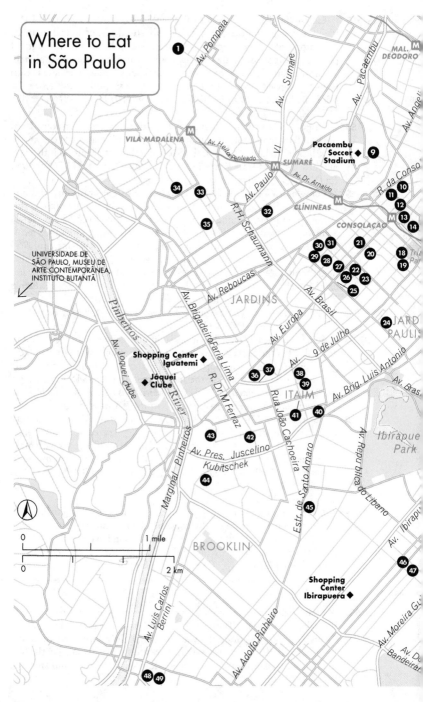

Where to Eat in São Paulo

Save room for papaya ice cream with mango soup or mango ice cream with papaya soup. ⊠ *Rua Manoel Guedes 474, Itaim Bibi* ☎ *011/ 3078–9884* ⊟ *AE, DC, MC, V.*

Eastern European

$ ✕ **Cecilia.** Get your gefilte fish, pickled herring, matzoh bread, and potato latkes at this small restaurant serving traditional (non-kosher) Jewish cuisine. Pastrami sandwiches are very popular and a special "Jewish feijoada" (with meat, white beans, barley, and potatoes) is served on weekends. The restaurant is family-run and the owner, Cecilia Judkrowitch, is always there. ⊠ *Rua Tinhorão 122* ☎ *011/ 3826–2973* ⊕ *www.restaurantececilia.com.br* ⊟ *AE, V* ☉ *Closed Mon.*

Eclectic

$$–$$$$ ✕ **La Tambouille.** This Italo-French restaurant with a partially enclosed garden isn't just a place to be seen; it also has some of the best food in town. Among chef Giancarlo Bolla's recommended dishes are the linguini with fresh mussels and prawn sauce and the filet mignon *rosini* (served with foie gras and saffron risotto). ⊠ *Av. Nove de Julho 5925, Jardim Europa* ☎ *011/3079–6276* ⊟ *AE, DC, MC, V.*

$–$$ ✕ **Bar des Arts.** A great place for lunch or drinks, and a favorite with businesspeople, the Bar des Arts is in a charming arcade near a flower shop, a wine shop, and a fountain. The Italian dishes are the best options, thanks to the Italian owner. Try the mozzarella-filled ravioli. ⊠ *Rua Pedro Humberto 9, at Rua Horacio Lafer, Itaim Bibi* ☎ *011/ 3078–0828* ⊟ *AE, DC, MC, V* ☉ *Closed Mon.*

★ **$–$$**   ✕ **Mestiço.** Tribal masks peer down from the walls of the large, modern dining room. Consider the Thai *huan-hin* (chicken with shiitake mushrooms in ginger sauce and rice) followed by a dessert of lemon ice cream with *baba de moça* (a syrup made with egg whites and sugar). An eclectic menu also includes Italian, Brazilian, and Bahian dishes. ⊠ *Rua Fernando de Albuquerque 277, Consolação* ☎ *011/3256–1539 or 011/ 3256–3165* ⊟ *AE, DC, MC, V* Ⓜ *Consolação.*

$ ✕ **Pitanga.** In a comfortable house in Vila Madalena, Pitanga has a diverse buffet every day (R$23 weekdays, R$32 Saturday, R$34 Sunday). Delicious salads, meat dishes, and feijoada are some of the buffet choices. ⊠ *Rua Original 162, Vila Madalena* ☎ *011/3816–2914* ⊟ *AE, MC, V* ☉ *Closed Mon.* Ⓜ *Vila Madalena.*

$ ✕ **Ritz.** An animated crowd chatters at this restaurant with Italian, Brazilian, French, and mixed cuisine, as contemporary pop music plays in the background. Although each day sees a different special, a popular dish is *bife à milanesa* (a breaded beef cutlet) with creamed spinach and french fries. ⊠ *Alameda Franca 1088, Jardins* ☎ *011/3088–6808* ⊟ *AE, DC, MC, V* Ⓜ *Consolação.*

¢–$ ✕ **Spot.** The closest thing to a chic diner that you'll find in São Paulo, Spot is just one door up from MASP. The salads and the pasta dishes are good bets; come early, though, as it gets crowded after 10 PM. ⊠ *Alameda Rocha Azevedo 72, Cerqueira César* ☎ *011/3284–6131 or 011/3283–0946* ⊟ *AE, DC, MC, V* Ⓜ *Consolação.*

French

$$–$$$$ ✕ **Freddy.** Leave the grunge and noise of the streets behind in this eatery with the feel of an upscale Parisian bistro. Try the duck with Madeira sauce and apple puree, the pheasant with herb sauce, or the hearty cassoulet with white beans, lamb, duck, and garlic sausage. ✉ *Praça Dom Gastão Liberal Pinto 111, Itaim Bibi* ☎ *011/3167–0977* 🖃 *AE, DC, MC, V* ⊘ *No dinner Sun., no lunch Sat.*

$$–$$$$ ✕ **La Casserole.** Facing a little Centro flower market, this charming bistro has been around for five decades. Surrounded by wood-paneled walls decorated with eclectic posters, you can dine on such delights as *gigot d'agneau aux soissons* (roast leg of lamb in its own juices, served with white beans) and cherry strudel. ✉ *Largo do Arouche 346, Centro* ☎ *011/3331–6283* 🖃 *AE, DC, MC, V* ⊘ *Closed Mon. No lunch Sat.* Ⓜ *República.*

$$–$$$$ ✕ **Le Coq Hardy.** This upscale restaurant has two chefs: one is a veteran of the top French kitchens in Brazil, and the other spent many years cooking in France. The grilled foie gras and mango, the escargots with mushrooms in an anise-and-wine sauce, and the roast duck are all highly recommended. ✉ *Rua Jerônimo da Veiga 461, Itaim Bibi* ☎ *011/3079–3344* 🖃 *AE, DC, MC* ⊘ *Closed Sun.*

$–$$$ ✕ **Bistrô Jaú.** Chef Roberto Eid runs the kitchen and the restaurant here. Businesspeople from Avenida Paulista appreciate the fine decor and the lunch menu, which is superb yet inexpensive (compared with the dinner menu). ✉ *Alameda Jaú 1606, Jardins* ☎ *011/3085–5573* 🖃 *AE, DC, MC, V* Ⓜ *Consolação.*

★ $–$$$ ✕ **La Tartine.** An ideal place for a cozy romantic dinner, this small bistro has a good wine selection and simple but comfortable furniture. The menu changes daily; a favorite is the classic coq au vin, or you can fill up on entrées from beef tenderloin to soups and quiches. It is usually crowded with São Paulo's trendy people, and you might have to wait to get a table on weekends. ✉ *Rua Fernando de Albuquerque 267, Consolação* ☎ *011/3259–2090* 🖃 *V* ⊘ *Closed Sun.–Mon.* Ⓜ *Consolação.*

Indian

$–$$$$ ✕ **Ganesh.** The traditional menu includes curries and *tandoori* dishes from many regions of India. Indian artwork and tapestries fill the interior. ✉ *Morumbi Shopping Center, Av. Roque Petroni Jr. 1089, Morumbi* ☎ *011/5181–4748* 🖃 *AE, DC, MC, V.*

Italian

$$$–$$$$ ✕ **Famiglia Mancini.** A huge wheel of provolone cheese is the first thing
Fodor'sChoice you see at this warm restaurant. An incredible buffet with cheeses, olives,
★ sausages, and much more makes finding a tasty appetizer a cinch. The menu has many terrific pasta options, such as the cannelloni with palm hearts and a four-cheese sauce. All dishes serve two people. ✉ *Rua Avanhandava 81, Centro* ☎ *011/3256–4320* 🖃 *AE, DC, MC, V* Ⓜ *Anhangabaú.*

$$$–$$$$ ✕ **Fasano.** A family-owned northern Italian classic, this restaurant is as famous for its superior cuisine as for its exorbitant prices. The chef, Sal-

vatore Loi, has added to the menu dishes like seafood ravioli with a white wine sauce. The luxe decor—marble, mahogany, and mirrors—has seen better days. ⊠ *Rua Vittorio Fasano 88, Jardins* ☎ *011/3062–4000* 🖃 *AE, DC, MC, V* ⊘ *Closed Sun. No lunch.*

$$–$$$$ ✕ **Ca' D'Oro.** This is a longtime northern Italian favorite among Brazilian bigwigs, many of whom have their own tables in the old-world-style dining room. Quail, osso buco, and veal-and-raisin ravioli are winners, but the specialty is the Piedmontese *gran bollito misto,* steamed meats and vegetables accompanied by three sauces. ⊠ *Grande Hotel Ca' D'Oro, Rua Augusta 129, Bela Vista* ☎ *011/3236–4300* 🖃 *AE, DC, MC, V* Ⓜ *Anhangabaú.*

$$–$$$$ ✕ **Don Pepe Di Napoli.** Good and simple Italian food is served here. Choose from a great variety of pastas, salad, and meat dishes. A good option is *talharina a Don Pepe,* pasta with meat, broccoli, and garlic. ⊠ *Rua Padre Joao Manoel 1105, Jardins* ☎ *011/3081–4080* 🖃 *AE, DC, MC, V.*

$$–$$$$ ✕ **Gigetto.** The theater posters that adorn the walls are a tribute to the actors who dine here after performing. The modest decor is offset by the elaborate menu's more than 200 delicious options. Try the cappelletti *à romanesca* (with chopped ham, peas, mushrooms, and white cream sauce). Main courses serve two people. ⊠ *Rua Avanhandava 63, Centro* ☎ *011/3256–9804* 🖃 *AE, DC, MC, V* Ⓜ *Anhangabaú.*

$$–$$$$ ✕ **La Vecchia Cucina.** Chef Sergio Arno changed the face of the city's Italian restaurants with his *nuova cucina,* exemplified by dishes like frogs' legs risotto and duck ravioli with watercress sauce. Well-to-do patrons dine in the glass-walled garden gazebo or the ocher-color dining room decorated with Italian engravings and fresh flowers. ⊠ *Rua Pedroso Alvarenga 1088, Itaim Bibi* ☎ *011/3079–4042* 🖃 *AE, DC, MC, V* ⊘ *No dinner Sun., no lunch Sat.*

★ $$–$$$$ ✕ **Roperto.** Plastic flowers adorn the walls at this typical Bixiga cantina. You won't be alone if you order the ever-popular fusilli *ao sugo* (with tomato sauce), or the traditional baby goat's leg with potatoes and tomatoes. ⊠ *Rua 13 de Maio 634, Bixiga* ☎ *011/3288–2573* 🖃 *DC, MC, V* Ⓜ *Brigadeiro.*

$–$$ ✕ **Jardim di Napoli.** The white, green, and red of the Italian flag is just about everywhere you look in this restaurant. People come for the unmatchable *polpettone alla parmigiana,* a huge meatball with mozzarella and tomato sauce. There are many other meat dishes, pasta selections, and pizza. ⊠ *Rua Doutor Martinico Prado 463, Higienópolis* ☎ *011/ 3666–3022* 🖃 *AE, V.*

Japanese

$$$–$$$$ ✕ **Kinoshita** In the heart of the Japanese neighborhood, this spot is popular for its tasting menu, which mixes the fresh catch of the day with Western and Japanese ingredients. ⊠ *Rua da Glória 168, Liberdade* ☎ *011/3105–4903* Ⓜ *Liberdade* 🖃 *DC, MC, V* ⊘ *Closed Sun.*

$$–$$$$ ✕ **Nagayama.** Low-key, trustworthy, and well loved, Nagayama consistently serves excellent sushi and sashimi. The chefs like to experiment: the California *uramaki* Philadelphia has rice, cream cheese, grilled salmon, roe, cucumber, and spring onions rolled together. ⊠ *Rua Bandeira Paulista 369, Itaim Bibi* ☎ *011/3079–7553* 🖃 *AE, DC, MC*

⊠ *Rua da Consolação 3397, Cerqueira César* ☎ *011/3064–0110* ⊟ *AE, DC, MC.*

$–$$$$ ✕ **Nakombi.** Chefs prepare sushi from a *kombi* (Volkswagen van) in the middle of the dining room at this eclectic and fun restaurant where tables are surrounded by a small artificial river teeming with fish. The menu includes a good variety of sushi and nonsushi dishes. Try the salmon fillet with *shimeji* mushrooms. ⊠ *Rua Pequetita 170, Vila Olímpia* ☎ *011/3845–9911* ⊟ *AE, DC, MC, V.*

Lebanese

★ **$–$$$$** ✕ **Arábia.** For more than 10 years, Arábia has served traditional Lebanese cuisine at this beautiful high-ceilinged restaurant. Simple dishes such as hummus and stuffed grape leaves are executed with aplomb. The lamb melts in your mouth. The reasonably priced "executive" lunch includes one cold dish, one meat dish, a drink, and dessert. Don't miss the pistachio marzipan covered in rose syrup for dessert. ⊠ *Rua Haddock Lobo 1397, Jardins* ☎ *011/3061–2203* ⊕ *www.arabia.com.br* ⊟ *AE, DC, MC.*

$ ✕ **Almanara.** Part of a chain of Lebanese semi-fast-food outlets, Almanara is perfect for a quick lunch of hummus, tabbouleh, grilled chicken, and rice. There's also a full-blown restaurant on the premises that serves Lebanese specialties *rodízio* style, meaning you're served continuously until you can ingest no more. ⊠ *Rua Oscar Freire 523, Jardins* ☎ *011/ 3085–6916* ⊟ *AE, DC, MC, V.*

Pan-Asian

$–$$$ ✕ **House of Siam.** Don't let the shopping mall atmosphere fool you. This Thai restaurant serves spicy food in a cozy space closed off from the retail outlets. Try the *Ped Yaang* (boneless duck with sweet and sour sauce and Thai spices) or the beef fillet with vegetables and oyster sauce. ⊠ *Shopping Morumbi, Av. Roque Petroni Jr. 1089, Morumbi* ☎ *011/ 5181–4748* ⊟ *AE, DC, MC, V.*

$–$$ ✕ **Kundun.** Inspired by food from China, Japan, Vietnam, Thailand, and Laos, chef Maria Yeh comes up with main courses like shrimp with lychee fruit, fresh tomatoes, and shiitake risotto; or zen duck, smoked with jasmine tea. Sushi is also served in this contemporary-casual space with floor-to-ceiling windows. ⊠ *Av. Horácio Lafer 362, Itaim Bibi* ☎ *011/ 3078–3519* ⊟ *AE, DC, MC, V.*

Pizza

$$–$$$$ ✕ **Pizzaria Camelo.** Though it's neither fancy nor beautiful, Pizzaria Camelo has kept paulistanos enthralled for ages with its wide variety of thin-crust pies. The *chopp* (draft beer) is great, too. Avoid Sunday night, unless you're willing to wait an hour for a table. ⊠ *Rua Pamplona 1873, Jardins* ☎ *011/3887–8764* ⊕ *www.pizzariacamelo.com. br* ⊟ *DC, MC, V.*

$–$$ ✕ **Braz.** Its name comes from one of the most traditional Italian neighborhoods in São Paulo and no one argues that it doesn't have the right. Each of the nearly 20 types of crisp-crusted pizzas is delicious, from the traditional margherita to the house specialty, pizza *braz*, with tomato

FodorsChoice
★

sauce, zucchini, and mozzarella and Parmesan cheeses. The *chopp* (draft beer) is also very good. ✉ *Rua Grauna 125, Moema* ☎ *011/5561–0905* ⊕ *www.casabraz.com.br* 🖃 *DC, MC, V.*

$–$$ ✕ **Galpão da Pizza.** Lights that shine from behind bottle bottoms embedded in exposed brick walls is one of the interesting design elements in this restaurant owned by an architect. Service is fast, and the arugula, sun-dried tomato, and mozzarella pizza is one of the best choices. ✉ *Rua Doutor Augusto de Miranda 1156, Pompéia* ☎ *011/3672–4767* 🖃 *DC, MC, V.*

★ **$–$$** ✕ **Oficina de Pizzas.** Both branches of this restaurant look like something designed by the Spanish artist Gaudí, but the pizzas couldn't be more Italian and straightforward. Try a pie with mozzarella and toasted garlic. ✉ *Rua Purpurina 517, Vila Madalena* ☎ *011/3816–3749* 🖃 *DC, MC, V* ✉ *Rua Inácio Pereira da Rocha 15, Vila Madalena* ☎ *011/3813–8389* 🖃 *DC, MC, V* ⊕ *www.oficinadepizzas.com.br.*

$–$$ ✕ **Piola.** Part of a chain started in Italy, this restaurant serves pizzas loaded with toppings like Gorgonzola, Brie, ham, salami, mushrooms, and anchovies. It also has good pasta dishes, like the penne with smoked salmon in a creamy tomato sauce. The young, hip crowd matches the trendy contemporary decor. ✉ *Alameda Lorena 1765, Jardins* ☎ *011/3064–6570* ⊕ *www.piola.com.br* 🖃 *AE, DC, MC, V.*

$–$$ ✕ **Speranza.** One of the most traditional pizzerias in São Paulo, this restaurant is famous for its margherita pie. The crunchy *pão de linguiça* (sausage bread) appetizers have a fine reputation as well. Pastas and chicken and beef dishes are also served. ✉ *Rua 13 de Maio 1004, Bela Vista* ☎ *011/288–8502* ⊕ *www.pizzaria.com.br* 🖃 *DC, MC, V.*

★ **¢** ✕ **Pedaço da Pizza.** Pizza is served by the slice here. Choose from the traditional ones such as pepperoni, or an innovation: pizza with oyster mushrooms and cabbage. It is a good late-night stop since it's open until 6 AM on weekends. The place is crowded with paulistas after movies let out. ✉ *Rua Augusta 2931, Jardins* ☎ *011/3891–2431* ✉ *Rua Augusta 1463, Cerqueira César* ☎ *3285–2117* 🖃 *No credit cards* Ⓜ *Consolação.*

Seafood

$$$$ ✕ **Amadeus.** Since it's not on the ocean, São Paulo isn't known for its seafood, but Amadeus is an exception. Appetizers such as fresh oysters and salmon and endive with mustard, and entrées like shrimp in a cognac sauce make it a challenge to find better fruits of the sea elsewhere in town. It's popular with the business-lunch crowd. ✉ *Rua Haddock Lobo 807, Jardins* ☎ *011/3061–2859* 🖃 *AE, V* ☉ *No dinner weekends* Ⓜ *Consolação.*

Vegetarian

¢–$ ✕ **Cheiro Verde.** One of the few places in São Paulo where you can eat tasty vegetarian food, Cheiro Verde has a simple menu with choices like whole-wheat mushroom pizza and the delicious *gratinado de legumes* (vegetables with Gorgonzola sauce). ✉ *Rua Peixoto Gomide 1413, Jardins* ☎ *011/3289–6853* 🖃 *AE, DC, MC, V* ☉ *No dinner* Ⓜ *Trianon.*

WHERE TO STAY

São Paulo's hotels are almost exclusively geared to business travelers, both homegrown and foreign. For this reason, most hotels are near Avenida Paulista, along Marginal Pinheiros, or in the charming Jardins neighborhood, where international businesses are locationed. But catering to business travelers doesn't necessarily make São Paulo's hotels stuffy or boring. On the contrary, the city has the largest concentration of high-quality, high-style hotels in Brazil. Many of them could be compared to the best hotels in London or New York.

You might get a discount for weekend stays; and breakfast is usually included in the room rate. São Paulo hosts many international conventions, so it's wise to make reservations well in advance. Hotel prices skyrocket during the annual Formule 1 auto race in September.

WHAT IT COSTS In Reais				
$$$$	**$$$**	**$$**	**$**	**¢**
FOR 2 PEOPLE over R$500	R$375–R$500	R$250–R$375	R$125–R$250	under R$125

Prices are for a standard double room in high season, excluding taxes.

Bela Vista

¢   **San Gabriel.** Expect no frills at this budget hotel very close to Avenida Paulista. Rooms are small (though there are some suites, which are larger), but have all the basics and are clean. The rates are unbeatable for this part of town. ⊠ *Rua Frei Caneca 1006, Bela Vista, 01307-002* ☎ *011/3253–2279* 🖷 *011/3253–2279 Ext. 5* ⊕ *www.sangabriel.com.br* 🛏 *75 rooms, 25 suites* ⚬ *Cable TV, refrigerators, parking (fee)* ▤ *AE, DC, MC, V* ⏲ *EP.*

Brooklin & Santo Amaro

$$$–$$$$ **Gran Meliá São Paulo.** This all-suites luxury hotel is in the same build-
FodorsChoice   ing as São Paulo's World Trade Center (WTC) and the D&D Decoração
★   & Design Center. Suites have king-size beds, two phone lines, living rooms with sofas, and small tables that are the perfect places to set up your laptop. Stay on one of the apartment floors and get special amenities like pass-key access and bathroom faucets that can be programmed to maintain your preferred water temperature. Off the large marble lobby is a bar whose comfortable leather chairs are perfect for unwinding after a day of meetings or shopping. ⊠ *Av. das Nações Unidas 12559, Brooklin, 04578-905* ☎ *011/3055–8000 or 0800/703–3399* 🖷 *011/3055–8000* ⊕ *www.solmelia.com* 🛏 *300 suites* ⚬ *Restaurant, room service, in-room safes, cable TV, in-room data ports, tennis court, indoor pool, gym, hair salon, massage, sauna, paddle tennis, bar, laundry facilities, business services, meeting room, parking (fee)* ▤ *AE, DC, MC, V.*

$$$–$$$$ **Transamérica.** Directly across the Pinheiros River from the Centro Empresarial office complex, the home of many U.S. companies, this hotel is a convenient choice for those working in the area. The skylighted

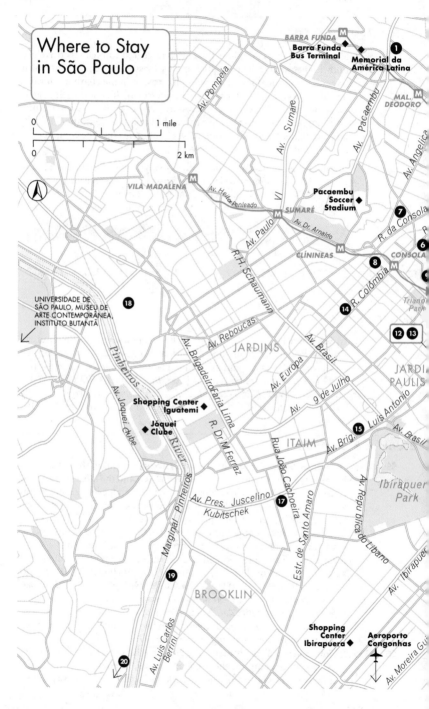

Where to Stay in São Paulo

0 _____ 1 mile

0 _____ 2 km

BARRA FUNDA
Barra Funda
Bus Terminal
Memorial da
América Latina ◆ **1**

Av. Pompéia

Av. Sumaré

Av. Pacaembu

MAL.
DEODORO

Av. Angélica

VILA MADALENA

Av. Heitor Penteado

Pacaembu
Soccer
Stadium ◆

7

R. da Consola

SUMARÉ

VI

R.H. Schaumann

Av. Paulo

Av. Dr. Arnaldo

6

CLÍNINEAS

CONSOLA

8

Triang
Park

14 R. Colômbia

UNIVERSIDADE DE
SÃO PAULO, MUSEU DE
ARTE CONTEMPORÂNEA,
INSTITUTO BUTANTÃ

18

Av. Reboucas

12 **13**

Av. Brasil

JARDINS

JARDI
PAULIS

Pinheiros

Av. Brigadeiro Faria Lima

Av. Europa

Av. 9 de Julho

Av. Joquei clube

Shopping Center
Iguatemi ◆

Jóquei
Clube ◆

R. Dr M Ferraz

Av.

Av. Brig. Luis Antonio

15

Av. Brasil

Pinheiros River

ITAIM

Ibirapuer
Park

Av. Repu blica do Libano

Marginal Pinheiros

Av. Pres. Juscelino
Kubitschek

17

Rua João Cacheoira

Av. Ibirapuer

19

BROOKLIN

Estr. de Santo Amaro

20

Av. Luís Carlos
Berrini

Shopping
Center
Ibirapuera ◆

Aeroporto
Congonhas ◆

Av. Ibirapuer

Av. Moreira Gu

lobby—in granite and marble, with Persian carpets, palm trees, leather sofas, and oversize modern paintings—is more impressive than the rooms, with their beige wall-to-wall carpets and floral fabrics, but they're clean, spacious, and quiet. ⊠ *Av. das Nações Unidas 18591, Santo Amaro, 04795-901* ☎ *011/5693–4511 or 0800/12–6060* 🖷 *011/ 5693–4990* ⊕ *www.transamerica.com.br* ⟿ *389 rooms, 11 suites* ⌂ *Restaurant, room service, cable TV, 9-hole golf course, 2 tennis courts, pool, gym, sauna, bar, laundry facilities, business services, parking (fee)* ▤ *AE, DC, MC, V.*

Centro & Environs

$$ 🏨 **Grande Hotel Ca' D'Oro.** Owned and run by a northern Italian family for more than 40 years, this old-world-style hotel near Centro has bar-side fireplaces, lots of wood and Persian carpeting, a great variety of classic European design styles, ultrapersonalized service, and the beloved Ca' D'Oro restaurant. All these amenities attract many repeat customers, including quite a few Brazilian bigwigs. ⊠ *Rua Augusta 129, Cerqueira César, 01303-001* ☎ *011/3236–4300* 🖷 *011/3236–4311* ⊕ *www.cadoro.com.br* ⟿ *240 rooms, 50 suites* ⌂ *Restaurant, room service, cable TV, indoor pool, gym, sauna, 2 bars, laundry facilities, parking (fee)* ▤ *AE, DC, MC, V* Ⓜ *Consolação.*

★ **$** 🏨 **Novotel Jaraguá.** Built in 1954 to be the headquarters of one of the main newspapers in the city, the building that now houses this hotel is a landmark in downtown São Paulo. The huge mural created by Di Cavalcanti is one of the 1950s attractions. All 415 rooms were renovated in 2004; their decor hovers somewhere between Scandinavian and airport lounge (albeit a well-maintained airport lounge). The furnishings are all blonde-wood and brushed steel of an indistinguishable contemporary style, which, all-in-all makes for pleasant rooms at good prices. ⊠ *Rua Martins Fontes 71, Centro, 01050-000* ☎ *011/3120–8000* ⊕ *www.novotel.com.br* ⟿ *309 rooms, 106 suites* ⌂ *Restaurant, cable TV with movies, in-room broadband in some rooms, Wi-Fi, Internet room, bar, shops, business center, parking (fee)* ▤ *AE, MC, V* ⦿ *BP.*

¢–$ 🏨 **Bourbon.** Both guests and furnishings are well cared for in this small hotel near the Largo do Arouche, a charming downtown district overtaken by the gay crowd at night. A brass-accented basement bar features live piano music. The lobby has upholstered print sofas, an abstract handcrafted black-and-white wall hanging, and granite flooring. Rooms are done in beige and blue and have marvelously large, sunlighted bathrooms. ⊠ *Av. Vieira de Carvalho 99, Centro, 01210-010* ☎ *011/ 3337–2000* 🖷 *011/3331–8187* ⟿ *123 rooms* ⌂ *Restaurant, sauna, bar, parking (fee)* ▤ *AE, DC, MC, V* Ⓜ *República.*

¢ 🏨 **Ibis São Paulo Expo.** This large hotel northwest of Centro has clean budget rooms. The decoration is contemporary with focus on function, not beauty. Rooms have either one queen-size bed or two or three twin beds. The professional staff helps you enjoy your stay. ⊠ *Rua Eduardo Viana 163, Barra Funda, 01133-040* ☎ *011/3824–7373* 🖷 *011/ 3824–7374* ⊕ *www.accorhotels.com.br* ⟿ *280 rooms* ⌂ *Restaurant, room service, cable TV, laundry facilities, meeting rooms, free parking* ▤ *AE, DC, MC, V.*

Higienópolis

$ ⊞ **Meliá Higienópolis.** In one of the city's oldest and most attractive residential neighborhoods, only a 10-minute taxi ride from Centro, this hotel, built in 2000, has bright and spacious rooms with contemporary light-wood furnishings. The 24-story building provides nice views of the city from the top floors. ⊠ *Rua Maranhão 371, Higienópolis, 01240-000* ☏ *011/3665–8200 or 0800/703–3399* 🖷 *011/3665–8201* ⊕ *www.solmelia.com* ⤴ *213 rooms* ⚬ *Restaurant, room service, cable TV with movies, in-room safes, minibars, in-room broadband, pool, gym, sauna, business center, Internet room, parking (fee)* ▤ *AE, DC, MC, V* ▯⊙▯ *BP.*

¢ ⊞ **Ville Hotel.** In the lively Higienópolis neighborhood of apartment buildings, bars, and bookstores abutting Mackenzie University, this hotel costs about R$100 a night. The small lobby has a black-and-pink-granite floor, recessed lighting, and leather sofas. Rooms are plain, with little decoration, but clean. ⊠ *Rua Dona Veridiana 643, Higienópolis, 01238-010* ☏ *011/3257–5288* 🖷 *011/3241–1871* ⊕ *www.hotelville.com.br* ⤴ *54 rooms* ⚬ *Restaurant, meeting room, parking (fee)* ▤ *AE, DC, MC, V.*

Itaim Bibi

$–$$ ⊞ **Blue Tree Towers Faria Lima.** In a good location for business travelers, the Blue Towers has 77 apartments that can be transformed into offices, with foldaway beds. Rooms are modern, with dark-wood furnishings and bright-white textiles. ⊠ *Avenida Brigadeiro Faria Lima 3989, Itaim, 04538-133* ☏ *011/3896–7544* 🖷 *011/3896–7545* ⊕ *www.bluetree.com.br* ⤴ *338 rooms* ⚬ *Restaurant, cable TV with movies, minibars, in-room broadband, Wi-Fi, pool, gym, massage, sauna, bar, parking (fee)* ▤ *AE, DC, MC, V* ▯⊙▯ *BP.*

Jardins

★ $$$$ ⊞ **Gran Meliá Mofarrej.** Just behind Avenida Paulista and next to Parque Trianon, the Mofarrej has rooms that are a mix of modern and classic styles. The softness of the decor belies the austere skyscraper that you see from the street. The service is fabulous all around, but the four butler-service floors offer other amenities that make you feel even more pampered. Rooms on the west side overlook the park. ⊠ *Alameda Santos 1437, Jardins, 01419-905* ☏ *011/3146–5900 or 0800/703–3399* 🖷 *011/3262–3368* ⊕ *www.solmelia.com* ⤴ *268 suites* ⚬ *2 restaurants, room service, cable TV, indoor pool, gym, massage, sauna, 2 bars, laundry facilities, business services, convention center, parking (fee)* ▤ *AE, DC, MC, V* Ⓜ *Trianon.*

★ $$$$ ⊞ **Inter-Continental São Paulo.** This exquisite hotel is one of the most attractive of the city's top-tier establishments and consistently gets rave reviews from patrons. Service is attentive, and both the private and public areas are well appointed. Creams, pastels, and marble come together with seamless sophistication and elegance. ⊠ *Al. Santos 1123, Jardins, 01419-001* ☏ *011/3179–2600 or 0800/11–8003* 🖷 *011/3179–2666*

⊕ *www.intercontinental.com* ☞ *189 rooms, 36 suites* ☖ *Restaurant, room service, cable TV, pool, health club, massage, sauna, bar, business services, helipad, parking (fee)* ▭ *AE, DC, MC, V* Ⓜ *Trianon.*

$$$$ ▦ **Renaissance São Paulo.** This elegant hotel has six Renaissance Club floors with suites, the price of which includes a buffet breakfast, evening hors d'oeuvres, butler service, express check-in and check-out, and fax machines. If you want to arrive in style, the hotel's helipad is key. For a lower rate, go for the large, cozy apartments, with couches and contemporary wood furnishings and king-size beds. ⊠ *Alameda Santos 2233, Jardins, 01419-002* ☎ *011/3069–2233, 800/703–1512 in the U.S.* 🖷 *011/3064–3344* ⊕ *www.renaissancehotels.com* ☞ *452 rooms, 52 suites* ☖ *3 restaurants, room service, cable TV, Wi-Fi, pool, health club, massage, squash, 3 bars, shops, laundry facilities, business services, helipad, travel services, parking (fee)* ▭ *AE, DC, MC, V* Ⓜ *Consolação.*

$$$$ ▦ **Unique.** Don't let the watermelon shape scare you. The design by Ruy

FodorśChoice Ohtake is one of the attractions of this boutique hotel, where technol-
★ ogy rules. Apartments have plasma TVs with DVD players, mobile phones, king-size beds, and whirlpool baths with remote control. Steps from Ibirapuera Park, the hotel is the home away from home for models and wealthy Brazilian jet-setters. ⊠ *Avenida Brigadeiro Luís Antônio 4700, Jardins, 01402-002* ☎ *011/3055–4710 or 0800/770–8771* 🖷 *011/ 3889–8100* ⊕ *www.unique.com.br* ☞ *95 rooms* ☖ *Restaurant, cable TV, in-room DVDs, in-room broadband, Wi-Fi, pool, health club, sauna, Internet room, parking (fee)* ▭ *AE, DC, MC, V* ▯◉▯ *BP.*

$$$ ▦ **Fasano.** One of the city's top hotels, Fasano is a vision in brown, with a decor that hints at 1940s modern, but is undeniably 21st century chic. *Architecture Digest*–worthy rooms have leather chairs and headboards, parquet floors with fashionable throw rugs, and huge windows. The staff gets rave reviews as being helpful, friendly, and unpretentious. Fasano rode into town on the coattails of its popular restaurant of the same name (⇨ Where to Eat, *above*) in 2003. ⊠ *Rua Vittorio Fasano 88, Jardins 01414-020* ☎ *011/3896-4077* 🖷 *011/3896-4156* ⊕ *www.fasano.com. br* ☞ *64 rooms* ☖ *Restaurant, room service, cable TV, in-room safes, minibars, in-room broadband, pool, spa, gym, bar, concierge, business center, dry cleaning, laundry service, airport shuttle, travel services, free parking, no-smoking floors* ▭ *AE, D, DC, MC, V* ▯◉▯ *EP.*

$$–$$$$ ▦ **L'Hotel.** Close to the major business hubs, this European-style hotel has rooms and suites decorated in somewhat sterile floral patterns. The place was modeled after the famous L'Hotel in Paris, and the small number of rooms allows it to focus on providing superior service. ⊠ *Alameda Campinas 266, Jardins, 01404-000* ☎ *011/2183–0500* 🖷 *011/2183–0505* ⊕ *www.lhotel.com.br* ☞ *80 rooms, 7 suites* ☖ *2 restaurants, room service, cable TV, pool, health club, sauna, pub, laundry facilities, business services, meeting room, parking (fee)* ▭ *AE, DC, MC, V* Ⓜ *Trianon.*

$$–$$$$ ▦ **Maksoud Plaza.** Once the top choice for luxury accommodations in São Paulo, Maksoud must now share the bill with a bevy of high-end hotels. Still, its facilities, comfort, and good location make it one of the best choices in the city. The multilingual staff provides professional service, the restaurants are excellent, and the in-house theater and the Maksoud 150 nightclub, where Frank Sinatra once played, offer entertainment. ⊠ *Alameda Campinas 1250, Jardins, 01404-900* ☎ *011/ 3145–8000* 🖷 *011/3145–8001* ⊕ *www.maksoud.com.br* 🛏 *416 rooms, 99 suites* ♻ *6 restaurants, room service, cable TV, indoor pool, health club, 3 bars, nightclub, theater, laundry facilities, business services, parking (fee)* ▭ *AE, DC, MC, V* Ⓜ *Trianon.*

Paraíso

¢ 🏨 **Hotel Formule 1.** One of the first hotels in São Paulo to offer high quality at low prices, this hotel has a simple and practical style. Rooms are small, but each has a queen-size bed with a twin bunk above, a table, and a closet. The service has its ups and downs, but the location is good—you can get nearly everywhere in the city from here, by subway or bus, and the area is safe for walking around. ⊠ *Rua Vergueiro 1571, Paraíso* ☎ *011/5085–5699* 🖷 *011/5085–5694* ⊕ *www.accorhotels.com.br* 🛏 *300* ♻ *Cable TV, business services, parking (fee)* ▭ *AE* Ⓜ *Paraíso.*

Pinheiros

$ 🏨 **Golden Tower.** Proximity to important hubs and to Vila Madalena make this a good choice. The hotel was built in 2001, and all rooms have non-allergenic carpet and sheets, as well as anti-noise windows and modern-looking furniture. Rooms are spacious, the location is ideal, and the Mediterranean restaurant is good. Views from the terrace and top floors are privileged. ⊠ *Rua Deputado Lacerda Franco 148, Pinheiros, 05418-000* ☎ *011/3094–2200 or 0800/10–1525* 🖷 *011/ 3094–2201* ⊕ *www.goldentowerhotel.com.br* 🛏 *88 rooms, 8 suites* ♻ *Restaurant, cable TV, minibars, in-room safes, in-room broadband in some rooms, Wi-Fi, pool, gym, Internet room, parking (fee), no-smoking floors* ▭ *AE, MC, V* ⦶ *BP.*

Vila Mariana

$$–$$$$ 🏨 **Hotel Sofitel São Paulo.** Near the Congonhas Airport and Ibirapuera Park, this modern, luxury hotel is noted for its French style. The restaurant serves French cuisine. Dark-wood furniture fills the rooms, many of which have views of park. It's rare in São Paulo to be able to see trees from your window. ⊠ *Rua Sena Madureira 1355, Bloco 1, Vila Mariana, 04021-051* ☎ *011/5087–0800* 🖷 *011/5575–4544* ⊕ *www. accorhotels.com.br* 🛏 *219 rooms* ♻ *Restaurant, room service, cable TV, tennis court, pool, gym, sauna, bar, laundry facilities, business services, meeting rooms, helipad, parking (fee)* ▭ *AE, DC, MC, V.*

NIGHTLIFE & THE ARTS

Nightlife

São Paulo's nightlife options are seemingly endless, and knowing where to go is key. The chic and wealthy head for establishments, many of which serve food, in the Vila Olímpia, Jardins, and Itaim neighborhoods. The Pinheiros and Vila Madalena neighborhood have a large concentration of Brazilian clubs and bars. The neighborhood of Jardins also has many gay and lesbian spots, whereas Pinheiros and Vila Madalena have a large concentration of youthful bars and clubs.

São Paulo is a city beset by trends, so clubs and bars come and go at a dizzying pace. Though the places listed here were all thriving spots at this writing, the nightlife scene is always changing, and it's best to check with hotel concierges and paulistanos you meet to confirm that a place is still open before heading out on the town.

Bars

The most sophisticated (and expensive) places are in Jardins, Vila Olímpia, and Itaim. Pinheiros and Vila Madalena are full of trendy places.

CENTRO

Fodor'sChoice
★

First opened in 1949, **Bar Brahma** (⊠ Av. São João 677, Centro ☎ 011/3333–0855 ⊕ www.barbrahmasp.com.br Ⓜ República) used to be the meeting place of artists, intellectuals, and politicians. The decor is a time-warp to the mid-20th century, with furniture, lamps, and a piano true to the period. This is one of the best places in São Paulo for live music, especially on Thursday and Sunday, when the traditional samba group Demônios da Garoa plays.

FREGUESIA DO Ó

A stop at off-the-beaten-path **Frangó** (⊠ Largo da Matriz de Nossa Senhora do Ó 168, Freguesia do Ó ☎ 011/3932–4818 or 011/3931–2285 ⊕ www.frangobar.com.br), northwest of Centro, makes you feel as if you've been transported to a small town. The bar has 150 varieties of beer, including the Brazilian dark beer Xingu. Its rich, molasses-like flavor nicely complements the bar's unforgettable *coxinhas de frango com queijo* (fried balls of chicken with cheese).

ITAIM & VILA
OLÍMPIA

Moça Bonita (⊠ Rua Quatá 633, Vila Olímpia ☎ 011/3846–8136 ⊕ www.mocabonitabar.com.br) is a popular bar with a maritime theme, complete with aquarium and miniature sailboats. The specialties are draft beer and seafood.

JARDINS

Crowded from happy hour on, **All Black** (⊠ Rua Oscar Freire 163, Jardins ☎ 011/3088–7990 ⊕ www.allblack.com.br) is an Irish pub with style—and a great variety of international beer brands. Irish soccer paraphernalia decorates the place, and a New Zealand flag betrays one of the owner's roots. This is one of the best places to have a Guinness in São Paulo. **Balcão** (⊠ Rua Doutor Melo Alves 150, Jardim Paulista ☎ 011/3088–3063 or 011/3088–6091 Ⓜ Consolação) means "balcony" in Portuguese, and this artsy place has a sprawling one. If you'd like a little food to accompany your drinks and conversation, try the sun-dried tomato–and-mozzarella sandwich.

PARAÍSO

Barnaldo Lucrécia (⊠ Rua Abílio Soares 207, Paraíso ☎ 011/3885–3425 ⊕ www.barnaldolucrecia.com.br Ⓜ Paraíso) draws crowds with live *música popular brasileira* (MPB; popular Brazilian music). The crowd is intense but jovial.

PERDIZES

Elias (⊠ Rua á 70, Perdizes ☎ 011/3864–4722) is a hangout for fans of the Palmeiras soccer team, whose stadium is just a few blocks away. If you want something to eat, the carpaccio is undoubtedly the best choice on the menu.

PINHEIROS &
VILA MADALENA
★

The '60s and '70s bohemian-chic decor at **Astor** (⊠ Rua Delfina 163, Vila Madalena ☎ 011/3815–1364) sends you back in time. The owner decided to open this place after the success of his other two bars, Pirajá and Original. The menu has good draft beer, snacks, and meals, and is full of specialties from classic bars in Brazil. Don't miss *picadinho à astor* (beef stew with rice and black beans, poached eggs, banana, farofa, and beef *pastel*).

Most patrons stop at **Empanadas** (⊠ Rua Wisard 489, Vila Madalena ☎ 011/3032–2116) for a beer en route to another Vila Madalena bar. It's a good place to "warm up" for an evening out with a quick drink and a bite to eat on the bar's sidewalk tables. Appropriately, the *empanadas* (Argentinian filled pastries) are particularly appealing. When it comes to ending the night, **Filial** (⊠ Rua Fidalga 254, Vila Madalena ☎ 011/3813–9226) is considered the best bar in town. Plenty of musicians stop by for an after-hours taste of its draft beer, along with the flavorful snacks (such as *bolinho de arroz,* or rice fritters) and meals (try *galinha afogada,* a stew with incredibly moist chicken and rice).

★

The fashionable patrons customers at **Grazie a Dio** (⊠ Rua Girassol 67, Vila Madalena ☎ 011/3031–6568 ⊕ www.grazieadio.com.br) may vary in age, but they always appreciate good music. The best time to go is at happy hour for daily live performances. On Saturday it's jazz, and on Friday, bossa nova. The natural decorations, including trees and constellations, complement the Mediterranean food served in the back. **Pirajá** (⊠ Av. Brigadeiro Faria Lima 64, Pinheiros ☎ 011/3815–6881), known for its draft beer and sandwiches, attracts a crowd of journalists and designers that work nearby. Pictures of Rio line the walls. The action starts at happy hour, after 6 PM. The *bolinhos de abóbora com carne seca* (pumpkin-and–jerked beef fritters) are very good.

Music Clubs

São Paulo's music clubs might have rock, jazz, or blues artists, but when it comes to Brazilian music, there are more options. On weekends you find MPB, samba, and *pagode* (similar to samba but with pop-music elements) in clubs throughout the city. At *forró* clubs, couples dance close to the fast beat and romantic lyrics of music that originated in the Northeast.

BIXIGA

Café Piu Piu (⊠ Rua 13 de Maio 134, Bixiga ☎ 011/3258–8066 ⊕ www.cafepiupiu.com.br) is best-known for jazz and blues, but it also hosts groups that play rock (between Friday and Sunday), bossa nova, and sometimes even tango. Statues, an antique balcony, and marble tables decorate the place. Doors open at 9 PM Tuesday–Sunday.

ITAIM BIBI

The decor at **Sem Eira Nem Beira** (⊠ Rua Fiandeiras 966, Itaim Bibi ☎ 011/3845–3444 ⊕ www.semeiranembeira.com.br) was inspired by Brazilian bars circa 1940. The club is famous for its live MPB performances on Friday and Saturday

JARDINS

At **Mr. Blues Jazz Bar** (⊠ Av. São Gabriel 558, Jardim Paulista ☎ 011/3884–9356), a traditional jazz, blues, rock, and soul venue, the audience drinks beer and whiskey and eats french fries with Parmesan cheese. Doors open at 9 PM Thursday–Saturday.

MOEMA   With a name right out of New Orleans, it's no wonder that **Bourbon Street** (⊠ Rua dos Chanés 127, Moema ☎ 011/5561–5095 or 011/5561–6100 ⊕ www.bourbonstreet.com.br) is where the best jazz and blues bands, Brazilian and international, play. Performances are Tuesday–Sunday, beginning at 9 PM. On Sundays you can merengue and mambo at the Caribbean dance party.

PINHEIROS   **Canto da Ema** (⊠ Av. Brigadeiro Faria Lima 364, Pinheiros ☎ 011/ 3813–4708 ⊕ www.cantodaema.com.br) is considered the best place to dance forró in town. Here you'll find people of different ages and styles coming together on the dance floor. *Xiboquinha* is the official forró drink, made with *cachaça* (a Brazilian sugarcane-based alcohol), lemon, honey, cinnamon, and ginger. Doors open at 10:30 PM Wednesday–Saturday and it's open 7–midnight on Sunday; admission is R$12–R$18.

A *carioca* is a person from Rio de Janeiro, and **Carioca Club** (⊠ Rua Cardeal Arcoverde 2899, Pinheiros ☎ 011/3813–8598 ⊕ www.cariocaclub. com.br) has the decor of old-style Rio clubs. Its large dance floor attracts an eclectic mix of up to 1,200 college students, couples, and professional dancers who move to *samba, gafieira,* and *pagode* Thursday–Saturday beginning at 10 PM, and Sunday 5–11.

Eclectic **KVA** (⊠ Rua Cardeal Arcoverde 2978, Pinheiros ☎ 011/ 3816–8000 ⊕ www.kvaproducao.com.br) can hold up to 4,000 people, and has three stages and two dance floors. The house plays Brazilian and other rhythms, but usually favors forró. Admission is R$10–R$15 and doors open at 10 PM Monday and Thursday–Saturday.

· VILA MADALENA   The tiny round tables at **Piratininga** (⊠ Rua Wizard 149, Vila Madalena ★   ☎ 011/3032–9775 ⊕ www.piratiningabar.com.br Ⓜ Vila Madalena ◒ Daily 4 PM), a small bar-restaurant, are perfect for a quiet rendezvous. The live MPB, bossa nova, blues, and jazz music, which start daily around 6:30 PM, add to the romance.

VILA OLÍMPIA   People come to tiny **All of Jazz** (⊠ Rua João Cachoeira 1366, Vila Olímpia ☎ 011/3849–1345 ⊕ www.allofjazz.com.br) to quietly listen to very good jazz and bossa nova. Local musicians jam Monday–Saturday beginning at 7:30 PM. Reserve a table on weekends.

Dance Clubs
Most clubs open at 9 PM, but people tend to arrive very late (around midnight), and dance until 5 or 6 AM. Still, you should arrive early to be at the front of the lines. Don't worry if the dance floor appears empty at 11 PM; things will start to sizzle an hour or so later.

BARRA FUNDA   **Villa Country** (⊠ Av. Francisco Matarazzo 810, Barra Funda ☎ 011/ 3868–5858 ⊕ www.villacountry.com.br Ⓜ Barra Funda) is *the* place to go for American country music and *sertanejo,* Brazilian country music. The huge club has restaurant, bars, shops, game rooms, and a dance floor. An Old West theme permeates the decor. It's open Thursday–Sunday.

CONSOLAÇÃO   Live or recorded indie rock is the musical menu at two-story **Funhouse** (⊠ Rua Bela Cintra 567, Consolação ☎ 011/3259–3793 ⊕ www.

funhouse.com.br Ⓜ Consolação), open Wednesday–Saturday. New Brazilian bands play every Saturday.

JARDINS DJs and live acts play rock, hip-hop, and electronic music at **Bunker Lounge Music Bar** (✉ Rua da Consolação 3589, Jardim Paulista ☎ 011/3061–1027 ⊕ www.bunkerlounge.com.br Ⓜ Consolação) Tuesday–Saturday. Some of the owners are members of Sepultura, a famous Brazilian heavy-metal band.

PINHEIROS Trendy **Ampgalaxy** (✉ Rua Fradique Coutinho 352, Pinheiros ☎ 011/3085–7867 ⊕ www.ampgalaxy.com.br) is not only a nightclub, but also a clothing store, bar, and café/lounge. DJs play mostly electro, house, techno, disco, punk, and alternative rock. It's open Tuesday and Thursday–Saturday. At **Avenida Club** (✉ Av. Pedroso de Morais 1036, Pinheiros ☎ 011/3814–7383 ⊕ www.avenidaclub.com.br) some Friday and Saturday nights are dedicated to Caribbean- or Brazilian dance parties; Sundays bring contemporary MPB and rock acts. The large wooden dance floor—one of the finest in town—attracts a crowd of twenty- and thirtysomethings.

Every night except Sunday, **Blen Blen Brasil** (✉ Rua Inácio Pereira da Rocha 520, Pinheiros ☎ 011/3812–2890 ⊕ www.blenblen.com.br ⊘ Mon.–Sat. 8 PM) has live music ranging from reggae to salsa jazz to Brazilian rock and MPB. The clientele varies depending on the music—rock generates a younger crowd; salsa jazz an older one. Arrive early and stay at the bar having a drink and snack before going upstairs to dance.

Urbano (✉ Rua Cardeal Arcoverde 614, Pinheiros ☎ 011/3085–1001 ⊕ www.urbanoclub.com.br ⊘ Mon., Thurs.–Sat. 10 PM Ⓜ Clínicas) draws an eclectic, hip audience. Mondays bring live soul and funk, Thursday is rock night, Friday is electronic, and Saturday draws a crowd with hip-hop and samba-rock.

VILA MADALENA At **Dolores Bar** (✉ Rua Fradique Coutinho 1007, Vila Madalena ☎ 011/3031–3604 ⊕ www.doloresbar.com.br ⊘ Fri.–Sat. 10 PM), DJs spin funk, soul, and hip-hop tunes for a crowd in its twenties and thirties. Friday nights are the most popular, and people really do fill up the floor only after midnight. Because **A Lanterna** (✉ Rua Fidalga 531, Vila Madalena ☎ 011/3031–0483 ⊕ www.lanterna.com.br) is a mixture of restaurant, bar, and nightclub, you can go early for dinner and stay late for dancing. Actors, dancers, and musicians give performances that add to the entertainment. The walls are decorated with local artists' works. It's open Tuesday–Sunday.

VILA OLÍMPIA **Buena Vista Club** (✉ Rua Atílio Innocenti 780, Vila Olímpia ☎ 011/3045–5245 ⊕ www.buenavistaclub.com.br) is a good place to take dance classes. On Sunday you can learn to dance *gafieira* and *zouk*. Live music and DJs heat up the dance floor for hours. The club also has good appetizers and drinks and is open Wednesday–Sunday. You might feel ★ like you're on the set of an Austin Powers movie at **Lov.e Club & Lounge** (✉ Rua Pequetita 189, Vila Olímpia ☎ 011/3044–1613 ⊕ www.loveclub.com.br). Before 2 AM the music isn't too loud, and you can sit and talk on the '50s-style sofas. Then the techno and house effects keep people on the small dance floor until sunrise. If you want a taste of *pancadão*, the unique carioca-style funk, don't miss Wednesday night with DJ Marlboro. The club is open Tuesday, Wednesday, and Friday–Sunday nights.

Gay & Lesbian Bars & Clubs

Most of the bars and cafes along Avenida Vieira de Carvalho are gay or mixed, but also rather run-down.

BARRA FUNDA & LAPA In a huge colonial blue house in an old industrial neighborhood, **Blue Space** (✉ Rua Brigadeiro Galvão 723, Barra Funda ☎ 011/3666–1616 ⊕ www.bluespace.com.br Ⓜ Marechal Deodoro) is one of the largest gay nightclubs in São Paulo. Every Saturday and Sunday, two dance floors and four bars, along with lounge and private rooms, fill with a large crowd interested in the house DJs and go-go-boy and drag shows. Popular **The Week** (✉ Rua Guaicurus 324, Lapa ☎ 011/3872–9966 ⊕ www.theweek.com.br) has a whooping 6,000 square meters area. Two dance floors, three lounge rooms, a deck with a swimming pool, six bars, and several DJs who play house, electro, and techno animate an often shirtless-crowd on Friday and Saturday nights.

BELA VISTA **A Lôca** (✉ Rua Frei Caneca 916, Cerqueira César ☎ 011/3159–8889 ⊕ www.aloca.com.br Ⓜ Consolação) has a crowded dance floor, a video room, and two bars. A mixed gay, lesbian, and straight crowd often dances until dawn, both to electronic music (Thursday to Saturday) and rock (on Sunday). On Friday and Saturday, you can end the night with a light breakfast (yogurt and fruits).

ITAIM BIBI Popular lesbian spot **Clube Z** (✉ Rua Tabapuã 1420, Itaim Bibi ☎ 011/3071–0030 ⊕ www.clubz.com.br), open Friday and Saturday, has Ancient Rome decor, red velvet sofas, and two DJs spinning house and techno.

The Arts

The world's top orchestras, opera and dance companies, and other troupes always include São Paulo in their South American tours. Most free concerts—with performances by either Brazilian or international artists—are presented on Sunday in Parque Ibirapuera. City-sponsored events are usually held in Centro's Vale do Anhangabaú area or in Avenida Paulista.

Listings of events appear in the "Veja São Paulo" insert of the newsweekly *Veja*. The arts sections of the dailies *Folha de São Paulo* and *O Estado de São Paulo* also have listings and reviews. Both papers publish a weekly guide on Friday.

Tickets for many events are available at booths throughout the city and at theater box offices. Many of these venues offer ticket delivery to your hotel for a surcharge. **Fun by Phone** (☎ 011/5087–3450 ⊕ www.funbynet.com.br) sells ticket to music concerts, theater, and theme parks. **Ticketmaster** (☎ 011/6846–6000 ⊕ www.ticketmaster.com.br) also sells tickets by phone and the Internet. **Show Tickets at Shopping Center Iguatemi** (✉ Av. Brigadeiro Faria Lima 1191, 3rd floor, Jardim Paulistano ☎ 011/

3031–2098) sells tickets to the main concerts and performances in town. It's open Monday–Saturday 10 AM–10 PM and Sunday 2–8.

Classical Music & Opera

Many operas and classical performances take place at Teatro Municipal, Teatro Alfa, and Teatro Cultura Artística (⇨ Concert Halls).

★ **Espaço Promonã** (✉ Av. Juscelino Kubitschek 1830, Itaim Bibi ☎ 011/ 3847–4111) hosts chamber music performances. **Sala São Paulo** (✉ Praça Júlio Prestes, Centro ☎ 011/3337–5414 ⊕ www.osesp.art.br Ⓜ Luz) is one of the most modern concert halls for classical music in Latin America. It's also home to the **São Paulo Symphony** (OSESP).

Built in neoclassic style in 1917 and entirely renovated in 1998, the **Teatro São Pedro** (✉ Rua Barra Funda 171, Barra Funda ☎ 011/3667–0499 ⊕ www.teatrosaopedro.sp.gov.br Ⓜ Marechal Deodoro) is the second-oldest theater in São Paulo. It's one of the best places in the city for chamber concerts and operas. There are free morning events Sunday and Wednesday.

Dance

Dance companies perform at Teatro Alfa, Teatro Cultura Artística, Teatro Municipal, and Via Funchal (⇨ Concert Halls).

Ballet da Cidade (✉ Praça Ramos de Azevedo, Centro ☎ 011/223–3022 ⊕ www.baledacidade.com.br Ⓜ Anhangabaú) is the city's official dance company. It only performs classical acts, mostly in its home theater, the Teatro Municipal. Contemporary pieces are performed by **Ballet Stagium** (✉ Rua Augusta 2985, 2nd floor, Cerqueira César ☎ 011/3062–3451 ⊕ www.stagium.com.br). **Cisne Negro** (✉ Rua das Tabocas 55, Vila Beatriz ☎ 011/3813–4966) is another esteemed contemporary dance company.

Concert Halls

Credicard Hall (✉ Av. das Nações Unidas 17995, Santo Amaro ☎ 011/ 6846–6010 ⊕ www.credicardhall.com.br) is of the biggest theaters in São Paulo and can accommodate up to 7,000 people. It housed concerts by famous Brazilian and international artists. Tickets can be bought by phone or Internet using the services of Ticketmaster. Opera, ballet, music, and symphony performances are held at **Teatro Alfa** (✉ Rua Bento Branco de Andrade Filho 722, Santo Amaro ☎ 011/5693–4000 ⊕ www.teatroalfa.com.br). It's one of the newest theaters in the country, with all the latest sound and lighting technology—and the biggest foreign stars grace the stage. Tickets can be bought by phone and through Show Tickets, then picked up a half hour before the performance.

Fine acoustics make **Teatro Cultura Artística** (✉ Rua Nestor Pestana 196, Cerqueira César ☎ 011/3258–3344 ⊕ www.culturaartistica.com.br Ⓜ Anhangabaú) perfect for classical music performances. It also hosts dance recitals and plays. Avoid walking from the metro stop at night; take a car instead.

Most serious music, ballet, and opera is performed at **Teatro Municipal** (✉ Praça Ramos de Azevedo, Centro ☎ 011/222–8698 or 011/223–3022 ⊕ www.prefeitura.sp.gov.br/theatromunicipal Ⓜ Anhangabaú), a classic theater built in 1911 with an intimate gilt and moss-green-velvet interior. Besides scheduled events, it hosts "guided concerts" (sort of a Classical Music 101) on some Wednesdays, Thursdays, and Fridays at 11 AM. **Teatro da Universidade Católica (TUCA)** (⊠ Rua Monte Alegre 1024, Sumaré ☎011/3670–8453 ⊕www.teatrotuca.com.br), the Catholic University theater, hosts plays and alternative concerts. **Via Funchal** (⊠ Rua Funchal 65, Vila Olímpia ☎011/3846–2300 or 011/3842–6855 ⊕www.viafunchal.com.br) is capable of seating more than 3,000 people, and is the site of many large international music, theater, and dance shows.

Samba Shows

From November to February, many *escolas de samba* (literally "samba schools," which are groups that perform during Carnaval) open their rehearsals to the public. Drummers get in sync with the singers, and everyone learns the lyrics to each year's songs.

Rosas de Ouro (⊠Av. Cel. Euclides Machado 1066, Freguesia do Ó ☎011/3931–4555 ⊕ www.sociedaderosasdeouro.com.br) has one of the most popular rehearsals. Up to 3,000 people at a time attend rehearsals at **Mocidade Alegre** (⊠ Av. Casa Verde 3498, Limão ☎ 011/3857–7525 ⊕ www.mocidadealegre.com.br) just before Carnaval.

Film

Centro Cultural São Paulo (⊠ Rua Vergueiro 1000, Paraíso ☎ 011/3277–3611 Ext. 279 Ⓜ Vergueiro ⊕ www.centrocultural.sp.gov.br) usually shows a series of films centered on a theme. Admission is free or nearly free. It also has plays, concerts, and art exhibits. **Reserva Cultural** (⊠ Av. Paulista 900, Jardim Paulista ☎ 011/3287–3529 ⊕ www.reservacultural.com.br Ⓜ Brigadeiro) has four movie theaters, a small café, a bar, and a nice deck-style restaurant from which you can see—and be seen by—pedestrians in Paulista Avenue.

Brazilian, European, and other non-blockbuster films are shown at the **Espaço Unibanco** (⊠ Rua Augusta 1470/1475, Consolação ☎ 011/3288–6780 Ⓜ Consolação). The **Unibanco ArtePlex** (⊠ Rua Frei Caneca 569, 3rd floor, Consolação ☎011/3472–2365 Ⓜ Consolação ⊕ www.unibancoarteplex.com.br) shows Hollywood, European, and independent films.

SPORTS & THE OUTDOORS

Check the air quality before you practice outdoor sports. During a dry season, the air can be bad. Don't take your cues from the paulistas—their lungs are made of steel.

Auto Racing

Racing fans from all over the world come to São Paulo in September for the **Formule 1** (Formula 1) race every September, bringing this city of 5.0 million cars to heights of spontaneous combustion, especially when a Brazilian driver wins. The race is held at **Autódromo de Interlagos** (⊠Av. Senador Teotônio Vilela 261, Interlagos ☎ 011/5666–8822 ⊕ www.autodromointerlagos.com), which also hosts other kinds of races on weekends. For ticket information on the Formule 1 race, contact the **Con-**

KING RONALDO

BRAZILIANS ARE SO PASSIONATE *about futebol (soccer) that popular wisdom says there are three subjects—soccer, women and religion—not to be discussed at a bar table among friends, to avoid quarrels. Of these, soccer is surely the most important. The sport, which arrived in Brazil in 1894 with immigrant British railroad workers, is as central to Brazilian culture as samba and the beach.*

Soccer is the national passion in no small part thanks to Brazil's world-champion status in 1958, 1962, 1970, 1994, and 2002. The greatest Brazilian soccer players—such as "King" Pelé, as he was known in the 1960s and '70s—are seen as gods, and are treated like royalty. Soccer stars in Brazil are probably more famous than the country¥s president.

The king of the ball in Brazil today is Ronaldo, who in 1994, at age 17, joined the World Cup team. He didn't play in

that game, but went on to score 42 goals in the next two years, in only 13 matches. Shortly afterwards he went to play in Europe, but remained an idol in Brazil, where he is known as "The Phenomenon," and is still a hot item in the press, both for his spectacular performances and his tabloid-worthy personal life.

Many lesser stars bring Brazilians to tears and shouts of joy every Sunday afternoon in thrilling games that can be watched live in the fields or on TV. And though soccer reigns supreme in Brazil, you don't have to be royalty to afford a game—even at the world's largest soccer stadium, Maracanã, in Rio, admission is just US$2.

federação Brasileira de **Automobilismo** (⊠ Rua da Glória 290, 8th floor, Rio de Janeiro, RJ 20241-180 ☎ 021/2221–4895 ⊕ www.cba. org.br).

Golf

The greens fee at the 18-hole **Clube de Campo** (⊠ Praça Rockford 28, Vila Represa ☎ 011/5929–3111 ⊕ www.ccsp.org.br) is R$50, but you need to be introduced by a member. It's open Monday, Tuesday, Thursday, and Friday 7–7. **Golf School** (⊠ Av. Guido Caloi 2160, Santo Amaro ☎ 011/5515–3372) is a driving range that has 40-minute classes. For R$50 you get 100 balls.

Golf & Gym (⊠ Rua Marquês de São Vicente 1700, Barra Funda ☎ 011/ 3611–0080 ⊕ www.golfgym.com.br) has a driving range and a putting green. The fees are R$45 for 30 minutes and 70 balls.

Horse Racing

Thoroughbreds race at the **São Paulo Jockey Club** (⊠ Rua Lineu de Paula Machado 1263, Cidade Jardim ☎ 011/2161–8300 ⊕ www.hcj.com.br), which is open Monday, Wednesday, and Thursday 7:30 PM–11:30 PM and weekends 2–9. Card-carrying Jockey Club members get the best seats, but you can also go there for its elegant restaurant with a nice view.

Soccer

Brazilians' reputation for being obsessed with soccer is rightfully earned. Some paulistas, however, prefer to watch soccer on TV at home or in a bar. São Paulo State has several well-funded teams with some of the country's best players. The four main teams—Corinthians, São Paulo, Palmeiras, and Santos—attract fans from other states. The two biggest stadiums are Morumbi and the municipally run Pacaembu. Covered seats offer the best protection, not only from the elements but also from rowdy spectators. Buy tickets at the stadiums or online at **www.ingressofacil. com.br.** Regular games usually don't sell out, but finals—where you can buy tickets up to five days in advance—always do.

At **Canindé** (✉ Rua Comendador Nestor Pereira 33, Canindé ☎ 011/3315–0400 ⊕ www.portuguesa.com.br), the main attraction, besides the game, are *bolinhos de bacalhau* (salt-cod fritters), popular among the Portuguese immigrants. **Morumbi** (✉ Praça Roberto Gomes Pedrosa s/n, Morumbi ☎ 011/3749–8000 ⊕ www.saopaulofc.net), the home stadium of São Paulo Futebol Clube, has a capacity of 80,000. The first games of the 1950 World Cup were played at the **Pacaembu** (✉ Praça Charles Miller s/n, Pacaembú ☎ 011/3661–9111 Ⓜ Clínicas) stadium, unofficial home of the Corinthians team.

Parque Antártica (✉ Rua Turiassu 1840, Barra Funda ☎ 011/3873–2111 ⊕ www.palmeiras.com.br Ⓜ Barra Funda), the home of Palmeiras since 1920, seats 32,000. The small **Rua Javari** (✉ Rua Javari 117, Moóca ☎ 011/6292–4833 ⊕ www.juventus.com.br Ⓜ Moóca) stadium is where Juventus plays. It's an ideal place to enjoy the stadium's Italian atmosphere—Moóca is a traditionally Italian neighborhood—and eat a cannoli while cheering for the home team.

SHOPPING

Shopping is an attraction in its own right in São Paulo, which is confirmed by the many South Americas who come from all over the continent to browse the city's wares—especially clothing, shoes, and accessories. Stores are usually open weekdays 9–6:30, Saturday 9–1, and are closed Sunday. Mall hours are generally weekdays and Saturday 10–10; malls open on Sunday at around 2 PM.

Areas

In **Centro,** Rua do Arouche is noted for leather goods. The area around Rua João Cachoeira in **Itaim** has evolved from a neighborhood of small clothing factories into a wholesale- and retail-clothing sales district. Several shops on Rua Tabapuã sell small antiques. Also, Rua Dr. Mário Ferraz is stuffed with elegant clothing, gift, and home-decoration stores. In **Jardins,** centering around Rua Oscar Freire, double-parked Mercedes-Benzes and BMWs point the way to the city's fanciest stores, which sell leather items, jewelry, gifts, antiques, and art. Jardins also has many restaurants and beauty salons. Shops that specialize in high-price European antiques are on or around Rua da Consolação. A slew of lower-price antiques stores line Rua Cardeal Arcoverde in **Pinheiros.**

Centers & Malls

D&D Decoração & Design Center (✉ Av. das Nações Unidas 12555, Brooklin ☎ 011/3043–9000 ⊕ www.dedshopping.com.br) shares a building with the World Trade Center and the Gran Meliá hotel. It's loaded with fancy home decorating stores, full-scale restaurants, and fast-food spots. **Shopping Center Ibirapuera** (✉ Av. Ibirapuera 3103, Moema ☎ 011/5095–2300 ⊕ www.ibirapuera.com.br) has more than 500 stores.

★ One of the newest shopping malls in São Paulo, **Shopping Pátio Higienópolis** (✉ Av. Higienópolis 618, Higienópolis ☎ 011/3823–2300 ⊕ www.patiohigienopolis.com.br) is a mixture of old and new architecture styles. It has plenty of shops and restaurants, as well as six movie theaters. **Shopping Center Iguatemi** (✉ Av. Brigadeiro Faria Lima 2232, Jardim Paulistano ☎ 011/3816–6116 ⊕ www.iguatemisaopaulo.com.br) is the city's oldest and most sophisticated mall and has the latest in fashion and fast food. Movie theaters often show films in English with Portuguese subtitles. The Gero Café, built in the middle of the main hall, has a fine menu. **Shopping Center Morumbi** (✉ Av. Roque Petroni Jr. 1089, Morumbi ☎ 011/5189–4500 ⊕ www.morumbishopping.com.br), in the city's fastest-growing area, is giving Iguatemi a run for its money. That said, it houses about the same boutiques, record stores, bookstores, and restaurants.

Markets

Almost every neighborhood has a weekly outdoor food market, complete with loudmouthed hawkers, exotic scents, and mountains of colorful produce. Nine hundred of them happen every week in São Paulo, so you'll be able to hit at least one; ask around to find out when and where the closest one happens.

On Sunday there are **antiques fairs** near the Museu de Arte de São Paulo (MASP) and (in the afternoon) at the Shopping Center Iguatemi's parking lot. Many stall owners have shops and hand out business cards so you can browse throughout the week at your leisure. An **arts and crafts fair** (✉ Praça da República, Centro)—selling jewelry, embroidery, leather goods, toys, clothing, paintings, and musical instruments—takes place Sunday morning. Many booths move over to the nearby Praça da Liberdade in the afternoon, joining vendors selling Japanese-style ceramics, wooden sandals, cooking utensils, food, and bonsai trees. **Flea markets** with second-hand furniture, clothes, and CDs take place on Saturday at the popular Praça Benedito Calixto in Pinheiros (where you can also eat at food stands and listen to music all day long) and on Sunday at the Praça Dom Orione in Bela Vista.

Specialty Shops

Antiques

Antiquário Paulo Vasconcelos (✉ Alameda Gabriel Monteiro da Silva 1935, Jardins ☎ 011/3062–2444) has folk art and 18th- and 19th-century Brazilian furniture, among other treasures. **Edwin Leonard** (✉ Rua

Oscar Freire 146, Jardins ☎ 011/3088–1394) is a collective of three dealers that sell Latin American and European antiques.

Head to **Patrimônio** (✉ Alameda Ministro Rocha Azevedo 1068, Jardins ☎ 011/3064–1750) for Brazilian antiques at reasonable prices. It also sells some Indian artifacts as well as modern furnishings crafted from iron. **Pedro Corrêa do Lago** (✉ Rua João Cachoeira 267, Itaim Bibi ☎ 011/3082–0066) represents Sotheby's. The shop sells and auctions rare and used books, as well as antique maps, prints, and drawings of Brazil. **Renée Behar Antiques** (✉ Rua Peixoto Gomide 2088, Jardins ☎ 011/3085–3622 ⊕ www.reneebehar.com.br) has 18th- and 19th-century antiques and temporary exhibitions of antique pieces.

Art

Arte Aplicada (✉ Rua Haddock Lobo 1406, Jardins ☎ 011/3062–5128 ⊕ www.arteaplicada.com.br) is the place for Brazilian paintings, sculptures, and prints. The staff at **Galeria Fortes Vilaça** (✉ Rua Fradique Coutinho 1500, Vila Madalena ☎ 011/3032–7066 ⊕ www.fortesvilaca.com.br) has an eye for the works of up-and-coming Brazilian artists.

At **Espaço Cultural Ena Beçak** (✉ Rua Oscar Freire 440, Jardins ☎ 011/3088–7322 ⊕ www.enabecak.com.br) you can shop for Brazilian prints, sculptures, and paintings and then stop in at the café. If *art naïf* is your thing, **Galeria Jacques Ardies** (✉ Rua Morgado de Mateus 579, Vila Mariana ☎ 011/5539–7500 ⊕ www.ardies.com Ⓜ Paraíso) is a must. As the name suggests, art naïf is simple, with a primitive and handcrafted look.

At **Galeria Renot** (✉ Alameda Ministro Rocha Azevedo 1327, Jardins ☎ 011/3083–5933 ⊕ www.renot.com.br) you find oil paintings by such Brazilian artists as Vicente Rego Monteiro, Di Cavalcanti, Cícero Dias, and Anita Malfatti. Many a trend has been set at **Mônica Filgueiras Galeria** (✉ Rua Bela Cintra 1533, Jardins ☎ 011/3082–5292), which has all types of art, but mostly paintings and sculpture.

Beauty

Anna Pegova (✉ Alameda Lorena 1582, Jardins ☎ 011/3081–2402 ⊕ www.annapegova.com.br) is a French beauty-product brand famous in Brazil. The shop has hair, skin, face, and body products for men and ★ women. The Jardins store is one of the best. Brazilian brand **O Boticário** (✉ Rua Pamplona 1551 store 20, Jardins ☎ 011/3885–8623 ⊕ www.oboticario.com.br) was created by dermatologists and pharmacists from Curitiba in the 1970s. Today it is one of the biggest franchising companies in the country, with products for men, women, and children. The company's Fundação O Boticário de Proteção a Natureza (Boticário Foundation for Nature Protection) funds ecological projects throughout Brazil. The shops can be found in most neighborhoods and malls in the city.

Beachwear

Beira Mar Beachwear (✉ Rua José Paulino 592, Bom Retiro ☎ 011/222–7999 ⊕ www.maiosbeiramar.com.br Ⓜ Tiradentes) was founded in 1948. Since then it has been known for innovative and good-quality products. The Brazilian brand has its own factory and produces a great variety of bikinis and swimming suits. **Track & Field** (✉ Rua Oscar Freire

959, Jardins ☎ 011/3062–4457 or 3048–1277 ⊕ www.tf.com.br) is a very good place to buy beachwear and sports clothing. The store sells bikinis and swimsuits from **Cia. Marítima** (⊕ www.ciamaritima.com. br), a famous Brazilian beachwear brand. The shops are in almost every mall in São Paulo.

Clothing

FOR KIDS Younger family members are the stars at **Petistil** (⊠ Av. Brigadeiro Faria Lima 2232, Shopping Center Iguatemi, Jardim Paulistano ☎ 011/ 3812–5073 ⊕ www.petistil.com.br), which sells colorful clothes for infants and children up to 11 years old.

FOR MEN & WOMEN Famous Brazilian designer **Alexandre Herchcovitch** (⊠ Rua Haddock Lobo 1151, Jardins ☎ 011/3063–2888 ⊕ www.herchcovitch.com.br) ★ sells prêt-à-porter and tailor-made clothes at his store. At **Cori** (⊠ Rua Oscar Freire 791, Jardins ☎ 011/3081–5223 ⊕ www.cori.com.br) everyday outfits with classic lines are the specialty.

Designer-label boutique **Daslu** (⊠ Avenida Chedid Jafet 131, Itaim Bibi ☎ 011/3841–4000 ⊕ www.daslu.com.br) has built a 17,000-square-meter (183,000-square-foot) megastore of luxurious items: clothes from Chanel, Dior, Pucci, Vuitton, Valentino, Armani, as well as jewelry, purses, objects, shoes, cars—even boats! **Ellus** (⊠ Rua Oscar Freire 990, Jardins ☎ 011/3061–2900 ⊕ www.ellus.com.br) is a good place to buy men's and women's jeans, sportswear, and street wear.

Fórum (⊠ Rua Oscar Freire 916, Jardins ☎ 011/3085–6269 ⊕ www. forum.com.br) has evening attire for young men and women, but it also sells sportswear and shoes. **Richard's** (⊠ Rua Oscar Freire 1129, Jardins ☎ 011/3082–5399) is one of Brazil's best lines of sportswear. Collections include outfits suitable for the beach or the mountains. The prices for suits, jackets, jeans, and some women's clothing (silk blouses, for example) at **Vila Romana Factory Store** (⊠ Via Anhanguera, Km 17.5, Osasco ☎ 011/3604–5293 ⊠ Av. Ibirapuera 3103, Shopping Ibirapuera, Moema ☎ 011/5535–1808 ⊕ www.vilaromana. com.br) are unbeatable. The store is a 40-minute drive from Centro. In-town mall branches are more convenient, but prices are higher. **Zoomp** (⊠ Rua Oscar Freire 995, Jardins ☎ 011/3064–1556 ⊕ www.zoomp. com.br) is famous for its jeans and high-quality street wear. Customers from 13 to 35 mix and match the clothes, creating some unusual combinations.

FOR WOMEN **Anacapri** (⊠ Alameda dos Arapanés 83, Moema ☎ 011/5052–4329) sells plus-size women's underwear, swimsuits, and clothes. **Le Lis Blanc** (⊠ Rua Oscar Freire 809, Jardins ☎ 011/3083–2549) is Brazil's exclusive purveyor of the French brand Vertigo. Look for party dresses in velvet and sheer fabrics. If you have money in your pocket, shop at **Maria Bonita** (⊠ Rua Oscar Freire 702, Jardins ☎ 011/3082–6649 ⊕ www.mariabonitaextra.com.br), which has elegant and fun women's clothes. At Maria Bonita Extra, right next door, the prices are a little lower.

The women's clothing at **Reinaldo Lourenço** (✉ Rua Bela Cintra 2167, Jardins ☎ 011/3085–8150 ⊕ www.reinaldolourenco.com.br) is sophisticated and of good quality. Young women are intrigued by the unique high-fashion designs of the swimsuits, dresses, shorts, shirts, and pants at **Uma** (✉ Rua Girassol 273, Vila Madalena ☎011/3813–5559 ⊕www. uma.com.br). At **Viva Vida** (✉ Rua Fidalga 593, Vila Madalena ☎ 011/ 3811–1840 ⊕ www.vivavida.com.br) long evening dresses—many in shiny, sexy fabrics—steal the show.

Handicrafts

Art Índia (✉ Rua Augusta 1371, Loja 117, Cerqueira César ☎ 011/ 3283–2102 Ⓜ Consolação) is a government-run shop that sells Indian arts and crafts made by tribes throughout Brazil. As its name suggests, **Casa do Amazonas** (✉ Al. Jurupis 460, Moema ☎ 011/5051–3098) has a wide selection of products from the Amazon. Since 1920, **Galeria de Arte Brasileira** (✉ Alameda Lorena 2163, Jardins ☎011/3062–9452 and 3085–8769 ⊕ www.galeriaartebrasileira.com.br) has specialized in art and handicrafts from all over Brazil. Look for objects made of pau-brasil wood, hammocks, jewelry, T-shirts, *marajoara* pottery (from the Amazon), and lace.

Marcenaria Trancoso (✉ Rua Harmonia 233, Vila Madalena ☎011/ 3032–3505 ⊕ www.marcenariatrancoso.com.br Ⓜ Vila Madalena) sells wooden products that are an elegant mixture of interior design and handicraft. At **Mundareu** (✉ Rua Mourato Coelho 988, Vila Madalena ☎ 011/3032–4649 ⊕ www.mundareu.org.br) browse through quality products made by different types of artisans from all over Brazil.

Jewelry

★ An internationally known Brazilian brand for jewelry, **H. Stern** (✉ Rua Oscar Freire 652, Jardins ☎011/3068–8082 ⊕ www.hstern.com.br) has shops in more than 30 countries. This one has designs made especially for the Brazilian stores. Carioca **Antonio Bernardo** (✉ Rua Bela Cintra 2063, Consolação ☎ 011/3083–5622 ⊕ www.antoniobernardo.com. br) is one of the most famous jewelry designers in Brazil. He can create custom pieces with gold, silver, and other precious stones and metals. The world famous **Tiffany & Co.** (✉ Rua Haddock Lobo 1594, Jardins ☎011/3081–8100 ⊕ www.tiffany.com) sells exclusive pieces for the very wealthy. Go for the diamonds—you know you want to.

Leather Goods & Luggage

One of the biggest brands for luggage and leather goods in Brazil, **Le Postiche** (✉ Av. Prof. Ascendino Reis 965, Vila Mariana ☎ 011/ 5082–4388 ⊕ www.lepostiche.com.br) has 81 shops around the country. You can find one in almost any mall in São Paulo.

An excellent chain store for travel and leather goods, **Comtesse** (✉ Rua Treze de Maio 1947, Shopping Paulista, Paraíso ☎ 011/3284–5726 ⊕ www.comtesse.com.br Ⓜ Paraíso) can also be found at major shopping malls. **Inovathi** (✉ Rua Oscar Freire 497, Jardins ☎011/3062–2692 ⊕ www.inovathi.com.br) has leather accessories at good prices. It's in nearly every mall in town.

Music

Baratos Afins (✉ Av. São João 439, 2nd floor, no. 314–318, Centro ☎ 011/223–3629 ⊕ www.baratosafins.com.br Ⓜ República) is heaven for music collectors. Opened in 1978, it's also a record label and was the brainchild of Arnaldo Baptista, guitar player in the influential 1960's Brazilian rock band Os Mutantes. The store sells all kinds of music, but specializes in Brazilian popular music (MPB). If you are looking for rare records, ask for the owner, Luiz Calanca.

In shopping malls, the best option is **Painel Musical** (✉ Av. Ibirapuera 3103, Shopping Ibirapuera, Jurupis floor, store 135, Moema ☎ 011/5561–9981 ⊕ www.painelmusical.com.br), a small record shop that carries CDs and DVDs. It usually has a good selection of instrumental Brazilian music and local rock. Browse through more than 100,000 records at **Ventania** (✉ Rua 24 de Maio 188, 1st floor, store 113, Centro ☎ 011/222–6273 ⊕ www.ventania.com.br Ⓜ República), a huge store specializing in MPB. You can find old vinyls 78s, contemporary CDs and everything in between.

SÃO PAULO ESSENTIALS

Transportation

Getting around the city by subway is quick and simple. Buses can be hard to navigate if you don't speak Portuguese. Take cabs or drive to farther-flung places.

For more information about transportation, *see* Smart Travel Tips A to Z, *at* the front of this book.

BY AIR

Nearly all international flights stop in São Paulo, so practically every airline that flies to Brazil flies to São Paulo, and it's very easy to get from São Paulo to everywhere else in Brazil. For airline information *see* Air Travel, *in* Smart Travel Tips A to Z.

AIRPORTS São Paulo's international airport, Aeroporto Cumbica, is in the suburb of Guarulhos, 30 km (19 mi) and a 45-minute drive (longer during rush hour or on rainy days) northeast of Centro. Aeroporto Congonhas, 14 km (9 mi) south of Centro (a 15- to 45-minute drive, depending on traffic), serves regional airlines, including the Rio–São Paulo shuttle.

🛫 Airports **Aeroporto Congonhas** ☎ 011/5090-9000. **Aeroporto Cumbica** ☎ 011/6445-2945.

AIRPORT EMTU buses—blue air-conditioned vehicles—shuttle between Cumbica
TRANSFERS Airport and Congonhas (5:30 AM–11:10 PM, every 30 minutes; midnight–5:30 AM, every 90 minutes) as well as between Cumbica and the Tietê bus terminal (5 AM–11:10 PM, every 50–60 minutes); the downtown Praça da República (5:40 AM–11:10 PM, every 30 minutes); and the Hotel Maksoud Plaza (6:10 AM–11:10 PM, every 60–70 minutes), stopping at most major hotels around Avenida Paulista. There are also lines that connect Cumbica to the Barra Funda terminal and the Shopping Eldorado. The cost is R$24.

The sleek, blue-and-white, air-conditioned Guarucoop radio taxis take you from Cumbica to downtown for around R$80. *Comum* (regular) taxis charge R$65 from Cumbica and around R$25 from Congonhas. 🚍**EMTU** ☎ 0800/19-0088 or 011/6445-2505 ⊕ www.airportbusservice.com.br. **Guaru-coop** ☎ 011/6440-7070.

BY BUS

ARRIVING & DEPARTING
All bus terminals in the city of São Paulo are connected to metro stations. The three bus stations in São Paulo serve more than 1,100 destinations combined. The huge main station—serving all major Brazilian cities (with trips to Rio every 10 minutes during the day and every half hour at night, until 2 AM) as well as Argentina, Uruguay, Chile, and Paraguay—is the Terminal Tietê in the north, on the Marginal Tietê Beltway. Terminal Jabaquara, near Congonhas Airport, serves coastal towns. Terminal Barra Funda, in the west, near the Memorial da América Latina, has buses to and from western Brazil. All stations have metro stops. You can buy tickets at the stations; although those for Rio de Janeiro can be bought a few minutes before departure, it's best to buy tickets in advance for other destinations and during holiday seasons.

Socicam, a private company, runs all of the bus terminals in the city of São Paulo and lists schedules on its Web site. Click on "*consulta de partidas de ônibus.*"
🚍**Socicam** ☎ 011/3235-0322 ⊕ www.socicam.com.br. **EMTU** ☎ 0800/19-0088 or 011/6445-2505. **Terminal Barra Funda** ✉ Rua Mário de Andrade 664, Barra Funda ☎ 011/3235-0322 ⊕ www.socicam.com.br Ⓜ Barra Funda. **Terminal Jabaquara** ✉ Rua Jequitibás, Jabaquara ☎ 011/3235-0322 ⊕ www.socicam.com.br Ⓜ Jabaquara. **Terminal Tietê** ✉ Av. Cruzeiro do Sul, Santana ☎ 011/3235-0322 ⊕ www.socicam.com.br Ⓜ Tietê.

GETTING AROUND
Municipal bus service is frequent and covers the entire city, but regular buses are overcrowded at rush hour and when it rains. If you don't speak Portuguese, it can be hard to figure out the system and the stops. Stops are clearly marked, but routes are spelled out only on the buses themselves. Buses do not stop at every bus stop, so if you are waiting, you'll have to flag one down.

The fare is R$2. You enter at the front of the bus, pay the *cobrador* (fare collector) in the middle, and exit from the rear of the bus. To pay, you can use either money or the electronic card *bilhete único,* introduced in 2004. The card allows you to take three buses in two hours for the price of one fare. Cards can be bought and reloaded at special booths at major bus terminals or at lottery shops.

For bus numbers and names, routes, and schedules, go to the (Portuguese-language) Web site of Transporte Público de São Paulo, the city's public transport agency, or purchase the *Guia São Paulo Ruas,* published by Quatro Rodas and sold at newsstands and bookstores for about R$30. 🚍**Transporte Público de São Paulo** ☎ 156 ⊕ www.sptrans.com.br.

BY CAR

ARRIVING & DEPARTING
The main São Paulo–Rio de Janeiro highway is the Via Dutra (BR 116 North), which has been repaved and enlarged in places. The speed limit is 120 kph (74 mph) along most of it, and although it has many tolls,

there are many call boxes you can use if your car breaks down. The modern Rodovia Ayrton Senna (SP 70) charges reasonable tolls, runs parallel to the Dutra for about a quarter of the way, and is an excellent alternative route. The 429-km (279-mi) trip takes five hours. If you have time, consider the longer, spectacular coastal Rio-Santos Highway (SP 55 and BR 101). It's an easy two-day drive, and you can stop midway at the colonial city of Paraty, in Rio de Janeiro State.

Other main highways are the Castelo Branco (SP 280), which links the southwestern part of the state to the city; the Via Anhanguera (SP 330), which originates in the state's rich northern agricultural region, passing through the university town of Campinas; SP 310, which also runs from the farming heartland; BR 116 south, which comes up from Curitiba (a 408-km/265-mi trip); plus the Via Anchieta (SP 150) and the Rodovia Imigrantes (SP 160), parallel roads that run to the coast, each operating one-way on weekends and holidays.

GETTING AROUND Driving in the city isn't recommended because of the heavy traffic (nothing moves at rush hour, especially when it rains), daredevil drivers, and inadequate parking. If you do opt to drive, there are a few things to keep in mind:

The high-speed beltways along the Rio Pinheiros and Rio Tietê rivers—called Marginal Tietê and Marginal Pinheiros—sandwich the main part of São Paulo. Avenida 23 de Maio runs south from Centro and beneath the Parque do Ibirapuera via the Ayrton Senna Tunnel. You can take avenidas Paulista, Brasil, and Faria Lima southwest to the Morumbi, Brooklin, Itaim, and Santo Amaro neighborhoods, respectively. The Elevado Costa e Silva, also called Minhocão, is an elevated road that connects Centro with Avenida Francisco Matarazzo in the west.

In most commercial neighborhoods you must buy hourly tickets (called Cartão Zona Azul) to park on the street during business hours. Buy them at newsstands, not from people on the street. Booklets of 10 tickets cost R$20. Fill out each ticket—you'll need one for every hour you plan to park—with the car's license plate and the time you initially parked. Leave the tickets in the car's window so they're visible to officials from outside. After business hours or at any time near major sights, people may offer to watch your car. If you don't pay these "caretakers," there's a chance they'll damage your car (R$3 is enough to keep your car's paint job intact). But to truly ensure your car's safety park in a guarded lot, where rates are R$5–R$7 for the first hour and R$1–R$2 each hour thereafter.

Invest in the *Guia São Paulo Ruas,* published by Quatro Rodas, which shows every street in the city. It's sold at newsstands and bookstores for about R$30.

🚘 Rental Agencies **Avis** ✉ Rua da Consolação 335, Centro ☎ 011/3259–6868 or 0800/19–8456. **Hertz** ✉ Rua da Consolação 439, Centro ☎ 011/3258–9384 or 4336–7300. **Localiza** ✉ Rua da Consolação 419, Centro ☎ 011/3231–3055 or 0800/99–2000.

BY SUBWAY

When you buy 10 tickets at once; note that ticket sellers often can't change large bills. You insert the ticket into the turnstile at the platform entrance, and it's returned to you only if there's unused fare on it. Transfers within the metro system are free, as are bus-to-metro (or vice-versa) transfers. You can buy a *bilhete integração* (integration ticket) on buses or at metro stations for R$3.60. You can print maps from the English-language Web site of the Metrô, where you can also find ticket prices and schedules.

Metrô ☎ 011/3286-0111 ⊕ www.metro.sp.gov.br.

BY TAXI

Taxis in São Paulo are white. Owner-driven taxis are generally well maintained and reliable, as are radio taxis. Fares start at R$3.20 and run R$1.80 for each kilometer (½ mi) or R$0.40 for every minute sitting in traffic. After 8 PM and on weekends fares rise by 25%. You'll pay a tax if the cab leaves the city, as is the case with trips to Cumbica Airport. Good radio-taxi companies usually accept credit cards, but you must call ahead and request the service. Delta takes calls in English.

Coopertaxi ☎ 011/6941-2555. **Delta Rádio Táxi** ☎ 011/5572-6611. **Ligue-Taxi** ☎ 011/3866-3030.

BY TRAIN

Most travel to the interior of the state is done by bus or automobile. Still, a few places are served by trains. Trains from Estação da Luz, near 25 de Março, run to some metropolitan suburbs and small interior towns. Trains from Estação Barra Funda serve towns in the west of the state. Estação Júlio Prestes, in Campos Elíseos, has trains to the southeast and some suburbs. Estação Brás serves the suburbs only.

Estação Barra Funda ⊠ Rua Mário de Andrade 664, Barra Funda ☎ 011/3392-3616 Ⓜ Barra Funda. **Estação Júlio Prestes** ⊠ Praça Júlio Prestes 148, Campos Elíseos ☎ 0800/55-0121. **Estação da Luz** ⊠ Praça da Luz 1, Luz ☎ 0800/55-0121 Ⓜ Luz. **Estação Brás** ⊠ Praça Agente Cícero, Brás ☎ 0800/55-0121 Ⓜ Brás.

Contacts & Resources

BANKS & EXCHANGE SERVICES

Avenida Paulista is the home of many banks (generally open 10–4), including Citibank. For currency exchange services without any extra fees, try Action. In Centro you can exchange money at Banco do Brasil and at Banespa. Several banks have automatic-teller machines (ATMs) that accept international bank cards and dispense reais.

Some banks accept only cards with Visa/Plus logos and others accept only cards with MasterCard/Cirrus logos. Banco24horas ATMs usually accept all cards, including American Express. *See* "Money Matters" *in* Smart Travel Tips A to Z for more information.

Action ⊠ Aeroporto Cumbica, TPS2 arrival floor, Guarulhos ☎ 011/6445-4458 ⊠ Rua Augusta 2766, Jardins ☎ 011/3086-1966 ⊠ Shopping Paulista, Rua 13 de Maio 1947, Paraíso ☎ 011/3288-4222 ⊕ www.actioncambio.com.br Ⓜ Brigadeiro. **Banco do Brasil** ⊠ Av. Paulista 2163, Jardins ☎ 011/3066-9322 ⊕ www.bancodobrasil.com.br Ⓜ Consolação. **Bank Boston** ⊠ Av. Paulista 800, Jardins ☎ 011/3285-3477 ⊕ www.bankboston.com.br Ⓜ Brigadeiro. **Citibank** ⊠ Av. Paulista 1111, Jardins ☎ 011/5576-1000 ⊕ www.citibank.com.br Ⓜ Trianon-Masp. **Santander Banespa** ⊠ Av. Paulista 2064 Jardins ☎ 011/3016-9955 ⊕ www.banespa.com.br Ⓜ Consolação.

EMERGENCIES

The three main pharmacies have more than 20 stores, each open 24 hours—Droga Raia, Drogaria São Paulo, and Drogasil. The police department in charge of tourist affairs, Delegacia de Turismo, is open weekdays 8–8.

🚩 Hotlines **Ambulance** ☎ 192. **Delegacia de Turismo (Tourism Police)** ✉ Av. São Luís 91, Centro ☎ 011/3214-0209 Ⓜ República. **Fire** ☎ 193. **Police** ☎ 190.

🚩 Hospitals **Albert Einstein** ✉ Av. Albert Einstein 627, Morumbi ☎ 011/3747-1233 ⊕ www.einstein.br. **Beneficência Portuguesa** ✉ Rua Maestro Cardim 769, Paraíso ☎ 011/3253-5022 ⊕ www.beneficencia.org.br Ⓜ Vergueiro. **Sírio Libanês** ✉ Rua. D. Adma Jafet 91, Bela Vista ☎ 011/3155-0200 ⊕ www.hsl.org.br.

🚩 24-Hour Pharmacies **Droga Raia** ✉ Rua José Maria Lisboa 645, Jardim Paulistano ☎ 011/3884-8235 or 011/3237-5000 (delivery) ⊕ www.drogaraia.com.br. **Drogaria São Paulo** ✉ Av. Angélica 1465, Higienópolis ☎ 011/3667-6291 ⊕ www.drogariasaopaulo. com.br. **Drogasil** ✉ Av. Brigadeiro Faria Lima 2726, Cidade Jardim ☎ 011/3812-6276 or 011/3767-2222 (delivery) ⊕ www.drogasil.com.br.

INTERNET

Internet service charges range from R$4 to R$8 per hour.

🚩 Internet Cafés **Coffee & Book at Saraiva Megastore** ✉ Shopping Morumbi, Av. Roque Petroni Jr. 1089, Morumbi ☎ 011/5181-7574 ⊕ www.livrariasaraiva.com.br. **Cyber Games e Internet** ✉ Rua Oscar Freire 1928, Pinheiros ☎ 011/3891-2526 ⊕ www. cyberlan.com.br Ⓜ Sumaré. **Frans Café at Fnac** ✉ Av. Pedroso de Morais 858, Pinheiros ☎ 011/4501-3000. **Monkey** ✉ Rua da Consolação 2961, Jardins ☎ 011/3085-4646 ⊕ www.monkey.com.br.

MAIL & SHIPPING

The central branch of the *correio* (post office) is in Centro, but there are several others throughout the city.

🚩 Post Office **Correio** ✉ Rua Líbero Badaró 595, Centro ⊕ www.correios.com.br Ⓜ São Bento ✉ Alameda Santos 2224, Jardins Ⓜ Consolação.

🚩 Express Services **DHL** ✉ Rua da Consolação 2721, Jardins ☎ 011/3618-3200 ⊕ www. dhl.com.br Ⓜ Consolação. **FedEx** ✉ Av. São Luís 187, Loja 45, Centro ☎ 011/5641-7788 ⊕ www.fedex.com.br Ⓜ República.

TOUR OPTIONS

You can hire a bilingual guide through a travel agency or hotel concierge (about R$15 an hour with a four-hour minimum), or you can design your own walking tour with the aid of information provided at Anhembi booths around the city. Anhembi also offers Sunday tours of museums, parks, and Centro that are less expensive than those offered in hotels. The tourist board (⇨ Visitor Information, *below*) has three half-day Sunday bus tours, one covering the parks, one centered on the museums, and one focused on the historical downtown area. Officially, none of the board's guides speaks English; however, it may be able to arrange something on request.

Gol Tour Viagens e Turismo has custom tours as well as car tours for small groups. A half-day city tour costs about R$40 a person (group rate); a night tour—including a samba show, dinner, and drinks—costs around R$100; and day trips to the beach or the colonial city of Embu cost R$80–R$90. Easygoing has fly-and-dine tours that include a helicopter trip and dinner. If you prefer something down-to-earth, try the carriage tours with Carruagens São Paulo. They tour the Centro Novo (New Downtown) or Centro Velho, or (Old Downtown). Both are available in English if you reserve by phone. The price is R$40 per person, plus R$35 per group for an English-speaking guides. For general sightseeing tours, try Check Point, whose daily tours are R$400 for four people.

🏷**Carruagens São Paulo** ☎ 011/3237-4976 or 011/9770-7311 ⊕ www.carruagemsaopaulo. com.br. **Check Point** ☎ 011/6091-1316. **Easygoing** ☎ 011/3801-9540 ⊕ www.easygoing. com.br. **Gol Tour Viagens e Turismo** ☎ 011/3256-2388 ⊕ www.goltour.com.br Ⓜ República. **Terra Nobre** ☎ 011/3662-1505 ⊕ www.terranobre.com.br.

BIKING TOURS Night Biker's Club has tours of the city at night. Sampa Bikers has city tours and excursions outside town. A day tour starts at R$50, including transport and lunch.

🏷 **Night Biker's Club** ✉ Rua Pacheco de Miranda 141, Moema ☎ 011/3871-2100 ⊕ www.nightbikers.com. **Sampa Bikers** ✉ Rua Baluarte 672, Vila Olímpia ☎ 011/ 3045-2722 ⊕ www.sampabikers.com.br.

VISITOR INFORMATION

The most helpful contact is the São Paulo Convention and Visitors Bureau, open 9–6. The sharp, business-minded director, Orlando de Souza, speaks English flawlessly and is extremely knowledgeable. Branches of the city-operated Anhembi Turismo e Eventos da Cidade de São Paulo are open daily 9–6.

The bureaucracy-laden Secretaria de Esportes e Turismo do Estado de São Paulo, open weekdays 9–6, is less helpful, but has maps and information about the city and state of São Paulo. SEST also has a booth at the arrivals terminal in Cumbica airport; it's open daily 9 AM–10 PM.

🏷 **Anhembi Turismo e Eventos da Cidade de São Paulo** ✉ Anhembi Convention Center, Av. Olavo Fontoura 1209, Santana ☎ 011/6224-0400 ⊕ www.cidadedesaopaulo.com ✉ Praça da República at Rua 7 de Abril, Centro Ⓜ República ✉ Av. Paulista, across from MASP, Cerqueira César Ⓜ Trianon-Masp ✉ Av. Brigadeiro Faria Lima, in front of Shopping Center Iguatemi, Jardim Paulista ✉ Av. Ribeiro de Lima 99, Luz Ⓜ Luz ✉ bus station, Tietê Ⓜ Tietê ✉ Cumbica Airport Terminals 1 and 2, Aeroporto de Guarulhos. **São Paulo Convention and Visitors Bureau** ✉ Alameda Ribeirão Preto 130, conjunto 121, Jardins ☎ 011/3289-7588 ⊕ www.visitesaopaulo.com. **Secretaria Estadual de Turismo do Estado de São Paulo** ✉ Rua Guaianazes 1058, Campos Elíseos ☎ 011/ 221-0474 ⊕ www.saopaulo.sp.gov.br/turismo.

Side Trips from São Paulo

WORD OF MOUTH

"I would recommend a trip from São Paulo to Campos de Jordão, not too far. A beautiful resort in the mountains."

—Larry

"Go to Ilhabela—just a great place. Amazingly beautiful! Go to Ubatuba, the town is not very nice but it has some wonderful beaches. These places are on the Rio–Santos Road. It runs along the coast from Rio de Janeiro to Santos (near São Paulo). It is one of the most beautiful roads I ever traveled."

—Alet

Updated by
Gabriela Dias
and Eduardo
Acquarone

SÃO PAULO'S SURROUNDINGS ARE PERFECT FOR ALL TYPES OF GETAWAYS.
The state has the best highways in the country, making it easy to travel
by car or bus to its many small, beautiful beaches, and even beyond to
neighboring states (Paraná, Rio de Janeiro, and Minas Gerais). Although most sandy stretches require one- or two-hour drives, good side
trips from the city can be as close as the 30-minute trip to Embu.

Embu is famous for its furniture stores, and artisans from throughout
Brazil sell their wares at its enormous weekend crafts fair; expect to see
all the sights in one afternoon. Also less than an hour away, 1500s Santana de Parnaíba mixes historical settings and regional attractions with
good restaurants.

For a weekend of relaxation, soak up the healing properties of Águas
de São Pedro's spas and springs. Farther away, in Brotas, you can go
white-water rafting or hike past waterfalls. If you like mountains, head
up in another direction: Campos de Jordão, where cafés and clothing
stores are often crowded with oh-so-chic *paulistanos* (natives of São Paulo
city; inhabitants of São Paulo State are called *paulistas*). Favor the
state's North Shore and Ilhabela (the name means "beautiful island"),
if you prefer the beach. The island is part of the Mata Atlântica (Atlantic Rain Forest) and has many waterfalls, trails, and diving spots.

History

The first inhabitants of the region that is now São Paulo State were the
Gaurani, Kaingang, Pankararu, and other indigenous tribes. In 1532 the
Portuguese made their first permanent settlement in the port town of
São Vicente. Sugarcane was farmed in the surrounding areas, and
shipped from São Vicente. The city of São Paulo was first settled by Jesuit missionaries bent on converting the natives, in 1554. Bandeirantes
(literally, "explorers") followed soon after, capturing native people to
work as slaves on sugar plantations, looking for gold, and returning escaped slaves. In the process, the bandeirantes "discovered" areas that
later became developed communities.

In the 19th century, farming, first of sugarcane, and then of coffee, was
São Paulo's major industry, and brought prosperity to the region. Most
farms congregated near the rich-soil areas around the Tietê and Paraíba
do Sul rivers. Unlike some other regions of Brazil, São Paulo was prepared for the abolition of slavery in 1888, and had contracted Italian
immigrants to work on the plantations, providing a fairly smooth tran-
sition. Between 1882 and 1934, Brazil received 4.5 million immigrants;
nearly half of them settled in São Paulo State thanks to government programs recruiting them to work on plantations.

At the beginning of the 20th century, the state's eponymous capital became the center for industry in Brazil, as factories were built at a rapid
pace, mostly by an immigrant workforce. By mid-century, São Paulo was
one of the largest industrialized centers in Latin America and the state
with the highest population in Brazil, thanks in part to mass immigration from within Brazil.

4

Beaches São Paulo has some of the most beautiful beaches in the country, especially on the North Shore—the stretch of land along the Rio-Santos Highway which unites the states of São Paulo and Rio de Janeiro. From surfer paradises such as Itamambuca, in Ubatuba, to small, sandy coves embraced by mountains and Atlantic rain forest such as Barra do Sahy, there's almost one beach for every taste. And don't forget the islands off the coast, like gorgeous Ilhabela.

Historic Towns Part of Brazil's colonial and rural history lies in São Paulo's cities outside the capital, like Embu and Santana de Parnaíba. They may not be as rich in impressive architecture as Minas Gerais's historic towns, but they certainly provide you with an idea of what it was like to live in 17th- to 18th-century Brazil.

Nature and Wildlife Luxuriant forests combine with impressive bodies of water and wildlife in São Paulo State. Trees, springs, waterfalls, and rivers abound in Águas de São Pedro, Brotas, and Ilhabela, where you can enjoy outdoor activities like diving and trekking. For mountains, fishing, and wildlife, try Campos de Jordão.

Today São Paulo is the richest and most multicultural state in the country. It has the largest Japanese community outside of Japan (an estimated 1 million people), about 1 million people of Middle Eastern descent, and about 6 million people of Italian descent.

About the Restaurants
Restaurants in coastal towns tend to be of the rustic beach-café sort, and predictably serve lots of seafood. Some of the best restaurants in the state, outside the capital, are in Campos do Joardão, a popular paulistano mountain retreat.

About the Hotels
Most of the towns in this chapter can be done as day trips from São Paulo—and the city has, by far, the best lodgings in the state. Elsewhere you'll generally find basic pousadas, with the occasional gems like Maison Joly and Pousada do Hibiscus in Ilhabela and Hotel Estalagem Quinta das Cachoeiras in Brotas.

WHAT IT COSTS In Reais					
	$$$$	**$$$**	**$$**	**$**	**¢**
RESTAURANTS	over R$60	R$45–R$60	R$30–R$45	R$15–R$30	under R$15
HOTELS	over R$500	R$375–R$500	R$250–R$375	R$125–R$250	under R$125

Restaurant prices are for a dinner entrée. Hotel prices are for two people in a standard double room in high season, excluding taxes.

THE NORTH SHORE

The cleanest and best *praias* (beaches) in São Paulo State are along what is known as the Litoral Norte (North Shore). Mountains and bits of Atlantic rain forest hug numerous small, sandy coves. Some of the North Shore's most beautiful houses line the Rio-Santos Highway (SP 055) on the approach to Maresias. On weekdays when school is in session, the beaches are gloriously deserted.

The city of São Paulo rests on a plateau 72 km (46 mi) inland. If you can avoid traffic, getaways are fairly quick on the parallel Imigrantes (BR 160) or Anchieta (BR 150) highways, each of which becomes one-way on weekends and holidays. Buses from São Paulo's Jabaquara terminal, near the Congonhas Airport, run along the coast.

Beaches often don't have bathrooms or phones right on the sands, but several rent beach umbrellas or chairs, especially during the summer and on holidays and weekends. They generally do have restaurants nearby, or at least vendors selling sandwiches, soft drinks, and beer.

São Sebastião

38 *204 km (127 mi) southeast of São Paulo*

São Sebastião stretches along 100 km (62 mi) of the North Shore. Its bays, islands, and beaches attract everyone from the youngsters who flock to Maresias and Camburi to the families who favor Barra do Sahy. Boating enthusiasts, hikers, and wildlife-seekers also come here, especially on weekends, when hotels are often crowded. Nightlife is good here—the best is in Boiçucanga. The "beautiful island" of Ilhabela (⇨ *below*) is just a 15-minute boat ride away from downtown São Sebastião.

★ Families with young children favor small, quiet **Praia da Barra do Sahy** (⊠ Rio-Santos Hwy. (SP 055), 157 km/97 mi southeast of São Paulo). Its narrow strip of sand (with a bay and a river on one side and rocks on the other) is steep but smooth, and the water is clean and very calm. Kayakers paddle about, and divers are drawn to the nearby Ilha das Couves. Area restaurants serve mostly basic fish dishes with rice and salad. Note that Barra do Sahy's entrance is atop a slope and appears suddenly—be on the lookout around marker Km 174.

The young and the restless flock to **Praia do Camburi** (⊠ Rio-Santos Hwy. (SP 055), 162 km/100 mi southeast of São Paulo) to sunbathe, surf, and party. At the center of the beach is a cluster of cafés, ice-cream shops, and bars and the Tiê restaurant. The service may be slow, but Tiê's menu is extensive, and the open-air setup is divine. Camburi is just north of Barra do Sahy. If you're coming from the south, take the second entrance; although it's unpaved, it's usually in better shape than the first entrance, at Km 166.

Praia de Maresias (⊠ Rio-Santos Hwy, Km 151 (SP 055), 177 km/109 mi southeast of São Paulo) is a 4-km (2-mi) stretch of white sand with clean, green waters that are good for swimming and surfing. Maresias is popular with a young crowd.

Ilhabela

39 *7 km (5 mi)/15-min boat ride from São Sebastião.*

Fodor's Choice
★

Ilhabela is favored by those who like the beach and water sports; indeed, many championship competitions are held here. This is the biggest sea island in the country, with 22 calm beaches along its western shore, which faces the mainland. The hotels are mostly at the north end, though the best sandy stretches are the 13 to the south, which face the open sea. Eighty percent of the island is in a state park area.

There are two small towns on the island: one is where the locals live; the other is where most visitors stay because of its hotels, restaurants, and stores. During the winter months most businesses that cater to tourists, including restaurants, are open only on weekends.

Scuba divers have several 19th- and early-20th-century wrecks to explore—this region has the most wrecks of any area off Brazil's coast—and hikers can set off on the numerous inland trails, many of which lead to a waterfall (the island has more than 300). Mosquitoes are a problem; bring plenty of insect repellent.

The best way to get around Ilhabela is by car, which you must rent on the mainland and transfer by ferry (there are no bridges to the island). *Balsas* (ferries) from São Sebastião to Ilhabela run every 30 minutes from 6 AM to midnight and hourly during the night. The **São Sebastião balsa** (☎ 0800/704–5510) transports vehicles as well as passengers. Make reservations, particularly December–February. Public buses cross the island from north to south daily. Fares range from R$10.70 (weekdays) to R$16 (weekends), including a car. To get to the ferry dock in São Sebastião, take Avenida São Sebastião from town to the coast.

Praia Grande (⊠ 13 km/8 mi south of ferry dock) has a long sandy strip with food kiosks, a soccer field, and a small church. At night people gather at **Praia do Curral** (⊠ 6 km/4 mi south of Praia Grande), where there are many restaurants and bars—some with live music—as well as places to camp. The wreck of the ship *Aymoré* (1921) can be found off the coast of this beach, near Ponta do Ribeirão, where you can also look for a waterfall trail.

A small church and many fishing boats add to the charm of **Praia da Armação** (⊠ 14 km/9 mi north of ferry dock). The beach was once the site of a factory for processing blubber and other resources from whales caught in the waters around the island. Today windsurfers stick to capturing the wind and the waves.

To reach **Baía dos Castelhanos** (⊠ 22 km/14 mi east of the ferry dock), you need a four-wheel-drive vehicle, and if it rains even this won't be enough. Consider arriving by sailboat, which demands a 1½- to 3-hour trip that can be arranged through local tour operators. With such an isolated location, you can see why slave ships once used the bay to unload their illicit cargo after slavery was banned in Brazil. If you're lucky, you might spot a dolphin off the shore of this 2-km (1¼-mi) beach—the largest on the island.

Where to Stay & Eat

$–$$$$ ✕ **Ilha Sul.** The best option on the menu is the grilled shrimp with vegetables. Fish and other seafood are also available. ⊠ *Av. Riachuelo 287* ☎ *012/3894–9426* ▤ *AE, DC, MC, V* ⊗ *Closed Mon.–Thurs. Apr.–June and Aug.–Nov.*

★ **$$–$$$**   ✕ **Viana.** *Camarão* (shrimp) is prepared in various ways at this traditional and petite restaurant with just a few tables. It's popular among locals, who come here to eat and enjoy the gorgeous view and sunsets. Grilled fish is also on the menu. ⊠ *Av. Leonardo Reale 1560* ☎ *012/3896–1089* ▤ *No credit cards* ⌂ *Reservations essential* ⊗ *Closed weekdays Apr.–June and Aug.–Nov.*

$$$$ ▥ **Maison Joly.** Past guests of this exclusive hotel at the top of the Can-
FodorśChoice   tagalo Hill range from kings of Sweden to the Rolling Stones. Upon arrival you're given a beach kit complete with mosquito repellent and a
★   hat. Each of the rooms has distinctive furnishings that are part of its theme, such as a piano, a billiard table, or a telescope—and all have balconies facing the sea. The restaurant ($$$$), open only to guests, is excellent. ⊠ *Rua Antônio Lisboa Alves 278* ☎ *012/3896–3500* 🖷 *012/3896–2364* ⊕ *www.maisonjoly.com.br* ⇱ *9 rooms* ⌂ *Restaurant, in-room safes, in-*

room hot tubs, minibars, cable TV, pool, massage, spa, bar, piano, Internet room, meeting rooms; no kids under 12 ☰ *DC, MC, V.*

★ $ ⚅ **Pousada dos Hibiscos.** North of the ferry dock, this red house has mid-size rooms, all at ground level. The friendly staff serves up a good breakfast and provides poolside bar service. Each room has its own unique decoration, but all have hardwood furnishings, and either tile or stone floors. ✉ *Av. Pedro de Paula Moraes 720* ☎☎ *012/3896–1375* ⊕ *www. pousadadoshibiscos.com.br* ⬀ *13 rooms* ⬧ *Fans, in-room safes, minibars, cable TV, pool, gym, sauna, bar* ☰ *AE, V.*

Sports & the Outdoors

BOATING & SAILING — Because of its excellent winds and currents, Ilhabela is a sailor's mecca. You can arrange boating and sailing trips through **Maremar Turismo** (✉ Av. São João 574 ☎ 012/3896–3679 ⊕ www.maremar.tur.br), one of the biggest tour agencies in Ilhabela. Maremar also has sailing courses and other activities, ranging from historical tours to off-road adventures.

For information on annual boating competitions that Ilhabela hosts, including a popular sailing week, contact **Iate Club de Ilhabela** (✉ Av. Força Expedicionária Brasileira 299 ☎012/3896–2300). **Ilha Sailing Ocean School** (✉ Av. Pedro de Paula Moraes 578 ☎ 012/9766–6619 ⊕ www. ilhasailing.com.br) has 12-hour sailing courses that cost about R$500.

HIKING — The **Cachoeira dos Três Tombos** trail starts at Feiticeira Beach (a nude beach) and leads to three waterfalls. **Trilha da Água Branca** is an accessible, well-marked trail. Three of its paths go to waterfalls that have natural pools and picnic areas. You can arrange guided hikes through local agencies such as **Cia. Aventura** (✉ Av. Princesa Isabel 809 ☎ 012/3896–2899 ⊕ www.ciaventura.tur.br).

SCUBA DIVING — Ilhabela has several good dive sites off its shores. In 1884, the British ship *Darth* sank near **Itaboca** (✉ 17 km/11 mi south of ferry dock). It still contains bottles of wine and porcelain dishes. **Ilha de Búzios** (✉ 25 km/15 mi offshore; take boat from São Sebastião), one of the three main Ilhabela islands, is a good place to see a variety of marine life, including dolphins. For beginners, the recommended diving and snorkeling spot is the sanctuary off the shore of islet **Ilha das Cabras** (✉ 2 km/1 mi south of ferry). It has a statue of Neptune at a 22-foot depth.

You can rent equipment, take diving classes, and arrange for a dive-boat trip through **Colonial Diver** (✉ Av. Brasil 1751 ☎ 012/3894–9459 ⊕ www.colonialdiver.com.br). The basic course takes three to four days and costs around R$960, which includes underwater videos and photographs, course material, and an international certificate.

SURFING — One of the best places to surf is **Baía de Castelhanos** (✉ 22 km/14 mi east of ferry dock). **Pacuíba** (✉ 20 km/12 mi north of ferry dock) has decent wave action. Surfing activities are among the specialties of **Lokal Adventure** (✉ Av. Princesa Isabel 171 ☎ 012/3896–5770 ⊕ www. lokaladventure.com.br), which also has tours to isolated communities on the island and rents buggies and motorbikes.

KITE- & WINDSURFING — Savvy kite-surfers and windsurfers head to **Ponta das Canas,** at the island's northern tip. Side-by-side beaches **Praia do Pinto and Armação** (✉ 12 km/7 mi north of ferry dock) also have favorable wind conditions. You can take kite-surfing, windsurfing, and sailing lessons at **BL3** (⊠ Av. Pedro Paulo de Moraes 1166 ☎ 012/3896–1034 ☒ Armação Beach ☎ 012/3896–1271 ⊕ www.bl3.com.br), the biggest school in Ilhabela. A 12-hour course costs R$400–R$550.

Ubatuba

40 *234 km (145 mi) southeast of São Paulo*

Many of the more than 70 beaches around Ubatuba are more than beautiful enough to merit the long drive from São Paulo. Young people, surfers, and couples with and without children hang out in the 90-km (56-km) area, where waterfalls, boat rides, aquariums, diving, and trekking in the wild are major attractions. Downtown Ubatuba also has an active nightlife, especially in summer. Ubatuba can be reached from São Paulo via the Carvalho Pinto (SP 070) and Oswaldo Cruz (SP 125) highways.

Lively **Praia Grande** (⊠ Off the Tamoios [SP 099] and Rio-Santos intersection) is one of Ubatuba's most popular beaches for its central location and loads of kiosks selling food and drink. The waters are good for swimming, though waves are big. Surfing is popular here. In stark contrast to Praia Grande, isolated and peaceful **Praia do Prumirim** (⊠ Off SP 055 at Km 23) is surrounded by nature and doesn't see much tourist traffic. You can hire local fishermen to take you by boat to a small undeveloped island offshore.

INLAND

São Paulo's inland region has beautiful mountains, springs, rivers, and waterfalls perfect for outdoor activities like hiking and rafting. Historic attractions are generally fewer than in other states. Save some time for clothing and crafts shopping, and for the lavish regional cuisine.

Highways that lead to inland towns are some of the best in the state. To get to Águas de São Pedro and Brotas, take Anhangüera–Bandeirantes (SP 330/SP 348); to Santana de Parnaíba, take Castelo Branco (SP 280); and to Campos de Jordão, take Ayrton Senna–Carvalho Pinto (SP 70). Embu is the exception—it's a 30-minute drive from the capital on the not-so-well-maintained Régis Bittencourt (BR 116). To go by bus, choose between the daily departures from the Tietê and Barra Funda terminals (⇨ Side Trips from São Paulo Essentials). Both are next to subway stations, making access fairly easy.

Águas de São Pedro

41 *180 km (112 mi) northwest of São Paulo.*

Although Águas de São Pedro is the smallest city in Brazil, at a mere 3.9 square km (1.5 square mi), its sulfurous waters made it famous countrywide in the 1940s and '50s. The healing hot springs were discovered by chance in the 1920s when technicians were drilling for oil.

Fonte Juventude is the richest in sulfur in the Americas and is often used to treat rheumatism, asthma, bronchitis, and skin ailments. The waters at Fonte Gioconda have minor radioactive elements (and, yes, they are reportedly good for you), whereas Fonte Almeida Salles's have chlorine bicarbonate and sodium (which are said to alleviate the symptoms of diabetes and upset stomachs).

You can access the springs at the Balneário Publico (public bathhouse) or through some hotels. Though a number of illnesses respond to the water, most visitors are just healthy tourists soaking in relaxation. Águas de São Pedro is compact, so it's easy to get around on foot.

☾ A walk through the woods in **Bosque Municipal Dr. Octávio Moura Andrade** is a chance to relax. Horseback riding costs around R$10 for a half hour. It's part of the Balneário complex (⇨ *below*). Saunas, baths, and massages cost R$8–R$33. ⊠ *Av. Carlos Mauro* ☎ *019/3482–1333* 🎫 *Free* ⊗ *Weekdays 7–noon, weekends 7–5.*

☾ A good option for those with kids is **Thermas Water Park,** with its 11 pools, eight water slides, and a small working farm. ⊠ *Km 189, SP 304* ☎ *019/3482–1011* 🎫 *R$32* ⊗ *Mon.–Sun. 8–6.*

Built in the Swiss style, the 18th-century **Capela Nossa Senhora Aparecida** (Our Lady of Aparecida Chapel) perches atop the highest part of the city. Twelve pine trees were planted around the chapel to represent the twelve apostles. ⊠ *Rua Izaura de Algodoal Mauro, Jardim Porangaba* ☎ *019/3482–1366* 🎫 *Free* ⊗ *Weekends 1–5.*

Balneário Municipal Dr. Octávio Moura Andrade has immersion baths in sulfurous springwater. You can swim in the pool or sweat in the sauna while you wait for your private soak, massage, or beauty appointment. A snack bar and a gift shop round out the spa services. ⊠ *Av. Carlos Mauro* ☎ *019/3482–1333* 🎫 *R$8–R$33* ⊗ *Mon.–Sun. 7–6.*

Where to Stay & Eat

$ ✕ **Patagônia.** This restaurant with international cuisine owes its contemporary flavor to the city's gastronomy students who do internships here. Duck, lamb, trout, risotto, and salt cod are good choices. ⊠ *Av. Presidente Kennedy 876* ☎ *019/3482–2338* ▭ *V* ⊗ *No lunch Thurs.–Sat. No dinner Sun.*

$$$–$$$$ ✕▦ **Grande Hotel São Pedro.** The beautiful art deco building was a casino during the 1940s. Now it's a teaching hotel and restaurant ($$–$$$) with all the comforts of a full-service spa. Many of the friendly staff members are students—including those who prepare dishes such as salt cod in pistachio sauce. The property is in the middle of a 300,000-square-meter (3.2 million-square-foot) park with more than 1 million trees and local wildlife. ⊠ *Parque Dr. Octávio de Moura Andrade* ☎ *019/3482–7600* 🖷 *019/3482–1665* ⊕ *www1.sp.senac.br/hoteis* ⇴ *96 rooms, 16 suites* ♨ *2 restaurants, room service, minibars, cable TV, tennis court, pool, gym, hair salon, sauna, spa, bar, recreation room, video game room, business services, meeting rooms* ▭ *AE, DC, MC, V.*

¢ ✕▦ **Avenida.** This hotel with an arcaded veranda resembles a large ranch house. Rooms are plain and sparsely decorated, but they're spacious. The restaurant (¢–$$$) serves homestyle Brazilian fare like *filé cubana* (steak with fried bananas) and has live music on Friday and Saturday. ⊠ *Av. Carlos Mauro 246* ☎ *019/3482–1221* 🖷 *019/3482–1223* ⊕ *www.hotelavenida.com.br* ➴ *53 rooms* ⚲ *Restaurant, room service, fans, pool, Internet room, some pets allowed; no a/c* ▤ No credit cards.

$ 🏨 **Hotel Jerubiaçaba.** The rooms in this 30-year-old hotel are bathed in light colors and filled with simple furnishings. The 120 rooms are divided into four types, from standard to luxury, but all of them are in a 17,000-square-meter (183,000-square-foot) green area with springs and a bathhouse. ⊠ *Av. Carlos Mauro 168* ☎ *019/3482–1411* ⊕ *www. hoteljerubiacaba.com.br* ➴ *120 rooms, 8 suites* ⚲ *Restaurant, room service, tennis court, pool, hair salon, massage, soccer, bar, recreation room, video game room, playground, business services, meeting rooms, no-smoking floors; no a/c in some rooms* ▤ *AE, DC, MC, V.*

Where to Stay & Eat

$–$$$ ✕ **Restaurante Casinha.** A lake view adds ambience to this family-owned restaurant. Try the delicious *pintado na brasa*, a charcoal-grilled fish made with garlic, onions, and lemon. ⊠ *Av. Lorival Jaubert da Silva Braga 1975* ☎ *014/3653–1225* ▤ *MC* ⊗ *Closed Mon.–Thurs. No lunch Fri. No dinner Sun.*

$ ✕ **Malagueta.** Those seeking a light meal after a rafting or hiking excursion can find it at Malagueta, which serves grilled meat, salads, and sandwiches. A green-and-red color scheme gives the place an upbeat modern look. *Salada portofino* (lettuce, sun-dried tomatoes, mozzarella, olives, and mustard dressing) is a noteworthy choice. ⊠ *Av. Mário Pinotti 243* ☎ *014/3653–5491* ▤ *DC, MC, V* ⊗ *Closed Mon. and Tues. No lunch Wed.–Fri.*

¢–$ 🏨 **Hotel Estalagem Quinta das Cachoeiras.** In front of a park and considered one of the best places in town, this Victorian-style hotel has a staff that prides itself on providing personal attention to their guests. You are treated to a breakfast that includes European pastries and classical music, besides getting to sleep in king-size beds with goose-feather pillows. ⊠ *Rua João Rebecca 225, Parque dos Saltos* ☎☎ *014/ 3653–2497* ⊕ *www.quintadascachoeiras.com.br* ➴ *12 rooms* ⚲ *Minibars, cable TV, pool, sauna, recreation room; no smoking* ▤ No credit cards �*Ol* BP.

¢   🏨 **Pousada Caminho das Águas.** The owners of this small downtown inn live on-site and provide a friendly place to rest—and a good breakfast. Rooms are very simply decorated and have ceramic-tile floors; some have verandas. ⊠ *Av. Mário Pinotti 1110* ☎☎ *014/3653–2428* ⊕ *www. cachoeiracassorova.com.br* ➴ *18 rooms* ⚲ *Fans, minibars, cable TV, pool; no a/c, no room phones* ▤ *MC, V* �*Ol* BP.

Sports & the Outdoors

White-water rafting on the Jacaré-Pepira River is best from November to May. The 9-km (5.6-mi) course ranges in difficulty from Class III to Class IV rapids, with drops of 3–9 feet.

Alaya (⊠ Av. Mário Pinotti 230 ☎ 014/3653–5656 ⊕ www.alaya.com. br) is the oldest rafting operator in town. It also has canyoning, mountain-biking, and hiking excursions. The basic rafting tour costs R$60, but there are more advanced options such as "raids," which are adventure races and other challenges, and "radical duck," which is an 8- to 10-km run through Class II–IV rapids that is done in an inflatable two-person kayak. Tours are Monday–Sunday 9–6.

Águas Radicais (⊠ Avenida Mário Pinotti 385 ☎ 014/3653–1699 ⊕ www.aguasradicais.com.br) has many rafting tours starting at R\$50, with trained guides and modern equipment. Cascading, trekking, tubing, and canyoning are also available.

Campos do Jordão

43 *184 km (114 mi) northeast of São Paulo.*

In the Serra da Mantiqueira at an altitude of 5,525 feet, Campos do Jordão and its fresh mountain air are paulistas' favorite winter attractions. In July temperatures drop as low as 32°F (0°C), though it never snows; in warmer months temperatures linger in the 13°C–16°C (55°F–60°F) range.

In the past some people came for their health (the town was once a tuberculosis treatment area), others for inspiration—including such Brazilian artists as writer Monteiro Lobato, dramatist Nelson Rodrigues, and painter Lasar Segall. Nowadays the arts continue to thrive, especially during July's Festival de Inverno (Winter Festival), which draws classical musicians from around the world.

Exploring Campos do Jordão without a car is very difficult. The attractions are far-flung, except for those at Vila Capivari.

Boulevard Genéve, a mall in the busy Vila Capivari district, is lined with cafés, bars, and restaurants, making it a nightlife hub. You can also find plenty of clothing stores, and candy shops selling chocolate, the town's specialty.

Palácio Boa Vista, the official winter residence of the state's governor, has paintings by such famous Brazilian modernists as Di Cavalcanti, Portinari, Volpi, Tarsila do Amaral, and Anita Malfatti. On the same property, the **Capela de São Pedro** (São Pedro Chapel) has sacred art from the 17th and 18th centuries. ⊠ *Av. Dr. Adhemar de Barros 3001* ☎ *012/3662–1122* ☞ *R\$5* ⊙ *Wed., Thurs., weekends 10–noon and 2–5.*

Horto Florestal is a natural playground for *macacos-prego* (nail monkeys), squirrels, and parrots, as well as for people. The park has a trout-filled river, waterfalls, and trails—all set among trees from around the world and one of the last *araucária* (Brazilian pine) forests in the state. ⊠ *Av. Pedro Paulo Km 13* ☎ *012/3663–3762* ☞ *R\$3–R\$4* ⊙ *Daily 8–5.*

Outside town a chair-lift ride to the top of **Morro do Elefante** (Elephant Hill) is a good way to enjoy the view from a 5,850-foot height. ⊠ *Av. José Oliveira Damas s/n* ☎ *012/3663–1530* ☞ *R\$7* ⊙ *Tues.–Fri. 1–5, weekends 9–5:30.*

The athletically inclined can walk 3 km (2 mi) and climb the 300-step stone staircase to **Pedra do Baú,** a 6,400-foot trio of rocks inside an eco-

OS BANDEIRANTES

IN THE 16TH AND 17TH CENTURIES *groups called bandeiras (literally, "flags," but also an archaic term for an assault force) set out on expeditions from São Paulo. Their objectives were far from noble. Their initial goal was to enslave Native Americans. Later, they were hired to capture escaped African slaves and destroy quilombos (communities the slaves created deep in the interior). Still, by heading inland at a time when most colonies were close to the shore, the bandeirantes inadvertently did Brazil a great service.*

A fierce breed, bandeirantes (bandeira members) often adopted indigenous customs and voyaged for years at a time. Some went as far as the Amazon River; others only to what is today Minas Gerais, where gold and precious gems were found. In their travels they ignored the 1494 Treaty of Tordesillas, which established a boundary between Spanish and Portuguese lands. (The boundary

was a vague north–south line roughly 1,600 km/1,000 mi west of the Cape Verde islands). Other Brazilians followed the bandeirantes, and towns were founded, often in what was technically Spanish territory. These colonists eventually claimed full possession of the lands they settled, and thus Brazil's borders were greatly expanded.

Near Parque Ibirapuera in the city of São Paulo there is a monument, inaugurated in 1953, to honor the bandeirantes. It is a huge granite sculpture created by Victor Brecheret, a famous Brazilian artist. Protests are occasionally staged here by those who don't believe the bandeirantes deserve a monument.

tourism park north of the city. A trail starts in nearby São Bento do Sapucaí, and it's recommended you hire a guide. In the park you can also practice horseback riding, canopy walking, trekking, or mountain-climbing and spend the night in a dormlike room shared with other visitors. Some of the activities are only available on weekends. ⊠ *Km 25, Estrada São Bento do Sapucaí* ☎ *012/3662–1106* ⊠ *R$5* ☾ *Weds.–Sun. 8–6.*

Where to Stay & Eat

$–$$$ ✕ **Baden-Baden.** One of the specialties at this charming German restaurant in the heart of town is sauerkraut *garni* (sour cabbage with German sausages). The typical dish serves two and is almost as popular as Baden-Baden's own brewery, which is open to visitors from 10–5 on weekdays. ⊠ *Rua Djalma Forjaz 93, Loja 10* ☎ *012/3663–3610* ▭ *AE, DC, MC, V.*

$–$$ ✕ **Itália Cantina e Ristorante.** As its name suggests, this place specializes in Italian food. The pasta and the meat dishes are delicious, but you can also try trout, lamb, fondue, and even boar dishes. ⊠ *Av. Macedo Soares 306* ☎ *012/3663–1140* ▭ *AE, DC, MC, V.*

¢–$ ✕ **Cyber Café.** Drink hot cocoa with crepes, fondue, or a slice of pie, while you browse the Internet at this downtown café. ⊠ *Rua Djalma*

Forjaz 100, Loja 15 ☎ *012/3663–6351* ⊕ *www.cybercafeboulevard. com.br* ▤ *MC, V.*

$–$$$ 🏨 **Pousada Villa Capivary.** A stay at this cozy guest house puts you in the gastronomic and commercial center of Campos. The friendly staff is helpful and efficient. Most apartments have balconies, and the five suites have whirlpool baths. ⊠ *Av. Victor Godinho 131* ☎ *012/ 3663–1746* 🖷 *012/3663–1736* ⊕ *www.capivari.com.br* ⊷ *10 rooms, 5 suites* ⌂ *In-room safes, some in-room hot tubs, minibars, cable TV, central heat, bar, recreation room* ▤ *AE, DC, MC, V.*

¢ 🏨 **Lausanne Hotel.** In an enormous ecopark 7 km (4 mi) outside town, this hotel has plenty of solitude, allowing you to commune with nature 5,850 feet above sea level. Rooms have forest views. ⊠ *Km 176, Rodovia SP-050* ☎ *012/3663–4806* 🖷 *011/3663–3247* ⊕ *www.lausannehotel. com.br* ⊷ *24 rooms* ⌂ *Restaurant, minibars, cable TV, heating, tennis court, pool, soccer, bar, recreation room, Internet, some pets allowed* ▤ *V.*

Shopping

Casa de Chocolates Montanhês (⊠ Praça São Benedito 45, Loja 6 ☎ 012/ 3663–1979 ⊕ www.chocolatemontanhes.com.br) is a well-known chocolate shop whose prices start at R$48 per kilo. The best handmade embroidered clothing in town is at **Maison Geneve** (⊠ Rua Djalma Forjaz 100, Lojas 1 a 3 ☎ 012/3663–2520 ⊕ www.geneve.com.br), open weekdays 10–7 and weekends 10–10. For knits try **Paloma Malhas** (⊠ Rua Djalma Forjaz 78, Loja 15 ☎ 012/3663–1218), open weekdays 10–7 and weekends 10–10.

Embu

㊹ *27 km (17 mi) west of São Paulo.*

Founded in 1554, Embu is a tiny Portuguese colonial town of whitewashed houses, old churches, wood-carvers' studios, and antiques shops. It has a downtown handicrafts fair every Saturday and Sunday. On Sunday the streets sometimes get so crowded you can barely walk. Embu also has many stores that sell handicrafts and wooden furniture; most of these are close to where the street fair takes place.

On weekends it's difficult to find a place to park in Embu, and parking lots can be expensive. You can easily walk to all the main sights in town.

Igreja Nossa Senhora do Rosário was built in 1690 and is a nice bet for those who won't have a chance to visit the historic cities of Minas Gerais. The church contains baroque images of saints and is next to a 1730 monastery now turned into a sacred-art museum. ⊠ *Largo dos Jesuítas 67* ☎ *011/4704–2654* 🎫 *R$2* ⊙ *Tues.–Sun. 9–5.*

㊢ In the Mata Atlântica you can visit the **Cidade das Abelhas** (City of the Bees), a farm with a small museum where you can watch bees at work. You can buy honey and other bee-related natural products while your kids climb the gigantic model of a bee. It's about 10 minutes from downtown; just follow the signs. ⊠ *Km 7, Estrada da Ressaca* ☎ *011/ 4703–6460* 🎫 *R$6* ⊙ *Tues.–Sun. 8:30–5.*

Where to Eat

$–$$ ✕ **O Garimpo.** In a large room with a fireplace or around outdoor tables, choose between Brazilian regional dishes such as the house specialty, *moqueca de badejo* (spicy fish-and-coconut-milk stew), and German classics such as *eisbein* (pickled and roasted pork shank). ✉ *Rua da Matriz 136* ☎ *011/4704–6344* ⊟ *AE, DC, MC, V.*

¢–$$ ✕ **Os Girassóis Restaurante e Choperia.** A great variety of dishes is served at this downtown restaurant next to an art gallery. The *picanha brasileira* (barbecued steak) with fries and *farofa* (cassava flour sautéed in butter) is recommended. ✉ *Largo dos Jesuítas 169* ☎ *011/4781–6671* ⊟ *AE, DC, MC, V* ⊘ *Closed Mon.*

$ ✕ **Casa do Barão.** In this colonial-style spot you find contemporary versions of country plates, but no salads or juices. Go for the exotic *picadinho jesuítico* (round-steak stew), served with corn, fried bananas, and farofa. Unlike most restaurants in the city, Casa do Barão serves single-person portions. ✉ *Rua Joaquim Santana 95* ☎ *011/4704–2053* ⊟ *MC, V* ⊘ *Closed Mon.*

Shopping

Cantão Móveis e Galeria (✉ Largo dos Jesuítas 169 ☎ 011/4781–6671) is a good place to buy ceramics, paintings, sculptures, and antique decorations. **Fenix Galeria de Artes** (✉ Rua Marechal Isidoro Lopes 10 ☎ 011/4704–5634) is a good place to find oil paintings as well as wood and stone sculptures.

Galeria Jozan (✉ Rua Nossa Senhora do Rosarío 59 ☎ 011/4704–2600) sells lovely antiques. **Guarani Artesanato** (✉ Largo dos Jesuítas 153 ☎ 011/4704–3200) has handicrafts made of wood and stone, including sculptures carved from *pau-brasil* (brazilwood). **Embuarte Móveis Rústicos** (✉ Av. Elias Yazbek 253 ☎ 011/4704–2083) is one of the many shops in town with colonial-style furniture.

Santana de Parnaíba

㊺ *42 km (26 mi) northwest of São Paulo.*

With more than 200 preserved houses from the 18th and 19th centuries, Santana de Parnaíba is considered the "Ouro Preto from São Paulo"—a town rich with history and colonial architecture. Santana was founded in 1580; by 1625 it was the most important point of departure for the *bandeirantes*.

In 1901 the first hydroelectric power station in South America was built here. Throughout the 20th century, Santana managed to retain its houses and charm while preserving a local tradition: a rural type of *samba* called "de bumbo," in which the pacing is marked by the *zabumba* (an instrument usually associated with rhythms from the northeastern states of Brazil). The proximity to a couple of São Paulo's finest suburbs explains the region's fine dining. Outdoors lovers feel at home with the canopy-walking and trekking options. On weekends parking is scarce in Santana de Parnaíba, and parking lots can be expensive.

Begin your trip by appreciating the 17th- and 18th-century colonial architecture of the **Centro Histórico,** with its more than 200 well-preserved houses. All of them are concentrated around three streets: Suzana Dias, André Fernandes, and Bartolomeu Bueno—two of which are named after famous bandeirantes.

Museu Casa do Anhanguera provides an even sharper picture of the bandeirantes era. In a 1600 house (the second-oldest in the state) where Bartolomeu Bueno—nicknamed Anhanguera, or "old devil," by the Indians—was born, the museum displays objects and furniture from the past four centuries. ⊠ *Largo da Matriz 9* ☎ *011/4154–5042* 🖅 *R$1* ⊗ *Weekdays 8–4:30, weekends 11–5.*

Baroque **Igreja Matriz de Sant'Anna** was built in the same square as Casa do Anhanguera in 1610 and restored in 1892. It has terra-cotta sculptures and an altar with gold-plated details. ⊠ *Largo da Matriz* ☎ *011/4154–2401* 🖅 *Free* ⊗ *Daily 8–5.*

Where to Eat

$$–$$$ ✕ **Dom Afonso de Vimioso.** A place like this would have reminded Portuguese colonists of the motherland. Options include fine wines and more than 10 dishes made with salt cod. Don't miss out on typical sweets such as *pastéis de Santa Clara* (yolk and sugar-filled pastries). ⊠*Km 36, Estrada dos Romeiros* ☎ *011/4151–1935* 🖃 *AE, DC, MC, V.*

☯ **$–$$$** ✕ **Aldeia Cocar.** This restaurant and outdoors complex was built in a former indigenous village. It occupies a 86,111-square-foot Mata Atlântica (Atlantic Forest) area with wildlife, and hosts indigenous exhibits in a reconstructed native tent. Aldeia serves more than 30 Brazilian specialties from all over the country, as well as a few typical dishes from countries which helped shape Brazil, like Italy, Japan, and, of course, Portugal. *Arrumadinho* (sun-dried beef with mashed pumpkin and collard greens) is an excellent choice. After the meal, take some time to rest on the hammocks. ⊠ *Estrada do Belo Vale 11, Km 32, SP-280* ☎ *011/ 4192–3073* ⊕ *www.aldeiacocar.com.br* 🖃 *AE, DC, MC, V* ⊗ *Closed Mon.–Wed.*

$–$$ ✕**São Paulo Antigo.** In a century-old ranch-style house, taste *caipira* (rural) dishes such as *dobradinha com feijão branco* (intestines and white-bean stew) or *galinha atolada* (rural-style hen stew). The grand finale is a free carriage ride around the town's main square. ⊠ *Rua Álvaro Luiz do Valle 66* ☎ *011/4154–2726* 🖃 *DC, MC, V* ⊗ *No dinner weekdays.*

$ ✕ **Bartolomeu.** In a 1905 house, this restaurant serves regional specialties like feijoada and *picadinho* (steak stew served with rice and beans, farofa, fried banana, and fried egg). Salmon and boar ribs are some additional choices. ⊠ *Praça 14 de Novembro 101* ☎ *011/4154–2679* 🖃 *DC, MC* ⊗ *Closed Mon.*

Sports & the Outdoors

Head back to the 21st century by participating in the weekend activities organized by the restaurant **Aldeia Cocar** (⊠ Estrada do Belo Vale 11, Km 32, SP-280 ☎ 011/4192–3073), which include walks through the forest canopy and trekking. A half-hour of canopy tour costs R$30. Activities take place Friday and Saturday 11–11 and Sunday 11–5.

Travessia do Caminho do Sol (☎ 011/4154–2422) is a 240-km (150 mi) trail that passes by 13 villages and crosses small rivers and cane plantations. The trail is considered the local version of the famous Camino de Santiago, in Spain. Call to join a group hike.

SIDE TRIPS FROM SÃO PAULO ESSENTIALS

Transportation

For more information about transportation, *see* Smart Travel Tips A to Z, *at* the front of this book.

BY BUS

ARRIVING &
DEPARTING

Buses to most cities in São Paulo State leave from the Terminal Tietê in the city of São Paulo. These include Piracicabana buses, which run daily to Águas de São Pedro; Pássaro Litorânea buses, which travel five times daily to São Sebastião (to the ferry dock) and six times a day to Ubatuba; and Expresso Mantiqueira buses, which leave for Campos do Jordão every two hours. Buses to Brotas, operated by Expresso de Prata, depart three times a day from the Terminal Barra Funda, in the western part of the city. There are two *executivo* (executive, or first-class) buses from São Paulo to Santana de Parnaíba and Embu, run by EMTU: Line 385 to Pirapora do Bom Jesus makes four daily rides between Barra Funda and Santana de Parnaíba, and Line 179 to Embu-Engenho Velho departs hourly from Anhangabaú. Regular (intermunicipal) buses travel more often: every 20 minutes, Line 033 leaves from Clínicas to Embu. The ride is less comfortable, though: you might have to stand up.

For locations of bus terminals within the city São Paulo, *see* São Paulo Essentials *in* Chapter 3.

🚍 **Expresso Mantiqueira** ☎ 011/6221-0244 ⊕ www.expressomantiqueira.com.br. **Expresso de Prata** ☎ 011/3392-7373 ⊕ www.expressodeprata.com.br. **Piracicabana** ☎ 011/6221-0032 ⊕ www.piracicabana.com.br. **Litorânea** ☎ 011/6221-0244 ⊕ www.litoranea.com.br.

GETTING
AROUND

For buses within towns, you can buy tickets directly on the bus. Service is mostly regular and cheap, but buses aren't always well maintained. Terminals and stands are usually easy to spot, as most streets have at least one, even in smaller towns. As a general rule, beware of pickpockets when on the bus and when waiting for it.

To travel between towns, just go to the local main terminal and ask for directions. It won't always be easy to go straight from one place to the other; between Embu and Santana de Parnaíba, for example, there's no direct connection.

When traveling between smaller towns, buses usually make several stops along the way, leaving and picking up passengers.

BY CAR

Roads in São Paulo State are generally in good condition and well marked; some of them are toll roads. Rent a car in São Paulo.

The drive from São Paulo to São Sebastião is about 2½ hours; take Rodovia Ayrton Senna–Carvalho Pinto (SP 070), followed by Rodovia Tamoios

(SP 099) to Caraguatatuba, and then follow the signs until you reach the ferry boat to Ilhabela. To reach Ubatuba, follow the same path to Caraguatatuba then turn right and head north on SP 055. Águas de São Pedro is about a 2½-hour drive on Anhangüera-Bandeirantes (SP 330/ SP 348) and then SP 304. Another 45-minute drive, along SP 304, will take you to Brotas. To reach Campos do Jordão from the city (also a 2½-hour drive), take Rodovia Carvalho Pinto (SP 070) and SP 123. To make the 30-minute drive from São Paulo to Embu, drive from Avenida Professor Francisco Morato to Rodovia Régis Bittencourt (BR 116) and then follow the signs. To reach Santana de Parnaíba from São Paulo—a 40-minute drive—take the express lane of Rodovia Castelo Branco (SP 280) and pay attention to the road signs.

Contacts & Resources

BANKS & EXCHANGING SERVICES

Some banks accept only cards with Visa/Plus logos and others accept only cards with MasterCard/Cirrus logos. Banco24horas ATMs usually accept all cards, including American Express. *See* "Money Matters" *in* Smart Travel Tips A to Z for more information.

It is best to change money in São Paulo.

🏧 **Banco do Brasil** ✉ Av. Rodolfo Guimarães 673, Brotas. **Banespa** ✉ Rua Dr. Carvalho 98, Ilhabela. **Bradesco** ✉ Praça Cel. Julião M. Negrão 29, Ilhabela ✉ Av. Frei Orestes Girardi 1037, Campos do Jordão ✉ Rua Nossa Senhora do Rosario 29, Embu ✉ Av. Carlos Mauro 336, Águas de São Pedro ✉ Praça Amador Simões 43, Brotas ✉ Largo de So Bento 30, Santana de Parnaíba. **Itaú** ✉ Av. Frei Orestes Girardi 859 Campos de Jordão.

EMERGENCIES

🏥 Hospitals & Clinics **Hospital Santa Ana** ✉ Rua Prof. Edgar de Moraes 707, Santana de Parnaíba ☎ 011/4154-2234. **Hospital São Paulo** ✉ Rua Agripino Lopes de Morais 1100, Campos do Jordão ☎ 012/3662-1722.

Pronto Socorro Municipal ✉ Rua Antônio Feijó 52, Águas de São Pedro ☎ 019/ 3482-1721. **Pronto Socorro Municipal** ✉ Av. Elias Yazbek 1415, Embu ☎ 011/4704-5744. **Pronto Socorro Municipal Governador Mário Covasú** ✉ Av. Prof. Malaquias de Oliveira Freitas 154, Ilhabela ☎ 012/3895-8789. **Santa Teresinha** ✉ Av. Rui Barbosa 703, Brotas ☎ 014/3653-2455.

📞 Hot Lines **Ambulance** ☎ 912. **Fire** ☎ 193. **Police** ☎ 190.

💊 Pharmacies **Drogaria Estância** ✉ Av. Carlos Mauro 375, Águas de São Pedro ☎ 019/3482-1347 ⏰ 8 AM-10 PM. **Drogaria Nossa Senhora das Dores** ✉ Av. Rui Barbosa 473, Centro, Brotas ☎ 014/3653-1619 ⏰ 24 hours. **Drogaria Nova Esperança** ✉ Rua da Padroeira 73, Ilhabela ☎ 012/3896-1183 ⏰ 8 AM-10 PM.

TOUR OPTIONS

Lokal Adventure leads tours of Ilhabela by boat, bike, horse, or jeep. Another Ilhabela operator is Maremar, which has scuba-diving, jeep, horseback-riding, and hiking tours. HS Turismo offers five tours in or around Campos do Jordão. Also in Campos do Jordão, trains depart from Estação Ferroviária Emílio Ribas on tours of the city and its environs, including the 47-km (29-mi) trip to Reino das Águas Claras, where there's a park with waterfalls.

Gol Tour Viagens e Turismo has day trips to Embu (R$80–R$90). Canoar is one of the best rafting tour operators in São Paulo State. Trilha Brazil arranges treks in forests around São Paulo. Reputable operators that have rain-forest, beach, and island excursions include Cia. Nacional de Ecoturismo and Venturas e Aventuras.

🚩 **Canoar** ☎ 011/3871-2282 ⊕ www.canoar.com.br. **Cia. Nacional de Ecoturismo** ☎ 011/5571-2525 ⊕ www.ciaecoturismo.com.br. **Estação Ferroviária Emílio Ribas** ✉ Av. Dr. Januário Miráglia, Vila Capivari, Campos do Jordão ☎ 012/3663-1531. **Gol Tour Viagens e Turismo** ☎ 011/3256-2388 ⊕ www.goltour.com.br Ⓜ República. **HS Turismo** ✉ Rua Ionel Strass 65, Campos do Jordão ☎ 012/3662-2759. **Lokal Adventure** ✉ Av. Princesa Isabel 171, Ilhabela ☎ 012/3896-5770 ⊕ www.lokaladventure.com. br. **Maremar** ✉ Av. São João 574, Ilhabela ☎ 012/3896-3679 ⊕ www.maremar.tur.br. **Trilha Brazil** ☎ 011/5925-1635 ⊕ www.trilhabrazil.com.br. **Venturas e Aventuras** ☎ 011/3872-0362 ⊕ www.venturas.com.br.

VISITOR INFORMATION

🚩 **Águas de São Pedro Informações Turísticas** ✉ Av. Carlos Mauro, in front of Balneário, Águas de São Pedro ☎ 019/3482-2173 or 3482-1096 ⊕ www.aguasdesaopedro. sp.gov.br. **Brotas Informações Turísticas** ✉ Av. Lourival Joubert da Silva Braga 101á, Brotas ☎ 014/3653-2288 ⊕ www.brotas.tur.br. **Campos do Jordão Tourist Office** ✉ At entrance to town, Campos do Jordão ☎ 012/3664-3525 ⊕ www.camposdojordao. com.br. **Embu Secretaria de Turismo** ✉ Largo 21 de Abril 139, Embu ☎ 011/4704-6565 ⊕ www.embu.sp.gov.br. **Ilhabela Secretaria do Turismo** ✉ Rua Bartolomeu de Gusmão 140, Ilhabela ☎ 012/3896-1091 ⊕ www.ilhabela.sp.gov.br. **Santana de Parnaíba Secretaria de Cultura e Turismo** ✉ Largo da Matriz 19, Santana de Parnaíba ☎ 011/4154-1874 or 011/4154-2377 ⊕ www.santanadeparnaiba.sp.gov.br.

The South

5

Updated by
Carlos G.
Tornquist

EXPECT THE UNEXPECTED IN THE SOUTHERN STATES of Paraná, Santa Catarina, and Rio Grande do Sul. The climate is remarkably cooler (the highest elevations even get a couple of inches of snow every year) and the topography more varied than in the rest of Brazil. You're also just as likely to find people of German and Italian ancestry as Portuguese. And as Brazil's breadbasket, the Região Sul (southern region) has a standard of living comparable to many developed nations.

The southern section of the Serra do Mar, a mountain range along the coast, stretches well into Rio Grande do Sul. It looks like one green wall—broken only by the occasional canyon or waterfall—separating the interior from the shore. Most mountainsides are still covered with the luxuriant Mata Atlântica (Atlantic Rain Forest), which is as diverse and impressive as the forest of the Amazon. The Serra do Mar gives way to hills that roll gently westward to the valleys of the *rios* (rivers) Paraná and Uruguay. Most of these lands were originally covered with dense subtropical forests interspersed with natural rangelands such as the Campos Gerais, in the north, and the Brazilian Pampas, in the south.

History

Although Portugal controlled the continent's Atlantic coast from the Amazon to the Rio de la Plata delta for more than a century after discovering Brazil, the Spanish influence was greatly felt throughout the interior. In the early 1600s Jesuit missionaries ventured into the valleys of the rios Paraná, Paraguay, and Uruguay, converting (and dominating) the region's native Guarani peoples. The Jesuits and their once semi-nomadic converts established self-sustaining *missões* (missions), locally known as *reduções* (missionary communities). As soon as those villages were more or less organized, the focus turned to building magnificent churches. In the late 1600s, several of these early settlements were destroyed by *bandeirantes* (Portuguese slave hunters and adventurers), who sought labor for the gold mines of Minas Gerais. The enduring Jesuits sought more remote regions in the Uruguay River basin for renewed expansion in the 1700s, ultimately building seven large missions in Rio Grande do Sul.

The demise of the Jesuit-Guarani period came with Treaty of Madrid (1750), which recognized Portuguese rule in what is roughly today's Brazil southern borders, and the decree of expulsion of the Jesuit order from all Portuguese territory in 1767. In a matter of a few years, the Jesuits were gone, the native peoples were either enslaved or dispersed in the wilderness, and most of the missões were abandoned. However, cattle ranching introduced by the Jesuits remained the activity of choice in the vast rangelands of central and western Rio Grande do Sul. As ranching evolved to an organized trade system in the late 1800s, a large number of *charqueadas* (ranches where cattle were slaughtered and the meat salted and sun-dried by slaves before export) were founded. This enterprise was so profitable that "cattle barons" turned villages into bustling commercial hubs. Although not as significant today, cattle culture still dominates the Brazilian Pampas, much like its Argentine counterpart.

If you have 5 days

Base yourself in 🚏 **Florianópolis** ⑮, taking time to visit the colonial forts and the bustling northern beaches on a schooner tour on your first day. Save the second day for the southern beaches of **Ilha de Santa Catarina** ⑭ and a trek to Lagoinha do Leste. On the third day take time to visit **Porto Belo** ⑬ or **Garopaba** ⑯ for diving, surfing, or whale-watching. On Day 4 fly to the remarkable 🚏 **Foz do Iguaçu** ⑩ and explore both the Brazilian side of the falls and the Itaipú Dam in one day. Spend your last day exploring the Argentine side of the falls.

If you have 7 days

Start off in 🚏 **Curitiba** ①–⑦, using Day 1 to visit Niemeyer's **Novo Museu** ⑦ and the Jardim Botânico and the other city parks; take the next day to travel by train to **Paranaguá** ⑧ through the scenic Serra da Graciosa. Then head out for a three-day visit to 🚏 **Foz do Iguaçu** ⑩. If you opt to drive, make a stop at **Parque Estadual de Vila Velha** ⑨. From Foz fly to 🚏 **Florianópolis** ⑮ for two days on the beaches of the island and the historical forts. Make sure to hike to the tiny secluded beach of Lagoinha do Leste.

If you have 10 days

For your explorations of southern Brazil, in 🚏 **Foz do Iguaçu** ⑩ reserve two days to visit both the Brazilian and Argentine side of the falls and the Itaipú Dam. Then move on to 🚏 **Curitiba** ①–⑦ to experience the European atmosphere and temperate climate; be sure to go to the Novo Museu ⑦. On Day 4 take the train tour to **Paranaguá** ⑧, returning to Curitiba in the evening. Next fly to 🚏 **Florianópolis** ⑮ to enjoy its many beaches by land on Day 5 and on a schooner tour the following day. Take Day 7 to go either to **Porto Belo** ⑬ or **Garopaba** ⑯ for whale-watching and snorkeling, or go to **Blumenau** ⑫ to experience German culture in southern Brazil. The following day fly to 🚏 **Porto Alegre** ⑰–㉔. Then head north for a visit to the Serra Gaúcha for one day. On your last day see the fantastic canyons at **Parque Nacional dos Aparados da Serra** ㉘ or get acquainted with the south's early history at the missions.

Perhaps the greatest transformation in the region followed the arrival of German and Italian colonizers. These immigrants brought along centuries of old-world farming and wine-making traditions. Many also contributed greatly to urbanization and industrialization, which in turn brought about socioeconomic improvements still evident today.

About the Restaurants

Southern Brazil is known for high-quality, inexpensive cuisine, much of it revolving around European fare brought here by the region's many European immigrants, and the quintessential *churrasco*, or Brazilian "barbecue," in which meats are slow-roasted and -grilled. At *churrascarias* (restaurants that specialize in churrasco), waiters bring skewers full of different meats to your table until you can eat no more. Good restaurants can be found even in remote villages in the south. In larger cities you can find a variety of international cuisines, albeit on a smaller scale than in São Paulo or Rio.

Café colonial is the elaborate 5 PM tea that's very popular among the Germans in the South. It"s a dieter's worst fear, with coffee and tea accompanied by a variety of breads, pies, German kuchen, honey, butter, and several kinds of jelly. For dessert there are fruit creams (pureed fruit mixed with cream) and ice cream. Café colonial is also the term used for the establishment where the afternoon tea is served.

About the Hotels

The south has a great variety of hotels and inns, though upscale facilities are limited. Except for in the smallest towns and most remote areas, however, you shouldn't have a problem finding comfortable accommodations. Pousadas in historic buildings are common, particularly in beach towns. Hotel-fazendas are popular in rural areas. For definitions of types of hotels in Brazil *see* Lodging *in* Smart Travel Tips A to Z.

Southern beaches attract many Argentine tourists, so seaside cities might become crowded from December through March, especially if the exchange rate favors the Argentine peso. There's usually enough lodging for this influx of visitors (though you'd be wise to reserve in advance), but traffic on highways and crowding on beaches can be nightmarish.

WHAT IT COSTS In Reais				
$$$$	$$$	$$	$	¢
RESTAURANTS over R$60	R$45–R$60	R$30–R$45	R$15–R$30	under R$15
HOTELS over R$500	R$375–R$500	R$250–R$375	R$125–R$250	under R$125

Restaurant prices are for a dinner entrée. Hotel prices are for two people in a standard double room in high season, excluding taxes.

Exploring the South

Touring this region—roughly the size of France—in a short time is a challenge, even though the transportation network is relatively efficient. The major hubs are Curitiba, capital of the region's northernmost state of Paraná; Florianópolis, capital of Santa Catarina State; and Porto Alegre, capital of the southernmost state of Rio Grande do Sul.

The region can be divided into two large but more or less homogeneous areas—the coast and the interior—both worth visiting. The coast in Paraná, Santa Catarina, and Northeastern Rio Grande do Sul has great beaches, forested slopes, canyons, and the peaks and valleys of the Serra do Mar. Foz do Iguaçu, far to the west, should not be missed by any means, but consider stops in Vila Velha and Curitiba in Paraná and the missões and canyons in Rio Grande do Sul.

When to Go

November through March is invariably hot and humid. Rainfall is quite frequent (but less than in the Amazon or some northern coastal regions) and evenly distributed throughout the year, although some years might

Waterworks

The mighty Foz do Iguaçu (Iguaçu Falls) is actually a 3-mile (5-km) series of 275 falls. At the southwestern tip of Paraná, it overlaps the Brazil–Argentina border. Thanks to the falls, you can visit another of Brazil''s top attractions nearby, the massive Itaipú Dam.

The Mata Atlântica

Only 5 percent of Mata Atlântica, or Atlantic rain forest, survives today, and the 5,000-square-km (1,900-square-mi) Serra do Mar in Paraná State is one of the largest tracts that remain. The best way to see it is on the Serra Verde Express, a train that chugs along 110 km (69 mi) of virgin rain forest, past waterfalls, and along the edge of 1,000-meter (3,300-foot) precipices with outstanding views. For more information, *see* Train Travel *in* The South Essentials.

5

Beaches

The coastline from Paraná to the city of Torres in Rio Grande do Sul has spectacular scenery dotted with great beaches. Some of the best and most visited are on large offshore island Ilha de Santa Catarina and near the city of Florianópolis.

Southern Wines

The slopes of the Serra Gaúcha (a mountain district in Rio Grande do Sul) were settled by Italians whose wine-making traditions flourished in the region's cold winters and fertile soils. Though Brazilian wine has a long way to go to reach the acclaim of its Chilean and Argentinean counterparts, some varieties from Caxias do Sul and Bento Gonçalves are deservedly earning praise.

Eating Well

One of the most famous foods of Brazil, *churrasco* (slow-grilled and -roasted meat), originated in Rio Grande do Sul. Meat is a staple of the diet here in cowboy country, but cuisine is eclectic, and rice and beans sit on southern tables beside Italian and German dishes, thanks to the south's many European immigrants. Look for *barreado*, a dish from coastal Paraná made by stewing beef, bacon, potatoes, and spices for several hours in a clay pot made airtight with moistened manioc flour.

---

have extremely rainy El Niño–related summers or, conversely, quite dry La Niña–affected years. January and February are top vacation months, so expect crowded beaches, busy highways, and higher prices. Winter (April–November) brings much cooler temperatures, sometimes as low as the upper 20s in the higher elevations at night. Major cold fronts blowing in from Patagonia can bring some gray, blustery days, usually followed by chilly days with deep blue skies.

PARANÁ

The state of Paraná is best known for the Foz do Iguaçu, a natural wonder, and the Itaipú Dam, an engineering marvel. But also worth a visit is Vila Velha, a series of strange sandstone formations in the center of Paraná that might remind you of the eerily moving landscapes of the western United States. At one time the rolling hills of the state's plateau were covered with forests dominated by the highly prized Paraná pine, an umbrella-shape conifer. Most of these pine forests were logged by immigrants half a century ago, and the cleared land of the immense interior is now where soybeans, wheat, and coffee are grown. (Still, be on the lookout for the occasional Paraná pine.) The state has a very short coastline, but the beaches are spectacular, as is the Serra do Mar, which still has pristine Atlantic forest and coastal ecosystems. Curitiba, the upbeat capital, ranks as a top Brazilian city in efficiency, innovative urban planning, and quality of life.

Curitiba

❶–❼ *408 km (254 mi) south of São Paulo, 710 km (441 mi) north of Porto Alegre.*

A 300-year-old city, Curitiba is on the Paraná plateau, at an elevation of 2,800 feet. It owes its name to the Paraná pinecones, which were called *kur-ity-ba* by the native Guaranis. In a region that already differs considerably from the rest of the country, the city of 1.5 million is unique for its temperate climate (with a mean temperature of 16°C/61°F) and the 50% of its population that is of non-Iberian European ancestry.

With one of the highest densities of urban green space in the world, Curitiba is known as the environmental capital of Brazil. This is not only because of its array of parks but also because since the 1980s it has had progressive city governments that have been innovative in their urban planning—a process spearheaded by former mayor and architect Jayme Lerner. The emphasis on protecting the environment has produced an efficient public transportation system and a comprehensive recycling program that are being used as models for cities around the globe.

Numbers in the text correspond to numbers in the margin and on the Curitiba Setor Histórico map.

Setor Histórico

Much as in other Brazilian cities, the history of the downtown district of Curitiba revolves around the first church built in the city, Igreja de São Francisco. In the early days it was the focal point where roads and streets converged, businesses set shop, the government established its representation, and urban sprawl unfolded. Development in the last 50 years moved the administrative and commercial district away from the original center, where symbols of early days are preserved.

A GOOD TOUR   Start your tour in the Setor Histórico (Historic District) at the **Museu Paranaense** ❶ ▶. Then circle the block and take Rua Monsenhor Celso north to the Praça Tiradentes. The **Catedral Basílica Menor** ❷ is on the opposite side of the square. Continue a couple of blocks north on Rua do Rosário to the Largo da Ordem, where you will find the **Memorial de Curitiba** ❸, several colonial houses, and the public water well for the

Copacabana, Rio.

(top left) Buggies on the cliff at Morro Branco, near Fortaleza. (bottom left) Recife. (top right) São Paulo.
(bottom right) Amazon River.

(top left) Christ the Redeemer statue at Corcovado, Rio. (top right) Foods at a market in Rio. (bottom) Brasília.

(top) Ipanema, Rio. (bottom) Carnival in Rio.

(top left) The Foz do Iguaçu cascades. (top right) Golden lion tamarin. (bottom) Spinning Brazilian samba.

(top) Salvador. (bottom) Farmworkers playing music in the Pantanal.

(top left) Toucan. (top right) Carnival in Recife. (bottom) A favela outside Rio.

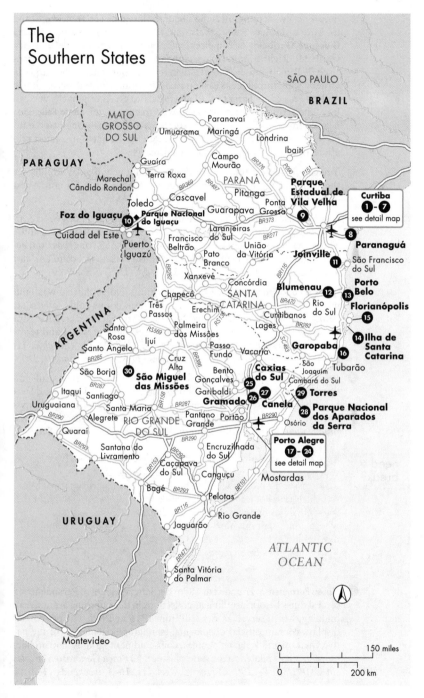

The
Southern States

SÃO PAULO

BRAZIL

MATO
GROSSO
DO SUL

Umuarama   Maringá   Londrina
Paranavaí
Ibaiti

PARAGUAY

Guaíra   Campo
Mourão
Terra Roxa
Marechal   **PARANÁ**
Cândido Rondon   Pitanga
Toledo   Cascavel   **Parque
                                           Estadual de
                          Guarapava Ponta Vila Velha**
Foz do Iguaçu **Parque Nacional**   Grossa   **9**
            10 **do Iguaçu**
Cuidad del Este   Laranjeiras
            Puerto   do Sul
            Iguazú   Francisco   União
                     Beltrão   da Vitória   **Joinville**
                         Pato   **11**
                         Branco
               Xanxevê   Concórdia   **Blumenau**
               Chapecó   **SANTA**   **12**
            Três   Erechim   **CATARINA**   Rio
            Passos   do Sul
                       Palmeira   Curitibanos
         Santa   das Missões   **Caxias**
         Rosa   Passo   Lages **282**
Santo Ângelo   Ijuí   Fundo   Vacaria
                    Cruz   São
         São Borja Alta   Bento   Joaquim Tubarão
                                 Gonçalves **25** Cambará do Sul
Itaqui   Santiago   Garibaldi **26** **27**
Uruguaiana   Santa Maria   **São Miguel**   **Gramado**
                           das Missões   **Canela**
         Alegrete   Pantano Portão
Quaraí   **RIO GRANDE** Grande
                     DO SUL
         Santana do   Encruzilhada
         Livramento   do Sul
                    Caçapava
                    do Sul   Canguçu
            Bagé
                       Pelotas
URUGUAY   Rio Grande
            Jaguarão

Curitiba
1-**7**
see detail map

8
Paranaguá

São Francisco
do Sul
**Porto
Belo**
13
Florianópolis
15
14 **Ilha de
Santa
Catarina**
Garopaba
16

29 **Torres**
28
**Parque Nacional
dos Aparados
da Serra**
Osório

Porto Alegre
17-**24**
see detail map

Mostardas

ARGENTINA

*ATLANTIC
OCEAN*

Santa Vitória
do Palmar

Montevideo

0   150 miles
0   200 km

horses. A few steps uphill is the site of the **Igreja de São Francisco** ❹ and its Museu de Arte Sacra. Walk one block southwest to find **Società Giuseppe Garibaldi di Beneficenza** ❺, on the northern side of Praça Garibaldi. Right behind the society building are the ruins of São Francisco de Paula Church. You can then retrace your steps to the Largo da Ordem, walk three blocks east on Rua São Francisco, and then go north on Rua Presidente Faria to the **Passeio Público** ❻. Alternatively, you can leave the Setor Histórico and head west to explore the **Santa Felicidade** neighborhood—with its many restaurants and shops—or go to the futuristic **Novo Museu (Museu de Arte do Paraná)** ❼, one of the latest creations of Brasilia's architect Oscar Niemeyer.

TIMING You can follow the tour in two hours, but allow half a day to fully see the sights. Shopping or people-watching in a park can fill up the rest of the day.

WHAT TO SEE **Catedral Basílica Menor.** The cathedral, also called Igreja de Nossa Senhora da Luz dos Pinhais, is on the site where the city was founded in 1693. ❷ The present neo-Gothic structure was finished in 1893 and was built according to the plan of an unknown cathedral in Barcelona, Spain. ⊠ *Praça Tiradentes s/n* ☎ *041/3222–1131* 🎫 *Free* ☉ *Daily 7 AM–9 PM.*

❹ **Igreja de São Francisco.** St. Francis, Curitiba's oldest church, was built in 1737 and was fully restored in 1981. Check out its gold-plated altar before ducking into the attached **Museu de Arte Sacra** (Sacred Art Museum), with its baroque religious sculptures made of wood and terracotta. ⊠ *Largo da Ordem s/n* ☎ *041/3223–7545 for church, 041/ 3321–3265 for museum* 🎫 *Free* ☉ *Tues.–Fri. 9–6, weekends 9–2.*

❸ **Memorial de Curitiba.** The triangle-shaped building with glass walls has three stories with space for art exhibits and workshops. The ground level has a theater and several sculptures by local artists representing the city's history. ⊠ *Rua Claudino dos Santos s/n* ☎ *041/3323–8594* ⊕ *www. fundacaoculturaldecuritiba.com.br* 🎫 *Free* ☉ *Weekdays 9–6, Sat. 9–1.*

need a break? **Rua 24 Horas.** To satisfy your hunger, head for Rua 24 Horas, a short downtown alley that's sheltered by a glass roof (with interior lighting) supported by a steel structure. The entrance is marked by stylish clocks that hint at the appealing ambience inside. You'll find souvenir shops and newsstands as well as coffeehouses and bars whose tables spill out onto the walkway. Most are open 24 hours a day, seven days a week. ⊠ *Rua Coronel Mena Barreto between Rua Visconde de Rio Branco and Rua Visconde de Nacar, Centro* ☎ *041/ 3225–1732.*

▶ ❶ **Museu Paranaense.** Founded in 1876, the State Museum of Paraná moved several times before installing its collections in this imposing art nouveau building, which served as city hall from 1916 to 1969. The permanent displays contain official documents, ethnographic materials of the native Guarani and Kaigang peoples, coins and photographs, and archaeological pieces related to the state's history. ⊠ *Praça Generoso Marques s/n* ☎ *041/3304–3300* 🎫 *Free* ☉ *Weekdays 10–5, weekends 11–3.*

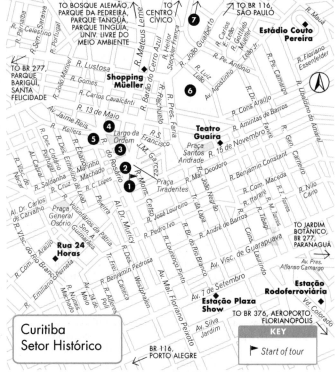

Curitiba
Setor Histórico

KEY

► *Start of tour*

❼ **Museu Oscar Niemeyer.** Pictures of Oscar Niemeyer's projects throughout the world are on display at this museum designed by the architect himself. (For more information about Niemeyer, the architect of Brasília, *see* "The Making of a Capital" CloseUp box *in* Chapter 7.) The museum also incorporates a collection of the works of Paraná's artists from the former Museu de Arte do Paraná with temporary modern art exhibits. Niemeyer's futuristic building design includes a long rectangular building, formerly a school. The main building, a suspended eye-shaped structure overlooking the adjacent John Paul II woods, has the major modern art exhibit. ⊠ *Rua Marechal Hermes 999, Centro Cívico* ☎ *041/3350–4400* ⊕ *www.novomuseu.org* ⊠ *Free* ☉ *Weekdays 10–5, weekends 11–3.*

❻ **Passeio Público.** Opened in 1886, the Public Thoroughfare was designed as a botanical and zoological garden. It soon became a favorite place for the affluent to spend their weekend afternoons. The main gate is a replica of that at the Cimetière des Chiens in Paris. Although it's no longer the official city zoo, you can observe several Brazilian primates and birds still kept in the park, as well as majestic sycamores, oaks, and the famed Brazilian *ipê amarelo.* ⊠ *Main Gate: Rua Pres. Faria at Pres. Carlos Cavalcanti* ☎ *041/3222–2742* ⊠ *Free* ☉ *Tues.–Sun. 6 AM–8 PM.*

off the beaten path

SANTA FELICIDADE – What was once an Italian settlement (it dates from 1878) is now one of the city's most popular neighborhoods. It has been officially designated as Curitiba's "gastronomic district," and, indeed, you'll find some fantastic restaurants—as well as wine, antiques, and handicrafts shops—along Via Veneto and Avenida Manuel Elias. The area also has some colonial buildings, such as the Igreja Matriz de São José (St. Joseph's Church).

❺ Società Giuseppe Garibaldi di Beneficenza. The stately neoclassical mansion housing the Garibaldi Beneficient Society—a philanthropic organization that once helped a great many Italian immigrants—was built with the help of donations from the Italian government and finished in 1890. Today the restored building sponsors a folkloric dance group and a choir. ⊠ *Praça Garibaldi s/n* ☏ *041/3222–8843* 🎫 *Free* 🕙 *By appointment only.*

Parks, Gardens & Forests

It would be a shame to visit Brazil's environmental capital without seeing one of its many parks. In addition to the Passeio Público, you can visit the Jardim Botânico (east from downtown). Also recommended are the Bosque Alemão, Parque da Pedreira, Parque Tangüá, Parque Tingüí, and Universidade Livre do Meio Ambiente (they're clustered northwest of Centro and the Setor Histórico). Tour on your own or as part of the 2½-hour Linha Turismo tour (➪ By Bus *in* The South Essentials).

PARKS TO SEE   **Bosque Alemão.** The 8-acre German Woods—which, as its name suggests, is a park honoring German immigration—is on a hill in the Jardim Schaffer neighborhood. On its upper side is the Bach Oratorium, a small concert hall that looks like a chapel; it's the site of classical music performances. The park also has a viewpoint with a balcony overlooking downtown, a library with children's books, and a path through the woods called Hans and Gretel Trail. Named after the Grimm Brothers' tale, the trail has the story depicted in 12 paintings along the way, ending at the Mural de Fausto, where there's a stage for music shows. ⊠ *Rua Nicolo Paganini at Rua Francisco Schaffer, Jardim Schaffer* ☏ *041/ 3338–6835* 🎫 *Free* 🕙 *Park daily sunrise–sunset. Library Mon.–Sat. 8–6.*

Jardim Botânico. Although not as old and renowned as its counterpart in Rio, the Botanical Garden has become a Curitiba showplace. Its most outstanding feature is the tropical flora in the two-story steel greenhouse that resembles a castle. The Municipal Botanical Museum, with its library and remarkable collection of rare Brazilian plants, is also worth visiting. There are several paths for jogging or just wandering. ⊠ *Rua Eng. Ostoja Roguski s/n, Jardim Botânico* ☏ *041/3362–1800* 🎫 *Free* 🕙 *Gardens daily 6 AM–8 PM. Museum weekdays 8–5.*

★ Parque da Pedreira. This cultural complex was built in the abandoned João Gava quarry and adjacent wooded lot. The quarry itself was converted to an amphitheater that can accommodate 60,000 people. The 2,400-seat **Opera de Arame** (Wire Opera House), also on the grounds here, is built of tubular steel and wire mesh, built above a water–field quarry pit. National and international musical events have given this

facility world renown. ⊠ *Rua João Gava s/n, Pilarzinho* ☎ *041/
3354–2662* ✆ *Free* ⊗ *Tues.–Sun. 8 AM–10 PM.*

Parque Tangüá. The latest addition to Curitiba"s recreational scene,
Tangüá Park, opened in 1996, is most-visited park in the city. Its interesting landscaping includes a pond in an abandoned quarry that creates
the backdrop for a tunnel (dug 45 meters/160 feet into the rock wall),
an artificial waterfall, and a walkway over the water. ⊠ *Rua Eugenio
Flor s/n, Pilarzinho* ☎ *041/3352–7607* ✆ *Free* ⊗ *Daily sunrise–sunset.*

Parque Tingüí. One of the city's most pleasant parks was designed to protect the upper basin of the Rio Barigüí from urban encroachment. It's best
known as the site of the **Ukrainian Memorial,** which includes a repro-
duction of a wooden church with onion domes built by Ukrainian Catholic
immigrants in 1900 in the town of Prudentópolis, 250 km (155 mi) away.
There is also a shop with traditional Ukrainian handicrafts. ⊠ *Rua Dr.
Bemben s/n, Pilarzinho* ☎ *041/3240–1103* ✆ *Free* ⊗ *Daily 6–8.*

Universidade Livre do Meio Ambiente. The Free University of the Environment, in the Bosque Zaninelli (Zaninelli Woods), opened in 1992
during the UN Conference on the Environment and Development being
held in Rio. Its main objective is to promote environmental awareness
through courses, conferences, and seminars. The impressive main structure is built of eucalyptus wood and has a scenic overlook on its top
level. Several paths through the woods make the Bosque Zaninelli a popular place to wander. ⊠ *Rua Victor Benato 210, Pilarzinho* ☎ *041/
3254–3734* ⊕ *www.unilivre.org.br* ✆ *Free* ⊗ *Daily 7–6.*

Where to Stay & Eat

As one of the major centers of industry, commerce, and tourism in
Brazil, Curitiba has wide a variety of lodging and dining options that
caters to hurried and demanding business travelers. The Santa Felicidade neighborhood carved a name for affordable restaurants that serve
locally influenced Italian cuisine.

$$$–$$$$ ✕ **Boulevard.** The sophisticated atmosphere and excellent wine selection
of this highly regarded small French restaurant won't fail to impress.
Try the wild boar ribs with herbs, truffles, and mustard sauce prepared
by renowned chef Celso Freire. ⊠ *Rua Voluntários da Pátria 539, Setor
Histórico* ☎ *041/3224–8244* ⊟ *AE, DC, MC, V* ⚙ *Reservations es-
sential* ⊗ *Closed Sun. No lunch Sat.*

$–$$$ ✕ **Durski.** This family-run restaurant has brought traditional Polish and
Fodor's Choice Ukrainian food center stage. The impeccable service by staff in tradi-
★ tional attire, as well as the borscht, pierogi, and *bigos* (a round loaf of
bread stuffed with sausages and sauerkraut), transport you to central
Europe. Another highlight is the home-brewed low-alcohol beer, made
of sugar, egg whites, and hops. ⊠ *Rua Jaime Reis 254, Setor Histórico*
☎ *041/3225–7893* ⚙ *Reservations essential* ⊟ *AE, DC, MC, V*
⊗ *Closed Mon. No dinner Sun.*

$$ ✕ **Devon's.** The service is excellent at this rodízio-style churrascaria. It's
very popular with businesspeople and visitors to the Centro Cívico
area. ⊠ *Rua Lysimaco Ferreira da Costa 436, Centro Cívico* ☎ *048/
3254–7073* ⊟ *DC, MC, V* ⊗ *No dinner Sun.*

THE MATA ATLÁNTICA

THE AMAZONIAN RAIN FOREST *is so famous that most tourists are amazed to learn that Brazil's southern states were once covered by an equally lush humid forest, teeming with animal and plant biodiversity. The Mata Atlântica (Atlantic Forest), really a series of forests, originally covered about a fourth of Brazil, mostly along the south-eastern seaboard. One of the most complex ecosystems on earth, these evergreen forests contained about 7% of all known vertebrates and more than 20,000 plant species.*

The major difference between the Amazon and the Mata Atlântica is the flora. In the Amazon plants are essentially lowland types adapted to the humid climate; those in the Atlantic forests have adapted to mountainous terrain, less rainfall, and lower mean annual temperatures. Unique Mata Atlântica fauna includes primates like the mico-leão dourado (golden-lion tamarin) and the muriqui (spider monkey), parrots, toucans, arapongas (bell birds), and the anta (tapir).

The flora is rich in pau-brasil (brazilwood) and, at higher elevations, araucária (Brazilian pine). The hundreds of orchid species, the yellow flowers of the ipê (Brazil's national flower) and the flowers of the manacá (princess flower tree) that turn from white to purple to violet within days compose a colorful spectacle.

The Mata Atlântica has been seriously overexploited since the 16th century, and is threatened by human encroachment and agricultural land conversion. Recent estimates indicate that only 8% of the original remains. Preservation, conservation, and recovery efforts by the national government and private organizations are ongoing. "Bright spots" include Foz do Iguaçu, Superagüi Island (a national park in Paranaguá), a golden tamarin reserve in southern Bahia State, and organizations that train farmers in sustainable agriculture practices.

$–$$ ✕ **Estrela da Terra.** In a colonial house, this restaurant is *the* place to try the local *barreado* (beef, bacon, potatoes, and spices stewed for several hours in a clay pot that is made airtight with moistened manioc flour) on weekends. The weekly menu also contains choices from other regions. ✉ *Rua Jaime Reis 176, Setor Histórico* ☎ *041/3225–5007* ▤ *DC, MC, V* ⊘ *No dinner.*

$–$$ ✕ **Schwarzwald.** One of the city's most popular German restaurants, Schwarzwald has carved a name for itself with great draft beer, including some imported brands and local bocks (German-style dark beers), which are hard to find here. Highly recommended entrées are the house version of *eisbein* (pig's leg served with mashed potatoes), *kassler* (beef fillet with a cream sauce), and duck with red cabbage. ✉ *Rua Claudino dos Santos 63, Setor Histórico* ☎ *041/3223–2585* ▤ *AE, DC, MC, V.*

$ ✕ **Madalosso.** An enormous hangarlike building that seats 4,800 houses the best-known restaurant in Santa Felicidade. The prix-fixe Italian menu includes a large selection of pastas and sauces, meat dishes, and salads. ✉ *Rua Manoel Ribas 5875, Santa Felicidade* ☎ *041/3372–2121* ▤ *AE, DC, MC, V* ⊘ *No dinner Sun.*

¢–$ ✕ **Baviera.** In the basement of an imposing house on a hillside, this is a popular choice for those visiting the Setor Histórico. Baviera is essentially a pizzeria, but the menu also includes Brazilian-style steak (thin-cut fillet, usually rare), grilled chicken, and hamburgers. ⊠ *Rua Augusto Stellfeld 18, Setor Histórico* ☎ *041/3232–1995* ⊟ *AE, DC, MC, V.*

$$ ⊞ **Bourbon & Tower.** Much like its counterpart in Foz do Iguaçu, this hotel is recommended for the sophisticated business or leisure traveler. The decor is sober, with custom antique-style furniture and textured wall-paper. The restaurant Le Bourbon serves French-Swiss dishes, but the Brazilian *feijoada* is the Saturday special. ⊠ *Rua Candido Lopes 102, Centro 80020-060* ☎ *041/3221–4600 or 0800/701–8181* ⊟ *041/ 3221–4601* ⊕ *www.bourbon.com.br* ⊃ *165 rooms, 10 suites* ⅄ *Restaurant, coffee shop, cable TV, indoor pool, gym, sauna, bar, business services, convention center* ⊟ *AE, DC, MC, V* ⦿ *CP.*

★ **$$** ⊞ **Grand Hotel Rayon.** A spacious lobby welcomes you to Curitiba's most sophisticated hotel. Superbly furnished standard rooms have soundproof windows and two phone lines, which are a blessing for the business traveler. Service is impeccable, and the location—in the heart of the financial district and right next to Rua 24 Horas—is convenient. Weekend stays get complimentary Linha Turismo bus-tour tickets. ⊠ *Rua Visconde de Nacar 1424, Centro 80411-201* ☎ *041/2108–1100 or 0800/41–8899* ⊕ *www.rayon.com.br* ⊃ *136 rooms, 11 suites* ⅄ *2 restaurants, coffee shop, room service, cable TV, outdoor pool, gym, sauna, bar, business services, meeting room, travel services* ⊟ *AE, DC, MC, V* ⦿ *CP.*

$ ⊞ **Bristol Multy Duomo Park Hotel.** Everything is shiny and comfortable at this small hotel. The rooms and suites are unusually spacious. Bathrooms are heated—hard to find in Brazil, but welcome in the cold Curitiba winters. Another draw is the location: one step from Rua 24 Horas. ⊠ *Rua Visconde de Rio Branco 1710, Centro 80420-200* ☎ *041/ 3321–1900 or 0800/41–1816* ⊟ *041/3224–1816* ⊕ *www.bristol-hotelaria.com.br* ⊃ *40 rooms, 8 suites* ⅄ *Restaurant, cable TV, bar, business services, sauna, fitness center, meeting rooms, airport shuttle* ⊟ *AE, DC, MC, V* ⦿ *CP.*

$ ⊞ **Slaviero Braz Hotel.** In a landmark building overlooking the walkway of Rua das Flores, Slaviero Braz has large rooms with wood paneling and matching furniture. Beds are king sized, with colorful spreads and cushions that invite you to relax. Rooms in the east wing are smaller and oddly shaped, and elevators there are cramped because of the original building plan. The second-floor Getúlio bar-café is a popular gathering spot for businesspeople. ⊠ *Av. Luiz Xavier 67, Centro 80020-020* ☎ *041/ 3017–1037 or 0800/704–3311* ⊟ *041/3322–2829* ⊕ *www.hotelslaviero. com.br* ⊃ *89 rooms, 2 suites* ⅄ *Restaurant, cable TV, gym, bar, business services, meeting rooms, airport shuttle* ⊟ *AE, DC, MC, V* ⦿ *CP.*

¢ ⊞ **Íbis Curitiba.** The Íbis leads the city's roster of budget lodging. The hotel combines comfort and efficiency in cream-color rooms with a no-frills approach to the extras. Be prepared to carry your own luggage. The reception desk and the restaurant are in restored historic houses that are detached from the main building. Íbis is one of the few hotels in Curitiba that has wheelchair-accessible rooms. ⊠ *Rua Comendador Araújo 730, Centro Cívico 80020-050* ☎ *041/2102–2000 or 0800/ 703–7000* ⊟ *041/2102–2001* ⊕ *www.accorhotels.com.br* ⊃ *150 rooms* ⅄ *Restaurant, cable TV, bar* ⊟ *AE, DC, MC, V.*

¢ ▦ **InterPalace.** What once was a school in downtown Curitiba, near Teatro Guaíra and Setor Histórico, is now a great budget choice. Rooms are basic, but extremely spacious and comfortable. ⊠ *Av XV de Novembro 950, Centro 80060-000* ☎ *041/3223–5282* ⊟ *041/3225–2224* ⊕ *www.interpalace.com.br* ⟿ *70 rooms* ⚲ *Restaurant, convention center; no a/c in some rooms* ⊟ *AE, DC, MC, V* ⏀ *CP.*

Nightlife & the Arts

Curitiba has a bustling cultural scene, a reflection of the European background of many of its citizens. Complete listings of events are published in the *Gazeta do Povo,* the major daily newspaper.

☾ In what was once a railway terminal, the **Shopping Estação** (⊠ Av. 7 de Setembro 2775, Centro ☎ 041/2101–9101) is a 210,000-square-meter (700,000-square-foot) covered area with a colorful and noisy collection of bars and restaurants, amusement parks, exhibits, and more than 100 shops. The small Museu Ferroviário (Railway Museum), a cineplex, and daily live musical shows add to the center's charm. The complex is open daily 10 AM–2 AM. The **Teatro Guaíra** (⊠ Rua 15 de Novembro s/n, Centro ☎ 041/3322–2628), formerly the Teatro São Teodoro (circa 1884), was totally rebuilt in its present location and reopened in 1974. It has a modern, well-equipped 2,000-seat auditorium, as well as two smaller rooms. Shows include plays, popular music concerts, and the occasional full-fledged opera.

Sports & the Outdoors

Curitiba has three professional soccer clubs: Coritiba, Atlético Paranaense, and Paraná Clube. Check local newspaper listings for upcoming game times and locations. Many of the area's parks have paths for jogging and bicycling.

Arena da Baixada (⊠ Rua Eng. Rebouças 3113, Água Verde ☎ 041/3333–4747) is home for Atlético Paranaense Club. It's the most modern sports facility in the country, with a 32,000-seat capacity, to be expanded to 50,000 in the future. **Estádio Couto Pereira** (⊠ Rua Ubaldino do Amaral 37, Alto da Glória ☎ 041/3362–3234) is the 60-year-old home of Coritiba FC and holds 40,000 fans. **Parque Barigüí** (⊠ Av. Candido Hartmann at Av. Gen. Tourinho, off Km 1, BR 277 ☎ 041/3335–2112) contains soccer fields, volleyball courts, and paths spread throughout 310 acres.

Shopping

Curitiba Outlet Center (⊠ Rua Brigadeiro Franco 1916, Batel ☎ 041/3224–1900) has a large array of clothing shops with rock-bottom prices. This government-sponsored shop offers a variety of wicker, clay, wood, and leather crafts as well as more traditional items such as Ukrainian *pessankes* (painted eggshells) and indigenous ornaments. Handmade toys are also available. **Artesanato do Paraná** (⊠ Alameda Dr. Muricy 950, Centro ☎ 041/3234–1118). Interact directly with the artisans every Sunday at the **Feira de Artesanato** (⊠ Largo da Ordem and Praça Garibaldi, Setor Histórico) from 9 to 3. **Shopping Center Müller** (⊠ Rua Candido de Abreu 127, São Francisco ☎ 041/3224–0510) is the city's prime shopping location, with branches of national chains, upscale fashion and jewelry stores, as well as small handicraft shops, restaurants and cafés, book-stores, and movie theaters.

Paranaguá

8 *90 km (56 mi) southeast of Curitiba.*

Most of Brazil's coffee and soybeans are shipped out of Paranaguá, the nation's second-largest port, which also serves as chief port for land-locked Paraguay. Downtown holds many examples of colonial archi-tecture and has been designated an official historic area. The city, founded in 1565 by Portuguese explorers, is 30 km (18 mi) from the Atlantic on the Baía de Paranaguá. The bay area is surrounded by Mata Atlântica, of which a great swatch on the northern side is protected; sev-eral islands in the bay also have rain forests as well as great beaches. You'll find other less scenic but popular sandy stretches farther south, toward the Santa Catarina border.

Although you can reach Paranaguá on BR 277, consider taking the more scenic Estrada da Graciosa, which follows the route taken by 17th-cen-tury traders up the Serra do Mar. This narrow, winding route—paved with rocks slabs in some stretches—is some 30 km (18 mi) longer than BR 277, but the breathtaking peaks and slopes covered with rain for-est make the extra travel time worthwhile.

Igreja Nossa Senhora do Rosário, the city's first church, was destroyed, sacked, and rebuilt several times, but its facade (circa 1578) is original. ⊠ *Largo Monsenhor Celso s/n* ☎ *No phone* 🖾 *Free* 🕑 *Daily 7* AM*–9* PM.

The **Museu de Arqueologia e Etnologia** (Archaeology and Ethnology Mu-seum) occupies a building that was part of a Jesuit school founded in 1752. The Jesuits left around 1768 when the Marques de Pombal from Portugal, trying to control the power of the Catholic church, had them expelled from the Portuguese kingdom (which included Brazil at that time). The collection includes pieces found in excavations in the area, most belonging to the Sambaqui, a coastal-dwelling native people, and temporary art exhibits. ⊠ *Rua General Carneiro 66* ☎ *041/3422–8844* 🖾 *R$3* 🕑 *Tues.–Sun. 1–5.*

Fodor's Choice ★ The 10-km-long (6-mi-long) **Ilha do Mel** (Honey Island), a state park in the Baía de Paranaguá, is the most popular destination on Paraná's coast. It's crisscrossed by hiking trails—cars aren't allowed, and the number of visitors is limited to 5,000 at any one time—and has two villages, Encantadas and Nova Brasília, and several pristine beaches. Local lore has it that the east shore's Gruta das Encantadas (Enchanted Grotto) is frequented by mermaids. On the south shore check out the sights around Farol das Conchas (Lighthouse of the Shells) and its beach. From Forte de Nossa Senhora dos Prazeres (Fort of Our Lady of Pleasures), built in 1767 on the east shore, take advantage of the great views of the for-est-clad northern bay islands. The most scenic ferry rides leave from Paranaguá between 8 AM and 1 PM; they take one and a half hours and cost R$50–R$75. More convenient are the ferries that depart from Pontal do Sul, 49 km (30 mi) east of Paranaguá every 30 minutes. Prices start at R$35. To ensure admission in the high season (December–March), it's best to book an island tour before you leave Curitiba. ✉ *Ferries depart from Alameda do Café s/n, Pontal do Sul* ☎ *041/3455–2616.*

The northern shore of Baía de Paranaguá is also home to the 92,000-acre **Parque Nacional de Superagüí** and its complex system of coves, saltwater marshes, and forested islands—including Ilha Superagüí and Ilha das Peças. Most of these pristine settings containing animal and bird species unique to the Mata Atlântica are closed to visitation. You can, however, see a lot of bird and animal species by basing yourself in the fishing village of Guaraqueçaba—reached by a three-hour ferry ride from Paranaguá's harbor—and then touring the bay and trails around the park. Your best bet for viewing wildlife is to explore the islands on a guided boat tour. ✉ *Park administration: 2 km (1 mi) north of Guaraqueçaba. Ferry Dock: Rua da Praia s/n* ☎ *041/3455–2616 ferry information, 041/ 3482–1262 park* 🖅 *Park free, ferry R$190–R$275* ☉ *Park daily 9–6; ferries from Guaraqueçaba at 1* PM *and 3* PM.

Where to Stay & Eat

$ ✕ **Casa do Barreado.** As its name suggests, this small, homey family-run buffet-style restaurant specializes in the traditional barreado, including an unusual chicken variety called *galinha na púcura*. Although the restaurant is officially open only on weekends, you can call ahead to arrange a dinner during the week. Barreado takes 24 hours to cook, so you must order it a day in advance. ✉ *Rua José Antônio Cruz 78* ☎ *041/3423–1830* ⚐ *Reservations essential* 🖃 *DC, MC* ☉ *Closed weekdays.*

$ ✕🏨 **Camboa Resort Hotel.** In the historic district, Camboa has comfortable facilities, a long roster of activities, and a dedicated staff that can arrange for tours in the region. Modern architecture and cheerful colors blend with the colonial surroundings. Ask to be on the north side for a bay view. Continental cuisine, with an emphasis on French, is served in the restaurant ($–$$). ✉ *Rua João Estevão s/n, 83203-020* ☎ *041/ 3420–5200 or 0800/411–077* 🖶 *041/3422–3637* ⊕ *www.hotelcamboa. com.br* ⟿ *114 rooms, 6 suites* ♿ *Restaurant, coffee shop, cable TV, 2 tennis courts, indoor pool, pool, gym, sauna, boating, soccer, volleyball, 2 bars, recreation room, shops, playground, business services, meeting room* 🖃 *AE, DC, MC, V* ¶�‖ *CP.*

¢ ✕🏨 **Tia Bela Pousada and Restaurant.** Right on the waterfront of the historic district, this small pousada allows easy access to the boats and ferries. The apartments are basic, yet cozy and neatly decorated. The friendly staff serves a king's breakfast in the morning before you depart to your explorations to visit the area attractions. The restaurant ($) has barreado and seafood dishes. ✉ *Rua General Carneiro, 83203-000* ☎🖶 *041/3424–3783* ⟿ *5 rooms* ♿ *Restaurant, fans; no a/c in some rooms* 🖃 *No credit cards* ¶❖‖ *CP.*

Parque Estadual de Vila Velha

❾ *97 km (60 mi) northwest of Curitiba.*

The 22 towering rock formations of the 7,670-acre Vila Velha State Park stand in sharp contrast to the green rolling hills of the Campos Gerais,

Paraná's high plains. Three hundred million years of rain and wind have carved these sandstone formations, whose names—the Lion, the Cup, the Mushroom, the Sphinx—reflect their shapes. You can visit these natural monuments on foot or in a tractor-pulled wagon along a well-marked 2½-km (1½-mi) trail that starts a mile from the visitor center. Traversing the path and viewing the formations on foot takes about two hours. ⊠ *Km 514, BR 376* ☎ *042/3228–1539* 🖼 *R$12* ☉ *Daily 8–6.*

Where to Stay & Eat

$ ✕ **La Taverne.** This is a great choice for pasta, pizzas, and beef in downtown Ponta Grossa, north of the Parque Vila Velha. The *picanha* (grilled steak served with a mushroom-and-herb sauce) is the highlight. ⊠ *Rua 7 de Setembro 1136, 23 km (13 mi) northwest of park, Ponta Grossa* ☎ *042/3224–3534* ⚏ *Reservations essential* ▤ *DC, MC, V.*

¢ ✕ **Pampeana.** This busy, *espeto-corrido*–style (called *rodízio* in the north-central states) churrascaria is the perfect place to satisfy a hearty appetite acquired touring Parque Estadual de Vila Velha. It has a great salad bar for those not crazy about the meat excesses of churrasco. Saturday special is the *feijoada.* ⊠ *Km 373, BR 376 (Avenida Presidente Kennedy), Ponta Grossa* ☎ *042/3229–2881* ▤ *DC, MC, V* ☉ *No dinner Sun.*

¢–$ ✕▥ **Vila Velha Palace.** The best luxury option in the city, Vila Velha Palace is also the largest hotel in the central region of Paraná State. Among the amenities is free access to the city's golf course. Rooms are ample and elegant, with queen-sized beds. The house restaurant ($–$$) serves Brazilian fare. ⊠ *Rua Balduino Taques 123, Ponta Grossa 84040-000* ☎☎ *042/3225–2200* ⊕ *www.convoy.com.br/~hvvelha/* 🗲 *90 rooms, 2 suites* ⚫ *Restaurant, golf privileges, gym, sauna, bar, business services, meeting rooms* ▤ *AE, DC, MC, V* ▥ *CP.*

☾ ¢–$ ▥ **Hotel Fazenda Capão Grande.** The 150-year-old Fazenda Capão Grande is a fully functional ranch that breeds *criollo* horses. You can fully experience gaucho traditions, from churrasco to cattle driving—a great way to round out your visit to Vila Velha. There are trails and waterfalls to explore within the farm. Riding classes are available. ⊠ *19 km (12 mi) along an unpaved road off Km 511, BR 376, Ponta Grossa* ☎☎ *042/3228–1198* 🗲 *8 rooms* ⚫ *Dining room, horseback riding, lounge* ▤ *No credit cards* ▥ *FAP.*

¢ ▥ **Planalto Palace.** This budget hotel in downtown Ponta Grossa is a preferred choice for business travelers. It has comfortable rooms and a reliable staff eager to inform you about the attractions of the Campos Gerais region. ⊠ *Rua 7 de Setembro 652, Ponta Grossa 84010-350* ☎☎ *042/ 3222–7900* ⊕ *www.hotelplanalto.com.br* 🗲 *66 rooms* ⚫ *Cable TV, gym, bar, business services, meeting rooms* ▤ *AE, DC, MC, V* ▥ *CP.*

Foz do Iguaçu

⑩ *637 km (396 mi) west of Curitiba, 544 (338 mi) west of Vila Velha.*

The Foz do Iguaçu cascades in a deafening roar at a bend in the Rio Iguaçu where southwestern Paraná State meets the borders of both Argentina and Paraguay. This Brazilian town and the Argentine town of Puerto Iguazú are the hubs for exploring the falls (the Paraguayan town of Ciudad del Este is also nearby).

The avalanche of water actually consists of some 275 separate falls (in the rainy season they can number as many as 350) that plunge 80 meters (250 feet) onto the rocks below. The backdrop is one of dense, lush jungle, rainbows, ferns, and butterflies over the reddish-black basalt walls. The falls and the lands around them are protected by Brazil's Parque Nacional do Iguaçu and Argentina's Parque Nacional Iguazú (where the falls are referred to by their Spanish name, the Cataratas de Iguazú).

The Brazilians are blessed with the best panoramic view of the falls (allow half a day to traverse the catwalks and stop at the lookouts); the Argentine side—where most of the falls are actually situated—offers better up-close experiences. Allow another half day for this tour. Local tour operators run trips that take you to both. To set your own pace, take one of the regularly scheduled buses to the Brazilian park and then take a taxi across the international bridge, Ponte Presidente Tancredo Neves, to Argentina. Note that immigration authorities keep the region under close watch, and you will have to go through immigrations and customs. To avoid delays, make sure you have a valid visa before attempting to cross the Argentina–Brazil border either way.

The summer months (November–March) are hot and humid, so if you're bothered by the heat, plan to visit between April and October. Be aware, however, that high waters from heavy rainfall on the upper Iguaçu River basin occasionally restrict access to some walkways. Whatever time of year you visit, bring raingear: some paths take you extremely close to the falling water, where the spray can leave you drenched.

Fodor'sChoice
★

The **Parque Nacional do Iguaçu** extends 25 km (16 mi) along a paved highway southwest of downtown Foz do Iguaçu. Park administration is handled by a private operator, which runs the visitor center and all tourist service and facilities. ATMs, a snack bar, a souvenir shop, and information and currency exchange are available at the center. You cannot drive into the park—park at the entrance by the visitor center and take an 11-km (7-mi) double-decker shuttle trip from there. The shuttle departs every 15 minutes and drops you by the trailhead, where the luxurious Tropical Cataratas EcoResort stands. The path to the falls is about 2 km (1 mi) long, and its walkways and staircases lead through the rain forest to concrete and wooden catwalks. (Much of the park's 457,000 acres are protected rain forest that is off-limits to visitors and home to the last viable populations of jaguars as well as of rare bromeliads and orchids.) There is a smaller visitor center with a snack bar, restaurant, and souvenir kiosk at the end of the trail, where you take the shuttle buses back to the main visitor center.

At the Salto Macuco (Macuco Falls) in the park, the crystal-clear waters of the Rio Macuco, a small tributary of the Iguaçu River, fall 18 meters (60 feet) into a natural pool. The only way to visit the falls is on a tour that takes about two hours and costs roughly R$140 per person. The trip requires a 7-km (5-mi) ride in a four-wheel-drive vehicle, followed by a short hike through the forest and a breathtaking 30-minute Zodiac ride on the Iguaçu to the falls.

Highlights of the Brazilian side of the falls include the Salto Santa Maria, from which catwalks branch off to Salto Deodoro and Salto Floriano, where you'll be doused by the spray. The end of the catwalk puts you right at the tallest and most popular falls, Garganta do Diabo (Devil's Throat), which extend for 3 km (1½ mi) in a 270-degree arc; the water thunders down 54 meters (180 feet).

In Argentina's **Parque Nacional Iguazú** (☎ 03757/420–2722), there are a couple of major *circuitos* (routes). The Circuito Inferior (Lower Circuit) is a loop trail that leads to the brink of several falls. It starts off the main path leading from the visitor center, which is open daily from 7 AM to 8 PM. Wear your bathing suit on this route so you can take a dip in the calm pools at the trail's edge. The Circuito Superior (Upper Circuit) is a 900-meter-long (3,000-foot-long) path that borders the ridge on the river's south side, along the top of the falls.

The Argentine side offers the chance to view Devil's Throat from a different perspective. From Puerto Canoas, 4 km (2½ mi) upriver from the visitor center, a small fleet of Zodiacs will take you to the remnants of the ½-km-long (¼-mi-long) catwalk that once spanned the river to the falls. Much of this structure was washed away by floods. An overlook lets you watch the mighty waters of the Iguaçu disappear right in front of you. ⊠ *Km 17, Rodovia das Cataratas* ☎ *045/3521–4400* ⊕ *www. cataratasdoiguacu.com.br* 🎟*Park R$11.85, parking R$9.90* ⊙ *Mon. 1–6, Tues.–Sun. 8–6.*

There are other notable sights near the national park, including the privately run **Parque das Aves** (Bird Park). Here, on 36 acres of mostly untouched tropical forest right outside the national park, are 8-meter-high (25-foot-high) aviaries with 160 species of birds, as well as reptiles and a butterfly collection. A gift shop and a restaurant round out the facilities. ⊠ *Km 17, Rodovia das Cataratas* ☎ *045/3529–8282* 🎟*R$18* ⊙ *Daily 9–6.*

★ Only slightly smaller than the Hoover Dam, the **Itaipú Dam** is the result of one of the engineering marvels of the world: the mighty Hidrelétrica de Itaipú (Itaipú Hydroelectric Power Plant). It is the largest hydroelectric power plant on earth, at 8 km (5 mi) long, producing 25 percent of Brazil's electricity and 78 percent of Paraguay's. Watch a 15-minute video about the construction of the dam at the visitor center and join the hour-long guided bus tour of the complex. Tours of the plant or dam must be booked in advance. Night tours—which include a light-and-sound show—begin at 8:30 Friday and Saturday. ⊠ *Km 11, Av. Tancredo Neves, 6 mi (10 km) up the Rio Paraná from the Foz do Iguaçu* ☎ *045/3520–6999* 🎟*$6* ⊙ *Mon.–Sat. 8–6.*

At the **Ecomuseu de Itaipú** (Itaipú Eco-Museum), funded by the dam's operator Itaipú Binacional, you can learn about the geology, archeology, and efforts to preserve the flora and fauna of the area since the dam was built. ⊠ *Km 10, Av. Tancredo Neves* ☎ *045/3520–5816* ⊕ *www. itaipu.gov.br* 🎟*Free* ⊙ *Daily 8–6.*

Where to Stay & Eat

Near the borders of two other countries, the town of Foz do Iguaçu has a cosmopolitan atmosphere that's reflected in the cuisine. The options are impressive for a city of its size. One noteworthy hotel is on the Argentine side—the Internacional Cataratas de Iguazú. For convenience, most visitors stay in the establishments that line BR 469 (Rodovia das Cataratas), the highway that runs from the city of Foz do Iguaçu to the national park and the falls. All major hotels can make arrangements for tours.

★ **$$–$$$** ✕ **Zaragoza.** In a quiet neighborhood on a tree-lined street, this cozy restaurant, owned by a Spanish immigrant, is very popular with the international crowd and with locals. The fare includes seafood paella, the house specialty, as well as several delicious fish options. The *surubi*, a regional fish, definitely merits a try. ✉ *Rua Quintino Bocaiúva 882* ☎ *045/ 3574–3084* ▭ *AE, DC. MC, V.*

$–$$ ✕ **Cantina 4 Sorelle.** The warm and cheerful atmosphere at this Italian restaurant makes it very popular among the locals. The efficient staff serves pasta dishes and pizzas. Try the *tortellone anatra ubriaco* (duck-filled pasta with spinach, tomato, and mozzarella in a wine–cognac reduction). ✉ *Rua Alm Barroso 1336* ☎ *045/3523–1707* ▭ *AE, DC, MC, V.*

$ ✕ **Cataratas Iate Clube.** The only restaurant where you can dine with the Paraná River as your backdrop, Cataratas Iate Clube is about a mile from downtown. The fish rodízio includes Foz do Iguaçu's best *moqueca de surubi* (stew made with surubi, a local fish) and *piapara ao vinagrete* (fried *piapara* fish marinated in vinegar sauce). ✉ *Km 0.5, Av. Gen. Meira* ☎ *045/3523–6776* ☾ *Closed Mon.* ▭ *No credit cards.*

¢ ✕ **Búfalo Branco.** This is the city's finest and largest churrascaria. The picanha stands out from the 25 grilled meat choices. The salad bar is well stocked, a boon for vegetarians. ✉ *Av. Rebouças 530* ☎ *045/ 3523–9744* ▭ *AE, DC, MC, V.*

$$$ ✕▦ **Bourbon Cataratas Resort & Convention Center.** The decor of this hotel is elegant, in light yellow tones, and the upper floors have views of the national park's lush rain forest in the distance. Most of the spacious rooms and guest facilities are in the main building; suites occupy the top floors of an adjacent tower. On the ground floor is a small shopping center. Hotel grounds have a jogging path that runs through a patch of rain forest. The highly regarded restaurant, Tarobá ($$–$$$), serves Brazilian and international fare. ✉ *Km 2½, Rodovia das Cataratas, 85863-000* ☎ *045/3529–0123 or 0800/45–1010* 🖷 *045/3529–0000* ⊕ *www. bourbon.com.br* ☞ *298 rooms, 13 suites* ♿ *3 restaurants, coffee shop, cable TV, 2 tennis courts, golf privileges, indoor pool, 2 outdoor pools, gym, health club, sauna, soccer, bar, shops, convention center, meeting rooms, car rental, travel services, no-smoking rooms, airport shuttle* ▭*AE, DC, MC, V* ¶◯ *CP.*

★ **$$$** ✕▦ **Sheraton International Iguazú.** The building may be an eyesore, but it's just a short walk from the falls, and half of the large, comfortable rooms have direct views of them. Be sure to reserve one of these well in advance (they're about 30% more expensive). Floor-to-ceiling windows reveal the inspiring scene to the lobby, restaurants, bars, and even the pool. As the harpist plucks away in the Garganta del Diablo ($) restaurant, one of the area's finest, you can savor expertly prepared dishes from the international menu. The trout in pastry and the surubí (catfish) in banana leaves are exquisite. The restaurant is only open for dinner, which starts after the last bus from here to Puerto Iguazú; if you're not a Sheraton guest, plan on laying out over 50 pesos (R$38) for the taxi trip back to your hotel. ⊠ *Parque Nacional Iguazú, Argentina 3370* ☎ *3757/49–1800* 🖷 *3757/49–1810* ⊕ *www.sheraton.com* ⋟ *176 rooms, 4 suites* ⟁ *2 restaurants, room service, in-room safes, minibars, cable TV, 3 tennis courts, outdoor pool, gym, sauna, bicycles, bars, lobby lounge, babysitting, laundry service, Internet room, business services, convention center, airport shuttle, car rental, travel services, free parking, no-smoking rooms* ⊟ *AE, DC, MC, V.*

$$$ ✕▤ **Tropical das Cataratas EcoResort.** Not only is this stately hotel *in* the
Fodor'sChoice   national park, with wonderful views of the falls from the front-side apart-
★   ments, but it also provides the traditional comforts of a colonial-style establishment: large rooms, terraces, vintage furniture, and hammocks. The main building, surrounded by verandas and gardens, is almost 100 years old and is a National Heritage Site. The Itaipú restaurant ($$–$$$$) serves a traditional Brazilian dinner, with feijoada and a variety of side dishes. Any entrées featuring fish from the Paraná basin are also recommended. ⊠ *Km 25, Rodovia das Cataratas, 85850-970* ☎ *045/3521–7000 or 0800/701–2670* 🖷 *045/522–1717* ⊕ *www.tropicalhotel.com.br* ⋟ *203 rooms* ⟁ *2 restaurants, coffee shop, cable TV, 2 tennis courts, pool, gym, volleyball, bar, shops, playground, airport shuttle* ⊟ *AE, DC, MC, V* ⦿ *CP.*

★ $$ ▤ **Bourbon Iguaçu Golf Club and Resort.** Even the most demanding visitors find the Iguaçu Golf Club unforgettable. The resort hosts a national pro golf tournament annually. Accommodations are in small eight-room buildings surrounded by spacious and plush gardens with tropical vegetation—a preview of what lies beyond in the national park. If you're traveling with family or a group of friends, ask for one of the separate guest houses, called *bangalôs.* ⊠ *Km 7, Rodovia das Cataratas, 85863-000* ☎ *045/3529–9999* 🖷 *045/3529–8888* ⊕ *www.bourbon.com.br* ⋟ *67 rooms, 4 guest houses* ⟁ *Restaurant, cable TV, driving range, 18-hole golf course, putting green, pool, health club, hot tub, bar, lounge, shops, airport shuttle* ⊟ *AE, DC, MC, V* ⦿ *CP.*

$ ▤ **Hotel Florença Iguassu.** In a sprawling wooded lot on the road to the national park, Florença combines budget rates with excellent service. Rooms are large and have walk-in closets and views of the gardens. ⊠ *Km 13, Rodovia das Cataratas, 85863-000* ☎ *045/3529–7755* 🖷 *045/3529–8877* ⊕ *www.hotelflorenca.com* ⋟ *63 rooms* ⟁ *Restaurant, cable TV, tennis court, pool, volleyball, bar, playground, meeting room* ⊟ *AE, DC, MC, V* ⦿ *CP.*

¢   ▤ **Foz Plaza.** This reliable budget choice has standard but comfortable rooms, and although the decor isn't tasteful, the staff is attentive. ⊠ *Rua Mal. Deodoro 1819, 85851-030* ☎ *045/523–1448* ⊕ *www.challengerhoteis.com.br* ⋟ *64 rooms* ⟁ *Restaurant, cable TV, pool, sauna, bar, recreation room* ⊟ *AE, V* ⦿ *CP.*

¢   ▤ **Foz Presidente.** The main draw of this budget hotel is the downtown location, with easy access to all attractions and the business district. Rooms are nondescript but comfortable, with queen-sized beds, and look out onto downtown Foz. ✉ *Av. Marechal Floriano 1851, 85851-030* 🏢 *045/3523–2318* 🛏 *115 rooms* ⚙ *Cable TV, pool, bar, lounge* 🖃 *AE, DC, MC, V* 🍴 *CP.*

SANTA CATARINA

The state of Santa Catarina, the south's smallest state, has almost 485 km (300 mi) of coastline (with many gorgeous beaches). The capital, Florianópolis, is on Ilha de Santa Catarina, an island with 42 beaches and many world-class hotels and resorts that has become a major travel destination in Brazil. North and south of Florianópolis along the coast are other great destinations where thousands of Brazilian and foreign tourists flock every summer. Santa Catarina is also home to the German settlements of Blumenau and Joinville, in the northern valleys. These highly industrialized cities still retain some of their German flavor, including a popular Oktoberfest.

Blumenau

⑫ *250 km (156 mi) northwest of Florianópolis.*

The cradle of the prosperous Vale do Itajaí region, Blumenau is a pleasant place, with clean streets and friendly people who take great pride in their community. The name of this city of more than 260,000 is indicative of its German origins. Downtown has been restored to preserve its early German architectural style—*enxaimel* (half-timber, half-brick construction)—and the annual Oktoberfest has attracted crowds from all over the south since its inception in 1984. Events spill from the festival site into downtown (around Rua 15 de Novembro) for three weeks, when almost 100,000 gallons of beer and matching amounts of wurst and sauerkraut are consumed.

For insight into the history of German immigration, check out the **Museu da Família Colonial** (Colonial Family Museum). The house, which was built in 1864 for the Gaertner family, some of the first settlers to the area, contains a collection of everyday objects that belonged to the city's first residents; its garden has many examples of regional flora. ✉ *Rua Duque de Caxias 78* 🏢 *047/3322–1676* 💲 *R$3* 🕐 *Tues.–Fri. 8–6, Sat. 9–4, Sun. 9–noon.*

The Blumenau area is home to an important glassware industry, whose high-quality products are aimed at the discriminating customer. At **Glaspark** you can see artisans at work, learn about the industry at a museum, and buy designer glassware at reasonable prices. ✉ *Rua Rudolf Roedel 147, Salto Weisbach* 🏢 *047/3327–1261* 💲 *Free* 🕐 *Mon.–Sat. 9–6.*

Where to Stay & Eat

$–$$ ✕ **Frohsinn.** On the outskirts of town is one of the best German restaurants in the region. The stuffed duck served with mashed potatoes, cassava, and red cabbage is a regional specialty. ✉ *Rua Gertrud Sierich s/n, Morro do Aipim* 🏢 *047/3322–2137* 🖃 *AE, DC, MC, V* 🕐 *Closed Sun.*

$ ✕🏨 **Plaza Blumenau.** Check in if you're looking for upscale accommodations, spacious rooms, and great facilities. The Terrace restaurant ($–$$)

THE EUROPEAN SOUTH

IN THE EARLY 1820S *Austrian-born Empress Dona Leopoldina, first wife of Dom Pedro I (Brazil's first emperor), envisioned the vast, sparsely populated Brazilian countryside settled with the kind of farmers she knew from Europe. Although European farmers had a poor track record in the tropics, it was felt that southern Brazil's cooler, subtropical climate wouldn't be so inhospitable. Agents hired by the Brazilian crown were dispatched to central Europe, where they touted the wonders of Brazil and the abundance of its "farmland" (actually covered by dense forest, home to native peoples—such as the Guarani and Kaigang—and wild animals like the South American puma). Beginning in 1824 and continuing for more than 50 years, thousands of Europeans—many of them German—were lured to central and eastern Rio Grande do Sul and to eastern Santa Catarina.*

High-end estimates place the number of German settlers in the 200,000–300,000 range (exact figures are hard to come by because of poor record-keeping by the Brazilian authorities and the tendency for colonists to indicate the region— Hunsrück, Pommern, Pfalz—from which they came rather than simply "Germany," which was not unified as a single country until 1871). Most who came were poor or landless farmers who faced famine in their homelands. Some were craftsmen who provided the goods and services needed to truly create settlements. The first New World community was established in São Leopoldo (named after Dona Leopoldina), 31 km (19 mi) north of Porto Alegre on the Rio dos Sinos (Bells River). This and the valley of the Rio Itajaí in Santa Catarina became cradles of Brazil's German immigrants.

The Germans brought their unswerving work ethic, their knowledge of intensive cash-crop agriculture, and their rich culture—much of which still thrives. Recent studies indicate that at least 500,000 Brazilians speak some German (usually dialects that speakers of the standard language would find hard to understand). Further, the Lutheran religion is still practiced by many people with German ancestry. Researchers of Rio Grande do Sul's rich folklore are keen to acknowledge that the rhythms of some regional music can be traced back to German polkas. German cuisine is so much a part of the region that hardly anyone here can conceive of a churrasco without pork sausages and Kartoffeln Salat (potato salad). And pastries are an essential part of the German-bred café colonial. Although most small local breweries have been incorporated into large national companies, prior to the 1970s the southern states had a long list of them. In addition, German immigrants and their descendants were behind such internationally renowned Brazilian companies as Varig Airlines, the steel company Gerdau, and the jeweler H. Stern.

If you visit such communities as Blumenau, Joinville, São Leopoldo, Novo Hamburgo, Gramado, Lageado, and Santa Cruz do Sul, you'll certainly experience a bit of Europe in Brazil. Indeed, Blumenau and Santa Cruz host large Oktoberfests. Crowds of German-Brazilians flock to these festivals to dance to their traditional rhythms (polkas and waltzes) and indulge in sausages, sauerkraut, and beer.

serves international cuisine with an emphasis on things German. ✉ *Rua 7 de Setembro 818, Centro 89010-200* ☎ *047/231–7000 or 0800/ 47–1213* 🖷 *047/3231–7001* ⊕ *www.plazahoteis.com.br* ⤴ *123 rooms, 8 suites* ♻ *Restaurant, cable TV, pool, gym, bar, business services, meeting rooms, no-smoking rooms* ▭ *AE, DC, MC, V* |◎| *CP.*

¢ ✕🖭 **Hotel Glória.** This best buy has rooms that are basic but comfortable and an attentive staff. The elegant British-style lobby—with wood paneling, wrought-iron lamps, and large leather chairs—is unique in Brazil. What really makes the place popular is the on-site KaffeHaus Glória (¢–$), which serves the traditional, lavish café colonial, with 50 kinds of pies and cakes. ✉ *Rua 7 de Setembro 954, Centro 89010-280* ☎ *047/ 326–1988* 🖷 *047/3326–5370* ⊕ *www.hotelgloria.com.br* ⤴ *105 rooms* ♻ *Restaurant, coffee shop, cable TV, bar, meeting rooms* ▭ *AE, DC, MC, V* |◎| *CP.*

Shopping

H Shopping Center (✉ Rua 15 de Novembro 759, Centro ☎ 047/326–2166) sells its own glassware and china, all at below-market prices.

Porto Belo

⓭ *69 km (43 mi) north of Florianópolis.*

The seafront town of Porto Belo lies at the base of a peninsula dotted with beaches, bays, and coves, and it has a great reputation among Argentine and Paraguayan tourists for its natural beauty, great beaches, and many water sports. It is a port of call for some of the Buenos Aires–Rio cruise lines. The calm waters of the Porto Belo bay are a haven of nautical sports—scuba diving, snorkeling, sailing. Fishing is very popular here, too. Porto Belo is the ideal place to make your base for exploring the paradisiacal landscapes of the region.

Where to Stay & Eat

$ ✕🖭 **Baleia Branca.** There are plenty of amenities to recommend this hotel, but the short distance to the beach is certainly the highlight. Expect impeccable service from one of the first hotels to open in the area. The chalets are a comfortable option for larger parties. The highly regarded restaurant ($) won't fail to impress either. ✉ *Alameda Nena Trevisan 98, 88210-000* ☎ *047/3369–4011* 🖷 *047/369–4114* ⊕ *www.hotelbaleiabranca. com.br* ⤴ *43 apartments, 11 chalets* ♻ *Restaurant, pool, sauna, beach, soccer, bar, playground, meeting room* ▭ *V.*

Ilha de Santa Catarina

⓮ Its nickname is the Magic Island, which is an appropriate moniker for this island with breathtaking shoreline, 42 easy-to-reach beaches—some with warm waters—and seemingly endless vacation activities. Every summer (December–March), thousands of Argentines and Paraguayans arrive here, adding to the constant influx of Brazilians, making this one of the country's top tourist destinations. Ilha de Santa Catarina is joined to the mainland by two bridges: the modern, multilane Ponte Colombo Sales and the 60-year-old Ponte Hercilio Luz—the latter now condemned. Scuba diving, surfing, sailing, and parasailing are among the

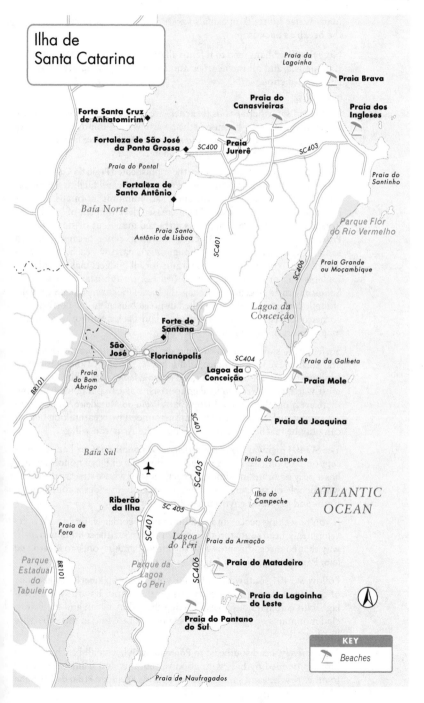

Ilha de Santa Catarina

Praia da Lagoinha

Praia Brava

Praia do Canasvieiras

Praia dos Ingleses

Forte Santa Cruz de Anhatomirim ◆

Fortaleza de São José da Ponta Grossa ◆

SC400

Praia Jurerê

SC403

Praia do Pontal

Praia do Santinho

Fortaleza de Santo Antônio ◆

Baía Norte

Praia Santo Antônio de Lisboa

SC401

Parque Flór do Rio Vermelho

Praia Grande ou Moçambique

SC406

Lagoa da Conceição

Forte de Santana ◆

São José ○

Florianópolis ○

SC404

Praia da Galheta

Lagoa da Conceição ○

Praia Mole

BR101

Praia do Bom Abrigo

SC401

Praia da Joaquina

Baía Sul

Praia do Campeche

✈

SC405

Ilha do Campeche

ATLANTIC OCEAN

Riberão da Ilha ○

SC 405

SC401

Praia de Fora

Lagoa do Peri

Praia da Armação

Parque Estadual do Tabuleiro

BR101

Parque da Lagoa do Peri

SC406

Praia do Matadeiro

Praia da Lagoinha do Leste

Praia do Pantano do Sul

Praia de Naufragados

KEY
Beaches

many water sports. You can also go for nature walks along trails with the ocean as backdrop.

Note that Brazilians tend to refer to all of Santa Catarina island as "Florianópolis," and all the beaches and forts on the island are under the city's jurisdiction.

Beaches

FodorśChoice
★

The island's northern *praias* (beaches) are considered the best—and are therefore the busiest—because of their warm waters. Impressive seascapes dominate the Atlantic beaches, and southern beaches have fewer sun worshipers and a more laid-back atmosphere.

You're strongly advised to explore the sophisticated **Praia do Canasvieiras,** which has calm, warm waters and great services and facilities. **Praia Jurerê,** home to an upscale resort and condominiums, normally has bigger waves than its neighbors. The increased development of beachfront hotels, restaurants, and shops has attracted many out-of-state visitors. **Praia dos Ingleses** (English Beach) acquired its name because a British sailboat sank here in 1700. Although it is a narrow beach, the unparalleled lineup of hotels and restaurants for all budgets makes Praia dos Ingleses one of the most popular beaches on the island. In summer Spanish with an Argentine accent is the local language. **Praia do Santinho** is a mile-long stretch of sand backed by green hills at the far-northeastern corner of the island. It was a secluded, laid-back neighborhood until a major resort opened in the 1990s.

Surfers have staked claims to **Praia da Joaquina,** the beach where several surfing events take place, including one round of the world professional circuit. Nudism is tolerated at **Praia Mole,** with white sands that mostly attract surfers and foreign tourists. You can paraglide here, and there are a number of beachfront bars. **Praia do Matadeiro,** quite popular among surfers, is a small beach surrounded by breathtaking hills. It can only be reached by a footpath from the Armação village.

The SC 404 highway takes you to **Lagoa da Conceição** (Our Lady of Conception Lagoon), 12 km (8 mi) east of downtown Florianópolis, which has a busy nightlife and dining district, most of whose streets are packed with people on weekend evenings. The region provides a combination fresh- and saltwater environment for water sports.

If you're seeking peace (and you don't mind colder waters and less development), head south through the Beira-Mar Sul (the southbound highway that connects downtown to the airport and beyond) to **Riberão da Ilha, Pântano do Sul,** and **Lagoinha do Leste.**

Follow SC 401 southwest and make your first stop **Riberão da Ilha,** one of the oldest Portuguese settlements on the island. Its little fishing village with colonial houses overlooking the balmy ocean and the forest-clad mountains on the continent beyond is a rare find in this otherwise bustling island.

Alternatively, head southeast to **Pântano do Sul,** a small beach community surrounded by hills with good restaurants and fishing-boat rides to other beaches and smaller islands nearby. Secluded **Praia da Lagoinha**

do Leste is a breathtaking beach that you can only reach by boat or by a steep, 5-km (3-mi) path that starts at the entrance of the Pântano do Sul village.

Forts

In the early days of the colony, the Portuguese built forts on the Baía Norte and Baía Sul to protect their investment. Today these forts can only be reached by taking a schooner tour.

One of the best-preserved forts open to the public is **Fortaleza de São José. Forte Santa Cruz de Anhatomirim** was built in 1744, opposite Fortaleza de São José at the entrance to the Baía Norte. It has a historical photo exhibit as well as a small aquarium. **Fortaleza de Santo Antônio** has marked trails to follow up to the fort. Check out the tropical vegetation along the way. The **Forte de Santana,** under Hercílio Luz Bridge, houses a firearms museum run by the state military police.

Where to Stay & Eat

$-$$$
Fodor'sChoice
★
✕**Chef Fedoca.** This restaurant, part of a marina complex, has a grand view of the Lagoa da Conceição, with surrounding green hills as the backdrop. The fare, organized by Chef Fedoca, a diver himself, includes a wide variety of seafood, with shrimp *moquecas* (stews) from Bahian cuisine as a highlight. ✉ *Marina Ponta da Areia, Rua Sen. Ivo D'Aquino Neto 133, Lagoa da Conceição, Florianópolis* ☎ *048/3232–0759* 🖃 *AE, DC, MC, V* ☉ *Closed Mon.*

$$
✕**Gugu.** This off-the-beaten path restaurant combines no-frills service and decor with an outstanding seafood menu. You can have the steamed oysters as an appetizer and move on to the seafood stew, the talk of the island. ✉ *Rua Antonio Dias Carneiro 147, Sambaqui, Florianópolis* ☎ *048/3335–0288* 🖃 *D, MC, V* ☉ *No lunch Mon.*

$-$$
✕**Arante.** At this rustic beachfront restaurant it's the tradition that before leaving, customers pin notes to the walls of their impressions of this restaurant—and the walls are covered with them. The Brazilian seafood buffet served at lunch is flawless; don't pass up the *pirão de caldo de peixe* (black beans cooked with a fish sauce), one of the dinner options. ✉ *Rua Abelardo Gomes 254, Pântano do Sul, Florianópolis* ☎ *048/ 3237–7022* 🖃 *DC, MC* ⚓ *Reservations essential weekends.*

$$$-$$$$
Fodor'sChoice
★
🏨**Jurerê Beach Village.** The four- to eight-person guest houses here are just steps from sophisticated Jurerê Beach. The efficient and attentive staff make each guest feel like a homeowner. The hotel is a prime destination for South American visitors, especially Argentines. The Z Perry restaurant serves international fare with seafood specialties. A minimum stay of one week is usually required in high season (December–March). ✉*Alameda César Nascimento 646, Praia de Jurerê, Florianópolis 88053-000* ☎ *048/3261–5100 or 0800/48–0110* 🖷 *048/3262–5200* ⊕ *www. jurere.com.br/jbv/* ➷ *202 apartments, 40 guest houses* ♨ *2 restaurants, kitchen, cable TV, tennis court, 2 pools, health club, sauna, beach, snorkeling, jet skiing, soccer, volleyball, bar, playground, business services, shops, airport shuttle, travel services* 🖃 *AE, DC, MC, V* ⭘⭘ *MAP.*

$$-$$$$
Fodor'sChoice
★
🏨**Costão do Santinho Resort.** The island's most sophisticated resort has a terrific location on Santinho Beach, 35 km (22 mi) north of Florianópolis. The ocean view from rooms that face north is one reason to stay here;

the surrounding 100-acre Atlantic forest is another (a trail leads to petroglyphs on the hill). The older buildings have full apartments with kitchens, available for longer stays.There are programs for children (Costão Kids) and teenagers (Costão Teen). ⊠ *Rua Ver. Onildo Lemos 2505, Praia do Santinho, Florianópolis 88001-970* ☎ *048/3261–1000 or 0800/ 701–9000* 🖷 *048/3261–1236* ⊕ *www.costao.com* 🖃 *451 rooms* ⚹ *3 restaurants, kitchens, cable TV, 8 tennis courts, 2 indoor pools, 4 outdoor pools, gym, hot tub, massage, sauna, spa, beach, snorkeling, hiking, paddle tennis, soccer, volleyball, 2 bars, lounge, recreation room, shops, children's programs (ages 4–6), playground, business services, convention center, airport shuttle, travel services, shops* ▤ *AE, DC, MC, V* ⎟⊙⎟ *MAP.*

$$ 🖫 **Lexus Internacional Ingleses.** Although it has much to offer, this midsize hotel's main attraction is its location on the popular (therefore crowded in high season) Praia dos Ingleses, 34 km (21 mi) northeast of downtown Florianópolis. The pool is one step from the beach, making the Lexus a great place to enjoy the warm northern waters. Choose the bay-facing apartments with balconies where you can hang your hammock and feel the sea breeze. Some apartments have a barbecue grill. ⊠ *Rua Dom João Becker 859, Praia dos Ingleses, Florianópolis 88058-601* ☎🖷 *048/3269–2622* ⊕ *www.hotellexus.com.br* 🖃 *63 rooms* ⚹ *Restaurant, kitchenette, cable TV, indoor pool, outdoor pool, sauna, beach, volleyball, bar* ▤ *AE, DC, MC, V* ⎟⊙⎟ *CP.*

$ 🖫 **Praia Mole Park Hotel.** Bordered by a lagoon on one side and a beach on the other, this hotel has neatly decorated rooms in light colors that enhance the green exterior. Colonial-style furnishings, and paintings by local artists contrast with the casual atmosphere. An almost unending lineup of amenities in a 16-acre wooded lot makes this a prime choice for relaxation. In high season (December–February) a four-day minimum stay is required. ⊠ *Rua Jornalista Manoel de Menezes (Estrada da Lagoa) 2001, Praia Mole, Florianópolis 88062-970* ☎ *048/3239–7500* 🖷 *048/3232–5482* ⊕ *www.praiamole.com.br* 🖃 *74 rooms, 18 chalets* ⚹ *Restaurant, cable TV, tennis court, 2 pools (1 indoor), fitness classes, massage, sauna, boating, marina, paddle tennis, bar, convention center, no-smoking rooms* ▤ *AE, DC, MC, V* ⎟⊙⎟ *BP.*

Sports & the Outdoors

The island has a great lineup of sports options. Sandboarding is practiced on the gigantic dunes at Praia da Joaquina. Windsurfing and jet skiing are popular on Lagoa da Conceição, but strict zoning rules are enforced and you must obtain a license by taking a course at an accredited outfitter or school—something most visitors won't have the time for.

Marina Ponta da Areia (⊠ Rua Sen. Ivo D'Aquino Neto 133, Lagoa da Conceição ☎ 048/3232–2290) is the place for boat and jet-ski rentals. Snorkeling and scuba diving are very popular on the northern beaches; check out **Parcel Dive Center** (⊠ Av. Luiz B. Piazza 2243, Cachoeira do Bom Jesus, Florianópolis ☎ 048/3284–5564 ⊕ www.parcel.com.br) for internationally accredited diving lessons, diver's certification, and for equipment sale, maintenance, and rentals. The cost to rent basic gear is about R$275 a day. **OpenWinds** (⊠ Av. das Rendeiras 1672, Lagoa da Conceição, Florianópolis ☎ 048/3232–5004 ⊕ www.openwinds.com.br) gives sandboarding, surf and windsurfing lessons; it also has a gear sales, rentals, and maintenance shop. **Parapente Sul** (✉ Rua João Antônio da Silveira 201, Lagoa da Conceição, Florianópolis ☎☎ 048/3232–0791 ⊕ www. parapentesul.com.br), a center for parasailing—a popular sport on this mountainous, windy coast of Santa Catarina—leads tandem flights with an instructor for about R$200. For enthusiasts, a full course is available.

Nightlife

Outside the city proper, the lively Lagoa da Conceição neighborhood has popular bars and live-music venues. During the summer expect heavy car and pedestrian traffic. **John Bull Pub** (✉ Av. das Rendeiras 1046, Lagoa da Conceição, Florianópolis ☎ 048/3232–8535 ⊕ www. johnbullpub.com.br) is *the* place for live music on the island. A roster of local and nationally known bands performs, from blues, rock and roll, and reggae to Brazilian popular music. It's also a great place for drinks and snacks.

Florianópolis

⑮ *300 km (187 mi) southeast of Curitiba, 476 km (296 mi) northeast of Porto Alegre.*

The city of Florianópolis played an important part in the history of the island of Santa Catarina. Settled by colonists from the Azore Islands, it was the southernmost post of Portuguese empire for some time, and it was the site of several skirmishes with the Spanish before the border disputes were settled. You might be lured by the beaches—which rank among the most beautiful in Brazil—but downtown Florianópolis also offers worthwhile attractions.

The **Alfândega** (Old Customs House), which dates from 1875, is the city's best example of neoclassical architecture. It now houses an artists' association and a handicrafts shop that sells *rendas de bilro* (handwoven tapestries) and pottery. ✉ *Rua Cons. Mafra 141, Centro* ☎ *048/3224–6082* 🎟 *Free* ⊗ *Weekdays 9–7, Sat. 9–noon.*

Beyond the Alfândega is the picturesque, 100-year-old **Mercado Público** (Public Market), a Portuguese colonial structure with a large central patio. The renovated market—which is filled with stalls selling fish, fruit, and vegetables—still preserves its Arabian-bazaar atmosphere. ✉ *Rua Cons. Mafra 255, Centro* ☎ *048/3225–3200* 🎟 *Free* ⊗ *Mon.–Sat. 7 AM–9 PM.*

The **Museu Histórico de Santa Catarina** is housed in the 18th-century Palácio Cruz e Souza, a mixture of baroque and neoclassical styles. The palace, whose stairways are lined with Carrara marble, was once the governor's home and office. The sidewalks around the building are still paved with the original stones brought from Portugal. The museum's collection delineates the state's history with documents, personal items, and artwork that belonged to former governors. ✉ *Praça 15 de Novembro 227, Centro* ☎ *048/3221–3504* 🎟 *Free* ⊗ *Tues.–Fri. 10–6, weekends 10–4.*

A great sight to visit by schooner is the **Baía dos Golfinhos** (Dolphin Bay). A few nautical miles up the coast from the island, this bay is home to hundreds of *botos-cinza* (gray dolphins). They tolerate boats moving in very close to them. *See* Tours *in* The South Essentials for information about schooner tours.

Where to Stay & Eat

★ **$–$$** ✕ **La Pergoletta.** A variety of fresh pasta dishes is the highlight here. Try the pasta with shrimp, *kani kama* (ground crabmeat), and white-wine sauce. ⊠ *Trv. Carreirão 62, Centro* 🕾 *048/3224–6353* ⚒ *Reservations essential* ▤ *DC, MC, V* ☉ *Closed Mon.*

¢ ✕ **Ataliba.** With 20-odd years in the business, you can expect nothing less than excellent service at this rodízio-style churrascaria. The meat selections—more than 20 kinds, from beef to mouton and rabbit—and the salad bar are both outstanding. ⊠ *Rua Irineu Bornhausen 5050, Agronomica* 🕾 *048/3333–0990* ⊕ *www.ataliba.com.br* ▤ *AE, DC, MC, V* ☉ *No dinner Sun.*

$ 🏨 **Baía Norte Palace.** Lush suites with hot tubs await discerning guests. Rooms are meticulously furnished, and those facing west have a grand view of the bay and Hercílio Luz bridge. From here, quick access to the business district or the beaches is guaranteed. ⊠ *Av. Beira-Mar Norte 220, Centro, 88000-000* 🕾 *048/3229–3144 or 0800/48–0202* 🖷 *048/3225–3227* ⊕ *www.baianorte.com.br* ⇄ *99 rooms, 9 suites* ⚐ *Restaurant, coffee shop, cable TV, outdoor pool, gym, bicycles, bar, meeting room, airport shuttle, travel services* ▤ *AE, DC, MC, V* ¶◐ *CP.*

¢ 🏨 **Íbis Florianópolis.** Íbis is a welcome retreat if you're looking for service and basic facilities like those you can find back home. "Functionality with comfort" is the motto here. It is one of the few hotels to offer rooms for people with disabilities. ⊠ *Av. Rio Branco 37, Centro 88015-200* 🕾🖷 *048/3216–0000 or 0800/703–7000* ⊕ *www.accorhotels.com.br* ⇄ *198 rooms* ⚐ *Restaurant, cable TV, gym, bar, lounge, Internet, business services* ▤ *AE, DC, MC, V.*

Shopping

For modern shops in a world-class mall, try **Beira-Mar Shopping Center** (⊠ Rua Bocaiúva 2468, Centro 🕾 048/3224–1563). If you're looking for beach apparel on your way to the beaches, a good spot is **Via Lagoa Shopping** (⊠ Rua Henrique Veras do Nascimento s/n, Lagoa da Conceição).

Garopaba

⑯
Fodor'sChoice
★

91 km (57 mi) south of Florianópolis, 380 (238 mi) northwest of Porto Alegre.

Around Garopaba you can find great beaches and sand dunes, green hills, and rocky cliffs that end right in the ocean. Praia do Rosa and Praia da Ferrugem have acquired national recognition for their awesome beauty and laid-back atmosphere. This is also prime sand-boarding and surfing territory, but watching the *baleia-franca* (right whales) breeding grounds off the coast—scheduled to become a protected area—is quickly becoming popular. The warm waters here attract whales from Patagonia (especially from Peninsula Valdéz) July through October.

Where to Stay & Eat

$ ✕🖬 **EcoResort Vida, Sol e Mar.** This pousada combines easy access to the beach and several amenities, including OnoKaii ($–$$), one of the best seafood restaurants south of Florianópolis. An in-house operator works in conjunction with Instituto Baleia Franca—a nongovernmental environmental organization—to offer whale-watching boat trips (R$100/person). Surfing classes are also available. ✉ *Km 6, Estrada Geral da Praia do Rosa, Imbituba 88780-0200* ☎ *048/3355–6111, 048/3254–4199 whale-watching* ⊕ *www.vidasolemar.com.br* 🛏 *14 rooms* ⚒ *Restaurant, beach, horseback riding, bar* ▭ *MC, V.*

off the beaten path

★

LAGUNA – Sixty-two kilometers (38 mi) south of Garopaba on BR 101, the city of Laguna is the second-oldest Portuguese settlement in the state of Santa Catarina. Most downtown buildings reflect the early colonial days. Known for its many beaches, Laguna has one of the liveliest Carnival festivities of southern Brazil. Part of the city faces Lagoa Imaruí (Imaruí Lake), which connects to the Atlantic 5 km (3 mi) farther east. You can drive or hire a boat on the beaches to get to the Imaruí Lake delta, where exploring the imposing Santa Marta Lighthouse and nearby beaches is well worth a day's outing.

RIO GRANDE DO SUL

The state of Rio Grande do Sul is almost synonymous with the *gaúcho,* the South American cowboy who is glamorized as much as his North American counterpart. There's more to this state, however, than the idyllic cattle-country lifestyle of the early days. As it is one of Brazil's leading industrial areas, its infrastructure rivals that of any country in the northern hemisphere. Its mix of Portuguese, German, and Italian cultures is evident in the food and architecture. Indeed, to be gaúcho (which is a term for all people and things from this state) may mean to be a vintner of Italian heritage from Caxias do Sul or an entrepreneur of German descent from Gramado as much as a cattle rancher with Portuguese lineage out on the plains.

The state capital, Porto Alegre, is a sophisticated metropolis of 1.3 million that rivals Curitiba in quality of life. This important industrial and business center has universities, museums, and convention centers. It is also one of the greenest cities in Brazil, with many parks and nature preserves. The slopes of the Serra Gaúcha were settled by Italian immigrants; thanks to their wine-making skills, the state now produces quality wines, particularly in the Caxias do Sul and Bento Gonçalves areas. Along the coast, basaltic cliffs drop into a raging Atlantic and provide an impressive backdrop for the sophisticated seaside resort of Torres. Farther inland, straddling the state's highest elevations, is the Aparados da Serra National Park, whose gargantuan canyons are the result of millions of years of erosion.

Porto Alegre

⑰–㉔ *476 km (296 mi) southwest of Florianópolis, 760 km (472 mi)
southwest of Curitiba, 1,109 km (690 mi) southwest of São Paulo.*

Porto Alegre's hallmark is the hospitality of its people, a trait that has
been acknowledged over and over by visitors, earning it the nickname
Smile City. The capital of one of Brazil's wealthiest states, it has many
streets lined with jacaranda trees that create violet tunnels when in full
spring bloom.

The city was founded on the banks of the Rio Guaíba in 1772 by immigrants from the Azores. The Guaíba is actually a 50-km-long (31-mi-
long) lagoon formed by four rivers that merge a few miles upstream from
the city. The city has an important port, connected to the Atlantic by
the Lagoa dos Patos.

Exploring

From Morro de Santa Teresa (Santa Teresa Hill), you get a grand view
of the skyline as it confronts the expanse of the Rio Guaíba. From this
spot and the numerous riverfront parks, the great spectacle of Porto Alegre's sunset is inspirational. As local poet Mário Quintana put it: "Skies
of Porto Alegre, how could I ever take you to heaven?" For another great
perspective of Centro, consider taking a riverboat tour of the Rio Guaíba
and its islands, which are part of a state park.

The heart of Porto Alegre lies within a triangle formed by Praça da Alfândega, the Mercado Público, and the Praça da Matriz. Not only is this
the main business district, it's also the site of many cultural and historical attractions. Outside this area, Casa de Cultura Mário Quintana and
Usina do Gasômetro are very active cultural centers, with movies, live
performances, art exhibits, and cafés.

*Numbers in the text correspond to numbers in the margin and on the
Porto Alegre Centro map.*

A GOOD WALK   Start at the two neoclassical structures on the northwest side of Praça
da Alfândega facing the river: the **Museu de Arte do Rio Grande do
Sul** ⑰ ☞ and the **Memorial do Rio Grande do Sul** ⑱. The adjacent grayish
building with imposing Roman columns is the **Centro Cultural Santander** ⑲. If you're ready for a break, stop for a meal at one of the **Mercado Público** ⑳ restaurants. Go three blocks uphill on Rua Gen Câmara
to **Theatro São Pedro** ㉔. Across Praça da Matriz are the **Catedral Metropolitana Nossa Senhora Madre de Deus** ㉒ and the adjacent **Palácio Piratini** ㉓.
Finish this tour at the **Museu Júlio de Castilhos** ㉑, one block to your right,
where you can catch a glimpse of gaúcho culture and history.

TIMING   You can follow this tour—and visit some of the exhibits in the museums—in about three hours.

WHAT TO SEE   **Catedral Metropolitana Nossa Senhora Madre de Deus.** Although its con-
㉒   struction began in 1921, this cathedral wasn't completed until 1986.
Its predominant style is Italian Renaissance, but note the twin bell towers, which were inspired by 17th-century Jesuit missions. The facade's

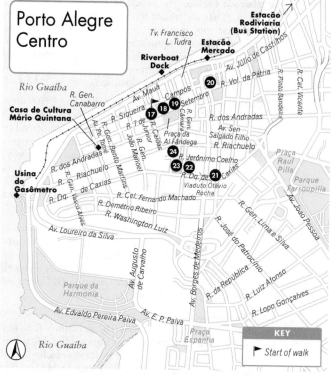

mosaic panels were made in the Vatican ateliers. ⊠ *Rua Duque de Caixas 1047, Centro* ☎ *051/3228–6001* ☞ *Free* ☉ *Daily 7–noon and 2–7.*

⓲ Centro Cultural Santander. This stately building has headquartered some local banks in its 100-year existence. Now owned by Banco Santander of Spain, it has been transformed into a cultural center and gallery for temporary exhibits. Guided tours (Portuguese only) show the intricate ironwork of the entrance door and second-floor balcony as well as the ceiling's neoclassical paintings. One curiosity: the massive bank vault now contains a small movie theater. ⊠ *Rua Sete de Setembro 1028 Centro* ☎ *051/3287–5500* ⊕ *www.santandercultural.com.br* ☞ *Free* ☉ *Daily 9–5.*

⓲ Memorial do Rio Grande do Sul. Built at the turn of the 20th century, the building was declared a national architectural landmark in 1981. It now houses a state museum. Although overall the style is neoclassical, German baroque influences are strong; the asymmetrical corner towers with their bronze rotundas are said to resemble Prussian army helmets. A permanent exhibit focuses on the state's history and the lives of important gaúchos, and on the second floor there's one of Brazil's largest collections of documents and manuscripts about Brazilian society. ⊠ *Praça da Alfândega s/n, Centro* ☎ *051/3224–7210* ⊕ *www.memorial. rs.gov.br* ☞ *Free* ☉ *Tues.–Sun. 9–5.*

㉟ Mercado Público. The neoclassical Public Market was constructed in 1869. It has undergone repeated renovations, the last of which added the glass roof that now covers the central inner plaza. With these changes, some of the produce stalls have been replaced by souvenir shops, cafés, and restaurants—taking away a bit of the boisterous bazaar ambience—but increasing the options for the visitor. ⊠ *Largo Glenio Peres s/n, Centro* ⊕ *www.mercadopublico.com.br* ⊗ *Mon.–Sat. 7 AM–11 PM.*

▶ **⑰ Museu de Arte do Rio Grande do Sul.** In the 1990s the old, neoclassical customs building was restored to house this art museum. German immigrant Theo Wiederspahn designed this and several other of the city's early buildings. A collection of his sketches and blueprints is on display. You can also see paintings, sculptures, and drawings by Brazilian artists from several periods. Two works of Di Cavalcanti—one of the country's most renowned painters—are exhibited as well as several pieces by local sculptor Xico Stockinger. ⊠ *Praça da Alfândega s/n, Centro* ☎ *051/3227–2311* ⊕ *www.margs.org.br* 🎫 *Free* ⊗ *Tues.–Sun. 10–7.*

㉑ Museu Júlio de Castilhos. The small Júlio de Castilhos Museum displays an impressive collection of gaúcho documents, firearms, clothing, and household utensils. The home belonged to Governor Julio de Castilhos, who lived here at the turn of the 20th century, before the Palácio Piratini was built. ⊠ *Rua Duque de Caxias 1231, Centro* ☎ *051/3221–3959* 🎫 *Free* ⊗ *Tues.–Fri. 10–5, Sat. 1–5.*

㉓ Palácio Piratini. The Piratini Palace is the stately governor's mansion, which also houses executive offices. The structure's Roman columns convey a solidity and permanence uncommon in official Brazilian buildings. Duck into the main room to see the murals (depicting gaúcho folktales) by Italian artist Aldo Locatelli. ⊠ *Praça da Matriz s/n, Centro* ☎ *051/3210–4170* 🎫 *Free* ⊗ *Weekdays 9–5.*

㉔ Theatro São Pedro. In a 130-year-old building that was thoroughly renovated in the 1980s, São Pedro hosts theatrical and musical performances—including those of the theater's own chamber orchestra (March–December). The popular Café Orquestra das Panelas, on the balcony above the lobby, has an ample view of the Praça da Matriz, the cathedral, and Palácio Piratini. ⊠ *Praça da Matriz s/n, Centro* ☎ *051/3227–5100* ⊕ *www.teatrosaopedro.rs.gov.br* 🎫 *Free; ticket prices vary* ⊗ *Closed Mon.*

off the beaten path

PARQUE ESTADUAL DE ITAPOÃ – Fifty-seven kilometers (35 mi) south of Porto Alegre, where the Rio Guaíba flows into Lagoa dos Patos, Itapoã State Park protects 12,000 acres of granitic hills and sandy beaches. At Ponta de Itapoã (Itapoã Point) there's a century-old lighthouse. Although the infrastructure is minimal, being able to bathe in the river, walk along marked trails, and watch magnificent sunsets attracts many visitors. Rare cacti and bands of *bugios* (howler monkeys) add to the list of local natural highlights. Boat tours to the park beaches and lighthouse depart from the marina in the small village of Itapoã, 45 km (28 mi) south of Porto Alegre. ⊠ *Park entrance: Km 1, Estrada das Pombas, Viamão* ☎ *051/494–8083* 🎫 *R$5.50* ⊗ *Wed.–Sun. 8–6.*

Where to Stay & Eat

Porto Alegre definitely lives up to the good and affordable food tradition of local restaurants in the south, and also has a roster of international cuisine.

$–$$$ ✕ **Al Dente.** Northern Italian dishes at this small restaurant include *gar-*
Fodor'sChoice *ganelli* (a variety of pasta from Emilia-Romagna) with salmon in wine
★ sauce and fettuccine *nere* (black fettuccine) with caviar sauce. ⊠ *Rua Mata Bacelar 210, Auxiliadora* ☎ *051/3343–1841* ⊟ *AE, D, MC, V* ⊘ *Closed Sun. No lunch weekdays.*

★ **$–$$** ✕ **Galpão Crioulo.** At one of Porto Alegre's largest churrascarias, everything is done the traditional way. The restaurant serves rodízio fare with a salad buffet whose premium beef is tenderer than that of most of its competitors. If rodízio is too much for you, ask for the *miniespeto* (one small skewer with a sampler of all meats). Gaúcho musical performances in the evening and a *chimarrão* (type of indigenous tea) tasting stand round out the highlights. ⊠ *Rua Loureiro da Silva s/n, Parque da Harmonia, Centro* ☎ *051/3226–8194* ⊟ *AE, DC, MC, V.*

$–$$ ✕ **Café do Porto.** One of the trendiest coffee shops in town, Porto serves several types of coffee, along with drinks, sandwiches, and pastries. Highly recommended is the antipasto *sott'olio* (Italian rolls with dried tomatoes and red and yellow peppers). Combine this with a glass of chardonnay from the regional vineyard, Casa Valduga, or with the house cappuccino. ⊠ *Rua Padre Chagas 293, Moinhos de Vento* ☎ *051/ 3346–8385* ⊕ *www.cafedoporto.com.br/* ⊟ *AE, DC, MC, V.*

¢ ✕ **Ilha Natural.** This is the place to compensate for the likely excesses of rodízio-style churrasco. The vegetarian buffet has carved a name for itself in the downtown business district for its variety of salads and vegetable stews, as well as for the ubiquitous rice and beans. ⊠ *Rua General Camara 60, Centro* ☎ *051/3224–4738* ⊟ *No credit cards* ⊘ *Closed Sat. No dinner.*

$$ ✕▦ **Holiday Inn Porto Alegre.** The first member of the Holiday Inn family in southern Brazil is in the booming business district of Bela Vista, which not too long ago was a purely residential neighborhood. The decor is modern; rooms have king-sized beds. Chef's Grill ($–$$), the house restaurant with Italian leanings, is increasingly popular on this side of the city. ⊠ *Av. Carlos Gomes 565, Bela Vista 90450-000* ☎ *051/3378–2727 or 0800/707–6444* ⊕ *www.holiday-inn.com* ⊟ *051/3378–2700* ⋤ *172 rooms* ⟨ *Restaurant, coffee shop, cable TV, gym, bar, Internet, business services, meeting rooms, no-smoking rooms* ⊟ *AE, DC, MC, V.*

$–$$ ✕▦ **Plaza San Rafael.** The Plaza has long been one of the city's most sophisticated hotels. All suites have whirlpool baths whose hot water is supplied by a thermal spring in the basement. All rooms have wireless Internet service. The restaurant Le Bon Gourmet ($$$–$$$$) has the best French cuisine in town and is very popular with international visitors. One highlight is the juicy fillet Camembert with a mushroom sauce. The Plaza Grill ($$–$$$) serves international fare. ⊠ *Rua Alberto Bins 514, Centro 90030-040* ☎ *051/3220–7000 or 0800/51–2244* ⊟ *051/3220–7001* ⊕ *www.plazahoteis.com.br/sao_rafael.htm* ⋤ *261 rooms, 23 suites* ⟨ *2 restaurants, in-room hot tubs, cable TV, in-room* data ports, indoor pool, gym, sauna, bar, Internet, business services, convention center, meeting rooms, travel services, no-smoking rooms ▤ AE, DC, MC, V ⏐⏐ MAP.

$$$$ ▦ **Sheraton Porto Alegre.** In the fashionable neighborhood of Moinhos

Fodor'sChoice de Vento, the Sheraton sets the city's standard of luxury. The level of

★ comfort is outstanding, from the lobby to the top-floor rooms. In the Brazil Suite you'll find 18th-century-style wooden furniture and copies of paintings by the French artist Debret, whose works depict rural scenes of colonial Brazil. The restaurant, Clos du Moulin, offers Mediterranean fare, which is accompanied by live piano performances each evening. Shoppers take note: the hotel is in the same complex as the Moinhos de Vento Mall. ✉ Rua Olavo Barreto Viana 18, Moinhos de Vento 90570-010 ☎ 051/3323–6000 or 0800/11–1345 📠 051/3323–6010 ⊕ www.sheraton-poa.com.br 🛏 156 rooms, 22 suites ⚘ Restaurant, in-room safes, minibars, cable TV, in-room data ports, health club, bar, concierge, Internet, business services, convention center, meeting rooms, no-smoking rooms ▤ AE, DC, MC, V ⏐⏐ CP.

★ **$$$–$$$$** ▦ **Blue Tree Towers.** A haven for those seeking a peaceful night's rest, the Blue Tree Towers is in the safe, scenic, and quiet residential Mont Serrat neighborhood. The spacious rooms have modern decor. Those at the back have superb views of downtown and the Guaíba. You can ask that a basic office be set up in your room. The Gaia restaurant serves Japanese fare. ✉ Rua Lucas de Oliveira 995, Mont Serrat 90940-011 ☎ 051/3333–0333 or 0800/15–0500 📠 051/3330–5233 ⊕ www. bluetree.com.br 🛏 130 rooms, 2 suites ⚘ Restaurant, cable TV, pool, health club, sauna, bar, Internet, business services, meeting rooms, no-smoking rooms ▤ AE, DC, MC, V ⏐⏐ CP.

$ ▦ **Everest.** This unassuming central hotel is close to the museums and cathedral. The staff is well trained and can help you find tours and activities. The top-floor restaurant, popular with businesspeople, has a view of the Guaíba riverfront. ✉ Av. Duque de Caxias 1357, Centro 90010-283 ☎ 051/3215–9500 or 0800/99–0095 📠 051/3228–4792 ⊕ www. everest.com.br 🛏 153 rooms ⚘ Restaurant, cable TV, bar, Internet, business services, meeting rooms, no-smoking rooms ▤ AE, DC, MC, V.

¢ ▦ **Continental Business.** Tourists are lured to this downtown budget option despite its many business amenities, such as two phone lines for every room. The hotel is close to attractions and the bus terminal, and access to the airport is quick and easy. ✉ Praça Otávio Rocha 49, Centro 90010-000 ☎☎ 051/3027–1600 ⊕ www.hoteiscontinental.com.br 🛏 126 rooms ⚘ Restaurant, cable TV, bar, Internet, no-smoking rooms ▤ AE, DC, MC, V.

Nightlife & the Arts

Porto Alegre has a very active cultural life. Complete listings of entertainment and cultural events are published in the daily papers Zero Hora and Correio do Povo.

The **Casa de Cultura Mário Quintana** (✉ Rua dos Andradas 736, Centro ☎ 051/3221–7147 ⊕ www.ccmq.rs.gov.br) occupies what was Porto Alegre's finest hotel at the turn of the 20th century, the Majestic. The building has two art-film cinemas, one theater, and several exhibit

BARBECUING BRAZILIAN-STYLE

ONCE THE STAPLE OF THE *GAÚCHO* (South-American cowboy) diet, churrasco (slow-grilled and -roasted meat) is now found all over Brazil, and many churrascarias have become fashionable restaurants in Rio de Janeiro, São Paulo, Brasília and other major cities. Churrasco is often referred to as "Brazilian barbecue," but it bears little resemblance to American barbecue, which is usually slathered with spicy sauce. The only seasonings used on traditional churrasco are salt for red meat, and a lime, garlic, and salt marinade for mutton (commonly found only in the south), poultry, and pork.

The most traditional method of roasting the meat is over coals in a pit dug in the ground. Some people still do it that way. But churrascarias (restaurants serving churrasco) use a system known as espeto-corrido (literally, "running skewer"), called rodízio (rotation) elsewhere in Brazil.

At a churrascaria everyone pays a fixed price for the all-you-can-eat meal, which includes infinite trips to the salad bar and usually a dessert. Waiters serve the meat to your table—each waiter circles the room with a different type of meat on a skewer. On your table will usually be some sort of indicator to tell the waiters whether to keep coming or let you digest in peace. At some restaurants it's a small chess-piece-like object painted red on one side and green on the other; at others it's a simple piece of cardboard. As the waiter cuts the meat, you should use the tongs provided to catch it and move it to your plate.

rooms. The popular Café Concerto Majestic, on the seventh floor, has regular jazz and classical music performances and is a popular happy-hour place. **Dado Bier** (⊠ Bourbon Country Center, Av. Túlio de Rose 100, Três Figueiras ☎ 051/3378–3000) started off as the city's first microbrewery. Local fashionistas and international tourists hang out at what is now an entertainment complex with a restaurant serving international fare and Dado Tambor, a live-music venue and dance club; the cover charge is R$20. The **Usina do Gasômetro** (⊠ Av. João Goulart 551, Centro ☎ 051/3212–5979), with its conspicuous 110-meter (350-foot) brick smokestack, was the city's first coal-fired powerhouse—built in the early 1920s, when the city experienced rapid growth. Today it's a cultural center with theaters, meeting rooms, and exhibit spaces on the bank of the Rio Guaíba. A terrace café overlooking the river is the perfect place to take in a sunset. The center is open daily 8 AM–midnight.

Sports & the Outdoors

Clube Veleiros do Sul (⊠ Av. Guaíba 2941, Asunção ☎ 051/3346–4382 ⊕ www.veleirosdosul.com.br) takes advantage of the great expanse of the Guaíba waters to offer sailing classes and boat rentals. **Estádio Beira-Rio** (⊠ Av. Padre Cacique 891, Praia de Belas ☎ 051/3231–4411), with a capacity of 70,000, is the home of Internacional—one of the city's major *futebol* (soccer) clubs. **Estádio Olímpico** (✉ Largo dos Campeões s/n, Azenha ☎ 051/3217–4466) is the stadium of Grêmio Football Portoalegrense, the city's other major futebol team. It seats 60,000.

Shopping

At the **Brique da Redenção,** on Rua José Bonifácio (southeast side of Parque Farroupilha), you can find antiques and crafts. The entire street is closed to vehicles and taken over by dealers and artisans every Sunday from 10 to 3. **Moinhos Shopping** (✉ Rua Olavo Barreto Vianna 36, Moinhos de Vento ☎ 051/3346–6013) is the smallest of the city's malls and caters to the sophisticated consumer. There is a six-theater cineplex on-site, and a Sheraton hotel is attached. **Shopping Center Iguatemi** (✉ Rua João Wallig 1831, Três Figueiras ☎ 051/3334–4500), the oldest of the world-class malls in the city, was extensively expanded in the late 1990s. It includes branches of large chain stores as well as high-end specialty shops. If you don't have the time to venture into Brazilian wine country, look for a sample to buy at **Vinhos do Mundo** (✉ Rua João Alfredo 557, Cidade Baixa ☎ 051/3226–1911).

Caxias do Sul

㉕ *150 km (93 mi) north of Porto Alegre.*

Caxias do Sul is the heart of the state's Italian region, where the first immigrants set foot in 1875. The mild climate and fertile soil helped spur development through agriculture. Now industry (especially the motor and furniture industries) is the leading economic activity in the area, although the production of grapes and other temperate fruits is still important.

The **Museu da Casa de Pedra** (Stone House Museum) was the residence (circa 1878) of the Lucchesi family, one of the first Italian families to arrive in the region. The basalt walls and hewn-wood window frames and doors are testaments to the hardiness of the early days. ✉ *Rua Matteo Gianella at Av. Ruben Alves* ☎ *054/3228–3344 Ext. 1925* 🎫 *Free* ☉ *Tues.–Sun. 9–5.*

Igreja São Pelegrino, finished in 1953, has 14 religious murals, including 12 depicting the *via crucis* (stations of the cross) painted by Italian classical painter Aldo Locatelli, who came to Rio Grande do Sul on a Vatican assignment and eventually became one of the state's most renowned artists. Another highlight is the replica of Michelangelo's *Pietá,* donated in 1975 by the Italian government to celebrate the centennial of immigration (1975). ✉ *Rua Itália 50* ☎ *No phone* 🎫 *Free* ☉ *Daily 7 AM–9 PM.*

Where to Stay & Eat

$ ✕ **La Vindima.** The city's most traditional eatery, this restaurant is nationally recognized for the *galeto al primo canto* (young fried chicken served with an herb cream sauce). The pasta is homemade, with locally produced wheat flour and eggs, "like in the olden days." If you're not driving, try the house wine; if you are driving, the house grape juice is also good. ✉ *Rua Borges de Medeiros 446, Caxias do Sul* ☎ *051/3221–1696* ▭ V ☉ *Closed Sun.*

$ ▦ **Reynolds International.** Impeccable service has become a hallmark at this small establishment, and a downtown location adds to the convenience. Because of this, it is attracting more and more international businesspeople. Rooms are spacious, with an emphasis on functionality. ✉ *Rua Dr. Montaury 1441, Caxias do Sul 95100-970* ☎ *054/3026–8000* 🖷 *054/3223–5843* ⊕ *www.reynolds.com.br* 🛏 *47 rooms* ⟠ *Restaurant, cable TV, gym, bar, Internet, business services, meeting rooms, free parking* ▤ *AE, DC, MC, V* ⦿ *CP.*

Vale dos Vinhedos

124 km (77 mi) north of Porto Alegre

The Serra Gaúcha produces 90% of Brazilian wine. Grapevines grow throughout the hilly terrain, but the heart of the winemaking country is within the municipality of Bento Gonçalves. Because the best-known Brazilian wineries are within a few miles in this region, the name Vale dos Vinhedos (Vineyard Valley) has become synonymous with quality wines.

Wineries

Casa Valduga is run by Luiz Valduga and his sons. Together they produce Seculum and Premium wines (the cabernets are highly regarded). In summer you can take a tour of the family-owned vineyards and purchase other house products such as grape juice and fruit jellies. ✉ *Km 6, RS 444, Vale dos Vinhedos, Bento Gonçalves* ☎ *054/2105–3122* ⊕ *www.casavalduga.com.br* 🎟 *Free* ⊙ *Tours Dec.–Feb. by appointment; wine tastings weekdays 8–11 and 2–6, weekends 9–5.*

Vinícola Cordelier offers guided tours through the facilities, which end in a wine-tasting session. It's smaller than the other wineries in the area and gives more personal attention. ✉ *Km 210, RS 470, Bento Gonçalves* ☎ *054/2102–2333* ⊕ *www.cordelier.com.br* 🎟 *Free* ⊙ *Weekdays 9–4, weekends 9–5.*

The Miolo family has carved a name for itself in the Brazilian wine industry with the **Vinícola Miolo.** The on-site restaurant—which adds to the fare Italian folk-songs sung by a small choir—and inn are among the best in the region. Tours of the premises include the vineyards and tasting the award-winning Miolo Reserva wines, which include outstanding chardonnays and cabernet sauvignons. ✉ *Km 9, RS 444, Bento Gonçalves* ☎ *054/2102–1500 or 0800/541–4165* ⊕ *www.miolo.com.br* 🎟 *Free* ⊙ *Tours daily 9–5.*

Where to Stay & Eat

$$ ✕ **Osteria Mamma Miolo.** This restaurant is connected to the Miolo Winery. In addition to local versions of Italian fare, you'll also find such game as wild boar on the menu. Try the Miolo Reserva Chardonnay as an accompaniment for your dinner. ✉ *Km 9, RS 444, Bento Gonçalves* ☎ *054/2102–1500* ▤ *MC, V* ⟠ *Reservations essential.*

$ ✕▦ **Pousada Valduga.** The Valduga winery maintains three redbrick houses with large, comfortable rooms overlooking the vineyards. The breakfast is almost a full café colonial served at the winery near the wine vats. The restaurant ($), which is closed weekdays, serves the best of Brazilian–Italian fare, such as cappelletti soup and pork polenta. ✉ *Km 6, RS 444, Bento Gonçalves 95700-000* ☎ *054/2105–3154* ⊕ *www. casavalduga.com.br* ⤝ *15 rooms* ✎ *Restaurant, shop* ▤ *D, MC, V.*

Gramado

❷❻ *115 km (72 mi) northeast of Porto Alegre.*

No doubt it was Gramado's mild mountain climate that attracted German settlers to the area in the late 1800s. They left a legacy of German-style architecture and traditions that attract today's travelers. Ample lodging options and a seemingly endless choice of restaurants have given this city a reputation with conventioneers and honeymooners. Every August the city hosts the Festival de Cinema da Gramado, one of Latin America's most prestigious film festivals. At Christmastime the city is aglow with seasonal decorations and musical performances—the Natal Luz (Christmas Lights) festivities. During peak periods around Christmas and July–August it can be difficult to find lodgings if you haven't made arrangements in advance.

Where to Stay & Eat

$$–$$$ ✕ **Gasthof Edelweiss.** The rustic atmosphere at this German restaurant is the ideal setting for duck *à la viennese* (with an orange-flavor cream sauce)—the house specialty. Some tables are in the wine cellar, which has more than 1,000 wine bottles. ✉ *Rua da Carriere 1119, Lago Negro* ☎ *054/3286–1861* ▤ *AE, DC, MC, V.*

¢ ✕▦ **Bavária.** If you're looking for a peaceful, natural setting, this is a good choice: the hotel is within a private park just off the busy shopping district. A small restaurant ($–$$$) of the same name serves German fare and is highly recommended. ✉ *Rua da Bavária 543, 95670-000* ☎☎ *054/3286–1362* ⊕ *www.hotelbavaria.com* ⤝ *56 rooms* ✎ *Restaurant, cable TV, indoor pool, sauna, paddle tennis, soccer, bar, Internet* ▤ *DC, MC, V.*

★ **$–$$$** ▦ **Serra Azul.** This prestigious hotel's name is almost synonymous with Gramado. It's the preferred choice of Brazilian TV and movie stars during the winter film festival. The location is prime for browsing the myriad clothing shops and enjoying café colonials and restaurants. The owners have a ranch outside the city, where you can experience the gaúcho lifestyle as part of your hotel package. ✉ *Rua Garibaldi 152, 95670-000* ☎ *054/ 3286–1082* 🖷 *054/3286–3374* ⊕ *www.serraazul.com* ⤝ *151 rooms, 18 suites* ✎ *Restaurant, cable TV, indoor pool, massage, sauna, bar, Internet* ▤ *AE, DC, MC, V.*

¢ ▦ **Pousada Zermatt.** This charming inn has a cozy atmosphere, especially in the rooms with Brazilian-pine floors and wall panels, fireplaces, and colorful locally made bedspreads. Add to this the reasonable rates and distance from the noisy downtown district. ✉ *Rua da Fé 187, Bavaria 95670-000* ☎ *054/3286–2426* ⊕ *www.pousadazermatt.com.br* ⤝ *9 rooms* ✎ *Cable TV, bar; no a/c* ▤ *MC, V.*

BRAZILIAN WINE

ALTHOUGH THE FIRST GRAPEVINES were brought to Brazil in 1532 by early Portuguese colonists, the Jesuits who settled in the south decades later were the first to establish true vineyards and wineries (to produce the wine needed for the Catholic mass). It wasn't until Italian immigrants arrived that Brazil's viticulture gained any importance. With the blessing of Italian-born empress Teresa Cristina, wife of Dom Pedro II, the first group of immigrants from northern Italy arrived in 1875. In the next decades at least 150,000 Italians came to settle the mountainous region of Rio Grande do Sul—the Serra Gaúcha. These newcomers were the first to produce significant quantities of wine, thereby establishing a truly Brazilian wine industry.

Although the region is suitable for growing grapes, the rainfall is often excessive from January to March—when the grapes reach maturity. This has traditionally made local winegrowers true heroes for being able to produce decent wines despite difficult conditions. Traditional grapes such as merlot and cabernet were grown to some extent, but most of the wine produced originated from less impressive American stock—Concord and Niagara grapes. These average wines are still produced for local markets.

New agricultural techniques and hybridization of grapes have brought modern viticulture to the area and allowed a dramatic expansion of higher-quality grapes. This has significantly improved wine quality and attracted such international industry heavyweights as Almadén, Moët et Chandon, and Heublein. Almadén broke new ground and established vineyards in the hills near the city of Santana do Livramento (about 480 km/300 mi southwest of Porto Alegre, on the Uruguay border), where, according to current agricultural knowledge, climate and soils are more apt to produce quality grapes. Other wineries are following its steps. There are more than 100 cantinas (winemakers) in Rio Grande do Sul, primarily in the Vale dos Vinhedos (Vineyard Valley) near Bento Gonçalves. The wine producers' association of the Vale dos Vinhedos IBRAVIN ⊕ www.ibravin.com.br has created a system similar to that used in European countries for controlled-origin wines to promote and warrant the quality of their products. The following wines have received mentions in 2005 international contests supervised by the Office International de la Vigne et du Vin (International Bureau of Wine): Casa Valduga Cabernet Sauvignon 2002 (from Casa Valduga); Aurora Chardonay 2004 and Espumante Aurora Brut (from Cooperativa Vin'cola Aurora); Miolo Cabernet Sauvignon Reserva 2002 (from Miolo).

Canela

㉗ *8 km (5 mi) east of Gramado, 137 km (85 mi) north of Porto Alegre.*

Gramado's "smaller sister" is quieter and more low-profile. Brazilians most immediately associate this city of 35,000 with the Caracol Waterfall, but it has many more attractions, including one of the largest Paraná pine trees on record and great shopping opportunities for cotton and wool-knit apparel, handmade embroidered items, and handicrafts. The impressive views of the forest-clad valleys with meandering rivers also bring many tourists.

The **Parque Estadual do Caracol** (Caracol State Park) has an impressive 120-meter (400-foot) waterfall that cascades straight down into a horseshoe-shape valley carved out of the basaltic plateau. For the best views try the lookout atop the 100-foot tower (R$3). The park also includes 50 acres of native forests with several well-marked paths, dominated by Paraná pine and an environmental education center for children. The entrance area is somewhat overcrowded with souvenir shops and snack tents. ⊠ *Km 9, Estrada do Caracol* ☎ *054/282–3035* ⊠ *R$8; Lookout Elevator ride: R$4* ☉ *Daily 9–7.*

Parque da Ferradura is a private nature preserve that has three lookouts to the Vale da Ferradura (Horseshoe Valley), formed by Rio Santa Cruz. You can walk trails in more than 500 acres of pine forests through hilly countryside. A 2-hour strenuous trek will reach Rio Caí near its source. Spotting deer, anteaters, and badgers is quite common. ⊠ *Km 15, Estrada do Caracol* ☎ *0800/51–2153 or 054/9969–6785* ⊠ *R$6; R$10 weekends* ☉ *Daily 9–6.*

Parque do Pinheiro Grosso is a small park that attracts hundreds of tourists, who come to see the 150-foot towering Paraná pine tree, which is about 700 years old. ⊠ *Km 5, Estrada do Caracol* ☎ *No phone* ⊠ *Free* ☉ *Daily 9–5.*

Where to Stay & Eat

$ ✕ **Al Pesto.** In the cold winters, the large fireplace in the main room warms guests at this Italian eatery. Traditional Brazilian–Italian *galeto* (fried chicken served with *polenta,* fried cornmeal pastry) is served, along with many homemade pasta options. ⊠ *Rua Helmut Schmidt 109* ☎ *054/282–1211* ⊟ *No credit cards* ☉ *Closed Mon–Tues. No dinner Sun.*

¢ ✕ **Castelinho Caracol.** The lofty two-story building surrounded by flower gardens is the oldest enxaimel house in the region, built in 1913 by the Franzen family, which ran a woodshop on the property for many years. Now this is the place for a hearty café colonial when returning from the Caracol Falls. Behind the house there's a small museum with woodworking tools and farming equipment from the early days of German immigration. ⊠ *Km 6, Estrada do Caracol* ☎ *054/272–3208* ⊟ *No credit cards* ☉ *No dinner.*

$ ▥ **Laje de Pedra.** Built near a cliff, this hotel has impressive views of the Vale do Quilombo from its west wing. On weekends it regularly hosts a variety of musical performances. Rooms in the main building are rather small and somewhat outdated. ⊠ *Km 3, Av. Pres. Kennedy,*

95680-000 ☎ 054/278–9000 or 0800/51–2153 🖷 054/282–4400 ⊕ www.lajedepedra.com.br ⇌ 250 rooms, 8 suites ⚐ Restaurant, cable TV, tennis court, indoor pool, outdoor pool, gym, health club, massage, sauna, spa, bar, theater, children's programs (ages 4–8), Internet, meeting rooms ☰ AE, DC, MC, V.

en route

If you are heading east of Canela on RS 235 to visit the canyons at Aparados da Serra National Park, consider staying in **São Francisco de Paula.** This mountain town, once a stopover for the cattle drives from the south to São Paulo, has many pousadas and hotels—more than you will find near the national park. The town's pride is Lago São Bernardo (St. Bernard Lake), just one step from downtown, with a paved walking path around it.

Parque Nacional dos Aparados da Serra

28 47 km (29 mi) north of Gramado, 145 km (91 mi) north of Porto Alegre.

Fodor's Choice
★

One of the oldest Brazilian national parks, Aparados da Serra was created to protect Itaimbezinho (the Tupi-Guarani language word for "cut" or "sharp rock"), one of the most impressive canyons that dissect the plateau in the north of Rio Grande do Sul State. In the last 10 years another park (Parque Nacional da Serra Geral) was established to protect the other great canyons farther north, the Malacara, Churriado, and Fortaleza. Winter (June–August) is the best time to take in the spectacular canyon views, as there's less chance of fog. The main entrance to the park, the Portaria Gralha Azul, is 20 km (13 mi) southeast of Cambará do Sul, the small town that serves as the park's hub. A visitor center provides information on regional flora and fauna, as well as the region's geology and history. Beyond the entrance you come to grassy meadows that belie the gargantuan depression ahead. A short path (a 45-minute walk, no guide necessary) takes you to the awesome Itaimbezinho Canyon rim, cut deep into the basalt bedrock to create the valley 725 meters (2,379 feet) below. The longest path requires a hired guide and trekking gear to traverse the strenuous path down into the canyon's interior. The local tourist office can also make arrangements for other trekking tours in the region. The park allows only 1,500 visitors each day, so it's best to arrive early, especially in the summer months. ✉ 20 km (12 mi) southeast of Cambará do Sul on unpaved Rd. ☎ 051/3251–1262, 051/3251–1277, 051/3251–1320 for tour guides (Cambará Municipal Visitor Center) 🎫 R$6 per person, R$5 parking ticket ⊙ Wed.–Sun. 9–5.

Where to Stay & Eat

¢ ✕ **Fogão Campeiro.** This churrascaria in a picturesque wooden bungalow has the ubiquitous southern Brazilian espeto-corrido, in addition to a fixed-price buffet with less advertised gaúcho dishes such as arroz de carreteiro (rice with dried beef), farofa (cassava flour), and cooked cassava. Traditional-music performances take place on Friday and Saturday. ✉ Rua José Trindade 351 ☎ 051/3251–1012 ☰ No credit cards ⊙ Closed Mon.

$ ⌂ **Preda Afiada Refúgio.** The most comfortable lodging on the down side of the canyons, this pousada has established its niche among adventure tourists, who depart from here to explore the Malacara and other canyons beyond. All northwest-facing rooms have balconies with views of the canyon walls. ⊠ *Estrada da Vila Rosa s/n, Praia Grande* ☎☎ *048/ 532–1059 or 051/3338–3323* ⇨ *9 rooms* ⚒ *Dining room, snack bar, hiking, horseback riding, lounge; no a/c, no room phones, no room TVs* ⊟ *No credit cards* ⏻⊙⏽ *MAP.*

¢ ⌂ **Pousada das Corucacas.** Step into the region's rugged world by staying at this inn on a working gaúcho horse farm—the 1,200-acre Fazenda Baio Ruano. This pousada has no frills but guest rooms are cozy, with central heating (rare in these parts), an ample lounge with a fireplace, and a great view of the surrounding hills covered with native grass meadows and dotted with Paraná pine trees. There are waterfalls and woods in the area: consider exploring them on horseback and perhaps trekking into the canyons beyond. ⊠ *Km 1, RS-020 (Estrada do Ouro Verde), 95481-970* ☎ *054/3251–1123* ⇨ *11 rooms* ⚒ *Dining room, horseback riding; no a/c, no room phones, no room TVs* ⊟ *MC, V* ⏻⊙⏽ *MAP.*

Torres

㉙ *205 km (128 mi) northeast of Porto Alegre.*

The beaches around the city of Torres are Rio Grande do Sul's most exciting. The sophistication of the seaside areas attracts international travelers, particularly Argentines and Uruguayans. Some of the best beaches are Praia da Cal, Praia da Guarita, and Praia Grande. The Parque Estadual da Guarita (Watchtower State Park), 3 km (2 mi) south of downtown, was set aside to protect the area's unique vegetation as well as the basalt hills that end abruptly in the Atlantic. Locals like to fish from these cliffs. A mile offshore, Ilha dos Lobos (Seawolf Island) is a way station for sea lions in their annual migrations along the south Atlantic coast. South of Torres, and extending well into Uruguay, the coastline is a 400-mi-long sandy stretch interrupted only by a few river deltas and lagoons.

Where to Stay & Eat

¢–$$ ✕ **Restaurante Parque da Guarita.** The thatched roof and tropical garden of this restaurant blend in perfectly with its beach setting. Seafood is the specialty here, and you can partake of your meal while enjoying the magnificent view of the surf and cliffs. ⊠ *Km 2, Estrada do Parque da Guarita* ☎ *051/3664–1056* ⊟ *DC, MC, V* ⊙ *No dinner Mar.–Nov.*

$ ⌂ **Solar da Barra Hotel.** In one of the best hotels in the city the decor is not distinguished, but rooms are large and comfortably furnished. Services are akin to those normally found only in larger resorts. Sightseeing boat trips to Ilha dos Lobos can be arranged by the hotel. ⊠ *Rua Plínio Kroeff 465, Mampituba 95560–000* ☎ *051/3664–1811 or 0800/ 54–16100* ⊟ *051/3664–1090* ⊕ *www.solardabarra.com.br* ⇨ *178 rooms* ⚒ *Restaurant, cable TV, 2 pools (1 indoor), sauna, paddle tennis, soccer, volleyball, bar, nightclub, playground, Internet, meeting room* ⊟ *AE, DC, MC, V.*

THE GAÚCHO: COWBOY OF THE SOUTHERN RANGES

WHEN EUROPEAN SETTLERS *moved into the South America grasslands known as the Pampas in the 16th century, cattle raising became the occupation of choice. Soon a new character gained notoriety in this rural landscape: the gaúcho. These men were loners, roaming the Pampas on horseback and taking odd jobs at the estancias (cattle ranches, similar to Mexican haciendas). They were often involved in some sort of contraband and even banditry, and the word "gaúcho" had, for long time, a denigrating meaning, akin to "vagabond" or "cattle rustler." But that image changed with the independence wars of the 1800s, when gaúchos took side against the colonial powers. Since then they've been painted as freedom-seeking heroes, romanticized in t he poetry, literature, and folk music of Argentina, Uruguay, and southern Brazil.*

Gaúcho attire has changed over time, but traditinally, the thick poncho, adopted

from pre-Colombian Andean cultures like the Incas, was ubiquitous. Bombachas, (loose, wide-brimmed cotton trousers) became popular by the 1860s. The gaúcho wore several types of hats, but the boina is the most common—a dark-color felt beret popular with Spanish settlers. Boleadeiras (a weapon made from rope, with rocks or metal balls tied at the end), adopted from native peoples, were used before the lasso to ensnare cattle and ema (rhea). Gaúcho boots were quite simple— just thick leather straps wrapped and tied around the feet.

Today in Brazil "gaúcho" is the nickname for natives of Rio Grande do Sul State— about half of its territory lies in the Pampas region. The gaúcho traditions, especially rodeos, music, and dances, are still very much revered and preserved through hundreds of CTGs (Centro de Tradições Gaúchas; Gaucho Tradition Centers).

São Miguel das Missões

★ ㉚ *482 km (300 mi) northwest of Porto Alegre.*

Jesuit missionaries moved into the upper Uruguay River basin around 1700. In the following decades the local Guarani peoples were converted to Christianity, leading them to abandon their seminomadic lifestyle and to congregate around the new missions—locally known as *reduções* (reductions). Seven of these existed in what is now Brazil, and several more were in Argentina and Paraguay—all linked by a closely knit trade and communication route. Historians have claimed that at the peak of their influence, the Jesuits actually had created the first de facto country in the Americas, complete with a court system and elections. After the Treaty of Madrid granted rights over the lands and native peoples in the area to the Portuguese crown, the Jesuits were under pressure to leave. Recurrent clashes with Portuguese militia precipitated the breakdown of the mission system, but the final blow came with the decree of expulsion of Jesuit order from Portuguese territory. Most of the Guaranis dispersed back into unexplored country. This important historical period was depicted in *The Mission,* starring Robert De Niro, with several scenes shot at Iguaçú Falls.

São Miguel das Missões is the best-preserved and best-organized Jesuit mission in Brazil. Circa 1745 an impressive church was built of reddish basalt slabs brought by the Guaranis from quarries miles away. The ruins are now a UNESCO World Heritage Site. There is a small museum on the grounds designed by Lucío Costa (who was instrumental in the development of Brasília). It holds religious statues carved by the Guaranis, as well as other pieces recovered from archaeological digs. Admission to the site includes a sound-and-light show that tells the mission's story, at 8 PM in summer and 6 PM in winter.

Tours of the missions can be booked through any tour operator in Porto Alegre. Other mission sites with ruins are São Lourenço and São Nicolau; however, there is less to be seen at these sites. ⊠ *Parque Histórico de São Miguel. From Porto Alegre follow BR 386 to Carazinho, then BR 285 to the São Miguel exit. From there drive 11 km (7 mi) to mission site via BR 466* ☎ *055/3381–3259* 🖼 *R$5* ⊙ *Museum daily 8–6; grounds daily 8 AM–dusk.*

Where to Stay & Eat

$ ✕ **Churrascaria Barichello.** This typical gaúcho restaurant is the best option in town. Savor the espeto-corrido, with more than a dozen kinds of meat. ⊠ *Av. Borges do Canto 1519* ☎ *055/3381–1272* 🖃 *MC, V.*

¢ 🖼 **Wilson Park Hotel Missões.** A world-class hotel catering to the discriminating tourist, the Wilson Park has large rooms painted in pastel colors, with colonial-style furnishings. Arched doorways echo the design of the mission a few blocks away. The well-trained staff is knowledgeable about the missions and other attractions in the region. ⊠ *Rua São Miguel 664, 98865-000* ☎ *055/3381–2000* ⊕ *www.wilsonparkhotel. com.br* 🖘 *78 rooms* ⌂ *Restaurant, cable TV, minibar, pool, horseback riding, bar, Internet, no-smoking rooms* 🖃 *AE, DC, MC, V* ⦿ *CP.*

THE SOUTH ESSENTIALS

Transportation

For more information about transportation, *see* Smart Travel Tips A to Z, at the front of this book.

BY AIR

Flights to the south from Canada, the U.S., and the U.K. stop first in São Paulo. Domestic carriers TAM, Varig, and Gol have flights from various Brazilian cities to Curitiba, Florianópolis, and Porto Alegre (⇨ Air Travel, *in* Smart Travel Tips A to Z). In addition, Aerolíneas Argentinas and OceanAir serve Porto Alegre.

🛪 Airlines **Aerolíneas Argentinas** ☎ 051/3221-3300 in Rio Grande do Sul. **OceanAir** ☎ 051/3358-2393, 0300/789-8160 in Rio Grande do Sul.

PARANÁ The flight from São Paulo to Curitiba is about an hour. Curitiba"s Aeroporto Internacional Afonso Pena (CWB) is 21 km (13 mi) east of downtown. A cab ride to downtown is around R$40. A minibus service (R$6) provides transportation between Rua 24 Horas and Estação Rodoferroviária and the airport.

Direct São Paulo–Foz do Iguaçu flights take about an hour and a half. Longer flights are routed through Curitiba. The Aeroporto Internacional Foz do Iguaçu (IGU) is 13 km (8 mi) southeast of downtown Foz. The 20-minute taxi ride should cost R$45, the 45-minute regular bus ride about R$2.50. Note that several major hotels are on the highway to downtown, so a cab ride from the airport to these may be less than R$30. A cab ride from downtown hotels directly to the Parque Nacional in Brazil costs about R$80, and a full tour including both the Brazilian and Argentine sides of the falls costs R$200 (entrance fees to the parks not included).

🛧 Airports **Aeroporto Internacional Afonso Pena** ⊠ Av. Rocha Pombo s/n, São José dos Pinhais, Curitiba ☎ 041/3381-1515. **Aeroporto Internacional Foz do Iguaçu** ⊠ Km 13, Rodovia das Cataratas ☎ 045/3521-4276.

SANTA CATARINA   Flights from São Paulo to Florianópolis are about an hour in length. The Aeroporto Internacional Hercílio Luz (FLN) is 12 km (8 mi) south of downtown Florianópolis. Taking a cab into town will run about R$38. In addition, there's *amarelinho* (minibus) service for R$8.50.

🛧 Airport **Aeroporto Internacional Hercílio Luz** ⊠ Km 12, Av. Deomício Freitas, Florianópolis ☎ 048/331-4000.

RIO GRANDE   It takes about an hour and a half to fly from São Paulo to Porto Ale-
DO SUL   gre. The Aeroporto Internacional Salgado Filho (POA) in Porto Alegre is one of Brazil's most modern air terminals. It is only 8 km (5 mi) northeast of downtown. The cost of cab ride is around R$30. At a booth near the arrivals gate you can prepay your cab ride. There's also a minibus shuttle into town for about R$3.25.

The closest airport to São Miguel das Missões is 60 km (38 mi) away, in Santo Angelo. It's served daily by OceanAir flights from Portão.

🛧 Airport **Aeroporto Internacional Salgado Filho** ⊠ Av. Severo Dulius 90010, Porto Alegre ☎ 051/3358-2000.

BY BUS

For the most part, each city is served by a different bus company. For long-distance trips it's best to opt for special services, often called *executivo* or *leito* (pullman) buses, which have air-conditioning, wide reclining seats, and restrooms. Regular buses are 20%–30% less but aren't nearly as comfortable.

Within the region's cities, the bus is the preferred form of public transportation. You can reach virtually any neighborhood, and the fares are modest. Crime can be a problem on little-traveled routes or during off-peak hours.

PARANÁ   Curitiba's main bus station is the Estação Rodoferroviária. Catarinense buses travel to Blumenau (4 hours) and Joinville (1½ hours). Penha buses run to and from São Paulo (5 hours). For trips to Porto Alegre (12 hours), try Pluma. Sulamericana buses make the 10-hour trip to Foz do Iguaçu. The Terminal Rodoviário in Foz do Iguaçu is 5 km (3 mi) northeast of downtown. For trips to Florianópolis (14 hours), contact Catarinense. Pluma buses make the 16-hour journey to São Paulo. For trips to Curitiba (10 hours), try Sulamericana.

In Foz do Iguaçu, Linha Cataratas and Parque Nacional buses depart hourly (8–6) from the Terminal Urbano for the visitor center at the park entrance. The fare is about R$3. Buses for Puerto Iguazú, Argentina, and Ciudad del Este, Paraguay, depart from the same terminal.

🚍 **Catarinense** ☎ 041/3224-9368 in Curitiba, 045/3223-2996 in Foz do Iguaçu. **Estação Rodoferroviária** ⊠ Av. Afonso Camargo 330, Curitiba ☎ 041/3320-3000. **Penha** ☎ 041/3322-8811. **Pluma** ☎ 041/3223-3641 in Curitiba, 045/3522-2515 in Foz do Iguaçu. **Sulamericana** ☎ 041/373-1000 in Curitiba, 045/3522-2050 in Foz do Iguaçu. **Terminal Rodoviário** ⊠ Av. Costa e Silva s/n, Foz do Iguaçu ☎ 045/3522-1027. **Terminal Urbano (Foz do Iguaçu)** ⊠ Av. Juscelino Kubitschek s/n, across from army barracks, Foz do Iguaçu ☎ 0800/45-1516.

SANTA CATARINA Several bus companies have regular service to and from Florianópolis's Terminal Rodoviário Rita Maria. For the 12-hour journey to São Paulo, the 3½-hour trip to Joinville, or the two-hour trip to Blumenau, try Catarinense. Pluma buses travel to Curitiba (5 hours). For trips to Porto Alegre (6 hours), try União Cascavel/Eucatur or Catarinense.

In Florianópolis a quick, convenient way to visit the beaches is by amarelinho (also known as executivo), or express minibuses, which cost about R$6. They leave regularly from designated places around Praça XV.

🚍 **Catarinense** ☎ 048/222-2260. **Pluma** ☎ 048/223-1709. **Terminal Rodoviário Rita Maria** ⊠ Av. Paulo Fontes 1101, Florianópolis ☎ 048/212-3100. **Terminal Urbano Florianópolis** ⊠ Praça 15 de Novembro s/n, Centro, Florianópolis ☎ 048/3324-1517. **União Cascavel/Eucatur** ☎ 048/224-2080.

RIO GRANDE DO SUL All bus lines to the interior—and to other states and countries—use the outdated, overcrowded Estação Rodoviária. Penha has service to São Paulo (19 hours). Pluma buses travel to Curitiba (12 hours). Florianópolis (6 hours) is served by Eucatur. To reach Foz do Iguaçu (14 hours), Unesul is the only option. Regular bus service to São Miguel das Missões is not designed for tourists: the trip is painfully slow. Instead, book a tour from Porto Alegre, either taking a regular flight or charter bus.

Porto Alegre has an extensive bus system as well as the *lotação* (express minibus). For service times and routes call Informações Municipais.

🚍 **Estação Rodoviária** ⊠ Largo Vespasiano Veppo s/n ☎ 051/3210-0101. **Informações Municipais** ⊠ Porto Alegre ☎ 051/158. **Penha** ☎ 051/3225-0933. **Pluma** ☎ 051/3224-9291. **Eucatur** ☎ 051/3228-8900. **Unesul** ☎ 051/3228-0029.

BY CAR

The southern states have extensive highway systems connecting major cities and tourist destinations. Be prepared for stretches that aren't in top condition; some are being renovated, and there may be delays. When planning a road trip, it's best to check the highway traffic conditions by calling the *plantão*, a 24-hour hotline operated by the Polícia Rodoviária Federal (Federal Highway Patrol) in each state. Privatized toll roads in Rio Grande do Sul and Paraná are generally in good shape, but you'll have to pay R$4–R$9. These provide rest areas next to the toll plazas, where tourist information and highway status reports can be obtained.

You can drive from Curitiba to Foz do Iguaçu on BR 277, which traverses Paraná State. It's a long drive, but this toll highway is kept in good shape. To visit Vila Velha State Park, a detour must be made on BR 376 toward Ponta Grossa. The BR 101 is the most direct route from Curitiba to other southern communities, but it's one of the country's busiest roads (there's lots of truck traffic night and day). The single-lane stretch south of Florianópolis to Porto Alegre is under major renovation and is extremely dangerous, especially during the vacation months of January and February.

BR 116, the Mountain Route, runs from Curitiba to Porto Alegre. Built 40 years ago, it was the first highway connecting the region with the rest of the country. Although it's scenic for much of the way—and a little shorter than other routes—it's also narrow, with many curves and many trucks.

Most of the 482-km (300-mi) route from Porto Alegre to São Miguel das Missões is a toll road. It's single-lane, but generally in good condition. Expect heavy truck traffic.

Traffic in Curitiba, Florianópolis, and Porto Alegre isn't as hectic as in São Paulo or Rio, so driving won't be overly daunting. Finding a place to park is relatively easy, except in the downtown districts during business hours. Parking lots are abundant in the cities, and one-hour tickets cost about R$4. Streets in downtown Porto Alegre have a parking-meter system, up to 2 hours, starting at 50 centavos for 30 minutes.

Don't expect to find rental vehicles in the luxury range of the car spectrum. Automatic transmission is not normally available, and there's a surcharge for air-conditioning.

Paraná Rental Agencies Avis ✉ Aeroporto Internacional Afonso Pena, Av. Rocha Pombo, São José dos Pinhais, Curitiba ☎ 041/3381-1370 ✉ Av. Salgado Filho 1491, Curitiba ☎ 041/3296-1889 ✉ Km 16.5, Rodovia das Cataratas, Foz do Iguaçu ☎ 045/3523-1510. **Hertz** ✉ Aeroporto Internacional Afonso Pena, Av. Rocha Pombo, São José dos Pinhais, Curitiba ☎ 041/3381-1382 ✉ Av. Nossa Senhora Aparecida 3731, Curitiba ☎ 041/3269-8000. **Localiza** ✉ Km 16.5, Rodovia das Cataratas, Foz do Iguaçu ☎ 045/3529-6300 ✉ Av. Juscelino Kubitschek 2878, Foz do Iguaçu ☎ 045/3522-1608.

Santa Catarina Rental Agencies Avis ✉ Aeroporto Internacional Hercílio Luz, Av. Deomício Freitas, Km 12, Florianópolis ☎ 048/236-1426 ✉ Av. Silva Jardim 495, Florianópolis ☎ 048/225-7777. **Hertz** ✉ Aeroporto Internacional Hercílio Luz, Av. Deomício Freitas, Km 12, Florianópolis ☎ 048/236-9955 ✉ Rua Bocaiuva 2125, Florianópolis ☎ 048/224-9955. **Localiza** ✉ Aeroporto Internacional Hercílio Luz, Av. Deomício Freitas, Km 12, Florianópolis ☎ 048/236-1244 ✉ Av. Paulo Fonte 730, Florianópolis ☎ 048/225-5558.

Rio Grande do Sul Rental Agencies Avis ✉ Aeroporto Internacional Salgado Filho, Av. Severo Dulius 90010, Porto Alegre ☎ 051/3371-4514 ✉ Av. Ceará 444, Porto Alegre ☎ 051/3342-0400. **Hertz** ✉ Aeroporto Internacional Salgado Filho, Av. Severo Dulius 90010, Porto Alegre ☎ 051/3337-7755. **Localiza** ✉ Aeroporto Internacional Salgado Filho, Av. Severo Dulius 90010, Porto Alegre ☎ 051/3358-2346 ✉ Av. Carlos

Gomes 190, Porto Alegre ☎ 051/3328-3150 ✉ Aeroporto Regional, Km 13, Estrada Ca-
tuipe, 60 km (38 mi) from São Miguel das Missões, Santo Ângelo ☎ 055/3312-1000.

BY TAXI

Taxis in Brazil are normally independently owned, and most are locally
organized into cooperatives that maintain phone numbers and dispatchers (hence the moniker *radio taxis*). These outfits have booths in
all airports, with posted rates (regulated by city authorities) for specific
destinations; you pay up front for the ride to town. Although it's best
to call for a cab in town to avoid delays, you can hail passing taxis. Cabs
have meters, but to avoid surprises, before departing ask for an estimate
of the fare to your destination. In Foz do Iguaçu independent tour operators (certified by the city government) offer their services outside hotel
lobbies. These special cabs are usually large sedans with air-conditioning. The driver doubles as a tour guide, and you can tailor the route
and pace according to your interests. A half-day trip to the Argentinean
Foz side of the falls from downtown costs about R$180.

🚖 Curitiba Taxi **radio taxi** ☎ 0800/600-6666 or 0800/41-4646.
🚖 Florianópolis Taxi **radio taxi** ☎ 240-6009.
🚖 Foz do Iguaçu Taxi **radio taxi** ☎ 045/3523-4800.
🚖 Porto Alegre Taxi **radio taxi** ☎ 051/3334-7444 or 051/3266-7000.

BY TRAIN

One of Brazil's few passenger rail lines runs from Curitiba to Paranaguá—
a fabulous 110-km (69-mi) trip. Trains traverse the Serra do Mar slope
from 1,000 meters (3,300 feet) down to 5 meters (17 feet) through bridges
and tunnels. There are great views of the peaks, waterfalls, and Atlantic
rain forest, which covers most of the slopes on the way. Two stops, at
the historic towns of Marumbi and Morretes, complete this great route.
Two kinds of trains operate: the faster motorcar *litorina* makes the trip
in 3½ hours, departs from Curitiba at 9 AM (Friday–Sunday and holidays), returns from Paranaguá at 3:30 PM, and costs R$75; the trip by
regular train takes four hours, departs at 8 AM (except Monday), returns
at 4 PM, and costs R$25. Note that in the low season (April–Novem-
ber), both trains run only on weekends and holidays. To make arrangements, contact Serra Verde Express.

🚂 **Serra Verde Express** ✉ Estação Rodoferroviária, Gate 8, Curitiba ☎ 041/3323-4008
⊕ www.serraverdeexpress.com.br.

Contacts & Resources

BANKS & EXCHANGING SERVICES

In general, banks are open weekdays 10–4 in major cities, 10–3 in the
countryside, though major airport branches have extended hours for currency exchange (daily 8 AM–9 PM); some also have weekend hours. For
security reasons most ATMs shut down after 8 PM and restart after 6 AM.

Some banks accept only cards with Visa/Plus logos and others accept
only cards with MasterCard/Cirrus logos. Banco24horas ATMs usually
accept all cards, including American Express. *See* "Money Matters" *in*
Smart Travel Tips A to Z for more information.

PARANÁ 🏦 **Banco ABN-AMRO Real** ✉ Av. Candido de Abreu 304, Centro Cívico, Curitiba ☎ 041/3252-2233. **Banco do Brasil** ✉ Aeroporto Internacional Afonso Pena, Av. Rocha Pombo, São José dos Pinhais, Curitiba ☎ 041/3381-1515 ✉ Av. Brasil 1377, Foz do Iguaçu ☎ 045/3521-2500. **BankBoston** ✉ Av. Mal. Deodoro 869, Centro, Curitiba ☎ 041/3322-5052. **STTC** ✉ Av. das Cataratas 1419, Foz do Iguaçu ☎ 045/3574-2527.

SANTA CATARINA 🏦 **Amplestur** ✉ Rua Jerônimo Coelho 293, Loja 01, Centro, Florianópolis ☎ 048/224-9422. **Banco do Brasil** ✉ Praça 15 de Novembro 20, Florianópolis ☎ 048/222-7000 ✉ Aeroporto Internacional Hercílio Luz, Av. Dep. Diomício Freitas s/n, Florianópolis ☎ 048/236-1717.

RIO GRANDE DO SUL 🏦 **American Express** ✉ Av. Carlos Gomes 466, Porto Alegre ☎ 0800/702-0777. **Banco do Brasil** ✉ Rua Uruguai 185, Centro, Porto Alegre ☎ 051/3214-7500 ✉ Aeroporto Internacional Salgado Filho, Av. Severo Dulius 90010, Porto Alegre ☎ 051/3371-1822. **Citibank** ✉ Praça Maurício Cardoso 176, Moinhos de Vento, Porto Alegre ☎ 051/3223-1000. **Exprinter** ✉ Rua Padre Chagas 185, Suite 306, Porto Alegre ☎ 051/3346-4211.

EMERGENCIES

PARANÁ For any emergency in Curitiba, dial ☎ 100.

🏦 Emergency Contacts **Ambulance** ☎ 192. **Fire** ☎ 193. **Police** ☎ 190.

Police Rodoviaria Federal ☎ 191.

🏦 Hospitals **Hospital Cajuru** ✉ Av. São José 300, Curitiba ☎ 041/3360-3000. **Hospital Internacional** ✉ Av. Brasil 1637, Foz do Iguaçu ☎ 045/3523-1404.

🏦 24-Hour Pharmacies **FarmaRede** ✉ Av. Brasil 46, Foz do Iguaçu ☎ 045/3523-1929. **HiperFarma** ✉ Rua P. Antonio Polito 1028, Curitiba ☎ 041/3286-5511.

SANTA CATARINA 🏦 Emergency Contacts **Ambulance** ☎ 192. **Fire** ☎ 193. **Police** ☎ 190.

Police Rodoviaria Federal ☎ 048/246–3799.

🏦 Hospitals **Hospital Universitário** ✉ Av. Beira-Mar Norte, Trindade, Florianópolis ☎ 048/331-9100.

🏦 24-Hour Pharmacies **Farmácia Rita Maria** ✉ Av. Paulo Fontes 1101, Terminal Rita Maria, Florianópolis ☎ 048/222-5016.

RIO GRANDE DO SUL 🏦 Emergency Contacts **Ambulance** ☎ 192. **Fire** ☎ 193. **Police** ☎ 190.

Police Rodoviaria Federal ☎ 051/3374–0003.

🏦 Hospitals **Hospital Pronto Socorro** ✉ Av. Osvaldo Aranha s/n, Porto Alegre ☎ 051/3330-9888.

🏦 24-Hour Pharmacies **Farmácia PanVel** ✉ Av. 24 de Outubro 722, Moinhos de Vento, Porto Alegre ☎ 051/3222-0188.

INTERNET

🏦 Internet Cafés **Digital Land** ✉ Av. das Cataratas 1118, Foz do Iguaçu ☎ 045/3523-4245. **Saraiva Mega Store** ✉ Shopping Center Praia de Belas, Av. Praia de Belas 1181, Menino Deus, Porto Alegre ☎ 051/3231-6868.

MAIL & SHIPPING

🏦 Express Services **FedEx** ✉ Rua Nossa Senhora da Penha 435, Curitiba ☎ 041/3362-5155 ✉ Rua Coronel Américo 912, Florianópolis ☎ 048/240-6232 ✉ Av. Ceará 255, Porto Alegre ☎ 051/3325-1333. **UPS** ✉ Rua Visconde do Rio Branco 279, Porto Alegre ☎ 051/3346-6854.

🏦 Post Offices **Curitiba post office** ✉ Av. Marechal Deodoro 298 ☎ 041/3310-2159. **Foz do Iguaçu post office** ✉ Praça Getúlio Vargas 72 ☎ 045/3523-0327. **Florianópolis**

post office ✉ Praça 15 de Novembro 242 ☎ 048/159. **Porto Alegre post office** ✉ Rua Siqueira Campos 1100, Porto Alegre ☎ 051/3220-8800.

TOUR OPTIONS

PARANÁ In Curitiba try Best Ways, which runs Serra Verde Express (⇨ Train Travel), for train tickets to the Paranaguá Bay and tours of the attractions including the national park; check OneTur for other Paraná state sights.

STTC Turismo in Foz do Iguaçu is reliable. Macuco Safari arranges Zodiac trips to Salto Macuco and on to the main falls. Helisul Táxi Aéreo offers helicopter tours of the falls between 9 and 6 and, if you like, of Itaipú Dam. The shortest flight (10 minutes) costs US$60 per person (with a minimum of three passengers).

Within Curitiba, the Linha Turismo is a special bus line maintained by the city that follows a 2½-hour circular route, which allows three stops along the way for the same fare. Buses depart every 30 minutes from 9 to 5:30 from the Praça Tiradentes, stopping at 22 attractions. Plan to spend an entire day on this route. There are taped descriptions of the sights (available in three languages—including English), and the fare is R$12.

🏂 **Best Ways** ✉ Estação Rodoferroviária, Gate 8, Curitiba ☎ 041/3323-4007. **Linha Turismo** ☎ 041/156. **OneTur** ✉ Rua Mal. Floriano 228, Suite 1107, Centro, Curitiba ☎ 041/3224-8509 ⊕ www.onetur.com.br. **Helisul Táxi Aéreo** ✉ Km 16.5, Rodovia das Cataratas, Foz do Iguaçu ☎ 045/3529-7474 ⊕ www.helisul.com. **Macuco Safari** ✉ Km 21, Rodovia das Cataratas, Foz do Iguaçu ☎ 045/3574-4244. **STTC Turismo** ✉ Av. Morenitas 2250, Padre Monti, Foz do Iguaçu ☎ 045/3523-1115 🖷 045/3523-3137 ⊕ www.sttcturismo.com.br.

SANTA CATARINA In Florianópolis try Amplestur for van tours of the city, the beaches, and destinations around the continent. Scuna Sul operates a schooner, on which you can take tours, especially of the northern part of the island. A highly recommended tour includes a stop for snorkeling off Ilha do Arvoredo, a nature preserve. For the more adventurous traveler there is a larger schooner outfitted for a 12-hour trip around the island, which costs R$120.

🏂 **Amplestur** ✉ Rua Jerônimo Coelho 293, Loja 01, Centro, Florianópolis ☎ 041/224-9422 ⊕ www.amplestur.com.br. **Scuna Sul** ✉ Rua Antonio Heil s/n, Canasvieiras, Florianópolis ☎ 048/266-1810.

RIO GRANDE DO SUL In Porto Alegre tours of the city, to the Serra Gaúcha, and of the coast can all be arranged by Galapagos Tour and Unesul Turismo. Caminhos do Sul Turismo offers the best tour packages to the Missions. Cisne Branco and Noiva do Caí run day and night boat trips on the Guaíba. Caá-Etê Ecotourismo & Aventura and Galapagos are good choices for adventure trips—rafting, horseback riding, or hiking excursions—to the national and state parks in Rio Grande do Sul.

The Linha Turismo, run by the Serviço de Atenção ao Turista (SAT; ⇨ Tourist Information, *below*), in double-decker buses, departs from the main SAT location in Cidade Baixa. One ticket for the 80-minute ride, stopping at most of city's points of interest, costs about R$7. Schedules vary seasonally.

🏂 **Caá-Etê Ecoturismo & Aventura** ✉ Av. Protásio Alves 2715, Suite 905, Porto Alegre ☎ 051/3338-3323 🖷 051/3338-1888 ⊕ www.caa-ete.com.br. **Caminhos do Sul Tur-**

ismo ✉ Rua Dr. Armando Barbedo 480, Suite 306, Porto Alegre ☎ 051/3268-0851 ⊟ 051/
3268-0851 ⊕ www.caminhosdosulturismo.com.br. **Cisne Branco** ✉ Port of Porto Alegre, Main Gate, Av. Mauá 1050, Centro, Porto Alegre ☎ 051/3224-5222. **Noiva do Caí**
✉ Usina do Gasômetro, Centro, Porto Alegre ☎ 051/3211-7662. **Farol de Itapuã** ✉ Av.
Nossa Senhora de Navegantes 6, Vila de Itapoã, Viamão ☎ 051/3019-7945 or 051/494-
1111. **Galápagos Tour** ✉ Av. Senador Salgado Filho 135, Suite 202, Centro, Porto Alegre ☎ 051/3286-7094 ⊕ www.galapagostour.com.br. **Unesul Turismo** ✉ Rua Vigário
José Inácio 621, Porto Alegre ☎ 051/3228-8111 ⊕ www.unesultur.com.br.

VISITOR INFORMATION

PARANÁ Paraná Turismo in Curitiba is open Monday and Tuesday 1 PM–7 PM at
the Centro Cívico location and daily 8 AM–10 PM at its Afonso Pena airport location.
🚩 **FozTur** ✉ Rua Alm. Barroso 1300, 2nd floor, Foz do Iguaçu ☎ 0800/45-1516
✉ Aeroporto Internacional Foz do Iguaçu, Km 13 ☎ 045/3521-4276. **Paraná Turismo**
(State Tourism Board) ✉ Rua Dep. Mário de Barros 1290, Centro Cívico, Curitiba ☎ 041/
3331-3500 or 041/3354-1516 Disque Turismo [24-hr hotline] ⊕ www.pr.gov.br/turismo
✉ Aeroporto Internacional Afonso Pena, Av. Rocha Pombo s/n, São José dos Pinhais
☎ 045/3381-1153.

SANTA CATARINA A reliable independent source about what's going on in Florianópolis
is *Guia Floripa,* which is free and can be obtained at newsstands or online at ⊕ www.guiafloripa.com.br.
🚩 **Portal Turístico** ✉ Rua Eng. Max de Souza 236, Coqueiros, mainland side of Ponte
Colombo Sales (Colombo Sales Bridge), São José ☎ 048/271-7028 ⊕ www.pmf.sc.gov.
br/turismo ✉ Terminal Rodoviária Rita Maria, Av. Paulo Fontes 1101, Centro, Florianópolis
☎ 048/212-3127. **SanTur** (State Tourism Authority) ✉ Rua Felipe Schmidt 249, 9th floor,
Florianópolis ☎ 048/244-5822 or 048/244-1516 ⊕ www.sc.gov.br/santacatarina/
turismo/contrastes/index.html.

RIO GRANDE 🚩 **Serviço de Atenção ao Turista** (SAT) ✉ Travessa do Carmo, 84, Cidade
DO SUL Baixa, Porto Alegre ☎ 0800/51–7686 or 051/3212–3464 ⊕ www.
portoalegre.rs.gov.br/turismo ✉ Mercado do Bom Fim, loja 12, Av. Osvaldo Aranha s/n, Bom Fim, Porto Alegre ☎ 051/3333–1873 ✉ Usina
do Gasometro, Av. João Goulart 551, Centro, Porto Alegre ☎ 051/
3333–5979. **Secretaria de Turismo** (State Tourism Authority) (Serviço de
Apoio ao Turista) ✉ Centro Administrativo, Av. Borges de Medeiros
1501, 10th floor, Porto Alegre ☎ 051/3288–5400 ⊕ www.turismo.rs.
gov.br ✉ Aeroporto Internacional Salgado Filho, Av. Severo Dulius
90010, Porto Alegre ☎ 051/3358–5423 ✉ Estação Rodoviária, Largo
Vespasiano Veppo s/n, Porto Alegre ☎ 051/3288–5410.

Minas
Gerais

WORD OF MOUTH

"Go to Ouro Preto and stay in a pousada overlooking the valleys and mountains. The tranquillity of Ouro Preto plus the magic of the city will forever remain in your memory."

—A.Lukosky

"In Minas Gerais you find small, friendly, finely restored towns—witnesses to a rich colonial past—like Tiradentes."

—Dilermando

Updated by
Jefferson
Santos and
Alessandra
Faria

THE CENTRAL MOUNTAINOUS REGION OF BRAZIL is dominated by this state whose name ("General Mines") was inspired by the area's great mineral wealth. In the 18th century the vast precious-metal reserves of Minas Gerais made the state, and particularly the city of Ouro Preto, the de facto capital of the Portuguese colony. That period of gold, diamond, and semiprecious-stone trading is memorialized in the historic towns scattered across the mountains and remains a tremendous source of pride for the *mineiros* (inhabitants of the state). Minas Gerais is one of the calmest and most conservative Brazilian states. Many say that it's because of the mountains that surround the state, which are also said to make the mineiro an introspective and friendly person. Yet Minas Gerais has also been a hotbed for movements that have triggered political, economic, and cultural development.

Though the Gold Towns (Ouro Preto, Mariana, Tiradentes, and Congonhas) are awe inspiring, Minas Gerais has other attractions. Roughly six hours south of the state capital of Belo Horizonte, several mineral-spa towns form the Circuito das Águas (Water Circuit). Thought to have healing powers, the natural springs of places like São Lourenço and Caxambu have attracted the Brazilian elite for more than a century. Close by is the unusual town of São Tomé das Letras—a place where UFOs are said to visit and where mystics and bohemians wait for the dawn of a new world.

Although justifiably proud of their state's artistic accomplishments, mineiros are also passionate about their politics. Minas Gerais has produced many of Brazil's most famous leaders, including Tiradentes, who led Brazil's first attempt at independence in the late 18th century; Juscelino Kubitschek, the president who made Brasília happen; and Tancredo Neves, who helped restore Brazilian democracy in the mid-1980s.

History

Exploration of Minas Gerais began in the 17th century, when *bandeirantes* (bands of adventurers) from the coastal areas came in search of slaves and gold. Near the town of Vila Rica, they found a black stone that was later verified to be gold (the coloring came from the iron oxide in the soil). Thus Vila Rica came to be called Ouro Preto (Black Gold), and at the beginning of the 18th century Brazil's first gold rush began. Along with the fortune seekers came Jesuit priests, who were later exiled by the Portuguese (for fear they would try to manipulate the mineral trade) and replaced by *ordens terceiros* ("third," or lay, orders). By the middle of the century the Gold Towns of Minas were gleaming with new churches built first in the baroque-rococo style of Europe and later in a baroque style unique to the region.

Minas, as it is known, was also blessed with a local artistic genius, Antônio Francisco Lisboa. The son of a Portuguese architect and a former slave, Lisboa was born in 1738 in what is today Ouro Preto. As an adult he acquired the nickname Aleijadinho (Little Cripple) because of an illness that left him deformed. Working in cedarwood and soapstone, Aleijadinho carved the passion of his beliefs in sculptures that grace churches throughout the state.

By the end of the 18th century the gold had begun to run out, and Ouro Preto's population and importance decreased. The baroque period ended at the start of the 19th century, when the Portuguese royal family, in flight from the conquering army of Napoléon Bonaparte, arrived in Brazil, bringing with them architects and sculptors with different ideas and artistic styles. Ornate twisted columns and walls adorned with lavish carvings gave way to simple straight columns and walls painted with murals or simply washed in white.

Today Minas is Brazil's second most industrialized state, after São Paulo. The iron that darkened the gold of Ouro Preto remains an important source of state income, along with steel, coffee, and auto manufacturing. Although some of its once heavily wooded areas have been stripped bare, Minas still has diverse and amazingly pristine ecosystems, including Atlantic forests, rain forests, wetlands, and grasslands. The traffic that the mines brought here in the 17th century thrust Brazil into civilization, and now, well into the wake of the gold rush, a steady sense of progress and a compassion for the land remain.

Exploring Minas Gerais

The peaks of the Serra do Mantiqueira separate Minas from Rio de Janeiro and give way to the Paraíba Valley. Although Minas is large, its major attractions, including Belo Horizonte, Ouro Preto, and the mineral-spa towns, are in the state's southeast, within driving distance of one another. The key historic cities—called the Gold Towns—are in the Serra do Espinhaço range, with Ouro Preto at 1,220 meters (4,000 feet) above sea level.

When to Go

The busiest and often most exciting times to travel are during the Christmas, Easter, and Carnaval periods—although Carnaval is much more subdued here than in Bahia or Rio. July, when the weather is cool and dry, is winter-break month for schoolchildren and another peak season. Temperatures are usually around 24°C (75°F) in the summer and 17°C (63°F) in the winter. To avoid crowds, travel from April to June or August to November. Discounts may be available during these months, although fewer services will be offered.

About the Restaurants

Mineiros tend to eat dinner after 8 (often closer to 10). Restaurants are busiest on weekends and may require reservations; many close on Monday.

About the Hotels

In the interior of Minas Gerais, especially in the historic cities and state parks, there are two types of traditional habitations for tourists: *pousadas* (inns), with simpler and familiar rooms, and *fazendas* (farms), which can be a fun option. In many cases hotel services aren't as good as they could be, but in recent years mineiros have been paying more attention to the importance of the tourism and improving the quality of lodgings. That said, most hotels remain small, lack English-speaking staffs, and have few of the amenities common in American and European chains.

6

If you have
5 days

Start your trip in 🏛 **Belo Horizonte** ❶–⓫, capital and main city of Minas Gerais. On your first day, do our Good Walk and get to know the city. At night, look for a pub or another cultural option. On Day 2, spend your day at the Feira de Artesanato on Avenida Afonso Pena. The following day, rent a car and head to the historic cities. Take the day to know **Sabará** ⑬ and **Mariana** ㉖, the oldest city of the state. Spend your last two days in 🏛 **Ouro Preto** ⑭–㉕, exploring its rich architecture, shopping, and absorbing the local folklore.

If you have
7 days

Follow the five-day itinerary above. For your remaining days you can either head north to 🏛 **Diamantina** (about 380 km/240 mi) or south through **Congonhas** ㉗ and 130 km (80 mi) south to the charming town of 🏛 **Tiradentes** ㉘

When you book, you'll likely be given a choice between a standard and a luxury room; the *apartamento de luxo* (luxury room) may be slightly larger, with air-conditioning and a better-equipped bathroom. Significant weekend discounts are common in Belo Horizonte.

AMETUR (✉ Rua Paraíba 1317 loja 15, Savassi, Belo Horizonte ☎ 031/3227–0006 or 031/3227–6886 ⊕ www.ametur.tur.br), the Association of Rural Tourism, is a group of respected, trustworthy ranch owners who have converted their fazendas into accommodations with luxurious yet down-home surroundings. You can visit one or more of these ranches, where relaxation, swimming, horseback riding, walks in the woods, and home-cooked meals are the order of the day. Suzana Sousa Lima runs AMETUR as well as her own fazenda, Boa Esperança, which has been rated among the top accommodations in the country.

WHAT IT COSTS In Reais				
$$$$	**$$$**	**$$**	**$**	**¢**
RESTAURANTS over R$60	R$45–R$60	R$30–R$45	R$15–R$30	under R$15
HOTELS over R$500	R$375–R$500	R$250–R$375	R$125–R$250	under R$125

Restaurant prices are for a dinner entrée. Hotel prices are for two people in a standard double room in high season, excluding taxes.

BELO HORIZONTE

444 km (276 mi) northwest of Rio and 741 km (460 mi) southeast of Brasília.

With more than 2 million inhabitants, Belo Horizonte, the capital of the state of Minas Gerais, still lives up to its nickname, the Garden City, which it earned in the 1940s and '50s, when the main avenue, Afonso Pena, was lined with huge trees. Also affectionately called BH (pronounced "bay ah-GAH") by residents, the city can look both like a metropolis—with traffic jams, tall buildings, and urban noise—and, in its tranquil downtown neighborhoods, like a simple country town.

Minas Gerais is better known for its historic towns, but Belo Horizonte is not an old city. Inspired by cities like Paris and Washington, Belo Horizonte was established in 1897 and was the first planned modern city in the country. That year the state capital moved to the city from Ouro Preto, whose location—wedged between mountains—did not allow for an expansion of the capital in line with the prosperity of the state. The construction of a new capital was a sign that modernity had arrived in the state and a celebration of the triumph of the new Brazilian republic over the old Portuguese monarchy.

Growth was slow at first but picked up speed in the 1920s, after World War I. At that time, with industries finally prospering, the city gained monuments like the Praça Sete's obelisk, knows as *Pirulito* (restored in 2003) and the Santa Tereza viaduct. Belo Horizonte also emerged on the Brazilian cultural scene with poets such as Carlos Drummond de Andrade and Pedro Nava, among others. In the 1940s, under the administration of mayor Juscelino Kubitschek, one of the most famous and respected Brazilian politicians, Belo Horizonte gained status as a metropolis. Kubitschek hired the young architect Oscar Niemeyer, who created some of landmarks of the city, including the Pampulha's Architectural Complex.

Today Belo Horizonte, the third-largest city in Brazil, is distinguished by its politics and its contributions to the arts. In the early 20th century the Brazilian political system was referred to as Café com Leite (Coffee with Milk), because the presidency was alternately held by natives of São Paulo (where much of Brazil's coffee is produced) and natives of Minas Gerais (the milk-producing state). The current system is more diverse, but mineiros are still very influential in the country's politics. Minas Gerais is also home to some of the most respected Brazilian theater companies, such as Grupo Galpão, and dance companies (Grupo Corpo, for one), and also to some of the most famous pop bands—such as Skank, Pato Fu, and Jota Quest. The artistic tradition is emphasized by the many festivals dedicated to all forms of art, from comic books to puppet theater and short movies to electronic music. The arts and nightlife scene, along with the stunning modern architecture, are reasons to visit Belo Horizonte before or after traversing Minas Gerais's peaceful countryside.

Exploring Belo Horizonte

Minas Gerais is a mountainous state, and you should be prepared for lots of hills when walking around Belo Horizonte. The central and original section of the city, which was planned in the 19th century, is surrounded by Avenida Contorno. The city's main attractions are downtown and in the southern zone. During the day these areas are not too crowded. To get to other neighborhoods, like Pampulha, you should take a taxi.

Architecture Ouro Preto and the other Gold Towns hold churches and other buildings built in a uniquely Brazilian baroque style. The interiors are often much more spectacular than the exteriors, and designs (naturally) incorporate a lot of gold.

Mineiro Cuisine One of the best places in Brazil for food lovers, Minas has authentically Brazilian cuisine, whereas food from other parts of Brazil tends to be heavily influenced by Africa and Europe. Many dishes that today are considered simply "Brazilian" originated in Minas Gerais. The mineiro diet is fish-free, since Minas Gerais has no coastline, and focuses on meat and chicken. Some of the best cachaças in Brazil are made here. For more information about the food of Minas Gerais, see "Eating like a Mineiro."

6

Gemstones Minas Gerais produces most of the world's colored gemstones, including the grande dame of them all—the imperial topaz, which is found nowhere else. The state's mines also produce amethysts, aquamarines, tourmalines, and emeralds. Ouro Preto, Belo Horizonte, and Tiradentes have good-quality jewelry and gem stores; prices are best in Ouro Preto.

Shopping Hand-carved wood and soapstone figures are sold by street vendors in all the historic cities. Other typical handicrafts are pottery and tapestries, in particular the handwoven *arraiola* tapestries for which the area around Diamantina is famous. Look for jewelry in Ouro Preto and Belo Horizonte, where you can buy authenticated pieces—often at heavily discounted prices—from top jewelers.

---

a good walk

On Avenida Afonso Pena in the center of Belo Horizonte the **Palácio das Artes** ⑦ ▶ incorporates the city's main theaters and art galleries. In front of the Conservatório (Music Conservatory), the **Parque Muncipal,** with its many trees, is an excellent place for a walk. On Sunday morning you'll find this part of the avenue crowded with tents for the Feira Artesanato (Artisans Fair). Take the Avenida Augusto de Lima, in front of the park's entrance, until you cross the Rua da Bahia, with its many historic buildings, which binds together two of the most bohemian neighborhoods of Belo Horizonte: Santo Antônio and Santa Tereza. The neo-Gothic building at the corner is **Centro de Cultura de Belo Horizonte** ⑥.

Head southwest five blocks on Rua da Bahia. Along the way you can see the Minas Gerais Writers Academy, the Vivaldi Moreira Auditorium, and the **Basílica de Lourdes** ⑤. Turn left to find the **Praça da Liberdade** ④, a good place to rest and appreciate the diverse architectural styles of the complex, including the **Palácio da Liberdade** ②, the **Museu de Mineralogia** ③, the Biblioteca Pública Luiz de Bessa (the Public Library), and the Niemeyer Building, one of the most beautiful examples of modernist architecture in the city.

Take Praça José Mendes Júnior, the small street to the right of the Palácio da Liberdade, and walk a short way to the Minas Tênis Clube. This art deco building was the venue for many high-society parties during the 1950s and '60s. Turn left onto Rua Espírito Santo until you arrive at the pleasant Rua Felipe dos Santos, in the Lourdes district. Keep walking to Rua Marília de Dirceu and turn left. Cross Avenida Contorno, where Rua Marília de Dirceu becomes Avenida Prudente de Morais. On your right, two blocks south, is the **Museu Histórico Abílio Barreto** ❶. Visit the museum and grab a snack at its coffee shop.

TIMING Reserve two hours for this walk. If you want to explore the Parque Municipal, add one more hour. Add another hour for the Sunday-morning Feira do Artesanato.

What to See

❺ **Basílica de Lourdes.** Conceived when the capital was founded but only inaugurated in 1923, Our Lady of Lourdes Church was elevated to the category of basilica by Pope Pius XII in 1958. Its Gothic architecture has received some adaptations, but it is still a magnificent building. ⊠ *Rua da Bahia 1596, Lourdes* ☎ *031/3218–7676* ⚏ *Free* ☉ *Daily 7 AM–8 PM.*

❻ **Centro de Cultura de Belo Horizonte.** The city's only example of the neo-Gothic style of Portuguese inspiration, this building was built in 1914 in order to house the first legislative assembly of the capital as well as the public library. In 1997 it was transformed into a cultural space, where local art exhibitions are scheduled. ⊠ *Rua da Bahia 1149, Centro* ☎ *031/3277–4014 or 031/3277–4607* ⚏ *Free* ☉ *Weekdays 9–7.*

⓫ **Conjunto Arquitetônico da Pampulha.** This modern complex was designed by Oscar Niemeyer and built in the 1940s on the banks of Lagoa da Pampulha. Opened in 1943, the **Casa do Baile** (Ballroom House; ⊠ Av. Otacílio Negrão de Lima 751, Pampulha ☎ 031/3277–7971) was a popular dance hall. It closed its doors shortly after the casino that is now the Pampulha Art Museum (⇨ *below*). Today the Casa do Baile is an art gallery. It's open Tuesday through Sunday 9–7, and admission is free. At **Igreja de São Francisco de Assis** (Church of St. Francis of Assisi; ⊠ Av. Otacílio Negrão de Lima, s/n Pampulha ☎ 031/3427–1644) has 14 panels, comprising the most important works painted by Portinari. The church is open Monday though Saturday 9–5 and Sunday 9–1; tickets are R$2. One of Niemeyer's first projects was the **Museu de Arte da Pampulha** (Pampulha Art Museum; ⊠ Av. Otacílio Negrão de Lima 16585, Pampulha ☎ 031/3443–4533 or 031/3277–7946), which has landscaped gardens by Burle Marx. The building was a casino until 1946, when gambling was prohibited in Brazil. Transformed into a museum in 1957, the building also has multimedia rooms, a small theater, a library, and a coffee shop. It's open Tuesday through Sunday 9–7; admission is free.

❽ **Mercado Central** (Central Market). There are more than 400 stores in this market, opened in 1929. You can find almost everything—from groceries to typical products from Minas Gerais, such as cheese, guava and milk sweets, arts and crafts, medicinal herbs and roots, and even pets. Many people (including local celebrities) stop by the popular bars inside the market to drink a beer and sample the famous appetizers, such as liver with onions. ⊠ *Av. Augusto de Lima 744, Centro* ☎ *031/3274–9434* ⊕ *www.mercadocentral.com.br* ✉ *Free* ☉ *Mon.–Sat. 7–6, Sun. 7–1.*

❾ **Museu de Artes e Ofícios.** In the main building of the Praça da Estação, in the center of the city, this museum houses almost 2,000 rudimentary tools and other items from the 17th to the 20th centuries used by Brazilian laborers. ⊠ *Praça da Estação s/n, Centro* ☎ *031/3248–8600* ⊕ *www.museudearteseoficios.com.br* ✉ *Free* ☉ *Tues.–Fri. 1–6, Sat. 1–5.*

❿ **Museu de História Natural e Jardim Botânico.** Although it has an area of more than 600,000 square meters (6.4 million square feet), with Brazilian fauna, flora, archaeology, and mineralogy, the museum's main attraction is the Presépio do Pipiripau (Pipiripau Crèche). This ingenious work of art narrates Christ's life in 45 scenes, with 580 moving figures. It was built by Raimundo Machado de Azevedo, who began assembling it in 1906 and finished in 1984. The Instituto do Patrimônio Histórico e Artístico Nacional (National Institute of the History and Arts) deemed it artistic patrimony in 1984. ⊠ *Rua Gustavo da Silveira 1035, Santa Inês* ☎ *031/3461–5805 or 031/3482–9723* ✉ *R$3* ☉ *Tues.–Fri. 8–11:30 and 1–4, weekends 10–5.*

❸ **Museu de Mineralogia Professor Djalma Guimarães.** More than 3,000 pieces extracted from sites all over the world are on display in the mineralogy museum, which is housed in a postmodern steel-and-glass building. ⊠ *Av. Bias Fortes 50, Funcionários* ☎ *031/3271–3415 or 031/3277–7159* ✉ *Free* ☉ *Tues.–Sun. 9–5.*

❶ **Museu Histórico Abílio Barreto.** Attached to an old colonial mansion, the Abílio Barreto Historical Museum (MHAB) has permanent and temporary exhibitions about the city of Belo Horizonte. Its comfortable coffee shop is open until midnight. ⊠ *Av. Prudente de Morais 202, Cidade Jardim* ☎ *031/3277–8575 or 031/3277–8572* ✉ *Free* ☉ *Tues.–Sun. 10–5.*

❷ **Palácio da Liberdade.** Built in 1898, the French-style Liberdade Palace is the headquarters of the Minas Gerais government and is the official residence of the governor. Of note are the gardens by Paul Villon, the Louis XV–style banquet room, the paintings in Noble Hall, and a panel by Antônio Pereira. The palace is opened to the public the last Sunday of every month. ⊠ *Praça da Liberdade s/n, Funcionários* ☎ *031/3250–6265 or 031/3250–6050* ✉ *Free* ☉ *Last Sun. of month, 8:30–2.*

❼ **Palácio das Artes.** Designed by Oscar Niemeyer and built in 1970, the
 Fodor'sChoice ★ Palace of the Arts is the most important cultural center in Belo Horizonte, comprising three theaters, three art galleries, a movie theater, a bookstore, a coffee shop, and the Centro de Artesanato Mineiro (Mineiro Artisan Center), which has such contemporary Minas handicrafts as wood and soapstone carvings, pottery, and tapestries—all for sale. The main theater, Grande Teatro, stages music concerts, plays, operas, ballets, and other productions by Brazilian and foreign artists. ⊠ *Av. Afonso Pena 1537, Centro* ☎ *031/3237–7399* ⊕ *www.palaciodasartes.com.br* ✉ *Free* ☉ *Tues.–Sat. 10–8, Sun. 4–8.*

Parque Municipal Américo Renné Giannetti. With 45 acres of green area, the Parque Municipal (municipal park) Américo Renné Giannetti, in-

Belo Horizonte

KEY

▶ *Start of walk*

spired by the design of French parks, was inaugurated in 1897. It shelters an orchid house, a school, a playground, and the Francisco Nunes Theater, a beautiful modern building designed by the architect Luiz Signorelli in the 1940s that still presents theatrical plays and musical performances. With more than 50 tree species, the Municipal Park is highly recommended for walks. ⊠ *Av. Afonso Pena s/n, Centro* ☎ *031/3277–4161 or 031/3277–4749 park, 031/3277–3235 or 031/3277–4203 Francisco Nunes theater* 🎟 *Free* 🕓 *Tues.–Sun. 6–6.*

❹ Praça da Liberdade (Liberdade Square). When the city was founded, this square was created to house public administration offices. Today, in addition to centenarian palm trees, fountains, and a bandstand, the square also has neoclassical, art deco, modern, and postmodern buildings. ⊠ *Between Avs. João Pinheiro and Cristóvão Colombro, Funcionários.*

Where to Eat

BRAZILIAN (MINEIRO) $ ✕ **Dona Lucinha.** Roughly 32 traditional Minas dishes, like *feijão tropeiro, frango com quiabo,* and *frango ao molho pardo,* are available at this reasonably priced self-serve eatery. The food is the only reason to go, as the place—in an old house devoid of taste—lacks charm. Children get significant discounts. ⊠ *Rua Padre Odorico 38, São Pedro* ☎ *031/3227–0562* 🖃 *AE, DC, MC, V* 🕓 *No dinner Sun.* ⊠ *Rua Sergipe 811, Savassi* ☎ *031/3261–5930 or 031/3227–3286* ⊕ *www.donalucinha.com.br* 🖃 *AE, DC, MC, V* 🕓 *No dinner Sun.*

CONTINENTAL ★ $$–$$$$ ✕ **Chalezinho.** There's only one reason to come here: romance. The dimly lighted chalet, with its elegant piano music (accompanied by the occasional saxophone), is a magical retreat in the hills above town. The specialty is fondue; the filet mignon cooked in a bowl of sizzling oil and paired with any of eight delicious sauces is a treat. Afterward, order a chocolate fondue, which comes with a mouthwatering selection of fruits waiting to be dipped. When you finish, step outside to the Praça dos Amores (Lovers' Plaza) for a kiss under the moonlit sky. ⊠ *Alameda da Serra 18, Vale do Sereno–Nova Lima* ☎ *031/3286–3155* ⊕ *www.chalezinho.com.br* 🖃 *AE* 🕓 *No lunch.*

$$–$$$$ ✕ **Splêndido Ristorante.** The food and the service at this cosmopolitan restaurant are exceptional. The kitchen blends French and northern Italian cuisines to produce a menu with a mix of pasta, seafood, and meat dishes. It's assured that anyone who's anyone will show up here at some point during a visit to Belo Horizonte. The restaurant has the best wine cellar in town, with about 300 bottles from all over the world. ⊠ *Rua Levindo Lopes 251, Funcionários* ☎ *031/3227–6446* 🖃 *AE, DC, MC, V* 🕓 *No lunch Sat. No dinner Sun.*

ECLECTIC $–$$ ✕ **Restaurante Varandão.** On the 25th floor of the Othon Palace hotel, this romantic restaurant has spectacular urban vistas. Start off with a cocktail at one of the outdoor candlelighted tables before coming inside for dinner, where a generous buffet serves as the dining room's centerpiece. Feijoada, pastas, salads, and various meats are on the buffet daily. On weekends the chef serves an innovative "soapstone barbecue," where you choose thinly sliced meats to grill on a hot soapstone; your meal also comes with potatoes, sauces, and toast. Live Brazilian music accompanies dinner nightly. ✉ *Av. Afonso Pena 1050, Centro* ☎ *031/3247–0000 or 031/3247–0001* ⊕ *www.othon.com.br* ▤ *AE, DC, MC, V.*

¢–$ ✕ **Casa dos Contos.** A popular gathering place for local journalists, artists, and intellectuals, Casa dos Contos has an unpretentious and varied menu with choices ranging from fish and pasta to typical mineiro dishes. In keeping with its bohemian clientele, Casa dos Contos serves well past midnight. ✉ *Rua Rio Grande do Norte 1065, Funcionários* ☎ *031/3261–5853* ▤ *AE, DC, MC, V.*

¢–$ ✕ **Restaurante Top Beer.** This trendy restaurant-bar makes an ideal launchpad for your evening. Students and executives alike plan their night out while sipping caipirinhas on the large outdoor patio. The inside dining room is an inviting tropical enclave, with fountains and trees surrounding the tables. The pasta dishes and grilled steaks are commendable. ✉ *Rua Tomé de Souza 1121, Savassi* ☎ *031/3282–7788* ▤ *AE, DC, MC, V.*

ITALIAN ✕ **Vecchio Sogno.** What is widely considered Belo Horizonte's best Italian restaurant attracts a well-heeled clientele. Tuxedo-clad waiters serve
★ $$–$$$$ selections from the extensive wine list as well as steak, seafood, and pasta dishes. Consider the grilled fillet of lamb with saffron risotto in a mushroom-and-garlic sauce; the gnocchi *di mare,* with spinach and potatoes, topped with a white clam and scallop sauce; or the *badejo,* a local white fish baked and dressed in a seafood sauce. ✉ *Rua Martim de Carvalho 75, Santo Agostinho* ☎ *031/3292–5251 or 031/3292–5180* ⊕ *www. vecchiosogno.com.br* ▤ *MC, V* ⌕ *Reservations essential* ☾ *No lunch Sat. No dinner Sun.*

★ ¢–$ ✕ **Memmo Pasta & Pizza.** This casual Italian eatery is popular with Brazilians celebrating the end of the workday for appetizers like the *champignon Recheado* (mushroom stuffed with shrimp and prosciutto), and entrées like *tournedo Amici Miei* (filet mignon wrapped in bacon and marinated in garlic and olive oil). The pizza is arguably the best in town. The restaurant is often packed both inside and on the large outdoor patio; you may need to wait for the staff to find you a table. ✉ *Rua Tome de Souza 1331, Funcionários* ☎ *031/3282–4992* ⊕ *www. memmo.com.br* ▤ *V* ☾ *No dinner Sun.*

MIDDLE EASTERN ✕ **Amigo do Rei.** The first Persian restaurant of Brazil appeared in Paraty,
$–$$ Rio de Janeiro, but it moved to the capital of Minas Gerais in 2002. The
Fodor'sChoice homey place has only 23 seats. The owner, Cláudio, is the host, and his
★ wife, Nasrin, is the chef. Before your order is ready, the waiter will be happy to inform you about Iranian culture. A recommended dish is the *fessenjhuhn,* small meat spheres with nuts and pomegranate, rice with saffron, and the typical borani gravy, made of zucchini. ✉ *Rua Quintiliano Silva 118, Santo Antônio* ☎ *031/3296–3881* ▤ *No credit cards* ⌕ *Reservations essential* ☾ *Closed Mon.–Tues. No lunch. No dinner Sun.*

Where to Stay

$$–$$$ 🛏 **Ouro Minas Palace Hotel.** The only five-star hotel in Belo Horizonte,
Fodor'sChoice the palatial Ouro Minas has rooms with large beds and well-appointed
★ bathrooms. A pillow menu with 10 different kinds of pillows, a pool with waterfalls, and a multilingual staff are a few of the many amenities here that are hard to find in Belo Horizonte. The largest of the three

EATING LIKE A MINEIRO

SOME GASTRONOMIC CRITICS *say there are only three native Brazilian cuisines: the cuisine from the north (particularly from Pará); the Capixaba cuisine from Espírito Santo; and comida mineira, the cuisine from Minas Gerais. Purportedly, all other Brazilian cuisines are originally from outside Brazil. Since Minas Gerais is one of the few states without access to the sea, its cuisine is strongly based on pork and chicken, and legumes and cereals (most notably beans and corn).*

The mainstay of comida mineira is tutu, a tasty mash of beans with roast pork loin, pork sausage, chopped collard greens, manioc meal, and boiled egg served with meat dishes. Another favorite is feijão tropeiro, a combination of beans, manioc meal, roast pork loin, fried egg, chopped collard greens, and thick pork sausage. Among meat dishes, pork is the most common, in particular the famed lingüiça (Minas pork sausage) and lombo (pork

tenderloin), which is often served with white rice and/or corn porridge. The most typical chicken dish is frango ao molho pardo, broiled chicken served in a sauce made with its own blood. Another specialty is frango com quiabo, chicken cooked in broth with chopped okra. The region's very mild white cheese is known throughout Brazil simply as queijo Minas (Minas cheese). Pão de queijo (bread baked with Minas cheese) is irresistible, and popular throughout Brazil. You'll realize very quickly that Minas Gerais isn't the place to start a diet.

presidential suites is more 300 square meters (3,000 square feet). The one downside of the Ouro Minas is that it's not centrally located. ⊠ *Av. Cristiano Machado 4001, Ipiranga* ☎ *031/3429–4001* 📠 *031/3429–4002* 🌐 *www.ourominas.com.br* 🛏 *343 rooms, 44 suites* ⚑ *Restaurant, room service, in-room safes, minibars, refrigerator, cable TV, in-room data ports, pool, health club, massage, piano bar, nightclub, recreation room, shop, babysitting, laundry service, Internet room, business services, convention center, car rental, no-smoking floors* 🞐 *AE, DC, MC, V* ❙⃝❙ *BP.*

$–$$ 🞐 **Othon Palace.** With the best location of any hotel in Belo Horizonte, the Othon is in the midst of ongoing renovations (a good thing, since it's age had begun to show), but the level of service remains high. Rooms are without much character but are comfortable and have spectacular city views, some of the tree-lined Parque Municipal. The rooftop pool and bar are the best in town, and the on-site Restaurante Verandão (⇨ Where to Eat, *above*) is excellent. ⊠ *Av. Afonso Pena 1050, Centro* ☎ *031/3247–0000 or 0300/789–8809* 📠 *031/3247–0001* 🌐 *www. hoteis-othon.com.br* 🛏 *266 rooms, 19 suites* ⚑ *Restaurant, room service, in-room safes, minibars, refrigerators, cable TV, pool, gym, massage, sauna, bar, laundry service, concierge floor, Internet room, business* *services, convention center, meeting room, no-smoking floor* ▭ *AE, DC, MC, V* ▯⊙▮ *BP.*

$ ▯▮ **Mercure Lourdes.** On a main city avenue, close to the Savassi area and not very far from Belo Horizonte's central region, the Mercure hotel is very popular among executives and artists. Its seven convention rooms occasionally stage music concerts. The restaurant's menus include French, Italian, and international dishes. If possible, choose a room on one of the higher floors for a privileged view of the city. ⊠ *Av. do Contorno 7315, Lourdes* ☎ *031/3298–4100* ▤ *031/3298–4105* ⊕ *www.accorhotels.com.br* ⤴ *374 rooms* △ *2 restaurants, cafeteria, room service, in-room safes, microwaves, refrigerator, cable TV, in-room data ports, pool, gym, sauna, steam room, bar, piano bar, laundry service, Internet room, business services, convention center, meeting rooms, no-smoking floors* ▭ *AE, D, MC, V* ▯⊙▮ *BP.*

¢–$ ▯▮ **Minas Hotel.** The lobby of this centrally located hotel, one of the city's oldest, is often crowded with conventioneers. Rooms are clean and in fine working order, but are inexpensively furnished and outdated stylewise. Many rooms have the same view of the city and surrounding mountains that you'll find from the small rooftop pool and bar. The rooms that don't have this view tend to be a bit dark. ⊠ *Rua Espírito Santo 901, Centro* ☎ *0800/31–1188 or 031/3248–1000* ▤ *031/3248–1100* ⊕ *www.dayrell.com.br* ⤴ *241 rooms, 4 suites* △ *Restaurant, cafeteria, dining room, room service, in-room safes, minibars, refrigerators, cable TV, in-room data ports, pool, gym, sauna, steam room, bar, piano bar, shop, laundry service, business services, convention center, meeting room* ▭ *AE, DC, MC, V* ▯⊙▮ *BP.*

¢–$ ▯▮ **Wembley Palace.** This aging high-rise has clean (albeit small) rooms, reliable service, and a central location. ⊠ *Rua Espírito Santo 201, Centro* ☎ *031/3273–6866* ▤ *031/3273–1601* ⊕ *www.wphpalacehotel.com.br* ⤴ *105 rooms, 2 suites* △ *Restaurant, room service, minibars, refrigerator, cable TV, in-room data ports, bar, laundry service, Internet room, convention center, no-smoking floor* ▭ *AE, DC, MC, V* ▯⊙▮ *BP.*

¢ ▯▮ **Hotel Amazonas Palace.** Clean, simply furnished, reasonably priced rooms are the ticket at this downtown hotel. The 11th-floor restaurant is good and has a nice view of the city. ⊠ *Av. Amazonas 120, Centro* ☎ *031/3201–4644* ▤ *031/3212–4236* ⤴ *76 rooms* △ *Cafeteria, dining room, room service, refrigerator, cable TV, 2 bars, babysitting, laundry service, Internet room, business services, convention center, no-smoking rooms* ▭ *AE, DC, MC, V* ▯⊙▮ *BP.*

¢ ▯▮ **Hotel Wimbledon.** A central location and a pleasant mix of elegance and warmth set this hotel above others in its price range. Attentive service makes it feel like a bed-and-breakfast. Rooms have polished hardwood floors, local artwork, and modern bathrooms; luxury rooms have whirlpool baths. The rooftop bar, next to the pool, is the perfect spot for an afternoon drink. ⊠ *Av. Afonso Pena 772, Centro* ☎ *031/3222–6160 or 0800/31–8383* ▤ *031/3222–6510* ⊕ *www.wimbledon.com.br* ⤴ *69 rooms, 1 suite* △ *Restaurant, room service, in-room safes, minibars, refrigerator, cable TV, in-room data ports, pool, bar, laundry service, Internet room, business services, convention center, no-smoking floor* ▭ *AE, DC, MC, V* ▯⊙▮ *BP.*

★ ¢ ☒ **Ibis.** The best budget hotel in town, in the best part of the city, Ibis is in the backyard of an old mansion. Its minimalist rooms are more contemporary than those of most hotels in this price range. (The hotel was constructed in 2003.) The mansion, just yards from the Praça da Liberdade, has been well maintained and now has a charming lobby ☒ *Rua João Pinheiro 602, Savassi* ☎ *0800/703–7001* ⊕ *www.accorhotels.com. br* ➼ *130 rooms* ⚹ *In-room safes, refrigerators, cable TV, in-room data ports, bar, Internet room, convention center* ⊟ *AE, D, MC, V* ¶⊙¶ *EP.*

Nightlife

No other city in Brazil has as many bars and coffee shops as Belo Horizonte—there are 14,000, or one for every 150 inhabitants. This isn't a recent trend: the first bar appeared in 1893, four years before the city was founded. The bar culture is the core of the city's nightlife. There is even a contest every year in April, called Comida di Buteco (the Bar Food Contest), to reward the best appetizers and the coldest beer.

BARS For some of Brazil's best cachaças and one of the city's best views, try **Alambique Cachaçaria e Armazém** (☒ Av. Raja Gabáglia 3200, Chalé 1D, Estoril ☎ 031/3296–7188 ⊕ www.alambique.com.br). **Arrumação** (☒ Av. Assis Chateaubriand 524, Floresta ☎ 031/3229–3952 or 031/3222–9794 ⊕ www.saulolaranjeira.com.br) is a traditional bar that's owned by Brazilian comedian and actor Saulo Laranjeira. Live music—usually MPB (*música popular brasileira*, or Brazilian popular music)—is performed occasionally at **Cervejaria e Bar Brasil** (☒ Rua Aimorés 108, Funcionários ☎ 031/3287–3299). It's open until the last customer leaves. **Bolão** (☒ Rua Mármore 689, Santa Tereza ☎ 031/3461–6211 ⊕ www.restaurantebolao. com.br) is a bar and restaurant in a quiet district next to Centro. Its clientele includes bohemians, musicians, and poets. The rock band Sepultura has been known to hang out here. A good house draft beer and an excellent feijoada are served Saturday at **Botequim Maria de Lourdes** (☒ Rua Bárbara Heliodora 141, Lourdes ☎ 031/3292–6905 or 031/3292–7203 ⊕ www.mariadelourdes.com.br).

Established in 1962, **Cantina do Lucas** (☒ Av. Augusto de Lima 233, Loja 18, Centro ☎ 031/3226–7153) is a Belo Horizonte cultural landmark. One of the best bars in town is **Mercearia do Lili** (☒ Rua São João Evangelista 696, Santo Antônio ☎ 031/3296–1951), which operates in a small grocery store in a bohemian area. During the day the shop sells eggs, cereals, and soap. When night comes, tables are placed on the sidewalk, and the owner serves iced beer and incomparable appetizers.

CAFÉS Casual **Café com Letras** (☒ Rua Antônio de Albuquerque 781, Savassi ☎ 031/3225–9973 ⊕ www.cafecomletras.com.br) is a good place to listen to a quiet music.

DANCE CLUBS Inside the Ponteio Mall **Na Sala** (☒ Rodovia BR 356, 2500, Loja 120D, Santa Lúúcia ☎ 031/3286–4705 ⊕ www.nasala.com.br) is the most modern and well-equipped nightclub in the city. It is the premier club for house music in Belo Horizonte. A hip and young crowd ranging in age from 18 to mid-30s gathers at **A Obra** (☒ Rua Rio Grande do Norte 1168, Savassi ☎ 031/3261–9431 ⊕ www.aobra.com.br), a basement-level pub with a dance floor. Music styles vary from indie rock to classic rock and more, but it's always the best place to go for something other than mainstream music.

GAY & LESBIAN **Josefiné** (✉ Rua Antônio de Albuquerque 729, Savassi ☎ 031/3225–2307 or 031/3225–2353 ⊕ www.josefine.com.br) is a popular nightclub for "GLS," which stands for *"gays, lésbicas, e simpatizantes"* (gays, lesbians, and sympathizers).

LIVE MUSIC Find typical Brazilian rhythms such as samba and forró at **Lapa Multshow** (✉ Rua Álvares Maciel 312, Santa Efigênia ☎ 031/3241–2074 ⊕ www.lapamultshow.com.br). **Utópica Marcenaria** (✉ Av. Raja Gabáglia 4700, Santa Lúcia ☎ 031/3296–2868 ⊕ www.utopica.com.br) is a furniture store and an architecture office during the day, but from Tuesday to Saturday nights it is a venue for jazz, blues, and Brazilian and Cuban rhythms. It also has a very cool decor, with chairs hung from the ceiling.

The Arts

Belo Horizonte could easily be dubbed the City of Festivals. Numerous arts festivals take palce here year-round. Choose from film, electronic music, and dance. Look for program listings in bars and cafés

CONCERT HALLS Inaugurated in 2003, the **Chevrolet Hall** (✉ Av. Nossa Senhora do Carmo 230, São Pedro ☎ 031/3228–7500 or 3209–8989 ⊕ www.chevrolethallbh.com.br) presents concerts by famous Brazilian and foreign musical artists. With the capacity to hold 3,700 people, the place is also used for volleyball and basketball games. The center of cultural life in Belo Horizonte is the downtown **Palácio das Artes** (✉ Av. Afonso Pena 1537, Centro ☎ 031/3237–7399 ⊕ www.palaciodasartes.com.br), where symphony orchestras and ballet, opera, and theater companies perform. The box office is open only when performances are coming up.

FILM **Espaço Unibanco Belas Artes Liberdade** (✉ Rua Gonçalves Dias 1581, Lourdes ☎ 031/3252–7232) screens foreign and art films. Art movies and European films are the main attractions of **Unibanco Usina de Cinema** (✉ Rua Aimorés 2424, Santo Agostinho ☎ 031/3337–5566).

Sports & the Outdoors

HORSEBACK RIDING **Nossa Tropa** (☎ 031/3292–2177 or 031/9972–8505) arranges day treks on horseback into the mountains surrounding Belo. The daily trips include breakfast and a snack and cost R$50. Reserve at least one week in advance.

RUNNING Most of the city's parks offer good, if short, jogging paths, and running is common during the day. One exception is **Parque das Mangabeiras** (✉ Av. José do Patrocínio Pontes, 580, Mangabeiras ☎ 031/3277–8272), on the slopes of Serra do Curral. At 568 acres, it's one of the largest urban parks in the country. The park is open Tuesday through Sunday 8–6. Shaded lawns and a sparkling lake make the **Parque Municipal** (✉ Av. Afonso Pena s/n, Centro ☎ 031/3277–4749 or 031/3277–4161) a good place to jog. It's open Tuesday through Sunday 6–6.

SOCCER The **Estádio Mineirão** (✉ Av. Antônio Abraão Caran 1001, Pampulha ☎ 031/3499–1100) is Brazil's third-largest stadium and the home field for Belo's two professional *futebol* (soccer) teams: Atlético

Mineiro and Cruzeiro. Admission to the stadium for a look around (there are no guided tours) is R$2; it's open daily 8–5, except when there's a match. Prices for games vary depending on the type of seat and how important the match is. Expect to pay R$10–R$30 or more for a big game.

SPELUNKING For amateur spelunkers the mountains of Minas are replete with caves to be explored, though they must be seen with a guided tour. The largest and most popular cavern, with six large chambers, is the **Gruta de Maquiné** (☎ 031/3715–1078 ⊕ www.cordisburgo.mg.cnm.org.br), 113 km/ (70 mi) northwest of Belo Horizonte near the town of Cordisburgo. Admission is R$8, and the cavern is open daily 8–5. The **Gruta da Lapinha** (☎ 031/3689–8422 ⊕ www.lagoasanta.mg.gov.br) is only 36 km/ (22 mi) north of Belo, near the city of Lagoa Santa, on the road leading from Confins Airport. You can tour the cave any day 8:30–4:30; the entry fee is R$5.

Shopping

In the fashionable Savassi and Lourdes neighborhoods you'll find the city's best antiques, handicrafts, and jewelry stores. For clothing, head to one of the major shopping centers. On Saturday morning Avenida Bernardo Monteiro (between Rua Brasil and Rua Otoni) is the site of an antiques fair and food market, offering a taste of mineiro cuisine. On Sunday morning head for the large (nearly 3,000 vendors) arts-and-crafts fair in front of the Othon Palace hotel, on Avenida Afonso Pena.

ANTIQUES **Arte Sacra Antiguidades** (⊠ Rua Alagoas 785, Savassi ☎ 031/3261–7256 or 031/3261–8158) has a fine selection of Minas antiques.

CLOTHING For a range of fashions, hit the malls and shopping centers (⇨ *below*). If you are looking for clothes influenced by Minas Gerais culture, pay a visit to the store of designer **Ronaldo Fraga** (⊠ Rua Raul Pompéia 264, São Pedro ☎ 031/3282–5379 or 031/3282–5347). **Santíssima** (⊠ Rua Tomé de Souza 815, Savassi ☎ 031/3261–9487) sells secondhand clothing and accessories.

HANDICRAFTS **Serjô** (⊠ Rua Antônio de Albuquerque 749, Loja 2, Savassi ☎ 031/ 3227–5251) sells handicrafts from different Minas Gerais regions. The **Centro de Artesanato Mineiro** (⊠ Av. Afonso Pena 1537, Centro ☎ 031/ 3272–9513 or 031/3272–9516), in the Palácio das Artes, has a wide range of regional crafts. In the main hall of the theater **Espaço Unibanco Belas Artes Liberdade** (⊠ Rua Gonçalves Dias 1581, Lourdes ☎ 031/3252–7232) there is a small store with aboriginal arts and crafts, plus a coffee shop and a bookstore. Modern objects made by up-and-coming Brazilian artists are found in the **Divina Obra** (⊠ Rua Paraíba 1358 l, Loja 11, Savassi ☎ 031/3281–5757).

For jewelry and gemstone shops, *see* "Finding a Gem" CloseUp *in* Ouro Preto section.

MALLS & **Bahia Shopping** (⊠ Rua Espírito Santo 1009, Centro ☎ 031/3247–6940)
CENTERS is a good place to shop for men's and women's clothing. In the downtown area, **Shopping Cidade** (⊠ Rua Rio de Janeiro 910, Centro ☎ 031/

Minas Gerais

3274–8300) is one of the most frequented malls. You can buy almost anything, from clothes to electronics. Many shops sell designer togs for men and women in Belo Horizonte's most exclusive mall, **BH Shopping** (⌧ BR 356 n. 3049, Belvedere ☎ 031/3228–4001).

Side Trips from Belo Horizonte

Less that two hours from Belo Horizonte are some wild, wonderful national parks—worth a day trip if you have the time.

Parque Nacional do Caraça

123 km (77 mi) southeast of Belo Horizonte.

Waterfalls, caves—like Gruta do Centenário, one of the world's largest quartzite caves—and natural pools fill this national park whose name means "big face," in homage to its mountain, which resembles a giant. Guided tours—walking, spelunking, and other activities—can be arranged at the administration office once you arrive. Beyond its natural attractions, the park also has some historical buildings, including a convent constructed in the 18th century, and the Igreja de Nossa Senhora Mãe dos Homens (Church of Our Lady, Mother of Men), built at the end of the 19th century, which has French stained-glass windows, a rare organ, baroque altars, and a painting of the Last Supper by Athaiçde. There was once a seminary in the park as well, but it caught fire in 1968. After the accident the building was transformed into an inn and small museum.

The park's most famous inhabitant is the *lobo guará*, a wolf threatened by extinction that makes the rounds in the park at night searching for food. ⊠ *From Belo Horizonte take BR 262 to Santa Bárbara* ☎ *031/3837–2698* 🗩 *R$10 per vehicle* ☉ *Daily 7–5.*

Parque Nacional Serra do Cipó
96 km (60 mi) northeast of Belo Horizonte.

Highlights of the Serra do Cipó National Park include the roaring Cachoeira da Farofa, a waterfall, and the sprawling Canyon das Bandeirantes. Numerous bird species as well as wolves, jaguars, anteaters, monkeys, and the poisonous *sapo de pijama* (colored pajama frog) make up the park's wildlife. Although it is difficult to reach and is lacking in infrastructure, the park has a beautiful landscape and ecological wealth that make it worth the trip. Facilities are poor, so consider visiting the area as part of an organized tour with **Cipó Aventuras** (☎ 031/3718–7014). If you're an intrepid traveler, you can rent a car; call the park's visitor center for some information, and head out on your own. ⊠ *Take MG 10 north from Belo Horizonte toward Lagoa Santa* ☎ *031/3718–7228 or 031/3718–7210, 031/3718–7237 visitor center* ⊕ *www.guiaserradocipo.com.br* 🗩 *R$3* ☉ *Daily 8–2.*

Where to Stay
Expect basic and rustic (no air-conditioning), though clean, accommodations near the park.

$–$$ 🏨 **Cipó Veraneio.** The area's best hotel is inside the park, and the reason to stay at this hotel is definitely its surroundings: it's right next to a river and has views of the forest. The pool area is beautiful. The rooms, however, are small, plain, and dark. ⊠ *Km 95, Rodovia MG 10, 3 km (1 mi) south of park entrance, Jaboticatubas* ☎ *031/3718–7000 or 031/3718–7018* ⊕ *www.cipoveraneiohotel.com.br* ⊟ *AE, DC, MC, V* 🗪 *32 rooms* ⟶ *Restaurant, cable TV, minibars, pool, sauna, playground* ❍❙ *FAP.*

$ **Fazenda Monjolos Pousada.** Bed down and board at this working farm. Horseback tours are available. ⊠ *Km 95, Rodovia MG 10, 4 km (2½ mi) south of park entrance, Santana do Riacho* ☎ *031/3718–7011 or 031/3718–7012* ⊕ *www.fazendamonjolos.com.br* ⊟ *V* 🗪 *21 rooms* ⟶ ❍❙ *FAP.*

THE COLONIAL AND GOLD TOWNS

Two hours southeast of Belo is Ouro Preto, a UNESCO World Heritage Site. The country's de facto capital during the gold-boom years, it was also the birthplace of Brazil's first independence movement: the Inconfidência Mineira. Today a vibrant student population ensures plenty of year-round activity, and lodging, dining, and shopping options abound.

All the Gold Towns—Ouro Preto, Mariana, Tiradentes, and Congonhas—are characterized by winding cobblestone streets, brilliant baroque churches, impressive mansions and museums, and colorful markets. Tiradentes is smaller than Ouro Preto but no less charming; this town truly seems to have stopped in time about midway through the 18th century. Between Ouro Preto and Tiradentes lies Congonhas, whose basilica is guarded by Aleijadinho's extraordinary sculptures of the 12 Old Testament prophets. In each of the towns you visit, from Sabará to Mariana to Diamantina, you'll discover a rich cultural history that sheds considerable light on colonial Brazil.

Diamantina

⑫ *290 km (180 mi) northeast of Belo Horizonte.*

Diamantina took its name from the diamonds that were extracted in great quantities here in the 18th century. Perhaps because of its remote setting in the barren mountains close to the *sertão* (a remote arid region), Diamantina is extremely well preserved, although its churches lack the grandeur of those in other historic towns. Its white-wall structures stand in pristine contrast to the iron red of the surrounding mountains. The principal attraction in Diamantina is the simple pleasure of walking along the clean-swept cobblestone streets surrounded by colonial houses—note the overhanging roofs with their elaborate brackets.

The city was the home of two legendary figures of the colonial period: diamond merchant João Fernandes and his slave mistress, Xica da Silva, today a popular figure in Brazilian folklore. According to legend, Xica had never seen the ocean; so her lover built her an artificial lake and then added a boat. Two area attractions are linked with her; to see them, you should contact the Casa da Cultura to arrange a guided tour.

The **Casa de Xica da Silva** was the official residence of João Fernandes and Xica da Silva from 1763 to 1771, and contains colonial furniture and Xica's private chapel. ⊠ *Praça Lobo de Mesquita 266* ☎ *038/3531–2491* 🕾 *Free* ☼ *Tues.–Sat. noon–5:30, Sun. 9–noon.*

The **Igreja Nossa Senhora do Carmo** is a church built in 1751 as a gift from Fernandes to his mistress. Supposedly, Xica ordered that the bell tower be built at the back of the building so the ringing wouldn't disturb her. The altar has gold-leaf paneling, and the organ has 514 pipes. ⊠ *Rua do Carmo s/n* ☎ *No phone* 🕾 *R$1* ☼ *Tues.–Sat. noon–5, Sun. 9–noon.*

The **Museu do Diamante,** the city's diamond museum, in a building that dates from 1789, displays equipment used in colonial-period mines. Other items on exhibit include instruments made to torture slaves as well as sacred art from the 16th to the 19th centuries. There are guided tours of the rooms where diamonds were classified and separated. ⊠ *Rua Direita 14* ☎ *038/3531–1382* 🕾 *R$1* ☼ *Tues.–Sat. noon–5:30, Sun. 9–noon.*

The **Casa de Juscelino Kubitschek** was the childhood home of one of Brazil's most important 20th-century presidents and the man who built Brasília. ⊠ *Rua São Francisco 241* ☎ *038/3531–3607 or 038/3531–1970* 🕾 *R$1* ☼ *Tues.–Sat. 9–5, Sun. 9–1.*

On Rua da Glória notice the covered wooden **footbridge** connecting the second stories of two buildings that once served as the headquarters of the colonial governors.

Where to Stay & Eat

$–$$ ✕ **Cantina do Marinho.** This well-respected restaurant specializes in comida mineira. Favorites are pork steak with tutu and pork tenderloin with feijão tropeiro. There's an à la carte menu as well as a self-service buffet for a fixed price of R$8.50. ⊠ *Rua Direita 113* ☎ *038/3531–1686* ▤ *AE, DC, MC, V.*

¢ ▥ **Tijuco.** This historic-district inn is paradoxically housed in an Oscar Niemeyer–designed structure. It's considered the best hotel in town; views of the city from this hotel certainly are outstanding. ⊠ *Rua Macau do Meio 211* ☎ *038/3531–1022* ⬩ *27 rooms* ⬩ *Café, room service, fans, refrigerator, laundry service, convention center* ▤ *AE, DC, MC, V* ⍟ *BP.*

Nightlife

Diamantina enjoys a special distinction as Brazil's center of serenading. At night, particularly on weekends, romantics gather in a downtown alley known as Beco da Mota, the former red-light district and now home to several popular bars frequented by students and young professionals. Strolling guitar players also gather on Rua Direita and Rua Quitanda.

Sabará

⓭ *19 km (12 mi) east of Belo Horizonte.*

Sabará's churches drive home the enormous wealth of Minas Gerais during the gold-rush days. In this former colonial town, today a sprawling suburb of 90,000, historic buildings are scattered about, requiring you either to join a tour or to drive. The interiors of the baroque churches are rich with gold-leaf paneling.

In the main square sits the unfinished **Igreja de Nossa Senhora do Rosário dos Pretos** (Church of Our Lady of the Rosary of the Blacks; circa 1767), which was built, like its counterpart in Ouro Preto, by slaves. Here, however, they ran out of gold before the project could be completed. When slavery was abolished in 1888, the church was left as a memorial. ⊠ *Praça Melo Viana s/n* ☎ *031/3671–1523* ⬩ *R$1* ⍟ *Tues.–Sun. 8–11 and 1–5.*

The ornate **Igreja de Nossa Senhora da Conceição** (Church of Our Lady of the Immaculate Conception), though small, is Sabará's main church and an outstanding example of Portuguese baroque architecture combined with elements of Asian art. Its simple exterior gives no indication of the wealth inside, typified by its luxurious gold altar and lavishly decorated ceiling. At this writing, the church is undergoing renovations but is still open for public visits. ⊠ *Praça Getúlio Vargas s/n* ☎ *031/ 3671–1724* ⬩ *R$1* ⍟ *Weekdays 9–5, weekends 9–noon and 2–5.*

Igreja de Nossa Senhora do Ó (Our Lady of Ó Church), one of Brazil's oldest and smallest churches, contains paintings said to have been completed by 23 Chinese artists brought from the former Portuguese colony of Macau. Other signs of Asian influence include the Chinese tower and the gilded arches. ✉ *Largo do Ó s/n* ☎ *031/3671–1724* 💳 *R$1* ⏱ *Weekdays 9–5, weekends 9–noon and 2–5.*

In the **Igreja de Nossa Senhora do Carmo** (Church of Our Lady of Carmel) are pulpits, a choir loft, and a doorway all designed by the famed Aleijadinho. This is one of several Minas churches that were the result of a collaboration between Aleijadinho and painter Manuel da Costa Ataíde, a brilliant artist in his own right. ✉ *Rua do Carmo s/n* ☎ *031/3671–2417* 💳 *R$1* ⏱ *Tues.–Sat. 9–11:30 and 1–5:30, Sun. 1–6.*

Ouro Preto

⓮–⓲ *97 km (60 mi) southeast of Belo Horizonte.*

The former gold-rush capital is the best place to see the legendary Aleijadinho's artistry. Now a lively university town, it has been preserved as a national monument and a World Heritage Site. The surrounding mountains, geometric rows of whitewashed buildings, cobblestone streets, and red-tile roofs that climb the hillsides, and morning mist and evening fog all give Ouro Preto an evocative air, as if at any moment it could be transported back three centuries.

In its heyday Ouro Preto (also seen as Ouro Prêto, an archaic spelling) was one of Brazil's most progressive cities and the birthplace of the colony's first stirrings of independence. A movement called the Inconfidência Mineira was organized to overthrow the Portuguese rulers and establish an independent Brazilian republic. It was to have been led by a resident of Ouro Preto, Joaquim José da Silva Xavier, a dentist known as Tiradentes (Tooth Puller). But the Minas rebellion never got off the ground. In 1789 word of Tiradentes's intentions reached the capital, Rio de Janeiro; he was hanged and drawn and quartered, and his followers were either imprisoned or exiled. Today the date he was executed, April 21, is a national holiday.

Exploring Ouro Preto

Ouro Preto has several museums as well as 13 colonial *igrejas* (churches) that are highly representative of mineiro baroque architecture. The Minas style is marked by elaborately carved doorways and curving lines. Most distinctive, though, are the interiors, richly painted and decorated lavishly with cedarwood and soapstone sculptures. Many interiors are unabashedly rococo, with an ostentatious use of gold leaf, a by-product of the region's mineral wealth.

All the town's sights are within easy walking distance of the central square, Praça Tiradentes, which teems with gossiping students, eager merchants, and curious visitors. From here the longest walk you'll make takes about 15 minutes. Note that many museums and churches are closed Monday.

Pay attention to the addresses, because the main streets of Ouro Preto have two names: one from the 18th century, still used by the city's inhabitants, and the other an official name, used on maps but not very popular. Therefore, Rua Conde de Bobadela is better known as Rua Direita, Rua Senador Rocha Lagoa as Rua das Flores, and Rua Cláudio Manoel as Rua do Ouvidor. Street signs sometimes use the official name

THE PASSION OF ALEIJADINHO

IT'S A TESTAMENT TO THE CREATIVE SPIRIT
that Brazil's most famous artist couldn't use his hands or feet. Born in 1738 in Vila Rica (today's Ouro Preto) to a Portuguese architect and a black slave, Antônio Francisco Lisboa developed a passion for art through exposure to his father's projects. In his mid-thirties he developed an illness (some say leprosy, others syphilis; most assume it was arthritis) that led to a life of torment. Nicknamed Aleijadinho (Little Cripple), he shunned human contact, going out only at night or before dawn. With the help of some assistants, he traveled between towns, sculpting and overseeing church construction. He died on November 18, 1814, and was buried in the church he attended as a child.

There's no hint of Aleijadinho's pain in the delicate, expressive features of his soapstone and cedarwood figures. Indeed, his art is distinguished by a striking liveliness and deep religious faith. His most cherished works, such as the larger-than-life Old Testament prophets at the church in Congonhas, were created with a hammer and chisel strapped to his wrists, a feat often compared to the suffering of Christ. After those in Congonhas, his best works are in Ouro Preto, where he designed the brilliant Igreja São Francisco de Assis, as well as sculptures and other churches.

and sometimes have two signs, each with a different name. We used the official names in this guide.

Numbers in the text correspond to numbers in the margin and on the Ouro Preto map.

A GOOD WALK Start at **Praça Tiradentes** ⑭ ▶, in the center of town. South of the square is the **Museu da Inconfidência** ⑮. Two blocks west, on Rua Brigadeiro Mosqueira, is the **Teatro Municipal** ⑯. Across from theater is the **Igreja de Nossa Senhora do Carmo** ⑰, with major works by Aleijadinho and Ataíde, and its neighboring **Museu do Oratório** ⑱.

Head back to Praça Tiradentes. Two blocks east is the distinctive twin-tower **Igreja de São Francisco de Assis** ⑲. Two blocks farther east is the **Igreja de Nossa Senhora da Conceição** ⑳ and its small Aleijadinho museum. From here head east on Rua da Conceição, which becomes Rua Santa Efigênia, to the **Igreja de Santa Efigênia** ㉑. Retrace your steps to Praça Tiradentes one more time. Walk north across the plaza to **Museu da Mineralogia e das Pedras** ㉒, inside the Escola de Minas. There are several restaurants and coffee shops in Rua Direita, a few meters from Praça Tiradentes. Choose one for lunch or a snack.

Head west on Rua Senador Rocha Lagoa (better known as Rua das Flores). One block ahead, on the corner of Rua José, is **Casa dos Contos** ㉓, the city's original mint. Continuing south on the same street, which becomes Rua Randolfo Bretas, you come to the **Igreja de Nossa Senhora do Pilar** ㉔, with its baroque interior. Head northwest on Rua Randolfo Bretas followed by Rua Getúlio Vargas to the less ornate but equally intriguing **Igreja de Nossa Senhora do Rosário dos Pretos** ㉕.

TIMING This is an all-day tour. Start out early, as some churches are only open in the morning. Unless you're an ecclesiastic, plan to spend about 20 minutes in each church and 30–45 minutes in each museum.

WHAT TO SEE **Casa dos Contos.** The colonial coinage house contains the foundry used
㉓ to mint the coins of the gold-rush period as well as examples of coins and period furniture. The museum building is considered one of the best examples of Brazilian colonial architecture. ⊠ *Rua São José 12* 🕾 *031/ 3551–1444* 💷 *R$3* ☉ *Tues.–Sat. 10–6, Sun. 10–4, Mon. 2–6.*

❶ **Igreja de Nossa Senhora do Carmo.** Completed in 1772, the impressive Our Lady of Carmel Church contains major works by Aleijadinho and Ataíde. It was originally designed by Aleijadinho's father, himself an architect, but was later modified by Aleijadinho, who added additional baroque elements, including the characteristic soapstone sculptures of angels that are above the entrance. ⊠ *Praça Tiradentes s/n* 🕾 *031/ 3551–4735* 💷 *R$1* ☉ *Tues.–Sun. 1–4:45.*

㉔ **Igreja de Nossa Senhora da Conceição.** The lavishly gilded Our Lady of the Conception Church, completed in 1760, contains the tomb of Aleijadinho as well as a small museum dedicated to the artist. ⊠ *Praça Antônio Dias s/n* 🕾 *031/3551–3282* 💷 *R$4* ☉ *Tues.–Sun. 9–11:45 and 1:30–5.*

㉔ **Igreja de Nossa Senhora do Pilar.** Built around 1711 on the site of an earlier chapel, this is the most richly decorated of Ouro Preto's churches and one of Brazil's best examples of baroque religious architecture. It's said that 400 pounds of gold leaf were used to cover the interior. ⊠ *Praça Monsenhor Castilho Barbosa s/n* 🕾 *031/3551–4735* 💷 *R$4* ☉ *Tues.–Sun. 9–10:45 and noon–4:45.*

㉕ **Igreja de Nossa Senhora do Rosário dos Pretos.** The small, intriguing Church of Our Lady of the Rosary of the Blacks was built by slaves, some of whom bought freedom with the gold they found in Ouro Preto. According to legend, the church's interior is bare because the slaves ran out of gold after erecting the baroque building. ⊠ *Largo do Rosário s/ n* 🕾 *031/3551–4735* 💷 *Free* ☉ *Tues.–Sun. noon–4:45.*

㉑ **Igreja de Santa Efigênia.** On a hill east of Praça Tiradentes, this interesting slave church was built over the course of 60 years (1730–90) and was funded by Chico-Rei. This African ruler was captured during Brazil's gold rush and sold to a mine owner in Minas Gerais. Chico eventually earned enough money to buy his freedom—in the days before the Portuguese prohibited such acts—and became a hero among slaves throughout the land. The clocks on the facade are the city's oldest, and the interior contains cedar sculptures by Francisco Xavier de Brito,

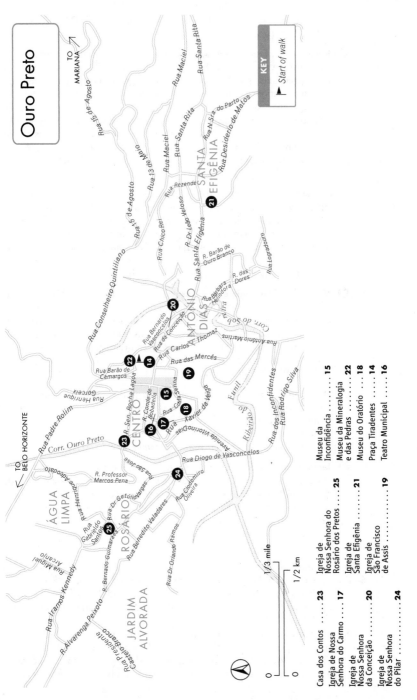

Ouro Preto

KEY
▲ *Start of walk*

TO MARIANA →

← TO BELO HORIZONTE

0 ___ 1/3 mile
0 ___ 1/2 km

Casa dos Contos **23**
Igreja de Nossa
Senhora do Carmo ... **17**
Igreja de
Nossa Senhora
da Conceição **20**
Igreja de
Nossa Senhora
do Pilar **24**

Igreja de
Nossa Senhora do
Rosário dos Pretos **25**
Igreja de
Santa Efigênia **21**
Igreja de
São Francisco
de Assis **19**

Museu da
Inconfidência **15**
Museu da Mineralogia
e das Pedras **22**
Museu do Oratório ... **18**
Praça Tiradentes **14**
Teatro Municipal **16**

Aleijadinho's teacher. ⊠ *Rua de Santa Efigênia s/n* ☏ *031/3551–5047* 🖃 *R$2* ⊘ *Tues.–Sun. 9–4:30.*

⑲ Igreja de São Francisco de Assis. Considered Aleijadinho's masterpiece, this church was begun in 1766 by the Franciscan Third Order and not completed until 1810. In addition to designing the structure, Aleijadinho was responsible for the wood and soapstone sculptures on the portal, high altar, side altars, pulpits, and crossing arch. The panel on the nave ceiling representing the Virgin's glorification was painted by Ataíde. Cherubic faces, garlands of tropical fruits, and allegorical characters carved into the main altar are still covered with their original paint. ⊠ *Largo de Coimbra s/n* ☏ *031/3551–5683* 🖃 *R$5* ⊘ *Tues.–Sun. 9–11:45 and 1:30–5.*

FodorśChoice ★

⑮ Museu da Inconfidência. A former 18th-century prison as well as the one-time city hall, this museum commemorates the failed Inconfidência Mineira rebellion with many artifacts. Among the displays are furniture, clothing, slaves' manacles, firearms, books, and gravestones, as well as works by Aleijadinho and Ataíde. The museum also holds the remains of the unlucky revolutionaries. ⊠ *Praça Tiradentes 139* ☏ *031/ 3551–1121* 🖃 *R$4* ⊘ *Tues.–Sun. noon–5:30.*

FodorśChoice ★

㉒ Museu da Mineralogia e das Pedras. Housed opposite the Museu da Inconfidência in the former governor's palace and inside the current Escola de Minas (School of Mines), the Mineral and Rock Museum contains an excellent collection of precious gems (including diamonds), gold, and crystals. The minerals have been organized according to their rarity, color, and crystallization. ⊠ *Praça Tiradentes 20* ☏ *031/ 3559–1597* 🖃 *R$4* ⊘ *Tues.–Sun noon–5.*

FodorśChoice ★

⑱ Museu do Oratório. Established in the old house of the St. Carmel Novitiate, this museum celebrates sacred art from the 18th and 19th centuries. Some of the oratories, which reflect ideas of religious beauty from the period, have been displayed at the Louvre. ⊠ *Rua Costa Senna 28* ☏ *031/3551–5369* ⊕ *www.oratorio.com.br* 🖃 *R$2* ⊘ *Daily 9:30–5:30.*

⑯ Teatro Municipal. The former opera house, built between 1746 and 1769, still presents shows and plays, making it Latin America's oldest municipal theater still in operation. There's no regular schedule for performances, however; check with the Associação de Guias for information on events. ⊠ *Rua Brigadeiro Musqueira s/n* ☏ *031/3559–3224* 🖃 *R$1* ⊘ *Tues.–Sun. noon–6.*

Where to Eat

BRAZILIAN
★ $–$$$

✕ **Café Geraes.** This cozy bilevel café is at the center of Ouro Preto's artistic and intellectual life. Students sip wine and feast on delicious sandwiches, soups, and other snacks. The pastries and the coffees are equally appealing. ⊠ *Rua Conde de Bobadela 122, Centro* ☏ *031/3551–5097* 🖃 *DC, MC, V.*

$–$$
FodorśChoice ★

✕ **Casa do Ouvidor.** Atop a jewelry store in the heart of the historic district, this popular restaurant has garnered several awards for such regional dishes as *tutu à mineira, feijão tropeiro,* and *frango com quiabo.* Portions are huge, so come with an empty stomach and be prepared for a noisy, ever-crowded dining room. ✉ *Rua Conde de Bobadela 42, Centro* ☎ *031/3551–2141* ⊕ *www.casadoouvidor.com.br* ▭ *AE, DC, MC, V.*

★ $ ✕ **Chafariz.** The best comida mineira in Ouro Preto is served in this informal eatery near the Casa dos Contos. The small, colorful dining room has hardwood floors, wood-beam ceilings, and wooden tables draped with blue, green, or white tablecloths. ✉ *Rua São José 167, Centro* ☎ *031/3551–2828* ⊘ *No dinner* ▭ *AE, DC, MC, V.*

ECLECTIC ✕ **O Profeta.** The friendly staffers at this cozy restaurant serve up mineira
$–$$ and international dishes. On weekends there's also live MPB. ✉ *Rua Conde de Bobadela 65, Centro* ☎ *031/3551–4556* ▭ *AE, DC, MC, V.*

FRENCH ✕ **Le Coq d'Or.** The finest restaurant in Minas Gerais and one of the best
$–$$ in Brazil is in Ouro Preto's Solar Nossa Senhora do Rosário hotel. An
Fodor'sChoice elegant atmosphere with formal place settings, attentive service, and soft
★ Brazilian music makes it ideal for a quiet, romantic dinner. The executive chef trained in Paris at the renowned Cordon Bleu culinary institute before introducing creative French-inspired cuisine to Brazilian gourmands. The ever-changing menu always includes an innovative selection of meat and fish dishes, and the wine list is excellent. ✉ *Rua Getúlio Vargas 270, Rosário* ☎ *031/3551–5200* ▭ *AE, DC, MC, V* ⊘ *No lunch Sun.–Fri.*

ITALIAN ✕ **Piacere.** If you want to escape from the typical comida mineira, the
$ Piacere is an excellent option. This Italian restaurant has modern decor, which contrasts with the architecture of the basement in which it is housed. ✉ *Rua Getúlio Vargas 241, Rosário* ☎ *031/3551–4297 or 031/3552–2422* ⊘ *Closed Mon. No lunch Tues.–Sat.; no dinner Sun.*

Where to Stay

Some families in Ouro Preto rent rooms in their homes, although usually only during Carnaval and Easter, when the city's hotels fill up. For a list of rooms to rent, contact the **Associação de Guias** (✉ Rua Padre Rolim s/n, São Cristóvão, Ouro Preto ☎ 031/3551–2655). The association also provides information on places to camp.

★ $–$$ ▦ **Pousada do Mondego.** This small, intimate inn is next to the Igreja de São Francisco de Assis in a house that dates from 1747. You'll find period furnishings, a colonial ambience, and highly personalized service. The hotel also gives two-hour city tours in a 1930s minibus, and it has its own antiques store and art gallery. ✉ *Largo de Coimbra 38, Centro* ☎ *031/3551–2040, 021/2287–1592 Ext. 601 for reservations in Rio* 🖷 *031/3551–3094* ⊕ *www.roteirosdecharme.com.br* 🛏 *24 rooms* ᐔ *Restaurant, café, room service, fan, high-speed Internet, in-room safes, refrigerator, cable TV, laundry service, concierge, meeting room, airport shuttle, car rental* ▭ *AE, DC, MC, V* ⫣ *BP.*

$ ▦ **Estalagem das Minas Gerais.** As it's near a nature preserve, this place is perfect for those who like to hike or walk in the woods. Rooms are modern, and those in front have wonderful views of the valley. The luxury chalets have two floors and granite details. Each can accommodate as many as five people with a double bed upstairs, single beds downstairs, and two bathrooms. The restaurant serves regional fare. ✉ *Km*

90, *Rodovia dos Inconfidentes* ☎ *031/3551–2122* 🖷 *031/3551–2709*
🖘 *114 rooms, 32 chalets △ Restaurant, dining room, room service, re-*
frigerator, cable TV, 2 pools, gym, sauna, steam room, squash, bar, piano
bar, library, playground, laundry service, Internet, business services,
convention center; no a/c ☰ AE, DC, MC, V ‖❙ *BP.*

$ 🏨 **Luxor Ouro Preto Pousada.** With stone walls that date back 200 years,
beautiful wood floors, and gracious antique furnishings, this hotel has
the feeling of a 19th-century lodge. The lobby leads to a small, romantic restaurant: typical mineira cooking is served to the lucky few at tables. Rooms enjoy views of the city, and some have original paintings
by famous Minas artist Chanina. ⊠ *Rua Dr. Alfredo Baeta 16, Antônio*
Dias ☎🖷 *031/3551–2244* ⊕ *www.luxorhoteis.com.br* 🖘 *19 rooms*
△ *Restaurant, room service, fan, refrigerator, in-room data ports, laun-*
dry service, Internet, some pets allowed ☰ AE, DC, MC, V ‖❙ *BP.*

$ 🏨 **Pousada Clássica.** Opened in 2000, this pousada is in an elegant
house a few yards from the main churches and museums. The rooms
are comfortable, and one of the suites, in the front of the building, has
a hydromassage bathtub. The city view from the balconies is spectacular, but the noise coming from the Rua Direita's bars, frequented by college students, can be a bother. Apartments in the back are more tranquil,
but the views are not as good. ⊠ *Rua Conde de Bobadela 96, Centro*
☎ *031/3551–3663* 🖷 *031/3551–6593* ⊕ *www.pousadaclassica.com.br*
🖘 *25 rooms, 2 suites △ Restaurant, room service, refrigerator, cable*
TV, laundry service, Internet, some pets allowed ☰ D, MC, V ‖❙ *BP.*

$ 🏨 **Solar Nossa Senhora do Rosário.** Superior service and the world-class
★ Le Coq d'Or restaurant are among this hotel's draws. The beautiful 19th-
century building feels like a bed-and-breakfast, with elegant yet comfortable decor, quiet floors, and charming guest rooms. When you're
not exploring the town, have a swim in the luxurious hilltop pool or
stop by the atrium for afternoon tea. The hotel even has a section of the
mine that originally was on this site, discovered during renovations. ⊠ *Rua*
Getúlio Vargas 270, Rosário ☎ *031/3551–5200* 🖷 *031/3551–4288*
⊕ *www.hotelsolardorosario.com.br* 🖘 *28 rooms, 9 suites △ Restau-*
rant, café, room service, in-room safes, refrigerator, whirlpool baths, cable
TV, in-room data ports, pool, wading pool, exercise equipment, steam
room, bar, babysitting, dry cleaning, laundry service, convention cen-
ter, meeting rooms, airport shuttle, car rental ☰ AE, DC, MC, V ‖❙ *BP.*

¢ 🏨 **Colonial.** Close to the main square, this is a good example of the small
no-frills inns found in most historic cities. What you'll get is a very basic,
clean room for a low price. Room 1 has a loft and can sleep up to five
people. ⊠ *Trv. Camilo Veloso 26, Centro* ☎ *031/3551–3133* 🖷 *031/*
3551–3361 🖘 *18 rooms △ Room service, fans, in-room data port, re-*
frigerator, laundry service, concierge, some pets allowed ☰ AE, DC,
MC, V ‖❙ *BP.*

¢ 🏨 **Grande Hotel de Ouro Preto.** As its name suggests, the Grande is Ouro
Preto's largest hotel—it's immense by local standards, though room sizes
are comparable to those at other hotels. The hotel is also the town's premier modernist structure—a curving two-story building on concrete pillars designed by world-acclaimed architect Oscar Niemeyer. Cultural purists
and aesthetes consider it an eyesore, however. ⊠ *Rua Senador Rocha Lagoa*

FINDING A GEM

GEMS VARY WIDELY in quality and value; don't buy them on the streets, and be wary about buying them from smaller shops. Do your research. Know that gold topaz, smoky topaz, and some other types of "topaz" are really quartz. It is very difficult to tell the difference between well-crafted synthetic lookalikes and the real deal. Get references for a jeweler before you buy.

Imperial topaz, sometimes called precious topaz, comes in shades of pink and tangerine. In general, the clearer the stone, the better the quality. The topaz can, at first glance, easily be confused with citrine quartz, found elsewhere in Brazil, but is harder, denser, and more brilliant.

Where to Buy

Ouro Preto has a reputation for the best selection and prices in Brazil. One of the best shops for gems, especially the rare imperial topaz, is **Ita Gemas** (✉ L Conde de Bobadela 139, Centro, Ouro Preto ☎ 031/3551–4895). An excellent store for authenticated gems—including imperial topazes, emeralds, and tourmalines—is **Luiza Figueiredo Jóias** (✉ Rua Conde de Bobadela 48, Centro, Ouro Preto ☎ 031/3551–2487). At **Brasil Gemas** (✉ Praça Tiradentes 74, Ouro Preto ☎ 031/3551–2976) you can visit the stonecutting and jewel assembly workshop.

Although not as upscale as the stores in Ouro Preto, **Artstones** (✉ Rua Ministro Gabriel Passos 22, Tiradentes ☎ 032/3355–1730) carries imperial topazes, emeralds, quartz, and tourmalines and also has some finished jewelry.

164, Centro ☎ 031/3551–1488 🖶 031/3551–5028 ⊕ www.hotelouropreto.com.br ↪ 35 rooms ↻ Restaurant, café, snack bar, room service, fan, high-speed Internet, in-room safes, refrigerator, pool, bar, shop, laundry service, convention center ▭ AE, DC, MC, V ▯ BP.

★ ¢ ▦ **Pousada Ouro Preto.** Popular with backpackers, this pousada has small rooms individually decorated with local art; some have beautiful views. Its open-air halls have flowers and paintings of Ouro Preto; the terrace in front of the lobby offers a peaceful view of the city center. The English-speaking staff does laundry for free. ✉ Rua das Mercês 72, Antônio Dias ☎☎ 031/3551–3081 ↪ 17 rooms ↻ Room service, refrigerators, laundry service, some pets allowed; no a/c ▭ DC, MC, V ▯ BP.

¢ ▦ **Pousada Recanto das Minas.** Its hilltop location at the edge of town is both a blessing and a curse. A stay at this comfortable pousada affords lovely views, but the walk to and from it is somewhat strenuous. It's a popular place with families and other groups. For more privacy and peace, opt for a simple but cozy chalet instead of a room in the main building. ✉ Rua Manganês 287, São Cristóvão ☎☎ 031/3551–3003 ↪ 11 rooms, 25 chalets ↻ Dining room, room service, refrigerator, 2 pools, sauna, billiards, recreation room, playground, laundry service, Internet, business services; no a/c ▭ AE, DC, MC, V ▯ BP.

Nightlife & the Arts

Even if the food and the service at **Acaso 85** (⊠ Largo do Rosário 85, Rosário ☎ 031/3551–2397) don't impress you, the incredibly high ceilings, stone walls, and medieval ambience will. It's popular with the late-night crowd. **Bardobeco** (⊠ Trv. do Arieira 25, Centro ☎ No phone) is the city's best *cachaçaria,* with more than 40 brands of cachaça, including the owner's own Milagre de Minas.

The best place for information about theater, arts, and musical performances is the **Posto Central de Informações Turísticas** (⊠ Praça Tiradentes 41, Centro ☎ 031/3559–3269). For an English-speaking guide who can take you to nightlife or arts attractions, contact **Pedro Paulo** (☎ 031/9906–7717). **Fundação de Artes de Ouro Preto** (FAOP; ⊠ Rua Getúlio Vargas 185, Rosário ☎ 031/3551–2014), the local arts foundation, hosts various art and photographic exhibitions throughout the year.

Shopping

HANDICRAFTS There are numerous handicrafts stores on Praça Tiradentes and its surrounding streets. At the daily **handicrafts fair** in front of the Igreja de São Francisco de Assis, vendors sell soapstone and wood carvings, paintings, and other goods.

For sculpture, head to **Bié** (⊠ Praça Professor Amadeu Barbosa 129 ☎ 031/3551–2309 or 031/3551–6525). **Gomides** (⊠ Beco da Mãe Chica 29, Barra ☎ 031/3551–2511 or 031/3551–4571) has a good selection of unique sculptures. For authentic Minas antiques and handicrafts, visit **Bureau d'Art** (⊠ Largo do Rosário 41, Rosário ☎ 031/3551–7438). If you're looking for religious souvenirs, don't miss **Ciríaco** (⊠ Rua Santa Efigênia 334, Antônio Dias ☎ 031/3551–5804). **Z Nelson** (⊠ Rua Randolpho Bretas 67, Pilar ☎ 031/3551–6434) sells crafts and religious objects.

For information about jewelry and gemstone shops, *see* the "Finding a Gem" CloseUp

en route   Between Ouro Preto and Mariana lies **Mina de Ouro de Passagem,** Brazil's oldest gold mine. During the gold rush thousands of slaves perished here because of its dangerous, backbreaking conditions. Although the mine is no longer in operation, you can ride an old mining car through 11 km (7 mi) of tunnels and see exposed quartz, graphite, and black tourmaline. Buses travel here from Ouro Preto (catch them beside the Escola de Minas) and cost about R$2; taxis are about R$20. ⊠ *Road to Mariana, 4 km (3 mi) east of Ouro Preto* ☎ *031/3557–5001* ⊑ *R$17* ☉ *Daily 9–5.*

Mariana

26 *11 km (7 mi) east of Ouro Preto, 110 km (68 mi) southeast of Belo Horizonte.*

The oldest city in Minas Gerais (founded in 1696) is also the birthplace of Aleijadinho's favorite painter, Manuel da Costa Ataíde. Mariana, like Ouro Preto, has preserved much of the appearance of an 18th-century gold-mining town. Its three principal churches showcase examples of the art of Ataíde, who intertwined sensual romanticism with religious themes. The faces of his saints and other figures often have mulatto features, reflecting the composition of the area's population at the time. Today Mariana is most visited for the weekly organ concerts at its cathedral.

The **Catedral Basílica da Sé,** completed in 1760, contains paintings by Ataíde, although it's best known for its 1701 German organ built by Arp Schnitger. Transported by mule from Rio de Janeiro in 1720, the instrument was a gift from the Portuguese court to the first diocese in Brazil. This is the only Schnitger organ outside Europe, and one of the best preserved in the world. Concerts take place Friday at 11 AM and Sunday at 12:15 PM. ✉ *Praça Cláudio Manoel s/n* ☎ *031/3557–1216* 🖃 *R$1 donation* ⏱ *Tues.–Sun. 8–noon and 2–6:30.*

Behind the cathedral is the **Museu Arquidiocesano de Arte Sacra de Mariana,** which claims to have the largest collection of baroque painting and sculpture in the state, including wood and soapstone carvings by Aleijadinho and paintings by Ataíde. ✉ *Rua Frei Durão 49* ☎ *031/ 3557–2516* 🖃 *R$3* ⏱ *Tues.–Sun. 8:30–noon and 1:30–5.*

Although the 1793 **Igreja de São Francisco de Assis** (Church of St. Francis of Assisi) has soapstone pulpits and altars by Aleijadinho, its most impressive works are the sacristy's ceiling panels, which were painted by Ataíde. They depict, in somber tones, the life and death of St. Francis of Assisi and are considered by many to be the artist's masterpiece. Sadly, however, they've been damaged by termites and water. ✉ *Praça Minas Gerais* ☎ *031/3557–1023* 🖃 *R$2* ⏱ *Tues.–Sun. 9–noon and 1–5.*

The **Igreja da Nossa Senhora do Carmo** (Our Lady of Carmel Church), with works by Ataíde and Aleijadinho, is noteworthy for its impressive facade and sculpted soapstone designs. Ataíde is buried at the rear of the church. At this writing, it is closed for renovations following a huge fire. ✉ *Praça Minas Gerais* ☎ *031/3558–1979* ⏱ *Tues.–Sun. 8–11 and 1–5.*

Congonhas do Campo

㉗ *50 km (31 mi) west of Mariana, 94 km (58 mi) south of Belo Horizonte.*

To see Aleijadinho's crowning effort, head to the small Gold Town of Congonhas do Campo. Dominating Congonhas is the hilltop pilgrim-
★ age church **Igreja Bom Jesus do Matosinho,** built in 1757 and the focus of great processions during Holy Week. At the churchyard entrance are Aleijadinho's 12 life-size Old Testament prophets carved in soapstone, a towering achievement and one of the greatest works of art from the baroque period. The prophets appear caught in movement, and every facial expression is unforgettable. Leading up to the church on the sloping hillside are six chapels, each containing a scene of the stations of the cross. The 66 figures in this remarkable procession were carved in cedar by Aleijadinho and painted by Ataíde. ✉ *Praça da Basílica 180* ☎ *031/3731–1590 or 031/3731–1591* 🖃 *Free* ⏱ *Tues.–Sun. 6–6.*

Tiradentes

28 *129 km (80 mi) south of Congonhas do Campo, 210 km (130 mi) southwest of Belo Horizonte.*

Probably the best historic city to visit after Ouro Preto, Tiradentes was the birthplace of a martyr who gave the city its name (it was formerly called São José del Rei) and retains much of its 18th-century charm. Life in this tiny village—nine streets with eight churches set against the backdrop of the Serra de São José—moves slowly. This quality attracts wealthy residents of Belo Horizonte, Rio, and São Paulo, who have sparked a local real-estate boom by buying up 18th-century properties for use as weekend getaways or to transform them into pousadas or restaurants.

In addition to the excellent selection of handicrafts—some 20 shops line Rua Direita in the town center—the principal attraction is the **Igreja de Santo Antônio.** Built in 1710, it contains extremely well-preserved gilded carvings of saints, cherubs, and biblical scenes. The church's soapstone frontispiece—a celebration of baroque architecture—was sculpted by Aleijadinho. ⊠ *Rua Padre Toledo s/n* ☎ *032/3355–1238* ☞ *R$2* ⊙ *Daily 9–5.*

Where to Stay & Eat

$$–$$$ ✕ **Tragaluz.** This mix of store, coffee shop, and restaurant serves unusual dishes, like chopped meat with cheese and potatoes. The desserts are delicious—try the fried banana with ice cream and chestnuts. ⊠ *Rua Direita 52* ☎ *032/3355–1424* ☰ *DC, MC, V* ⊙ *Closed Tues.*

$–$$$ ✕ **Theatro da Villa.** On the site of an old Greek-style amphitheater, this restaurant offers dinner theater; most performances involve local folk music and dance. The menu is filled with international fare, including meat and fish dishes. ⊠ *Rua Padre Toledo 157* ☎ *032/3355–1275* ☰ *AE, DC, MC, V* ⊙ *Closed Mon.–Wed. No lunch Thurs. and Fri.*

★ $$ ✕ **Estalagem do Sabor.** The Estalagem draws rave reviews for its feijão tropeiro and frango ao molho pardo, just two of the dishes that are part of the self-service buffet. Although it's small, it has an elegant atmosphere. Light music and a quiet, attentive staff make for a relaxing meal. ⊠ *Rua Ministro Gabriel Passos 280* ☎ *032/3355–1144* ☰ *No credit cards* ⊙ *Closed Mon.*

$–$$
FodorśChoice
★
✕ **Viradas do Largo.** One of the best restaurants in the country for typical comida mineira, the Viradas do Largo (or Restaurante da Beth) serves dishes such as chicken with *ora pro nobis* (a Brazilian cabbage) and feijão tropeiro with pork chops. Some of the ingredients, such as the *borecole* (kale), are cultivated in the restaurant's backyard. The portions are generous, enough for three or four people, but you can ask for a half order of any dish. The restaurant is also a market, with typical arts and crafts from Minas Gerais. Reservations are essential on weekends. ⊠ *Rua do Moinho 11* ☎ *032/3355–1111 or 032/3355–1110* ☰ *D, MC, V.*

★ $ ⊡ **Pouso Alforria.** Alforria enjoys a quiet, peaceful location with a fabulous view of the São José Mountains. The light-filled lobby—with its stone floors, high ceilings, and beautiful Brazilian artwork (some of it from Bahia)—leads to a charming breakfast space and courtyard. Rooms have considerable natural light and are individually decorated; mattresses are firm and bathrooms modern. ⊠ *Rua Custódio Gomes 286* 🖂🖂 *032/ 3355–1536* ⊕ *www.pousoalforria.com.br* 📞 *9 rooms* ⚇ *Café, room service, in-room safes, refrigerators, pool, library, laundry service, concierge, Internet room; no a/c, no kids under 16* ⊟ *DC, MC* 🍽 *BP.*

¢–$ 🖼 **Solar da Ponte.** In every respect—from the stunning antiques to the comfortable beds to the elegant place settings—this inn is a faithful example of regional style. Breakfast and afternoon tea (included in the rate) are served in the dining room, overlooking well-tended gardens. With advance notice, the English owner and his Brazilian wife can arrange historical, botanical, and ecological tours on foot or horseback. ⊠ *Praça das Mercês s/n* 🖂 *032/3355–1255, 021/2287–1592 for reservations in Rio* 🖂 *032/ 3355–1201* 📞 *12 rooms* ⚇ *Café, dining room, room service, fans, refrigerators, cable TV, pool, croquet, massage, steam room, bar, library, laundry service; no a/c, no kids under 12* ⊟ *AE, DC, MC, V* 🍽 *BP.*

Fodor's Choice ★

¢ 🖼 **Pousada Três Portas.** This pousada is in an adapted colonial house— with hardwood floors and locally made furniture and artwork—in the historic center of Tiradentes. The owner runs a small puppet theater adjacent to the breakfast room. Rooms are clean and modern. Note that prices jump dramatically on weekends. ⊠ *Rua Direita 280A* 🖂 *032/ 3355–1444* 🖂 *032/3355–1184* ⊕ *www.pousadatresportas.com.br* 📞 *8 rooms, 1 suite* ⚇ *Room service, fan, refrigerators, cable TV, in-room data ports, pool, steam room, 2 bars, laundry service, business services; no a/c* ⊟ *No credit cards* 🍽 *BP.*

The Arts

Cultural life in Tiradentes revolves around the **Centro Cultural Yves Alves** (⊠ Rua Direita 168 🖀 032/3355–1503 or 031/3355–1604 ⊕ www.centroculturalyvesalves.org.br), which has theatrical performances, films, concerts, and art exhibitions. On weekends the **Theatro da Villa** (⊠ Rua Padre Toledo 157 🖀 032/3355–1275) has musical shows that accompany dinner.

Shopping

Local artwork is the biggest draw here, with painters and sculptors famous throughout Brazil working in their gallerylike studios. The main street for galleries and antiques shops is Rua Direita.

ART **Atelier José Damas** (⊠ Rua do Chafariz 130 🖀 032/3355–1578) belongs to Tiradentes's most famous artist. He paints local scenes—such as a train winding through the mountains or a dusty afternoon street—on canvas and on stones. The small and quiet city **Bichinho** (⊠ 6 km/4 mi northeast of Tiradentes) is recognized in the region for the quality of its arts and crafts.

For jewelry and gemstone shops, *see* "Finding a Gem" CloseUp *in* Ouro Preto section.

THE MINERAL-SPA TOWNS

Known for the curative properties of their natural springs, a collection of mineral-spa towns in southern Minas Gerais forms the Circuito das Águas (Water Circuit). For more than a century people in need of physical, mental, and spiritual rejuvenation have flocked to these mystical towns, bathing in the pristine water parks and drinking from the bubbling fountains. Today they're especially popular among older, wealthier Brazilians, who come to experience the fresh air and beautiful landscapes and to get relief for their hypertension, arthritis, allergies, diabetes, and various stomach problems.

You'll be told that a minimum of three weeks of drinking the waters is required for their healing powers to take hold. Despite the curative properties of the mineral waters in the spa towns, don't drink too much when you first arrive unless you want to cleanse your system thoroughly. Usually, a one- or two-day visit is enough to experience a helpful placebo effect.

Parque Nacional da Serra do Canastra

㉙ *320 km (200 mi) southwest of Belo Horizonte.*

Serra do Canastra National Park was created to preserve the springs of Rio São Francisco, one of the most important rivers in South America, which cuts through five Brazilian states. Its main attractions are its waterfalls, including the 186-meter (610-foot) Casca D'Anta. The park is in the city of São Roque de Minas, almost on the border with São Paulo State. The Brazilian Institute of the Environment (IBAMA) manages the park from its headquarters in São Roque de Minas. The ecological group **Os Canastras** (⊕ www.canastra.com.br) has a good Portuguese-language Web site about the Serra da Canastra and surrounding region. ⊠ *From Belo Horizonte take MG 050 southwest to Pium-i, then take the road to São Roque de Minas; entrance to park is 35 km (21 mi) west of São Roque de Minas* ☎ *037/3433–1840 or 037/3433–1195 for IBAMA* ☑ *R$3* ☉ *Daily 8–6.*

Where to Stay

The park has a camping area, but nearby towns have some simple inns.

$ 🏨 **Paraíso da Serra.** Just 500 meters (¼ mi) from the main attraction at Parque Nacional da Serra do Canastra—the waterfall Casca D'Anta—this pousada has beautiful views from its rooms. ⊠ *Serra da Canastra, Portaria 4* ☎ *037/3433–2062 or 037/9988–8004* ⊕ *www.pousadaparaisodaserra.com.br* ⇦ *8 rooms* ♨ *Restaurant, cafeteria, dining room, room service, fans, minibars, refrigerators, 2 pools, steam room, bicycles, horseback riding, bar, shop, babysitting, playground, laundry service, business services, some pets allowed, no-smoking rooms; no a/c, no phones in some rooms* ⊟ *No credit cards* ❢◎❢ *FAP.*

¢ 🏨 **Pousada da Limeira.** On the bank of the São Francisco River, 15 km (9 mi) from the waterfall Casca D'Anta, this is a simple but comfortable pousada. ⊠ *Km 07, Estrada Cachoeira Casca D'Anta, Vargem Bonita* ☎🏨 *037/3435–1118* ⊕ *www.pousadadalimeira.com.br* ⇦ *13 rooms* ♨ *Restaurant, café, picnic area, fans, refrigerator, cable TV, high-speed Internet, pool, lake, horseback riding, laundry service; no a/c, no room phones, no TV in some rooms* ⊟ *No credit cards* ❢◎❢ *BP.*

BRAZILIAN BAROQUE

IN THE 17TH CENTURY the Portuguese, to ensure their control of the mining industry when gold was discovered in Minas Gerais, exiled the traditional religious orders, which led to the formation of third orders. Attempts by these lay brothers to build churches based on European models resulted in improvisations (they had little experience with or guidance on such matters) and, hence, a uniquely Brazilian style of baroque that extended into the early 19th century. Many churches from this period have simple exteriors that belie interiors whose gold-leaf-encrusted carvings are so intricate they seem like filigree.

As the gold supply diminished, facades became more elaborate—with more sophisticated lines, elegant curves, and large round towers—and their interiors less so, as murals were used more than carvings and gold leaf. Many sculptures were carved from wood or soapstone.

Today Minas Gerais has the largest concentration of baroque architecture and art of any state in Brazil. You can see several outstanding examples of baroque architecture, many of them attributed to the legendary Aleijadinho (⇨ "The Passion of Aleijadinho" CloseUp), in Ouro Preto (where there are 13 such churches) and the other Gold Towns of Minas: Mariana, Tiradentes, and Congonhas.

São Lourenço

30 *387 km (240 mi) south of Belo Horizonte.*

This most modern of the mineral-spa towns is a good base from which to visit the other Circuito das Águas communities. From here taxis and tour operators happily negotiate a day rate for the circuit, usually around $50.

São Lourenço's **Parque das Águas** (Water Park) includes a picturesque lake with art deco pavilions, fountains, and gorgeous landscaping. The center of activity is its *balneário,* a hydrotherapy spa where you can immerse yourself in bubbling mineral baths and marble surroundings. There are separate bath and sauna facilities for men and women, and you can also get a massage. ⊠ *Praça Brasil s/n* ☎ *035/3332–3066 or 035/3332–7111* ⊡ *R$4* ⊘ *Park daily 8–5:20. Balneário daily 8–noon and 2–4:50.*

If your experience at the park fails to rid you of all ailments, head to the **Templo da Eubiose,** the temple of a spiritual organization dedicated to wisdom and perfection through yoga. The Eubiose believe this will be the only place to survive the end of the world. ⊠ *Praça da Vitória s/n* ☎ *035/3331–1333* ⊡ *Donations accepted* ⊘ *Weekends 2–4.*

Where to Stay & Eat

$-$$ ⌨ **Hotel Brasil.** This luxury hotel is just across from the Parque das Águas at the Praça Duque de Caxias. It has its own pools, fountains, and mineral waters. Ask for a room with a park view. The restaurant has a prix-fixe regional-cuisine buffet. ⊠ *Alameda João Lage 87* ☎ *035/3332–2000* 🖷 *035/3331–1536* ⊕ *www.hotelbrasil.com.br* ⥺ *142 rooms* ⌂ *Restaurant, cafeteria, room service, minibar, refrigerators, cable TV, tennis court, 5 pools, health club, billiards, Ping-Pong, soccer, volleyball, bar, piano bar, nightclub, recreation room, shop, babysitting, children's programs (ages 2–12), playground, laundry service, Internet, convention center, meeting room, some pets allowed, kennel; no a/c in some rooms* ▭ *DC, MC, V* ⏍ *FAP.*

★ ¢-$ ⨉⌨ **Emboabas Hotel.** About a half hour's walk from the Parque das Águas, this gracious fazenda is more like a private estate than a rural farm. Its carefully decorated rooms have bucolic views; at night the only sounds you hear are those of various animals roaming the countryside. Occasional performances take place in the fazenda's theater, and there are numerous other activities to keep you amused. The restaurant ($) has prix-fixe buffets of at least three regional dishes as well as salads and dessert. ⊠ *Alameda Jorge Amado 350* ☎ *035/3332–4600* 🖷 *035/ 3332–4392* ⊕ *www.emboabashotel.com.br* ⥺ *57 rooms, 3 suites* ⌂ *Restaurant, cafeteria, room service, fans, refrigerators, cable TV, in-room data ports, tennis court, 3 pools, gym, hair salon, massage, sauna, steam room, billiards, horseback riding, soccer, squash, volleyball, 2 bars, piano bar, cinema, dance club, library, recreation room, theater, babysitting, children's programs (ages 4–12), playground, laundry service, Internet room, business services, convention center, some pets allowed; no a/c* ▭ *MC, V* ⏍ *FAP.*

¢ ⨉⌨ **Pousada Le Sapê.** The pousada's six tiny rooms are reasonable, low-budget options for a night or two. All rooms are very simple but have verandas and hammocks. The restaurant (¢–$), open to the public only December–March, specializes in comida mineira. ⊠ *Via Ramon s/n* ☎ *035/3331–1142* ⥺ *6 rooms* ⌂ *Restaurant, fans, minibars, 2 pools, soccer, volleyball, playground; no a/c, no room phones* ▭ *No credit cards* ⏍ *BP.*

¢ ⌨ **Hotel Fazenda Vista Alegre.** The many facilities and the low price of accommodations at this farm compensate for the lack of proximity to the water park (around 4 km/3 mi away). You can go boating on the lake in front of the cottages. If you're interested, the employees can teach you how to milk a cow. The chalets, in front of the lake, can house up to five people. The hotel also has rooms for two or four people. ⊠ *Km 1, Estrada Aeroporto Conquista* ☎ *035/3332–4730* 🖷 *035/3332–4730* ⊕ *www.hfvistaalegre.com.br* ⥺ *9 chalets, 35 suites* ⌂ *Restaurant, dining room, room service, fans, refrigerators, cable TV, 2 pools, lake, massage, sauna, steam room, boating, fishing, bicycles, billiards, horseback riding, Ping-Pong, soccer, bar, recreation room, shop, children's programs (ages 5–12), playground, laundry service, Internet room, business services, some pets allowed; no a/c, no room phones* ▭ *V* ⏍ *FAP.*

Caxambu

③ *30 km (19 mi) northeast of São Lourenço.*

A 19th-century town once frequented by Brazilian royalty, Caxambu remains a favorite getaway for wealthy and retired *cariocas* (residents of Rio). Although most people spend their time here relaxing in bathhouses and drinking curative waters, you can also browse in the markets where local sweets are sold or take a horse-and-buggy ride to a fazenda.

Towering trees, shimmering ponds, and fountains containing various minerals—each believed to cure a different ailment—fill the **Parque das Águas.** Lavish pavilions protect the springs, and the balneário, a beautiful Turkish-style bathhouse, offers saunas and massages. In addition, hundreds of thousands of liters of mineral water are bottled here daily and distributed throughout Brazil. ☒ *Town center* ☎ *035/3341–3999* ⊕ *www.caxambu.mg.gov.br* ☞ *R$2* ☉ *Park daily 7–6. Balneário Tues.–Sun 8:30–noon and 2–5.*

Overlooking the springs is the **Igreja Isabel da Hungria.** The small Gothic church was built by Princess Isabel, daughter of Dom Pedro II, after the springs were believed to have restored her fertility. ☒ *Rua Princesa Isabel s/n* ☎ *035/3341–1582* ☞ *Donations accepted* ☉ *Daily 8–noon.*

You could take a chairlift (daily 9–5; R$10) from near the bus station to the peak of the **Cristo Redentor** (☎ 035/9983–2223), a smaller version of the one in Rio. The summit has a small restaurant and an impressive city view.

Where to Stay & Eat

★ **$–$$** ✕ **La Forelle.** Inside the Fazenda Vale Formoso hotel, La Forelle is the best restaurant in town. Besides typical food from Minas Gerais, it also serves Danish cuisine. The specialty of the house is baked trout with potatoes. The filet mignon, the salmon, and the shrimp are among the extensive menu's stellar entrées. You can also find delicious fondues and freshly made breads. ☒ *Km 8, Estrada do Vale Formoso* ☎ *035/ 3343–1900 or 035/3343–2556* ▭ *No credit cards* ☉ *Closed Mon.–Thurs.*

$–$$ ▦ **Hotel Glória.** Although it's just across from Caxambu's Parque das Águas, this luxury resort has its own rehabilitation pool and sauna as well as a variety of sports amenities. Rooms are well equipped and have marble baths. Meals are served in an antiques-filled dining room. ☒ *Av. Camilo Soares 590* ☎☎ *035/3341–3000* ⊕ *www.hotelgloriacaxambu.com.br* ⤺ *120 rooms* ⌂ *Restaurant, cafeteria, room service, fans, in-room safes, refrigerators, cable TV, tennis court, 2 pools, gym, health club, hair salon, massage, sauna, steam room, billiards, Ping-Pong, soccer, squash, 3 bars, piano bar, cinema, recreation room, video game room, shop, babysitting, children's programs (ages 05–12), playground, laundry service, Internet room, convention center; no a/c in some rooms* ▭ *DC, MC, V* ◐ *FAP.*

¢–$ ▦ **Fazenda Vale Formoso.** A 19th-century coffee plantation transformed into a hotel, this fazenda hotel on more than 740 acres is surrounded by mountains, lakes, and virgin forest. The original machinery of the plantation is on display, and some of it is still working, such as the 19th-century water-operated sawmill. The farm also has a cachaça distillery. ⊠ *Km 8, Estrada do Vale Formoso* ☎ *035/3343–1900* ⊕ *www. hotelvaleformoso.com.br* ⊋ *17 rooms* ⟁ *Restaurant, café, picnic area, room service, fans, minibars, refrigerators, cable TV, driving range, 2 pools, lake, mountain bikes, billiard, horseback riding, 2 bars, laundry service, Internet room, convention center, helipad, some pets allowed; no a/c, no kids under 12* ⊟ *D, MC, V* ⵏⵎ *FAP.*

São Tomé das Letras

③② *54 km (33 mi) northwest of Caxambu.*

With its tales of flying saucers, its eerie stone houses that resemble architecture from outer space, and its 7,500 inhabitants who swear to years of friendship with extraterrestrials, São Tomé das Letras may be one of the oddest towns on earth. Set in a stunning mountain region, it attracts mystics, psychics, and flower children who believe they've been spiritually drawn here to await the founding of a new world. Most visitors make São Tomé a day trip from Caxambu, smartly escaping nightfall's visiting UFOs.

A center of religious activity and one of the few nonstone buildings in São Tomé, **Igreja Matriz** is in São Tomé's main square and contains frescoes by Brazilian artist Joaquim José de Natividade. Next to the Igreja Matriz is the **Gruta de São Tomé**, a small cave that, in addition to its shrine to São Tomé, features some of the mysterious inscriptions for which the town is famous. Just 3 km (2 mi) from São Tomé, two **caverns**, Carimbado and Chico Taquara, both display hieroglyphs. A short walk from the caves puts you in view of Véu da Noiva and Véu da Eubiose, two powerful waterfalls.

MINAS GERAIS ESSENTIALS

Transportation

A flight from Rio de Janeiro or São Paulo to Belo Horizonte is less than an hour. By bus or car the trip from Rio or São Paulo takes approximately eight hours. Many parts of the Brazilian highways aren't very well maintained, and the truck traffic between Belo Horizonte and the two main Brazilian cities is constant. Flying is by far the easier option.

For more information about transportation, *see* Smart Travel Tips A to Z, *at* the front of this book.

BY AIR

Belo Horizonte, with its two airports, is the gateway to Minas Gerais. Nearly all international flights to Belo Horizonte go through São Paulo. TAM, Gol, and Varig (⇨ Air Travel, *in* Smart Travel Tips A to Z) have domestic flights between Belo Horizonte and most cities in Brazil.

AIRPORTS & TRANSFERS

Aeroporto Internacional Tancredo Neves—also known as Aeroporto de Confins—is 39 km (24 mi) north of Belo Horizonte and serves most domestic and international flights. Taxis from Confins to downtown cost about R$60 and take roughly a half hour. *Executivo* (air-conditioned) buses leave every 45 minutes and cost R$12. Aeroporto Pampulha is 9 km (5 mi) northwest of downtown and serves some domestic flights. A taxi ride from here to downtown costs about R$15.

🛫 Airports **Aeroporto Internacional Tancredo Neves** ✉ MG 10, Confins ☎ 031/3689-2700. **Aeroporto Pampulha** ✉ Praça Bagatelle 204, Pampulha, Belo Horizonte ☎ 031/3490-2001.

BUS TRAVEL

BELO HORIZONTE Frequent buses (either air-conditioned executivos or warmer, less comfortable, but cheaper coaches) connect Belo Horizonte with Rio (R$50–R$95; seven hours), São Paulo (R$65–R$110; eight hours), and Brasília (R$82–R$135; 12 hours). Get advance tickets at holiday times. All buses arrive at and depart from (punctually) the Rodoviária. Bus companies include Cometa, for Rio and São Paulo; Gontijo, for São Paulo; Itapemirim, for Brasília; and Útil, for Rio.

Within Belo Horizonte, the municipal bus system is safe and efficient, although buses are crowded during rush hour (7–9 and 5–7). They're clearly numbered, and you can get route information at Bhtrans, the city's transit authority. Fares depend on the distance traveled but are always less than R$3.

🚌 Bus Information **Bhtrans** ☎ 031/3277-6500 ⊕ www.bhtrans.pbh.gov.br. **Cometa** ☎ 031/3201-5611 ⊕ www.viacaocometa.com.br. **Gontijo** ☎ 031/2104-6300 ⊕ www.gontijo.com.br. **Itapemirim** ☎ 031/3271-1019 ⊕ www.itapemirim.com.br. **Terminal Rodoviário Israel Pinheiro da Silva** ✉ Av. Afonso Pena at Praça Rio Branco, Centro, Belo Horizonte ☎ 031/3271-3000 or 031/3271-8933 ⊕ www.pbh.gov.br/rodoviaria. **Útil** ☎ 031/4004-4646 or 031/2105-4699 ⊕ www.util.com.br.

ELSEWHERE IN MINAS GERAIS Coaches connect Belo Horizonte with Ouro Preto (R$15; 2–3 hours) and from there on to Mariana (R$3; 30 mintue); Diamantina (R$43; 5 hours); and Tiradentes, via São João del Rei (R$33; 3½ hours). From Belo Horizonte a bus to São Lourenço or Caxambu takes roughly seven hours and costs about R$45. To reach São Tomé das Letras from Belo Horizonte, Caxambu, or São Lourenço, you must change buses in Três Corações. The entire journey from Belo Horizonte takes 5½ hours and costs about R$50.

Companies with regular service from Belo Horizonte include Gardênia, for São Lourenço, Caxambu, and Três Corações; Pássaro Verde, for Ouro Preto, Diamantina, and Mariana; and Sandra, for São João del Rei. To get to Tiradentes, you must go to São João del Rei and transfer to a Vale do Ouro bus. Buses run every hour and the trip is about R$3.

Buses leave from the Terminal Rodoviário Israel Pinheiro da Silva (⇨ *above*) in Belo Horizonte.

🚌 Bus Information **Gardênia** ☎ 031/3491-3300 or 031/3495-1010 or 035/3231-3844. **Pássaro Verde** ☎ 031/3280-9410 or 0300/789-4400 ⊕ www.passaroverde.com.br. **Sandra** ☎ 031/3201-2927. **Rodoviário Ouro Preto** ✉ Rua Padre Rolim 661, São Cristóvão, Ouro Preto ☎ 031/3559-3252. **Vale do Ouro** ☎ 032/3371-5119.

BY CAR

BR 040 connects Belo Horizonte with Rio (444 km/276 mi), to the southeast, and Brasília (741 km/460 mi), to the northwest; BR 381 links the city with São Paulo (586 km/364 mi). The roads are in good condition, although exits aren't always clearly marked.

Belo Horizonte's rush-hour traffic can be heavy, and parking can be difficult (for on-street parking you must buy a sticker at a newsstand or bookshop). Narrow cobblestone streets inside the historic cities, however, weren't designed for cars, and some alleys can make for a tight squeeze. Parking isn't a problem in the smaller communities, except during holidays.

The historic cities and spa towns are for the most part connected by fairly decent minor routes to one of the region's main highways. There's no ideal direct route from Belo Horizonte to Diamantina; your best bet is north on BR 040 and then east on BR 259. Sabará is slightly east of Belo, just off BR 262. From Belo you can take BR 040 south and BR 356 (it becomes MG 262) east to Ouro Preto and beyond to Mariana. To reach Tiradentes from Belo, take BR 040 south (Congonhas do Campo is on this route) and then BR 265 west. São Lourenço, Caxambu, and São Tomé das Letras are south of Belo off BR 381, parts of which are under construction. As an alternative, you can take BR 040 south to BR 267 west.

🚗 Rental Agencies **Localiza** ✉ Aeroporto de Confins, Belo Horizonte ☎ 031/3689-2070 ⊕ www.localiza.com ✉ Av. Bernardo Monteiro 1567, Funcionários, Belo Horizonte ☎ 0800/99-2000 or 031/3247-7957. **Lokamig** ✉ Aeroporto de Confins, Belo Horizonte ☎ 031/3689-2020 ⊕ www.lokamig.com.br ✉ Av. Contorno 8639, Belo Horizonte ☎ 031/3335-8977.

BY TAXI

Taxis in Belo Horizonte are white and can be hailed or called. The meter starts at about R$3.10 and costs about R$1.60 for every kilometer traveled (slightly higher at night and on weekends). Two reputable companies are BH Taxi and Coopertaxi.

In the historic towns it's hard to drive on the narrow cobblestone streets, so taxis aren't abundant. Besides, these towns are small enough to explore on foot. You'll find plenty of eager taxis in both Caxambu and São Lourenço waiting to take you around the Circuito das Águas. A taxi between São Lourenço and Caxambu or São Lourenço and Tomé das Letras runs about R$500.

🚕 **BH Taxi** ☎ 0800/35-3939 or 31/3215-8081. **Coopertaxi** ☎ 0800/99-2424 or 031/3421-2424.

Contacts & Resources

BANKS & EXCHANGING SERVICES

Outside Belo Horizonte, exchanging currency can be challenging and expensive, so change money before you arrive or plan to do it at your hotel. You can change money at Confins Airport weekdays 10–6 and Saturday 10–4 (you're out of luck if you arrive on Sunday). Banco Sudameris has good exchange rates. Banco do Brasil also offers exchange services, though the rates aren't the best.

Some banks accept only cards with Visa/Plus logos and others accept only cards with MasterCard/Cirrus logos. Banco24horas ATMs usually accept all cards, including American Express. *See* "Money Matters" *in* Smart Travel Tips A to Z for more information.

🏧 **Banco do Brasil** ⊠ Rua Rio de Janeiro 750, Centro, Belo Horizonte ☎ 0800/78-5678 ⊕ www.bb.com.br. **Banco Sudameris** ⊠ Av. João Pinheiro 214, Centro, Belo Horizonte ☎ 031/3277-3100 ⊕ www.sudameris.com.br.

EMERGENCIES
🏥 Emergency Contacts **Ambulance** ☎ 192. **Police** ☎ 190. **Fire** ☎ 193.

🏥 Hospital **Hospital João XXIII** ⊠ Av. Alfredo Balena 400, Santa Efigênia, Belo Horizonte ☎ 031/3239-9200.

🏥 24-Hour Pharmacy **Drogaria Araújo** ☎ 031/3270-5577 in Belo Horizonte.

INTERNET
Internet service is slowly making its way to the region and may be available at your hotel's business center. In Belo Horizonte the Monkey Lanhouse lets you hook up for $3 an hour. At Internet Club Café the price is $6 an hour. If you have a laptop with wireless capabilities, you can connect for free at Café com Letras.

💻 Internet Cafés **Café com Letras** ⊠ Rua Antônio de Albuquerque 781, Savassi ☎ 031/3225-9973 ⊕ www.cafecomletras.com.br. **Internet Club Café** ⊠ Rua Fernandes Tourinho 385, Savassi, Belo Horizonte ☎ 031/3282-3132 or 031/3284-7074. **Monkey** ⊠ Rua Paraíba 1323 loja 3, Savassi, Belo Horizonte ☎ 031/3223-1125 ⊠ Rua Timbiras 1560, Lourdes, Belo Horizonte ☎ 031/3226-2854.

MAIL & SHIPPING
Belo Horizonte's main post office is open weekdays 9–7, Saturday 9–1.

📮 Post Office **Belo Horizonte** ⊠ Av. Afonso Pena 1270, Centro ☎ 0800/570-0100 ⊕ www.correios.com.br.

TOUR OPTIONS
CLN Tourism and Transportation Services offers exceptional tours of Ouro Preto and the historic cities. CLN's Cláudio Neves speaks fluent English, knows a great deal about the region's history, and can arrange airport pickup and other transportation.

AMO-TE, Minas's Association of Ecological Tourism, offers many fascinating tours. A great way to get acquainted with the history and topography of Minas is on a one- to five-day horseback trip with AMO-TE's Tulio. His English is perfect, his knowledge impressive, and his horses—native Mineiros themselves—have a unique step (not unlike the lambada) that makes extensive trips more comfortable than you might imagine.

The Associação de Guias, formed by Ouro Preto's professional tour guides, can provide general information on the city weekdays 8–6. Its well-informed, courteous guides also conduct six- to seven-hour walking tours (in English) of the historic area. Be prepared for some hiking up and down numerous hills.

YTUR Turismo can arrange hotel bookings, transportation plans, and tours of Belo Horizonte and beyond.

🎫 **AMO-TE** ✉ Rua Monte Verde 125, São Salvador, Belo Horizonte ☎ 031/3477-7757. **Associação de Guias** ✉ Rua Padre Rolim s/n, São Cristóvão, Ouro Preto ☎ 031/3551-2655 or 031/3551-2504. **Associação de Guias de Turismo** ✉ Praça Tancredo Neves s/n, Mariana ☎ 031/3557-1158 ⊕ www.mariana.mg.gov.br.

CLN Tourism and Transportation Services ✉ Rua Conselheiro Quintiliano 405, Lajes, Ouro Preto ☎ 031/3552-1100. **YTUR Turismo** ✉ Av. do Contorno 8000, Loja 2, Lourdes, Belo Horizonte ☎ 031/3275-3233 ⊕ www.ytur.com.br.

VISITOR INFORMATION

BELO HORIZONTE Belotur, the municipal tourist board, is open daily 8 AM–10 PM at the airports and weekdays 8–7 elsewhere.

🎫 **Belotur** ✉ Rua Pernambuco 282, Funcionários ☎ 031/3277-9797 ⊕ www.belotur.com.br ✉ Mercado das Flores at Av. Afonso Pena 1055, Centro ☎ 031/3277-7666 ✉ Rodoviária, Av. Afonso Pena at Praça Rio Branco, Centro ☎ 031/3277-6907 ✉ Mercado Central at Av. Augusto de Lima 744, Centro ☎ 031/3277-4691 ✉ Shopping 5a Avenida at Rua Alagoas 1314, Savassi ☎ 031/3277-5049 ✉ Confins Airport ☎ 031/3689-2557.

ELSEWHERE IN MINAS GERAIS Setur, the state tourism authority, is based in Belo Horizonte, but supplies information on the historic cities and other attractions weekdays 12:30–6:30. Diamantina's Casa da Cultura has information on the town, including all cultural events. It's open weekdays 8–6, Saturday 9–5, and Sunday 9–noon. In Ouro Preto contact the Associação de Guias (open daily 8 AM–10 PM), which has an office on the edge of town, or the tourist information desk (open daily 8–6) in the center of town. In Mariana contact the Associação de Guias de Turismo for general information on the city. Its hours are Tuesday–Saturday noon–5:30. In Tiradentes the Secretária de Turismo is the best place to go for information (weekdays 8–6). São Lourenço has a small tourist kiosk in front of the water park. It's open weekdays 8–11 and 1–6. In Caxambu there's an equally small tourist desk that's open weekdays 8–6.

🎫 **Associação de Guias de Turismo** ✉ Praça Tancredo Neves s/n, Mariana ☎ 031/3557-1158 ⊕ www.mariana.mg.gov.br. **Associação de Guias** ✉ Praça Tiradentes 41, Ouro Preto ☎ 031/3559-3269. **Caxambu Tourist Desk** ✉ Rua João Carlos 100, Caxambu ☎ 035/3341-1298 ⊕ www.caxambu.mg.gov.br. **Diamantina Casa da Cultura** ✉ Praça Antônio Eulálio 53, Diamantina ☎ 038/3531-9527 or 038/3531-9532. **Posto de Informação Turística** ✉ Praça Tiradentes 41, Centro, Ouro Preto ☎ 031/3559-3269. **São Lourenço Tourist Kiosk** ✉ Praça João Lage s/n, São Lourenço ☎ 035/3332-4490 ⊕ www.saolourenco.mg.gov.br. **Setur** ✉ Praça da Liberdade s/n, Funcionários, Belo Horizonte ☎ 031/3272-8567 or 031/3272-9240. **Tiradentes Secretaria de Turismo** ✉ Rua Resende Costa 71, Tiradentes ☎ 032/3355-1212.

Brasília & the West

WORD OF MOUTH

"Brasília is famous for its futuristic modern architecture by Oscar Niemeyer. The city was designed in the shape of an airplane."
—Katherine

"The Pantanal is a wildlife photographer's dream: a ton of exotic birds, and giant anteaters and jaguars, both difficult to spot."
—AdrenalineBoy

"Bonito is an unforgettable place. Lots of caverns, rivers, trekking, snorkeling, waterfalls, etc."

—adriana

Updated by
Mariane
Oliveira

VISITING BRASÍLIA IS LIKE LEAPING INTO THE FUTURE. Rising from the red earth of the 3,000-foot Planalto Central (Central Plateau) and surrounded by the *cerrado* (Brazilian savanna) is one of the world's most singular cities. Its structures crawl and coil along the flat landscape and then shoot up in shafts of concrete and glass that capture the sun's rays.

All around this wonderland of modernity nestles the old Brazil—the land of soybean plantations, beef cattle, and sluggish rivers. Nevertheless, those who flock to the rugged yet beautiful west have their eyes on the future. The surreal collection of migrants includes opportunists with get-rich-quick schemes; frontier folk with hopes of a solid, stable tomorrow; mystics and prophets who swear by the region's spiritual energy; and dreamers who are convinced that extraterrestrials visit here regularly. For most earthly visitors, however, the high point of the west is the Pantanal, a flood plain the size of Great Britain that's home to an amazing array of wildlife and the ever-present possibilities for adventure.

History

The occupation of the center-west of Brazil did not keep up with the pace of occupation in the other regions. It was not until the discovery of gold in the mid-18th century in the states of Mato Grosso and Goiás that the first prominent urban centers were established in the region: Cuiabá (1727), Vila Boa (1739), and Santíssima Trindade (1752). The roads opened by the first bandeirantes (explorers) in the 1820s—probably following the trails of the Indian tribes who lived in the area, the macro-jê or tapuias—were used by approximately 6,000 people at the time. The region was an important economic hub 250 years before the construction of Brasília.

Between 1906 and 1910, the government-sponsored Rondon Expedition set out to explore and map an area the size of France. Explorers faced some indigenous Xavantes tribes in the area of Araguaia River, who attacked to defend their territory. Colonization of the center-west was intensified in the '50s, with the construction of Brasília and the new integration roads, together with the increase in agricultural practices in the region.

The creation of Brasília began long before its construction in 1956. The idea of moving the capital to the countryside was first voiced in the 18th century, allegedly by the Portuguese Marquis of Pombal. Several sites were proposed, in different central states. A team was commissioned to study the climatic conditions of inland Brazil and demarcate an area for the future capital. The team's final report was submitted in 1894, but it wasn't until 1946 that the plan of moving the capital to the Central Plateau became a reality with the advent of a new Constitution. President Juscelino Kubitschek ordered the construction of Brasília in 1956.

The mystic part of the history of Brasília revolves around bishop Dom Bosco and the prophetic dream he had in the 19th century, 75 years before the construction of the city. Dom Bosco dreamed about Brasília being

7

If you have
3 days
in
Brasília

On Day 1, take a morning tour of the west part of the Eixo Monumental: go to the Praça dos Três Podores, Esplanada dos Ministérios (an esplanade along the Eixo Monumental, with identical government buildings on either side), **Palácio do Itamaraty** ⑧ (Ministry of Foreign Affairs), the **Cathedral Metropolitana** ⑦, then take a cab to **Vila Planalto** ㉑, Brasília's first residential area, to have lunch at Rosental, a restaurant, operated by the chef for the late President Kubitschek (founder of Brasília). In the afternoon, go to the **Torre de TV** ⑤, **Memorial JK** ①, and the **Parque da Cidade** ④. On Day 2, take a boat tour ride on Paranoá Lake under the **Ponte JK** ⑪ and explore the lake's shores: Pontão and Pier 21. Take the afternoon to go to **Ermida Dom Bosco,** and visit the Mosteiro Benedictine. The monks there sell paintings and homemade cookies, candies, and liqueurs to help support the monastery. Take a cab to Lago Sul, to tour one of the fanciest neighborhoods in Brasília. On your final day, do a trip to **Poço Azul** (80 km/50 mi away from the Plano Piloto), with its crystal-clear pools cut into quartz.

If you have
5 days
in
Brasília

Follow the three-day tour above. On Days 4 and 5, head to **Parque Nacional da Chapada dos Veadeiros** ㉓ (250 km/155 mi from Brasília) either by car or by plane. Spend the weekend trekking around the waterfalls, the Moon Valley, the Morada do Sol (Dwelling of the Sun), the Zen Backwoods, and the Crystal River. On your last day, walk through the Vila de São Jorge, a small village 2 km (1 mi) outside the park's entrance that is known for ecotourism. Alternatively, go to **Pirenópolis** ㉔ (130 km/80 mi from Brasília), and explore Fazenda Vagafogo and the Tree Canopy Ride, a high ropes course in the trees. While in Pirenópolis, also explore the waterfalls, the historical sites, and the good restaurants and live music along Rua do Rosário.

If you have
5 days
in the
Pantanal

Fly to either **Cuiabá** ㉗ or **Campo Grande** ㉙ and explore the Pantanal, the largest concentration of wildlife in Latin America. Activities include horseback riding, piranha fishing, bird-watching, searching for anacondas and jaguars, caiman spotting at night, boat trips through Paraguay River and car safaris through the swampy grasslands. Make sure you spend at least one day in **Bonito** ㉚ exploring the Gruta do Lago Azul (Blue Lake Cave).

the "promised land, flowing with milk and honey and inconceivable riches" between parallels 15 and 20. Dom Bosco's dream was used as one of the mottos to justify the moving of the capital to the interior of the country.

Brasília was unveiled in 1960. In 1987, UNESCO declared the city a World Heritage Site. Since its founding, Brasília has seen important political and social changes, such as the enactment of the current Brazilian Constitution in 1988 (the first after the military dictatorship stepped down) and rallies against President Fernando Collor de Mello, the only Brazilian president to be impeached, in 1992.

Exploring Brasília & the West

Brasília is 1,600 km (1,000 mi) from the Atlantic, on the flat plateau known as the Planalto Central. This is the domain of the vast cerrado, whose climate and vegetation are akin to those of the African savanna. The capital is actually in the Distrito Federal (Federal District), a 55,000-square-km (21,000-square-mi) administrative region. Also in this district are the *cidades-satélite* (satellite cities), which originated as residential areas for Brasília workers but which now qualify as cities in their own right. Cidades-satélite are essentially the suburbs of Brasília.

The Distrito Federal is flanked by Goiás State, part of the virtually untamed west and the country's agricultural heart, which, apart from Goiás, also includes the westernmost frontier states of Mato Grosso and Mato Grosso do Sul. The west is also the starting point for two massive Amazon tributaries: Rio Araguaia and Rio Tocantins.

The first settlers in the west were mostly after gold and precious stones, but agriculture and ranching are the mainstays now. This is Brazil's breadbasket, and the landscape is one large chessboard of crops and pastures. The main hubs—such as Goiânia, Cuiabá, and Campo Grande—are, for the most part, sophisticated trading outposts for farmers and ranchers. Most visitors venture to western Brazil to see the impressive wildlife in the world's largest wetlands: the Pantanal. This area of watery terrain and rich, unique wildlife, has been the target of a major preservation effort and is one of Brazil's top tourist destinations. But some tourists are also slowly discovering the charms of the colonial towns of Pirenópolis, Goiás, and Miranda, as well as the quasi-mystical mesa of Chapada dos Guimarães; the haven of Bonito, with its great water sports.

When to Go

In Brasília and much of the west you can count on clear days and comfortable temperatures from March to July (the mean temperature is 22°C/75°F). The rainy season runs from December to February; in August and September the mercury often rises to 38°C (100°F). When congress adjourns (July and January–February), the city's pulse slows noticeably and hotel rooms are easier to come by. It's nearly impossible to get a room during presidential inaugurations (January 2007 is the next one) and other large political events. On the other hand, popular holidays such as Carnaval are much less hectic than in other cities.

The best season in the Pantanal depends on what you intend to do. If the plan is to take photos of wildlife, the dry season is the ideal time to go (July–October). But for fishing, the best season is August to October, since in November fish go up the river to spawn, a phenomenon called piracema, and fishing is prohibited.

About the Restaurants

As the capital, Brasília attracts citizens from throughout the country as well as dignitaries from around the world. Hence you can find a variety of regional cuisines as well as international fare. Brasília also has plenty of "per kilo" restaurants, usually decently priced cafeterialike places where you pay according to the weight of your plate. In the West the

Architecture

Urban planning, engineering, architecture, and landscape design were applied so harmoniously in Brasília that the city seems like one gigantic sculpture. Though many buildings are massive, they're generally low and linear and set in grand spaces—conveying a sense of both light and lightness.

Eating Out

Brasília is ranked a laudable third in the national gastronomic ranking, right after São Paulo and Rio. There are good restaurants for every taste and pocket in the commercial blocks in Asa Sul and Norte. Variety is what makes Brasília's restaurant scene so great, but the Italian, mineiro (from Minas Gerais State), and goiana (from Gaoiás State) restauarants are some of the country's best.

Craftwork

Diversity is the word that best describes the craftwork in Brasília. Materials used range from dried fruit and plants, flowers, patches, ceramic, wood. Inspired by the city, artisans sell their beautiful work in traditional places like the TV Tower, art galleries, and fairs.

Parks

With the largest green area per inhabitant in Brazil, Brasília offers a variety of parks for cycling, jogging, and skating (the City Park, for example, in the middle of the city, has 10 km/6 mi of paved path). Some of the parks are also home for rare species of fauna and flora. Brasília Botanical Gardens are allegedly the largest in Latin America.

Pantanal Safaris

In the lush Pantanal wetlands it's easy to see birds (more than 600 species flock here), monkeys, caimans, and the famous piranha. You may also catch a glimpse of *capivaras* (capybaras, the world's largest rodents), wild boar, anteaters, and many types of snakes (including the anaconda). To see the elusive jaguar, however, you'll have to tour deep into the Pantanal—and have plenty of luck and patience.

---

dishes aren't as interesting or as flavorful as those found elsewhere in the country. That said, the food is hearty, and the meals are large; affordable all-you-can-eat buffets are everywhere.

About the Hotels

Brasília's master plan called for its hotels to be built in commercial areas. Many hotels cater primarily to businesspeople and government officials. Budget options such as *pousadas* (inns) are mainly in the Asa Sul (South Wing) and in the Hotel Sectors. Upscale hotels can be found in the Hotel Sectors and along the shores of Lago Paranoá. Stay in one of the Hotel Sectors to be close to a number of good, inexpensive restaurants.

The frontier towns west of Brasília have few deluxe accommodations. In the Pantanal, the *fazendas* (farms) where most people stay are quite spartan; pack a pillow and bug spray (not all fazendas have netting for their beds). A few jungle lodges are full-blown resorts with nearly everything you could need.

When you book a room, in addition to its normal fee, you also pay a 10% service charge and R$1.50 for tourism fees.

	WHAT IT COSTS In Reais				
	$$$$	$$$	$$	$	¢
RESTAURANTS	over R$60	R$45–R$60	R$30–R$45	R$15–R$30	under R$15
HOTELS	over R$500	R$375–R$500	R$250–R$375	R$125–R$250	under R$125

Restaurant prices are for a dinner entrée. Hotel prices are for two people in a standard double room in high season, excluding taxes.

BRASÍLIA

The idea of moving Brazil's capital to the interior dates from the early days of the country's independence, but it wasn't until 1955 that the scheme became more than a pipe dream. Many said Brasília couldn't be built; others simply went ahead and did it. The resolute Juscelino Kubitschek made it part of his presidential campaign platform. On taking office, he organized an international contest for the city's master plan. A design submitted by urban planner Lúcio Costa was selected, and he and his contemporaries—including architect Oscar Niemeyer and landscape artist Roberto Burle Marx—went to work. The new capital was built less than five years later, quite literally in the middle of nowhere.

Costa once mused, "The sky is the sea of Brasília." He made sure that the city had an unhindered view of the horizon, with buildings whose heights are restricted, wide streets and avenues, and immense green spaces. The sky here is an incredible blue that's cut only by occasional clusters of fleecy clouds. The earth is such an amazing shade of red that it seems to have been put here just for contrast. At night it's hard to tell where the city lights end and the stars begin. The renowned contemporary architect Frank O. Gehry said of Brasília, "It's a different city. I call it holy land, an untouchable icon of architecture."

Brasília is a great place for those interested in architecture and in a different city experience from Rio, Salvador, or São Paulo. Everything is divided into sectors (hotels, residences, swimming places, etc.), and the streets were designed without sidewalks—it's said that Brasília is a driver's paradise, but a pedestrian's nightmare. Because of this, Brasília has long been known as "the city without corners."

Exploring Brasília

Numbers in the text correspond to numbers in the margin and on the Brasília map.

Shaped like an airplane when seen from above, the *Plano Piloto* (Pilot Plan) is the name of the original design for the city conceived by Lúcio Costa and for the urban area that resulted. The plan had four basic fea-

THE MAKING OF A CAPITAL

AS FAR BACK AS 1808, *Brazilian newspapers ran articles discussing Rio's inadequacies as a capital (Rio became the capital in 1763, following Brazil's first capital, Salvador), the argument being that contact with Pará and other states far from Rio was difficult. Also, Rio was right on the water, and an easy target for enemy invasion. In 1892 congress authorized an overland expedition to find a central locale where "a city could be constructed next to the headwaters of big rivers" and where "roads could be opened to all seaports." Within three months the expedition leaders had chosen a plateau in the southeastern Goiás region.*

But it was not until the mid-1950s that Juscelino Kubitschek made the new capital part of his presidential campaign agenda, which was summarized in the motto "Fifty Years in Five." When he was elected in 1956, he quickly set the wheels in motion. Within a few days, the site was selected (in Goiás, as proposed by the 1892 expedition), work committees were set up, and Niemeyer was put in charge of architectural and urban development. The design, called the Plano Piloto (Pilot, or Master, Plan), was the work of Lúcio Costa, chosen from an international contest. The concept was simple and original: "Brasília was conceived by the gesture of those who mark a place on a map: two axes intersecting at a right angle, that is, the sign of a cross mark." The Plano Piloto's most important gardens were to be created by famed landscape designer Roberto Burle Marx.

Among Costa's objectives were to do away with a central downtown, design highways that were as accident-free as possible, and ensure that the vast horizon would always be visible. Construction officially began in February 1957—with 3,000 workers onsite.

Building a modern seat of power for Latin America's largest nation was a monumental undertaking. Before paved roads were built, supplies had to be flown in from the eastern cities. The majority of the workers were immigrants from the Northeast, and unskilled They learned fast and worked hard, however. Settlements of shacks and tents sprang up around the construction site. The largest, Freetown (now the suburb Nucleo Bandeirante), was home to close to 15,000 workers and their families.

In Rio, opposition to the new capital was heated. Debates in the senate turned into fistfights. Government employees feared that Rio's business would decline and its real-estate values would drop, and were reluctant to leave Rio's comforts and beaches. Kubitschek's government induced them with 100% salary increases, tax breaks, early retirement options, ridiculously low rents, and even discounts on home furnishings.

On April 21, 1960, the city was inaugurated. The day began with mass in the uncompleted cathedral and ended with a fireworks display, where the president's name burned in 15-foot-high letters. A new era of pioneering and colonization followed the realization of Kubitschek's vision of a "nation of the future," looking westward from the coast.

tures: well-ventilated housing near green spaces; work spaces that were separate from housing; spaces for cultural activities near residential space; and the separation of vehicle and pedestrian pathways.

The Eixo (pronounced *eye*-shoo) Monumental, the "fuselage" portion of the plan, is lined with government buildings, museums, monuments, banks, hotels, and shops. It runs roughly from the Praça do Cruzeiro to the "cockpit," or the Praça dos Três Poderes. Intersecting the Eixo Monumental to form the Plano Piloto's "wings" is the Eixo Rodoviário. The Asa Sul, or South Wing, is almost totally built up; the Asa Norte, or North Wing, still has spaces for development. In and around the two main axes are streets and avenues that connect still more residential and commercial areas, parks and gardens, and the Lago Paranoá, formed by a dam built about 16 km/10 mi southeast of the Plano Piloto. Along the outer shores of this lake are several residential areas.

For information about Brasília's unique system of addresses, *see* the CloseUp box "The Method to the Madness."

NAVIGATING BRASÍLIA
The public transportation system in Brasília is poor and does not cover every part of the city. The best way to get around is by car—either taxi or a rental car. It's best to tackle the Eixo Monumental and the Esplanada dos Ministérios first and then to visit the Praça dos Três Poderes. The sights in these areas are easy to reach by bus, cab, or organized tour. Staying at a hotel in the nearby Setor Hoteleiro Norte or Setor Hoteleiro Sul (SHN or SHS; Hotel Sector North or Hotel Sector South) keeps traveling time to a minimum. If you have time, get a taxi to the Entorno (literally, "surroundings"), the city's suburbs and cidades-satélites. Before heading out, get as detailed an address as possible, check that your cabbie knows where to go, and agree on a fare up front.

Eixo Monumental

Most of the Plano Piloto's major sights are along or just off the grand 8-km-long (5-mi-long) Eixo Monumental and its multilane boulevards. The distances are too far to see everything on foot, so if you want to explore on your own rather than as part of a tour, you'll have to combine walking with bus and/or cab rides.

A GOOD TOUR
Start at the Praça do Cruzeiro, at a commanding height above the Eixo Monumental. It's an easy 600-foot walk to Niemeyer's **Memorial JK** ❶ ▶, where you can learn about the man who made Brasília happen. From here it's another short walk to the **Memorial dos Povos Indígenas** ❷, a round structure containing indigenous artifacts. You can continue (by taxi or bus) to the other Eixo Monumental sights, starting with the **Torre de TV** ❺, one of the best places to buy souvenirs and enjoy a great view of the city.

Head southeast and cross the Eixo Rodoviário to the pyramid that houses the **Teatro Nacional Cláudio Santoro** ❻. At the other side of the Eixo Monumental and a little farther southeast is the unique **Catedral Metropolitana de Nossa Senhora da Aparecida** ❼, a Niemeyer masterpiece. You're just a few steps from the Esplanada dos Ministérios, a gigantic corridor formed by 17 identical government buildings lined up along

THE METHOD TO THE MADNESS

ADDRESSES IN BRASÍLIA'S PLANO PILOTO
can make even surveyors scratch their heads. Although the original layout of the city is very logical, it can be hard to get chapter-and-verse addresses, making them seem illogical. Some necessary vocabulary, with abbreviations:

Bloco *(Bl.):* A large building

Conjunto *(Cj.):* Building subdivision

Loja *(Lj.):* Literally "store," but here a type of subdivision within a larger building

Lote *(Lt.):* Lot

Quadra *(Q.)* Block

Quadra Interna *(QI.)* Internal block

Setores *(S.):* Sectors

Superquadras *(SQ):* Supersquares

The Eixo Rodoviário has a line of superquadras made up of two (usually) quadras numbered from 100 to 116, 200 to 216, or 300 to 316 and consisting of six-story blocos. Quadras numbered 400 and above have been added outside the initial plan.

In addresses, compass points are sometimes added: norte (north), sul (south), leste (east), oeste (west). So an address might include SQN, meaning "superquadra norte." The Lago (Lake) region of the city is divided into the Lago Sul and Lago Norte districts. The residental areas on the shores of the lake include the Setores de Habitações Individuais (SHI) and the Setores de Mansões (SM).

Some important neighborhoods are:

Setor Hoteleiro Norte (SHN): for hotels in the northern part of the city

Setor Hoteleiro Sul (SHS): for hotels in the southern part of Brasilia.

Setor de Diversões Sul (SDS): where the malls are located

---

either side of the Eixo Monumental. The buildings that face each other at the far end of the Esplanada (just before the Praça dos Três Poderes) are two more world-renowned Niemeyer works: the **Palácio do Itamaraty** ⑧ and **Palácio da Justiça** ⑨. Take a cab to **Pontão do Lago Sul** ⑩, an outdoor area where you can rest in front of a panoramic view, and to the modern-design **Ponte JK** ⑪, the city's most aesthetically striking bridge, alternately known as Terceira Ponte do Lago Sul (Third Bridge in Lago Sul).

TIMING &
PRECAUTIONS

You need at least a day (6–8 hours) to visit and fully appreciate all the sights. Wear comfortable shoes and drink plenty of water. Avoid doing this tour on foot in the hotter months (August–October); drive or take a cab to major sights instead. Note that all government buildings frown on shorts, tank tops, and the like, so dress comfortably but conservatively.

WHAT TO SEE
⑦
Fodor'sChoice
★

Catedral Metropolitana de Nossa Senhora da Aparecida. The city's only cathedral is a Niemeyer masterpiece that was finished in 1967. The circular structure consists of 16 reinforced concrete "fingers" that arch skyward. They support huge panes of glass that shelter a subterranean church awash in natural light. Inside, *Os Anjos* (*The Angels*)—an aluminum sculpture by Brazilian modern artist Alfredo Ceschiatti—hovers above the altar. The city's first mass was held at the Praça do Cruzeiro, on May 3, 1957; the *cruz* (cross) used is now here at the cathedral. Above ground, the cathedral resembles a crown of thorns and is surrounded by a reflecting pool. Its entrance is guarded by four majestic bronze statues, also by Ceschiatti, *Os Evangelistas (The Evangelists)*. The outdoor carillon is a gift of the Spanish government. ☒ *Esplanada dos Ministérios* ☎ *061/3224–4073* ☒ *Free* ☉ *Daily 8–6.*

❸ **Instituto Histórico e Geográfico.** The small collection of photographs and memorabilia in the saucer-shape History and Geography Institute documents the city's story with emphasis on the period from the demarcation of the area to its completion. The exhibit includes a vintage Jeep used by Kubitschek to visit the construction site in the late 1950s. ☒ *Av. W-5, SEPS 703/903* ☎ *061/3226–7753* ☒ *Free* ☉ *Tues.–Sun. 8–noon and 2–6.*

▶ ❶ **Memorial JK.** This Niemeyer structure is a truncated pyramid and has a function similar to its Egyptian counterpart: it's the final resting place of former president Juscelino Kubitschek (JK), the city's founding father, who died in 1981. The mortuary chamber has a lovely stained-glass roof by local artist Marianne Peretti. JK's office and library from his apartment in Rio have been moved to the memorial's north wing. The bronze statue of JK—his hand raised as if in blessing—surrounded by a half-shell (a trademark of Brasília) looks down upon the Eixo Monumental and makes this one of the capital's most moving monuments. Permanent and changing exhibits here document the city's construction. ☒ *Praça do Cruzeiro at Eixo Monumental Oeste* ☎ *061/3225–9451* ☒ *R\$2* ☉ *Tues.–Sun. 9–6* ⊕ *www.memorialjk.com.br.*

FodorśChoice
★

❷ **Memorial dos Povos Indígenas.** Another Niemeyer project, slated to contain a memorial to native peoples, was transformed into an art museum at completion by the city government. A popular uproar ensued, and the building was overtaken by indigenous peoples' organizations. The cylindrical structure has a spiraling ramp around a center plaza and houses a small museum with crafts made by the Kayapó and the Xavante, and other indigenous peoples who once lived on the cerrado and now dwell in the Xingu area of the Amazon. ☒ *Eixo Monumental Oeste* ☎ *061/ 3226–5206* ☒ *Free* ☉ *Tues.–Fri. 9–5, weekends 10–5.*

★ ❽ **Palácio do Itamaraty.** For the home of the Foreign Ministry, Niemeyer designed a glass-enclosed rectangular structure with a detached concrete shelter whose facade is a series of elegant arches. The whole complex rests amid a Burle Marx–designed reflecting pool that augments the sense of spaciousness and isolation. The building and the water create a perfect backdrop for the *Meteoro (Meteor)*, a round, abstract Carrara-marble sculpture by Brazilian-Italian artist Bruno Giorgi. On the guided tour of the interior, you see an astounding collection of modern art—including paintings by Brazilian artists like Candido Portinari—and a Burle Marx tropical garden. Make reservations for tours. Buses 104 and 108 go to Palácio do Itamaraty. ☒ *Esplanada dos Ministérios* ☎ *061/3411–6159* ☒ *Free* ☉ *Tours (in English) weekdays 2–4:30, weekends 10–3:30.*

❿ Palácio da Justiça. The front and back facades of Niemeyer's Justice Ministry have waterfalls that cascade between its arched columns. Inside there's an important library (not open to the public) that contains one of the few complete original sets of Shakespeare's works—a gift from Queen Elizabeth to Kubitschek. ⊠ *Esplanada dos Ministérios* ☎ *061/3429–3877* ▣ *Free* ☉ *Tours (in English) weekdays 10–noon and 3–5.*

❹ Parque da Cidade. A few blocks from the Instituto Histórico and Geográfico, you can relax in the shade of City Park, a collaborative effort by Costa, Niemeyer, and Burle Marx. Recent improvements include a state-of-the-art lighting system and more security guards, making an evening walk, run, or bike ride along a path more agreeable than ever. There's also a go-cart racetrack. ⊠ *Entrances at Q. 901 S and Q. 912 S* ☎ *061/3225–2451* ☉ *Daily 24 hrs.*

❻ Teatro Nacional Cláudio Santoro. Another of Niemeyer's "pyramid projects," this theater is adorned with an array of concrete cubes and rectangles designed by Brazilian architect Athos Bulcão. Its three stages host a variety of performances, and its several small art galleries offer changing exhibits. ⊠ *SCN, via N2* ☎ *061/3325–6240* ▣ *Free* ☉ *Daily 3–8.*

❺ Torre de TV. The observation room of this 670-foot TV tower has spectacular views, particularly at night. On a lower level, the small **Museu Nacional das Gemas** has an impressive collection of Brazilian gems, a shop that sells stones and crafts, and a café with a view of the Eixo. From the 72 m-high platform (Salão Panorâmico) you'll have a 360-degree view of the city. This is a great place to buy souvenirs. Guided tours are available in English. ⊠ *Eixo Monumental* ☎ *061/3323–1881 museum* ▣ *Salão panorâmico free, museum R$3* ☉ *Deck Mon. 2–9, Tues.–Sun. 9–9; museum weekdays 1–6.*

Praça dos Três Poderes

Buildings housing the government's three branches symbolically face each other in the Plaza of the Three Powers, the heart of the Brazilian republic. Here both power and architecture have been given balance as well as a view of Brasília and beyond. Indeed, the cityscape combined with the planalto's endless sky have made the plaza so unusual that Russian cosmonaut Yuri Gagarin once remarked, "I have the impression of landing on a different planet, not on Earth!"

A GOOD TOUR Start at the plaza's western end, where twin high-rises and two bowl-shape structures make up the Congresso Nacional ⓬ ▶. Directly in front of it is the **Museu Histórico de Brasília** ⓭, whose facade is adorned with a sculpture of Kubitschek. To one side of the museum and beneath the plaza is the **Espaço Lúcio Costa** ⓴, with exhibits depicting the planner's ideas for the city, beyond which you'll find the **Supremo Tribunal Federal** ⓯. To the other side of the museum is Giorgi's famous sculpture *Os Candangos* ⓰, which sits in front of the **Palácio do Planalto** ⓱, the executive office. Heading eastward across the plaza, you'll come to the **Mastro da Bandeira** ⓲ and the **Panteão da Pátria** ⓳. Head eastward along the path in the lawn to the **Espaço Cultural Oscar Niemeyer** ⓴, where several of the renowned architect's projects are displayed and explained.

Brasília

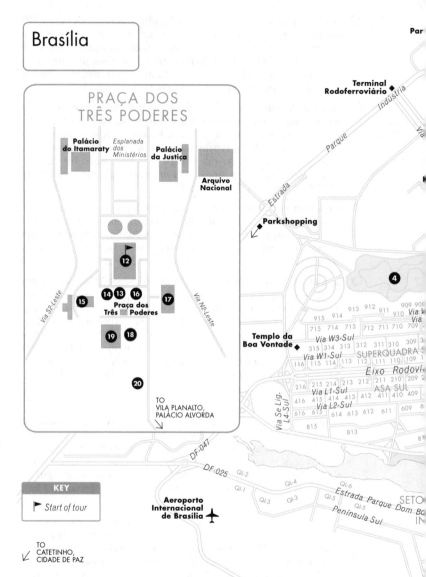

PRAÇA DOS
TRÊS PODERES

Palácio
do Itamaraty

Esplanada
dos
Ministérios

Palácio
da Justiça

Arquivo
Nacional

Parkshopping

12

14 **13** **16**

15

17

Praça dos
Três Poderes

Via N2-Leste

Via S2-Leste

19 **18**

Templo da
Boa Vontade

Via W3-Sul

913 912 911 910 909 908
915 914 712 711 710 709
715 714 713
315 314 313 312 311 310 309
Via W1-Sul
116 115 114 113 112 111 110 109

20

TO
VILA PLANALTO,
PALÁCIO ALVORDA

Eixo Rodovi

216 215 214 213 212 211 210 209
Via L1-Sul   ASA SUL
416 415 414 413 412 411 410 409
Via L2-Sul
616 615 614 613 612 611 609

Via Se Lig.
L4-Sul

815   813

Terminal
Rodoferroviário

Indústria

Parque

Estrada

4

SUPERQUADRA S

DF-047

DF-025 QL-2

QI-1 QI-3 QI-3

QL-4

QL-6

QL-5 QL-5

Estrada Parque Dom Bo

Península Sul

SETO

IN

KEY

▶ Start of tour

Aeroporto
Internacional
de Brasília ✈

TO
CATETINHO,
CIDADE DE PAZ

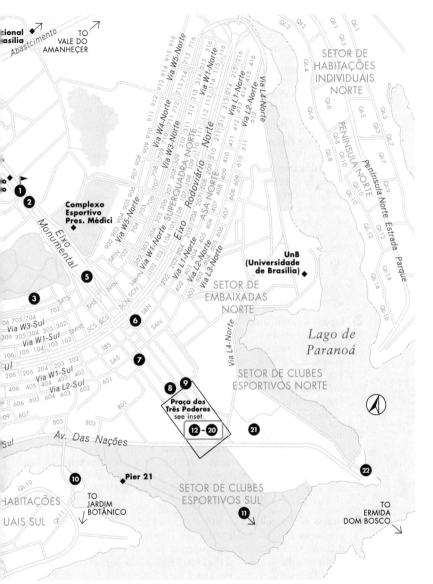

TO
VALE DO
AMANHEÇER

tional
asília

Abastcimento

Complexo
Esportivo
Pres. Médici

Eixo Monumental

Via W5-Norte
Via W4-Norte
Via W3-Norte
SUPERQUADRA NORTE
Eixo Rodoviário Norte
ASA-NORTE
Via L1-Norte
Via L2-Norte
Via L4-Norte

SETOR DE
HABITAÇÕES
INDIVIDUAIS
NORTE

PENÍNSULA NORTE

Península Norte Estrada Parque

UnB
(Universidade
de Brasília)

SETOR
DE
EMBAIXADAS
NORTE

Lago de
Paranoá

SETOR DE CLUBES
ESPORTIVOS NORTE

Via W3-Sul
Via W1-Sul
Via W1-Sul
Via L2-Sul

Praça dos
Três Poderes
see inset

Av. Das Nações

Pier 21

SETOR DE CLUBES
ESPORTIVOS SUL

HABITAÇÕES
UAIS SUL

TO
JARDIM
BOTÂNICO

TO
ERMIDA
DOM BOSCO

TIMING All the plaza's sights are close to one another, so you can easily complete this tour on foot in about two hours if you don't go into the museum or Espaço Cultural Lúcio Costa.

WHAT TO SEE **Os Candangos.** This 25-foot-tall bronze sculpture by Giorgi has become
⑯ the symbol of Brasília. The laborers, many from the northeast, who built the city from scratch were called *candangos*. The statue, which consists of graceful elongated figures holding poles, is right across from the Palácio do Planalto.

▶ ⑫ **Congresso Nacional.** One of Niemeyer's most daring projects consists of two 28-story office towers for the 500 representatives of the Câmara dos Deputados (House of Representatives) and the 80 members of the Senado (Senate); a convex structure, where the Câmara meets; and a concave structure, where the Senado convenes. The complex is connected by tunnels to several *anexos* (office annexes) and contains works by such Brazilian artists as Di Cavalcanti, Bulcão, and Ceschiatti as well as French designer Le Corbusier. The indoor gardens were done by Burle Marx. An hourly guided tour takes you through major sites within the building. Guided tours in English are available. No shorts, tank tops, or flip-flops are allowed. ⊠ *Praça dos Três Poderes* ☎ *061/3318–5107* 🖾 *Free* ⊙ *Weekdays 9:30–11:30 and 2:30–4:30, weekends 9–3:45.*

⑳ **Espaço Cultural Oscar Niemeyer.** This branch of the Oscar Niemeyer Foundation—which is based in Rio and was created to preserve and present the architect's work—houses a collection of sketches and drafts as well as a database with texts and images from Niemeyer's archives. The small auditorium hosts a variety of presentations, which have included talks by the architect himself—after all, this is also the site of his Brasília office. ⊠ *Praça dos Três Poderes, Lt. J* ☎ *061/3226–6797* 🖾 *Free* ⊙ *Weekdays10–6.*

⑭ **Espaço Lúcio Costa.** As a tribute to the urban planner who masterminded Brasília, this underground complex was added to the plaza in the late '80s. It has a 1,500-square-foot display of the city's blueprint, and you can read Costa's original ideas for the project (the text is in Portuguese and English). ⊠ *Praça dos Três Poderes* ☎ *061/3321–9843* 🖾 *Free* ⊙ *Tues.–Sun. 9–6.*

⑱ **Mastro da Bandeira.** This 300-foot steel flagpole supporting a 242-square-foot Brazilian flag is the only element of Praça dos Três Poderes that was not designed by Niemeyer. In the morning, on the first Sunday of the month, members of the armed forces take part in a *troca da bandeira* (flag change) ceremony. This is a good spot to contemplate the Brazilian flag's elements. The green background symbolizes the forests that once spanned much of the country. The yellow diamond represents the gold-mining period that so influenced the nation's history. The blue circle in the center is a homage to the great blue skies that dominate the territory; inside it are 27 stars—one for each state and the Federal District—from the southern skies and a white band with the national motto, "*Ordem e Progresso*" ("Order and Progress").

⑬ Museu Histórico de Brasília. Brasília's first museum has a small collection of pictures of the city and writings about it by such luminaries as Pope Pius XII, Kubitschek, and Niemeyer. The statue of Kubitschek on its facade is a 1960 work of Brazilian sculptor José Pedrosa. ⊠ *Praça dos Três Poderes* ☏ *061/3325–6244* 🖾 *Free* ◷ *Tues.–Sun. 9–6.*

㉒ Palácio da Alvorada. At the tip of a peninsula projecting into Lago Paranoá, the president's official residence—with its trademark slanting supporting columns of white marble—was Niemeyer's first project and was finished in June 1958. You can't go inside, but you can appreciate the grand view of the palace and gardens from the reflecting pool next to the gate. The interior is not open to the public. You need to take a cab to go from Plaza of the Three Powers to the Palace. ⊠ *SHTN, Via Presidencial s/n.*

⑰ Palácio do Planalto. Niemeyer gave this highly acclaimed structure an unusual combination of straight and slanting lines, a variation of the design of Palácio da Alvorada. The access ramp to the main entrance is part of the national political folklore, because it represents the rise to power (presidents go up the ramp when inaugurated). ⊠ *Praça dos Três Poderes* ☏ *061/3411–2317* 🖾 *Free* ◷ *Sun. 9:30–1.*

★ ⑲ Panteão da Pátria. Designed by Niemeyer in 1985, this building honors the nation's heroes, including the beloved Tancredo Neves (it's also known as the Panteão Tancredo Neves), whose untimely death prevented him from being sworn in as Brazil's first democratically elected president after the military dictatorship ended. Inside the curved structure, which resembles a dove, are works by Bulcão and João Camara. One set of panels, *Os Inconfidentes,* depicts the martyrs of the 18th-century Inconfidência Mineira movement, which was organized in Minas Gerais State to overthrow the Portuguese and establish an independent Brazilian republic. ⊠ *Praça dos Três Poderes* ☏ *061/3325–6244* 🖾 *Free* ◷ *Tues.–Sun. 9–6.*

⑮ Supremo Tribunal Federal. The Brazilian Supreme Court has the structural lightness that is the backbone of Niemeyer's work. The Tribunal Pleno, the highest court in Brazil, convenes on the ground floor. The top floor houses an 80,000-volume library, which you can visit on a guided tour. The 10-foot granite statue set to the left of the main entrance is *The Justice,* by Ceschiatti. ⊠ *Praça dos Três Poderes* ☏ *061/3217–3000* 🖾 *Free* ◷ *Weekends 10–3:30.*

㉑ Vila Planalto. Not far from the Palácio da Alvorada, this neighborhood was where the architects, engineers, topographers, accountants, and other professionals stayed while Brasília was under construction. They all lived in prefabricated wooden houses that are representative of an architectural trend within modernism called *racionalismo carioca* (Rio's rationalism), based on Le Corbusier's work. Some of the houses still can be seen along Avenida dos Engenheiros (Avenue of the Engineers). Vila Planalto is a down-to-earth middle- to low-income residential area that maintains a boomtown spirit. It's the perfect place to find a *buteco* (bar) for a late-evening *seresta* (impromptu musical soirée).

Beyond the Plano Piloto

If you have the time, head beyond the Plano Piloto and explore Lago Paranoá's outer perimeter, which has parks, gardens, and several interesting neighborhoods. Here you encounter the cult communities that reflect Brasília's mystical side. In 1883 an Italian priest named Dom Bosco (St. John Bosco) had a vision of a new civilization rising around a lake between the 15th and 20th parallels. "This will be the promised land," he proclaimed. The futuristic architecture; the location between the 15th and 16th parallels in the vast, eerie cerrado; and the fantastic sky views reinforced by the flatness of the region have led many to believe that Brasília is the realization of Bosco's vision. (Bosco never actually set foot in Brazil, making his vision seem even more mysterious.) Since its inception the city has attracted a variety of religious groups.

★ **Catetinho.** When Rio was the capital, the president resided in the Palácio Catete (Catete Palace). Although the new capital was being built, Kubitschek's temporary lodging was called the *Catetinho* (Little Catete). The barrackslike wooden edifice was built in 10 days during the summer of 1956. A nearby landing strip allowed the president to fly in from Rio for his frequent inspections. The building is a must-see museum for those interested in the city's history. It's surrounded by woods in which there's a small springwater pool where the president and his entourage once bathed. ⊠ *Km 0, BR 040, 16 km (10 mi) southeast of Estação Rodoviária* ☎ *061/3338–8694* ⛵ *Free* ⊙ *Daily 9–5.*

Ermida Dom Bosco. This lakefront sanctuary is dedicated to the saint who inspired so many of those who settled in the new capital. The project is attributed to Niemeyer, though he denies it vehemently. It's adjacent to the impressive postmodern architecture of the Mosteiro São Bento (São Bento Monastery). There is a small store in the Monastery where the monks sell homemade cookies, cakes, and liqueurs—the profit is entirely donated to charity. A scenic overlook with a view of the Plano Piloto and a tranquil Burle Marx–designed garden make it an ideal place to watch the sun set. There's an environmental preserve on the monastery grounds; the entrance is before the ermida's gate. ⊠ *Estrada Parque Dom Bosco, next to Paranoá Dam, Lago Sul, S. de Mansões Dom Bosco, Cj. 12, 24 km (15 mi) east of the Plano Piloto* ☎ *061/367–4505* ⛵ *Free* ⊙ *Daily dawn–dusk.*

Parque Nacional de Brasília. The 60,000-acre Brasília National Park, also called Água Mineral (Mineral Water), is in the northeastern area of the Federal District. The typical cerrado vegetation includes grasslands, woodland savannas, and taller gallery woods on the bottomlands. A 5-km (3-mi) trail through mostly flat terrain starts at the visitor center, where you can pick up maps and brochures. The park also has two pools (fed by natural springs), dressing rooms, and picnic and barbecue areas. ⊠ *EPIA, 9 km (6 mi) from bus terminal* ☎ *061/3465–2016* ⛵ *R$3* ⊙ *Daily 8–4.*

★ ⓫ **Ponte JK.** Opened in late 2002, the third bridge in Lago Sul is a combination of utility—it links the Clubs Sector to Lago Sul—and beauty, as its architecture is consistent with the city's modernist aesthetic. Its lakeshore location and promenade attract many people to walk and enjoy the sunset. ⊠ *S. de Clubes Sul, between QL 24 and 26* ⛵ *Free* ⊙ *Daily 24 hrs.*

10 **Pontão do Lago Sul.** Brasília may not have beaches, but it does have a shore. This large parklike area is in front of Lago Paranoá and has space to jog, to walk, and to rest, but the interesting bars and restaurants, shops, and beautiful view are the main attractions. Thousands of people head here each weekend. The entrance to the lakefront area is styled after the Arc de Triomphe in Paris, a controversial move, since Brasília has modern architecture. You need a car to get here. ⊠ *SHIS QL 10, Lago Sul* ☎ *061/3364–0580* 🖃 *Free* ☉ *Daily 8–midnight.*

Templo da Boa Vontade. This temple is adjacent to the national headquarters of the Legião da Boa Vontade (Goodwill Legion), a religious and philanthropic organization. The pyramid-shaped building is open to all denominations for worship or meditation. At the top sits a 21-kilogram (46-pound) quartz crystal, the largest ever found in Brazil. ⊠ *SGAS 915, Lt. 75/6, 8 km (5 mi) south of Eixo Monumental* ☎ *061/3245–1070* 🖃 *Temple free, Egyptian room R$2* ☉ *Temple daily 24 hrs; Egyptian room, gallery, memorial place, and noble room daily 10–6.*

Where to Eat

Brazilian

$$$$ ✕ **Porcão.** Deservedly one of Brazil's most famous *churrascarias* (barbecue restaurants), Porcão has branches in Rio, Belo Horizonte, Recife, and Miami. Brasília's Porcão is huge, seating more than 1,000 people. Close to the lake, it has many rooms for special and/or private events. The prix-fixe includes a buffet with salads, sushi, and side dishes, and *rodízio* service, in which waiters bring various types of meat off the spit to your table every few minutes. ⊠ *SCES trecho 02, Cj. 35, S. de Clubes Sul* ☎ *061/3223–2002* 🖃 *AE, DC, MC, V* ⊕ *www.porcao.com.br.*

Fodor'sChoice ★

$ ✕ **Feitiço Mineiro.** Live Brazilian music, usually bossa nova, is a nightly feature at this restaurant with high-quality *mineira food* (food from the state of Minas Gerais). Try the *costelinha ao Véio Chico* (fried ribs with manioc) while you wait for the shows. ⊠ *CLN 306 Bl. B, Lj. 45 and 51* ☎ *061/3272–3032* 🖃 *DC, MC, V* ☉ *No dinner Sun.*

Eclectic

$$$$ **Universal Diner.** The kitschy decor is one of the main attractions of this modern restaurant—bras hang from the bar on the lower level and kitschy objects like bulldog statuettes, miniature porcelain dolls, used vinyl LPs (hanging from the ceiling), and a 1960s-era fridge. The chef and owner, Mara Alckamin, is always on hand, asking whether you liked the food. Try the "Sexy Shrimp": prawns with caviar and champagne sauce, served with a strawberry risotto. Dance music is played every Friday. ⊠ *CLS 210, Bl. B, Lj. 30* ☎ *061/3443–2089* 🖃 *DC, MC, V* ☉ *No lunch Mon. No dinner Sun.* ⊕ *www.universaldiner.com.br.*

$$–$$$ **Patu Anú.** At the edge of Paranoá Lake with a beautiful view of the city, this romantic restaurant has excellent food. It is hard to find, but well worth the hunt. To get here by boat ($20 per person), take the road that goes to Ermida Dom Bosco and Paranoá Dam, following signs to the pier. Try the boar fillet with rum and honey sauce, served with cinnamon-and-cashew rice. ⊠ *Setor de Mansões do Lago Norte, trecho 12,*

Cj. 1, casa 7 ☎ *061/3369–2788* 🖃 *DC, MC, V* ⊕ *www.patuanu.com. br* ☉ *Closed Mon.*

$ ╳ **Carpe Diem.** If you are a bibliophile or a fan of the arts, you might enjoy the constant book launchings and exhibits at this restaurant frequented by politicians and academics. The menu includes *feijoada* (meat stew with black beans) and a special buffet on Sunday. It is close to the southern and northern hotel sectors. ⊠ *SCLS 104, Bl. D, Lj. 1* ☎ *061/ 3225–8883* 🖃 *AE, DC, MC, V.*

French

★ **$$$–$$$$** ╳ **La Chaumière.** For more than 30 years, this small but cozy restaurant has been highly regarded for its classical French fare—especially the steak with green pepper sauce and the steak with Roquefort. ⊠ *SCLS, Q. 408, Bl. A, Lt. 13* ☎ *061/3242–7599* 🖃 *AE, D, MC* ☉ *Closed Mon. No lunch Sat.; no dinner Sun.*

German

$–$$$ ╳ **Fritz.** In business for decades, this restaurant is synonymous with German cuisine. Try the *Eisbein* (pig's leg with mashed potatoes) or *Ente mit Blaukraut und Apfelpurée* (duck cooked in wine served with red cabbage and applesauce). ⊠ *SCLS, Q. 404, Bl. D, Lj. 35* ☎ *061/3223–4622* 🖃 *AE, DC, MC, V* ☉ *No dinner Sun.*

Italian

$$$–$$$$ ╳ **Villa Borghese.** The cantina ambience and fantastic cuisine (including many freshly made pastas) make you feel as if you're in Italy. The *tagliatelli negro* (pasta with squid ink), served with a garlic, herb, and shrimp sauce, is divine. ⊠ *SCLS, Q. 201, Bl. A, Lj. 33* ☎ *061/3226–5650* 🖃 *DC, MC, V* ☉ *Closed Mon.*

Spanish

$$ ╳ **La Torreta.** The success of this famous restaurant can be attributed to the personalized service and the variety of dishes—including the traditional *paella*—and wines from Spain, Argentina, Chile, and Brazil. ⊠ *CLS 402, Bl. A, Lj. 9, Asa Sul* ☎ *061/3321–2516* 🖃 *AE, MC, V* ☉ *No dinner Sun.*

Vegetarian

$$–$$$ **Oca da Tribo.** This place looks like it's straight out of the rain forest, and was built to resemble an Amazonian riverside *oca* (hut), complete with straw roof. It serves an excellent, well-seasoned vegetarian buffet in addition to à la carte plates at dinner. The food is a healthy mixture of vegetables and wild game meat such as boar, duck, quail, buffalo fillet, ostridge, and emu. Visit at night, when a fire is lit inside. ⊠ *SCES, Section 2, near the Meditation Club* ☎ *061/3226–9880* 🖃 *V* ☉ *No dinner Sun. and Mon.*

Where to Stay

★ **$$–$$$$** 🏨 **Naoum Plaza Hotel.** Brasília's most sophisticated hotel attracts heads of state (Prince Charles, Nelson Mandela, and Fidel Castro have stayed in the Royal Suite) and their diplomats. Rooms have tropical-wood furniture and beige color schemes. The service is impeccable. Two upscale restaurants, the Falls (with eclectic international cuisine) and Mitsubá (with Japanese fare), add to the hotel's appeal. ✉ *SHS, Q. 05, Bl. H/I, 70322-914* ☎ *061/3322–4545 or 0800/61–4844* 📠 *061/3322–4949* ⊕ *www.naoumplaza.com.br* 🛏 *171 rooms, 16 suites* ☺ *2 restaurants, coffee shop, room service, cable TV, pool, gym, sauna, bar, Internet room, business services, meeting rooms, travel services, free parking* 🖃 *AE, DC, MC, V* ¦◯¦ *BP.*

★ **$$–$$$** ⌧ **Blue Tree Park.** Staying so far from the city can be worthwhile to experience this spacious luxury hotel. On the Paranoá Lake shore, near the Palácio da Alvorada, the modern-design hotel is surrounded by greenery. Many events are held here, since the convention center can accommodate up to 750 and the ballroom up to 1,000. ✉ *SHTN Trecho 01, Cj. 1B, Bl. C, 70800-200* ☎ *061/3424–7000* 📠 *061/3424–7001* ⊕ *www.bluetree.com.br* 🛏 *380 rooms* ☺ *Restaurant, coffee shop, room service, cable TV, pool, gym, sauna, bar, Internet room, business services, convention center, free parking* 🖃 *AE, DC, MC, V* ¦◯¦ *BP.*

$$–$$$ ⌧ **Bonaparte Hotel Residence.** A sober granite lobby with sophisticated
Fodor'sChoice accent lighting make the Bonaparte an appealing choice. All rooms
★ could be considered small apartments, with plush carpeting, king-sized beds, and large bathtubs in every bathroom. The business services here are outstanding, and the on-site restaurant, La Via Vechia, is one of the best in town. ✉ *SHS, Q. 02, Bl. J, 70322-900* ☎ *061/3218–6600 or 0800/61–9991* 📠 *061/3321–1831* ⊕ *www.bonapartehotel.com.br* 🛏 *267 rooms* ☺ *2 restaurants, coffee shop, room service, cable TV, pool, gym, sauna, bar, Internet room, business services, convention center, free parking* 🖃 *AE, DC, MC, V* ¦◯¦ *BP.*

★ **$$–$$$** ⌧ **Meliá Brasília.** The newest hotel in Brasília has one entire floor made of reforested wood. Rooms are comfortable and suitable for long stays. This is one of the most reliable, modern, well-run, and well-situated hotels in town. ✉ *SHS, Qd. 6, Bl. D* ☎ *061/3218–4700, 0800/703–3399 reservations* ⊕ *www.solmelia.com* 🛏 *334 rooms* ☺ *In-room safes, refrigerators, pool, sauna, gym, Internet room, bar* 🖃 *AE, MC, V..*

$$ ⌧ **Academia de Tênis Resort.** What was once merely a tennis club on the
Fodor'sChoice shore of Lago Paranoá has, over the course of 30 years, become a
★ sprawling resort. Suites are in chalets on landscaped grounds with gardens and wooded areas. Chalets are surrounded by palm trees and arranged around the pools, some free-form with waterfalls. Some suites have whirlpool baths. ✉ *SCES, Trecho 4, Cj. 5, Lt. 1-B, 70200-000* ☎ *061/3316–6161* 📠 *061/3316–6268* ⊕ *www.academiaresort.com. br* 🛏 *220 suites* ☺ *6 restaurants, coffee shop, room service, cable TV, 21 tennis courts, indoor pool, 6 outdoor pools, gym, sauna, 3 bars, theater, Internet room, business services, meeting rooms, free parking* 🖃 *AE, DC, MC, V* ¦◯¦ *BP.*

$$ ⌧ **Hotel Nacional.** Echoing Brasília's modernist architecture, the Hotel Nacional, though slightly outdated, is still one of the city's best options. It has accommodated any number of distinguished guests, including Queen Elizabeth. The Taboo Grill is a great place for grilled meat or seafood, and the Tropical Coffee shop offers a different buffet table for each day of the week. ✉ *SHS, Q. 01, Bl. A, 70322-900* ☎ *061/3321–7575* 📠 *061/3223–9213 or 0800/644–7070* ⊕ *www.hotelnacional.com.br*

🛏 *346 rooms* ♨ *Restaurant, coffee shop, room service, cable TV, indoor pool, gym, sauna, bar, nightclub, Internet room, business services, meeting rooms, travel services, free parking* ▭ *AE, DC, MC, V* ⬛ *BP.*

★ **$$** ⬚ **Kubitschek Plaza.** High-caliber service and upscale amenities are the hallmarks here. The lobby is decorated with antiques, Persian rugs, and original paintings by renowned Nippo-Brazilian artist Tomie Otake. Rooms have a sedate modern decor. After a hard day conducting affairs of state and/or business, many people head for the on-site Plaza Club, a restaurant–bar with a dance floor. ✉ *SHN, Q. 02, Bl. E, 70710-908* ☎ *061/3329–3333 or 0800/61–3995* 🖷 *061/3328–9366* ⊕ *www. kubitschek.com.br* 🛏 *246 rooms* ♨ *2 restaurants, coffee shop, room service, cable TV, indoor pool, gym, sauna, 3 bars, Internet room, business services, meeting rooms, travel services, free parking* ▭ *AE, DC, MC, V* ⬛ *BP.*

$$ ⬚ **Metropolitan.** This low-key hotel has a lower price tag than its sister property, the Bonaparte. The rooms are fully furnished apartments. It's convenient to the Brasília Shopping mall and gives special rates for extended stays. The Francisco Norte restaurant is highly recommended. ✉ *SHN, Q. 02, Bl. H, 70710-030* ☎ *061/3424–3500 or 0800/61–3939* 🖷 *061/3327–3938* ⊕ *www.atlantica-hotels.com* 🛏 *115 apartments* ♨ *Restaurant, cable TV, pool, gym, sauna, bar, Internet room, meeting rooms, free parking* ▭ *AE, DC, MC, V* ⬛ *BP.*

$ ⬚ **Eron Brasília Hotel.** Rooms at this hotel have high-tech amenities like full stereo systems. Request a room on the 10th floor or higher to avoid traffic noise. The Restaurante Panorâmico and its piano bar have a grand view of the Eixo Monumental and are popular with political types. ✉ *SHN, Q. 05, Bl. A, 70710-300* ☎ *061/3329–4000 or 0800/61–0999* 🖷 *061/3326–2698* ⊕ *www.eronhotel.com.br* 🛏 *170 rooms, 10 suites* ♨ *Restaurant, cable TV, in-room data ports, gym, bar, nightclub, Internet room, meeting rooms, travel services, free parking* ▭ *AE, DC, MC, V* ⬛ *BP.*

Nightlife & the Arts

Nightlife

BARS If you want to experience a typical Brazilian happy hour, go to **Bar Brasília** (✉ SHC/S CR, Q. 506, Bl. A, Lj. 15, Parte A, Asa Sul ☎ 061/3443–4323), which has been repeatedly elected the Best Bar in Town by a yearly poll conducted by *Veja,* one of Brazil's most popular magazines. **Beirute** (✉ SCLS 109, Bl. A, Lj. 02/04 ☎ 061/3244–1717), an eclectic bar-restaurant with an Arab flair, has been in business since 1966. During its first decade it drew politicians for postsession discussions; today it attracts intellectuals and is gay- and lesbian-friendly. It is also known for its ice-cold beer.

Gates Pub (✉ SCLS 403, Bl. B, Lj. 34 ☎ 061/3322–9301) is popular with those who appreciate jazz and blues. For drinks and light food, go to **Marietta Café** (✉ SCLS 210, Bl. C, Lj. 6 ☎ 061/3244–8344), famous for its natural sandwiches, ice cream, and fruit juices. **Mormaii Surf Bar** (✉ Pontão do Lago Sul ☎ 061/3364–6025) has a lively ambience and a view of the lake and the city. It serves sandwiches and Japanese food.

DANCE CLUBS In Brasília's clubs some nights are devoted to such northeastern Brazilian rhythms as *forró*—the result of the large number of *nordestinos* (northeasterners) that settled here. **Café Cancun** (⊠ Liberty Mall, SCN, Q. 02, Bl. D, Lj. 52 ☎ 061/3327–1566) is known for its variety of music. Each day of the week is dedicated to a certain type, and you can dance to forró, *axé* (music from Bahia), and techno. If you like the good, old rock 'n' roll, the place of choice is **UK Brasil Pub** (⊠ SCLS 411, Bl. B, Lj. 28, Asa Sul ☎ 061/3346–5214), with live presentations of local bands (usually cover bands) and an excellent selection of American and Brazilian songs of the '80s and '90s.

The Arts

The **Clube do Choro** (⊠ Eixo Monumental ☎ 061/3327–0494 ⊕ www.clubedochoro.com.br) presents good Brazilian music. The main building of the **Fundação Brasileira de Teatro** (Brazilian Theatrical Foundation; ⊠ SDS, Bl. C, Lj. 30 ☎ 061/3226–0182) has two theaters for plays and concerts: the Teatro Dulcina de Moraes and the Teatro Conchita de Moraes. The **Teatro Nacional Cláudio Santoro** (⊠ SBN, Via N2 ☎ 061/3325–6109, 061/3325–6105 symphony tickets) has three stages and several practice rooms used by the Orquestra Sinfônica do Teatro Nacional, which performs here from March through November. The **Centro Cultural Banco do Brasil** (CCBB; ⊠ SCES Trecho 2, Cj. 22 ☎ 061/3310–7087) hosts art exhibits, dance shows, and plays.

Sports & the Outdoors

Most spectator sporting events are held in the Centro Desportivo Presidente Medici complex, on the north side of the Eixo Monumental.

Participatory Sports

GOLF At the tip of Eixo Monumental, not far from the Palácio da Alvorada, you can golf on the 18-hole course at the **Clube de Golfe de Brasília** (⊠ SCES, Trecho 2, Lt. 2 ☎ 061/3224–2718). Greens fees are R$60 weekdays and R$90 weekends.

HIKING If you just want to wander along a trail, head to the **Parque Nacional de Brasília** (⇨ Beyond the Plano Piloto *in* Exploring Brasília, *above*). To learn about local vegetation while you walk, try one of the three trails at the **Jardim Botânico** (⇨ Beyond the Plano Piloto *in* Exploring Brasília, *above*).

SWIMMING The **Parque Nacional de Brasília** (⇨ Beyond the Plano Piloto *in* Exploring Brasília, *above*) has pools filled with mineral water. Take your dip in the morning to beat the crowds.

On the Sidelines

AUTO RACING The **Autódromo Internacional Nelson Piquet** (☎ 061/3273–6586), named after three-time Formula I champion and Brasília native Nelson Piquet, has a 5-km (3-mi) racetrack that hosts such events as Formula III and stock car races.

SOCCER The modern, 66,000-seat **Estádio Mané Garrincha** (☎ 061/3225–9860) is where Gama FC plays, a second-tier *futebol* (soccer) team that has occasionally risen to the major league. **Ginásio Cláudio Coutinho** (☎ 061/

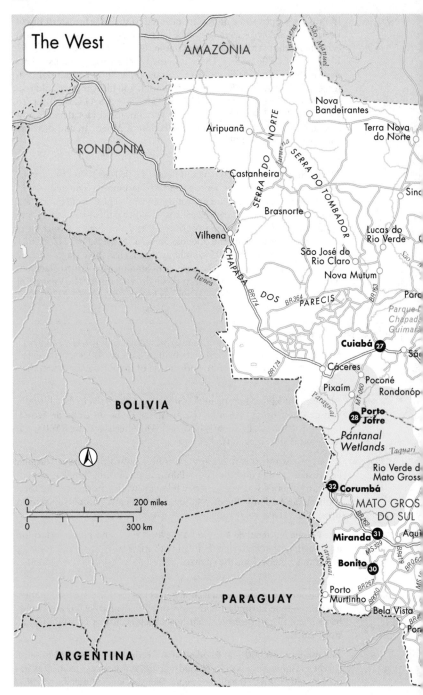

3225–5977) is a small, 6,000-seat facility used mostly for practice by national teams.

Shopping

There are two major shopping districts along the Eixo Monumental: the Setor Comercial Norte (SCN; Northern Commercial Sector) and the Setor Comercial Sul (SCS; Southern Commercial Sector). In addition, almost every *superquadra* has its own commercial district.

Centers & Malls

Housed in an odd arch-shaped building, **Brasília Shopping** (⊠ SCN, Q. 05 ☎ 061/3328–2122), the most sophisticated mall in the city, has several international chain stores, as well as movie theaters, restaurants, and snack bars. The mall is close to both hotel sectors and is open Monday–Saturday 10–10 and Sunday 2–10. **Pátio Brasil Shopping** (⊠ SRTV, Q. 701 ☎ 061/3314–7400) often has free concerts and is very close to most hotels. It has a full range of shops and movie theaters and is open Monday–Saturday 10–10:30. **Parkshopping** (⊠ SAI/Sudoeste, Q. A-1 ☎ 0800/61–4444), Brasília's largest shopping center, has 183 shops as well as a Burle Marx–designed central garden, the site of many cultural events. It's open Monday–Saturday 10–10.

Markets

The **BSB Mix and Feira da Lua (Moon Fair)** (⊠ Centro Comercial Gilberto Salomão, SHIS, QI. 5) are held alternately every two weekends, 8–4. In over 100 stalls you can find reasonably priced arts and crafts, furniture, jewelry, clothing, homemade food, and much more. The **Feira de Antiguidades** (Antiques Fair; ⊠ Centro Comercial Gilberto Salomão, SHIS, QI. 5) is held on the last weekend of each month from 8 to 6 and offers a great variety of decorative objects. At the **Feira de Artesanato** (Artisans' Fair; ⊠ Foot of Torre de TV, Eixo Monumental) you can find semiprecious-stone jewelry, bronze items, wood carvings, wicker crafts, pottery, and dried flowers. It's held weekends 9–6.

Gemstones

For quality stones head to the **Museu Nacional das Gemas** (⊠ Torre de TV, Eixo Monumental ☎ 061/3322–3227 Ext. 201). The shop is open Tuesday–Friday 10–6.

Side Trips from Brasília

By driving no more than an hour or two from your hotel you can get to the beautiful waterfalls and natural areas that surround Brasília, many within the 2,200-square-mi (5,700-square-km) Distrito Federal (Federal District). If you don't have a car, you can go with a tour. Note that tours leave very early in the morning. The **State Tourism Secretariat** (⊕ www.setur.df.gov.br/) lists multiple companies that arrange these tours on its Web site. For tour companies we especially recommend, *see* Tour Options *in* "Brasília and the West Essentials," *at* the end of this chapter.

Poço Azul is an ecological park with waterfalls and brilliant-blue natural pools enclosed in quartz. In the park you can do rappelling, hiking, and diving, or just cool off in the shallow natural pools. The park does not have restaurants or snack bars, so you should bring your own food and drinks. When leaving the park, you are reimbursed R$5 if you collect your garbage and hand it to the park's administration. ⊠ *DF 001, at Km 105; from Eixo Norte, take DF 001 toward Sobradinho and Lago Oeste to end of highway (about 12 mi/20 km), then take dirt road (follow signs) for 9 km (6 mi)* ☎ *0061/9648–1559* 💰 *R$15 per car* ⊙ *Daily 5 AM–7 PM.*

The **Cachoeira da Saia Velha** is a natural preserve with cerrado vegetation and several waterfalls. It has barbecue grills, horseback riding, a kid's park, and camping areas. A restaurant is nearby. All in all, it's a nice place to spend a hot day. ⊠ *BR 040, Saida Sul, 22 mi/35 km south of Brasília* ☎ *061/3627–0000* 💰 *R$7 weekdays, R$10 weekends* ⊙ *Daily 8–4.*

Salto do Itiquira (Itiquira Falls) are 551 feet (168 meters) high, making them the second-highest accessible waterfall in Brazil after Iguaçu. Below the falls, the river forms a series of small waterfalls, rapids, and deep natural pools, in terrain covered by dense tropical vegetation. There are several restaurants, a campground, and a platform for ultralight flights. ⊠ *Hwys 020 and 030 to Formosa, then Hwy GO 44 Formosa, 68 mi/110 km northeast of Brasília* ☎ *061/3503–5108* 💰 *R$10* ⊙ *Daily 9–5:30.*

GOIÁS STATE

Brasília's Distrito Federal is surrounded completely by Goiás State, in the geographical heart of Brazil. Exploring Goiás means getting to know some of its historic cities, which started as settlements around gold mines, such as Goiás Velho and Pirenópolis, examples of colonial Brazil in their architecture and local culture. To the south is the hinterland of Caldas Novas, the world's largest hydrothermal resort. North of Brasília is the region of the Chapada dos Veadeiros, with its strange rock formations, fantastic waterfalls, and moonlike scenery that surrounds the town of Alto Paraíso (High Paradise), considered by spiritualists to be the city of the third millennium.

Parque Nacional da Chapada dos Veadeiros

㉓ *250 km (155 mi) north of Brasília.*

This national park lies on the oldest part of the continent, Araí Plate, formed 1.8 billion years ago. The plateaus of Chapada dos Veadeiros form, according to NASA, the most luminous point seen from the Earth's orbit. This is due to the quantity of quartz crystals in the soil. The area is famous for its waterfalls, hiking trails, and unforgettable landscape. Place-names are suggestive of the park's beauty: the Crystal River, Zen Backwoods, Abyss Waterfall, and Moon Valley. There is no ideal season to go to the Chapada—the climate is comfortable year-round. But the flora is more exuberant between May and October, when the rivers have receded a bit. You must be accompanied by a guide to explore the park; you can make arrangements at the park's entrance. Local guides are accredited by IBAMA, the Brazilian Institute of Environment and Renewable Natural Resources. ⊠ *GO 327, Km 34, 40 km (25 mi) from Alto Paraíso de Goiás* ☏ *061/3459–3388* ⊕ *www. chapada.com* ✉ *R$3* ⊙ *Tues.–Sun. 8–5; entrance allowed only 8–noon.*

Alto Paraíso de Goiás (High Paradise of Goiás) is Chapada dos Veadeiros's main town. The majority of the residents are Brazilians from outside the region and foreigners, mostly Europeans. It is considered a center of mysticism, spiritualism, and ecotourism. Crossed by Parallel 14, as is Machu Picchu, in Peru, Alto Paraíso has fantastic stories about flying saucers and extraterrestrial beings. ⊠ *GO 118 at GO 327.*

Vila de São Jorge is the gateway to Parque Nacional da Chapada dos Veadeiros. With 500 inhabitants, the village is one of the coolest towns in the region, with parties every night and good infrastructure, with inns, camping areas, and restaurants. There are no pharmacies though; be sure you take you own medicine and repellents. ⊠ *GO 327, 40 km from Alto Paraíso.*

Where to Stay & Eat

$–$$ ✕ **Jambalaya.** The most refined restaurant in town, Jambalaya has a superb view of the county from its hilltop location. It has a self-service vegetarian buffet at lunchtime, à la carte European dishes for dinner, and a good variety of wine (mostly Italian). There are music and events on weekends. ⊠ *S. Mirante Estância Paraíso* ☏ *062/3446–1456* ☰ *V* ⊙ *Closed Mon.*

¢–$ ✕ **Oca Lila.** In the evening during high season, this restaurant is packed with teens and twenty-somethings. It's worth the wait for the varied healthfood menu, which includes many sandwiches and pizzas. Live music plays on weekends. A store in the restaurant sells arts and crafts. ⊠ *Av. João Bernardes Rabelo 449* ☏ *062/3446–1773* ☰ *V.*

¢ ✕ **Jatô.** Local artists and intellectuals meet over vegetarian and traditional Goiás dishes. Lunch is a self-service buffet, with six types of meat, as well as *arroz integral* (whole-grain rice) and salad. ⊠ *Rua Coleto Paulino 522* ☏ *061/3446–1339* ☰ *V* ⊙ *No dinner.*

$ 🏨 **Casa das Flores.** Exotic attractions like Arabian dance and live Brazilian music add to the romance of this attractive inn. Stay in rooms or two-story cabanas. Breakfast is served in the bangalos veranda. ⊠ *Vila de São Jorge, Rua 10, Q. 2, Lt. 14* ☏ *061/3234–7493* ⊕ *www. pousadacasadasflores.com.br* ➘ *8 apartments, 13 cabanas* ⚹ *Restaurant, pool, sauna, bar; no a/c in some rooms* ☰ *No credit cards* ⦿ *MAP.*

¢–$ 🏨 **Alfa & Ômega.** The owner, one of the first settlers in this town, is a father figure in the region. This interesting place has a meditation area, Indian decoration, and Ayurvedic massage. Chaletlike modules are divided into four rooms, and the most sophisticated apartments have an inner garden. Alternative therapies and meditation rooms are available. ⊠ *Rua Joaquim de Almeida 15, 73770-000* ☏ *062/446–1225* 🖷 *062/3446–1225* ⊕ *www.veadeiros.com.br* ➘ *12 rooms* ⚹ *Pool, massage, sauna; no room phones* ☰ *D, M.*

¢–$ 🏨 **Camelot Inn.** King Arthur's castle, complete with ramparts and parapets, has been transported to the cerrado with this thematic inn. Each room's decor is based on a different character from the Knights of the Round Table legend. You can enjoy the rivers and the waterfalls of the area or take a walk around the hills. ⊠ *Km 168, Rodovia GO 118, 73770-000* ☎ *062/3446–1449* ⊕ *www.pousadacamelot.com.br* ⇨ *20 rooms* ⚒ *Cable TV, 3 pools, hot tub, massage, sauna, bar, shop, helipads* ⊟ *MC, V* ⟡ *BP.*

Pirenópolis

㉔ *159 km (99 mi) west of Brasília.*

Settled in the 18th century at the height of the Goiás gold rush, Pirenópolis was abandoned by the early 19th century after most of its gold was mined. Some locals say the years of isolation were a blessing, as they've helped to preserve the town's character: most streets in the historic downtown district retain the original pavement, which has slivers of quartzite, an abundant mineral that's still quarried north of town. In 1989 the federal government gave national monument status to what was once virtually a ghost town, drawing attention from the tourism industry. On weekends people flee from the modern concrete and glass of Brasília to immerse themselves in Pirenópolis's colonial flavor. The town has several blocks of historic houses, churches, charming restaurants, and quaint resorts, along with several well-respected jewelers.

The **Praça da Matriz** is part of the old neighborhood of the city. The oldest cathedral in the state (Igreja Matriz) and the Teatro de Pirenópolis (Pirenópolis Theater) are here. ⊠ *Rua do Rosário at Rua Direita.*

The once-handsome, colonial **Igreja Nossa Senhora do Rosário–Matriz** is the oldest church in Goiás (c. 1728–32). A fire almost destroyed it on September 5, 2002, and the church is being restored. ⊠ *Praça da Matriz, Rua do Rosário, at Rua do Bonfim* ☎ *No phone.*

The **Museu das Cavalhadas** displays the outlandish medieval costumes worn by participants in the Festa do Divino Espírito Santo. First celebrated in 1891, this three-day event, which has the atmosphere of a Renaissance fair, takes over the town six weeks after Easter Sunday. Among the roster of activities is a staged battle between Moors and Christians (the Christians win every year). The museum is in a private home—Dona Maria Eunice, the owner, will guide you. ⊠ *Rua Direita 39* ☎ *062/3331–1166* ⊠ *R$2* ⊗ *Fri.–Sun. 9–5.*

Cachoeiras Bonsucesso is the most popular of the several waterfalls and swimming holes in the Rio das Almas because it's closest to town. A campsite, soccer fields, beach volleyball courts, and trails surround the falls. ⊠ *Rua do Carmo, 7 km (4 mi) north of town* ☎ *062/3321–1217* ⊠ *R$3* ⊗ *Daily 8–6.*

Fazenda Vagafogo is a 57-acre ecological preserve with a medium-size waterfall that crashes into a natural pool. It also has a small forest, hiking trails, and a little café. The adrenaline-rush Tree Canopy Ride is a high ropes course among trees. A brunch of fruits and farm produce is served Friday through Sunday. ⊠ *Rua do Carmo, 6 km/4 mi north of town center* ☎ *062/9969–3090* ⊠ *R$3* ⊗ *Tues.–Sun. 8–5.*

Where to Stay & Eat

$–$$ ✕ **Restaurante e Pizzaria Pireneus.** At lunch, this outstanding eatery serves Goiás-style barbecue (beef roasted over coals or on a grill, instead of using rodízio-style skewers). At dinner it takes advantage of its traditional brick stove and becomes a pizzeria. ✉ *Praça da Matriz 31, in front of the church* ☎ *062/3331–1577* ▭ *MC, V.*

¢–$ ✕ **Aravinda.** This eatery is also a "spiritual" center—the raspy-voice aging-hippie owner is the town's mother figure. The food is colorful and tasty with an emphasis on vegetarian fare, though the fish dishes are delicious, particularly the *peixe na telha,* served with tomatoes, potatoes, and rice. On weekends the live music could be anything from blues to salsa. ✉ *Rua do Rosário 25* ☎ *062/3331–2409* ▭ *No credit cards* ⊙ *Closed Mon.–Tues.*

¢–$ ✕ **Caffe & Tarsia.** Probably the best restaurant in town, Caffe & Tarsia is run by a young Italian man and his Brazilian wife. A wide variety of quality Mediterranean dishes are served; there's a self-service buffet on Saturday. Sit at the far end and enjoy the vines on the roof, which are covered with ice each day so they can endure the hot climate of the cerrado. Live music accompanies meals on Saturday and Sunday. ✉ *Rua do Rosário 34* ☎ *062/3331–1274* ▭ *V* ⊙ *Closed Mon.–Thurs.*

¢ ✕ **As Flor.** Popular with locals because of the affordable buffet-style service, As Flor serves traditional Brazilian fare—both the lunch and the dinner menu consist mainly of cured meats with rice and beans. ✉ *Sizenando Jaime 16* ☎ *062/3331–1276* ▭ *No credit cards.*

¢ ✕🏨 **Hotel Quinta de Santa Bárbara.** Across from the Igreja Nosso Senhor do Bonfim this family-oriented resort has colonial-style bungalows. Each has two rooms with comfortable beds and flagstone floors; a veranda has views of the town that are particularly beautiful at sunset. The open-air all-you-can-eat restaurant serves excellent Goiás specialties cooked in a massive kilnlike stove. ✉ *Rua do Bonfim 1* ☎🖳 *062/3331–1304* ⇌ *20 rooms* ♨ *Restaurant, minibars, cable TV, 2 pools, sauna, fishing, bar* ▭ *V.*

$ 🏨 **Pousada dos Pireneus.** The main lodge of this activities-rich hotel is an adobe Spanish Colonial–style house. It contains the restaurant and bar, which looks out at the pools, tennis courts, and beyond the landscaped grounds to town. Rooms are in what can only be described as a 17th-century condo complex, a five-minute walk from the main lodge; ground-floor quarters have decks and hammocks. ✉ *Chácara Mata do Sobrato* ☎ *062/3331–1345* 🖳 *062/3331–1462* ⇌ *103 rooms* ⊕ *www.pousadadospireneus.com.br* ♨ *Restaurant, cable TV, tennis court, 2 pools, fitness classes, massage, sauna, spa, bicycles, horseback riding, bar, recreation room, shops, convention center* ▭ *AE, DC, MC, V* ❙O❙ *MAP.*

FodorʼsChoice
★

$ 🏨 **Pousada Walkeriana.** This pousada is named after *Cattleya walkeriana,* one of several rare Brazilian orchids on display in the garden. The main building housed different city government offices over the years before it was declared an Architectural Heritage Site in 1990. An antiques shop in the west wing specializes in furniture, and the pousada's small, comfortable rooms are furnished with pieces from the shop. ✉ *Praça do Rosário 2, Centro* ☎🖳 *062/3331–1260* ⇌ *16 rooms* ♨ *Cable TV, pool, bar, shop* ⊕ *www.pireneus.com.br* ▭ *V* ❙O❙ *CP.*

Nightlife

Most nightlife is along or just off the **Rua do Rosário** (Leisure Street), which is closed to vehicular traffic on weekends, when bar and restaurant tables take over the narrow sidewalks and the street proper. The liveliest bars are Lanchonete da Chiquinha, Varanda, and Choperia Santo Graal.

Shopping

The number of art and antiques shops in Pirenópolis keeps growing, but the jewelry shops around the commercial district remain the highlight of the town. **Galleria** (⊠ Rua do Bom Fim 18 ☎ 062/3331–1483) has jewelry made from gold, silver, and semiprecious stones. **Pica Pedra** (⊠ Beira Rio at Rua do Rosário ☎ No phone) specializes in silver and stones, especially emeralds, amethysts, and quartz. At **Shanti** (⊠ Rua do Bom Fim 20 ☎ 062/9969–3161) you can shop for local handicrafts and indulge in an ice cream or an espresso.

Caldas Novas

㉕ *380 km (236 mi) west of Brasília.*

In the crater of a 600-million-year-old volcano, Caldas Novas is the world's greatest hydrothermal resort. The hot waters were discovered only in the early 1700s by adventurers seeking gold and precious stones. Together with Rio Quente (to the west), it has the largest number of hotels, resorts, and water-park resorts in Brazil's midwestern region. Among the therapeutic properties of the water are stress release, muscle relaxation, relief of digestive and rheumatic diseases, and stimulation of the endocrinal glands.

Where to Stay & Eat

¢ ✕**Restaurante Bella Nápoles.** This Italian restaurant and pizzeria has 28 types of pasta and pizza, plus salad, barbecue, and tropical fruit for dessert. ⊠ *Av. Orcalino Santos 136* ☎ *64/3453–1620* ▭ *No credit cards.*

¢ ✕**Restaurante e Churrascaria Picanha na Brasâ.** More than 20 à la carte dishes are available at this restaurant with a self-service buffet. Brazilian barbecue and *peixe na telha* (fish with tomatoes, potatoes, and cheese) are served. ⊠ *R. Pedro Branco de Souza 241, Centro* ☎ *64/3453–7318 or 64/3453–7318* ▭ *V.*

$–$$ ▦**Hotel Parque das Primaveras.** Playgrounds, waterfalls, and a minizoo make this hotel in the middle of a park and ideal place to entertain children. Four types of units include a chalet, where artificial rain and fans take the place of air-conditioning; basic rooms; and "luxury" and "super luxury" rooms, which are carpeted and more nicely decorated than the basic rooms. All rooms have whirlpool baths. ⊠ *Rua do Balneário 1* ☎ *64/3453–1355* 🖷 *062/3453–1294* ⊕ *www.hpprimaveras.com.br* ➭ *23 rooms, 1 chalet* ⚠ *In-room safes, minibars, refrigerators, cable TV, outdoor hot tub, sauna* ▭ *V* ❢◯❙ *MAP.*

$–$$ ▦**Thermas di Roma Hotel Clube.** This huge complex has eight thermal swimming pools, a water park, and rooms and apartments of all sizes. There's an astonishing panoramic view of the cerrado and the Serra de Caldas Novas (Caldas Novas Mountains). Rooms are bright white, with stone flooring; some have patios. ⊠ *Rua São Cristóvão s/n* ☎ *64/3453–1718 or 0800/99–1012* ⊕ *www.diroma.com.br* ⇌ *234 rooms, 4 suites* ⌂ *Restaurant, refrigerators, cable TV, 8 pools, hair salon, hot tub, sauna* ⊟ *V.*

Goiás Velho

❷❻ *320 km (200 mi) west of Brasília.*

The city of Goiás, better known as Goiás Velho, was founded in 1727 by the *bandeirantes* (explorers whose initial goals were to enslave Indians and, later, to capture African slaves who had escaped into the interior), who settled here when they found gold and diamonds. By order of the king of Portugal, a mint was built here in 1774 to process the large amounts of gold found in the Serra Dourada (Golden Sierras)—a mountain range surrounding the city. The town kept growing well into the 1800s but became stagnant as the gold, silver, and gemstones disappeared.

It was the state's capital until 1937, when the government moved to a more central location in the new planned city of Goiânia. Goiás seemingly lost its importance overnight, but most of the baroque-colonial architecture was preserved, and today it is a UNESCO World Heritage Site.

Cidade de Goiás is the site of the Procissão do Fogaréu (Fire Procession), a popular Holy Week celebration. Hooded participants toting burning stakes reenact Christ's descent from the cross and burial. In addition, much like Pirenópolis, Goiás is an important handicrafts center. It is also known for being the hometown of Cora Coralina, one of Brazil's most renowned poets. The house where she lived (⇨ below) has become a museum.

The **Chafariz de Cauda,** a baroque fountain, was built around 1778 to provide water for the population. Water was drawn from the Chapéu de Padre mine and carried by pipes carved in stone blocks—some are on display at the Palácio Conde dos Arcos. ⊠ *Praça Brasil Caiado, Largo do Chafariz, s/n.*

The handsome baroque **Igreja São Francisco de Paula,** built in 1761, is the oldest church in Goiás. The murals, depicting the life of St. Francis, were painted by local artist André da Conceição in 1870. ⊠ *Praça Zacheu Alves de Castro s/n* ☎ *Free* ⊙ *Tues.–Sat. 9–5, Sun. 9–1.*

The imposing two-story **Museu das Bandeiras** (c. 1766) housed the regional government, court, and jail for almost 200 years. Inside are a cell, vintage furniture, church relics, and indigenous artifacts. ⊠ *Praça Brasil Caiado s/n* ☎ *062/3371–1087* ☎ *R$3* ⊙ *Tues.–Sat. 9–5, Sun. 8–1.*

The **Palácio Conde dos Arcos** housed the Goiás executive government from 1755 until the capital moved to Goiânia in 1937. Now the government returns here for three days every July in recognition of the city's historical importance. ⊠ *Praça Tasso Camargo 1* ☎ *062/3371–1200* ☎ *R$3* ⊙ *Tues.–Sat. 8–5, Sun. 8–noon.*

Goiás's most important poet, Cora Coralina (1889–1985), started writing at 14 but published her first book when she was 75. The **Casa de**

Cora Coralina is the house owned by her family since 1784, now a museum. Her bedroom and the house's kitchen are kept exactly the way she left them when she died. ⊠ *Rua D. Cândido 20* ☎ *062/3371–1990* 🎫 *R$3* ⊙ *Tues.–Sat. 9–5, Sun. 9–4.*

Where to Stay & Eat

¢–$ ✕ **Flor do Ipê.** This simple homey restaurant may be nondescript when it comes to decor, but it is the best place to experience *comida goiana* (food from the state of Goiás) such as *arroz com pequi* (rice with souari nuts) and *galinhada* (chicken and rice with spices and berries). ⊠ *Rua Boa Vista 32-A* ☎ *062/3372–1133* ▤ *D, MC* ⊙ *Closed Mon. No dinner Sun.*

$ 🏠 **Fazenda Manduzanzanâ.** At this working farm you can milk cows early in the morning, go horseback riding, and enjoy the natural pools and waterfalls on the property. Rooms are plain and rustic, but comfortable. ⊠ *Rodovia Municipal Goiás, Km 7* ☎ *062/9982–3373* 🛏 *10 rooms* ⚒ *Restaurant, bar* ▤ *No credit cards* ⊺⊙⫾ *MAP.*

★ ¢–$ 🏠 **Vila Boa.** On a hill outside town, this pousada has great views. Although accommodations are standard, this is the best option in town, and the staff makes every possible effort to make your stay comfortable. ⊠ *Av. Dr. Deusdete Ferreira de Moura, Morro do Chapéu de Padre* ☎ *062/3371–1000* 🖷 *062/3371–1000* ⊕ *www.hotelvilaboa.com.br* 🛏 *33 rooms* ⚒ *Restaurant, pool, bicycles, bar* ▤ *No credit cards.*

¢ 🏠 **Pousada do Ipê.** This cozy place next to the Chafariz da Carioca allows you to blend easily into the local way of life because it is in the center of town, close to the old church and the museums. The rooms are simple and clean; eight are are simple, with TV and a fan. The other 13 are larger and more comfortable, with air-conditioning. ⊠ *Rua do Fórum 22* ☎ *062/337–1265* 🛏 *21 rooms* ⚒ *Restaurant, pool, hot tub, bar; no a/c in some rooms* ▤ *No credit cards.*

Sports & the Outdoors

The hills of Serra Dourada are covered with dense forest and are a great place to hike. There are also waterfalls and swimming holes in the creeks and the Rio Vermelho (Red River). **Balneário Santo Antônio** (⊠ Km 125, GO 070) is a popular bathing spot near town. The Rio Vermelho also has rapids and a first-come, first-served free camping site. **Pé no Chão Excursionismo** (☎ 062/3372–1782) organizes guided tours and rafting trips.

Shopping

Associação dos Artesãos de Goiás (⊠ Largo do Rosário s/n ☎ 062/371–1116) sells pottery, wicker, and terra-cotta pieces, all by local artists.

THE PANTANAL

Fodor'sChoice
★ Smack in the middle of South America, the **Pantanal Wetlands** cover a gigantic flood plain of the Rio Paraguay and its tributaries. Its area is about 225,000 square km (96,500 square mi), two-thirds of which are in Brazil. Much of the land is still owned by ranching families that have been here for generations. The Portuguese had begun colonizing the area by the late 18th century; today it's home to more than 21 million head

of cattle and some 4 million people (most of them living in the capital cities). Yet there's still abundant wildlife in this mosaic of swamp, forest, and savanna. From your base at a *fazenda* (ranch) or lodge—with air-conditioning, swimming pools, and well-cooked meals—you can experience the *pantaneiro* lifestyle, yet another manifestation of the cowboy culture. Folklore has it that pantaneiros can communicate with the Pantanal animals.

It's widely held that the Pantanal is the best place in all of South America to view wildlife. (It is slated to become a UNESCO Biosphere Reserve.) More than 600 species of birds live here during different migratory seasons, including *araras* (hyacinth macaws), fabulous blue-and-yellow birds that can be as long as three feet from head to tail; larger-than-life rheas, which look and walk like aging modern ballerinas; the *tuiuiú*, known as the "lords of the Pantanal" and one of the largest birds known (their wingspan is 5–6 feet), which build an intricate assemblage of nests (*ninhais*) on trees; as well as cormorants, ibis, herons, kingfishers, hawks, falcons, and egrets, to name a few. You're also sure to spot *capivaras* (capybaras; the world's largest rodents—adults are about 60 cm/2 feet tall), tapirs, anteaters, marsh and jungle deer, maned wolves, otters, and one of the area's six species of monkeys.

The amphibian family is well represented by *jacarés* (caiman alligators), whose population of 200 per square mile is a large increase from the 1970s, when poaching had left them nearly extinct. (The skin of four animals made just one pair of shoes.) Jacarés are much more tranquil than their North American and African relatives—they don't attack unless threatened. Almost blind and deaf, and lacking a sense of smell, caimans catch the fish they eat by following vibrations in the water. It's hard to spot jaguars and pumas during the day; a night photographic safari is the best way to try your luck. Native guides (some are actually converted hunters) take you safely to the animals' roaming areas. Sightings are not uncommon in the fazendas that go the extra mile to protect their fauna. Though all commercial hunting and the pelt trade in wild species has been illegal since 1967, some ranchers still kill jaguars that prey on livestock. Don't let scary tales about *sucuri* (anacondas), which can grow to 30 feet in length, worry you. Sightings of the snakes are extremely rare and instances of them preying on humans are even rarer.

When to Go

October is the beginning of the Pantanal's rainy season, which peaks in March but lasts through May (later in El Niño years). The land is much greener in the rainy season, but the wildlife is harder to spot. In the dry season (July–October), when some trees shed their leaves and grasses die, mammal sightings are more frequent. As the waters continue to disappear, fish get caught in the remaining pools and attract birds, meaning that the best fishing season is May–October. *Piraputanga* and *dourado* are the most prized catches, but the abundant *pacú, pintado,* and *traíra* are also popular. Piranhas are endemic to the area, but much like caimans, seldom cause trouble—they only attack animals or humans with open wounds.

Health Concerns

Malaria is quite rare in tourist areas. Yellow fever is of greater concern. It's best to get a yellow fever shot before arriving, but if you decide to travel at the last minute, it is possible to get shots at the airport; all airports have a Ministry of Health booth (open 8–5). Dengue fever, for which there is no vaccination or preventive medication, has also appeared around the Pantanal during summer. The best way to prevent it is to avoid being bitten by mosquitoes. Pousadas and hotels in the Pantanal have insect-tight screened windows, doors, and verandas. Use strong insect repellent at all times. For more information, *see* Health *in* Smart Travel Tips A to Z.

Navigating

The Pantanal is accessible by car and boat, but flights are the most popular—and easiest—mode of arrival. Main airports are in Campo Grande, Corumbá, and Cuiabá. Cuiabá is also the starting point to trips to Chapada dos Guimarães. Tour guides are indispensable for getting around—you're not allowed to enter the Pantanal Wetlands without a guide. Many hotels, inns, and pousadas offer the services of good, reliable tour guides. The best ones are those who were born in the region; check ahead of time to make sure the guide speaks English.

Cuiabá

㉗ *1,130 km (700 mi) west of Brasília, 1,615 km (1,000 mi) northwest of São Paulo.*

The northern gateway to the Pantanal Wetlands, Cuiabá is also the southernmost gateway to the cerrado and the Amazon beyond. You can visit one of several museums while you're waiting for a tour into the wetlands or take a jaunt to Chapada dos Guimarães, a mountain range with impressive gorges, waterfalls, and vistas. The capital of Mato Grosso, Cuiabá is well known for being the hottest city in Brazil: mean annual temperature is a sizzling 27°C (81°F). Daily highs surpass 45°C (113°F) several times during the year. The city name comes from the Bororo native people, who lived in the area—it means "place where we fish with spears." It was originally settled in the 18th century, when gold was found in the nearby rivers.

The **Museu História Natural e Antropologia** displays everything from ancient Indian artifacts to contemporary art. ⊠ *Palácio da Instrução, Praça da República* ☎ *065/3321–3391* 🎟 *R$5* ⊙ *Weekdays noon–6, Sat. 8–noon.*

The **Museu de Pedras Ramis Bucair** has a stunning collection of local fossils and stones, including what's purportedly a meteorite. ⊠ *Rua Galdino Pimentel 155, Calçadão, northeast of main Sq.* 🎟 *R$5* ⊙ *Weekdays 8:30–5:30.*

🕑 **Museu do Rio Cuiabá,** on the west bank of Cuiabá River, has maps and models of the river. The **Aquário Municipal** (Municipal Aquarium), with typical fish of the Pantanal, is here. ⊠ *Av. Beira Rio s/n, Porto* ☎ *065/3617–0928 or 65/3617–0929* ⊙ *Tues.–Sun. 9–5.*

Morro da Luz, a hill in downtown Cuiabá, has gardens and a beautiful view of the city. ⊠ *Av. Tenente Coronel Duarte.*

Where to Stay & Eat

$$$ ✕ **Morro de St. Antônio.** This surf-and-turf place has a Polynesian vibe and caters to a yuppie crowd. Many entrées are enough for two people. Dinner is served nightly until 1 AM. It's a good place to drink and be merry into the wee hours on weekends. ⊠ *Av. Isaac Póvoas 1167, Centro* ☎ *065/3622–0502* ▤ *AE, DC, MC.*

$$ ✕ **Getúlio Grill.** If you've had your share of fish from the Pantanal, this is a good choice. The menu is full of churrasco, but other options such as steak parmigiana are highly recommended. There is a dance club on the second floor. ⊠ *Av. Getulio Vargas 1147, Goiabeiras* ☎ *065/ 3624–9992* ◷ *Closed Mon.* ▤ *AE, DC, MC, V.*

★ ¢–$ ✕ **Peixaria Popular.** This is the place in town for Pantanal fish; don't miss the delicious *piraputanga,* either prepared in a stew or fried. Other options are the *pintado* (a large freshwater fish) and *pacu* (a smaller, piranhalike fish). All orders include a side serving of *pirão* (a thick fish gravy with cassava flour) and *banana frita* (fried bananas). ⊠ *Av. São Sebastião 2324, Goiabeiras* ☎ *065/3322–5471* ▤ *DC, MC, V* ◷ *No dinner Sun.*

¢–$ ✕ **O Regionalíssimo.** In the same building as the Casa do Artesão (⇨ Shopping, *below*), this self-service eatery has regional cuisine and Brazilian staples such as rice and beans. ⊠ *Av. 13 de Junho 38, Porto* ☎ *065/ 3623–6881* ▤ *DC, MC, V* ◷ *Closed Mon. No dinner.*

$$–$$$ ✕▦ **Paiaguás Palace.** Rooms are simple and small but charming. The top-floor restaurant ($), which has a buffet of international fare, is highly regarded by local businesspeople and has good views—on clear nights you can see the plains. Location is one of the main draws of this hotel; it's right in the business district with easy access to the airport. ⊠ *Av. Rubens de Mendonça 1718, Bosque da Saúde* ☎ *065/3642–5353* 🖷 *065/3642–2910* ⊕ *www.hotelpaiaguas.com.br* ⤶ *121 rooms* ⚘ *Restaurant, gym, bar, sauna, swimming pool, Internet room, business services, travel services* ▤ *AE, DC, MC, V* ⑩ *CP.*

$–$$ ▦ **Eldorado Cuiabá.** A vision in glass and brass (but no gold, as the name would suggest), this hotel has some of the best rooms in town. The pleasant decor, air-conditioning, and cable TV are a departure from the typically sparse Pantanal fazendas. ⊠ *Av. Isaac Póvoas 1000, Centro, 78045-640* ☎ *065/3624–4000 or 0800/17–1888* 🖷 *065/3624–1480* ⊕ *www.hoteiseldorado.com.br/hcuiaba.htm* ⤶ *147 rooms, 6 suites* ⚘ *Restaurant, cable TV, pool, bar, shops, Internet room, business services, convention center, meeting rooms* ▤ *AE, DC, MC, V* ⑩ *CP.*

Nightlife

Toward the newer part of the city, along Avenida C.P.A. and side streets, there are many sports bars and nightclubs. If you're looking for a wholesome evening, try one of the many ice-cream parlors, such as **Alaska** (⊠ Av. Alziro Zarur, 148, Boa Esperança ☎ 065/3627–1144). **Entretanto** (⊠ Rua Mal. Floriano 401 ☎ 065/3623–3786) has tables in a tree-lined garden and has daily performances of Brazilian and international pop music.

Shopping

For Indian handicrafts try the shop run by the Brazilian Indian agency FUNAI: **Artíndia** (✉ Rua Pedro Celestino 301 ☎ 065/3623–1675). For wicker, cotton, and ceramic crafts from local artists, go to **Casa do Artesão** (✉ Rua 13 de Junho 38 ☎ 065/3321–0603). The shop inside the **Museu de Pedras Ramis Bucair** (✉ Rua Galdino Pimentel 155, Calçadão) sells semiprecious stones, such as emeralds, tourmalines, and agates. **Goiabeiras Shopping** (✉ Av. Lava Pés 500, Duque de Caxias ☎ 065/3624–4760) has more than 50 shops of all kinds.

en route   Along the road to Chapada dos Guimarães from Cuiabá, you pass the **Portão do Inferno** (Hell's Gate; ✉ 30 mi/48 km northeast of Cuiabá), a scenic viewpoint over the chasm that was created as Rio Cuiabá's waters eroded the mesa.

Side Trips from Cuiabá

The areas in and around the **Parque Nacional Chapada dos Guimarães** are the most popular attractions in the region after the Pantanal. Traveling northeast of Cuiabá, you see the massive sandstone formations from miles away, rising 3,000 feet above the flat cerrado landscape. The **Cachoeira Véu de Noiva** (Bridal Veil Falls), with a 250-foot freefall, is the most impressive of the five falls in the park. You can enjoy lunch at the nearby open-air restaurant. Beyond this point there are hills, caves, more falls, and archaeological sites. The **Circuito das Cachoeiras** (Waterfalls Circuit) is a set of seven waterfalls 2 mi (3.5 km) from the visitor center.

If you have time, arrange a guided visit to **Caverna Aroe Jari** (✉ 40 km from Guimarães Town). The cave's name means "home of souls" in the Bororo language. This mile-long sandstone cave (one of Brazil's largest) can only be reached after a 4.8-km (3-mi) hike through the cerrado. Walk about 30 minutes beyond the Caverna Aroe Jari to **Gruta da Lagoa Azul** (Grotto of Blue Lagoon), a crystal-clear water lagoon (bathing is prohibited). Visits are limited to 50 people a day. At the **Cidade de Pedra** (Stone City), is a huge formation of rocks and canyons carved by wind and rain inside the park. There are two great red walls that echo at each other. To get here, take MT-251 northeast of Guimarães Town.

Contact **Ecoturismo Cultural** (✉ Praça Dom Wunibaldo 464 ☎ 065/3301–1393) to arrange for a tour guide in the park. Packages are R$80 per person. Book in advance if you plan on going in July, during summer or holidays.

✉ *Visitor center off MT 251 at Km 51, 40 mi (74 km) north of Cuiabá* ☎ *065/3301–1113* 🎫 *R$3* 🕐 *Daily 8–5.*

After navigating the steep and winding MT 251 through breathtaking canyons to reach the top of the mesa, you discover the pretty **town of Chapada dos Guimarães** (✉ 8 mi/13 km east of national park), which still retains some of its colonial charm. If you're going to Chapada dos Guimarães around the second fortnight of June, don't miss the **Winter Festival**, with art and music workshops and various concerts with local artists. The **Igreja de Nossa Senhora de Santana do Sacramento** (✉ Praça

OTHERWORLDLY VISITORS

MANY BELIEVE THAT THE CERRADO *and the Chapada dos Guimarães (south of the 14th parallel) are landing spots of choice for UFOs. This assertion goes back to Brasília's early days, when an air force officer claimed that his weekend home just outside the city was one such spot. A popular story in the Chapada tells of a bus left powerless for several minutes after being encircled by beams of colored light.*

In 1996 officials in Barra do Garças, 420 km (260 mi) northwest of Brasília on the Goiás–Mato Grosso border, designated 12 acres for the world's first UFO "airport"—the Interspace Aerodrome. Though the aerodrome was never built, the publicity it received fueled the notion that the cerrado is a hotbed of UFO activity.

In mid-1997 members of a small farming community 258 km (160 mi) northeast of Cuiabá were convinced that a local farmer and his son were hiding aliens

after a fiery ball was seen to crash on their property. The next year people all over the west, from Campo Grande to Cuiabá, reported seeing a large shiny cylinder pass silently overhead. Other mass and individual sightings have been reported, as have alien abductions. Many cerrado residents will warn you to beware of nighttime attacks . . . not by jaguars, but by aliens.

Many people and religious fanatics of the Osho Lua sect believe that Alto Paraíso de Goiás will be the capital of the world after the apocalypse. They claim the region hides the world's biggest diamond, which attracts "energetic vibrations."

D. Wunibaldo ☏ No phone) is a handsome colonial church (c. 1779) with some exceptional gold-plated interior flourishes. It's open daily 7–9. In 1972 satellite images proved that the continent's true center was not in Cuiabá, where a monument had been built, but at **Mirante do Centro Geodésico** (✉ 8 km/5 mi southwest of town) on the mesa's edge. If the geodesic center doesn't hold spiritual meaning for you, come for the fantastic view—on a clear day you can see as far as the Pantanal.

Where to Stay & Eat

$-$$ ✕ **Morro dos Ventos.** The fantastic scenery at this restaurant right on the edge of a cliff matches the fantastic regional dishes such as *vaca atolada*, or beef ribs served in cooked cassava chunks (literally "cow stuck in the mud"). The restaurant is in a condominium complex; parking is R$5. ✉ *Av. do Penhasco (Rua 17); take the road to Campo Verde, ½ mi/1½ km east of town* ☏ *065/3301–1030* ⌕ *Reservations essential* ▭ *DC, MC* ☾ *No dinner.*

¢-$ ✕ **Nivo's Fogão Regional.** True to its motto, QUALIDADE: INGREDIENTE FUNDAMENTAL DE BOA COZINHA, which translates as "quality: the basic ingredient of good cooking," this restaurant has delicious fish entrées such as pacu and *dourado*. Entrées are always served with pirão and *farofa* *de banana* (cassava flour with bananas). ⊠ *Praça Dom Wunibaldo 63* ☎ *065/3791–1284* ⊟ *V* ☺ *Closed Mon. No dinner.*

$ ⊡ **Pousada Penhasco.** Clinging to the mesa's edge, this small resort may be far from the Chapada dos Guimarães's town center, but it has tremendous views of the cerrado. The sunny rooms are in cabins scattered about the property. All rooms have access to verandas with great vistas. The staff frequently arranges soccer matches at the on-site field and en masse outings to area sights. ⊠ *Av. Penhasco s/n, Bom Clima* ☎ *065/3624–1000 in Cuiabá* ☎🖨 *065/3301–1555* ⊕ *www.penhasco.com.br* 🛏 *40 rooms* ⚘ *Restaurant, cable TV, Internet room, 2 pools, sauna, bicycles, hiking, soccer, bar, playground, meeting rooms; room phones* ⊟ *V* ⊠⃓ *CP.*

$ **Solar do Inglês.** Great care is taken with the decor at this charming hotel full of antiques and with a nice garden; the hotel's motto is "Enjoy Chapada dos Guimarães with an English touch." A delicious afternoon tea is served at 5 PM. Some rooms have fireplaces. ⊠ *Rua Cipriano Curvo 142* ☎ *3301–1389* ⊕ *www.chapadadosguimaraes.com.br/solardoingles* 🛏 *7 rooms* ⚘ *In-room safes, bar, sauna, pool; no kids under 14* ⊟ *V.*

Porto Jofre

🟤28 *236 km (147 mi) south of Cuiabá.*

The hotels here are some of the closest to the Pantanal Wetlands. There are many well-trained guides in town, who have lived here all their lives. (Be sure to specify if you need an English-speaking guide.) The Rodovia Transpantaneira (MT 080) was originally planned to cut a north–south line through the Pantanal. Lack of funds and opposition from environmentalists resulted in a stalemate. Today the road dead-ends at the banks of the Cuiabá River, in a village called Porto Jofre, about 150 km (93 mi) south of the town of Cuiabá. Still, the Transpantaneira makes it possible to observe the abundant fauna and plush vegetation of the northern part of the wetlands. A large number of fazendas and pousadas organize popular activities such as fishing and photo safaris.

This "highway" is actually a dirt road with some 125 log bridges, some of which have caved in when cars passed over them. Traversing the Transpantaneira is time-consuming and relatively dangerous. It's best to join an organized tour; leave the driving to experienced guides in four-wheel-drive vehicles.

Where to Stay

$$ ⊡ **Pousada Araras EcoLodge.** Rooms are impeccably clean at this ecolodge,
Fodor's Choice and the restaurant serves great Pantanal fish. Environmental education
★ and awareness is the motto here: this pousada goes the extra mile to keep the environmental impact of tourism to a minimum and explains why and how they do it. One highlight is the 3,000-foot wooden walkway over the wetlands that ends on a 75-foot-high lookout, well above the treetops. From there you have a bird's-eye view of the surroundings. There's a two-day minimum stay, which leaves you time to join the trekking, canoe, horseback, or other tours of the area. ⊠ *Km 33, Rodovia Transpantaneira, Pixaim* ☎ *065/3682–2800 or 65/9603–0529* 🖨 *065/3682–1260* ⊕ *www.araraslodge.com.br* 🛏 *19 rooms* ⚘ *Restau-*

*rant, pool, boating, marina, fishing, hiking, horseback riding, bar, air-
port shuttle; no room phones, no room TVs* ▤ *AE, DC, MC, V* ❙◯❙ *FAP.*

$–$$ ▥ **Pantanal Mato Grosso Hotel.** Rooms at this Best Western chain may
be sparsely decorated but are comfortable enough to make your stay
pleasant. The hotel arranges fishing expeditions, guided horseback tours
and hikes, and visits to the Campo Largo ranch, an adjoining working
ranch owned by the hotel. ✉ *Km 65, Rodovia Transpantaneira, Pix-
aim* ☎▤ *065/3391–1324 or 65/3628–1500* ⊕ *www.hotelmatogrosso.
com.br* ↵ *36 rooms* ♨ *Restaurant, pool, boating, marina, fishing, bicycles, hiking, horseback riding, airport shuttle, airstrip; no room TVs*
▤ *DC, MC* ❙◯❙ *FAP.*

Campo Grande

➋➒ *1,025 km (638 mi) west of São Paulo, 694 km (430 mi) south of Cuiabá.*

Campo Grande is the gateway to the southern Pantanal and to the
water-sports-rich areas around Bonito. Nicknamed the Cidade Morena
(Brunette City) because of the reddish-brown earth on which it sits, this
relatively young city (founded in 1899) was made the capital of Mato
Grosso do Sul in 1978, when the state separated from Mato Grosso.
Campo Grande's economy traditionally relied on ranching, but in the
1970s farmers from the south settled in the region, plowed the flat lands,
and permanently changed the landscape. Today, ecotourism is gaining
on agriculture as the main industry. The Brazilian Health Ministry rec-
ommends that tourists take the yellow fever vaccination 10 days before
going to Campo Grande.

It is worth going to **Mercado Municipal** (✉ Rua 15 de Novembro) to
try the typical *sopa paraguaia* (Paraguayan soup), which, despite its
name, is a corn pie with cheese, onions, and spices. The market is open
daily 8–6.

To get acquainted with Mato Grosso's indigenous population, which
includes more than 50,000 Terenas, Kaiowas, Guaranis, and Kadiweu,
visit the **Memorial da Cultura Indígena**, a 25-foot-high bamboo *maloca*
(Indian hut) built in the middle of an urban Indian reservation (Aldeia
Marçal de Souza), the first urban reservation in Brazil. You can shop
for pottery and tapestries. The reservation is in the Tiradentes neighborhood. ✉ *BR 262, exit to Tres Lagoas* ☎ *067/3341–6729.*

The **Museo Dom Bosco,** known as the Museu do Índio, has more than
5,000 indigenous artifacts of the Bororo, Kadiweu, and Carajás tribes.
Noteworthy are the taxidermy exhibits of the Pantanal fauna and the
formidable seashell collection (with 12,000 pieces). Don't miss the collection of 9,000 butterflies from all over the world, and the bug room,
whose walls are covered from floor to ceiling with insects. ✉ *Rua
Barão do Rio Branco 1843* ☎ *067/3312–6491* ↵ *R$3* ◷ *Tues.–Sat.
8–6, Sun. 8–noon and 2–6.*

Where to Stay & Eat

¢–$$$ ✕ **Radio Clube.** One of the fanciest places in town, this restaurant/
nightclub adds some energy to the somewhat lifeless Praça da República.

THE BRAZILIAN SAVANNA

BRAZIL'S VAST *CERRADO* (SAVANNA) is the most biologically rich grassland in the world. More than 100,000 species of plants are found in this 500-million-acre (200-million-hectare) territory that covers about 25% of Brazil, and nearly 50% of them are endemic to Brazil. Its small trees, shrubs, and grasses are adapted to the harshness of the dry season, when temperatures in some parts rise well above 38°C (100°F) and humidity drops to a desert low of 13%. Palm species usually stand out among the shrubby vegetation— thick bunches of buriti usually grow around springs and creeks. Cacti and bromeliads are also abundant. Look also for the pequi, a shrub that produces berries used in local cuisine, which are called *souari* nuts.

Unfortunately, only about 2% of the cerrado is protected. Since development— mostly in the form of soy and corn farming and cattle ranches—it has become harder to spot such species of cerrado wildlife as deer, jaguars, and giant anteaters. Emus, however, can be seen wandering through pastures and soybean plantations.

You can stop by for a drink or a meal of Continental fare. ⊠ *Rua Padre João Crippa 1280* ☎ *067/321–0131* ⊟ *AE, DC, MC, V* ⊘ *Closed Mon.*

¢–$$ **Fodor'sChoice** ★ ✗ **Fogo Caipira.** This is *the* place for regional cuisine. The standout here is the *picanha grelhada na pedra* (grilled picanha steak). The *carreteiro* (rice with sun-dried meat) is also recommended. Call ahead for stuffed pacu. ⊠ *Rua José Antôonio Pereira 145, Centro* ☎ *067/3324–1641* ⊟ *DC, MC, V.*

¢ **Soba Shimada.** A typical Japanese restaurant, Soba Shimada serves *soba* (wheat-noodle soup with pork or chicken, eggs, and coriander) throughout the year, though it is traditionally served on New Year's Eve in Japanese communities. The soup is meant to ensure prosperity and longevity. The Japanese have a big influence in Campo Grande, having immigrated from Okinawa in the beginning of the 19th century to work on the city's railway. ⊠ *Av. Mato Grosso 621* ☎ *067/3321–5475* ⊘ *No lunch* ⊟ *No credit cards.*

$ **Jandaia.** The Jandaia is so thoroughly modern that it almost seems out of place in this wild-west town. Though it has little character—it's geared toward businesspeople, so convenience wins over aesthetics—it does have all the facilities and amenities you'd expect at a deluxe hotel. The upscale Imperium restaurant, on the second floor, serves international fare with Brazilian options. ⊠ *Rua Barão do Rio Branco 1271, 79002-174* ☎ *067/3321–7000* 🖨 *067/3321–1401* ⊕ *www.jandaia. com.br* ⛵ *140 rooms, 10 suites* ⎝ *2 restaurants, pool, gym, bar, meeting room* 🚭 *AE, DC, MC, V.*

$ **Novotel.** This clean hotel is not terribly sophisticated, with basic decoration. Rooms, although a bit small, are fully equipped with standard features. Showers are a high point, with excellent water pressure. Service is good, and the Internet connection is fast. ⊠ *Av. Mato Grosso 5555, Jardim Copacabana* ☎ *067/3326–1177 or 0800/703–7000* 🖨 *067/3326–6633* ⊕ *www.accorhotels.com.br* ⛵ *87 rooms* ⎝ *Restaurant, cable TV, pool, game room, Internet room, no-smoking rooms* 🚭 *AE, MC, V.*.

¢–$ 🏨 **Metropolitan.** Near Avenida Afonso Pena, this hotel is popular with business travelers. Rooms are nicely decorated. The tile floors make the rooms feel extra cool—you might even forget to turn on the air-conditioning. ⊠ *Av Pres. Ernesto Geisel 5100, 79006-000* ☎ *067/3389–4600* 🖨 *067/3389–4601* ⊕ *www.hotelintermetro.com.br* ⛵ *80 rooms* ⎝ *Cable TV, pool, bar, meeting room, Internet* 🚭 *AE, DC, MC, V.*

Nightlife

Campo Grande is wilder than Cuiabá; parts of town (particularly the area near the bus station) are downright dangerous and best avoided at night. On the better side of the tracks is **Choperia 4 Mil** (⊠ Av. Afonso Pena 4000 ☎ 067/3325–9999), a microbrewery that caters to an eclectic crowd of all styles and ages. It's open for drinks and snacks Wednesday–Sunday from happy hour until after midnight. The dance club **D-Edge Club** (⊠ Rua Arthur Jorge 326 ☎ 067/3324–2861) plays mostly American dance and electronic music and is frequented by a young trendy crowd. It's open until the last customer leaves.

Shopping

For baskets of all shapes, beautiful wood handicrafts, and interesting ceramics made by Pantanal Indians, head to **Casa de Artesão** (⊠ Rua Calógeras 2050, at Av. Afonso Pena ☎ 067/3383–2633). It's open weekdays 8–6 and Saturday 8–noon. The **Feira Indígena,** adjacent to the Mercado Central and just across Avenida Afonso Pena from the Casa de Artesão, is a good place to shop for locally made crafts. It's open Tuesday–Sunday 8–5. The massive **Shopping Campo Grande** (⊠ Av. Afonso Pena 4909) has everything you'd expect in an American- or European-style mall, but the many boutiques are what makes it shine.

Bonito

30 *277 km (172 mi) southwest of Campo Grande.*

The hills around this small town of 15,000, whose name rightly means "beautiful," are the on the southern edge of the Pantanal, not too far from the Bodoquena Mountain range. The route to the Pantanal is longer than from Campo Grande, but you are well compensated with top-notch hotels that starkly contrast with the rustic Pantanal lodgings. In Bonito you can swim and snorkel among schools of colorful fish in the headwaters of several crystal-clear rivers. Fishing, rafting, rappelling, hiking, and spelunking are popular activities in this area. Tour guides can be hired on Bonito's main avenue.

At **Parque Ecológico Baía Bonita** you can go snorkeling along a 1-km (½-mi) section of the Baía Bonita River, where you can see an incredible diversity of Pantanal fish. You can also swim in the river or jump on a trampoline. A small museum describes the region's ecosystems. Equipment rental and lunch are included in the admission price. ⊠ *Road to Jardim, at Km 7* ☎ *No phone* ✆ *R$115* ⊙ *Daily 9–5.*

The 160-foot-deep **Gruta do Lago Azul** (Blue Lagoon Grotto) has a crystal-clear freshwater lake at the bottom and smaller side caves in the calcareous rock. The best time to visit is from mid-November to mid-January, at around 8:30 AM, when sunlight beams down the entrance, reflecting off the water to create an eerie turquoise glow. See stalagmites and stalactites in various stages of development. ⊠ *Fazenda Jaraguá, road to Campo dos Índios, 12 mi (20 km) west of Bonito* ☎ *No phone* ✆ *R$25* ⊙ *Daily 9–5.*

The approximately 1½-hour rafting trip on the **Rio Formoso** takes you through clear waters and some rapids while you observe the fish and the birds of the Pantanal. You might also see and hear bands of *macaco-prego* (nail monkeys), the region's largest primates. The tour ends at Ilha do Padre (Priest's Island), where there's a complex of waterfalls emerging through thick riverine vegetation. To best appreciate this attraction, make sure there hasn't been any rain in the previous days—the river gets quite muddy. ⊠ *Hotel Fazanda Cachoeira, 11 km (7 mi) east of Bonito on road to Ilha do Padre* ☎ *067/3255–1213* ✆ *R$50* ⊙ *Tours by appointment.*

Where to Stay & Eat

$–$$ ✕ **Cantinho do Peixe.** Despite its modest appearance, this establishment is your best choice for Pantanal fish. The highlight is *pintado,* which is prepared in 24 ways. The cheese sauce is a good accompaniment to any of the available fish. ⊠ *Rua 31 de Março 1918* ☎ *067/3255–3318* ▭ *DC, MC, V* ⊙ *Closed Sun.*

$ **Castellabate** This restaurant at the entrance to Bonito specializes in typical dishes and pizza. Try the caiman stew. ⊠ *Rua Coronel Pilad Rebuá 2168* ☎ *067/3225-1713* ▭ *DC, MC, V* ⊙ *Closed Mon..*

★ $$$$ ✕▥ **Zagaia Eco-Resort Hotel.** This resort has international-class facilities. The main building was inspired by the architecture of the Kadiweu Indians. The rooms—in single-story bungalows—are large, with colorful furnishings and native ornaments. Most rooms have great views of the gardens and forest-covered hills that lie beyond the complex. The restaurant serves international fare, but Pantanal fish are always available. ⊠ *Km 0, Rodovia Bonito–Três Morros* ☎ *067/3255–1280, 0800/ 99–4400 for reservations* 🖷 *067/3255–1710* ⊕ *www.zagaia.com.br* 🛏 *100 rooms, 30 suites* ⌂ *Restaurant, refrigerators, cable TV, tennis court, 3 pools, gym, hair salon, massage, sauna, bicycles, hiking, horseback riding, soccer, volleyball, bar, shops, playground, business services, convention center, meeting rooms, airstrip, travel services* ▭ *DC, MC, V* ⦿| *MAP.*

$$ Wetega. Large, luxurious, and expertly designed and landscaped Wetega, opened in 2002, is the standard by which other Bonito hotels are measured. Rooms are large, with tile floors and indigenous-inspired decorative objects. Most rooms have a living room and some have verandas. The design is dramatic, with rustic elements like log beams and rough-cut rocks interspersed with modern lighting and stainless steel. ⊠ *Rua Coronel Pilad Rebuá 679* ☎ *067/3255–1699* ⊕ *www.wetegahotel.com.br* ⬎ *67 rooms, 4 suites* ⚂ *Restaurant, refrigerators, cable TV, in-room safes, pool, hot tub, bar, recreation room, Internet room, laundry, gym, parking (fee)* ▭ *DC, MC, V.*

$ 🏠 **Pousada Rancho Jarinu.** A family business, Rancho Jarinu has friendly owners who go to great lengths to help you feel at home and choose the best tour. The redbrick and tile-roof building helps keep the air cool, a boon in the heat of the tropics. You're just steps from the main business district in Bonito. ⊠ *Rua 24 de Fevereiro 1965, 79290-000* ☎ *067/3255–2094* ⊕ *www.pousadaranchojarinu.com.br* ⬎ *9 rooms* ⚂ *Cable TV, phones, refrigerators, Internet room, pool, travel services* ▭ *DC, MC, V.*

Shopping

The town's main avenue has great handicraft shops with native art and other pieces by local artists. **Além da Arte** (⊠Rua Pilad Rebuá 1966 ☎067/3255–1485) has beautiful bamboo and feather handicrafts and colorful ceramics made by the Kadiweu and Terena peoples.

Miranda

③ *205 km (128 mi) west of Campo Grande.*

This tiny settlement on the Miranda River grew into a city after the construction of the railway linking São Paulo to Corumbá and on to Bolivia. In its heyday the railway was called Ferrovia da Morte (Death Railway) because of the many cattle thieves, train robbers, and smugglers that rode the rails. Since the 1980s the railway has been closed to passengers. A portion of the railway opened for tourist use in January 2006. The *Trem do Pantanal* (Pantanal Train) travels between Campo Grande and Corumbá. The first part of the project, 52 mi (84 km) connecting Corumbá to Porto Esperança, was set to open in November 2005, but at this writing is not yet open. Stretches leading to Corumbá, Aquidauana, Porto Esperança, Miranda, and Piraputanga are pending government investment.

Ecotourism is Miranda's main source of revenue. Comfortable pousadas and farms allow you to get acquainted with the *pantaneiro* lifestyle. The Rio Miranda area has abundant fauna, including a sizable population of jaguars. Here is a great opportunity to practice *focagem,* a local version of a photographic safari: as night falls, guides take you into the Pantanal in 4×4 pickup trucks with powerful searchlights that mesmerize the animals for some time, so you can get a really close look.

Where to Stay & Eat

¢–$ ✕ **Cantina Dell'Amore.** Make this small restaurant your choice for pasta, topped with the owner's original tomato sauce, and fish. You can also try caiman meat here. Owner Angelo Dell'Amore, an Italian expatriate, came to the Pantanal as a professional hunter and later became a caiman breeder. ✉ *Rua Barão do Rio Branco 515* ☎ *067/3242–2826* 🚫 *No credit cards.*

$$$$
Fodor'sChoice
★
▦ **Caiman Ecological Refuge.** This 100,000-plus-acre ranch pioneered the idea of ecotourism in the Pantanal. The service is excellent—from the professional manner of the kitchen and bar staffs to the knowledgeable guides, all of whom hold a degree in biology or a related science and most of whom speak English. Lodges are spread out over the ranch. The main lodge has the nicest common areas. The Baiazinha (Small Bay) lodge, which is surrounded almost entirely by water, is another great choice. Activities include horseback rides through the wetlands and boat trips to islands on the refuge's vast holdings. ✉ *23 mi (37 km) north of Miranda, 146 mi (235 km) west of Campo Grande* 🏠 *Rua Campos Bicudo 98-112, São Paulo 04536-010* ☎ *067/3242–1450, 11/3079–6622 reservations* 📠 *067/3242–1450 or 11/3079–6037* 🌐 *www.caiman.com.br* ➬ *29 rooms* ⚿ *Restaurant, Internet room, pool, boating, bicycles, hiking, horseback riding, volleyball, bar, airstrip, airport shuttle; no room phones, no room TVs* ▭ *AE, DC, MC, V* ⦿ *FAP.*

$–$$$
▦ **Fazenda Rio Negro.** This 25,000-acre farm gained notoriety when a popular Brazilian soap opera (called *Pantanal*) was shot here. The farm now belongs to the Brazilian chapter of Conservation International, which preserves its wildlife and habitat. The good regional food is one lure of this rustic but charming farm built in 1920. Although facilities aren't up to international hotel standards, rooms are comfortable and kept spotless by the attentive staff. The only way to reach this property is by plane (roughly R$650) from either Campo Grande or Aquidauana. ✉ *About 200 km (125 mi) northwest of Campo Grande* ☎📠 *067/3751–5191, 67/3751–5248 reservations* 🌐 *www.fazendarionegro.com.br* ➬ *10 rooms* ⚿ *Restaurant, boating, hiking, horseback riding, airstrip; no room phones, no room TVs* ▭ *No credit cards* ⦿ *FAP.*

¢
▦ **Pousada Águas do Pantanal.** A recommended budget choice in the city, this inn is in a historic house with antique furniture. You receive a warm welcome by the friendly staff and the owner, Fátima, who also runs a travel agency next door. The hearty breakfast, with several kinds of bread, jelly, and pastries, is a rarity in a region where buttered bread and coffee are the norm. ✉ *Av. Afonso Pena 367, Centro, 79380-000* ☎ *067/242–1314* 📠 *067/242–1242* 🌐 *www.aguasdopantanal.com.br* ➬ *17 rooms* ⚿ *Pool, bar, travel services, a/c in every room, room TVs; no room phones* ▭ *AE, MC, V* ⦿ *CP.*

Sports & the Outdoors

The last reluctant ranchers are beginning to see tourism as a viable economic alternative in this region, which means you can visit a working ranch or farm for a day. **Fazenda San Francisco** (✉ BR 262, 36 km/22 mi west of Miranda on BR 262 ☎ 067/3325–6606 🌐 www. fazendasanfrancisco.tur.br) is a 15,000-hectare (37,000-acre) working ranch where you can go on a photo safari in the morning and a boat tour on Rio Miranda in the afternoon. The R$95 fee includes a lunch of rice and beans with beef and vegetables. **Reserva das Figueiras** (✉ BR 262, 20 km/12 mi west of Miranda ☎ 067/9988–4082 Miranda, 062/

3384–9862 Campo Grande ⊕ www.reservadasfigueiras.com.br) has
guided wildlife-sighting trips via canoe on Rio Salobra for R$60.

Corumbá

🕘 *435 km (272 mi) west of Campo Grande.*

This port city on the Rio Paraguai's banks is a couple of miles from the
Bolivian border. Often called the "capital of the Pantanal" because it's
the only municipality within the Pantanal borders, the 100,000-inhab-
itant city itself is not particularly pretty, with the exception of the riverfront area where you can see some 19th-century buildings (which are
National Historic Landmarks) and the wetlands well into Bolivia. Corumbá means "faraway place" in the Tupi language, and the main lures
of this far-flung region are the chartered fishing trips in fully outfitted
riverboats and the yachts that travel up the Paraguay river into the heart
of the Pantanal. Waters are clearest and fish are most concentrated during the dry season (May–September).

Corumbá's most significant historical building, and a Brazilian military
outpost to this day, is **Forte Coimbra.** The fort was built in the late 1700s
overlooking the Paraguay river, which was then the de facto borderline.
This was the westernmost outpost of the Portuguese empire in those days.
Check out the massive British- and American-made cannons and the great
views of the river and adjacent lowlands from one of the four turrets.
To visit the fort, book a tour, as reservation are required. ⊠ *3-hr boat
trip from Porto Morrinhos, which is 72 km (39 mi) southeast of Corumbá on BR 262* ☎ *067/3231–9866* ☒ *Free* ☉ *By appointment only.*

off the beaten path

ESTRADA-PARQUE – The only remaining portion of the first road
into the region, blazed in the late 1800s to bring telegraph lines to the
wild frontier, this 120-km (75-mi) dirt road, which merges with BR
262 near the Rio Miranda, is a great chance to see Pantanal wildlife
outside scheduled tours. Here you can spot caimans, tuiuiús (also
known as jaburu) and other birds, and occasionally deer and
anteaters. Along the way there are several great places for fishing.
Attempt this only with a four-wheel-drive vehicle during the day.
⊠ *BR 262, 8 km (5 mi) south of Corumbá.*

Where to Stay & Eat

¢–$ ✕ **Peixaria do Lulu.** The fare at this family-run restaurant is essentially
Pantanal fish, which can be fried, grilled, or stewed and is served with
several side dishes such as *pirão* (a thick fish gravy with cassava flour).
⊠ *Rua Don Aquino Correia 700* ☎ *067/3231–5081* ☒ *Reservations
essential* ⊟ *DC, MC* ☉ *No dinner Sun.*

¢ 🏨 **Nacional Palace.** This hotel is the best in the region, with comfortable rooms and reliable air-conditioning—an absolute necessity in the
tropical heat. Amenities are few, but service is good, and the staff is helpful in recommending local attractions and tours. ⊠ *Rua América 936,
79301-060* ☎ *067/3231–6868* 🖷 *067/3231–6202* ⊕ *hnacional.com.br*
🛏 *98 rooms* ☐ *Cable TV, pool, bar, playground, Internet room, business services, meeting rooms* ⊟ *AE, DC, MC, V.*

Sports & the Outdoors

Corumbá is known across the country as port of call for comfortable riverboats and yachts with weeklong fishing trips—called locally *barcos-hotel* (hotel boats). Daily sightseeing trips are also available. A great travel agency and tour operator is **Pérola do Pantanal** (☎ 067/3231–1470 ⊕ www.peroladopantanal.com.br), which has several boats and yachts of different sizes, including the largest on the Paraguay river, the *Kalypso*. This luxury riverboat has 28 cabins with air-conditioning, plus a pool, a restaurant, a satellite phone link, and freezers for the fish you catch. The minimum trip is seven days.

BRASÍLIA & THE WEST ESSENTIALS

Transportation

For more information about transportation, *see* Smart Travel Tips A to Z, *at* the front of this book.

BY AIR

Airlines that serve Brasília include American Airlines, British Airways, Air Canada, Gol, Varig, and TAM. The west and the Pantanal towns are served by Gol, Varig, TAM, BRA, and Trip Linhas Aéreas. For airline contact information, *see* Air Travel *in* Smart Travel Tips A to Z.

BRASÍLIA The Aeroporto Internacional de Brasília (BSB), 12 km (7 mi) west of the Eixo Monumental, is considered South America's first "intelligent" airport, with computer-controlled communications and baggage-handling operations.

To get from the international airport in Brasília to the city center, taxis are your only real option (city buses, which cost about R$1, don't have room for your luggage). Trips to the hotel sectors along the Eixo Monumental take roughly 15 minutes and cost about R$30. Double-check costs at the dispatcher booth near the arrival gate, and reconfirm the fare with your driver.

🛫 Airport **Aeroporto Internacional de Brasília** ☎ 061/3364–9000.

THE WEST Major western airports are Aeroporto Santa Genoveva (GYN), in Goiânia; Aeroporto Marechal Rondon (CGB), in Cuiabá; and Aeroporto Internacional de Campo Grande (CGR).

The western airports are all close to their respective cities, so a taxi is your best bet. The fare into Goiânia and Campo Grande is about R$15; into Cuiabá it's R$20.

🛫 Airports **Aeroporto International de Campo Grande** ✉ 7 km (4 mi) west of downtown, Campo Grande ☎ 067/3368–6000. **Aeroporto Marechal Rondon** ✉ 7 km (4 mi) south of Cuiabá ☎ 065/3614–2500. **Aeroporto Santa Genoveva** ✉ 6 km (4 mi) northeast of Goiânia ☎ 062/3265–1500.

BY BUS

BRASÍLIA The interstate bus station is the Estação Rodoferroviária. To make the 14-hour trip to São Paulo, try Real. Itapemirim buses run to and from Rio de Janeiro (17 hours) and Belo Horizonte (11 hours). Expresso São Luiz buses make the 12-hour journey to Cuiabá. Auto Viação Goinésia operates most of the buses between Pirenópolis and Brasília (2½ hours, $3).

Within Brasília, virtually all buses depart from Estação Rodoviária. Route names (usually coinciding with the final destination) and departing times appear on digital displays. Rides within the Plano Piloto cost about R$2. There are also a few air-conditioned express buses, which make fewer stops and cost about R$3.50. Of these, the Terminal Rodoferroviária and Palácio da Alvorada buses are good for sightseeing along the Eixo Monumental.

🚍 Bus Lines **Auto Viação Goinésia** ✉ Terminal Rodoviário L Norte, Brasília ☎ 061/ 3562-0720. **Expresso São Luiz** ☎ 061/3233-7961 or 062/3581-1313 ⊕ www. expressosaoluiz.com.br. **Itapemirim** ☎ 061/3361-4505 or 0800/99-2627 ⊕ www. itapemirim.com.br. **Real** ☎ 061/3361-4555 ⊕ www.viacaoreal.com.br.

🚍 Bus Stations **Estação Rodoferroviária** ✉ Westernmost tip of Eixo Monumental ☎ 061/ 3233-7200. **Estação Rodoviária** ✉ Eixo Monumental, at intersection of Asa Norte and Asa Sul ☎ 061/3223-0557 or 061/3223-3247.

GOIÁS & THE PANTANAL Although the distances in the west are great, buses remain the primary mode of transportation because of high airfares and limited air service. Andorinha has frequent service connecting Cuiabá and Campo Grande (10 hours, R$70); Cuiabá and Chapada dos Guimarães (two hours, R$15); and Campo Grande and Corumbá (seven hours, R$65).

🚍 Bus Lines **Andorinha** ☎ 067/3383-5314.

🚍 Bus Stations **Rodoviária de Campo Grande** ✉ Dom Aquino and Joaquim Nabuco, east of downtown ☎ 067/3383-1678. **Rodoviária de Cuiabá** ✉ Av. Marechal Deodoro, Alvorada, north of city center ☎ 065/3621-2429. **Rodoviária de Goiânia** ✉ Av. Goiás, Ferroviário Norte sector ☎ 062/3224-8466.

BY CAR

Expect to pay at least R$175 a day for a compact car with air-conditioning, including insurance and taxes. Because the roads are in such bad shape, a 15% surcharge is added to car rentals in Campo Grande and Cuiabá. Contacts below are local numbers, for nationwide rental agency numbers, *see* Car Travel, *in* Smart Travel Tips A to Z.

BRASÍLIA Brasília is connected with the rest of the country by several major highways. BR 050 is the shortest way south to São Paulo (1,015 km/632 mi). From the city of Cristalina (113 km/70 mi south of Brasília), it's another 612 km (380 mi) on BR 040 to Belo Horizonte. The westbound route, BR 060, runs to the Pantanal and intersects with BR 153, the north–south TransBrasíliana Highway, which stretches another 1,930 km (1,200 mi) north to Belém in the Amazon. BR 020 runs northeast from Brasília to Salvador (1,450 km/900 mi).

When they were first built, Brasília's wide north–south and east–west multilane highways—with their nifty cloverleafs, overpasses, and exits—allowed quick access to all major points. Nowadays you can expect traffic jams at rush hour. Parking is easy in the residential areas but can be tricky in the commercial sectors.

🚗 Rental Agencies **Avis** ☎ 061/3365-2344 ⊕ www.avis.com.br. **Hertz** ☎ 061/ 3365-2816 ⊕ www.hertz.com.br. **Localiza** ☎ 061/3365-2782 ⊕ www.localiza.com. **Unidas** ☎ 061/3365-2266 ⊕ www.unidas.com.br.

GOIÁS & THE PANTANAL Driving isn't recommended to visit the western attractions, as in some stretches highways are in bad shape and there is heavy truck traffic. Also consider that Brazilian truck drivers are frightening in their disregard for basic rules of the road. Further, getting around on your own by car is difficult without a very good working knowledge of Portuguese. Outside the cities, few people speak English, making it hard to get directions if you get lost. In short, it's best to avoid traveling to and within the west by car.

🚩 Rental Agencies **Avis** ☎ 067/3325-0072 in Campo Grande, 65/3682-7360 in Cuiabá ⊕ www.avis.com.br. **Hertz** ☎ 065/3682-6767 in Cuiabá ⊕ www.hertz.com.br. **Localiza** ☎065/3624-7979 in Cuiabá ⊕www.localiza.com. **Unidas** ☎067/3363-2145 in Campo Grande ⊕ www.unidas.com.br.

BY TAXI

BRASÍLIA Fares in Brasília are a bit lower than in the rest of the country, and most cabs are organized into cooperatives with dispatchers. It's best to call for one of these "radio taxis," particularly in the evening; unlike those in other Brazilian cities, some offer discounted rates for cabs ordered by phone—inquire when calling.

🚩 **Rádio Táxi Turismo** ☎ 061/3325-3030. **Rádio Táxi Cidade** ☎ 061/3321-8181.

GOIÁS & THE PANTANAL As most of the tourist areas in western cities are compact, you rarely need a cab except for trips to the airport, the bus depot, or to and from your hotel at night. But they're all metered, so you shouldn't have to haggle. They're safe and comfortable, and you can hail them on the street. Tips aren't expected.

🚩 **CooperTáxi** ✉ Campo Grande ☎ 061/3361-1111. **Rádio Táxi Cuiabana** ✉ Cuiabá ☎ 065/3322-6664.

Contacts & Resources

BANKS & EXCHANGE SERVICES

Banking hours are weekdays 11–4 in major cities, 10–3 in the interior. Major banks are equipped with ATMs (dispensing reais), and a few are available 24 hours—for withdrawals limited to R$600. Outside state capitals, most ATMs operate from 8 AM–10 PM. Most ATMs run on the Plus (Visa) network; if your card is only affiliated with Cirrus (MasterCard), plan accordingly. Banco24horas ATMs usually accept all cards, including American Express. See "Money Matters" in Smart Travel Tips A to Z for more information. Banco do Brasil is the best establishment for cashing traveler's checks, with relatively low fees and decent exchange rates. Throughout the region, the better hotels will either exchange money for you (though rates aren't great) or tip you off to the area's best casas de câmbio (exchange houses).

BRASÍLIA 🚩 **American Express** ✉ Beltour, CLS 410, Bl. A, Lj. 29, Brasília ☎ 061/3244-5577. **Banco do Brasil** ✉ SBN, Q. 01, Bl. A, Brasília ☎ 061/3310-2000 ✉Aeroporto Internacional, Brasília ☎061/3365-1183. **BankBoston** ✉ SCS, Q. 06, Bl. A, Lj. 200, Brasília ☎ 061/3321-7714 or 0800/55-1784. **Citibank** ✉ SCS, Q. 06, Bl. A, Lj. 186, Brasília ☎ 061/3225-9250. **Kammoun Câmbio** ✉ SHS, Q. 3, Bl. J, Brasília ☎ 061/3321-1983.

In Pirenópolis Banco do Brasil ATMs are available from 6 AM to 10 PM.

Banco do Brasil's main Cuiabá branch is in the middle of town and is open weekdays 10–4, with ATMs that operate from 6 AM to 10 PM; there are also ATMs at the airport. Several little câmbios line Rua Cândido Mariano, including Guimel He Tour, which is open weekdays 8:30–6 and offers good rates.

All the major banks have offices in the center of Campo Grande, along Avenida Afonso Pena. Try Banco do Brasil, which is open weekdays 10–5; there are also a branch and several ATMs at the airport.

🏦 **Banco do Brasil** ⊠ Av. Afonso Pena at Rua 13 de Maio, Campo Grande ⊠ Av. Getúlio Vargas and Rua Barão de Melgaço, Cuiabá ⊠ Av. Sizenando Jayme 15, Centro, Pirenópolis. **Guimel He Tour** ⊠ Rua Cândido Mariano 402, Cuiabá ☎ 065/3624-1667.

EMERGENCIES

🏛 General Numbers **Ambulance** ☎ 192. **Fire** ☎ 193. **Police** ☎ 190. **Tropical Disease Control Hotline** ☎ 061/3225-8906. **24-Hour Pharmacy Hotline** ☎ 132.

In Brasília, Drogaria Rosário is open 24 hours a day and has delivery service.

🏛 Hospital **Hospital de Base do Distrito Federal** ⊠ S. Hospitalar Sul ☎ 061/3225-0070.

🏛 24-Hour Pharmacy **Drogaria Rosário** ⊠ SHCS 102, Bl. C, Lj. 05 ☎ 061/3323-5901, 061/3323-1818 for deliveries.

There's a late-night pharmacy in Cuiabá near the corner of Avenida Getúlio Vargas and Rua Joaquim Murtinho. In Campo Grande try the late-night pharmacy at the corner of Avenida Afonso Pena and Rua 14 de Julho. Elsewhere in the region, use the 24-Hour Pharmacy Hotline (⇨ *above*).

🏛 Hospitals **Hospital Ernestina Lopes Jayme** ⊠ Rua dos Pirineus, Pirenópolis ☎ 062/3331-1530. **Hospital Santo Antônio** ⊠ Rua Quinco Caldas, Chapada dos Guimarães ☎ 065/3391-1116. **Hospital Santa Casa** ⊠ Rua Eduardo Santos Pereira 88, Campo Grande ☎ 067/3321-5151. **Hospital Santa Casa** ⊠ Praça Seminário 141, Cuiabá ☎ 065/3624-4222.

INTERNET

Internet cafés in Brasília range from about R$6 to R$10 per hour. Iris, in Campo Grande, is one of the few cybercafés in the west and charges R$14 per hour.

🏛 Internet Cafés **Cotidiano Livraria** ⊠ SCLS 201, Bl. C, Lj. 15 a 19, Asa Sul, Brasília ☎ 061/3224-3439. **Media Cyber** ⊠ Brasília Shopping, 1o subsolo G1, Lj. 34/43, Brasília ☎ 061/3036-4202 ⊕ www.mediacyber.com.br. **Iris** ⊠ Av. Afonso Pena 1975, Campo Grande ☎ 067/3384-6002.

MAIL & SHIPPING

Fax services are available at major *correio* (post office) branches and hotels. Most city hotels have full-fledged business centers.

🏛 Express Service **DHL** ⊠ SCS, Q. 06, Bl. A, Suite 1A, Brasília ☎ 061/3225-9263.

🏛 Post Offices **Correio Brasília** ⊠ SBN, Q. 1, Bl. A, Brasília. **Correio Campo Grande** ⊠ Av. Calógeras 2309, at corner of Rua Dom Aquino, Campo Grande ⊠ Rua Barão do Rio Branco, across from bus depot, Campo Grande. **Correio de Cuiabá** ⊠ Praça da República, center of town, just south of tourist office, Cuiabá ⊠ Aeroporto Marechal Rondon, 2nd floor.

TOUR OPTIONS

BRASÍLIA Most hotels have an associated travel agency that arranges tours. Popular excursions include a basic day trip along the Eixo Monumental, a shorter night version with stops at clubs, and an uncanny "mystical tour" to the cult communities around town. ESAT Aerotáxi has 10-minute helicopter tours (R$180 for three people) above the city every Sunday from 9 to 7. MS Turismo has city tours as well as trips into the cerrado. Voe-Tur has a variety of tours.

🚩 **ESAT Aerotáxi** ✉ Monumental Axis at TV Tower ☎ 061/3323-8777 ⊕ www. esataerotaxi.com.br. **MS Turismo** ✉ SHCS/EQS 102/103, Bl. A, Lj. 04/22 ☎ 061/3224-7818. **VoeTur** ✉ Brasília Shopping, SCN, Q. 05, Bl. A, Lj. 235-A ☎ 061/3327-1717.

GOIÁS & THE In Pirenópolis Estação Aventura has bus, bike, or horseback tours of
PANTANAL the ecological spots surrounding the town. Diniz, of Ecotur, is another good Pirenópolis guide who does similar "ecological" trips.

Arriving in one of the Pantanal's gateway cities without having a tour already booked isn't a problem. Just be careful when choosing a guide upon arrival—some budget travelers have had bad experiences. To avoid being overcharged, compare prices. Also be sure your guide has adequate equipment, sufficient knowledge about area wildlife, and good English-language skills.

In southern Pantanal you may choose to book tours out of Bonito, where more than a dozen establishments vie for your business—you will need to contact local agents because all local attractions require booking. PantTour is a reliable operator with good knowledge of the best spots in the region.

Pantanal Adventure in Cuiabá, Pérola do Pantanal in Corumbá, Impacto Turismo in Campo Grande, and Agência AR in Bonito run large tours into the north and south of the Pantanal—including longer river trips in luxurious riverboats (locally known as "hotel-boats") that are equipped with many amenities and comfortable air-conditioned cabins. These boat tours usually stop in fazendas for treks into the wetlands by horseback, 4×4 vehicle, by zodiac, and by foot—whatever it takes to get the best animal sightings. The cost is about R$150 per person, per day, with everything included; most tours last 4–7 days.

🚩 **Agência AR** ✉ Rua Cel. Pilad Rebuá 1184, Bonito ☎ 067/3225-1008 ⊕ www. agenciaar.com.br. **Ecotur** ✉ Rua Emílio 21, Pirenópolis ☎ 062/3331-1392. **Estação Aventura** ✉ Rua da Prata 9, Pirenópolis ☎ 062/3331-1069. **Impacto Turismo** ✉ Rua Padre João Crippa 496, Campo Grande ☎ 067/3325-1333 🖷 067/3384-8179 ⊕ www. impactotour.com.br. **Pantanal Adventura** ✉ Rua Commandante Costa 649, Cuiabá ☎ 065/3333-6352 ⊕ www.pantanaladventure.com.br. **PantTour** ✉ Rua Senador Felinto Müller 578, Bonito ☎ 067/3255-1000 🖷 067/3255-1707. **Pérola do Pantanal** ✉ Rua Manoel Cavassa 255, Corumbá ☎ 067/3231-1460 ⊕ www.peroladopantanal. com.br.

VISITOR INFORMATION

BRASÍLIA Visit the main office of the Federal District Tourism Development Agency (ADETUR). There's a small information kiosk at Praça dos Três Poderes (across from the Panteão da Pátria).

🚩 **ADETUR** ✉ SDC, Centro de Convenções Ulisses Guimarães, 1st floor ☎ 061/3325-5730.

Goiás's AGETUR has a lot of information, but it's far from comprehensive. In Pirenópolis you can collect information at PIRETUR. The staff members in Campo Grande's Morada dos Baís can give you information about everything under the sun in Campo Grande and environs. SEDTUR, in Cuiabá, doesn't have much information; your hotel is probably a better option.

🚩 **AGETUR** ✉ Rua 30 at Rua 4, Centro de Convenções, Goiás ☏ 062/3217-1000 ⊕ www.agetur.go.gov.br/agetur.htm. **Atendimento Turismo** ✉ Praça Central, Bonito ☏ 067/3251-1799. **Morada dos Baís: Centro de Informação Turística e Cultura** ✉ Av. Noroeste at Av. Afonso Pena, Campo Grande ☏ 067/3324-5830. **PIRETUR** ✉ Rua do Bom Fim s/n, Pirenópolis ☏ 062/3331-1299 Ext. 119. **SEDTUR** ✉ Praça da República 131, Cuiabá ☏ 065/3624-9060 ⊕ www.sedtur.mt.gov.br.

Salvador & the Bahia Coast

WORD OF MOUTH

"My favorite [city] was Salvador—it has a unique African/Portuguese flavor, the market is wonderful, the main square is charming, and the artwork in the cathedral is fascinating."

—hdm

"Salvador is a nice city but what I love is the totally virgin, undeveloped 'Cocoa Coast,' which is the region stretching between Ilhéus and Itacaré. . . . It is not full of family resorts, big hotels or much of anything other than mile after mile of gorgeous, totally undeveloped, unspoiled beaches."

—liz

Updated by
Carlos
Tornquist

IN "THE LAND OF HAPPINESS," as the state of Bahia is known, the sun shines almost every day. Its Atlantic Ocean shoreline runs for 900 km (560 mi), creating beautiful white-sand beaches lined with coconut palms—while inland is Parque Nacional da Chapada Diamantina (Chapada Diamantina National Park), with 152,000 hectares (375,000 acres) of mountains, waterfalls, caves, natural swimming pools, and hiking trails. And in Bahia's capital, Salvador, the beat of bongo drums echoing through the narrow cobblestone streets of Pelourinho (the center of the Historic District) is a rhythmic reminder of Brazil's African heritage.

History

Portuguese navigator and explorer Pedro Alvares Cabral's first sight of Brazil—on Easter Sunday, April 22, 1500—was an isolated mountain of about 530 meters (1,600 feet) immediately named *Monte Pascoal* (Mount Easter), 750 km (466 mi) south of Salvador. The Portuguese flotilla soon dropped anchor most likely at what is now the fishing village of Curumuxatiba. The explorers were met by the Tupinambá, who were welcoming and eager to accept gifts and provide food and water. Proceeding up the coast about 130 km (81 mi), the ships landed at what is now Santa Cruz de Cabrália. On a knoll on the Coroa Vermelha beach, the first mass on this new-found land was held. In his journal, the journey's log keeper, Pero Vaz de Caminha, extolled the future colony—"where the land is so fertile that all that is sown will give a bountiful harvest". Within a few years more Portuguese expeditions arrived to comb the coastal forests for highly prized *pau-brasil* (brazilwood) trees, the first of many natural resources to be exploited by the colonial landlords.

In 1549 Tomé de Sousa was appointed Brazil's first governor-general, with orders to establish the colony's capital in Bahia. The deep waters at the mouth of Baía de Todos os Santos (All Saint's Bay) and the nearby hills, which provided a commanding view of the region and protection in case of attack by pirates, indicated a favorable site. Within a few decades, the city of Salvador had become one of the most important ports in the southern hemisphere, and remained so until the 18th century. In 1763 the capital was moved to Rio de Janeiro, and the city lost part of its economic importance and prestige.

Due to its continental dimensions, Brazil's diverse culture is sometimes a mosaic, more often a blend of European, African, and indigenous backgrounds. But in Bahia the historical and cultural influence is predominately African. The demeanor of the large African-Brazilian population (comprising more than 70% of the population), the rhythms with mesmerizing percussion line, the scents on the streets of Salvador immediately evoke the other side of the Atlantic.

Until slavery ended officially in 1888, it is estimated that more than 4 million slaves were brought to Brazil from Africa, and the port of Salvador was a major center of the slave trade. By contrast, only around 600,000 slaves where brought to the United States. This large African slave population and generally lenient attitude of Portuguese masters and the Catholic Church led to greater preservation of African customs

If you have 5 days

Your gateway to Bahia should be **Salvador** ①–⑲, the cradle of 300 years of Portuguese rule in Brazil. On your first night, have dinner at one of the city's best, Trapiche Adelaide, or see an Afro-Brazilian show at Solar do Unháo while you dine. The next day start your Salvadorian cultural immersion early with our Good Walk (⇨ Cidade Alta, *below*). Have a light lunch at Uauá or Escola Senac, then take the **Elevador Lacerda** ③ down to the **Mercado Modelo** ① for an eclectic shopping experience. Move on to the Terminal Marítmo (ferry wharf), and make arrangements for next day's trip to the **Ilha de Itaparica (Itaparica Island)** or **Morro de São Paulo** ⑳, where you can spend a day or two lazing on the beach or snorkeling the reefs. On the fourth day either take a guided tour or, for more freedom, rent a car and traverse the Green Line highway to the former fishing village (now tourist village) of **Praia do Forte** ㉑. During turtle-hatching season (October–May), walk over to Projeto Tamar to help baby turtles find their way to sea. Browse the tiny shops and kiosks, take a sightseeing flight, and, to finish the day, head to the beach for a late-day swim. On the fifth day finish your shopping, explore the pristine forest at Sapiranga Natural Reserve, or go snorkeling or diving on the reefs of Praia do Forte.

If you have 7 days

Follow the itinerary above, but at the end of Day 4 return to Salvador. On the next day take an early flight to **Porto Seguro** ㉗ not too long ago a laid-back fishing village, now a prime tourist destination in the northeast. Spend Day 5 enjoying the local beaches north of town or across Rio Brunhaém in **Arraial da Ajuda** ㉘. Don't miss the *luaus na praia* (beach luaus) that take place almost every day on different beaches. Spend the rest of your time sailing to offshore reefs, diving, or visiting the Atlântica forest at **Estação Vera Cruz** natural reserve, 12 km (8 mi) west of the city. On Day 6, take a bus or rent a car to visit **Trancoso** ㉙ on a bluff overlooking the Atlantic. Formerly a secluded hippie village, it is now a trendy resort with upscale shops and restaurants. Return to Porto Seguro and spend your last day at Curuípe Beach before your flight home.

If you have 10 days

Follow the seven-day itinerary, but on Day 7 fly back to Salvador and take a connecting flight to **Lençóis,** once the center of gold and diamond seekers in Bahia, and the gateway to **Parque Nacional da Chapada Diamantina** ㉙. Go hiking, explore caves, take a swim in natural pools, or go mountain climbing, or just absorb one of Bahia's most beautiful reserves. Join one of the many guided tours or get a rental car to explore on your own. Spend two full days in Chapada Diamantina and return to **Salvador** ①–⑲ on Day 10.

Alternatively, after Porto Seguro go south to Caravelas for a two-day road and sea excursion to visit Parque Nacional Marinho de Abrolhos, for snorkeling, scuba diving, and whale-watching.

8

there than in other countries. The indigenous tribes, forced to work with the Portuguese to harvest pau-brasil trees, either fled inland to escape slavery or were integrated into the European and African cultures.

After slavery was abolished, former slaves became sharecroppers, tenant farmers, or urban laborers. Unlike in the United States and other countries, in Brazil, and especially Bahia, people of African, native Brazilian, and Portuguese descent intermarried—interracial relationships were more the norm than the exceptions. This is reflected in the "melting pot" of cultures today; nearly everyone you meet has ancestors from all three ethnic groups.

Today Bahia faces several challenges. As Brazil's fourth-largest state, it is struggling to juggle population growth and the economic boom that started 50 years ago when oil was found in its territory. In more recent times, tourism—national and international—has emerged as a major economic determinant defining the future of Bahia and its cultural and natural wonders. The race is on to preserve its way of life and its landscapes, especially the remaining patches of Atlantic rain forest, coral reefs, mangroves, and interior sierras. Significant investments have been made from federal and local governments to preserve its natural treasures and its unique mix of Brazilian and African cultures.

Exploring Salvador & Bahia

The State of Bahia is huge, covering nearly 570,000 square km (220,000 square mi). The coast, with its beautiful beaches and vibrant capital Salvador, gets most of the attention. The interior of the state is hilly and drier than the coast. The central and northwest portions are arid and covered with grass- and scrubland. Southern Bahia is more humid, and the formerly forested land is dominated by farms, pastures, and eucalyptus plantations.

Salvador is by far the largest city in Bahia, with about 2.5 million people. The coastal city in the northern part of the state lies on the tip of a peninsula, fronting a bay, the Baía de Todos os Santos. Salvador is the hub for all travel in Bahia.

Bahia's Costa do Coqueiros (Coconut Coast), north of Salvador up to the village of Mangue Seco, on the border of Sergipe State, has 190 km (118 mi) of beautiful beaches. Several large international resorts are on Costa do Sauípe, the single largest tourist development scheme in Brazil.

South of Salvador, from Baía de Todos os Santos and its islands (Itaparica and Tinharé) to Itacaré is the Dendê Coast, so called because this is where you find the African palms that produce the dendê oil used in Bahian cooking. The mid-section of Bahia's coast, around Ilhéus, is known as the Cocoa Coast. Cocoa plantations dominate the landscape and the economy, although not as much as in its heyday during the 1960s.

Farther south, the Discovery Coast, from Santa Cruz de Cabrália to Barra do Caí, has many sites linked with the first Portuguese explorers to arrive in Brazil, including Monte Pascoal and the surrounding national park. The last bit of Bahia's coast heading south is the Whale Coast,

Beaches Warm waters year-round and a continuous lineup of beautiful beaches from south to north make Bahia one of the premier destinations in Brazil for soaking up the sun. The beaches in Salvador are usually crowded and lively, with capoeiristas showing their stunts and vendors hawking wares. The calm-water beaches north and south of Salvador are fringed with palm trees. Many consider the beaches in the south of Bahia to be the most beautiful in Brazil.

8

Bahian Cuisine Bahia's African influence on Portuguese and native Brazilian food has resulted in a very distinct regional cuisine. In particular, coconut milk, *óleo de dendê* (palm oil), and a wide assortment of spices like coriander, garlic, and especially chile peppers (hotter than elsewhere in Brazil) give Bahian cuisine a flavor all its own. And in a state with over 900 km (560 mi) of coastline, it's no surprise that seafood is a staple. For more information about the food of Bahia, *see* the CloseUp "Eating Bahian."

Salvador's Carnival Many argue that Rio's Carnival has become commercial and excessively elaborate, and Salvador is where the party is *really* at. In Salvador, Carnival means dancing night after night for a whole week, instead of the usual four nights elsewhere in Brazil. To call it "lively" would be an understatement: nearly 2 million people crowd the streets. Unique to Salvador's Carnival are the famous *axé* (Brazilian pop) music stars that perform, and the "Afro groups" (led by percussion band Olodum), and *Afoxés*, who parade wearing African-inspired costumes, singing and dancing to a beat called *ijexá*.

Religous Festivals Some religious holidays during the year, such as St. John's festival in June, can be just as lively and intense as Carnival. The slew of religious holidays begins in spirit January 1 with the Bom Jesus dos Navegantes (Festival of the Good Jesus of the Mariners), when hundreds of boats travel through All Saints' Bay carrying the image of the Bom Jesus dos Navegantes from Conceic(cx)ão da Praia church to the chapel at Boa Viagem. Other festivals include St. Peter's and St. Anthony's days in June, St. Rocco's Day in August, and Sts. Cosmo and Damiano's in September. Celebrations start with mass and later become all-out street parties.

Bahian Music Bahia is most popular in Brazil for its gut-wrenching drum beats that came with the African slaves, along with religion and chants. But there's much more to Bahian music. Shortly after MPB (*música popular brasileira*), a combination of bossa nova and samba, swept the country in the 1960s, a local spin-off was created in Bahia, dubbed the Tropicalismo movement, which quickly rose to international notoriety. Tropicalismo spiced up MPB with Bahian-African drum rhythms, the electric guitar borrowed from rock-and-roll music from North America and Europe, and politically charged lyrics. Names such as Gilberto Gil, Caetano Veloso, Gal Costa, Maria Bethânia, who were some of the musicians nicknamed Novo Baianos (New Bahians), are de facto ambassadors of Bahian music. They still draw multitudes to concert halls throughout Brazil and worldwide.

near the towns of Caravelas and Alcobaça. Humpback whales come from the southern Atlantic to the Abrolhos Archipelago offshore to mate and give birth from June to November.

About the Restaurants

The laid-back lifestyle of Bahians is reflected in its food. In urban areas, breakfast is a minor meal—maybe just a cup of coffee with a lot of sugar (typical throughout Brazil) and a sandwich. Lunches are usually casual and not strictly defined by the clock, as the hottest part of the day is not the best for large meals. This is where street and beach kiosks come in handy. Dinner is the main meal, and starts late, usually after 9. Bahians love to eat out, so you'll rub elbows with locals at the many restaurants in Salvador and tourist hot spots. Bahian cuisine is unique and delicious and a definite must (⇨ Top Reasons to Go, *below*). The ever-present *oleo de dendê* (palm oil) is one ingredient that sets it apart from other Brazilian cuisines.

About the Hotels

Lodging options in Salvador range from modern high-rises with an international clientele and world-class service to cozy, often family-run *pousadas* (inns). The one place you'll find big resorts is Costa do Sauípe. Pousadas are usually the only option in remote beaches or in fishing villages. Apartment hotels, where guest quarters have kitchens and living rooms as well as bedrooms, are available in some places. Low-end pousadas may not have air-conditioning or hot water; be sure to ask before you book.

WHAT IT COSTS In Reais				
$$$$	**$$$**	**$$**	**$**	**¢**
RESTAURANTS over R$60	R$45–R$60	R$30–R$45	R$15–R$30	under R$15
HOTELS over R$500	R$375–R$500	R$250–R$375	R$125–R$250	under R$125

Restaurant prices are for a dinner entrée. Hotel prices are for two people in a standard double room in high season, excluding taxes.

When to Go

Peak seasons for Brazilians to travel are from December to March (South American summer) and the month of July, when schools have winter breaks. Most international visitors come in the months of August and September. Make reservations far in advance for stays during these months, especially if you plan to visit during Carnival (February or March). As the weather is sunny and warm year-round, consider a trip in the off-season, when prices are lower and the beaches less crowded. Mean temperatures are about 25°C (77°F) during winter (July and August), when there is usually more rainfall, including the occasional tropical downpour. Summer temperatures are a few degrees higher (28°C/82°F), but humidity is somewhat lower.

SALVADOR

Though the city of Salvador, founded in 1549, lost its status as capital of Brazil in 1763 when that honor was given to Rio (and later to

Brasília), it remains the capital of Bahia. At least 70% of its 2,250,000 population is classified as Afro-Brazilian. African rhythms roll forth everywhere—from buses and construction sites to the rehearsals of percussion groups. The scents of coriander, coconut, and palm oil waft around corners, prepared and sold by turbaned women, *baianas,* in voluminous lace-trim white dresses, who take great pride in preserving their Afro-Brazilian culture.

Salvadorians may tell you that you can visit a different church every day of the year, which is almost true—the city has about 300. Churches whose interiors are covered with gold leaf were financed by the riches of the Portuguese colonial era, when slaves masked their religious beliefs under a thin Catholic veneer. And partly thanks to modern-day acceptance of those beliefs, Salvador has become the fount of Candomblé, a religion based on personal dialogue with the *orixás,* a family of African deities closely linked to nature and the Catholic saints. The influence of Salvador's African heritage on Brazilian music has also turned this city into one of the musical capitals of Brazil, with many of its exponents like Gilberto Gil, Caetano Veloso, and Daniela Mercury acquiring international notoriety.

Salvador's industry today is focused on telecommunications and tourism. The still-prevalent African culture draws many tourists—this is the best place in Brazil to hear African music, learn or watch African dance, and see *capoeira,* a martial art developed by slaves. In the district of Pelourinho, many colorful 18th- and 19th-century houses remain, part of the reason that this is the center of the tourist trade. But by no means is Salvador overrun with tourists. Local officials are trying to change that though, and continuous renovation will be part of the city's landscape for years to come.

Exploring Salvador

Salvador sprawls across a peninsula surrounded by the Baía de Todos os Santos on one side and the Atlantic Ocean on the other. The city has about 50 km (31 mi) of coastline. The original city, referred to as the Centro Histórica (Historical Center), is divided into the *Cidade Alta* (Upper City), also called Pelourinho, and *Cidade Baixa* (Lower City).

The Cidade Baixa is a commercial area—known as Comércio—that runs along the port and is the site of Salvador's largest market, Mercado Modelo. You can move between the upper and lower cities on foot, via the landmark Elevador Lacerda, behind the market, or the Plano Inclinado, a funicular lift, which connects Rua Guindaste dos Padres on Comércio with the alley behind Cathedral Basílica.

From the Cidade Histórica you can travel north along the bay to the hilltop Igreja de Nosso Senhor do Bonfim. You can also head south to the point, guarded by the Forte Santo Antônio da Barra, where the bay waters meet those of the Atlantic. This area on Salvador's southern tip is home to the trendy neighborhoods of Barra, Ondina, and Rio Vermelho, with many museums, theaters, shops, and restaurants. Beaches such as Amaralina, Jardim dos Namorados, and Itapuã, north of Forte

Santo Antônio da Barra and along the Atlantic coast, are among the city's cleanest. Many are illuminated at night and have bars and restaurants that stay open late.

Numbers in the text correspond to numbers in the margin and on the Salvador and Salvador Cidade Histórica map.

Neighborhoods

Pelourinho

In colonial Salvador, Pelô, as the locals call it, was the heart of the trade district. *Pelourinho* means "whipping post," which refers to the plaza (Largo do Pelourinho) where runaway slaves were flogged in public. Pelourinho has been undergoing restoration since 1968, but it didn't really take off until 1991. In 1985 the district was honored with UNESCO World Heritage recognition. Walking down the narrow cobblestone alleys lined with colorful, restored *sobrados* (two-story colonial residences) momentarily transports you to the 1700s. Tuesday evenings bring Terça da Benção (Blessed Tuesday), when special services are held in the churches and musical performances happen on almost every corner, including the rehearsals of the famous Olodum percussion group.

Barra

The area around Forte da Barra has many hotels and shops, although the beaches have little sand and the water is sometimes polluted. (Ask about current pollution advisories at your hotel.) Still, it is cleaner than inner-bay beaches. The sidewalks along the oceanfront roads Avenida Oceanica and Avenida 7 de Setembro are packed with joggers and bicyclists on weekends. Sometimes you can catch *capoeiristas* (athletes who "play" *capoeira,* a dancelike martial art) practicing their fluid kicks and spins on Farol da Barra or Morro do Cristo.

Campo Grande

Most buildings in this, one of Salvador's most modern neighborhoods, date from the 1960s when the city experienced renewed growth from oil and mineral trade. The center of the district is Largo de Campo Grande plaza, with Teatro Castro Alves on the west side. During Carnival this is a hub from which you can watch the *trio elétricos* (floats blasting music) and so-called Afro-groups from bleachers installed along Avenida 7 de Setembro.

Tororó

Some fine restaurants and bars make a trip to this mostly residential neighborhood ringing an artificial lake (Dique de Tororó) worthwhile. Eight metal statues of Candomblé saints dot the lake.

Safety

Salvador is no different from most big cities in Brazil—crime is a major concern in most neighborhoods. The Centro Histórico area, especially Cidade Alta during daytime, is one of the safest places in Salvador. There are tourist police on almost every corner. However, precautions are recommended, especially at night. Stick to the main tourist areas and don't walk down streets that appear to be deserted. It's a good idea to stay away from any deserted area, including a beach. At night take a taxi (registered vehicles only—white with blue stripe) to wherever you want to go. Cidade Baixa and the Comércio neighborhood are notorious for petty crime, and pickpocketing is common on buses and ferries and in crowded places.

During Carnival there are *huge* crowds in the streets. If you want to join the street party, do it in an organized *bloco de Carnaval,* an informal association of revelers, which is surrounded by a rope with security guards. Contact Bahiatursa about joining a bloco (⇨ Visitor Information *in* Salvador & Bahia Essentials). If you don't join a bloco, travel in groups of four or more.

Cidade Histórico

The heart of the original colonial city, the Cidade Alta section, incorporates the Comércio and Pelourinho neighborhoods and is a riveting blend of European and African cultures. More than 500 of the 2,982 buildings have been restored, earning Salvador the reputation of having the finest examples of baroque architecture in South America. Along the winding and sometimes steep streets, whose cobbles were laid by slaves, are restored 17th- and 18th-century buildings. Many of the restored buildings are now occupied by restaurants, museums, bars, and shops that sell everything from clothing, film, musical instruments, and handicrafts to precious stones. They are painted in bright colors, which, along with the sounds of vendors, street musicians, and capoeiristas, add to the festive atmosphere.

The Cidade Baixa (Lower City) is the section of historic Salvador that fronts the Atlantic Ocean. Its star attraction is the Mercado Modelo, one of Salvador's landmarks, with dozens of stalls that sell everything from Bahian lace dresses and musical instruments to amulets believed to ward off evil or bring good luck. Around the building gathers a mixed crowd of locals and visitors, impromptu entertainers, fortune tellers, and handicrafts vendors.

In the port of Salvador, the Forte de São Marcelo serves as a backdrop for cruise ships, schooners, and an assortment of small boats jockeying for space. Ferryboats and catamarans leave from different docks for Ilha de Itaparica (Itaparica Island), Morro de São Paulo, and other destinations within Baía de Todos os Santos. The area is busy during the day but is practically deserted at night, especially near the base of the Lacerda Elevator. Take a taxi at night.

A GOOD WALK Early morning is a good time for a walk in Salvador's historic neighborhood, especially during the hot summer months (November–March). Start at **Mercado Modelo** ➊ ▶ when the fresh produce has just been put out. Across the plaza, Terminal Maritimo is the gateway for **Forte de São Marcelo** ➋, the fortress that protected Salvador from the onslaught of pirates and Dutch invaders. Cross Rua Conceição da Praia to get to the lower deck of the **Elevador Lacerda** ➌. The short ride from Cidade Baixa to Cidade Alta takes you to the Municipal Square, with a spectacular view of the Todos os Santos Bay and, unfortunately, also of the

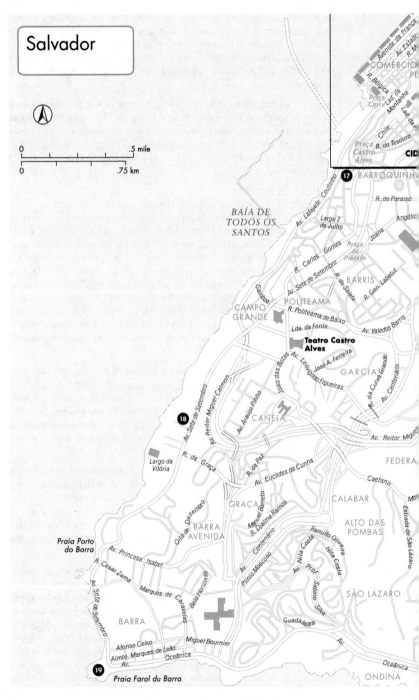

Salvador

.5 mile

.75 km

BAÍA DE
TODOS OS
SANTOS

Avenida da França

R. Estado

R. M

COMÉRCIO

R. Bélgica

PE

Praça
Cayru

Lad. da
Montanha

Chile

Lad. da Fi

Praça
Castro
Alves

R. do Tesouro

17 BARROQUINHA

CID

R. do Paraíso

Av. Lafayete Coutinho

Largo 2
de Julho

Angélic

R. Carlos Gomes

Joana

Praça
da
Piedade

Av. Sete de Setembro

R. do Salete

R. Gen. Labatut

BARRIS

Gamboa

POLITEAMA

CAMPO
GRANDE

R. Politeama de Baixo

Av. Val dos Barris

Lda. da Fonte

**Teatro Castro
Alves**

Av. Leovigildo Figueiras

José A. Ferreira

GARCIA

João das Botas

Av. da Curva Grande

Av. Centenário

18

Av. Sete de Setembro

Av. Reitor Miguel Calmon

Av. Araújo Pinho

CANELA

Av. Reitor Migu

FEDERA

R. da Graça

R. da Paz

Largo da
Vitória

Av. Euclides da Cunha

Caetano

CALABAR

GRAÇA

Manuel Barreto

R. Djalma Ramos

Ranulfo Oliveira

ALTO DAS
POMBAS

Oito de Dezembro

BARRA
AVENIDA

Av.
Centenário

Nila Costa

Nila Costa

Estrada de São Lázaro

Praia Porto
do Barra

Av. Princesa Isabel

R. Cesar Zama

Marques de Caravelas

Belo Horizonte

Av.
Plínio Moscoso

Av. Prof. Sabino Silva

SÃO LÁZARO

Av. Sete de Setembro

BARRA

Afonso Celso

Almte. Marques de Leão

Av. Oceânica

Miguel Bournier

Guadalajara

Av.

Av.
Oceânica

ONDINA

19

Praia Farol du Barra

"temporary" City Hall, an oblong cement building on columns with large, round, yellow pipes around the sides. It was erected around 1987, to be replaced within two years, but is still standing. Also on the square is the **Palácio Rio Branco** ❹. Take Rua da Misericórdia, heading northeast past the Igreja da Misericórdia and onto the plaza at Praça da Sé—named after the original cathedral from 1600s, the Igreja da Sé, which was razed by fire and demolished in 1933. Excavation sites revealing some of the foundations of this building and historical markers dot the area. The next corner on Rua da Misericórdia opens to a larger plaza, the **Terreiro de Jesus** ❺. On your left, at the northwest end, is the 17th-century **Catedral Basílica** ❻. Next to the cathedral is the **Museu Afro-Brasileiro** ❼. From here walk to the south side of the Terreiro de Jesus Square and **Igreja São Domingos de Gusmão da Ordem Terceira** ❽. Proceed through the Praça Anchieta, with its statue of the patron saint of Salvador, São Francisco de Xavier, on a cross, to the 18th-century baroque **Igreja de São Francisco** ❾, the Convento and the Igreja da Ordem Terceira de São Francisco. Continue enjoying the renovated colonial houses—now occupied by shops and restaurants—through the alleys of Rua da Ordem Terceira and Rua Maciel de Baixo onto the famed plaza called **Largo do Pelourinho** ❿. Visit **Fundação Casa de Jorge Amado/Museu da Cidade** ⓫, where you can see memorabilia of the internationally renowned Bahian author of *Dona Flor e Seus dos Maridos* (*Dona Flor and Her Two Husbands*), as well as exhibits on Candomblé. To the north stands the baroque **Igreja de Nossa Senhora do Rosário dos Pretos** ⓬. If you're hungry, good places to finish your tour with a bite to eat is Casa de Gamboa or Escola SENAC.

TIMING & TIPS — Walking this route will take about four hours, longer if you linger in the churches. (Exploring Salvador's churches in full could take the better part of a day.)

WHAT TO SEE — **Catedral Basílica.** The masonry facade of this 17th-century masterpiece ★ ❻ is made of Portuguese sandstone, brought as ballast in shipping boats; the 16th-century tiles in the sacristy came from Macau. Hints of Asia permeate the decoration, attributed to a Jesuit monk from China, a gifted painter. Note the Asian facial features and clothing of the figures in the transept altars; and the intricate ivory-and-tortoise shell inlay from Goa on the Japiassu family altar, third on the right as you enter. The altars and ceiling have a layer of gold—about 10 grams per square meter. ⊠ *Terreiro de Jesus, Pelourinho* 🕾 *071/3321–4573* 🎫 *R$3* 🕘 *Tues.–Sat. 8–11 and 3–6, Sun. 10–1.*

❸ **Elevador Lacerda.** For just a few centavos, ascend 236 feet in a minute in this elevator that runs between the Paço Municipal, in the Upper City, and Praça Visconde de Cayrú and the Mercado Modelo. Built in 1872, the elevator ran on hydraulics until its 1930 restoration, when it was electrified. Bahians joke that the elevator is the only way to "go up" in life. Watch out for pickpockets when the elevator's crowded. ⊠ *West side of Praça Visconde de Cayrú, Comércio* 🎫 *R$0.05* 🕘 *Daily 5 AM–midnight.*

❷ **Forte de São Marcelo.** Jorge Amado jokingly called this doughnut-shaped fortress near the Terminal Marítimo pier, the "belly button of the world," because Bahia's economy essentially revolved around this focal point: the slave trade, the Mercado Modelo, and the port are all clustered practically within arm's reach. The fort, built from 1650 until around 1680 in a mix of medieval and colonial styles, housed the Imperial Army for over 200 years, as they staved off buccaneers and other invaders. Closed off to tourists for many years, it reopened in 2005. Historical tours, about an hour in length, depart from Terminal Maritimo. Inside you can see the armory and soldier's quarters and get a great view of the bay from the lookouts. ⊠ *Av. França, s/n, Comércio* ☎ *071/ 3321–5286* ✉ *R$ 5* ⊗ *By appointment only.*

⓫ **Fundação Casa de Jorge Amado/Museu da Cidade.** The Jorge Amado House contains Bahia's best known and most beloved writer's photos and book covers, as well as a lecture room. Amado lived in the Hotel Pelourinho when it was a student house, and he set the locale of many of his books in this part of the city. Next door is the Museu da Cidade, with exhibitions on African culture, with an emphasis on Candomblé. ⊠ *Largo do Pelourinho, Pelourinho* ☎ *071/3321–0122* ✉ *R$3* ⊗ *Fundação: Mon.–Sat. 9:30 AM–10 PM. Museum: Mon. and Wed.–Sat. 10–5.*

★ ⓬ **Igreja de Nossa Senhora do Rosário dos Pretos.** Built by and for slaves between 1704 and 1796 to honor Our Lady of the Rosary of the Blacks, this church didn't receive due attention outside the local Afro-Brazilian community until long after it was built. After extensive renovation, it is worth a look at the side altars to see statues of the Catholic church's few black saints. African rhythms pervade the services. ⊠ *Largo do Pelourinho s/n, Pelourinho* ☎ *071/3327–9701* ✉ *Free* ⊗ *Weekdays 8–5, Sat 9–5, Sun. 10–13.*

⓰ **Igreja de Nosso Senhor do Bonfim.** North of the Centro Histórico, the Itapagipe Peninsula extends into the bay. Atop a hill is Salvador's iconic Igreja do Bomfim, which is central to African religious traditions because of its patron "saint," Oxalá, the father of all the gods and goddesses in Candomblé mythology. Here each Thursday before the third Sunday in January is the Lavagem do Bonfim ritual; a procession of *baianas*—women dressed in petticoat-puffed white dresses and adorned with turbans and ritual necklaces—comes here to wash the steps with holy water. Built in the 1750s, the church has many ex-votos (wax, wooden, and plaster replicas of body parts), objects of devoted prayer believed to be capable of miraculous cures. Outside the church, street vendors craft a bizarre mixture of figurines, such as St. George and the Dragon, devils, Indians, monks, sailors, and warriors. The church is the source of nationally renowned printed wrist ribbons of Bonfim. Sellers will try to tie one around your wrist with three knots (and sell 20 more to take home to friends), each good for one wish if you wear the ribbon until it falls off, and then throw it into the ocean. Each color represents a Catholic saint and Candomblé deity. The morning mass on the first Friday of the month draws a huge congregation, most wearing white, with practitioners of Candomblé on one side and Catholics on the other. ⊠ *Praça do Senhor do Bonfim, Alto do Bonfim, 8 km/5 mi north of Cidade Histórico* ☎ *071/316–2196* ✉ *Free* ⊗ *Tues.–Sun. 8–noon and 2:30–6:30.*

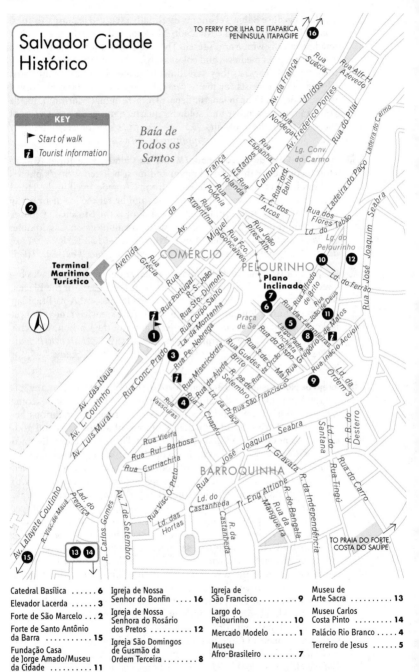

Salvador Cidade
Histórico

★ **8** **Igreja São Domingos de Gusmão da Ordem Terceira.** The baroque Church of the Third Order of St. Dominic (1731) houses a collection of carved processional saints and other sacred objects. Such sculptures often had hollow interiors and were used to smuggle gold into Portugal to avoid taxes. Asian details in the church decoration are evidence of long-ago connections with Portugal's colonies of Goa and Macau. Upstairs are two impressive rooms with carved wooden furniture used for church meetings. ⊠ *Terreiro de Jesus, Pelourinho* ☎ *071/3242–4185* 🎟 *Free* ☉ *Sun.–Fri. 8–noon and 2–5.*

9 **Igreja de São Francisco.** One of the most impressive churches in Salvador, *Fodor's*Choice the Church of St. Francis was built in the 18th century on the site of ★ earlier church burned down during the Dutch invasion in early 1600s. The ceiling was painted in 1774 by José Joaquim da Rocha, a mulatto who founded Brazil's first art school. The ornate cedar-and-rosewood interior writhes with images of mermaids, acanthus leaves, and caryatids—all bathed in gold leaf. Guides say that there's as much as a ton of gold here, but restoration experts maintain there's much less, as the leaf used is just a step up from a powder. At the end of Sunday-morning mass (9–11 and 11–11:45), the lights go off to catch the wondrous subtlety of gold leaf under natural light. The **Convento de São Francisco** (☎ 071/3322–6430), part of the Franciscan order complex at the site, has an impressive series of 37 white-and-blue tile panels lining the walls of the claustrum, each with a scene from Greco–Roman mythology and a moral aphorism in Latin. The **Ordem Terceira de São Francisco** (☎ 071/321–6968), on the north side of the complex, has an 18th-century Spanish plateresque sandstone facade—the only one of its kind in Brazil—that is carved to resemble Spanish silver altars made by beating the metal into wooden molds. ⊠ *Largo Padre Anchieta, Pelourinho* ☎ *071/322–6430* 🎟 *R$3* ☉ *Mon.–Sat. 8–noon and 2–5, Sun. 8–noon.*

★ **10** **Largo do Pelourinho** (Pelourinho Square). Today this small plaza commemorates the day in 1888 when Princesa Isabel, daughter of Dom Pedro II, while her father traveled abroad, signed the decree that officially ended slavery. It was at this spot where runaway or uncooperative slaves were tied to a pillory and publicly beaten, which was legal in Brazil until 1835. The plaza is now the setting for one of the largest and most charming groupings of Brazilian colonial architecture and a thriving cultural renaissance. There are four public stages in Pelourinho, at least two of which have music nightly, all named after characters in Jorge Amado novels. There is usually dancing on Tuesday and Sunday evenings. The **Projeto Pelourinho Dia & Noite** (⊕ www.fundacaocultural.ba.gov.br ☎ 071/ 3320–9358), maintained by FUNCEB (Bahian Cultural Foundation), keeps track of all Pelourinho's music shows and other artistic events, listed on its Web site in Portuguese. It also publishes a monthly schedule, available in tourist offices and hotels. ⊠ *Intersection of Rua Alfredo de Brito and Ladeira do Ferrão, Pelourinho.*

▶ **1** **Mercado Modelo.** Slaves were kept in chains at the basement of this building upon arrival from Africa in the 17th through 19th centuries. The market has seen many changes since it headquartered slave business through the mid-1800s. Today it's a convenient place to buy handicrafts. Bargaining is expected here, for goods like *cachaça* (sugarcane liquor), cashew nuts, pepper sauces, cigars, leather goods, hammocks, musical instruments, African sculptures, and semi-precious stones. *Repentistas* (impromptu folksingers) and fortunetellers gather outside. ⊠ *Praça Visconde de Cayrú 250, Comércio* ☎ *071/3241–2893* 🖻 *Free* ☉ *Mon.–Sat. 9–6, Sun. 9–2.*

★ ❼ **Museu Afro-Brasileiro.** Next to the Catedral Basílica, the Afro-Brazilian Museum has a collection of more than 1,200 pieces of a religious or spiritual nature, including pottery, sculpture, tapestry, weavings, paintings, crafts, carvings, and photographs. There's an interesting display on the meanings of Candomblé deities, with huge carved wood panels portraying each one. The two other museums that share the building are the Memorial de Medicina (Old School of Medicine Memorial) and the Museu Arqueologia e Etnologia (Archaeology and Ethnology Museum); both are closed for extensive renovation that is projected to finish sometime in 2007. ⊠ *Terreiro de Jesus, Pelourinho* ☎ *071/3221–2971* 🖻 *R$3* ☉ *Weekdays 9–5.*

❹ **Palácio Rio Branco.** The building dates back to 1549, when it was the headquarters of the colonial government of Brazil. The current construction, finished in 1919, is the result of several renovations and expansions and has resulted in an eclectic style that leans toward neoclassical. Today it houses Salvador's Chamber of Commerce, the Fundação Cultural (Cultural Foundation of the State of Bahia), and Bahíatursa, the state tourist office. On the first floor there's a small memorial to the state's governors, depicting the last two centuries of local history. Get a great view of Cidade Baixa and the bay from the east-side balcony. ⊠ *Praça Tomé de Souza s/n, Pelourinho* ☎ *071/3241–4333* ☉ *Tues.–Sat. 10–6.*

❺ **Terreiro de Jesus.** The wide plaza lined with churches and 17th-century houses is the heart of historic Salvador. Where nobles once strolled under imperial palm trees, now there is a crafts fair on weekends, and occasionally a group of locals might practice capoeira—a stylized dance-like fight with African origins—to the *thwang* of the *berimbau*, a rudimentary bow-shape musical instrument. ⊠ *Intersection of Rua das Laranjeiras and Rua João de Deus, Pelourinho.*

Cidade Baixa (The Lower City)

This historic district was made up of the port of Salvador and adjoining warehouses and businesses. There's little to interest tourists here—most of the original structures have been demolished and replaced with private and government office buildings from the early 20th century.

⓯ **Forte de Santo Antônio da Barra.** Since 1583 St. Anthony's Fort has stood guard for Salvador. The lighthouse atop the fort wasn't built until 1696, after many a ship wrecked on the coral reefs around Baía de Todos os Santos entrance. Inside the fort, the **Museu Nautico** (☎ *071/264–3296*) has permanent exhibitions of old maps, navigational equipment, artillery, model vessels, and remnants of shipwrecks found by archaeologists off the Bahian coast. An eatery, Café do Farol, is open until 11 PM. ⊠ *Praça*

SPIRITUAL SALVADOR

EVIDENCE THAT BRAZIL IS OFFICIALLY *a Roman Catholic country can be found everywhere. There are beautiful churches and cathedrals—from the colonial to the baroque to the modern—across the nation. Most Brazilians wear a religious medal or two, bus and taxi drivers place pictures of St. Christopher prominently in their vehicles, and two big winter celebrations (in June) honor St. John and St. Peter. For many Brazilians, however, the real church is that of the spirits.*

When Africans were forced aboard slave ships, they may have left their families and possessions behind, but they brought along an impressive array of gods. Foremost among them were Olorum, the creator; Yemanja, the goddess of the rivers and water; Oxalá, the god of procreation and the harvest; and Exú, a trickster spirit who could cause mischief or bring about death. Of lesser rank but still very powerful were Ogun, Obaluayê, Oxôssi, and Yansan, to name but a few.

The Catholic Church, whose spiritual seeds were planted in Brazil alongside the rows of sugarcane and cotton, was naturally against such religious beliefs. As a compromise, the slaves took on the rituals of Rome but kept their old gods. Thus, new religions—Candomblé in Bahia, Macumba in Rio, Xangó in Pernambuco, Umbanda in São Paulo— were born.

Yemanja had her equivalent in the Virgin Mary and was queen of the heavens as well as queen of the seas; the powerful Oxalá became associated with Jesus Christ; and Exú, full of deception to begin with, became Satan. Other gods were likened to saints: Ogun to St. Anthony, Obaluayê to St. Francis, Oxôssi to St. George, Yansan to St. Barbara. On their altars, crosses and statues of the Virgin, Christ, and saints sit beside offerings of sacred white feathers, magical beads, and bowls of cooked rice and cornmeal.

Salvadorans are eager to share their rituals with visitors, though often for a fee (you can make arrangements through hotels or tour agencies). The Candomblé temple ceremony, in which believers sacrifice animals and become possessed by gods, is performed nightly except during Lent.

Temples, usually in poor neighborhoods at the city's edge, don't allow photographs or video or sound recordings. You shouldn't wear black (white is preferable) or revealing clothing. The ceremony is long and repetitive, and there are often no chairs and there's no air-conditioning; men and women are separated.

A pãe de santo or mãe de santo (Candomblé priest or priestess) can perform a reading of the búzios for you; the small brown shells are thrown like jacks into a circle of beads—the pattern they form tells about your life. Don't select your mãe or pãe de santo through an ad or sign, as many shell readers who advertise are best not at fortune-telling but at saying "100 dollars, please" in every language.

Almirante Tamandaré s/n, Barra ☎ *071/3264–3296* 🖃 *R$4* ⊘ *Museum Tues.–Sun. 9–7.*

⑬ Museu de Arte Sacra. Housed in a former Carmelite monastery, the museum and the adjoining **Igreja de Santa Teresa** (St. Theresa Church) are two of Salvador's best-cared-for repositories of religious objects. An in-house restoration team has worked miracles that bring alive Salvador's golden age as Brazil's capital and main port. See the silver altar in the church, recovered from the fire that razed the original Igreja da Sé in 1933, and the blue-and-yellow-tile sacristy replete with a bay view. ✉ *Rua do Sodré 276, Centro* ☎ *071/3243–6310* 🖃 *R$5* ⊘ *Weekdays 11:30–5:30.*

⑭ Museu Carlos Costa Pinto. A collection of more than 3,000 objects collected from around the world by the Costa Pinto family, including furniture, crystal, silver pieces, and paintings, is on display at this museum. Included in the collection are examples of gold and silver *balangandãs* (or *pencas*), chains with large silver charms in the shapes of tropical fruits and fish, which were worn by slave women around the waist. A prized slave was given a chain by her master, who continued to reward loyalty and service with gifts of charms, sometimes freeing the slave after her chain was full. The balangandã usually included a *figa*—a closed fist with a thumb sticking out through the fingers—which, according to African legend, could increase warriors' fertility. In Brazil it's simply considered a good-luck charm. For it to work, though, it must always be a gift. ✉ *Av. 7 de Setembro 2490, Vitória* ☎ *071/3336–6081* 🖃 *R$12* ⊘ *Mon. and Wed.–Fri. 2:30–7, weekends 3–6.*

City Beaches

In general, the farther east and north from the mouth of the bay, the better the beaches. To avoid large crowds, don't go on weekends. Regardless of when you go, keep an eye on your belongings and take only what you need to the beach—petty thievery is a problem. There are no public bathrooms. You can rent a beach chair and sun umbrella for about R$10.

Beaches are listed in geographical order, beginning with Piatã, north of the city on the Baía de Todos os Santos, and then to Praia da Barra, near the peninsula's tip, and northeast to other Atlantic beaches.

Praia Piatã. Heading north and leaving the more built-up areas of the city behind, the first truly clean beach you'll come to is the wide Piatã. Its calm waters and golden sand attract local families. ✉ *northeast of Praia Corsário, along Av. Oceânica Piatã.*

Praia da Barra is a popular beach in Barra that's a convenient option if you're staying in the hotel districts of Ondina and Rio Vermelho, where rock outcroppings make swimming dangerous, and pollution is often a problem. ✉ *Along Av. Oceânica just east of Santo Antônio da Barra, Barra.*

One of the nicest beaches along Avenida Oceánica is **Praia Corsário**, a long stretch popular with surfers and the young crowd. There are kiosks where you can sit in the shade and enjoy seafood and an ice-cold beer or soft drink from the kiosks. ✉ *South of Parque Metropolitan de Pituaçu, along Av. Oceánica and Av. Otávio Mangabeira, Pituaçu.*

Praia Itapuã. Frequented by artists that live in the neighborhood, the Itapuã beach has an eclectic atmosphere. There are food kiosks—including Acarajé da Cira, one of the best places to get *acarajé* (a spicy fried-bean snack) in Salvador—and bars with live music. The area was once a whale cemetery, and bones are still an occasional find. Inland from Itapuã, a mystical freshwater lagoon, the **Lagoa de Abaeté**, and surrounding sand dunes are now a municipal park. Itapuã's dark waters are a startling contrast to the fine white sand of its shores. ⊠ *16 km/10 mi northeast of downtown, Itapuã.*

The northernmost beach in the Salvador municipality along the Avenida Oceánica is **Praia Stella Maris,** popular with surfers and the young crowd. There are myriads of food and drinks kiosks, more than at any other beach— it's the perfect place to sooth your thirst with *água de côco* (coconut water). ⊠ *20 km/12 mi north of downtown, after Itapuã, Stella Maris.*

---

off the beaten path

★

ILHA DE ITAPARICA – The largest of 56 islands in the Baía de Todos os Santos, Itaparica was originally settled because its ample supply of fresh mineral water was believed to have rejuvenating qualities. Its beaches are calm and shallow, thanks to the surrounding reefs, which are avidly sought by windsurfers, divers, and snorkelers. The main port of entry on the north of the island is the town of Bom Despacho, where the ferries from Salvador dock. The best beaches are near the villages of Vera Cruz, Mar Grande, and Conceição, the latter almost entirely owned by Club Med Itaparica.

Instead of buses or taxis, small Volkswagen vans (called *kombis*) provide the most convenient local transportation around the island. You can hail vans and hop from beach to beach along the 40 km (25 mi) of BA-001, the coastal highway that connects Itaparica village on the north part of the island to the mainland via Ponte do Funil (Funnel Bridge) on the southwest side. The drive from Salvador to the island takes about four hours. Bicycle rentals are readily available in the island's towns, so you don't really need a car.

Full-day schooner tours, run by several companies, include lunch and music (R$30–R$50) and depart from the **Terminal São Joaquim** (⊠ Av Oscar Pontes 1051 ☎ 071/3319–2890). You can book your passage at the terminal, or through a travel agency. Ferries to the island run daily 6–midnight from the São Joaquim Terminal; the trip is an hour. Ferry tickets range from R$8 to R$25, depending on the quality of the boat.

Where to Eat

You can easily find restaurants serving Bahian specialties in most neighborhoods. Pelourinho and Barra, full of bars and sidewalk cafés, are good places to start. There are also many good spots in bohemian Rio Vermelho and a slew of places along Orla, the beachfront drive beginning around Jardim de Alah. The regional cuisine leans toward seafood, but some meat dishes should be tried. And, like anywhere else in Brazil, there are *churrascarias* for beef-lovers. One main course often serves two; ask about portions when you order. Beware that regional food is normally spicy and hot.

Brazilian

$$–$$$ ✕ **Casa da Gamboa.** A longtime favorite of Bahian writer Jorge Amado, this is a Bahian cooking institution. *Casquinha de siri* (breaded crab in the shell) comes as a complimentary starter; then try the *peixe com risoto de ostras* (grilled fish with oyster risotto) or the *bobó de camarão* (shrimp stew in cassava flour) followed by a traditional dessert such as *cocada* (sweet coconut cream cake). ⊠ *Rua João de Deus 32, Pelourinho* ☎ *071/3321–3393* ▤ *AE, D, MC, V* ☉ *Closed Sun.*

$$–$$$ ✕ **Maria Mata Mouro.** At this small intimate restaurant, in a *sobrado* (two-story colonial house) right in the Pelourinho, you almost feel as if you're at a friend's home for dinner. Bahian food is lighter than in most restaurants. Try the *badejo* (grouper) in ginger sauce. The roasted leg of lamb is a great choice if you want to depart from seafood. Entrée servings are more than enough for two. ⊠ *Rua Inácio Acciole 8, Pelourinho* ☎ *071/3321–3929* ▤ *AE, D, MC, V.*

$$–$$$ ✕ **Trapiche Adelaide.** It's almost impossible to have a bad meal in this Fodor'sChoice city, but this restaurant along the harbor and near the Mercado Mod- ★ elo still stands out for its unique blend of Italian, French, and Bahian cuisines and for its fresh fish. Try the seafood risotto or quail in *farofa* (cassava flour). Having drinks before dinner on the deck overlooking the Todos os Santos Bay is a pleasant way to wind down after a day of sightseeing. ⊠ *Praça dos Tupinambás, Av. Contorno 02, Comércio* ☎ *071/3326–2211* ⊕ *www.trapicheadelaide.com.br* ▤ *AE, D, MC, V* ☉ *No dinner Sun.*

★ $–$$$ ✕ **Solar do Unhão.** You get a lot for your money at this restaurant on the bay. Dinner is buffet style, with emphasis on Bahian dishes, but you have several international choices. The evening show presents Afro-Brazilian dance, still an integral part of Bahian culture today. The building is part of an 18th-century colonial estate, which has housed a sugar mill and a tobacco factory. The restaurant is in the former slave quarters. On a corner of the estate, the small **Museu de Arte Moderna** has temporary exhibits of Brazilian artists such as Di Cavalcanti and Volpi. ⊠ *Av. do Contorno 08* ☎ *071/329–5551* ⌔ *Reservations essential* ▤ *AE, MC, V.*

$–$$ ✕ **Encontro dos Artistas.** This simple Bahian restaurant has both alfresco and indoor dining. The fish-and-shrimp moqueca, a stew made with coconut milk and *dendê* (a type of palm) oil, is a must here. The charm of this neighborhood establishment lies in its casual ambience, surroundings in a centuries-old part of town, and local clientele, who gather here after work. Service can be slow—order an appetizer or salad and drinks as soon as you sit down. ⊠ *Rua Francisco Muniz Barreto 15 at Rua das Laranjeiras, Pelourinho* ☎ *071/3321–1721* ▤ *AE, D, MC, V.*

$ ✕ **Escola SENAC.** This restaurant, which opened in 1975, is a cooking school where new generations of Bahian chefs hone their skills under supervision of experienced teachers. More than 40 typical Bahian and Brazilian dishes are served buffet style in this old colonial house. It is regarded as one of the best restaurants in town. The bargain prices are

AFRO-BRAZILIAN HERITAGE

OF ALL OF BRAZIL'S STATES, Bahia has the strongest links with its African heritage. There are few other countries with such a symphony of skin tones grouped under one nationality. This rich Brazilian identity began when the first Portuguese sailors were left to manage the new land. From the beginning Portuguese migration to Brazil was predominantly male, a fact that unfortunately led to unbridled sexual license with Indian and African women.

The first Africans arrived in 1532, along with the Portuguese colonizers, who continued to buy slaves from English, Spanish, and Portuguese traders until 1855. All records pertaining to slave trading were destroyed in 1890, making it impossible to know exactly how many people were brought to Brazil. It's estimated that from 3 to 4.5 million Africans were captured and transported from Gambia, Guinea, Sierra Leone, Senegal, Liberia, Nigeria, Benin, Angola, and Mozambique. Many were literate Muslims who were better educated than their white overseers and owners.

It was common in the main houses of sugar plantations, which relied on slave labor, for the master to have a white wife and slave mistresses. In fact interracial relationships and even marriage was openly accepted. It was also fairly common for the master to free the mother of his mixed-race offspring and allow a son of color to learn a trade or inherit a share of the plantation.

When the sugar boom came to an end, it became too expensive for slave owners to support their "free" labor force. Abolition occurred gradually, however. It began around 1871, with the passage of the Law of the Free Womb, which liberated all Brazilians born of slave mothers. In 1885 another law was passed, freeing slaves over age 60. Finally, on May 13, 1888,

Princess Isabel, while Emperor Dom Pedro II was away on a trip, signed a law freeing all slaves in the Brazilian empire.

The former slaves, often unskilled, became Brazil's unemployed and underprivileged. Although the country has long been praised for its lack of discrimination, this veneer of racial equality is deceptive. Afro-Brazilians still don't receive education on a par with that of whites, nor do they always receive equal pay for equal work. There are far fewer black or mulatto professionals, politicians, and ranking military officers than white ones.

Subtle activism to bring about racial equality and educate all races about the rich African legacy continues. For many people the most important holiday is November 20 (National Black Consciousness Day). It honors the anniversary of the death of Zumbi, the leader of the famous Quilombo (community of escaped slaves) de Palmares, which lasted more than 100 years and was destroyed by bandeirantes (slave traders) in one final great battle for freedom.

an extra incentive. ⊠ *Praça José de Alencar 13–19, Pelourinho* ☎ *071/ 3324–4550* ▭ *MC, V* ☉ *Closed Sun.*

$ ✕ **Uauá.** The cuisine here is representative of many Brazilian regions, making Uauá one of the most popular restaurant chains in Salvador, and therefore almost always crowded. The cuisine is representative of many Brazilian regions, with special attention to northeastern dishes. Don't skip the *guisado de carneiro* (minced mutton), here with calabrese sausage. ⊠ *R. Gregório de Matos 36, Pelourinho* ☎ *071/3321–3089* ⊠ *Av. Dorival Caymi 46, Itapuã* ☎ *071/3249–9579* ▭ *AE, DC, MC, V* ⌫ *Reservations not accepted* ☉ *Closed Mon.*

Eclectic

$$ ✕ **Boi Preto.** Beef is cooked to perfection at one of the best barbecue places in Salvador. Seafood, including lobster, crab, and sushi, and more exotic fare like alligator or wild boar are also on the menu. A piano bar keeps the atmosphere light. ⊠ *Av. Otávio Mangabeira s/n, Jardim Armação* ☎ *071/3362–8844* ⊕ *www.boipretogrill.com.br* ▭ *AE, MC, V.*

French

$$$$ ✕ **Chez Bernard.** *Soteropolitanos* (Salvadorans) consider this the best French restaurant in town, with over 40 years of service. Everything is worth trying, but the *filet de boeuf* (steak) with several sauce options is particularly *fantastique*. ⊠ *Gamboa de Cima 11, Aflitos* ☎ *071/ 3329–5403* ⊕ *www.chezbernard.com.br* ▭ *AE, MC, V* ☉ *Closed Sun.*

Seafood

★ $$–$$$ ✕ **Yemanja.** A bubbly underwater theme—replete with aquariums and sea goddess murals—sets the tone for the fabulous seafood here. Small portions of acarajé can be ordered as appetizers. The service is somewhat slow, but most patrons don't seem to mind, concentrating instead on plowing through enormous portions of moqueca, or *ensopado*, seafood cooked in a similar but lighter sauce. Reservations are essential on weekends. ⊠ *Av. Otávio Mangabeira 4655, Jardim Armação* ☎ *071/3461–9010* ⊕ *www.restauranteyemanja.com.br* ▭ *AE, DC, MC, V.*

$–$$ ✕ **Bargaço.** Great Bahian seafood dishes are served at this old favorite. *Pata de caranguejo* (vinegared crab claw) is hearty and may do more than take the edge off your appetite for the requisite moqueca *de camarão* (with shrimp) or moqueca *de siri mole* (with soft-shell crab); try the cocada for dessert, if you have room. ⊠ *Rua P, quadra 43, Jardim Armação* ☎ *071/3231–9300* ▭ *AE, MC, V.*

Where to Stay

There are only a few hotels in the Cidade Histórico. Heading south into the Vitória neighborhood along Avenida 7 de Setembro there are many inexpensive establishments convenient to beaches and sights. In the yuppie Barra neighborhood, many hotels are within walking distance of cafés, bars, restaurants, and clubs. The resorts in the beach areas of Ondina and Rio Vermelho are a 20-minute taxi ride from downtown. High seasons are from December to March and the month of July. For Carnival, reservations must be made months in advance, and prices are substantially higher.

★ **$$$–$$$$** ▦ **Catussaba Resort Hotel.** In a garden of flowers and palm trees, this hotel has large rooms, some of which have beautiful wicker furniture, with balconies and ocean views. The resort complex opens directly onto Itapuã beach, one of the cleanest and most famous in Salvador. The hotel is 40 km (25 mi) from downtown, near the airport. If you tire of saltwater and sand, head for the large pool area. ⊠ *Alameda da Praia, Itapuã, 41600-270* ☎ *071/3374–8000* 🖷 *071/3374–4749* ⊕ *www. catussaba.com.br* ⤳ *186 rooms, 4 suites ⚐ Restaurant, room service, minibars, cable TV, 4 tennis court, pool, health club, sauna, bar, Internet room, convention center, meeting rooms, travel services, free parking* ▱ *AE, MC, V.*

$$$ ▦ **Bahia Othon Palace Hotel.** A short drive from most sights, nightspots, and restaurants, this busy, modern hotel sits on a cliff overlooking Ondina Beach. Top local entertainers often perform at the hotel's outdoor park, and in high season the friendly staff organizes poolside activities and trips to better beaches. ⊠ *Av. Oceanica 2294, Ondina, 40170-010* ☎ *071/ 3203–2000* 🖷 *071/3245–4877* ⊕ *www.othon.com.br* ⤳ *300 rooms, 25 suites ⚐ Restaurant, coffee shop, in-room safes, minibars, cable TV, pool, health club, sauna, dance club, free parking* ▱ *AE, DC, MC, V.*

☾ **$$$** ▦ **Sofitel Salvador.** This branch of the international Sofitel chain sits in
Fodor's Choice a tropical park near Itapuã Beach and the Abaeté Lagoon, about 5 km
★ (3 mi) from the airport. It's the only hotel in Salvador with its own golf course, albeit a 9-hole one. As it aims for the business as well as the purely tourist clientele, rooms are more sober than other beachfront hotels. The Oxum restaurant has an excellent regional menu. The hotel provides transportation to the Centro Histórico. ⊠ *Rua da Passargada s/n, Itapuã, 41620-430* ☎ *071/2106–8500* 🖷 *071/2106–8536* ⊕ *www.sofitel. com* ⤳ *206 rooms ⚐ 2 restaurants, room service, in-room safes, cable TV, 9-hole golf course, 3 tennis courts, 2 outdoor pools, health club, hair salon, massage, boating, billiards, 3 bars, shops, babysitting, dry cleaning, children's program (ages 4–12), concierge, Internet room, business services, meeting rooms, airport shuttle, travel services, free parking* ▱ *AE, DC, MC, V.*

$$–$$$ ▦ **Blue Tree Towers Salvador.** Though it doesn't have close sea views, the local member of Blue Tree chain in the Ondina district has easy access to the historic center and the beaches. Rooms with king-sized beds and other facilities follow the Blue Tree standard of quality and functionality. From here it is a short distance to the many restaurants and bars of the Barra district. ⊠ *Rua Monte Conselho 505, Ondina, 41940-370* ☎ *071/2103–2233* 🖷 *071/2103–2200* ⊕ *www.bluetree.com.br* ⤳ *200 rooms ⚐ Restaurant, coffee shop, room service, in-room safes, minibars, cable TV, outdoor pool, health club, sauna, laundry service, Internet room, in-room data ports, business services, meeting rooms, parking (fee)* ▱ *AE, DC, MC, V* ⦿❘ *BP.*

$$ ▦ **Fiesta Bahia Hotel.** In the city's financial district and attached to the convention center, the Fiesta has wheelchair-accessible rooms and rooms with direct phone lines, fax and PC terminals, and queen-sized beds— amenities that distinguish it from its competitors. ⊠ *Av. Antônio Carlos Magalhães 711, Itaigara, 41125-000* ☎ *071/3352–0000* 🖷 *071/ 3352–0050* ⊕ *www.fiestahotel.com.br* ⤳ *236 rooms, 8 suites ⚐ Restau-*

rant, coffee shop, room service, in-room safes, minibars, cable TV, in-room data ports, 2 pools, health club, hair salon, bar, nightclub, shops, business services, meeting rooms, free parking 🖃 *AE, DC, MC, V.*

$$ ▦ **Ondina Apart Hotel Residência.** In the resort hotel district, a short drive from the sights, nightlife, and restaurants of Salvador, this outstanding beachside complex has simple modern furniture. Businesspeople and families opt for this hotel when they're staying in Salvador for extended periods, as all rooms have a small kitchen. ✉ *Av. Oceanica 2400, Ondina, 40170-010* ☏ *071/3203–8000* 🖷 *071/3247–9434* ⊕ *www.ondinaapart. com.br* ◗ *100 rooms* ❑ *Restaurant, coffee shop, in-room safes, kitchenettes, minibars, cable TV, tennis court, pool, gym, bar, babysitting, laundry service, parking (fee)* 🖃 *AE, DC, MC, V.*

$$ ▦ **Tropical Hotel da Bahia.** Owned by Varig Airlines and often included in package deals, this centrally located hotel is a bit tattered, but it's practical for those whose priority is Salvador's history and culture. The hotel is away from the beaches, but there's a free beach shuttle. Some rooms overlook Largo de Campo Grande, one of the hubs of Carnival in Salvador. ✉ *Praça 2 de Julho 02, Campo Grande, 40080-121* ☏ *071/ 3255–2000* 🖷 *071/3255–2005* ⊕ *www.tropicalhotel.com.br* ◗ *275 rooms* ❑ *Restaurant, coffee shop, room service, cable TV, 2 pools, massage, sauna, bar, dance club, concierge, parking (fee)* 🖃 *AE, DC, MC, V.*

$ ▦ **Hotel Bahia do Sol.** Decor might be simple, but this budget hotel has a prime location close to museums and historic sights. Some rooms have a partial ocean view, but those in the back are quieter. The restaurant Zarzuela is somewhat eclectic, but you can certainly find some Bahian dishes. ✉ *Av. 7 de Setembro 2009, Vitória, 40080-002* ☏ *071/ 3338–8800* 🖷 *071/ 3338–8801* ⊕ *www.bahiadosol.com.br* ◗ *90 rooms, 2 suites* ❑ *Restaurant, cable TV, bar, meeting rooms, free parking* 🖃 *AE, DC, MC, V.*

$ ▦ **Hotel Mercure Salvador.** A high-quality chain hotel in a high-rise building, the Mercure has a prime business location. The ambience is relaxing, as all apartments face the Atlantic Ocean. The Casarãao restaurant has tables on a deck overlooking the ocean. ✉ *Rua Fonte de Boi 215, Rio Vermelho, 40210-090* ☏ *071/3330–8200* ⊕ *www.accorhotels. com.br* ◗ *175 rooms* ❑ *Restaurant, bar, minibars, cable TV, sauna, fitness room, meeting rooms, business services, Internet room, in-room safes, free parking* 🖃 *AE, D, MC, V* ¶◎¶ *BP.*

$ ▦ **Pestana Bahia.** This hotel built atop a seaside cliff in the trendy Rio Vermelho neighborhood has carved itself a tradition of excellent services for tourists and conventioneers. It was thoroughly renovated in 2003. It is a short walk from the neighborhood's bars and restaurants. ✉ *Rua Fonte de Boi 216, Rio Vermelho, 40170-010* ☏ *071/2103–8000 or 800/26–6332* 🖷 *071/2103–80001* ⊕ *www.pestana.com.br* ◗ *430 rooms* ❑ *Restaurant, coffee shop, in-room safes, minibars, cable TV, pool, gym, bar, babysitting, laundry service, parking, shuttle service* 🖃 *AE, DC, MC, V.*

¢ ▦ **Âmbar Pousada.** The highlight of this small and simple pousada is the service—the staff is attentive and rooms are kept impeccably clean. Location is a draw too, as here you are just a couple of streets away from the eclectic Barra neighborhood. If you're braving Salvador at Carnival time, the parade passes noisily just two blocks away on Avenida

Oceânica. There's a nice terrace and courtyard. ⊠ *Rua Afonso Celso 485, Barra, 40140-080* ☎ *071/3264–6956* 🖷 *071/3264–3791* ⊕ *www. ambarpousada.com.br* ⤳ *5 rooms* ⚭ *Fans, Internet room; no room TVs* ⊟ *AE, MC, V* ⚭ *BP.*

¢ 🏨 **Hotel Catharina Paraguaçu.** Rooms and suites in this intimate hotel in a 19th-century mansion are small but comfortable, and include six split-level suites. Extra attention is devoted to the decor, with pottery and embroidery from local artisans. It's family run and in a neighborhood of many restaurants and bars. The kitchen serves snacks and meals, from fettuccine to salmon. It has one room for guests with disabilities, including wheelchair access, unusual for a small hotel like this. ⊠ *Rua João Gomes 128, Rio Vermelho, 40210-090* ☎🖷 *071/3334–0089* ⊕ *www.hotelcatharinaparaguacu.com.br* ⤳ *23 rooms, 6 suites* ⚭ *Dining room, minibars, cable TV* ⊟ *MC, V* ⚭ *BP.*

FodorsChoice
★

★ ¢ 🏨 **Pousada das Flores.** The Brazilian-French owners have made this inn, northeast of Pelourinho and within walking distance of the historical district, one of the city's best budget options. Rooms are large and have high ceilings and hardwood floors. For peace and quiet as well as an ocean view, opt for a room on an upper floor. If you feel like splurging, request the penthouse, which has a fantastic view of the harbor. Breakfast is served on the patio. ⊠ *Rua Direita de Santo Antônio 442, Santo Antônio, 40301-280* ☎🖷 *071/3243–1836* ⊕ *www.pflores.com.br* ⤳ *6 rooms, 3 suites* ⚭ *Restaurant, fans, mini-bar, Internet room* ⊟ *AE, DC, MC, V.*

Nightlife & the Arts

Pelourinho is filled with music every night and has more bars and clubs than you can count. Most bars serve food as well as drink. Activity also centers along the seashore, mainly at Rio Vermelho and between the Corsário and Piatã beaches, where many hotels have bars or discos.

Salvador is considered by many artists as a laboratory for the creation of new rhythms and dance steps. As such, this city has an electric performing arts scene. See the events calendar published by Bahiatursa or check local newspapers for details on live music performances as well as rehearsal schedules. In Pelourinho, groups often have practices open to the public on Tuesday and Sunday nights.

Nightlife

After dark, Praça Terreiro de Jesus is a hot spot, especially on Tuesday and Saturday nights, when stages are set up here and at other squares around the city for live performances. This plaza is especially popular with tourists because it has been painted, cleaned up, and gentrified. Although there may be impromptu musical performances any night, you can always count on it on Tuesday.

BARS There are many bars in the Pelourinho area, as well as on the beachfront avenues. The shopping complex Aeroclube Plaza on Avenida Otávio Manguabeira has also become quite popular among the young crowd, with bars, restaurants, and nightclubs.

Enjoy live music and typical Bahian food at **Casquinha de Siri** (⊠ Av. Otávio Mangabeira s/n, Piata ☎ 071/ 3367–1234). The two branches

of the traditional bar **Habeas Copos** (✉ Rua Marques de Leão 172, Barra
☎ 071/3247–7895 ✉ Praça Quincas Berro D'Agua, Pelourinho
☎ 071/3321–1798) are famous for their moqueca and *carne-de-sol*
(sun-dried meat).

Sancho Panza (✉ Av. Otávio Mangabeira 122, Pituba ☎ 071/3248–3571)
is a great place for sangria and typical Spanish fare. Sooner or later you
must have a *caipirinha* (lime and sugar-cane brandy cocktail) at **Cantina
da Lua** (✉ Praça Terreirro de Jesus 2, Pelourinho ☎ 071/3322-4041).

DANCE SHOWS Shows at the **Moenda** (✉ Rua P, Quadra 28, Lote 21, Jardim Armação
☎ 071/3231–7915) begin daily at 8 PM. There are Afro-Brazilian dinner shows at the **Solar do Unhão** (✉ Av. do Contorno 08, Comércio ☎ 071/
3321–5551). The unforgettable Afro-Bahian show at the **Teatro Miguel
Santana** (✉ Rua Gregório de Mattos 47, Pelourinho ☎ 071/3321–0222)
has the town's best folkloric dance troupes. This is an entertaining way
to learn about Afro-Brazilian culture.

NIGHTCLUBS Have dinner or drinks and listen to quality jazz, blues, soul, and pop
at the **French Quartier** (✉ Aeroclube Plaza complex, Av. Otávio
Mangabeira 2323, Lote 1, Jardim dos Namorados ☎ 071/3240–1491
⊕ www.frenchquartier.com.br). Happy hour is between 6 PM and 8 PM.
The view of the bay is fantastic, but ocean breezes are cool, so bring a
coat or sweater.

The **Queops** disco (✉ Rua Manoel Antônio Galvão 100, Patamares
☎ 071/3206–0138), open Wednesday to Saturday, has a large dance floor
and occasional performances of local rock-and-roll bands. **Rock in Rio
Café** (✉ Av. Otávio Mangabeira 6000, Jardim Armação ☎ 071/
3461–0300) is in the shopping-and-entertainment complex Aeroclube
Plaza. The atmosphere here is more like Miami than Salvador.

The Arts

CARNIVAL Afro-Brazilian percussion groups begin Carnival rehearsals—which are
REHEARSALS really more like creative jam sessions—around midyear. **Ilê Aiyê** (✉ Rua
★ do Curuzu 197, Liberdade ☎ 071/3256–1013), which started out as a
Carnival bloco, has turned itself into much more in its 25-year history.
It now has its own school and promotes the study and practice of
African heritage, religion, and history. Public practices are held every
Saturday night at Forte de Santo Antônio and should not be missed.

Olodum, Salvador's best-known percussion group, gained international
fame when it participated in Paul Simon's "Rhythm of the Saints" tour
and recordings. The group has its own venue, the **Casa do Olodum** (✉ Rua
Gregório de Matos 22, Pelourinho ☎ 071/3321–5010). Olodum also
has a percussion school, **Escola Criativa Olodum** (✉ Rua das Laranjeiras 30, Pelourinho ☎ 071/3322–8029). Pre-Carnival rehearsals take
place at Largo do Pelourinho Tuesday evenings and Sunday afternoons.

MUSIC, THEATER **Teatro Casa do Comércio** (✉ Av. Tancredo Neves 1109, Pituba ☎ 071/
& DANCE 3341–1310) hosts music performances and some theatrical productions. Classical and popular music performances, operas, and plays are
all held at **Teatro Castro Alves** (✉ Praça 2 de Julho s/n, Campo Grande
☎ 071/3532–2323 ⊕ www.tca.ba.gov.br), Salvador's largest theater. The

CARNIVAL IN SALVADOR: BRAZIL'S WILDEST PARTY

FORGET RIO'S COMMERCIALIZED SPECTACLE. *The most accessible and authentic large-scale Carnival in Brazil is in Salvador—an explosion of hundreds of thousands of revelers, all dancing in frenzied marching crews, called blocos, or hopping parade-side as pipoca, or popcorn. At the center of each bloco is the trio elétrico, a creeping stage whose towering speakers blare walls of energetic, ribcage-rattling axé music—a danceble and distinctly Bahian mix of African rhythms, rock, and reggae. Top pop stars like Daniela Mercury or Ivete Sangalo perform their party-stoking Carnival favorites.*

To be part of the action, and to avoid the hordes of pickpockets that are unfortunately part of the "excitement," join a bloco, which is roped off from the general public. Each bloco has its own all-purpose beer, first-aid, and toilet truck—and you'll have instant camaraderie with your crewmates. (A warning: it's not unusual for women to be kissed by strangers. It might sound feeble, but having a male friend close may deter unwanted groping.)

Favorite bloco themes include Egyptian-garbed percussion band Olodum, and axé acts Are Ketu and Timbalada. Alternatively, there's the peaceful Filhos de Ghandy (Children of Ghandi), a white sea of robes and jeweled turbans. Once you've chosen your bloco, all you have to do is lay down upwards of US$100 to buy a crew-specific t-shirt, called an abadá, purchased at Central do Carnival kiosks, or at markets from scalpers.

Blocos travel along specific circuitos (routes) through the city. Seaside Dodô (about 1 mile/5 hours) is the route of choice for Carnival's biggest stars and begins at Farol da Barra. Osmar (about 2 miles/6 hours), beginning near Campo Grande, is large and traditional. The less-populated and calmer Batatinha, which clings to historic Pelourinho, allows an intimate look at smaller percussionist groups and is popular with families. Prepare by checking the the maps at www.carnaval.salvador.ba.gov.br (click on Mapas do Circuito).

Add to all of these fine reasons to patronize Salvador's Carnival the more than 20 pre-Carnival warm-up celebrations and its honor in the Guinness Book of World Records as the biggest street carnival on the planet, and it's hard to argue that, come Carnival season, true partiers shouldn't be anywhere but Salvador.

— Joe Gould

For a flip-side opinion, see "Carnival in Rio: Spectacle of Spectacles" in Chapter 1.

Teatro ACBEU (Associação Cultural Brasil-Estados Unidos) (⊠ Av. 7 de Setembro 1883, Vitória ☎ 071/3337–4395 ⊕ www.acbeubahia.com. br) has contemporary and classical music, dance, and theater performances by Brazilian and international artists.

Sports & the Outdoors

CAPOEIRA You can see capoeira in almost any beach or park in Salvador and Bahia. Some places are traditional gathering points for practitioners. One such place is the parking lot of Forte de Santo Antônio on Tuesday, Thursday, and Saturday early evenings. Two schools practice here, of which the Grupo de Capoeira Angola is the best known.

There are several capoeira schools in Salvador for anyone who wants to learn the art that trains both the mind and body for combat. Mestre Bamba (Rubens Costa Silva) teaches at **Bimba's Academy** (⊠ Rua das Laranjeiras 01, Pelourinho ☎ 071/3322–0639). A 10-day course costs around R$100.

Soccer

Bahia and Vitória are the two local teams that play in the first division of Brazilian soccer federation. Schedules vary, but there are games year-round in the **Estádio da Fonte Nova** (⊠ Av. Vale do Nazaré, Tororó ☎ 071/3243–3322). Advance tickets sales are available, but games hardly ever sell out. The best seats are in the higher-priced *arquibancada superior* (upper level section).

Shopping

Areas & Malls

Aeroclube Plaza Shopping (⊠ Av. Otavio Mangabeira 6000, Jardim Armação ☎ 071/3461–0300) is a beachfront mall with live music venues, cinemas, restaurants, and jewelry shops, open daily 10–10. It has the only bowling alley in Salvador.

For paintings, especially art naïf, visit the many galleries in the Cidade Alta and around the **Largo do Pelourinho** (⊠ Rua Alfredo de Brito at Ladeira do Taboão). The **Mercado Modelo** is your best bet for local handicrafts, such as lace, hammocks, wood carvings, and musical instruments.

Shopping Barra (⊠ Av. Centenário 2992, Barra) is the best shopping mall in Salvador. It isn't far from the historic center and has cinemas, restaurants, and local boutiques, as well as branches of the major Rio, São Paulo, and Minas Gerais retailers. It is open from 10 to 10 weekdays and from 9 to 8 on Saturday. Many hotels provide transportation to the mall, but you can also take the Rodoviária bus line.

Specialty Stores

ART Top local artists (many of whom use only first names or nicknames) including Totonho, Calixto, Raimundo Santos, Joailton, Nadinho, Nonato, Maria Adair, Carybé, Mário Cravo, and Jota Cunha have their crafts and paintings at **Portal das Artes** (⊠ Rua Gregório de Matos 20, Pelourinho ☎ 071/3222–9890).

CAPOEIRA: THE FIGHT DANCE

DANCE AND MARTIAL ARTS IN ONE, capoeira *is purely Brazilian. The early days of slavery often saw fights between Africans from rival tribes who were thrust together on one plantation. When an owner caught slaves fighting, both sides were punished. To create a smoke screen, the Africans incorporated music and song into the fights. They brought a traditional berimbau string-drum instrument (a bow-shape piece of wood with a metal wire running from one end to the other, where there's a hollow gourd containing seeds) to the battles. Tapped with a stick or a coin, the berimbau's taut wire produces a throbbing, twanging sound whose rhythm is enhanced by the rattling seeds. Its mesmerizing reverberations were accompanied by singing and chanting, and when the master appeared, the fighters punched only the air and kicked so as to miss their opponents.*

The fights have been refined into a sport that was once practiced primarily in Bahia and Pernambuco but has now spread throughout Brazil. Today's practitioners, called capoeristas, *swing and kick—keeping their movements tightly controlled, with only hands and feet touching the ground—to the beat of the* berimbau *without touching their opponents. The goal is to cause one's opponent to lose concentration or balance. Capoeira is traditionally performed in a* roda *(wheel), which refers both to an event of continuous capoeira and to the circle formed by players and instrumentalists. Strength, control, flexibility, artistry, and grace are the tenets of capoeira. In any exhibition the* jogadores, *or players, as they are called—with their backs bending all the way to the floor and their agile foot movements (to avoid an imaginary knife)—as well as the compelling music, make this a fascinating sport to watch.*

BOOKS **Livraria Siciliano** (✉ Shopping Barra, Av. Centenário 2992, 2nd floor ☎ 041/3364–2191) is the local branch of a major Brazilian chain that has lots of foreign-language books and international magazines. **Graúna** (✉ AeroClube Plaza Shopping, Av. Otavio Mangabeira 6000 ✉ Rua Barão de Itapoã, Porto da Barra ☎071/3286–0455) has a wide assortment of English-language books, both new and used.

HANDICRAFTS The **Casa Santa Barbara** (✉ Rua Alfredo de Brito s/n, Pelourinho ☎ 071/244–0458) sells Bahian clothing and lacework of top quality, and at high prices. It's closed Saturday afternoon and Sunday. Of Salvador's state-run handicrafts stores, the best is the **Instituto de Artesanato Visconde de Mauá** (✉ Praça Azevedo Fernandes 2, Porto da Barra ☎ 071/3264–5440 ✉ R. Gregorio de Mattos 27, Pelourinho ☎ 071/3321–5501), which promotes local artisans. Look for exquisite lace, musical instruments of African origin, weavings, and wood carvings. **Kembo** (✉ Rua João de Deus 21, Pelourinho ☎071/3322–1379) carries handicrafts from Brazilian native peoples, such as the Pataxós, Karajá, Xingú, Tikuna, Caipós, and Yanomami.

JEWELRY & GEMSTONES Bahia is one of Brazil's main sources of stones. Agates, amethysts, aquamarines, emeralds, and tourmalines are the most abundant. Prices for these stones are usually cheaper here than elsewhere in Brazil, but you should have an idea of what stones are worth before you go. The well-known, reputable **H. Stern** (✉ Largo do Pelourinho s/n, Pelourinho ☎ 071/3322–7353) has several branches in Salvador, most of them in malls and major hotels. **Simon** (✉ Rua Ignácio Accioli s/n, Pelourinho ☎ 071/3242–5218), the city's most famous jeweler, allows you to peer through a window into the room where goldsmiths work.

SIDE TRIPS FROM SALVADOR

Although attractions in Salvador can keep you entertained for more than a week, there are great places for a one- or two-day break in more relaxing environs. On a two-day tour to Morro de São Paulo, you can enjoy the near-pristine beaches and tropical forest. Or plan a day trip to Praia do Forte or the other northern beaches; they're less crowded and more beautiful than those in and near Salvador.

Morro de São Paulo

★ ⓴ On Ilha de Tinharé, just south of Itaparica, Morro de São Paulo is the most popular place on the island, most of which is covered with thick Atlantic forest protected by a state park. Private cars are not allowed here; you can walk to the beaches, take tractor-pulled trolleys, or hire a small boat to "beach-hop" about the island. Popular beaches dot the 40-km (25-mi) Atlantic side of Tinharé. Starting at the Morro de São Paulo village, beaches begin with Primeira (First) and go on to Segunda, Terceira (Second, Third), and so forth. Waters are calm thanks to the coral reef just off the surf, whose abundant marine life (mostly in the form of small fish) makes scuba diving or snorkeling worthwhile. The number of tourists nearly triples from December to February (Brazil's summer), when Brazilians and foreigners fill the pousadas for festival and Carnival season. The southernmost beaches near Boca da Barra are usually quieter even during peak season.

To reach Morro de São Paulo, either take the air shuttle from Salvador (⇨ By Air, *in* Salvador & Bahia Essentials) or take a *lancha* (small boat carrying up to five passengers) or larger *catamarã* (catamaran) from **Terminal Marítimo** (✉ Av. da França 1 ☎ 071/3319–2890). Launch and catamaran services run by several different companies leave daily from 8 AM to 2 PM, and return from Morro de São Paulo from noon to 4 PM; fares range from R$50 to R$70 depending on services, like food, drinks, and live music.

North Coast Beaches

To reach some of Bahia's more pristine and less crowded beaches, head north of Salvador on the Estrada do Coco (Coconut Road), leaving the baroque churches and colonial dwellings behind in favor of miles of quiet road lined with coconut palms. At the fishing village and turtle haven of Praia do Forte, take the Linha Verde (Green Line/Highway BA 099) up the coast. Each of the little roads cutting east off Linha Verde leads to a different palm-tree-covered beach.

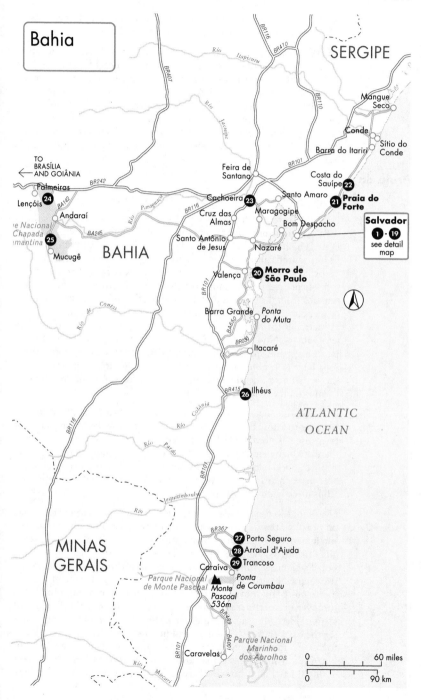

Bahia

Bus transportation to this area is readily available, but driving is fairly safe and the convenience of your own wheels is justified here.

Barra do Jacuípe. A river runs down to the ocean at this long, wide, pristine beach lined with coconut palms. There are beachfront snack bars, and the Santa Maria/Catuense bus company operates six buses here daily. ✉ *40 km (25 mi) north of Salvador.*

Guarajuba. With palm trees and calm waters banked by a reef, this is the nicest beach of them all, though it's lined with condos. The bus to Barra do Jacuípe continues on to Guarajuba, which has snack kiosks, fishing boats, surfing, dune buggies, and a playground. ✉ *60 km (38 mi) north of Salvador.*

Praia do Forte

㉑ *72 km (45 mi) northeast of Salvador.*

Praia do Forte was first settled in 1549 by Garcia D'Avila, a clerk for the Portuguese crown. For reasons lost in the mists of history, Garcia D'Avila had acquired a fortune and became a landowner. With foresight, he introduced cattle ranching and coconut-palm cultivation in the area. To protect the coast, a medieval-style castle was built that served as a fort—hence the town's name, which means "Fortress Beach." All that remains from the castle is just the outer walls, and there isn't too much to see, but it now has a helpful visitor center. Today the area's biggest attraction is the headquarters of a sea-turtle preservation project (Projeto Tamar). Now, instead of earning their living by killing turtles for meat, eggs, and shells, local fishermen are better paid to protect them. Jobs have also been provided by the bars, restaurants, pousadas, and shops that now line the three brick-paved streets. Almost everything in town is on the main street, Alameda do Sol.

On a relaxing day trip from Salvador you can visit Praia do Forte's village, get to know the sea-turtle research station, swim, or snorkel. The town also has a beautiful coconut-lined beach. If you decide to stay longer, there are many lodging options and the nightlife, although toned down a few decibels from that in Salvador, is still lively. You can book a trip here through any Salvador tour operator or travel agent, or simply take a bus directly on a day trip.

Fodor's Choice
★

Five of the seven extant sea-turtle species in the world roam and reproduce on Brazil's Atlantic coast, primarily in Bahia. The headquarters of **Projeto Tamar,** established in 1980, has turned what was once a small, struggling fishing village into a tourist destination with a mission—to save Brazil's giant sea turtles and their hatchlings. During the hatching season (September through March), workers patrol the shore at night to locate nests and move eggs or hatchlings at risk of being trampled or run over to safer areas or to the open-air hatchery at the Tamar base station. Here you can watch adult turtles in the swimming pools and see the baby turtles that are housed in tanks until they can be released to the sea. Eighteen other Tamar base stations on beaches along 1,000 km (621 mi) of coastline in five northeastern Brazilian states protect about 400,000 hatchlings born each year. The headquarters also has educational videos, lectures, and a gift shop where you can buy turtle-themed gifts (proceeds help support the project). From December to February, you can sign up for the "Tartaruga by Night" project to help release hatchlings from the station hatchery to the sea. ⊠ *Alameda do Sol s/n* ☎ *071/3676–1020* ⊕ *www.tamar.org.br* 🎫 *R$12* ☉ *Daily 9–7.*

Swim or snorkel in the crystal-clear (and safe) waters of the **Papa Gente,** a 3-meter-deep (10-foot-deep) natural pool formed by reefs at the ocean's edge. Snacks are sold at little huts on the beach, but if you're really hungry, a restaurant, in the Sobrado Da Vila Pousada, is nearby.

If you have a couple of days to visit Praia do Forte, spend one of them on a jeep tour. These tours make their way through the **Reserva de Sapiranga,** with 600 hectares (1,482 acres) of Atlantic forest that contains rare orchids and bromeliads. The reserve is a sanctuary for endangered animals. White-water rafting is possible on the Rio Pojuca, which flows through the park, and Lago Timeantube, where more than 187 species of native birds have been sighted. You can rent a car, or preferably a jeep, and drive yourself through the reserve or arrange for a tour in town at the **Centro Turistico** (Tourist Center; ⊠ Alameda do Sol s/n ☎ 071/676–1091 🖷 071/3676–1392 ⊕ www.prdoforte.com.br).

Where to Stay & Eat

$$ ✕ **Sabor da Vila.** It isn't surprising that seafood fresh from the ocean is the specialty at this small modest restaurant on Praia do Forte's main street. After visiting Praia do Forte's attractions, stop here for a fish-and-shrimp moqueca. ⊠ *Av. ACM s/n* ☎ *071/3676–1156* ▤ *D, MC, V.*

¢ ✕ **Bar do Souza.** Make this well-known bar your choice for a Bahian snack of *acarajés* (shrimp-filled bean-flour pastries fried in palm oil). The restaurant serves up other excellent Bahian specialties, including fish stews, grilled lobster, and shellfish stew. It's a favorite with the locals, especially on Friday and Saturday nights, when there's live music. ⊠ *Alameda do Sol* ☎ *No phone* ▤ *AE, MC, V.*

$$ ✕🏠 **Pousada Praia do Forte.** You have your own thatch-roof bungalow with a hammock hanging on the open porch here. Bungalows are small, but you're only there to sleep—the beach and the pools that are left when the tide goes out are too inviting to miss. Redbrick paths curve through the landscaped grounds to 12 km (8 mi) of beaches lined with coconut trees and to the Tamar sea-turtle project. In the evening you can relax in the pousada's outdoor pool and take a walk on the beach, and then end the day with dinner in the restaurant, enjoying international and Bahian cuisine. ⊠ *Av. do Farol s/n, Mata de São João, Praia do Forte, 48280-000* ☎ *071/676–1116* 🖷 *071/676–1033* ⊕ *www.pousadapraiadoforte.com.br* ⇨ *19 bungalows* ♿ *Restaurant, fans, pool* ▤ *DC, MC, V* ⍾ *MAP.*

$ ✕🏠 **Pousada Sobrado Da Vila.** Leave your computer and pocket organizer at home and forget about time management, this is a laid-back pousada right on the main drag where you can kick back and relax. The rooms are plain but comfortable, and the restaurant is superb, with all Bahian specialties. If you've never tried a *queijo de coalho frito* (roasted cheese ball), try it here. ⊠ *Av. ACM 7* ☎ *071/676–1088* ⊕ *www.*

sobradodavila.com.br ⇱ *23 rooms* ⚴ *Restaurant, refrigerators, cable TV* ⊟ *AE, MC, V.*

🕭 **$$$$** 🏨 **Praia do Forte Eco Resort.** Relax on a hammock and contemplate the
Fodor'sChoice sea from your private veranda at this sprawling beachfront resort. You'll
★ be within walking distance of the village in case you need more action,
but there is a full roster of activities available including horseback riding, volleyball, kayaking, sailing, and snorkeling. All rooms face the ocean,
and a large part of the grounds still have the original Atlantic forest vegetation that once covered the region. The restaurant and other facilities
are open only to resort guests. ⊠ *Av. do Farol s/n, Praia do Forte, Mata
de São João 48280-000* ☎ *071/676–4000 or 0800/71–8888* ☎ *071/676–
1112* ⊕ *www.praiadoforte.com* ⇱ *250 rooms* ⚴ *2 restaurants, in-
room safes, cable TV, 4 tennis courts, 5 pools, gym, beach, snorkeling,
windsurfing, boating, 3 bars, dance club, children's programs (ages
4–12)* ⊟ *AE, DC, MC, V* ⏇ *MAP.*

Shopping
Pietra Rara (⊠ Av. ACM ☎ No phone) sells ceramics, wood carvings,
paintings, clothing, and antiques.

en route If you have rented a jeep, you can turn off the main road and drive
between the sand dunes to **Santo Antônio** and walk through the
village with only 30 houses, up a sand dune, and then down onto a
nearly deserted beach. Drinks are available in the little village store,
handicrafts are sold by villagers, and sometimes a stand is open on
the beach for drinks and snacks. ⊠ *Just before the entrance to Costa
do Sauípe.*

Costa do Sauípe

㉒ *114 km (71 mi) northeast of Salvador 42 km (26 mi) northeast of Praia
Do Forte.*

An hour's drive north from Salvador along the Atlantic coast brings you
to the Costa do Sauípe resort complex. Its five hotels, convention center, re-created local village with six pousadas, and sports center are all
part of a 500-acre development in an environmental protection area bordered by rain forest. To get around during your stay within the complex, you can either hop the resort van that makes continuous loops or
take a horse and carriage.

If you prefer small lodgings to grand resorts, opt for a stay in one of the
six themed pousadas (inns) in Vila Nova da Praia, a re-creation of a typical northeastern village, with cobblestone lanes, crafts shops, restaurants, bars, and street entertainment. Vila Nova da Praia is also a great
place to find special gifts, especially ceramics, and to buy resort wear.
⊠ *Km 76, Rodovia BA 099, Costa do Sauípe, Mata de São João,
48280-000.*

Where to Stay
Regardless of where you stay, you have access to all the resort's amenities, including those of the sports complex, with its 18-hole PGA golf

course, 15 tennis courts, equestrian center, water-sports facilities, 4 paddleball courts, 2 squash courts, and a soccer field.

♨ $$$$ 🏨 **Marriott Resort & Spa.** The view from your balcony is of the garden's swaying palm fronds and a clean sweep of beach. Inside your large room, the dark-wood furniture is offset by bright fabrics. Have drinks or a typical Brazilian meal at the poolside bar and restaurant or retreat inside to the lobby bar or a restaurant with an ocean view that serves sushi, Korean barbecue, and other Asian cuisine. Dance the night away with the other guests in the ballroom. The spa has facial treatments and body treatments that include shiatsu massage and hot-stone therapy. ☎ 071/2104–7000 ⊕ *www.marriott.com* ⇨ *239 rooms, 17 suites ♨ 3 restaurants, room service, in-room safes, minibars, cable TV, in-room data ports, pool, health club, spa, beach, 2 bars, babysitting, children's program (4–12), dry cleaning, laundry service, concierge, business services, airport shuttle* ▤ *AE, DC, MC, V* ❮◉❯ *BP*.

♨ $$$$ 🏨 **Sofitel Costa do Sauípe.** Replicas of early sailing ships hanging in the lobby hint at the hotel's themes: sailing and the discovery of Brazil. The Porão da Nau Pub & Club, off the lobby, is decorated in the style of a ship's hold, making it a unique place for drinks and dancing. If you prefer a cocktail in the sun, head for the enormous poolside bar. The main restaurant, the Île de France, serves fine French cuisine. Rooms look almost like the staterooms of an elegant ship with their dark-wood furniture and beige walls and drapes. Sliding-glass doors lead out to individual balconies with hammocks that overlook the gardens, with tall palm trees and the beautiful beach beyond. ☎ 071/2104–7600 ⊕ *www.sofitel.com* ⇨ *392 rooms, 12 suites ♨ 3 restaurants, coffee shop, room service, in-room safes, minibars, cable TV, in-room data ports, pool, gym, hair salon, hot tub, massage, sauna, beach, snorkeling, windsurfing, boating, bicycles, basketball, billiards, horseback riding, Ping-Pong, squash, bar, pub, dance club, shops, babysitting, children's programs (ages 3–12), playground, dry cleaning, laundry service, concierge, business services, meeting rooms, airport shuttle, car rental* ▤ *AE, DC, MC, V* ❮◉❯ *MAP*.

$$$$ 🏨 **Sofitel Suites.** This hotel is evocative of the days when large coconut groves filled the Bahian landscape. Rooms are done in subdued shades of brown and gold, and wood and natural fibers are used throughout. From the lobby bar you can see the free-form pool, which surrounds small islands planted with coconut trees, and the Atlantic beyond. From the Tabuleiro bar-restaurant watch the chef prepare traditional Bahian dishes. The more sophisticated Casa Grande restaurant serves French and other international fare. All rooms have verandas and hammocks. ☎ 071/2104–8000 ◵ 071/467–2001 ⊕ *www.sofitel.com* ⇨ *198 suites ♨ 2 restaurants, room service, fans, in-room safes, minibars, cable TV, in-room data ports, pool, hair salon, 2 bars, shops, babysitting, children's programs (ages 4–12), playground, dry cleaning, airport shuttle, car rental* ▤ *AE, DC, MC, V* ❮◉❯ *BP*.

♨ $$$$ 🏨 **SuperClubs Breezes Costa do Sauípe.** At this family resort, kids are kept busy all day with circus workshops and an extensive Kids' Club program. Meanwhile, resident tennis pros keep you busy on the courts. The dining areas look out over a large free-form pool. Behind the pool is a beautiful, wide Atlantic beach. You can walk for miles; if you trek to the little village of San Antônio, you can buy souvenirs or a cold drink from the ladies sitting on their porches. In addition to the large buffet and grill, there are four restaurants: Japanese, Italian, Bahian, and Mediterranean. You can arrange tours or reconfirm airline tickets in the lobby tour office. There is a strict no-tipping policy. Reservations are essential for all restaurants except for Jimmy's Buffet and the Tropical Restaurant. ☎ *071/2104–8888* ⊕ *www.superclubs.com* ⤳ *324 rooms, 16 suites* ♻ *5 restaurants, in-room safes, cable TV, in-room data ports, pool, wading pool, health club, windsurfing, boating, bicycles, billiards, Ping-Pong, 3 bars, dance club, recreation room, children's programs (ages 3–12), complimentary weddings, airport shuttle, travel services* ☐ *AE, DC, MC, V* ▯◯▯ *AI.*

$$$ ▦ **Renaissance Costa do Sauípe Resort.** The open-air lobby has a casual feel and a restaurant that looks out over sand dunes. If you opt to dine in the Mediterranean restaurant, your choices include specialties from Provence and southern Italy; some of the dishes are even cooked in a wood-burning oven. Tile-floor rooms are breezy and pleasant. With breakfast and dinner included and a beautiful beach right out your door, it's a real bargain. ☎ *071/466–2000* 🖷 *071/466–2001* ⊕ *www. renaissancehotels.com/ssabr* ⤳ *237 rooms, 17 suites* ♻ *2 restaurants, snack bar, room service, in-room safes, minibars, cable TV, in-room high-speed Internet, pool, gym, sauna, beach, babysitting, dry cleaning, laundry service, concierge, business services, meeting rooms, airport shuttle, car rental* ☐ *AE, DC, MC, V* ▯◯▯ *MAP.*

$$ ▦ **Vila Nova da Praia.** The six Costa Sauípe pousadas in this planned village are nearly identical—all have the same amenities and are of equal quality—though each has a different theme and number of rooms. The village is very small, and the pousadas are close together. Resources available to anyone staying at the pousadas are banks, a convenience store, an eco-tourism agency, a car-rental agency, a medical center, bars and restaurants, several kilometers of beaches, and shops selling clothing, jewelry, and handicrafts. Each pousada has its own pool. **Pousada Gabriela** (20 rooms) resembles colonial architecture of downtown Ilhéus, south of Salvador. It's named after a character from a Jorge Amado novel. With its bright colors, **Pousada Carnaval** (39 rooms) captures the spirit of Bahia's pre-Lenten festivities. **Pousada do Agreste** (18 rooms) echoes the colonial architecture of the interior of northeastern Brazil. Art and antiques fill **Pousada da Torre** (28 rooms, 2 suites), which tries to recreate the Garcia D'Avila mansion at Praia do Frote. As its name implies, **Pousada do Pelourinho** (38 rooms) is a replica of a house in Salvador's historic district. **Pousada Aldeia** (20 rooms) makes you feel as if you're staying in a 16th-century coastal village. A sun deck has hammocks for lazy afternoons. ☎ *071/ 2104–8200, 0800/7020203 in Brazil* ⊕ *www.costadosauipe.com.br* ♻ *Dining room, in-room safes, minibars, cable TV, in-room data ports, pool, laundry service, airport shuttle* ☐ *AE, D, DC, MC, V* ▯◯▯ *BP.*

Sports & the Outdoors

The **Costa do Sauípe Sports Complex** (☎ 071/353–4544) has an 18-hole golf course with a clubhouse, a tennis center with 15 courts, a water-sports center, an equestrian center that offers trail rides and ecological tours, a soccer field, and squash courts. There is also a small "farm" where you can learn how to milk a cow or watch a hog burrow in the mud. Your hotel staff members can help you make arrangements to participate in either the active or spectator sports of your choice.

Cachoeira

㉓ *109 km (67 mi) northwest of Salvador.*

This riverside colonial town dates from the 16th and 17th centuries, when sugarcane was the economy's mainstay. It has been designated a national monument and is the site of some of Brazil's most authentic Afro-Brazilian rituals. After Salvador it has the largest collection of baroque architecture in Bahia. A major restoration of public monuments and private buildings was finished in 2003, and included revitalized streets and plazas in town. On an excursion to Cachoeira you can walk through the colorful country market and see architecture preserved from an age when Cachoeira shipped tons of tobacco and sugar downriver to Salvador.

One of the most interesting popular events is the festival held by the Irmandade da Boa Morte (Sisterhood of Good Death). Organized by descendants of 19th-century slaves who founded an association of black women devoted to abolition, it's held on a Friday, Saturday, and Sunday in the middle of August.

Devotion to Nossa Senhora da Boa Morte (Our Lady of Good Death) began in the slave quarters, where discussions on abolition and prayer meetings honoring those who had died for liberty took place. The slaves implored Our Lady of Good Death to end slavery and promised to hold an annual celebration in her honor should their prayers be answered.

The festival begins with a procession by the sisters who, heads held high, carry an 18th-century statue of their patron saint through the streets. The statue is adorned in a typical all-white Bahian dress that signifies mourning in the Candomblé religion practiced by many of the sisters. Sunday, the festival's main day, sees a solemn mass followed by a joyful procession that begins with the traditional samba *de roda,* which is danced in a circle.

The **Capela da D'Ajuda,** built in the 16th century, is one of the most remarkable examples of early baroque architecture in this part of Brazil. ⊠ *Largo D'Ajuda s/n* ☎ *No phone* ☞ *R$3* ☉ *Inquire at Museu da Boa Morte to gain entrance to chapel.*

Museu da Boa Morte displays photos and ceremonial dresses worn by members of the Sisterhood of Our Lady of Good Death during their rituals and festivals. You may also meet some of the elderly but always energetic women whose ancestors protested slavery. The ladies at the museum will let you in to see the chapel and the church. ⊠ *Largo D'Ajuda s/n* ☎ *075/425–1343* ☞ *By donation* ☉ *Weekdays 10–1 and 3–5.*

Where to Stay & Eat

¢ ✕🏠 **Pousada do Convento.** You can stay overnight in one of the large rooms or have a good lunch at this one-time Carmelite monastery that dates from the 17th century. The meeting room adjacent to the hotel main room was formerly a church. ⊠ *Praça da Aclamação s/n* 🕾🕾 *075/ 425–1716* 🖃 *26 rooms* ⚲ *Restaurant, minibars, pool, playground, meeting room* 🖃 *D, MC, V.*

Lençois

★ ❷ *427 km (265 mi) west of Salvador; 1,133 km (704 mi) northeast of Brasília*

The largest community in the Chapada Diamantina area and the gateway to Chapada Diamantina National Park, Lençóis arose from the hundreds of makeshift tents of white cotton fabric built by *garimpeiros* (gold- and precious stone–seekers). (*Lençois* means "bedsheet.") The precious-stone frenzy began in 1822 with the discovery of diamonds in riverbeds around the town of Mucugê, which brought hundreds of garimpeiros to the region. Many fortunes were made, but the golden age ended in 1889, when most of the stones had been hauled away, and the city was forgotten.

The current population is about 5,000, but since the national park was established in 1985, the city has enjoyed a renaissance. Lençóis has been designated a national monument for its 19th-century residential architecture. More than 250 *sobrados* are in the process of being restored. Other important towns in the area are Andaraí, Mucugê, and Palmeiras.

At **Poço Encantado,** south of Lençois, sunlight beams through the entrance to the cave and lights up the clear blue lake about 100 meters (300 feet) below. This spectacle is best seen between April and August from 10 AM to 1 PM. ⊠ *From Lençois, drive 2 hours south on BA 142.*

From the town of **Xique-Xique de Igatú,** a 19th-century stone road leads to a diamond-rush ghost camp. Here you can visit the miners' abandoned homes among the rocks and caves. ⊠ *30 km (19 mi) south of Poço Encantado.*

Lençóis has one tourist information center: **Bahiatursa** (⊠ Old City Hall, Praça Otaviano Alves 01 🕾 075/3334–1380).

Where to Stay and Eat

There are a growing number of pousadas in the area, all of which have good-quality, ranch-style accommodations, complete with hearty meals and a wide array of activities such as horseback riding, tennis, and swimming.

$ 🏨 **Pousada de Lençóis.** On the edge of Lençóis and next to the Parque Nacional da Chapada Diamantina is this homey pousada. A stay in one of its extra-large rooms (some sleep up to five people) truly makes you feel as if you're a guest in someone's country house. The large pool is surrounded by flower gardens. The restaurant and bar are open to the public, and an in-house tour agency arranges park trips. ⊠ *Rua Altina Alves 747, Lençóis* 🕾 *075/3334–1102* 🖷 *075/3334–1180* 🖃 *48 rooms* ⚲ *Restaurant, in-room safes, minibars, cable TV, pool, gym, bar, travel services* 🖃 *AE, D, MC, V* ⑩ *CP.*

$ 🏨 **Hotel Canto das Águas.** One of the first hotels to open after the national park was created, Canto das Águas is inspired by the colonial architecture of the nearby historic center. Arched hallways open to the garden that surrounds the main building. The Lençóis River runs through the backyard. The staff will arrange local guides and transportation to the park. ⊠ *Av. Sr. dos Passos 1, Lençóis* ☎ *075/3334–1154* 🖷 *075/ 3334–1188* ⊕ *www.lencois.com.br* 🖅 *44 rooms, 8 suites* ♿ *Restaurant, minibars, cable TV, pool, bar* ▤ *AE, D, MC, V.*

Sports & the Outdoors

In Lençóis, **Lentur Turismo Ecológico** (⊠ Av. 7 Setembro 10 ☎🖷 075/ 3334–1271) has trained guides for trekking expeditions in the Chapada. Other services include guided van tours of the area.

Parque Nacional Chapada Diamantina

㉕ *Park office (Palmeira): 60 km (37 mi) west of Lençóis*

Fodor's Choice
★

The Chapada Diamantina (Diamond Plateau), a series of mountain ranges with an average altitude of 3,000 feet, is among Brazil's most fascinating natural wonders. Here table-top mountains, natural pools, caves, valleys, and waterfalls abound. The flora and fauna of the area, which include wild orchids, bromeliads, and more than 200 bird species, have been the subject of two extensive studies by the Royal Botanical Gardens at Kew in England.

Established in 1985, the 1,520-square-km (593-square-mi) national park is one of the most scenic places in Brazil, comparable to the Grand Canyon in the U.S. Crystal-clear creeks and rivers, with rapids and waterfalls, the tall peaks of the Sincorá Range, with the highest point in Bahia at Barbados Peak (2,080 meters, or 7,000 feet), and over 70 grottos and caverns. The best time to visit the park is in the dry season from March to October. Mean temperature is 24°C (75°C), but expect lower night temperatures from May to July.

Bus or car is the usual way to get to Chapada Diamantina, although the road is not in perfect condition between Feira de Santana and Lençóis. The trip is about eight hours. Overnight buses leave from Salvador frequently. The quickest option is the daily flight from Salvador. At this writing, the park does not have a visitor center, only a small office run by IBAMA (the Brazilian Environmental Insitute) in Palmeira, with limited tourist information.

The tallest waterfall in Brazil, 1,312-foot **Cachoeira da Fumaça** (Smoke Waterfall), is the fifth-highest in the world. Most of the falling water turns into a thin mist and evaporates before reaching the ground, hence its name. ⊠ *20 km (12 mi) west of Lençóis.*

One of the most popular hiking trails, called the **Rio Serrano**, runs along the river of the same name. It has sand caves to explore, and natural pools that are highly polished by erosion so that they look a bit like marble hot tubs. There are three waterfalls along the way. ⊠ *Trailhead about 1 km (½ mi) north of Lençóis.*

A 20-minute climb of about 1,000 feet to the top of **Morro do Pai Inácio** provides the most fabulous 360-degree view of the Chapada Diamantina. ⊠ *20-minute drive northwest on BR-242 from Lençóis.*

A 30-minute climb down to the mouth of the **Lapa Doce** cave and a 40-minute walk through it (by appointment only) leads to stunning stalagmites and stalactites. This cave system has been mapped to about 25 km (16 mi), but only the first kilometer is open to visitors—the rest is on private property. ⊠ *From Lençois, take BR 242 west 25 km (16 mi), then take the road to Irecê for about 18 km (11 mi)* ☎ *075/3229–4117* 🎫 *R$10* ⊙ *By appointment.*

THE COCOA COAST

The best driving tour in this region is from Salvador north along the coast on the Estrada do Coco (Coconut Highway), picking up the Linha Verde (Green Highway, an extension of BA 099) at Praia do Forte. Along the way are fishing villages, endless beaches, restaurants, and small hotels and pousadas, stretching to Mangue Seco at the Sergipe state border. Regional bus service to towns on the Cocoa Coast departs from Salvador's Terminal Rodoviário.

Ilhéus

❷❻ *460 km (286 mi) south of Salvador.*

In Brazil, Ilhéus (literally meaning "islanders") is synonym with cocoa and Jorge Amado, one of Brazil's best-known contemporary writers. Amado spent his childhood here, and the house he lived in is now a cultural center. Many of his world-famous novels are set in places in and around Ilhéus. Catedral de São Sebastião (San Sebastian Cathedral) is the heart of the central area—a plaza surrounded by colonial-period buildings akin to those in Pelourinho.

Ilhéus has many beaches and a small harbor at the mouth of the Rio Cachoeira. The palm-tree-covered beaches to the south of the city are the most scenic; you can get a good view of them from hills that surround the city, such as Morro de Pernambuco (Mount Pernambuco). Ilhéus experienced fast development earlier in the 20th century with the export of cacau (cocoa) from plantations nearby. The spread of a bacterial disease in the 1980s almost wiped out the plantations; in recent times improved agricultural techniques and higher cocoa market prices are leading the way to economic resurgence in the region, tourism being another of the main pillars. Throngs of tourists descend during Carnival—the street festivities last just as long as and are as lively as in Salvador.

Ilhéustur (⊠ Praça do Teatro, Av. 7 Setembro 10 ☎☎ 071/3634–8142) is the municipal tourist board that provides information on lodging and local attractions.

Bar Vesúvio (⊠ Praça Dom Eduardo 190) was the inspiration for Jorge Amado's *Gabriela Cravo e Canela,* in 1958. Back then it was a favorite among the cocoa plantation-owners.

Where to Stay and Eat

The Cocoa Coast has a few upscale resorts and hotels and many budget pousadas with good-quality, ranch-style accommodations, complete

BEACH SAVVY

- As a rule, the farther away from the downtown area, the better the beach in terms of water cleanliness and number of people, especially on weekends

- Beaches in Bahia, as in most of Brazil, tend not to have facilities like bathrooms or showers

- Pickpocketing and minor theft can be a problem. Bring as few items to the beach as possible, and just enough money for the day. Never leave anything unattended.

- Vendors, no matter what age or gender, tend to be aggressive and overly persistent in Bahia, sometimes bordering on harassment. You might have to say no many times before they move on. Be patient or look for police officers (there are usually several on duty at Centro Historico for this reason alone).

- Larger cities such as Salvador, Ilhéus, and Porto Seguro have quick and comfortable public transportation to beaches, like the ônibus executivo (executive bus; a minibus or van, usually labeled ROTEIRO DAS PRAIAS).

- Be careful when entering the water for the first time—a few steps in can put you in deep waters

- Be aware of rock outcroppings and coral reefs that can cut your feet

- If you plan to snorkel, bring your own gear. Rentals are not always available.

- Food and drink are available at almost every beach, except those you have to hike to. However, if you're squeamish about eating food from a beach vendor, bring your own.

---

with hearty meals and a wide array of activities such as horseback riding, tennis, and swimming.

🕙 **$$$$**
Fodor'sChoice
★
🏨 **Transamérica Ilha de Comandatuba.** On an island with a giant coconut grove, this hotel has a private beach. The best accommodations are the bungalows—each has a balcony and a hammock. The many activities include fishing and various water sports. An airstrip has a weekly charter jet landings from São Paulo. ✉ *Ilha de Comandatuba s/n, Una 45690-000, 70 km (43 mi) south of Ilhéus* 🏠🏠 *073/3686–1122 or 0800/ 12–6060* ⊕ *www.transamerica.com.br* ⤴ *259 rooms, 110 bungalows* ♨ *2 restaurants, 3 bars, room service, in-room safes, minibars, cable TV, 2 pools, health club, spa, 18-hole golf course, 4 tennis courts, babysitting, children's program (ages 4–8), laundry service, concierge, business services, meeting rooms, convention center, airport shuttle, airstrip, shops* ➡ *AE, D, MC, V* ▧ *FAP.*

🕙 **$$**
🏨 **Ecoresort Tororomba.** This small beachfront resort is beside a beach with turquoise waters. The resort's main attractions are the sports facilities, such as the climbing wall, sea kayaks, and mountain bikes. ✉ *Praia de Canabrava , Km 21 Rod BA-001, Olivҫa, 45653-970, 25 km (16 mi) south of Ilhéus* 🕾 *073/3269–1200* 🖷 *073/3269–1090*

⊕ *www.tororomba.com.br* ⤳ *86 rooms, 4 bungalows* ⚙ *Restaurant, 2 bars, room service, in-room safes, minibars, cable TV, pool, sauna, health club, 2 tennis courts, beach, babysitting, children's program (ages 10–14), laundry service, concierge, business services, meeting rooms, airport shuttle* ☰ *AE, MC, V* ¶⊙¶ *MAP.*

THE DISCOVERY COAST

Protected areas where you can experience nature in its pristine state form the backdrop to the birthplace of Brazil.

Porto Seguro

㉗ Not too long ago, Porto Seguro (Safe Harbor) was a serene fishing village. Now it's one of the prime tourist destinations in the country, with international flights from several Europeans cities. Hotels, inns, and restaurants have risen to please nearly every need or taste.

Porto Seguro has an intense atmosphere comparable only to Salvador in Bahia. Picture a city whose main drag is called "Passarela do Alcool" (Booze Walkway). Carnival is a major event here, drawing hundreds of thousands of tourists. The beaches north of the city, such as Mutá are recommended for those looking for calmer grounds.

Fodor'sChoice ★ One of the most biodiverse places on the planet, **Estação Vera Cruz** is a 6,000-hectare nature preserve, and a great way to take a break from the beach. This the largest private Atlantic forest protected area in Brazil, owned by one of the largest paper pulp mills in the world (50 km/31 mi west of here). Call ahead to announce your visit. The visitor center introduces you to the ecology of the area. From there, knowledgeable guides lead you on a 2-km (1.2-mi) trail through the forest. Highlights are the *pau-brasil* (brazilwood) and *jatobá* (South American locust) trees, and birds—especially the colorful toucans and parrots. ⊠ *BR 367, at Km 37.5* ☏ *073/9985–1808* 🎫 *Free* ⊗ *By appointment.*

Where to Stay & Eat

$$$ ✕ **Bistrô da Helô.** One of the best-known restaurants in Porto Seguro. The fare is international, with emphasis on seafood. The seafood casserole and fish fillet in *maracujá* (passion flower fruit) sauce are recommended. ⊠ *Trv. Assis Chateubriand* ☏ *073/ 3288–3940* ☰ *MC, V* ⚙ *Reservations essential* ⊗ *Closed Mon.*

$ ✕ **Recanto do Sossego.** This restaurant right on Mutá beach, is very popular—on weekends you'll have to wait in line. But it's worth the wait. Fare is Italian—start with appetizers such fish carpaccio and move on to gnocci with pesto sauce. ⊠ *Praia do Mutá, Av. Beira Mar* ☏ *073/ 3672–1266* ☰ *AE, D, MC, V.*

★ $$ ⌂ **Villagio Arcobaleno.** Porto Seguro's five-star choice is right on hip Taperapuã Beach. Apartments are comfortable and decorated in tune with the tropical surroundings. The hotel maintains a large awning and wooden deck on the beach. ⊠ *Av. Beira Mar, at Km 6.5, 45810-000* ☏ *073/3679–1284 hotel, 0800/284–5222 reservations* 🖷 *073/3679–1269* ⊕ *www.hotelarcobaleno.com.br* ⤳ *160 rooms, 5 suites* ⚙ *Restaurant,*

EATING BAHIAN

WHEN AFRICAN SLAVES ARRIVED IN BAHIA, *they insinuated coconut milk, dendê (palm) oil, and hot spices into Portuguese and Indian dishes, transforming them into something quite new. Additional basic raw materials are lemon, coriander, tomato, onions, dried shrimp, salt, and hot chili peppers. Seafood is the thing in Bahia, and most regional seafood dishes are well seasoned, if not fiery hot. Bahia's most famous dish is moqueca, a seafood stew made with fish and/or shellfish, dendê oil, coconut milk, onions, and tomatoes, cooked quickly in a clay pot over a high flame. Bobó is equally tasty, but creamier version of moqueca, due to the addition of cassava flour. Other classics include vatapá, a thick puree-like stew made with fish, shrimp, cashews, peanuts, and a variety of seasonings; caruru, okra mashed with ginger, dried shrimp, and palm oil; ximxim de galinha, chicken marinated in lemon or lime juice, garlic,*

and salt and pepper and then cooked with dendê and peanut oil, coconut milk, tomatoes, and seasonings; and efo, a bitter chicorylike vegetable cooked with dried shrimp. Sarapatel is a Portuguese dish, a stew of pig meat and inner organs, that has been incorporated seamlessly into Bahian cuisine.

A popular snack is acarajé, a pastry of feijão fradinho (black-eyed beans) flour deep-fried in dendê oil and filled with camarão (sun-dried shrimp) and pimenta (hot-pepper sauce). A variation is abará, peas or beans boiled in a banana leaf instead of fried. Note that palm oil is high in saturated fat and hard to digest; you can order these dishes without it. Restaurants in Bahia usually serve hot pepper sauce on the side of all dishes, which is unusual elsewhere in Brazil.

---

bar, room service, in-room safes, minibars, cable TV, Internet room, pool, indoor pool, sauna, health club, 2 tennis courts, gym playground, laundry service, concierge, airport shuttle ▭ *D, MC, V* ⦿ *CP.*

$ ▦ **La Torre.** This hotel is very popular with international visitors because of its location on quiet Mutá Beach. Rooms are run-of-the-mill, but spacious. The restaurant serves international fare with some Bahian dishes. ✉*Praia do Mutá Av. Beira Mar 9999, 45650-000* ☎*073/3672–1243* 📠*073/ 3672–1616* ⊕ *www.latorreaparthotel.com.br* ↗ *74 rooms, 6 suites* ♨ *Restaurant, room service, kitchenette, in-room safes, gym, pool, sauna, minibars, cable TV, Internet room, airport shuttle* ▭ *AE, D, MC, V.*

Arraial d'Ajuda

28 The municipality of Arraial starts just across Rio Buranhém from Porto Seguro, a 10-min ferry ride. The town is about 4 km (2.5 mi) south of the river. Founded by Jesuits that arrived in 1549 with the Portuguese official Tomé de Souza, the first governor-general of Brazil. Its name is a tribute to Our Lady of Help, a much-revered saint in Portugal. The church and parish were the center of the Catholic church in Brazil for over a century.

In the 1970s, laid-back Arraial d'Ajuda attracted Brazilian hippies and then a slew of foreign adventurers moved here, giving the place an eclectic atmosphere and the nickname "Corner of the World."

Coroa Vermelha beach, to the south, is where the first mass in Brazil was celebrated. Other great beaches are Mucugê, Parracho, and Pitinga.

Where to Stay & Eat

$$ ✕ **Boi nos Aires.** If you have had your share of Bahian and seafood, a great change of taste is this Argentine-style steakhouse, with Argentine beef flown in from Buenos Aires. After a full day on the beach, the *asado* (Argentine-style grilled meat) should replenish your energy. ⊠ *Estrada do Mucugê 200* ☎ *073/3575–2554* ▭ *D, MC, V.*

¢ ✕ **A Portinha.** This popular buffet-style restaurant attracts many foreign visitors because of the many salad-bar and entrée options that include dishes from Bahia and Minas Gerais State. ⊠ *Estrada do Mucugê s/n* ☎ *073/3575–1717* ▭ *D, MC, V.*

★ ☾ **$$$** ▣ **Arraial d'Ajuda Eco Resort.** This resort should be your choice if you're looking for a beachfront hotel with ample activities—beside lazing on the beach. You can sail, windsurf, and dive; classes are offered for the neophyte. A water park next to the resort has many pools, water slides, and water games to keep children and adults entertained for the whole day. ⊠ *Ponta do Apaga Fogo, 45810-000* ☎ *073/3575–8500* 🖷 *073/ 575–1016* ⊕ *www.arraialresort.com.br* 🛏 *157 rooms, 9 suites* ☾ *Restaurant, bar, room service, in-room safes, minibars, cable TV, Internet room, pool, indoor pool, sauna, health club, children's program (ages 4–10), tennis court, gym, playground, laundry service, concierge, business center, convention center, meeting rooms, airport shuttle, shop* ▭ *AE, D, MC, V* �“❘ *MAP.*

$ ▣ **Manacá Pousada Parque.** The main draw are the comfortable and well decorated rooms, all with king-sized beds. Each room has a balcony with hammock. The pousada has a large garden surrounding its facilities, and is just one step from the beach ⊠ *Estrada Arraial 500, 4581–6000* ☎🖷 *073/575–1442* ⊕ *www.pousadamanaca.com.br* 🛏 *20 rooms* ☾ *Restaurant, minibars, cable TV, Internet room* ▭ *AE, V* ❘❘❘ *CP.*

Trancoso

㉙ Smaller that its northern neighbors Arraial and Porto Seguro, Trancoso moves at a much slower pace. Founded by Jesuit missionaries in 1586, its first name was St. John Baptist of the Indians. Life here circles around the downtown plaza called "Quadrado" (the Square), where pedestrians have the right of way—no cars allowed. This is where everybody goes for shopping, dining, and people-watching. In recent years Trancoso has become a boomtown of sorts, and a haven for high-society Brazilians from São Paulo, especially. As a result, it now has several upscale developments, such as the Club Med and a US$90-million 18-hole golf course.

Where to Stay & Eat

Compared to its northern neighbors, Trancoso has fewer lodging options, but you are sure to find a pousada that meets your taste. Or, if you prefer, go for the resort with a golf course. Some of the restaurants attract people from Porto Seguro and Arraial on weekends.

★ $$ ✕ **O Cacau.** Unique versions of Bahian dishes are served at this restaurant catering to international visitors. A must is the *arrumadinho,* with sun-dried meat, beans, cassava flour, and *pico-de-gallo* sauce. ⊠ *Praça São João s/n* ☎ *073/3668–1266* ▭ *MC, V* ⊙ *Closed Mon.*

$ ✕ **Capim Santo.** Capim Santo, right on the central square, is *the* place in Trancoso for seafood. A popular dish is the fish fillet in shrimp sauce. Servings are small. ⊠ *Praça São João s/n* ☎ *073/3668–1122* ▭ *AE, MC, V* ⊙ *Closed Sun.*

★ $$$–$$$$ ⌂ **Club Med Trancoso.** Built on the beachfront hills south of Trancoso's village, this Club Med chain went to great lengths to merge the sprawling resort with the landscape, with minimal environmental impact. Services are first rate, as this is one of the higher ranking hotels in this worldwide chain. The spa is very good. ⊠ *Km 18, Estrada do Arraial, 45818-000, 6 km/4 mi south of Trancoso* ☎ *073/3575–8400 or 0800/ 707–3782 (reservations)* ⎙ *073/3575–8484* ⊕ *www.clubmed.com.br* ⇱ *250 rooms, 50 suites* ⅋ *2 restaurants, 3 bars, beach, room service, in-room safes, minibars, cable TV, Internet room, 2 pools, sauna, spa, 8 tennis courts, gym playground, laundry service, concierge, convention center, meeting rooms, business center, airport shuttle* ▭ *AE, MC, V* ⌸ *FAP.*

$$ ⌂ **Pousada Etnia** This small pousada is designed for the most demanding guest. The Italian owners and managers also keep an art and antiques shop nearby. Most of the furniture in the pousada's public areas come from the shop. Each bungalow has a theme decor, like the Moroccan bungalow. Among the draws here are the several massage options and artsy activities taught by art therapists that assist you with painting and pottery that are designed to help you reach the highest level of relaxation. ⊠ *Rua Principal s/n, 45818-000* ☎ *073/ 3668–1137* ⎙ *073/3668–1549* ⊕ *www.etniabrasil.com.br* ⇱ *5 bungalows* ⅋ *Restaurant, room service, in-room safes, gym, pool, sauna, massage, minibars, cable TV, Internet room, airport shuttle; no children under 14, no smoking* ▭ *D, MC, V* ⌸ *FAP.*

FodorsChoice ★

$ ⌂ **Pousada Mata N'ativa.** Location is prime here, right on Trancoso's riverbank, only three minutes from the beach and the downtown square. As the name implies—Mata Nativa means "native forest"—the pousada is virtually hidden under the canopy of Atlantic forest. In the rooms, large beds with bedposts holding mosquito nets add to the rugged ambience. ⊠ *Estrada do Arraial s/n, 45818-000* ☎ *073/3668–1830* ⊕ *www.matanativapousada.com.br* ⇱ *6 rooms* ⅋ *Dining room, minibars, cable TV* ▭ *No credit cards* ⌸ *CP.*

off the beaten path

FodorsChoice ★

PARQUE NACIONAL MARINHO DE ABROLHOS – The first Brazilian (and South American) marine park, Marinho de Abrolhos, 856 km (532 mi) south of Salvador, was created to protect these remote the gigantic coral reefs teeming with marine wildlife. Charles Darwin's expedition made a stop here in 1832, and noted the abundant bird, whale, turtles, and fish population. The archipelago, 36 km (23 mi) off the coast of southern Bahia, is made up of five islands, four of which are within the park. Ilha Santa Barbara is a naval base with a lighthouse run by the Brazilian Navy. The shallow waters on the continental shelf are the Abrolhos Banks, containing one of the major coral formations in the Atlantic.

There are 15 different coral species in Abrolhos. The most impressive are mushroom-like columnar reefs rising about 90 feet from the ocean floor. The endemic "brain coral" is found on top of these structures. A growing population of about 2,000 humpback whales migrate 5,000 km (3,200 mi) from the South Atlantic to mate, birth, and play in these warm and food-rich waters around Abrolhos.

The town of **Caravelas** is the gateway to the Marine Park, where several operators have guided day trips on schooners and yachts to Abrolhos—visitors are only allowed with accredited tour operators. Paradise (⇨ Tours, *below*) is a recommended operator. The highlights of these excursions are scuba-diving and snorkeling in the reefs, an experience that has been equated to diving in an aquarium. The wreck of the steamer *Rosalina*, which sank in 1939 with a cargo of cement and beer, can also be explored. There is also a mile-long hiking trail around Ilha Siriba (the only one open to visitors), where you can see nesting areas of several bird species and colorful fish in reef pools. ⊠ *Praia do Quitongo (Park Administration), Caravelas* ☎ *073/3297–1111* ✉ *R$10 (included in tour price)* ☉ *By guided tour only.*

SALVADOR & BAHIA ESSENTIALS

Transportation

For more information about transportation, *see* Smart Travel Tips A to Z, *at* the front of this book.

Most side-trip destinations from Salvador can be easily reached by car. Morro de São Paulo and Chapada Diamantina have flights. To visit the Discovery Coast, fly to Porto Seguro (723 km/450 mi south of Salvador), and then rent a car to explore other beaches and attractions. For Ilhés and Itacaré (Cocoa Coast), you can fly directly to Ilhéus, 460 km (286 mi) south of Salvador.

BY AIR

Salvador's airport has become one of the busiest in Brazil. In the last few years several international carriers have opened direct service from abroad, especially from Europe. TAM is the only airline that flies directly from the U.S. (Miami). Most international flights require a change of plane in São Paulo. For major airline information (including TAM), *see* Air Travel *in* Smart Travel Tips A to Z.

OceanAir is the regional carrier for Chapada Diamantina. The daily one-hour flight to Lençóis costs about R$730 (round-trip).

A handful of small flight operators, including AeroStar and Adey, have service to Morro de São Paulo from Salvador. The 20-minute flight costs about $R350.

🛪 Airport **Aeroporto Deputado Luís Eduardo Magalhães** ✉ Praça Gago Coutinho s/n, São Cristovão ☎ 071/3204-1214 or 071/3204-1444.

🛪 Regional Airlines **AeroStar** ☎ 071/3377-4406. **Adey** ☎ 071/3377-2451. **OceanAir** ☎ 0300/789-8160.

AIRPORT TRANSFERS The Salvador airport, Aeroporto Luís Eduardo Magalhães, is quite far from downtown—37 km (23 mi) to the northeast. A trip from the airport to central hotels should cost about R$60. Choose one of the many taxi companies that have booths outside the arrival gate. You can prepay your ride to the hotel. The *ônibus executivo,* an air-conditioned bus, runs daily from 6 to 9, ask for a timetable at hotel lobbies; it costs about R$12 and takes an hour to reach downtown, stopping at hotels along the way. Several companies operate these buses, of which the largest is Transportes Ondina. Drivers don't speak English and might have difficulty understanding your hotel name.

🚌 **Transportes Ondina** ✉ Av. Vasco da Gama 347 ☎ 071/3245-6366.

BY BOAT

Itaparica and the other harbor islands can be reached by taking a ferry or a launch (small boat that carries up to five passengers) from Salvador, by hiring a motorized schooner, or by joining a harbor schooner excursion—all departing from two docks. Launches cost about R$2 and leave every 45 minutes from 7 to 6 from the Terminal Turístico Marítimo. The ferry takes passengers and cars and leaves every half hour between 6 AM and 10:30 PM from the Terminal São Joaquim. The fare is around R$2 for passengers and R$14–R$18 for cars, and it takes 45 minutes to cross the bay.

Morro de São Paulo, can be reached by catamaran or launch from Terminal Turístico Marítimo for about R$50 to R$70.

From Caravelas (865 km/537 mi from Salvador) you can book a boat trip to the Arquipelago de Abrolhos (Abrolhos Archipelago), Bahia's first underwater marine park, for about R$300.

🚢 **Disque Ferry** (Dial-a-Ferry hotline) ☎ 071/3319-2890. **Terminal Marítimo São Joaquim** ✉ Av. Oscar Ponte 1051, São Joaquim ☎ 071/3321-7100. **Terminal Turístico Marítimo** ✉ Av Fraṇa, s/n, Comércio ☎ 071/3243-0741.

BY BUS Long-distance bus tickets are sold at the Terminal Rodoviário in Salvador, from which all buses heading out of the city depart. Itapemirim has three buses a day to Recife (13 hours, R$140), Fortaleza (19 hours, R$175), and Rio (28 hours, R$250).

Within Bahia, Águia Branca offers daily overnight service to Porto Seguro (11 hours, R$95) leaving Salvador at 8 PM. Santa Maria has hourly service to Praia do Forte starting at 5 AM, with the last bus returning to the city at 6 PM; tickets cost about R$15. Camurujipe has hourly service to Cachoeira between 5:30 AM and 7 PM, for R$17. Real Expresso buses make the 8-hour trip to Chapada Diamantina (Lençóis) for about

R$35, with departures at 11:30 PM daily and at 7 AM Tuesday, Thursday, and Saturday. Return is at 11:30 PM daily, with additional departures at 7:30 AM Monday, Wednesday, and Friday.

Within Salvador, use the *executivo* (executive) buses. Although other buses serve most of the city and cost a pittance (R$1.40), they're often crowded and dirty, and pickpocketing is a problem. Fancier executivo buses (R$3.50) serve tourist areas more completely. The glass-sided green, yellow, and orange Jardineira bus (marked PRAÇA DA SÉ; R$6) runs every 40 minutes 7:30 to 7:30 daily from the Praça da Sé in Pelourinho to the Stella Maris Beach, traveling along the Orla Marítima series of avenues. Hop off when you see a beach you like. The Santa Maria/Catuense company operates six buses (marked PRAIA DO FORTE) daily that stop at Barra do Jacuípe Beach.

The municipal Circular buses, operated by both Transportes Ondina and Transportes Rio Vermelho, cost mere centavos and run along the beaches to downtown, ending at São Joaquim, where ferries depart for Ilha de Itaparica. For Setor Histórico, get off at the Elevador Lacerda stop, across from Mercado Modelo.

🚍 Bus Information **Águia Branca** ☎ 071/3460-4400. **Camurujipe** ☎ 071/3450-2109. **Itapemirim** ☎ 071/3450-5644 ⊕ www.itapemirim.com.br. **Real Expresso** ☎ 075/3334-1112 in Lençóis, 071/450-9310 in Salvador ⊕ www.realexpresso.com.br. **Santa Maria/Catuense** ☎ 071/3450-0321. **Terminal Rodoviário** ✉ Av. Antônio Carlos Magalhães 4352, Pituba, Salvador ☎ 071/3450-3871.

BY CAR Most of Bahia's highways and secondary roads near the coast are generally in good condition. Traffic can be daunting especially in the industrial district west of Salvador (BR 101, BR 116, and BR 262). Many soteropolitanos are reckless drivers, making driving quite an adventurous proposition, especially on rush hours during weekdays. Limited parking spaces in Setor Historico can be frustrating. To visit Setor Historico, the best alternative is to park in one of the paid lots near Mercado Modelo and take the elevator to Cidade Alta. Things are much calmer on weekends.

You can combine a road trip to Cachoeira and Chapada Diamantina. From Salvador, take BR 324 north for about 55 km (34 mi), then head west on BR 420 through the town of Santo Amaro. The trip takes 1½ hours. The route to Chapada Diamantina goes through the town of Santo Estevão, then south on BR-116 until the intersection with BR-242. Then it's straight west on BR-242 to Lençóis.

To reach Praia do Forte by car, take the Estrada do Coco (BA-099) north and follow the signs. From there on, it's called Linha Verde (Green Line), to Costa do Sauípe and the northern beaches all the way to the Sergipe border.

🚗 Rental Agencies **Avis** ✉ Aeroporto Luís Eduardo Magalhães, Salvador ☎ 071/3251-8500 or 0800/198-456 ⊕ www.avis.com.br ✉ Aeroporto Porto Seguro, Av. do Aeroporto s/n, Porto Seguro ☎ 073/3288-4033. **Hertz** ✉ Aeroporto Luís Eduardo Magalhães, Salvador ☎ 071/3377-3633 or 0800/701-7300 ⊕ www.hertz.com.br. **Localiza** ✉ Aeroporto Luís Eduardo Magalhães, Salvador ☎ 071/377-2272, 0800/99-2000 in Brazil ⊕ www.localiza.com.br ✉ Aeroporto Porto Seguro, Av. do Aeroporto s/n, Porto Seguro ☎ 073/3288-3106.

BY TAXI Taxis in Salvador are metered and most are organized through cooperatives. Tipping isn't expected. Beware that sometimes drivers might try to jack up the fare by "forgetting" (or, in some cases, refusing) to turn on the meter. You can hail a *comum* taxi (white with a blue stripe) on the street or at designated stops near major hotels, or summon one by phone. You can hire a comum taxi for the whole day for about R$135. The more expensive taxis, usually air-conditioned full-size sedans, are called *especial* (special taxis), and congregate outside major hotels. Cometas is a reliable company.

🛈 **Cometas** ☎ 071/3244-4500. **Rádio-Táxi** ☎ 071/3243-4333.

Contacts & Resources

BANKS & EXCHANGING SERVICES

Major banks have money exchange booths in some branches. In Salvador, try Citibank or Banco do Brasil. In Porto Seguro, Banco do Brasil is your only option. Credit cards and sometimes dollar bills are welcome in most areas of tourist-friendly Bahia, but rarely if you are traveling to smaller towns or the interior. For your own safety, never exchange money on the streets. It is also illegal.

Some banks accept only cards with Visa/Plus logos and others accept only cards with MasterCard/Cirrus logos. Banco24horas ATMs usually accept all cards, including American Express. *See* "Money Matters" *in* Smart Travel Tips A to Z for more information.

🛈 **Banco do Brasil** ✉ Praça Padre Anchieta 11, Pelourinho, Salvador ☎ 071/3321-6842 ✉ Av. Dos Navegantes 22, Centro Porto Seguro ☎ 073/3288-8700 **Citibank** ✉ Rua Miguel Calmon 555, Comércio ☎ 071/4009-6201.

EMERGENCIES

In an emergency, dial ☎ 192 for Pronto Socorro (first aid). In Salvador there is a special tourist police force. The tourist police precinct (Delegacia de Proteção do Turista) is on Largo de São Francisco south of Terreiro de Jesus. It deals as best it can (on a shoestring budget) with tourist-related crime after the fact. Officers, some of whom have rudimentary second-language skills, wear armbands that say POLÍCIA TURÍSTICA. The regular police is known as the POLÍCIA MILITAR.

Emergência (☎ 136) is a pharmacy hot line.

🛈 Emergency Services **Delegacia de Proteção do Turista** ☎ 071/3320-4103.
🛈 Hospitals **Hospital Espanhol** ✉ Av. 7 de Setembro 4161, Barra ☎ 071/3264-1500. **Hospital Português** ✉ Av. Princesa Isabel 914, Santa Isabel ☎ 071/3203-5555.
🛈 Hotlines **Police** ☎ 190. **Pronto Socorro** (First Aid) ☎ 192.
🛈 24-Hour Pharmacies **Farmácia Estrela Galdino** ✉ Aeroclube Plaza Shopping Center, Liberdade ☎ 071/3388-6493.

INTERNET

All hotels and even many small pousadas have Internet services for a small fee. There are also Internet cafés scattered around the city. One convenient location in the Barra neighborhood is Café Spaghetteria.

🛈 Internet Cafés **Internet Café Spaghetteria** ✉ Av. 7 de Setembro 37001, Porto da Barra ☎ 071/3267-1644.

MAIL & SHIPPING

Salvador's main post office is in the Cidade Baixa's Praça Inglaterra. Other branches are in Pelourinho, Mercado Modelo, and at the Barra shopping mall. There is a branch at the airport that stays open 24 hours; all others are open weekdays 8–5. All branches offer express-mail service.

Correios (✉ Rua Alfredo de Brito 43, Pelourinho ☎ 071/3243–9383).

TOUR OPTIONS

Salvador's large group tours are cursory, and their guides often speak minimal English; such tours are also targeted by hordes of street vendors. Private tours with an accredited Bahiatursa guide can be hired through your hotel or a travel agency or at a Bahiatursa office (⇨ Visitor Information). Prices vary depending on the size of the group; most include hotel pickup and drop-off. Do not hire "independent" guides who approach you at churches and other sights; they are normally not accredited and will very likely overcharge.

Tatur Tours is renowned for its African-heritage tours of Bahia. Its attentive personnel can arrange personalized special-interest city tours and top-notch excursions from Salvador. Top Hilton Turismo has the usual city tours and interesting boat cruises, including a trip around Baía de Todos os Santos in a trimaran and a schooner cruise to the islands. It also has a tour to the nudist beach at Massarandupió, along the northern coast.

Several travel agencies offer half-day minibus tours with hotel pickup and drop-off for about R$90–R$120. Agencies also offer daylong harbor tours on motorized schooners (about R$100) and night tours (about R$125) that include dinner and an Afro-Brazilian music-and-dance show.

BBTUR has excellent buses and vans; request an English-speaking guide ahead of time. The company has a full line of tours not only of Salvador but also of surrounding areas; there's also a branch in the lobby of the Breezes Costa do Sauípe resort. Bahia Adventure Ecoturismo can help you arrange jeep tours, rafting, and other adventure treks in the Praia do Forte area. Odara Turismo, in the arcade at the Praia do Forte Eco Resort Hotel, arranges four-wheel-drive tours of the area plus horseback and hiking trips. In Praia do Forte, Fly and Fun has scenic flights over Coconut Coast and the interior.

🚩 **Bahia Adventure** ✉ Km 76, Rodovia BA 099, Costa do Sauípe, Mata de São João ☎ 71/464–2525 ⊕ www.bahiaadventure.com. **BBTUR** ✉ Vila Nova da Praia, suites 22–23, Costa do Sauípe, Mata de São João ☎ 071/3464–2121 ✉ Av. Tancredo Neves 2421, Suite 1700, Centro Empresarial Redenção, Pituba, Salvador ☎ 071/3341–8800. **Fly and Fun** ☎ 071/3676–1540. **Odara Turismo** ✉ Praça da Música s/n, Praia do Forte, Mata de São João ☎ 071/676–1080. **Tatur Tours** ✉ Av. Tancredo Neves 274, Suite 304, Centro Empresarial Iguatemi, Bloco B, Iguatemi, Salvador ☎ 071/3450–7216 ⊕ www.tatur.com.br. **Top Hilton Turismo** ✉ Rua Fonte do Boi 05, 41940-360, Rio Vermelho, Salvador ☎ 071/3334–5223 ⊕ www.tophilton.com.br. **Paradise** ✉ Avenida das Palmeiras 313, 45900-000, Centro, Caravelas ☎ 071/3297–1433.

VISITOR INFORMATION

Bahiatursa, the state tourist board, is the best source of information about areas outside of Salvador. There are branches in Salvador and major tourist areas. Emtursa, Salvador's tourist board, is open weekdays 8–6 and operates mobile tourist information units in the Centro Histórico area (Pelourinho). Its main branch is conveniently located in the Elevador Lacerda building. Some receptionists are bilingual, and there are leaflets with information on current events, restaurants, and tours.

Bahiatursa ⊠ Centro de Convenções, Av. Simon Bolivar s/n, Jardim Armação, Salvador ☎ 071/370–8400 ⊕ Institutional: www.bahiatursa.ba.gov.br; Tourist Information: www.bahia.com.br ⊠ Aeroporto Internacional Luís Eduardo Magalhães s/n, Salvador ☎ 071/3204–1244 ⊠ Av. Antônio Carlos Magalhães 4362, Terminal Rodoviário, Salvador ☎ 071/3450–0871 ⊠ Rua das Laranjeiras 12, Pelourinho, Salvador ☎ 071/3321–2133 ⊠ Mercado Modelo, Praça Visconde de Cayrú 250, Comércio, Salvador ☎ 071/3241–0242 ⊠ Av. do Farol s/n, Praia do Forte ☎ No phone ⊠ Praça Manoel Ribeiro Coelho s/n, Centro, Porto Seguro ☎ 073/3268–1390 ⊠ Antiga Prefeitura, Rua Otaviano Alves 01, Lençóis ☎ 075/3334–1380. **Emtursa** ⊠ Upper Deck, Elevador Lacerda, Cidade Alta ☎ 071/3380–4200 ⊕ www.emtursa.salvador.ba.gov.br.

Recife, Natal & Fortaleza

WORD OF MOUTH

"The beaches in Recife are so much better than in Rio and not as touristy."

—cb

"Many beaches near Fortaleza could surprise you with their beauty. Jericoacoara beach is really a once-in-a-lifetime beach experience."

—Gustavo

"Recife and Olinda are cultural havens . . . In Olinda you will feel like you are in a time centuries past. Recife will give you big-city bustle, but small-town friendliness."

—daniel lee

Updated by
Alessandra
Faria, Jefferson
Santos, and
Brad Weiss

LIKE THE WHOLE OF BRAZIL, the Far Northeast is a place of contrasts. Churches, villas, and fortresses in Recife, Natal, and Fortaleza tell the tale of Portuguese settlers who fought Dutch invaders and amassed fortunes from sugar. The beaches in and around these cities evoke Brazil's playful side and its love affair with sun, sand, and sea. West of the cities, the rugged, often drought-stricken *sertão* (bush) shows Brazil's darker side—one where many people struggle for survival. This warp and weave of history and topography is laced with threads of culture: indigenous, European, African, and a unique blend of all three that is essentially Brazilian.

Brazil's northeastern cities are experiencing a renaissance whose changes strike a balance between preservation and progress. Recife remains a place of beautiful waters, and nearby Olinda is still a charming enclave of colonial architecture—though bohemians have long since replaced sugar barons. On Ceará State's 570-km-long (354-mi-long) coast, Fortaleza continues to thrive against a backdrop of fantastic beaches with both new amenities and timeless white dunes. Although smaller and with a less storied past, Natal and the surrounding region are experiencing dizzying growth in tourism and other major industries.

History

To protect Brazil from other European "invaders," the Portuguese crown divided the territory up into governed and defended captaincies in the 16th century. The northeastern captaincy of Pernambuco covered an area that today includes the states of Ceará, Rio Grande do Norte, Paraíba, and Alagoas. A number of captaincies failed, due largely to the inexperience of the captains, but Pernambuco thrived. Its captain, Duarte Coelho, adeptly established good relations with the area's native people and was among the first to employ African labor. At one point Pernambuco had more sugar *engenhos* (mills) than any other captaincy. Olinda, its capital, was filled with elegance and luxury, financed by sugar barons. Recife, the capital of what is now Pernambuco State, also began to evolve as a major port.

In 1611 Martim Soares Moreno was dispatched from Portugal to a captaincy in the far northeast, with orders to fend off the French, who were threatening the area. Captain Moreno fell in love with the place—parts of which became the state of Ceará and its capital, Fortaleza—and with its people. He was especially taken with a native woman, whom he married. (The love affair was immortalized in the 19th-century classic Brazilian novel *Iracema,* named for the Indian woman, by José de Alencar. Contemporary Fortaleza's Mucuripe Bay has a famous statue of Iracema by Corbiano Lins, a sculptor from Pernambuco.)

Although the French had posed an early threat to Brazil, it was the Dutch who truly tested its mettle. In 1621 they established the Dutch West India Company, and began attacks in northeastern Brazil. They took brief control of Pernambuco, but the Portuguese ousted them in 1654. Before the Dutch arrived, Olinda had been the center of power and wealth in Pernambuco. But the Dutch had developed Recife into a thriving port that eventually surpassed Olinda economically. Eventually, Recife became the capital of Pernambuco. Ceará State, to the north, was too arid for farming, and instead became the cattle ranching center of the northeast, producing beef and leather products.

The 19th century brought a series of revolutions in the northeast, opposing the creation of an empire in Brazil. Pernambuco led a struggle—aided by Ceará, Paraíba and Rio Grande do Norte—to create an independent nation from the rest of Brazil, but was defeated. Freedom and independence were central themes in the northeast in the 19th century, when there were revolts and rebellions for free speech, workers' rights, abolition of slavery, and other issues. (Ceará was the first state to abolish slavery, in 1881.) In 1825 the continent's first newspaper, the *Diário de Pernambuco,* was begun here; in 1828 the first law school in Brazil was founded in Olinda.

During the 19th century the sugar trade declined, leaving the northeast economically behind Rio and São Paulo. Many workers left Pernambuco and Ceará for coffee plantations in the south, or rubber plantations in the Amazon. Northeasterners felt, in the early 20th century, that the new republic's government was neglecting the northeast, leading to support for Getúlio Vargas in the Revolution of 1930, which unseated the incumbent government.

In the 20th century the northeast continued to rely on a dwindling sugarcane and cattle-ranching markets, placing much stress on the land and people. Agrarian reform is badly needed here, and parts of the northeast are some of the poorest in Brazil. But the cities of Olinda—now a UNESCO World Heritage Site—Recife, Natal, and Fortaleza are highly developed, and increasingly earning income from industry and tourism rather than sugar and cattle.

Exploring Recife, Natal & Fortaleza

The Nordeste (Northeast) of Brazil includes the coastal states from Bahia to Maranhão. Right in the middle of this region are three of the largest (after Salvador) and most vibrant cities: Recife, Natal, and Fortaleza. Several good main and secondary roads, some of them right along the coast, run north–south through the region. Still, considering the distances, it's best to fly between the cities. From each you can rent a car, take a bus, or sign up for a guided tour and explore other coastal communities or inland areas.

When to Go
High season corresponds to school vacations (July) and Carnival (late December–mid-March). Prices are better off-season, but if you've come to partake in festivities, Olinda has one of the best Carnival celebrations in the country. Also, the region has two of the most popular out-of-season Carnival celebrations: Carnatal in Natal, on the first weekend in December; and Fortal in Fortaleza, on the last weekend in July. Temperatures hover between about 20°C and 35°C (70°F and 95°F) year-round—temperatures get hotter the farther north you go. Rain is heaviest from May to August in Recife. In Fortaleza, March and April are the rainiest months. Natal sits at about 25°C (75°F) year-round; it sees much less rain than Fortaleza or Recife, but March–July are the wettest months.

If you have
5 days

Fly into **Recife ❶–⓬** and go straight to 🏨 **Olinda ⓭**, where you should spend two nights. In a day you can easily explore the colonial area. The next day spend a few hours in nearby Recife, which has several museums and sites worth visiting. On the third day either take a short flight or the four-hour bus ride to 🏨 **Natal ⓯**. Stay in the Ponta Negra area and use it as a base to explore the nearby beaches. Reserve one day to visit Genipabu and take a dune-buggy ride through its remarkable sand dunes. Also head to **Praia de Pipa ⓰**—be sure to take the boat trip to see the dolphins.

9

If you have
7 days

Do the same as above, but make sure to get in a quick trip to 🏨 **Fernando de Noronha,** which has some of the most beautiful beaches on the continent. While there, you should scuba dive or snorkel, as the marine wildlife in the protected archipelago is spectacular. It's best to spend three days at Fernando de Noronha. You should be able to save a day from the itinerary above by skipping the Recife tour and by avoiding the trip between Recife and Natal: Fly from **Recife ❶–⓬** to Fernando de Noronha but take the return flight to 🏨 **Natal ⓯**.

If you have
10 days

Follow the seven-day itinerary and tack on a trip to **Cariri ⓱** at the end of your trip. This will give you a taste for the vastly different landscapes and culture of the interior. Highlights are mysterious rock formations and well-preserved rock paintings. It takes about four hours by car from Natal to get to Cariri. You should go with a tour operator, as transport is rather difficult.

About the Restaurants

The restaurants (all of which are indicated by a ✕) that we list are the cream of the crop in each price category. Properties indicated by a ✕🏨 are lodging establishments whose restaurant warrants a special trip.

About the Hotels

We always list the facilities that are available at the lodgings that we list (all indicated with a 🏨), but we don't specify whether they cost extra: when pricing accommodations, always ask what's included. Most hotels charge as little as half the rack rate during high season and significantly less during low season. Properties indicated by a ✕🏨 are lodging establishments whose restaurant warrants a special trip.

WHAT IT COSTS In Reais					
	$$$$	**$$$**	**$$**	**$**	**¢**
RESTAURANTS	over R$60	R$45–R$60	R$30–R$45	R$15–R$30	under R$15
HOTELS	over R$500	R$375–R$500	R$250–R$375	R$125–R$250	under R$125

Restaurant prices are for a dinner entrée. Hotel prices are for two people in a standard double room in high season, excluding taxes.

RECIFE

Just over 3.2 million people call the capital of Pernambuco State home. This vibrant metropolis 829 km (515 mi) north of Salvador has a spirit that's halfway between that of the modern cities of Brazil's south and of the traditional northeastern centers. It offers both insight on the past and a window to the future.

It was in Pernambuco State, formerly a captaincy, that the most violent battles between the Dutch and the Portuguese took place. Under the Portuguese, the capital city was the nearby community of Olinda. But beginning in 1637 and during the Dutch turn at the reins (under the powerful count Maurício de Nassau), both Olinda and Recife were greatly developed.

The Dutch had hoped that Brazilian sugar planters wouldn't resist their rule, but many took up arms. In 1654, after a series of battles around Recife, the Dutch finally surrendered. In the 17th century Pernambuco maintained much of the affluence of the earlier sugar age by cultivating cotton. With several rivers and offshore reefs, Recife proved to be an excellent port and began to outgrow Olinda.

Today Recife is a leader in health care and design, among other things. It's also Brazil's third-largest gastronomic center—it's almost impossible to get a bad meal here. Nearby Olinda has been recognized by UNESCO as part of Humanity's Natural and Cultural Heritage. It has attracted artists who display their canvases on easels behind the iron-barred windows of well-preserved colonial homes.

Recife is built around three rivers and connected by 49 bridges. Its name comes from the *arrecifes* (reefs) that line the coast. Because of this unique location, water and light often lend the city interesting textures. In the morning, when the tide recedes from Boa Viagem Beach, the rocks of the reefs slowly reappear. Pools of water are formed, fish flap around beachgoers, and the rock formations dry into odd colors. And if the light is just right on the Rio Capibaribe, the ancient buildings of Recife Antigo (Old Recife) are reflected off the river's surface in a watercolor display.

Exploring Recife

Recife is spread out and somewhat hard to navigate. Centro consists of three areas: Recife Antigo, the old city; Recife proper, with the districts of Santo Antônio and São José; and the districts of Boa Vista and Santo Amaro. The first two areas are on islands formed by the Rivers Capibaribe, Beberibe, and Pina; the third is made into an island by the Canal Tacaruna.

Centro—with its mixture of high-rises, colonial churches, and markets—is always busy during the day. The crowds and the narrow streets can make finding your way around even more confusing. With the exception of Recife Antigo, Centro is dead at night and should be avoided as a safety precaution.

Beaches

Some of Brazil's most beautiful and peaceful beaches lie along the coast from Fortaleza to Recife. The Atlantic waters throughout the region are warm year-round, and many beaches, particularly those near Fortaleza, have dunes high enough to ski down. The BA 099 highway, called the Linha Verde (Green Line), links cities and beaches and is part of an effort to protect Brazil's green spaces.

Carnatal & Fortal

The out-of-season Carnival celebrations in Natal and Fortaleza are two of the largest in Brazil. Natal's celebration is called Carnatal, and is held the first weekend in December. Fortaleza's Fortal is held the last week in July.

9

Carnival

The highly animated Carnival in Olinda is considered to be among the three best in Brazil, along with those in Rio and Salvador. Olinda's celebration is much more like the Carnivals of yesteryear, with forró and maracatu music and tamer costumes. Olinda is famous for its brightly costumed and painted *bonecos de pano* (giant cloth dolls) that rise above the crowds, operated by men on stilts, and *mamulengos* (marionettes).

Northeastern Cuisine

Lobster, shrimp, crabs, and squid find their way to most menus in this part of the country. Also common is *carne de sol,* or sun-dried beef, generally served with rice, beans, and manioc root. A popular northeastern side dish is *paçoca* (ground-up carne de sol, sliced onions, and manioc flour). Fried tapioca pancakes, a typical dessert, are filled with bananas, grated coconut, or cheese. Pineapples, mangos, guavas, and cashews are found here in abundance. Sugarcane, which grows beside many roadways, is pressed into the delicious *caldo de cana* (sugarcane juice), but is more often drunk in its distilled form, as *cachaça.* The liquor is used in Brazil's national drink, the *caipirinha* (cachaça, lime, and sugar).

Six kilometers (4 mi) south of Centro is the upscale residential and beach district of Boa Viagem, reached by bridge across the Bacia do Pina. Praia da Boa Viagem (Boa Viagem Beach), the Copacabana of Recife, is chockablock with trendy clubs and restaurants as well as many moderately priced and expensive hotels.

Numbers in the text correspond to numbers in the margin and on the Recife map.

What to See

❻ **Casa da Cultura.** In this 19th-century building, the old cells, with their heavy iron doors, have been transformed into shops that sell clay figurines, wood sculptures, carpets, leather goods, and articles made from woven straw. One of the cells has been kept in its original form to give you an idea of how the prisoners lived. ⊠ *Rua Floriano Peixoto s/n, Santo Antônio* ☎ *081/3224–2850* ⊕ *www.fundarp.pe.gov.br* ☎ *Free* ☉ *Weekdays 9–7, Sat. 9–6, Sun. 9–2.*

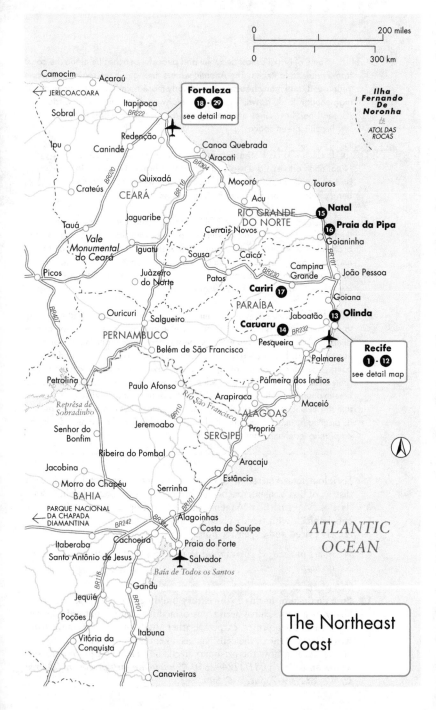

The Northeast Coast

4 **Catedral de São Pedro dos Clérigos.** The facade of this cathedral, which was built in 1782, has fine wood sculptures; inside is a splendid trompe-l'oeil ceiling. The square surrounding the cathedral is a hangout for artists, who often read their poetry or perform folk music. It's lined with many restaurants, shops, and bars. A museum has exhibits on Carnival and an art gallery. ⊠ *Pátio de São Pedro, São José* ☎ *081/3224–2954* 🖭 *Free* ☉ *Tues.–Fri. 8–11 and 2–4, Sat. 8–10:30.*

8 **Fortaleza do Brum** (Military Museum). To safeguard their control, the Dutch wisely yet futilely built more than one fortress. In this one (c. 1629) you find reminders of those precarious days in the on-site **Museu Militar**, with its collection of old cannons, infantry weapons, and soldiers' utensils; there's even a skeleton of a soldier that dates from 1654. The fort also has a restaurant. ⊠ *Praça Comunidade Luso-Brasileiro s/n, Recife Antigo* ☎ *081/3224–4620 or 081/3224–7559* 🖭 *R$2* ☉ *Tues.–Fri. 8–4:30, weekends 2–5.*

9 **Forte das Cinco Pontas.** The Dutch used mud to build the original five-sided fort in 1630. It was rebuilt in 1677 with stone and mortar; it now only has only four sides, but it has retained its original name. Inside is the **Museu da Cidade,** where maps and photos illustrate Recife's history. Before becoming a museum, it was used as a military headquarters and a prison. ⊠ *Praça das Cinco Pontas, São José* ☎ *081/3224–8492* 🖭 *R$1* ☉ *Tues.–Fri. 9–6, weekends 1–5.*

5 **Igreja e Convento do Carmo.** The historic baroque-style church and convent are constructed of wood and white gold. The main altar has a life-size statue of Our Lady of Carmel. ⊠ *Praça do Carmo s/n, Santo Antônio* ☎ *081/3224–3341 or 081/3224–3174* 🖭 *Free* ☉ *Weekdays 6:30 AM–8 PM, Sat. 7 AM–noon, Sun. 10–noon and 6 PM–9 PM. Mass weekdays at 6:30, 6, and 7; Sat. at 7; Sun. at 10 and 7.*

2 **Igreja da Ordem Terceira de São Francisco.** Built in 1606, this church has beautiful Portuguese tile work. Don't miss the adjoining Capela Dourada (Golden Chapel), which was constructed in 1697 and is an outstanding example of Brazilian baroque architecture. The complex also contains a convent—the Convento Franciscano de Santo Antônio—and a museum displaying sacred art. ⊠ *Rua Imperador Dom Pedro II s/n, Santo Antônio* ☎ *081/3224–0530* 🖭 *R$2* ☉ *Weekdays 8–11:30 and 2–5, Sat. 8–11:30.*

3 **Mercado de São José.** In the city's most traditional market, vendors sell handicrafts, produce, and herbs. It's housed in a beautiful cast-iron structure that was imported from France in the 19th century. ⊠ *Trv. do Macêdo s/n, São José* ☉ *Mon.–Sat. 6–6, Sun. 6–noon.*

10 **Museu do Estado de Pernambuco.** The state historical museum is in a mansion once owned by a baron and seems more like a home filled with beautiful antiques than a museum. There are a grand piano, a dining-room table set with 18th-century china, an ornate 19th-century crib, and many beautiful paintings. ⊠ *Av. Rui Barbosa 960, Graça* ☎ *081/3427–9322* 🖭 *R$1* ☉ *Tues.–Fri. 10–5, weekends 2–5.*

11 **Museu do Homem do Nordeste.** With three museums under one roof—one has displays about sugar, another anthropological exhibits, and the third regional handicrafts—the Museum of Northeastern Man offers great insight into Brazil's history. There are utensils made by indigenous peoples, European colonizers, and African slaves; religious articles used in Catholic and Candomblé rituals; and ceramic figurines by such artists as Mestre Vitalino and Mestre Zé. ⊠ *Av. 17 de Agosto 2187, Casa Forte* ☎ *081/3441–5500* 🖃 *R$5* ☉ *Weekdays 9–5, weekends 1–5.*

⑫ **Oficina Cerâmica Francisco Brennand.** In the old São José sugar refinery, this museum-workshop houses more than 2,000 pieces by the great (and prolific) Brazilian artist Francisco Brennand. Having studied in France, he was influenced by Pablo Picasso and Joan Miró, among others, and his works include paintings, drawings, and engravings as well as sculptures and ceramics. About 15 km (9 mi) from Recife Antigo, the museum's location amid forest and fountains is almost as appealing as its displays. ⊠ *Propriedade Santo Cosme e Damião s/n, Av. Caxangá, Km 16 Várzea* ☎ *081/3271–2466* ⊕ *www.brennand.com.br* 🖃 *R$4* ☉ *Weekdays 8–5.*

▶ ❶ **Praça da República.** Republic Square was originally known as the Field of Honor, a nod to those who were drawn and quartered here during the Republican movement of 1817. The structures around the square showcase the city's architecture from the 19th through the 20th centuries. Highlights include the Teatro Santa Isabel (St. Isabel Theater, 1850); the Palácio do Campo das Princesas, also known as the Palácio do Governo (Government House, 1841); and the Palácio da Justiça (Court House, 1930).

Recife Antigo. Most of Old Recife's colonial public buildings and houses have been restored. The area between Rua do Bom Jesus and Rua do Apolo is full of shops, cafés, and bars, making it the hub of downtown life both day and night; on some weekends there's dancing in the streets. A handicrafts fair is held every Sunday from 1 to 10 on Rua do Bom Jesus.

❼ **Sinagoga Kahal Zur Israel.** Opened in 2003 after a lengthy period of excavation and restoration, this synagogue was Latin America's first, opened in 1637. All that remain of the original synagogue are the walls and the ground, which can be viewed through glass floor panels. An excellent museum provides explanations of the Jewish experience in Brazil. Some monitors speak English. ⊠ *Rua do Bom Jesus 197, Recife Antigo* ☎ *081/3224–7376 or 081/3224–2128* ⊕ *www.arquivojudaicope.org. br* 🖃 *R$2* ☉ *Tues.–Fri. 9–5, Sun. 2–7.*

Beaches

★ **Boa Viagem.** Coconut palms line Recife's most popular beach, the 7-km-long (4-mi-long) Praia da Boa Viagem. A steady Atlantic breeze tames the hot sun, and reef formations create pools of warm water that are perfect for swimming. Sailors and fishermen beach their *jangadas* (handcrafted log rafts with beautiful sails), and vendors sell coconut drinks from kiosks. Avenida Boa Viagem separates a row of hotels and apartments from the beach, which is lined by a wide blue *calçadão* (sidewalk) that's perfect for runs, bike rides, or evening promenades. On weekend afternoons there's a handicrafts fair in Praça da Boa Viagem. Surfing and swimming beyond the reef are not recommended because of the presence of sharks. ⊠ *Just south of Recife.*

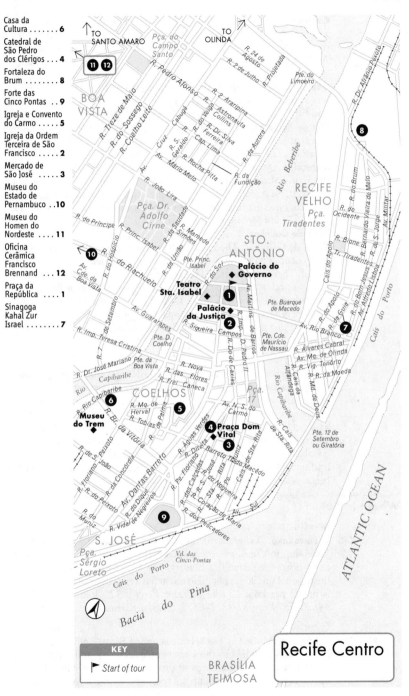

KEY

▶ *Start of tour*

Recife Centro

Cabo de Santo Agostinho. One of Pernambuco's finest beaches, Cabo de Santo Agostinho is good for swimming, though surfing has been banned due to the danger of shark attacks. In the town of Cabo de Santo Agostinho you can walk around the ruins of the Forte Castelo do Mar. ⊠ *35 km (22 mi) southeast of Recife.*

Gaibu. Quiet, beautiful Gaibu is surrounded by palm trees. Its blue waters are good for surfing, and it's also the site of volleyball competitions and fishing and sailing events. ⊠ *30 km (19 mi) south of Recife.*

Ilha de Itamaracá. This island is off the coast of the historic city of Igarassu. The best beach is Forte Orange, next to Coroa do Avião. ⊠ *39 km (24 mi) north of Recife, Igarassu.*

Maracaípe. Quiet Maracaípe Beach hosts surfing competitions; it hosted the World Surfing Games in 2000 (Brazil won first place in that competition). Maracaípe is a tiny hamlet with three dune buggies, two beach bars, and a small hotel. The beach's appeal is seclusion and surfing. ⊠ *73 km (46 mi) southwest of Recife.*

Porto de Galinhas. You'll find cool, clean waves and several resorts at Porto de Galinhas. The beach, which follows the curve of a bay lined with coconut palms and cashew trees, gets crowded on weekends year-round. There are plenty of jangadas for rent; other boats can take you to the island of Santo Aleixo. ⊠ *70 km (43 mi) south of Recife.*

Tamandaré. Although it's in the middle of an important nature reserve, developers have their eye on Tamandaré. Come quick, before its beaches—such as Praia dos Carneiros and Praia de Guadalupe—become one big resort area. ⊠ *110 km (68 mi) south of Recife.*

Recife's Carnival

In Recife people attend Carnival *bailes* (dances) and *bloco* (percussion group) practice sessions for two months prior to the main festivities. The beat of choice is *frevo* (a fast-pace, frenetic music that normally accompanies a lively dance performed with umbrellas). Galo da Madrugada, the largest of Recife's 500 blocos, opens Carnival and has drawn up to 20,000 costumed revelers. The blocos are joined by *escolas de samba* (samba schools or groups), escolas de frevo, *caboclinhos* (who dress in traditional Indian garb and bright feathers), and *maracatus* (African processions accompanied by percussionists).

Where to Eat

Brazilian

¢–$ ✕ **Parraxaxá.** Waiters wear the bent orange hats of Lampião, a Jesse James–like folk hero who made his way through the interior of the northeast during the early 20th century. The buffet has a wide selection of the regional specialties Lampião might have encountered back then. Food is priced per kilo. ⊠ *Rua Baltazar Pereira 32, Boa Viagem* ☎ *081/34630–7874 or 081/3327–0572* ⊕ *www.parraxaxa.com.br* ⊟ *V.*

Eclectic

★ $–$$$ ✕ **Leite.** Established in 1882, Leite is one of Brazil's oldest restaurants. Some tables are filled by the same people each day, and several waiters are following in the footsteps of generations of family members who have worked here. Roast lamb is a specialty. ⊠ *Praça Joaquim Nabuco*

147, Santo Antônio ☎ *081/3224–7977* ⊕ *www.restauranteleite.com. br* ▭ *DC, MC, V* ⊘ *Closed Sat. No dinner.*

Italian

$–$$ ✕ **Barbarico Bongiovani.** A sophisticated setting and a high-quality Italian menu are the draws here. Try the scaloppine al Marsala. ✉ *Av. Engenheiro Domingos Ferreira 2655, Boa Viagem* ☎ *081/3325–4268* ▭ *AE, DC, MC, V* ⊘ *Closed Mon. No lunch Tues.–Sat.*

$–$$ ✕ **Buongustaio.** This Italian restaurant has a diverse menu for all palates. Although the dishes often change, you cannot go wrong if you order the lamb or cod. ✉ *Av. Domingos Ferreira 467, Boa Viagem* ☎ *081/ 3327–5001 or 081/3325–8930* ▭ *DC, MC, V* ⊘ *No dinner Fri. or Sun.*

$–$$ ✕ **Famiglia Giuliano.** This outstanding restaurant is in a replica of a medieval Italian castle, replete with a moat, candelabras, coats of armor, and a stained-glass ceiling. It's open from lunchtime until the last diner leaves. The seafood fettuccine is an excellent choice. ✉ *Av. Eng. Domingos Ferreira 3980, Boa Viagem* ☎ *081/3465–9922* ▭ *AE, DC, MC, V.*

Portuguese

$$–$$$$ ✕ **Tasca.** The menu is more Portuguese than Brazilian, so, not surprisingly, one of the best dishes is *bacalhau a calí*—codfish cooked with olive oil, onion, garlic, tomatoes, potatoes, and white wine. ✉ *165 Rua Dom José Lopes, Boa Viagem* ☎ *081/3326–6309* ▭ *AE, MC* ⊘ *No lunch Tues.–Sat., no dinner Sun. Closed Mon.*

Seafood

$$–$$$$ ✕ **Bargaço.** People come to this pleasant restaurant for the renowned dishes from the state of Bahia. If you don't mind a heavy dish, try the outstanding *moqueca baiana* (fish cooked with onion, tomatoes, peppers, parsley, and coconut milk). ✉ *Av. Boa Viagem 670, Pina* ☎ *081/ 3465–1847* ▭ *DC, MC, V.*

★ **$–$$** ✕ **Restaurante Porta da Terra.** At least one evening out in Recife Antigo is a must on your trip. Although there are many good restaurants along Rua Bom Jesus, Restaurante Porta da Terra stands out for its shrimp dish, *camarão Maurício de Nassau*. Space is limited inside, but most diners opt for the sidewalk tables. ✉ *Rua do Bom Jesus 180, Recife Antigo* ☎ *081/3224–5453* ▭ *DC, MC, V* ⊘ *No dinner. No lunch Sat.–Sun.*

Where to Stay

Most of Recife's top hotels are about 20 minutes from the airport, across from the Boa Viagem and Pina beaches or along Piedade Beach, in the municipality of Jaboatão dos Guararapes.

$$–$$$ ▦ **Atlante Plaza Hotel.** Facing Recife's most popular beach, this high-rise's blue-glass windows make even the sky look pale. All rooms have sea views, but be sure to take a ride in the glass-enclosed elevator for a truly memorable ocean panorama. Ask for a room without carpets, as some have a faint mildew smell. A buffet breakfast is served in the Brasserie restaurant, where you can also have an à la carte or buffet lunch. The Mirage restaurant serves international or Brazilian dinners. ✉ *Av. Boa Viagem 5426, 51030-000* ☎ *081/3302–3333* 🖷 *081/3302–3344* ⊕ *www.*

BRAZIL'S NATIONAL DISH

THE FIRST FEIJOADA was reputedly made in Recife, and while the popular story of its origins is that it was a dish that slaves made for themselves with the scraps of meats from the masters' tables, some historians now believe that feijoada was, in fact, made for the masters. It has a certain semblance to the Portuguese dish cozido (a meat and vegetable stew), and the unusual cuts of meat used—including pig's feet and ears—are thought to have been parts prized by the Portuguese elite.

Feijoada, served at most Brazilian restaurants on Saturdays, is accompanied by rice, collard greens, farofa (finely ground manioc fried in butter), rice, aipîm frito (fried yucca), torresminho (pork rinds), and orange slices—the citrus supposedly counteracts the fat. Try it with a caipirinha.

Making Feijoada
Ingredients:

2 cups (1 pound) black beans, rinsed and picked over

¾ lb. pork butt or shoulder, trimmed of fat

6 ounces slab bacon

½ lb. smoked pork sausages

½ lb. hot Portuguese sausage such as linguiça

1 or 2 lbs. ham hock or shank, cut into 1-inch rounds

1 large yellow onion, chopped

3 garlic cloves, minced and sautéed in 1 tablespoon vegetable oil

6 green onions, including tops, chopped

1 yellow onion, chopped

½ cup chopped fresh parsley

2 bay leaves, crumbled

1½ tablespoons dried oregano, crushed

Salt and ground black pepper to taste

Chopped fresh cilantro or parsley

Directions:

Soak the beans overnight in enough water to cover by several inches. Drain.

Place the drained beans in a saucepan and add enough water to cover by 3 inches. Bring to a boil, reduce the heat to low, cover, and simmer until the beans are tender, 2–2½ hours. Add additional water as needed to keep the beans covered.

While the beans are cooking, prepare the meats. Preheat an oven to 375 degrees. Dice the pork butt or shoulder and the bacon into ½-inch cubes. Place the pork, sausages, and bacon in a large baking pan. Roast until well done. The sausages will be ready in 35–40 minutes and the other meats in 45–60 minutes.

Cook the ham hock at the same time as the meats are roasting. In a saucepan combine the ham hock rounds and onion with water to cover. Bring to a boil, reduce heat to a simmer, and cook until tender, about 1 hour. Remove the ham from the water and remove the meat from the bones; set aside. Or leave the rounds intact for serving alongside the beans. Strain the cooking liquid into a bowl. Add the strained onions to the beans. Add the cooking liquid to the beans if needed to keep them immersed.

Once the beans are almost cooked, check to make sure there is plenty of cooking liquid in the pot. It should be rather soupy at this point. Cut the sausages into rounds and add them and all the other cooked meats to the pot. Then add all the seasonings. Simmer for another 30 minutes, or until the beans are very tender.

Taste and adjust the seasonings. Sprinkle with chopped cilantro or parsley just before serving.

atlanteplaza.com.br ⟳ *70 room, 27 suites* ♨ *2 restaurants, minibars, cable TV, in-room broadband, pool, health club, 2 bars, business services, meeting rooms* ⊟ *AE, DC, MC, V.*

¢–$$ 🏨 **Golden Beach.** This beachfront apartment hotel is ideal for families or larger groups. Each spacious unit has one or two bedrooms, a living room, and a fully equipped kitchenette. ⊠ *Av. Bernardo Vieira de Melo 1204, Piedade, Jaboatão dos Guararapes 54410-001* ☎ *081/3468–3002* 🖷 *081/3468–1941* ⊕ *www.goldenbeach-pe.com.br* ⟳ *122 apartments* ♨ *Restaurant, kitchenettes, minibars, cable TV, Internet room, pool, health club, sauna, 2 bars* ⊟ *AE, DC, MC, V.*

¢–$$ 🏨 **Hotel do Sol.** This reasonably priced hotel faces Praia do Pina on Avenida Boa Viagem. Rooms are simple but comfortable. All have ocean views, some more direct than others. ⊠ *Av. Boa Viagem 978, Pina, 50030-010* ☎ *081/3091–0991* 🖷 *081/3465–5278* ⟳ *120 rooms* ♨ *Minibars, pool, bar* ⊟ *No credit cards.*

$ 🏨 **Mar Hotel Recife.** Location is one of this hotel's main draws: it's a five-minute drive from the airport, a 20-minute drive from Recife Antigo, and very close to Boa Viagem. Rooms are only medium-size but are nicely decorated and well equipped with desks that have swivel chairs, two phone lines, and fax and modem lines. When you're ready to call it a day, you can relax by the pool, which has a soothing waterfall. ⊠ *Rua Barão de Souza Leão 451, Boa Viagem 51030-300* ☎ *081/3302–4444* 🖷 *081/3302–4445* ⊕ *www.marhotel.com.br* ⟳ *207 rooms, 32 suites* ♨ *2 restaurants, minibars, cable TV, in-room broadband, pool, health club, sauna, bar, meeting room* ⊟ *AE, DC, MC, V.*

¢–$ 🏨 **Recife Monte Hotel.** Just a block from Boa Viagem Beach, this hotel has all the amenities of a luxury hotel, including a lovely pool. A must during your stay here is the Sunday *feijoada* (Brazilian national dish consisting of black beans, smoked meats, oranges, and whatever else the chef may decide to throw in) in the Marruá restaurant. ⊠ *Rua dos Navegantes 363, Boa Viagem 51021-010* ☎ *081/2121–0909* 🖷 *081/2121–0997* ⊕ *www.recifemontehotel.com.br* ⟳ *152 rooms, 21 suites* ♨ *Restaurant, minibars, cable TV, Internet room, pool, hair salon, bar* ⊟ *DC, MC, V* ¶◎ *BP.*

¢–$ 🏨 **Recife Plaza.** Overlooking the Rio Capibaribe, this simple downtown hotel emphasizes function over form. Beds are a bit flimsy and floors are tile. Some rooms have views of the river and the city; the pool has this view, too. ⊠ *Rua da Aurora 225, Boa Vista 50060-000* ☎☎ *081/3231–1200* ⊕ *www.recifeplazahotel.com.br* ⟳ *80 rooms* ♨ *Restaurant, minibars, pool, sauna* ⊟ *AE, DC, MC, V.*

Nightlife & the Arts

Nightlife

Pólo Pina, the calçadão in the Pina district, is a popular area near the beach for nighttime activities. In the streets off Rua Herculano Bandeira you can find close to two-dozen bars and restaurants. Between Rua do Apolo and Rua do Bom Jesus (or Rua dos Judeus) in Recife Antigo, people gather in a seemingly endless variety of bars, cafés, and nightclubs. On Saturday the market in Praça de Boa Viagem comes alive with forró dancers.

BARS **O Biruta** (✉ Rua Bem-te-vi 15, Brasília Teimosa ☎ 081/3326–5151 ⊕ www.birutabar.com.br) is a great spot to watch the moon rise over the beach. Chilled draft beer, tasty snacks, and excellent service make **Boteco** (✉ Av. Boa Viagem 1660, Boa Viagem ☎ 081/3325–1428) one of the most popular bars in town. **Depois** (✉ Av. Rio Branco 66, Recife Antigo ☎ 081/3424–7451 ⊕ www.depoisdancingbar.com.br) is in an old building in the heart of a bohemian neighborhood. Hits from the '60s and '70s are a hit with an over-30 crowd. **Galeria Joana D'Arc** (✉ Rua Herculano Bandeira 513, Pina) is a cluster of small cafés and bars, among them Café Poire, Anjo Solto, Barnabé, and Oriente Médio. It's a premier gay and lesbian hangout.

DANCE CLUBS **Downtown** (✉ Rua Vigário Tenório 105, Recife Antigo ☎ 081/3424–6317 ⊕ www.downtownpub.com.br), a club with a London pub look, is a good place to be on Saturday nights when local bands play. The club is popular with teenagers and twentysomethings. Local rock bands play every Sunday at **Musique Design Bar** (✉ Rua Tenente João Cícero 202, Boa Viagem ☎ 081/2102–9191 ⊕ www.musique.com.br). On Wednesday it has jazz and soul bands; DJs play Friday and Saturday.

The Arts
Built in 1850, the **Teatro Santa Isabel** (✉ Praça da República s/n, Santo Antônio ☎ 081/3224–1020 or 081/3224–0005), reopened in 2002 after 30 years and a major restoration. The neoclassical theater is the setting for operas, plays, and classical concerts.

Sports & the Outdoors

Sailing
At Boa Viagem, fishermen with jangadas offer sailing or fishing trips. The waters are shallow and calm at Maria Farinha Beach, on the north coast at the mouth of the Rio Timbó. Here you can rent jet skis, take ultralight flights, and enjoy motorboat and catamaran rides.

Scuba Diving
For centuries the treacherous offshore reefs that gave Recife its name have struck fear into the hearts of sailors. Many a vessel has failed to navigate the natural harbor successfully. Seventeen wrecks have been identified as good and safe dives for underwater explorers of various experience levels. The *Vapor de Baixo* is one such ship. Bombed by the Germans during World War II, it's 20 meters (65 feet) down and is crawling with lobsters and turtles. Though diving is practiced year-round, visibility is best between October and May, when the wind and water are at their calmest. The **Seagate** (✉ Rua Ministro Marcos Freire 257, Olinda ☎ 081/3494–3216 ⊕ www.seagaterecife.com.br), in Bairro Novo in Olinda, is a dive operation that offers courses, rents equipment, and runs trips for certified divers.

Shopping

Vendors at the **Mercado de São José** (✉ Praça Dom Vital s/n, São José ☎ 081/3424–4681) sell clothes and handicrafts as well as produce. It's open weekdays 6–6, Saturday 6–4, and Sunday 6–noon. The **Feira Hip-**

pie (Hippie Fair), held in the seafront Praça da Boa Viagem on afternoons starting at 4, has handicrafts.

Shopping Center Guararapes (⊠ Av. Barreto de Menezes 800, Piedade, Jaboatão dos Guararapes ☎081/2122–2211 ⊕www.shoppingguararapes. com.br) has everything the Shopping Center Recife has but on a smaller scale. It's near Piedade Beach. The enormous **Shopping Center Recife** (⊠ Rua Padre Carapuceiro 777, Boa Viagem ☎081/3464–6000 ⊕www. shoppingrecife.com.br) is the perfect place for a day of shopping. In addition to a good variety of both Brazilian and international stores, you can find restaurants, banks, a post office, pharmacies, and a business center. It's not far from Boa Viagem Beach.

SIDE TRIPS FROM RECIFE

Olinda

🔞 *7 km (4 mi) north of Recife.*

The name of Pernambuco State's original capital means "beautiful," and this must have been what came to mind when the first Europeans stood atop the forested hills and gazed at ocean and beach spread out before them. Today the town's natural beauty is complemented by colonial buildings painted in a rainbow of colors, making it a stunning slice of the old northeast.

Founded by the Portuguese in 1535, Olinda was developed further by the Dutch during their brief turn at running Pernambuco in the 1600s. The narrow cobblestone streets of this UNESCO World Cultural Site curve up and down hills that, at every turn, offer spectacular views of both Recife and the Atlantic. The scenery is just as nice up close: many houses have latticed balconies, heavy doors, and stucco walls. The zoning laws are strict, resulting in a beautiful, compact city that artists, musicians, and intellectuals have made their own.

The city center is hilly but fairly easy to explore by foot. You may want to hire a guide to help provide some historical background on the city and its principal sites. Look for the official guides (they have ID cards) who congregate in the Praça do Carmo. They are former street children, and half the R$45 fee for a full city tour goes to a home for kids from the streets.

Olinda's Carnival
Many rate Carnival in Olinda as one of the three best in Brazil (Rio and Salvador being the other two). It's considered Brazil's most traditional Carnival—the most like original Carnivals, and with noticeably less skin. Music is generally the slower-paced forró, in contrast to Rio's *samba* and Salvador's *axé*. Carnival here lasts a full 11 days. Highlights include the opening events—led by a bloco of more than 400 "virgins" (men in drag)—and a parade of *bonecos de pano* (huge dolls) and *mamulengos* (marrionettes) in the likenesses of famous northeasterners. The dolls and puppets are made of Styrofoam, fabric, and papier-mâché.

What to See

On Olinda's southern edge is the **Centro de Convenções Pernambuco,** one of the most modern convention centers in Latin America, which houses Empetur, the state tourism office. Cultural performances are often held in the center's theater and auditorium. ⊠ *Complexo Viário Vice Governador Barreto Guimarães s/n, Salgadinho* ☎ *081/3427–8000* ⊕ *www. empetur.com.br.*

The **Convento de São Francisco,** built in 1577, was the first Franciscan convent built in Brazil. The floors are Portuguese tile work, ceilings are frescoed, and walls are made of ground-up local coral. ⊠ *Rua São Francisco 280, Carmo Olinda* ☎ *081/3429–0517* ⊠ *R$1* ⊙ *Weekdays 7–noon and 2–5, Sat. 7–noon.*

The main chapel of the **Mosteiro de São Bento,** a Benedictine monastery, is considered one of Brazil's most beautiful. It once housed the nation's first law school. The 10 AM Sunday mass features Gregorian chants. ⊠ *Rua de São Bento s/n* ☎ *081/3429–3288* ⊠ *Free* ⊙ *Daily 8–11 and 2–5.*

The **Alto da Sé** is the most scenic spot for viewing Olinda, Recife, and the ocean. It's also a good place see some historic churches as well as to sample Bahia-style *acaraje* (black-eyed pea fritters) and Pernambuco's famous tapioca cakes. Have a seat at one of the outdoor tables here, or browse in the shops that sell handicrafts—including lace—and paintings. To get here, just walk up on Ladeira da Sé.

Built in 1540 and restored in 1654, the **Igreja da Misericórdia** (Mercy Church) has rich sculptures of wood, gold, and silver. It's atop the Alto da Sé. ⊠ *Alto da Misericórdia s/n, Carmo* ☎ *081/3429–2922* ⊠ *Free* ⊙ *Daily 9–1 and 2–6.*

The last of many renovations to the 1537 **Igreja da Sé,** on the Alto da Sé, was in 1983. It has now been restored as much as possible to its original appearance. From its side terrace you can see the Old City and the ocean. ⊠ *Rua Bispo Coutinho s/n* ⊠ *Free* ⊙ *Daily 8–11:30 and 2–5.*

At the **Museu do Mamulengo-Espaço Tiridá,** everyday life and northeastern folk tales are the stuff of shows, presented using some of the more than 300 puppets made of wood and cloth that are on display in this whimsical museum. ⊠ *Rua do Amparo 59* ☎ *081/3429–6214* ⊠ *R$2* ⊙ *Tues.–Fri. 9–5, weekends 10–5.*

Where to Stay & Eat

$$ ✕ **Oficina do Sabor.** Everything is tasty at this regional restaurant, but do try the *abóbora com camarão,* pumpkin stuffed with shrimp and served with a *pitanga* cherry sauce. ⊠ *Rua do Amparo 335* ☎ *081/3429–3331* ⊕ *www.oficinadosabor.com* ⊟ *AE, DC, MC, V* ⊙ *No dinner Sun. Closed Mon.*

$ ✕ **Goya.** The two artist-owners display their work on the walls of the colorful bilevel restaurant. Their creativity is also apparent in the preparation and presentation of French–Brazilian fusion dishes. The coconut shrimp is especially tasty. ⊠ *Rua do Amparo 157* ☎ *081/3439–4875* ⊟ *AE, DC, MC, V* ⊙ *No lunch Wed.–Sat. Closed Tues.*

★ **$–$$$** ▦ **Pousada do Amparo.** This lovely pousada is made up of two colonial houses with 12-meter (39-foot) ceilings. Wood and brick details, original artwork, and an indoor garden lend considerable warmth to the cavernous spaces. It is a member of the exclusive Brazilian Roteiros de Charme hotels group. ⊠ *Rua do Amparo 199, 53020-190* ☎ *081/ 3439–1749* ⊕ *www.pousadadoamparo.com.br* ↵ *11 rooms* ⚙ *Restaurant, minibars, pool, sauna, bar* ▭ *DC, MC, V.*

$–$$ ▦ **Hotel 7 Colinas.** This hotel sits in an off-street hollow amid the trees and flowers of a tangled garden. From here it's just a short hike up to Alto da Sé. Rooms are comfortably furnished, and all look out on the grounds. ⊠ *Ladeira de São Francisco 307, 53120-070* ☎ *081/3439–6055* ⊕ *www.hotel7colinasolinda.com.br* ↵ *39 rooms* ⚙ *Restaurant, minibars, pool, bar, meeting room* ▭ *AE, DC, MC, V.*

¢–$ ▦ **Hotel Pousada Quatro Cantos.** In a converted mansion, this pousada has rooms that vary considerably in size, quality, and price. The suites, with hardwood floors, rival those at the best hotels, but the standard rooms are just average. The individually decorated deluxe rooms are considerably nicer. Carnival decorations enliven the lobby. The Mercado da Ribeira is within walking distance. ⊠ *Rua Prudente de Morais 441* ☎ *081/3429–0220* ⊕ *www.pousada4cantos.com.br* ↵ *16 rooms, 2 suites* ⚙ *Restaurant, minibars, bar* ▭ *AE, DC, MC, V.*

¢–$ ▦ **Pousada Peter.** You may wonder whether this grand mansion is a pousada or an art gallery. Peter Bauer, whose paintings have hung in many galleries, is both the owner and the resident artist. The large guest rooms lead out to a terrace where you can enjoy a view of the gardens, Olinda, and Recife. During Carnival, for which the pousada has special packages, revelers dance along the street out front. ⊠ *Rua do Amparo 215, 53020-170* ☎ *081/3439–2171* ⊕ *www.pousadapeter.com. br* ↵ *8 rooms* ⚙ *Minibars, pool.*

Shopping

For crafts, head to the **Casa do Artesão** (⊠ Rua de Sáo Bento 170 ☎ 081/ 3429–2979 ⊕ www.associarte.org.br). It's open weekdays 9–6 and Saturday 9–2.

Caruaru

⑭ *134 km (83 mi) west of Recife.*

Caruaru and its crafts center, Alto do Moura (6 km/4 mi south of Caruaru), became famous in the 1960s and '70s for clay figurines made by local artisan Mestre Vitalino. There are now more than 500 craftspeople working in Alto do Moura. All are inspired by Vitalino, whose former home is now a museum, open Monday–Saturday 8–noon and 2–6 and Sunday 8–noon. At the crafts center you can buy not only figurines, which depict northeasterners doing everyday things, but also watch the artisans work.

In Caruaru a great open-air market, **Feira de Artesanato** (⊠ Parque 18 de Maio), is held every Saturday, when, as the songwriter Luis Gonzaga put it, "It is possible to find a little of everything that exists in the world." Look for pottery, leather goods, ceramics, hammocks, and baskets.

Where to Stay

¢ ⊞ **Caruaru Park Hotel.** On the outskirts of town, the Caruaru Park's colorful rooms and chalets are sparsely decorated but neat and clean. Balconies have hammocks and decent views of town. ⊠ *Km 134, BR 232, 55030-400* ☎ *081/3722–9191* ⊟ *081/3722–7397* ⊕ *www.caruaruparkhotelonline.com.br* ➘ *68 rooms* ⚘ *Restaurant, minibars, cable TV, pool* ⊟ *AE, DC, MC, V.*

NATAL

❶❺ Natal, with a population now exceeding 700,000, has been growing by leaps and bounds over the past decade. The capital of Rio Grande do Norte has become an important industrial center, yet no industry has had more effect on the economy than tourism. The past few administrations have invested heavily in the infrastructure and promotion, effectively placing it on the map as one of the prime tourism destinations in Brazil.

Although it has little in the way of historical or cultural attractions, the city's main asset is its location along one of the most beautiful stretches of coast in Brazil. In fact, Natal's foundation and much of its history have been all about location. In 1598 the Portuguese began construction of the Fortaleza dos Reis Magos in present-day Natal. Its location was strategic for two reasons. First, it was at the mouth of the Rio Potengi. Second, it was near the easternmost point of the continent and therefore was closest to Europe and Africa. On December 25, 1599, the city was founded and named Natal, the Portuguese word for "Christmas."

Because of its valuable location, Natal was a target for the Dutch, who ultimately seized control of the city in 1633 and renamed it New Amsterdam. The Portuguese repossessed Natal after the Dutch abandoned the city in 1654. Yet it was never a major colonial center for the Portuguese. The city had to wait nearly three centuries to regain importance, again due to its location. In World War II the United States built several military bases in and around the city that they deemed "the springboard to victory"—its position at the far-eastern point of the continent made it ideal for launching aerial attacks into Europe.

Exploring Natal

Few tourists stay in the city itself, and many do not even visit, and instead head straight to Ponta Negra (⇨ Beaches, *below*), a rapidly developing beach area 10 km (6 mi) south of the city center. Ponta Negra is still small enough that it can easily be explored on foot—most hotels and restaurants are on or just a few blocks from the beach. Natal's few museums and historic buildings are mostly clustered in the Cidade Alta (Upper City), the oldest part of the city, and are within easy walking distance of each other. Just half a mile to the northeast of Cidade Alta is Praia dos Artistas. It was formerly the center of tourist activity but has taken on a bit of a seedy quality. Its bars and clubs remain popular, but take taxis as night and avoid walking alone.

What to See

Museu Câmara Cascudo. This well-conceived museum has exhibits from a variety of disciplines: archaeology, paleontology, mineralogy, ethnography, and popular culture. A highlight is the collection of dinosaur fossils. ⊠ *Av. Hermes da Fonseca 1398, Tirol* ☎ *084/3212–2795* 🖂 *R$1* 🕑 *Tues.–Sun. 8–11:30 and 2–5:30.*

Praça 7 de Setembro. The two most notable buildings around this center of old Natal are the Victorian-style governor's mansion, built in 1873, and the uninspiring cathedral, built in 1862. The square is rather lifeless except for in the month of December, when a play retelling the Christmas story is performed.

Beaches

Búzios. This beach has been endowed with great natural beauty yet does not usually have many visitors. The barrier reef creates an area of clear, calm waters ideal for bathing, snorkeling, and scuba diving. In the background are some impressive dunes, covered with palm trees and other vegetation. The modest infrastructure consists of just a few small pousadas and restaurants. ⊠ *RN 063 (Rota do Sol); 35 km (21 mi) south of Natal.*

Genipabu. Massive dunes have made this one of the best-known beaches in the country. The area is most commonly explored on thrilling, hour-long dune-buggy rides. You have two choices: *com emocão* (literally, "with emotion"), which rivals any roller-coaster, or *sem emocão* (without emotion), a little calmer but still fairly hair-raising. Buggy operators, who usually find you before you find them, charge around R$150 for five people. You can also explore the dunes on camels imported from southern Spain. Other activities include half-hour boat rides and sky-boarding (also called sky-surfing)—which is basically snowboarding down the dunes. The beach is attractive, although it gets very crowded during high season. Because Genipabu is close to Natal, it is primarily a day-trip destination. There are a few small pousadas and restaurants near the beach, but the town shuts down at night. Buses leave from the Rodoviário Velho every half hour or so. ⊠ *Take BR 101 north to Pitanguí access road; 10 km (6 mi) north of Natal.*

Maracajaú. The principal draw at Maracajaú is the large coral reef 6 km (4 mi) off the coast. Teeming with marine life, the sizable reef offers the best snorkeling in the Natal area. There are no hotels for overnight stays, but **Ma-noa Parque Aquático** (Ma-noa Aquatic Park; ⊠ Enseada Pontas dos Anéis, Maracajaú ☎ 084/3234–9321 or 084/3234–9344 ⊕ www.ma-noa.com.br) has all that day visitors require: a restaurant, water rides, a huge pool, boat trips to the reef with snorkeling equipment provided, and even transport to and from Natal hotels. Entrance to the park costs R$20, and the snorkel trip costs R$45. Go now, as the ecosystem will not be able to handle the up to 1,000 daily visitors indefinitely. Ma-noa has a shuttle service from Natal. ⊠ *Take BR 101 north to Maracajaú access road; 55 km (34 mi) north of Natal.*

Pirangi do Norte. This long white-sand beach is an extremely popular summer vacation destination for residents of Natal. Boat rides to nearby coral reefs and beaches run frequently. Near the beach is the world's largest cashew tree, according to the *Guinness Book of World Records*. Its circumference measures 500 meters (1,650 feet), and it is as big as roughly 70 normal cashew trees. ⊠ *RN 063 (Rota do Sol); 28 km (17 mi) north of Natal*.

Ponta Negra. Nearly all tourism development has focused on or around this beach in the past few years. It has a multitude of pousadas, restaurants, and shops and even a few large resorts at the northern end. The beach itself, around 2½ km (1½ mi) long, can no longer be called pristine, but is still reasonably clean and attractive. Large waves make it popular with surfers. Ponta Negra's distinguishing feature is the Morro da Careca (Bald Man's Hill), a 120-meter (390-foot) dune at the southern end. You can catch a taxi or a bus at various stops along the Via Costeira south of Natal. ⊠ *Via Costeira; 10 km (6 mi) south of Natal*.

Where to Eat

$$ ✕ Peixada da Comadre. If you were wondering where locals go for the town's best fish, this is it. The decor is rather simple, but tables in the back have excellent views of the Praia dos Artistas through large glass windows. Dishes are easily large enough for two. ⊠ *Rua Dr. José Augusto Bezerra de Medeiros 4, Praia do Meio* ☎ *084/3202–3411* ▭ *No credit cards* ⊗ *No dinner Sun. Closed Tues.*

★ $$ ✕ Tererê. Consider fasting for several days before visiting what is considered by locals to be the town's best churrascaria. Unless you indicate otherwise, waiters bring choice cuts of beef, lamb, chicken, and pork until you have passed out on the table. If you're not as carnivorous as most Brazilians, you can sneak food off the salad table, which has a good selection of lighter fare. ⊠ *Estrada de Ponta Negra 2326, Ponta Negra* ☎ *084/3219–4081* ⊕ *www.terere.com.br* ▭ *AE, DC, MC, V.*

$–$$ ✕ Piazzale Italia. During the high season (July and December–mid-March) make a reservation, or you'll be among the many waiting outside, salivating from smells of fresh tomato sauce and garlic. The restaurant's popularity is a result of reasonable prices, proximity to the Ponta Negra Beach (a five-minute taxi ride), and skillful preparation of pasta and seafood dishes. Particularly recommended is the *tagliolini allo scoglio* (pasta with lobster, shrimp, and mussels). ⊠ *Av. Dep. Antônio Florêncio de Queiroz 12, Ponta Negra* ☎ *084/3236–2697* ▭ *AE, DC, MC, V* ⊗ *No lunch Mon. or Tues.*

¢–$ ✕ Mangai. Choose from more than 40 delicious regional specialties at this **FodorsChoice** immensely popular per-kilo restaurant. Tourists and town residents eat **★** together at communal wood tables, which fit the typical rustic decor of the sertão. To top off your meal, consider ordering the *cartola*, a popular dessert made of caramelized banana, cheese, and cinnamon. ⊠ *Av. Amintas Barros 3300, Lagoa Nova* ☎ *084/3206–3344* ▭ *V* ⊗ *Closed Mon.*

Where to Stay

★ $$$–$$$$ ✕▢ Manary Praia Hotel. It is hardly surprising that this small all-star hotel was chosen as a member of the prestigious Roteiros de Charme group. Both the service and decor reflect tremendous attention to detail. The restaurant serves skillfully prepared dishes such as grilled

OFF-SEASON CARNIVALS

Carnatal

When Natal's Carnatal began in 1991, it was the country's first carnaval *fora da epoca*, or out-of-season Carnival. (Off-season Carnivals are also sometimes called *micaretas*.) More than a dozen other cities have since instituted similar celebrations, but this remains one of the largest. Always on the first weekend in December, it unites party seekers from throughout the country and beyond. There are about 10 blocos, each with room for 3,000 revelers. They travel along a 2-km (1-mi) route that starts just outside the soccer stadium. Performances are given by some of the country's top acts. Tickets often sell out early, especially for the more popular blocos. You can reserve tickets online through ⊕ www.carnatal.com.br.

Fortal

Fortaleza's Fortal, one of the country's foremost Carnival *fora da epoca*

celebrations, began in 1992. It is held the last week in July on a 4-km (2½-mi) stretch along the seaside Avenida Beira-Mar. Its scale is impressive: There are six blocos, each with 2,500 revelers. An average of 500,000 participate in the festivities each of the four days, 200,000 of them tourists. Like Carnatal, Fortal attracts top acts. For more information visit ⊕ www.fortal.com.br.

seafood in the pretty pool area that overlooks the beach. The location is ideal, as it is just beyond the crowded portion of Ponta Negra. The owner also runs Natal's only ecotourism operator, which has top-flight trips to area beaches and fascinating inland destinations such as Cariri and Dinosaur Valley. ⊠ *Rua Francisco Gurgel 9067, Ponta Negra, 59090-050* ☎ *084/3204–2900* 🖷 *084/3204–2908* ⊕ *www.manary. com.br* 🖙 *23 rooms, 1 suite* ⟨ *Restaurant, minibars, cable TV, pool, bar* ⊟ *AE, DC, MC, V.*

$$$–$$$$ 🏨 **Pestana Natal Beach Resort.** This attractive resort manages to avoid some of the traditional problems associated with megacomplexes: its beige color allows it to blend into its sandy surroundings, room furnishings all have original artwork and other strokes of personality, and personalized service makes guests feel like more than just a number. ⊠ *Av. Senador Dinarte Mariz 5525, Via Costeira, 6 km north of Ponta Negra, 59090-001* ☎ *084/3220–8900* 🖷 *084/3220–8920* ⊕ *www.pestana. com* 🖙 *184 rooms, 5 suites* ⟨ *3 restaurants, minibars, cable TV, pool, health club, sauna, bars, business services* ⊟ *AE, DC, MC, V.*

$$–$$$$ 🏨 **Rifóles.** The eclectic architectural style of this hotel is both attractive and confusing; pirate and cave-painting motifs are cultivated through the use of materials such as old driftwood, plaster, marble, and *tijolo* *aparente*—locally produced beige bricks. The beach in front is uncrowded, as it is a mile or so from the busy part of Ponta Negra. You can also bathe in one of the two pools, but the nearby karaoke machine ruins any semblance of peace. Rooms are well equipped and adequately sized. ⊠ *Rua Cel. Inácio Vale 8847, Ponta Negra 59090-040* ☎ *084/ 3646–5000* 🖷 *084/3646–5005* ⊕ *www.rifoles.com.br* ⤴ *202 rooms* ☼ *Restaurant, minibars, cable TV, 2 pools, sauna, bar, recreation room* 🖃 *AE, DC, MC, V.*

$–$$ 🖭 **Divi-Divi.** Just one block from the beach, this small hotel is a great value if you're willing to forgo a beachside location. Apart from the elevator, the three-story hotel seems more like a guesthouse. Rooms are thoughtfully decorated, well equipped, and comfortable. The small, stylish pool in front helps compensate for the lack of beach. ⊠ *Rua Elias Barros 248, Ponta Negra, 59090-140* ☎ *084/4006–3900* 🖷 *084/ 3219–4195* ⊕ *www.dividivi.com.br* ⤴ *32 rooms, 2 suites* ☼ *Minibars, pool, bar, Internet room* 🖃 *AE, DC, MC, V.*

¢–$ 🖭 **O Tempo e o Vento.** The four-star-quality rooms at this hotel are highly incongruous with the two-star-quality lobby. Luckily, prices are more representative of the latter. The small hotel is just a block from the beach, with a pool in front. All rooms have balconies; request those with direct sea views, since they cost the same. ⊠ *Rua Elias Barros 66, Ponta Negra, 59090-140* ☎🖷 *084/3219–2526* ⤴ *22 rooms* ☼ *Minibars, pool, bar, Internet* 🖃 *DC, MC, V.*

$ 🖭 **Residence Praia Hotel.** This modern hotel a block from Praia dos Artistas is a good option for those who want all major amenities but don't want to pay Ponta Negra prices. The hotel is easily recognizable by its blue-glass facade. Rooms are pleasant and colorful, with pastel-painted brick walls. The downside is that the area is no longer in vogue and can get a bit seedy at night. ⊠ *Av. 25 de Dezembro 868, Praia do Meio, 59010-030* ☎🖷 *084/3202–4466* ⊕ *www.residencepraia.com.br* ⤴ *118 rooms* ☼ *Restaurant, minibars, cable TV, pool, meeting room* 🖃 *AE, DC, MC, V.*

Shopping

The best place to go for local crafts and artwork is the **Centro de Turismo** (⊠ Rua Aderbal de Figueiredo 980, Petrópolis ☎ 084/3211–6149). Little shops are housed within the cells of the former prison. It's open daily 8–7. Natal also has several malls and shopping centers. The largest is **Natal Shopping** (⊠ Km 02, Rodovia BR 101, Candelária ☎ 084/ 3209–8199). **Praia Shopping** (⊠ Av. Engenheiro Roberto Freire 8790, Ponta Negra ☎ 084/4008–0800 ⊕ www.praiashopping.com.br) is the most convenient shopping mall for those staying in Ponta Negra.

Nightlife & the Arts

Nightlife

Natal has a fairly active nightlife, supported by nearly year-round tourists. Some of the most frequented bars and clubs are in Praia dos Artistas. Other popular spots are scattered downtown and in Ponta Negra.

Every Thursday the Centro de Turismo hosts a live forró band as part of the long-running "Forró com Turista" program, which is aimed at acquainting tourists with this important piece of local culture.

BARS You won't have to worry about getting stale beer at **Cervejaria Via Costeira** (✉ Av. Sen. Dinarte Maris 4197, Parque das Dunas ☎ 084/3202–1089), which is both a bar and brewery. A bar with character, **Taverna Pub** (✉ Rua Dr. Manuel Augusto Bezerra de Araújo 500, Ponta Negra ☎ 084/3236–3696) is in the basement of a stylized medieval castle. It's popular with locals in their twenties and tourists who stay in the hostel upstairs. A common nighttime destination for Ponta Negra tourists is **Praia Shopping** (✉ Av. Engenheiro Roberto Freire 8790, Ponta Negra ☎ 084/4008–0800 ⊕ www.praiashopping.com.br), which has a cluster of small bars and restaurants.

DANCE CLUBS **Downtown** (✉ Rua Chile 11, Bairro da Ribeira ☎ 084/611–1950), modeled after typical London clubs, has live rock music Thursday through Saturday. **Chaplin House Club** (✉ Rua Presidente Café Filho 27, Praia do Meio ☎ 084/3202–1199), near Praia dos Artistas, has three distinct environments, each with a different type of live music: *pagode* (a popular, mellow samba derivative), forró, and rock. A R$20 cover charge doesn't prevent up to 1,500 local youngsters and tourists from pouring in.

Sports & the Outdoors

Most outdoor activity options are found at the beaches outside Natal: Genipabu has dune-buggy rides, Maracajaú has prime snorkeling, and Búzios is great for scuba diving.

SIDE TRIPS FROM NATAL

Praia da Pipa

🔟 *85 km (51 mi) south of Natal.*

This was a small fishing village until it was "discovered" by surfers in the '70s. Word of its beauty spread, and it is now one of the most famous and fashionable beach towns in the northeast. It is also rapidly gaining a reputation for having an extremely active nightlife. Praia da Pipa receives a truly eclectic mix of people: hippies, surfers, foreign backpackers, Brazilian youth, and, most recently, high-end visitors attracted by the increasingly upscale restaurants and pousadas.

On either side of the town is a string of beaches with amazingly varied landscapes created by stunning combinations of pink cliffs, black volcanic rocks, palm trees, and natural pools. You can spend hours exploring the various beaches, most of which are deserted because they fall within environmentally protected areas. Another recommended activity is the boat ride to see dolphins, which often frequent the surrounding waters. The 90-minute boat ride leaves regularly from the north end of the principal beach and costs R$15.

For active travelers a good option is the **Santuário Ecológico de Pipa** (Pipa Ecological Sanctuary), a 120-hectare (300-acre) protected area. Sixteen short, well-maintained trails pass through Atlantic forest vegetation and allow for some great views of the ocean. ⊠ *Estrada para Tibau do Sul, 2 km (1 mi) northwest of town* ☎ *084/3211–6070* 🎟 *Free* 🕘 *Daily 9–5.*

Where to Stay & Eat

$$–$$$ ✕ **La Provence.** This exquisite, unpretentious French restaurant is a true find. Among its specialties is the succulent *magret de canard avec pruneaux* (duck breast with prunes). ⊠ *Rua da Gameleira* ☎ *084/3246–2280* ▤ *AE, DC, MC, V* 🕘 *Closed May–June.*

★ $$$–$$$$ 🏠 **Toca da Coruja.** Although many pousadas have been built since this one opened back in 1991, when Pipa was still a fishing village, none can top Toca da Coruja. The chalets are more spacious and expensive than the apartments, and feel more like jungle lodges—one even has an "outdoor" bathtub. But all units are beautifully furnished. This is a Roteiros de Charme hotel. ⊠ *Av. Baía dos Golfinhos 464, 59173-000* ☎ *081/3246–2226* ⊕ *www.tocadacoruja.com.br* 🛏 *6 apartments, 5 chalets* ⚪ *Pool, sauna, bar* ▤ *AE, DC, MC, V.*

$ 🏠 **Pousada da Ladeira.** Made from local wood and tijolo aparente, this simple pousada has clean rooms—some with balconies overlooking the pool. Because it is right on the main road, it may not be the best choice for those looking for peace and quiet. ⊠ *Av. Baía dos Golfinhos 802, 59178-000* ☎ *084/3246–2334 or 084/3502–2310* ⊕ *www.pipa.com.br* 🛏 *34 rooms* ⚪ *Pool, bar* ▤ *AE, DC, MC, V.*

Cariri

🔟 *333 km (200 mi) southwest of Natal.*

This largely uninhabited region in the interior of Paraíba State is worth visiting for its spectacular **rock formations.** Its otherworldly appearance makes it ideal for those that tire of visiting only beaches. Only three other places in the world can compare in terms of the size, shape, and amount of rounded granite blocks (the others are in the Erongo Mountains of Namibia, the Hoggar region of Algeria, and the Australian outback). Despite this distinction, Cariri is seldom visited. Only one company, **Cariri Ecotours** (☎ *084/3204–2900, 084/3604–0782 or 084/9928–0198* ⊕ www.manarycaririecotours.com.br), has English-language tours to Cariri. Poor roads and a lack of public transport makes the trip difficult for independent travelers.

In Cariri tours visit several areas with enormous granite boulders; some lean against each other at precarious angles, and others have bottoms carved out so they look like helmets. On the way to Cariri, tours stop in **Ingá,** which has a huge monolith with mysterious prehistoric paintings. On the premises there is also a small, interesting museum with fossils and bones of prehistoric creatures that inhabited the area. At a site called **Saca de Lã,** huge rectangular rocks are mysteriously stacked upon each other. Visits include a trip into **Cabaçeiras,** a typical small town in the sertão.

FORTALEZA

Called the "City of Light," Fortaleza claims that the sun shines on it 2,800 hours a year. And it's a good thing, too, as the coastline stretches far beyond the city. To the east, along the Litoral Leste or the Costa Sol Nascente (Sunrise Coast) are many fishing villages. To the west, along the Litoral Oeste or the Costa Sol Poente (Sunset Coast), there are pristine stretches of sand. The shores here are cooled by constant breezes and lapped by waters with an average temperature of 24°C (72°F).

The city originally sprang up around the Forte de Schoonemborch, a Dutch fortress built in 1649. After the Portuguese defeated the Dutch, the small settlement was called Fortaleza Nossa Senhora da Assunção (Fortress of Our Lady of the Assumption). It didn't fully burgeon until 1808, when its ports were opened and the export of cotton to the United Kingdom commenced.

Today Fortaleza, a large, modern state capital with more than 2 million inhabitants, is Brazil's fifth-largest city. It's also on the move, with one of the country's newest airports, a modern convention center, a huge cultural center with a planetarium, large shopping malls, several museums and theaters, and an abundance of sophisticated restaurants. At Praia de Iracema there's a revitalized beachfront area of sidewalk cafés, bars, and dance clubs. But if you wander along the shore, you're still bound to encounter fishermen unloading their catch from traditional jangadas—just as they've done for hundreds of years.

Numbers in the text correspond to numbers in the margin and on the Fortaleza Centro Histórico map.

Exploring Fortaleza

Fortaleza is fairly easy to navigate on foot because its streets are laid out in a grid. Its business center lies above the Centro Histórico (Historic Center) and includes the main market, several shopping streets, and government buildings. East of the center, urban beaches are lined with high-rise hotels and restaurants. Beyond are the port and old lighthouse, from which Praia do Futuro runs 5 km (3 mi) along Avenida Dioguinho. Be on guard against pickpockets—particularly in the historic district.

What to See

off the beaten path

BEACH PARK ACQUA CENTER – Just 30 minutes from downtown on the idyllic Porto das Dunas Beach is this enormous water park. A 14-story-high water slide dumps you into a pool at a speed of 105 kph (65 mph), or if you prefer slow-paced attractions, visit its museum, which has the country's largest collection of jangadas, the wooden sailing rafts used by fishermen. An open-air restaurant at the beach serves excellent seafood dishes. There is no bus from downtown, and a taxi costs around R$50. ⊠ *Rua Porto das Dunas 2734, Aquiraz* ☎ *085/4012–3000* ⊕ *www.beachpark.com.br* ☏ *R$70* ☾ *July–mid-Dec., daily 10–5; mid-Dec.–June, Thurs.–Mon. 10–5.*

㉒ Catedral Metropolitana. Inspired by the cathedral in Cologne, Germany, the city cathedral was built between 1937 and 1963 and has a dominant Gothic look. Its two spires are 75 meters (250 feet) high, and it can accommodate 5,000 worshipers, who are no doubt inspired by its beautiful stained-glass windows. ⊠ *Praça da Sé s/n, Centro* ☎ *085/ 3231–4196* ⊕ *www.arquidiocesedefortaleza.org.br* 🎫 *Free* ⊙ *Mon.–Fri. 8–5, weekends 8–11.*

㉕ Centro Dragão do Mar de Arte e Cultura. Not far from the Mercado Central, this majestic cultural complex is an eccentric mix of curves, straight lines, and angular and flat roofs. What's inside is as diverse as the exterior. There's a planetarium as well as art museums with permanent exhibitions of Ceará's two most famous artists, Raimundo Cela and Antônio Bandeira. Another museum presents Ceará's cultural history, with exhibits of embroidery, paintings, prints, pottery, puppets, and musical instruments. When you need a break, head for the center's romantic Café & Cultura, which serves a variety of cocktails made with coffee as well as little meat or vegetarian pies. The center's bookstore has English-language titles as well as souvenirs and cards. ⊠ *Rua Dragão do Mar 81, Praia de Iracema* ☎ *085/3488–8600* ⊕ *www.dragaodomar.org.br* 🎫 *Museums R$2, planetarium R$8* ⊙ *Tues.–Sun. 2–9:30.*

㉗ Centro de Turismo. Originally a prison, this building was structurally changed in 1850 along simple, classical lines. It's now the home of the state tourism center, with handicraft stores as well as the Museu de Minerais (Mineral Museum) and the Museu de Arte e Cultura Populares (Popular Art and Culture Museum), whose displays of local crafts and sculptures are interesting. ⊠ *Rua Senador Pompeu 350, Centro* ☎ *085/ 3488–7410* 🎫 *R$2* ⊙ *Weekdays 7–6, Sat. 8–5, Sun. 8–noon.*

㉘ Farol do Mucuripe. Erected by slaves and dedicated to Princess Isabel, the monarch who eventually put an end to slavery, this lighthouse was inaugurated in 1846. Surrounded by a system of battlements, it operated for 111 years and was not deactivated until 1957. In 1982 it underwent a restoration and was designated a municipal historic monument. It now houses the Museu de Fortaleza, better known as the Museu do Farol, with exhibits on the city's history. ⊠ *Av. Vicente de Castro s/n, Mucuripe* ☎ *085/3263–1115* 🎫 *Free* ⊙ *Mon.–Sat. 7–5, Sun. 7–11.*

㉔ Forte de Nossa Senhora da Assunção. Built by the Dutch in 1649, this fort was originally baptized Forte Schoonemborch. In 1655 it was seized by the Portuguese and renamed after the city's patron saint, Nossa Senhora da Assunção. It was rebuilt in 1817 and is now a military headquarters. The city took its name from this fortress (*fortaleza*), which still has the cell where the mother of one of Ceará's most famous writers, José de Alencar, was jailed. ⊠ *Av. Alberto Nepomuceno s/n, Centro* ☎ *085/3255–1600* 🎫 *Free* ⊙ *Daily 8–4.*

㉙ Iracema. Along the Praia do Mucuripe on Avenida Beira-Mar is the statue of *Iracema,* an Indian girl who waited at the port for her lover to return. Inspired by the work of Ceará writer José de Alencar, the statue shows Iracema with an arrow in her hand as she looks at Martinho, a Portuguese soldier seated in front of her, holding their son, Moacir.

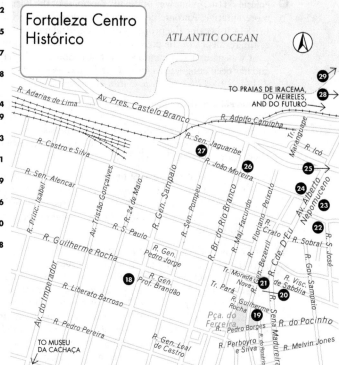

Fortaleza Centro Histórico

ATLANTIC OCEAN

TO PRAIAS DE IRACEMA,
DO MEIRELES,
AND DO FUTURO

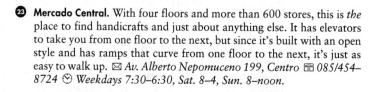

Mercado Central. With four floors and more than 600 stores, this is *the* place to find handicrafts and just about anything else. It has elevators to take you from one floor to the next, but since it's built with an open style and has ramps that curve from one floor to the next, it's just as easy to walk up. ⊠ *Av. Alberto Nepomuceno 199, Centro* ☎ *085/454–8724* ☉ *Weekdays 7:30–6:30, Sat. 8–4, Sun. 8–noon.*

off the
beaten
path

MUSEU DA CACHAÇA – It's a toss-up whether coffee or cachaça is Brazil's national drink. This museum just west of Fortaleza offers tastings of the latter in a tavern. Of course, this happens after you tour the plant and learn the history of what has been a family business for four generations. In the tavern you see a 374,000-liter (98,736-gallon) wooden barrel, the largest in the world. ⊠ *Turn left off CE 65 just before small town of Maranguape; look for signs* ☎ *085/3341–0407* ⊕ *www.museudacachaca.com.br* ⊠ *R$5* ☉ *Tues.–Sun. 8–5.*

Museu do Ceará. Housed in the former Assembléia Provincial (Provincial Assembly Building), this museum's exhibits are devoted to the history and anthropology of Ceará State. ⊠ *Rua São Paulo s/n* ☎ *085/251–1502* ⊠ *R$2* ☉ *Tues.–Fri. 8:30–5, Sat. 8:30–noon, Sun. 2–5.*

⑲ Palácio da Luz. What was originally the home of the Portuguese crown's representative, Antônio de Castro Viana, was built by Indian laborers. In 1814 it became the property of the imperial government and served as the residence of the provincial president. The next important occupant was painter Raimundo Cefa. It now houses a display of his work and has been designated a historic landmark. ✉ *Rua do Rosário* ☎ *085/ 231–5699* 💺 *R$5* ☾ *Mon.–Sat. 8–noon and 2–5.*

㉖ Passeio Público. Also called the Praça dos Mártires, this landmark square dates from the 19th century. In 1824 many soldiers were executed here in the war for independence from the Portuguese crown. It has a central fountain and is full of century-old trees and statues of Greek deities. Look for the ancient baobab tree.

⑳ Praça dos Leões (Praça General Tibúrcio). Built in 1817, this square is officially named after a Ceará general who fought in Brazil's war against Paraguay. However, it's also commonly referred to as the Praça de Leões because of its bronze lions, which were brought over from Paris in the early 20th century.

⑱ Theatro José de Alencar. The José de Alencar Theater is a rather shocking example (especially if you come upon it suddenly) of the eclectic phase of Brazilian architecture. It's a mixture of neoclassical and art nouveau styles. The top of the theater, which looks as if it was designed by the makers of Tiffany lamps, really stands out against Ceará's perpetually blue sky. It was built in 1910 of steel and iron (many of its cast-iron sections were imported from Scotland) and was restored in 1989. It's still used for cultural events—including concerts, plays, and dance performances—and houses a library and an art gallery. Some of the tour guides speak English; call ahead for reservations. ✉ *Praça do José Alencar s/n, Centro* ☎ *085/3101–2596* 📠 *085/3101–2565* ⊕ *www.secult. ce.gov.br* 💺 *R$4* ☾ *Weekdays 8–5, Sat. 8–3.*

Beaches

Fortaleza's enchanting coast runs 22 km (14 mi) along the Atlantic between the Rio Ceará, to the west, and the Rio Pacoti, to the east. The feel of this great urban stretch of sand along with its scenery varies as often as its names: Barra do Ceará, Pirambu, Formosa, Iracema, Beira-Mar, Meireles, Mucuripe, Mansa, Titanzinho, Praia do Futuro, and Sabiazuaba.

In the city center and its immediate environs, feel free to soak up the sun and the ambience of the beaches, but stay out of the water—it is too polluted for swimming. However, you can find clean waters and amazing sands just a little way from Centro and beyond. Surfing is fine at several beaches, including those near the towns of Paracuru and Pecém, to the west of Fortaleza, and Porto das Dunas, to the east.

Fodor'sChoice
★   **Canoa Quebrada.** Hidden behind dunes, the stunning Canoa Quebrada Beach was "discovered" in the 1970s by French doctors working in the area. The spectacular scenery includes not only dunes with colored sands used to make pictures in bottles but also jangadas, red cliffs, and groves of palm trees. Carved into a cliff is the symbol of Canoa: a crescent moon with a star in the middle. Although it was originally settled

by Italian hippies, the village itself has moved on with the times and now has good roads, several comfortable pousadas, and bars and restaurants. The best way to get here is on a trip offered by one of Fortaleza's many tour operators, but bus companies also have daily departures from Fortaleza. ⊠ *Take BR 116 to BR 304; 164 km (101 mi) east of Fortaleza.*

Iguape. The white-sand dunes at this beach are so high that people actually ski down them. The water is calm and clean. In the nearby village you find both fishermen and lace makers (lace is sold at the Centro de Rendeiras). There's also a lookout at Morro do Enxerga Tudo. Buses depart from Fortaleza for this beach several times daily. ⊠ *CE 040, 50 km (31 mi) east of Fortaleza.*

Flexeiras. The ocean is always calm at this beach. Coconut trees, lagoons, and sand dunes surround it. During low tide the reefs surface, and you can see small fish and shells in the rocks. When the tide comes in and the natural pools form, you can grab your mask and go snorkeling. In a 5-km (3-mi) stretch between Flexeiras and Mundaú—another almost-deserted beach—there are several fishing villages and a working lighthouse. A river joins the ocean at Mundaú, forming a large *S* on the sand; on one side is a line of coconut trees and on the other, fishermen with their jangadas—the scene conveys the very essence of Ceará. Flexeiras is about a 90-minute drive from Fortaleza. You can take the Rendenção bus or arrange a trip here with a tour operator. As yet there are no luxury resorts here, but there are several simple, clean pousadas. ⊠ *CE 085, 177 km (110 mi) northwest of Fortaleza.*

Porto das Dunas. Its water-sports options, including surfing, and its sand dunes are enough to draw many people to this beach. But it has much more, including an all-suites hotel and a water park and entertainment complex that might make Disney jealous. You can get here on the *jardineira* bus from Centro or from along Avenida Beira-Mar. ⊠ *Take Av. Washington Soares, then follow signs to Estrada da Cofeco and Beach Park; 22 km (14 mi) southeast of Fortaleza.*

Where to Eat

Along Praia de Iracema and Praia do Mucuripe there are several good seafood restaurants. Be sure to try *lagosta ao natural* (lobster cooked in water and salt and served with homemade butter). Sun-dried meat with *paçoca* (manioc flour seasoned with herbs and red onions) and *caldeirada* (shrimp soup with vegetables and strong spices and herbs) are also popular regional dishes.

Brazilian

$–$$ ⨯ **Caicó.** Locals come for arguably the city's most famous sun-dried meat and paçoca, though dishes of chicken and lamb are also recommended. Ambience is at a minimum in the simple, outdoor seating area on a busy road. ⊠ *Av. Engenheiro Santana Jr. 1002, Papicu* ☎ *085/3234–1915* ▭ *DC, MC, V.*

$–$$ ⨯ **Colher de Pau.** Ana Maria Vilmar and her mother opened this restaurant 10 years ago in a small rented house in the Varjota district. It became so popular that they had to open in a larger building down the street. The original place still serves meals to faithful patrons who are mostly locals; the newer branch is popular with visitors. At both branches the sun-dried meat is served not only with paçoca but also with banana and *baião-de-dois* (rice and beans). The shellfish dishes, many prepared using regional recipes, are also standouts. ⊠ *Rua Frederico Borges 204, Varjota* ☎ *085/3267–3773* ⊠ *Rodovia dos Tabajaras 412, Praia de Iracema* ☎ *085/3219–4097* ▭ *AE, DC, MC, V* ⊘ *No lunch at Iracema branch.*

Eclectic

¢–$$ ✕ **Santa Grelha.** The international fare with local accents smartly matches the attractive decor that employs traditional local materials. In a restored colonial house about a mile from the beach, Santa Grelha is off the tourist path. ⊠ *Rua Vicente Leite 1062, Aldeota* ☎ *085/3224–0249* ▭ *MC, V* ⊘ *Closed Mon.*

French

$–$$ ✕ **La Bohème.** If you like original art, you must have dinner at La Bohème. Only one room inside this former colonial home is for dining; the others are part of an art gallery that you can wander through while waiting for your first course. Be sure to see the wall with photos from films of the 1930s. There's plenty of seating on the patio out front, where a small combo entertains, competing with a combo at a restaurant across the street. Although La Bohème specializes in French cuisine, it also has a small selection of regional seafood dishes. ⊠ *Rua Silva Jataí 1404, Meireles* ☎ *085/3242–6541* ▭ *DC, MC, V* ⊘ *Closed Sun.–Tues. No lunch.*

Fodor'sChoice
★

Italian

$–$$ ✕ **Pulcinella.** You can feast on this restaurant's classic Italian fare (sometimes given a regional twist) in either the air-conditioned dining room with a no-smoking section or in the alfresco seating area. Among the most popular dishes are spaghetti in garlic sauce with shrimp and pimiento and veal in a mushroom-and-herb sauce. ⊠ *Rua Osvaldo Cruz 640, Aldeota* ☎ *085/3261–3411* ▭ *AE, DC, MC, V.*

Seafood

★ $–$$$ ✕ **Cemoara.** A sophisticated decor with clean lines adds to the appeal of this traditional seafood restaurant. Although the *bacalão* (salt cod) selections are fabulous, you can't go wrong with the grilled lobster in a caper sauce or any of the flambéed dishes. The piano in the corner is there for a purpose: a musician accompanies your dinner with nice, soft music. Cemoara has air-conditioning and a no-smoking area. ⊠ *Av. Abolição 3340-A, Meireles* ☎ *085/3263–5001* ▭ *DC, MC, V.*

$–$$ ✕ **Al Mare.** Facing as it does out to the sea, it seems appropriate that the building housing this establishment is shaped like a ship. The grilled seafood *al mare*—a medley of fish, lobster, shrimp, octopus, and squid in an herb sauce—is the specialty. A few dishes, like the aforementioned specialty, are priced much higher than the rest of the menu. ⊠ *Av. Beira-Mar 3821, Meireles* ☎ *085/3263–3888* ▭ *AE, DC, MC, V.*

¢–$ ✕ **Picanha Iracema.** Although the decor is sparse, the location—amid Praia de Iracema's hopping nightlife—is terrific, and you can eat shrimp, fish, or steaks here for very little money. The most expensive dish is Mistão Mar (R$87), but this medley of seafood is enough for four people. Top your meal off with an espresso that costs the equivalent of 5 U.S. cents. ✉ *Av. Historiador Raimundo Girão 574* ☎ *085/3219–0488* 🚻 *AE, DC, MC, V.*

Where to Stay

Most hotels are along Avenida Beira-Mar (previously known as Avenida Presidente John Kennedy). Those in the Praia de Iracema are generally less expensive than those along Praia do Mucuripe. Iracema, however, is also a more interesting area to explore, and it's full of trendy restaurants and bars.

$$$$ 🏨 **Beach Park Suites Resort.** There's very little this pleasant all-suites resort doesn't offer. It faces the beautiful Porto das Dunas Beach, and the Beach Park Acqua Center—arguably the most fantastic facility of its kind in Latin America—is within a five-minute walk (hotel guests get a 15% discount on admission). All the spacious suites have balconies, and the dozens of pots of flowers in the lobby give the whole place a cheerful atmosphere. ✉ *Rua Porto das Dunas 2734, Aquiraz, 61700-000* ☎ *085/ 4012–3000* 🖷 *085/4012–3040* ⊕ *www.beachpark.com.br* 🛏 *198 suites* ♨ *Restaurant, minibars, cable TV, 2 tennis courts, pool, health club, hair salon, sauna, beach, bar, children's programs (ages 4–12), Internet* 🚻 *AE, DC, MC, V.*

★ $$$$ 🏨 **Gran Marquise By Sol Meliá.** On Praia do Mucuripe, just a 15-minute drive from either the airport or Centro, this luxury hotel can certainly include "convenient location" in its list of features. Marble and black granite give the building a modern, sleek look. One of the on-site restaurants serves Brazilian fare, another French; the third, Mariko, is noteworthy for Japanese food and buffets of lobster, shrimp, sushi, sashimi, and oysters. The view from the pool area on the 20th floor is fantastic. ✉ *Av. Beira-Mar 3980, Mucuripe, 60165-121* ☎ *085/3466–5000* 🖷 *085/3466–5111* ⊕ *www.solmelia.com.br* 🛏 *185 rooms, 45 suites* ♨ *3 restaurants, room service, in-room safes, minibars, cable TV, pool, health club, hot tub, massage, sauna, steam room, 2 bars, business services, convention center* 🚻 *AE, DC, MC, V.*

$$$ 🏨 **Seara Praia.** There's plenty of action at the Meireles Beach across the street. The lobby is decorated with works by local artists. Rooms have tile floors, modern art, and furniture with clean, classic lines. For an ocean view, ask for a deluxe room or suite. Don't despair if such a room isn't available; simply head for the rooftop pool and deck and partake of the glorious sunsets. ✉ *Av. Beira-Mar 3080, Meireles, 60165-121* ☎ *085/4011–2200* ⊕ *www.hotelseara.com.br* 🛏 *203 rooms, 14 suites* ♨ *Restaurant, minibars, cable TV, pool, hair salon, bar, Internet room* 🚻 *AE, DC, MC, V.*

$$–$$$ 🏨 **Vila Galé Fortaleza.** This family-friendly resort is the newest, most upscale hotel in the Praia do Futuro area. Extremely well run, it represents the Portuguese chain's foray into Brazil. Although the exterior lacks distinction, the grand lobby is impressive in its design and decor. Services and amenities are top-notch, which is fortunate since there's no nightlife to speak of in the area. ✉ *Av. Dioguinho 4189, Praia do Futuro 60182-001* ☎ *085/3486–4400* 🖷 *085/486–4430* ⊕ *www.vilagale.com.br* 🛏 *285 rooms, 15 suites* ♨ *Restaurant, minibars, cable TV, pool, gym,* *sauna, bar, recreation room, business services, meeting rooms* 🖃 *AE, DC, MC, V.*

★ **$$** 🏨 **Ponta Mar Hotel.** This refined and modern hotel is across the street from a popular beach. A handicrafts fair and a shopping plaza are nearby. Rooms are extra large, and those with great sea views cost just R$15 more than those without. ⊠ *Av. Beira-Mar 2200, Meireles, 60165-121* ☎ *085/ 4006–2200 or 085/4006–2222* 🖷 *085/4006–2223* ⊕ *www.pontamar. com.br* 🛏 *260 rooms, 12 suites* ⏦ *Restaurant, minibars, cable TV, pool, gym, bar, Internet, business services, meeting rooms* 🖃 *AE, DC, MC, V.*

$$ 🏨 **Praiano Palace.** This hotel is a surprisingly affordable option in the chic Praia do Meireles area. Its rooms are simple but comfortable, and nearly all have sea views. Windows alongside the lobby look out on a small garden and a waterfall. ⊠ *Av. Beira-Mar 2800, Meireles, 60165- 121* ☎ *085/4008–2200* ⊕ *www.praiano.com.br* 🛏 *189 rooms* ⏦ *Restaurant, minibars, cable TV, pool, bar, Internet, business services* 🖃 *AE, DC, MC, V.*

$–$$ 🏨 **Marina Park.** Designed to look like a huge ship, the resort overlooks a calm bay and is connected to a marina from which you can take boat trips. It is rather far from the center of everything, but it does have an uncrowded 5-km-long (3-mi-long) beach, as well as an enormous free-form pool. ⊠ *Av. Presidente Castelo Branco 400, Praia de Iracema, 60312–060* ☎ *085/4006–9595* 🖷 *085/3253–1803* ⊕ *www.marinapark. com.br* 🛏 *305 rooms, 10 suites* ⏦ *5 restaurants, coffee shop, in-room safes, minibars, cable TV, in-room data ports, 4 tennis courts, pool, hair salon, massage, sauna, dock, volleyball, bar, shops, playground, business services, meeting room, helipad* 🖃 *AE, DC, MC, V.*

$–$$ 🏨 **Othon Palace Fortaleza.** The Othon Palace Fortaleza sits on a small hill right where the beach makes a big curve, affording guests a spectacular view of the beach and Mucuripe Bay. There's comfortable seating in the stylish lobby, where a spiral staircase leads up to meeting rooms. Tastefully decorated rooms are more like minisuites. ⊠ *Av. Beira-Mar 3470, Mucuripe, 60165-121* ☎ *085/3466–5500* 🖷 *085/3466–5501* ⊕ *www.othon.com.br* 🛏 *121 rooms, 13 suites* ⏦ *Restaurant, coffee shop, minibars, cable TV, gym, business center, meeting rooms* 🖃 *AE, DC, MC, V.*

★ **$** 🏨 **Holiday Inn Fortaleza.** Because of the way the Iracema Beach curves, all rooms here have either ocean or harbor views. There isn't anything opulent about the hotel, but rooms are well designed, large, and immaculate. Also, the location is great: a block off the beach and within walking distance of Centro Dragão do Mar, Ceará's largest cultural center. The pool is on the top deck, and there's a small French restaurant. ⊠ *Av. Historiador Raimundo Girão 800, Praia de Iracema, 60165-050* ☎ *085/3455–5000* 🖷 *085/3455–5055* ⊕ *www.holiday-inn.com/fortaleza* 🛏 *273 rooms* ⏦ *Restaurant, coffee shop, minibars, cable TV, pool, gym, sauna, bar, business services, convention center* 🖃 *AE, DC, MC, V.*

¢–$ 🏨 **Parthenon Golden Flat.** The comfortable apartments here are perfect for families and visitors in the city for a long stay. Each unit has one or two bedrooms, a living room, and a fully equipped kitchen. If you get tired of preparing your own meals, you can head for the restaurant or the coffee shop. ⊠ *Av. Beira-Mar 4260, Mucuripe, 60165–121* ☎ *085/*

3466–1413 🖨 *085/3466–1323* ⊕ *www.accorhotels.com.br* 🛏 *132 apartments* ↻ *Restaurant, coffee shop, minibars, cable TV, pool, sauna, bar* 🖃 *AE, DC, MC, V.*

¢ 🖼 **Malibu Praia Hotel.** Being six blocks from the beach means you do not pay a lot for a decent-size room with all major amenities. Its only major flaws are small beds and dim lighting. Tacky paintings and plastic flowers lend a comical touch to the lobby. ⊠ *Av. Rui Barbosa, Iracema, 60115-220* ☎ *085/3261–5755 or 085/3261–8687* 🛏 *29 rooms* ↻ *Restaurant, minibars* 🖃 *AE, DC, MC, V.*

Nightlife & the Arts

Nightlife

Fortaleza is renowned for its lively nightlife, particularly along Avenida Beira-Mar and Rua dos Tabajaras in the vicinity of Praia de Iracema. The action often includes live forró, the traditional and very popular music and dance of the northeast. As the story goes, U.S. soldiers based in Fortaleza during World War II always invited the townsfolk to their dances, saying they were "for all," which the Brazilians pronounced "forró."

BARS **Itapariká** (⊠ Av. Zezé Diogo 6801, Praia do Futuro ☎ 085/3265–3213) is the place to feast on crabs while enjoying live daily MPB shows. Although it's open for lunch daily, Thursday is the only evening it remains open for dinner.

DANCE SHOWS & Just outside Fortaleza are establishments that blend forró shows with
RODEOS *vaquejada,* a traditional rodeo in which farmhands try to wrangle bulls and wild horses. For a lively mix of vaquejada with samba, reggae, forró, and other types of music, drop in at **Clube do Vaqueiro** (⊠ Quarto Anel Viário de Fortaleza, Km 14, BR 116, Eusébio ☎ 085/3278–2000 ⊕ www.clubedovaqueiro.com.br).

NIGHTCLUBS A young crowd grooves to MPB and rock and roll at **Boite Domínio Público** (⊠ Rua Dragão do Mar 212, Praia de Iracema ☎ 085/219–3883). **Mucuripe Club** (⊠ Travessa Maranguape 108, Centro ☎ 085/3230–3020 or 085/3254–3020 ⊕ www.mucuripe.com.br) houses two separate clubs: Comodore is designed with a nautical theme and Submarino with an underwater theme. In Papicu Tuesday and Thursday nights are hottest at **Oásis** (⊠ Av. Santos Dumont 6061 ☎ 085/3234–4970), when live music from years past draws a crowd to the large dance floor.

The Arts

The large, white **Centro Dragão do Mar de Arte e Cultura** (⊠ Rua Dragão do Mar 81, Praia de Iracema ☎ 085/3488–8600), near the Mercado Central, has several theaters and an open-air amphitheater that host live performances. There are also classrooms for courses in cinema, theater, design, and dance. The **Centro Cultural Banco do Nordeste** (⊠ Rua Floriano Peixoto 941, Centro ☎ 085/488–4100) often hosts plays, concerts, and art exhibitions.

The beautiful, early-19th-century **Theatro José de Alencar** (⊠ Praça do José Alencar s/n Centro ☎ 085/3101–2596 🖨 085/3101–2565 ⊕ www. secult.ce.gov.br) is the site of many concerts, plays, and dance performances. Alongside the main theater is a smaller venue (it seats about

120 people) for more intimate events. There's also a small stage in the theater's garden.

Sports & the Outdoors

The sidewalk along Avenida Beira-Mar is a pleasant place for a walk, run, or bike, and there's usually a pickup volleyball or soccer game in progress on the beach—don't hesitate to ask the players whether you can join in. There are also running tracks and sports courts in the 25-km-long (16-mi-long) Parque do Cocó, on Avenida Pontes Vieira.

Kite- and Windsurfing

Open seas and constant trade winds make Ceará's beaches perfect for windsurfing. You can take lessons and rent equipment at the **Fortaleza Windclub** (✉ Av. Beira-Mar 2120, Praia dos Diários ☎ 085/8818–1966 ⊕ www.kitewind.cjb.net).

Scuba Diving

Off the coast of Ceará are some good dive sites with coral reefs, tropical fish, and wrecks. To rent equipment and arrange lessons and/or trips, contact **Projeto Netuno** (✉ Rua Osvaldo Cruz 2453, Dionísio Torres ☎ 085/3264–4114 ⊕ www.pnetuno.com.br). If you're a novice, you can benefit from its courses, with presentations on equipment and dive techniques as well as marine biology.

Shopping

Fortaleza is one of the most important centers for crafts—especially bobbin lace—in the northeast. Shops sell a good variety of handicrafts, and others have clothing, shoes, and jewelry along Avenida Monsenhor Tabosa in Praia de Iracema. Shopping centers both large and small house branches of the best Brazilian stores. Markets and fairs are the best places to look for lacework, embroidery, leather goods, hammocks, and carvings. More than 600 artisans sell their work at the nightly **feirinha de artesanato** (✉ Av. Beira-Mar, in front of Imperial Othon Palace), on Praia do Meireles.

For lace aficionados, a trip to the town of **Aquiraz** (✉ 30 km/19 mi east of Fortaleza) is a must. Ceará's first capital (1713–99) is today a hub for the artisans who create the famous *bilro* (bobbin) lace. On the beach called Prainha (6 km/4 mi east of Aquiraz) is the Centro de Rendeiras Luiza Távora. Here, seated on little stools, dedicated and patient women lace makers explain how they create such items as bedspreads and tablecloths using the bilro technique.

SIDE TRIPS FROM FORTALEZA

Vale Monumental do Ceará

158 km (98 mi) southwest of Fortaleza.

Ecological parks and huge monoliths fill the Vale Monumental do Ceará (Monumental Valley), an area of nearly 247,100 acres of sertão a two-hour drive over good roads from Fortaleza. Activities include mountain climbing, biking, hiking, horseback tours, paragliding, hang gliding, geology treks, and birding (400 species of birds have been identified).

Sports & the Outdoors

You can hire guides to take you on hikes along the Trilha das Andorinhas (Andorinhas Trail). The valley is filled with giant rocks sculptured by the elements into unusual formations. Trails have been mapped out for moderate hikes to grottos, caves (some of which have prehistoric etchings), lagoons, canyons, and tunnels. Contact **Sertão & Pedras** (⊠ Rua Basílio Pinto 365, Quixadá ☎ 088/3412–5995 ⊕ www.sertaoepedras. com.br) to arrange a trek or rock-climbing/rappelling trips.

Thermal wind conditions are just right for paragliding off a mountaintop near the towns of Quixadá and Quixeramobim, about two hours southwest of Fortaleza (BR 116 to BR 122). One person's excursion of 6½ hours in the air made it into the *Guinness Book of World Records*. Once you're harnessed up, it's just a short downhill run before the wind grabs you and off you go. The most popular month for competitions is November because it's dry. Chico Santos at **Go Up Brazil** (⊠ Estrada das Canoas 722, Bloco 4, Apto. 207, São Conrado, Rio de Janeiro, RJ 22610–210 ☎ 021/3322–3165 or 021/9177–9134 ⊕ www. goup.com.br) can help you make arrangements for paragliding trips in the Vale Monumental. If you'd like to learn to paraglide, contact Claudio Henrique Landim, an instructor with **Escola de vôo Livre** (☎ 085/ 9984–1330). The course is R$680 for 30 hours.

Jericoacoara

FodorśChoice ★ *300 km (186 mi) northwest of Fortaleza.*

It could be the sand dunes, some more than 30 meters (100 feet) tall; it could be the expanse of ocean that puts no limits on how far your eyes can see; or it could be that in the presence of this awesome display of nature, everyday problems seem insignificant. Jericoacoara, a rustic paradise on Ceará State's northwest coast, affects everyone differently but leaves no one unchanged—just like the sand dunes that change their shape and even their colors as they bend to the will of the winds.

In Jericoacoara, or Jerí, time seems endless, even though in the back of your mind you know you'll be leaving in a day or two (or a week or two, if you're lucky). It's the ultimate relaxing vacation, and not because there isn't anything to do. You can surf down sand dunes or ride up and down them in a dune buggy. Also, you can take an easy hike to the nearby Pedra Furada, or Arched Rock, a gorgeous formation sculpted by the waves.

Jerí is said to be one of the 10 most beautiful beaches in the world, yet it has managed to avoid mass tourism. Although a few more small businesses open every year, growth is tempered by its remoteness and its status as an Environmental Protection Area. The pousadas, restaurants, and bars that have sprung up are owned in large part by former tourists, especially from Europe, who were lured back to stay, as if by a siren's call.

The six-hour trip between Jericoacoara and Fortaleza can be arranged through **Heliance Turismo** (✉ Rua Virgílio Távara 150, sala 102, Meireles ☎ 085/3433–9383 or 085/3433–9384 ⊕ www.heliance.com.br).

Where to Stay & Eat

¢–$$ ✕ **Carcará.** This highly regarded restaurant has a wide variety of seafood dishes, from local specialties to international favorites such as sashimi and seviche. You can choose between pleasant indoor and outdoor seating areas. ✉ *Rua do Forró 530* ☎ *088/3669–2013* ▤ *DC, MC, V* ⊗ *No lunch Sun. Closed Apr.*

★ $ ▦ **Pousada Ibirapuera.** Wind chimes, candles, and mobiles help create a sense of peace and tranquillity at this splendid pousada. Colorful duplex apartments have windows looking out into the garden and hammocks in front. The dining area is decorated with a mix of modern art and antiques. ✉ *Rua S da Duna 06, 62598-000* ☎ *088/3669–2012 or 088/9961–5544* ⊕ *www.jericoacoara.tur.br/ibirapuera* ⇨ *8 apartments* ♨ *Minibars, bar; no room TVs* ▤ *AE, DC, MC, V.*

Sports & the Outdoors

Casa do Turismo (☎ 084/621–0211 ⊕ www.jericoacoara.com) can set you up for a 9-km (5-mi) self-guided hike through the dunes using a handheld GPS (global positioning system) monitor. When you arrive at the oasislike Lagoa do Paraiso, you are picked up in a canoe and taken to a restaurant where Italian chef Fred treats you to a divine five-course meal.

FERNANDO DE NORONHA

322 km (200 mi) off the coast of Recife.

This group of 21 islands is part of the Mid-Atlantic Ridge, an underwater volcanic mountain chain more than 15,000 km (9,315 mi) long. It was discovered in 1503 by the Italian explorer Amérigo Vespucci, but was taken over by Fernando de Noronha of Portugal. Its attackers have included the French, Dutch, and English, but the Portuguese built several fortresses and, with cannons in place, fought them off. In later years the Brazilians took advantage of its isolated location and built a prison on one of the islands; it was later used as a military training ground. As word of its beauty and spectacular underwater life spread, however, it was turned over to Pernambuco State and designated a protected marine park. Today fierce regulations protect the archipelago's ecology.

The mountainous, volcanic main—and only inhabited—island of Fernando de Noronha is ringed by beaches with crystal-clear warm waters that are perfect for swimming, snorkeling, and diving. In summer surfers show up to tame the waves. There are shipwrecks to explore and huge turtles, stingrays, and sharks (14 species of them) with which to swim. Diving is good all year, but prime time is from December to March on the windward side (facing Africa) and from July to October on the leeward side (facing Brazil).

If you're an experienced diver, be sure to visit the *Ipiranga*, a small Brazilian destroyer that sank in 1987. It sits upright in 60 meters (200 feet) of water and is swarming with fish, and you can see the sailors' personal effects, including uniforms still hanging in closets. Another good site is the Sapata Cave, which has an antechamber so large that it has been used for marriage ceremonies (attended by giant rays, no doubt).

Well-maintained trails and well-trained guides make for enjoyable hikes. You can also enjoy the landscape on a horseback trek to the fortress ruins and isolated beaches where hundreds of seabirds alight. In addition, Projeto Tamar has an island base for its work involving sea turtles. One of the most fascinating exploring experiences, however, is an afternoon boat trip to the outer fringes of the Baía dos Golfinhos (Bay of the Dolphins), where dozens of spinner dolphins swim south each day to hunt in deep water.

There are two daily departures to Fernando de Noronha from both Recife and Natal; flight time from either is around an hour. Only 90 visitors are allowed here each day, and there's a daily tourist tax of R$28, including the day you arrive and the day you leave. Divers pay an additional R$20 a day. Bring enough reais to last the trip, as credit cards are not widely accepted and changing money is difficult.

Where to Stay & Eat

$$$–$$$$ ✕ **Ecologiku's.** This very small restaurant is known for its seafood, especially lobster. If you can't decide what to order, the *sinfonia ecologiku* is a sampling of every type of seafood on the menu. ⊠ *Estrada Velha do Sueste, near airport* ☎ 081/3619–1807 ⊟ MC, V ☻ No lunch.

$–$$ ✕ **Tartarugão.** One of island's best restaurants also operates a little rent-a-buggy business on the side. The phenomenal steak is big enough for two people and comes with rice and a salad. ⊠ *Alameda do Boldró; west side of island* ☎ 081/3619–1331 ⊕ www.tartarugao.com.br ⊟ MC, V.

$$$$ 🏨 **Pousada Zé Maria Paraíso.** Although this friendly, popular pousada isn't on the beach, you can see the ocean, which is a 15-minute walk away. It sits atop a hill, surrounded by vegetation. ⊠ *Rua Cordeiro 1, Floresta Velha, 53990-000* ☎ 081/3619–1258 ⊕ *www.pousadazemaria.com.br* ⤳ *6 rooms, 13 bungalows* ♨ *Restaurant, minibars, cable TV, pool.*

$$$–$$$$ 🏨 **Pousada Dolphin.** Just a five-minute walk from the beach, this pousada has large, attractively decorated rooms. ⊠ *Alameda Boldró s/n, BR 363, 53990-000* ☎ 081/3465–7224 ⊕ *www.dolphinhotel.tur.br* ⤳ *11 rooms* ♨ *Restaurant, minibars, pool, hot tub, sauna, bar, recreation room* ⊟ DC, MC, V ⧫ MAP.

Sports & the Outdoors

For dive trips, **Atlantis Divers** (⊠ Fernando de Noronha, Caixa Postal 20, 53990-000 ☎ 081/3619–1371 ⊕ www.atlantisnoronha.com.br) has excellent English-speaking staffers and good boats.

RECIFE, NATAL & FORTALEZA ESSENTIALS

Transportation

For more transportation information, *see* Smart Travel Tips A to Z, *at* the beginning of this book.

BY AIR

The main airlines operating in Recife, Natal, and Fortaleza are TAM, Varig, and Gol. Fernando de Noronha is a one-hour flight from Recife or Natal on Trip Linhas Aéreas, TAM, or Varig (⇨ Air Travel, *in* Smart Travel Tips A to Z).

RECIFE The Aeroporto Internacional Guararapes is 10 km (6 mi) south of Recife, just five minutes from Boa Viagem, and 15 minutes from the city center. In the lobby of Recife's airport, on the right just before the exit door, is a tourist information booth, and next to that is a taxi stand. You can pay at the counter; the cost is about R$23 to Boa Viagem and R$34 to downtown. A cab from the airport to Olinda costs R$40–R$55. There are also regular buses and microbuses (more expensive). The bus labeled AEROPORTO runs to Avenida Dantas Barreto in the center of the city, stopping in Boa Viagem on the way. To reach Olinda, take the AEROPORTO bus to Avenida Nossa Senhora do Carmo in Recife and then take the CASA CAIADA bus.

🛈 Airport **Aeroporto Internacional Guararapes** ✉ Praça Ministro Salgado Filho s/n, Imbiribeira, Recife ☎ 081/3464-4188.

NATAL The Aeroporto Internacional Augusto Severo is 15 km (9 mi) south of the town center. There are no buses connecting the Natal airport with Ponta Negra. Taxis to Ponta Negra or downtown Natal cost around R$25.

🛈 Airport **Aeroporto Internacional Augusto Severo** ✉ BR 101, Parnamirim ☎ 084/3644-1110.

FORTALEZA The Aeroporto Internacional Pinto Martins is 6 km (4 mi) south of downtown. Fortaleza's fixed-price *especial* (special) taxis charge about R$23 for trips from the airport to downtown on weekdays, R$41 on weekends. City buses also run from here to the nearby bus station and Praça José de Alencar in Centro.

🛈 Airport **Aeroporto Internacional Pinto Martins** ✉ Av. Senador Carlos Jereissati, Serrinha, Fortaleza ☎ 085/477-1200.

BY BUS

RECIFE The Terminal Integrado de Passageiros (TIP), a metro terminal and bus station 14 km (9 mi) from the Recife city center, handles all interstate bus departures and some connections to local destinations. To reach it via metro, a 30-minute ride, enter through the Museu do Trem, opposite the Casa da Cultura, and take the train marked RODOVIÁRIA. Several buses a day go to Salvador (12–14 hours, R$90), Fortaleza (12 hours, R$70), and Natal (four hours, R$30); there are also daily departures to Rio (40 hours, R$200) and frequent service to Caruaru (two hours, R$12).

In Boa Viagem you can take the PIEDADE/RIO DOCE bus to Olinda. Buses to Igarassu and Ilha de Itamaracá leave from the center of Recife, at Avenida Martins de Barros, in front of the Grande Hotel.

Buses are free when using the metro and vice-versa.

📧 **Terminal Integrado de Passageiros (TIP)** ✉ Km 15, Rodovia BR 232, Curado, Jaboatão dos Guararapes ☎ 081/3452-2824.

NATAL Natal has two bus stations. For most destinations you use the Rodoviário de Natal, 5 km (3 mi) from Ponta Negra. It's often referred to as the *terminal nova* (new terminal). Several buses daily go to Praia da Pipa (1½ hours; R$7), Recife (four hours; R$30), Fortaleza (eight hours; R$75), and Rio de Janeiro (44 hours; R$205).

The other bus station, the Rodoviário Velho (old bus station), is downtown. Buses to Genipabu leave every half hour for the half-hour trip. The fare on city buses is R$1. Buses run fairly frequently between Ponta Negra and downtown. From Ponta Negra to downtown, look for buses marked CENTRO or CIDADE ALTA. On the return, look for buses marked PONTA NEGRA. Buses run between Ponta Negra and downtown.

📧 **Terminal Rodoviário de Natal** ✉ Av. Capitão Mor. Gouveia 1237, Cidade de Esperança ☎ 084/3232-7219. **Rodoviário Velho** ✉ Praça de Augusto Severo ☎ No phone.

FORTALEZA The main bus station, Terminal Rodoviário João Tomé, is 6 km (4 mi) south of Centro. In low season you can buy tickets at the station right before leaving. São Benedito runs five buses daily to Beberibe and Morro Branco Beach (2½ hours; R$8.40), and three daily to Aracati and Canoa Quebrada (3½ hours; R$15). Expresso Guanabara has five daily buses to Recife (12 hours; R$88–R$102). Itapemerim has one daily to Salvador (22 hours; R$149) and daily buses to Rio de Janeiro (48 hours; R$258–R$319). Penha runs buses to São Paulo (52 hours; R$331–R$339).

The fare on city buses is R$1.20. Those marked 13 DE MAIO or AGUANAMBI 1 or 2 run from Avenida General Sampaio and pass the Centro de Turismo; from here (Rua Dr. João Moreira), you can take the bus labeled CIRCULAR to Avenida Beira-Mar and Praia de Iracema and Praia do Meireles. From Avenida Castro e Silva (close to Centro de Turismo), PRAIA DO FUTURO and SERVILUZ buses run to Praia do Futuro. For beaches west of the city, take a CUMBUCO bus from Praça Capistrano Abreu on Avenida Tristão Gonçalves or from along Avenida Beira-Mar. For the eastern beach of Porto das Dunas and the water park, take a BEACH PARK bus from Praça Tristão Gonçalves or from along Avenida Beira-Mar.

📧 **Bus Information Expresso Guanabara** ☎ 085/4011-1992. **Itapemirim** ☎ 085/3256-4511. **Penha** ☎ 085/3256-4511. **São Benedito** ☎ 085/3452-1980. **Terminal Rodoviário Engenheiro João Tomé** ✉ Av. Borges de Melo 1630, Fátima ☎ 085/3256-2100.

BY CAR

RECIFE The main north–south highway through Recife is BR 101. To the north it travels through vast sugar plantations; it's mostly straight, with only slight slopes. To travel south, you also can take the scenic coastal road, PE 060, which passes through Porto de Galinhas Beach. To reach Caruaru, take BR 232 west; the trip takes 1½ hours. Because of horrible rush-hour traffic and careless drivers, it's best to rent a car only for side trips from Recife.

Rental Agencies Hertz ☎ 081/3338-2103 ⊕ www.hertz.com.br. **Localiza** ☎ 081/3341-2082 or 081/3341-0477 ⊕ www.localiza.com.

NATAL Natal lies at the northern end of BR 101, making it an easy trip from Recife, which is due south on BR 101. To reach Praia da Pipa, head south on BR 101 and then take RN 003 to the east. To Fortaleza, take BR 304 northwest and then head north on BR 116. Although traffic is increasing, it is still fairly easy and quick to drive around Natal.

Rental Agencies Avis ☎ 084/3644-2503 ⊕ www.avis.com.br. **Hertz** ☎ 084/3644-1228 ⊕ www.hertz.com.br. **Localiza** ☎ 084/3643-1557 ⊕ www.localiza.com.

FORTALEZA The main access roads to Fortaleza are the BR 304, which runs southeast to Natal and Recife and which is in good condition; the BR 222, which has a few poor sections and which travels west to the state of Piauí and on to Brasília; the BR 020 southwest, which goes to Picos, in Piauí State, and on to Brasília and is in decent shape; and the BR 116, which runs south to Salvador and has several stretches in poor condition. The CE 004, or Litoránea, links the coastal towns to the southeast as far as Aracati. Many of the secondary routes are paved, though there are also some dirt roads in fair condition.

It's easy to drive in Fortaleza. Major routes take you easily from one side of town to the other. Although rush hour sees traffic jams, they aren't nearly as bad as they are in other big cities.

Rental Agencies Avis ☎ 0800/198-456 or 085/3242-3115 ⊕ www.avis.com.br. **Hertz** ☎ 0800/7017300 or 085/3242-5425 ⊕ www.hertz.com.br. **Localiza** ☎ 0800/992-000 or 085/3477-5050 ⊕ www.localiza.com.

BY SUBWAY

Recife is the only northeastern city with a subway system.

A single ride on the metro is R$1.10. You can find a map at the Metrorec Web site (click on MAPA DA REDE). Transfer tickets and city bus tickets cost R$1.10–R$2.30. Buses are clearly labeled and run frequently until about 10:30 PM. Many stops have signs indicating the routes. To reach Boa Viagem via the metro, get off at the Joana Bezerra stop (a 20-minute ride) and take a bus or taxi (R$15) from here. Buses are free when using the metro and vice-versa.

Metrorec ⊕ www.metrorec.com.br.

BY TAXI

RECIFE Taxis are cheap (fares double on Sunday), but drivers seldom speak English. All use meters. You can either hail a cab on the street or call for one. Recommended services are Coopertáxi, Radiotáxi Recife, and Teletáxi.

Coopertáxi ☎ 081/3424-8944 ⊕ www.coopertaxi.com.br. **Radiotáxi Recife** ☎ 081/3423-7777. **Teletáxi** ☎ 081/3429-4242 ⊕ www.teletaxirecife.com.br.

NATAL All taxis have meters and are easy to locate in Ponta Negra and downtown. Some of the best-known companies are Rádio Táxi, Rádio Táxi Relámpago, and Rádio Cooptáxi.

Rádio Táxi ☎ 084/3221-5666 ⊕ www.taxinatal.com.br. **Rádio Táxi Relámpago** ☎ 084/3223-5444. **Rádio Cooptáxi** ☎ 084/3205-4455.

FORTALEZA   You can call cabs or hail them on the street—all have meters. Fares are affordable, though they double on Sunday. Few drivers are English speakers. Reliable taxi services include Coopertáxi, Disquetáxi, Ligue Táxi, and Rádio Táxi.

🚖 **Coopertáxi** ☎ 085/3295-8258. **Disquetáxi** ☎ 085/3287-7222 ⊕ www.disquetaxifortaleza.com.br.

Contacts & Resources

For more contacts and resources and in-depth information, *see* Smart Travel Tips A to Z, at the beginning of this book.

BANKS & EXCHANGING SERVICES

Some banks accept only cards with Visa/Plus logos and others accept only cards with MasterCard/Cirrus logos. Banco24horas ATMs usually accept all cards, including American Express. *See* "Money Matters" *in* Smart Travel Tips A to Z for more information.

RECIFE   Recommended *casas de câmbio* (exchange houses) in the city center include Mônaco Câmbio and Norte Câmbio Turismo. In Boa Viagem try Norte Câmbio Turismo or Colmeia Câmbio & Turismo. Banco do Brasil has multiple locations, including the airport. Most banks are open weekdays 10–4.

🏦 **Banco do Brasil** ⊠ Av. Dantas Barreto 541, Santo Antônio ☎ 0800-785678 ⊠ Rua Barão de Souza Leão 440, Boa Viagem. **Colmeia Câmbio & Turismo** ⊠ Rua dos Navegantes 784, Loja 4, Boa Viagem. **Mônaco Câmbio** ⊠ Praça Joaquim Nabuco 159, Santo Antônio. **Norte Câmbio Turismo** ⊠ Rua Mathias de Albuquerque 223, Sala 508, Boa Viagem ⊠ Rua dos Navegantes 691, Loja 10, Boa Viagem.

NATAL   Money can be exchanged in the airport at VIP Câmbio or at Paria Câmbio in the Praia Shopping. Banco do Brasil has an office in Natal Shopping. Bank hours are generally weekdays 10–4.

🏦 **Banco do Brasil** ⊠ Natal Shopping, Rodovia Br. 101 Km 02, Loja 233, Candelária ☎ 084/3235-8191. **Praia Câmbio** ⊠ Praia Shopping, Av. Engenheiro Roberto Freire 8790, Ponta Negra. **VIP Câmbio** ⊠ Aeroporto Internacional Augusto Severo, BR 101, Parnamirim.

FORTALEZA   The main Banco do Brasil branch is open weekdays 10–3; the Meireles branch on Avenida Abolição has the same hours. There are lots of casas de câmbio in Meireles as well.

🏦 **Banco do Brasil** ⊠ Av. Duque de Caxias 560, Centro ☎ 085/3255-3000 ⊠ Av. Desembarcador Moreira 1195, Aldeota ☎ 085/3266-7800.

EMERGENCIES

RECIFE   🚑 Emergency Services **Ambulance** ☎ 192.

🏥 Hospitals **Centro Hospitalar Albert Sabin** ⊠ Rua Senador José Henrique 141, Ilha do Leite ☎ 081/3421-5411. **Real Hospital Português** ⊠ Av. Agamenon Magalhães s/n, Derby ☎ 081/3416-1122.

💊 Pharmacies **Drogafácil** ⊠ Rua Real da Torre 570, Madalena ☎ 081/3326-6498. **Farmanossa** ⊠ Av. Visconde de Jequitinhonha 1144, Boa Viagem ☎ 081/3341-2169.

NATAL   🚑 Emergency Services **Ambulance** ☎ 192.

🏥 Hospitals **Hospital Memorial** ⊠ Av. Juvenal Lamartine 979, Tirol ☎ 084/3211-3636. **Hospital Walfredo Gurgel** ⊠ Av. Senador Salgado Filho s/n, Tirol ☎ 084/3232-7500.

⚑ Pharmacies Farmácia Nobre ☒ Av. Praia dos Búzios 9036, Ponta Negra ☎ 084/3219-3381. **Cooperfarma** ☒ Av. Praia de Ponta Negra 8936, Ponta Negra ☎ 084/3219-3471.

FORTALEZA **⚑ Emergency Services Ambulance** ☎ 192. **Surfing emergencies** ☎ 193.
⚑ Hospitals Hospital Antônio Prudente ☒ Av. Aguanambi 1827, Fátima ☎ 085/3277-4000. **Hospital Batista** ☒ Rua Prof. Dias da Rocha 2530, Aldeota ☎ 085/3268-3308.
⚑ Pharmacies Farmácia Aldesul ☒ Av. Abolição 2625, Meireles ☎ 085/3242-7071. **Farmácia Portugal** ☒ Av. Abolição 2950, Meireles ☎ 085/3242-4422.

RECIFE Livraria Brandão has used English-language books; the shop also sells books from stalls on Rua do Infante Dom Henrique. Espaço Nossa Livraria is a large emporium with a huge stock, including many foreign-language titles. You can find English-language books, magazines, and newspapers at Sodiler.
⚑ Bookstores Livraria Brandão ☒ Rua da Matriz 22, Boa Vista ☎ 081/3222-4171. **Espaço Nossa Livraria** ☒ Rua Riachuelo 267, Boa Vista ☎ 081/3302-6070. **Sodiler** ☒ Guararapes Airport, Praça Ministro Salgado Filho s/n, Imbiribeira ☎ 081/3342-0828 ☒ Shopping Center Recife, Rua Padre Carapuceiro 777, Boa Viagem ☎ 081/3326-9094 or 081/3326-3809.

NATAL A.S. Book Shop has a decent selection of English-language books and periodicals.
⚑ Bookstores A.S. Book Shop ☒ Praia Shopping, Av. Engenheiro Roberto Freire 8790, Ponta Negra ☎ 084/3219-5373 ⊕ www.aslivros.com.br.

FORTALEZA You can find English-language publications at Edésio.
⚑ Fortaleza Bookstores Edésio ☒ Rua Guilherme Rocha 185, Centro ☎ 085/3231-3981.

INTERNET
Cyber-café Alô Brazil also provides Internet access. The Guararapes shopping center, just outside Recife, has Internet services at Cyber Café do Shopping Guararapes. For Internet service in Fortaleza, try Company Office, which also has fax and secretarial services.
⚑ Internet Cafés Alô Brasil ☒ Rua Alto Bonito 46, Santa Terezinha, Fortaleza ☎ 085/3263-3309. **Company Office** ☒ Caesar Park Hotel, Av. Beira-Mar 3980, Mucuripe, Fortaleza ☎ 085/263-1133. **Cyber Café do Shopping Guararapes** ☒ Av. Barreto de Menezes 800, near Piedade Beach, just south of Recife, Jaboatão dos Guararapes ☎ 081/3464-2488. **Interjato** ☒ Praia Shopping Av. Roberto Freire 3796, Ponta Negra, Natal ☎ 084/3219-5510. **Lan House Net Inside** ☒ Av. Dois Rios 1515, sala 3, Ibura de Baixo, Recife ☎ 081/3339-3945.

MAIL & SHIPPING
Express-mail service is available at post offices in Recife, Natal, and Fortaleza.
⚑ Overnight Services DHL ☒ Av. Luciano Carneiro 2090, Fortaleza ☎ 0800/701-0833 in Brazil ⊕ www.dhl.com.br ☒ Av. Conselheiro Aguiar 1415 loja 01, Recife. **FedEx** ☒ Km 10, BR 116, Fortaleza ☎ 085/3274-1966 ⊕ www.fedex.com.
⚑ Post Offices Fortaleza post offices ☒ Rua Senador Alencar 38, Centro ☒ Monsenhor Tabosa 111, Iracema. **Natal post office** ☒ Av. Engenheiro Hilderando Góis 221. **Recife post office** ☒ Av. Gurarapes 250.

TOUR OPTIONS

RECIFE   Agência Luck's vans pick up from all the hotels for city tours. Make arrangements for these and excursions outside Recife with Andratur. Catamarã Tours books day and night river trips by catamaran and other small boats from its office at the port in Recife Antigo on Praça Rio Branco (Marco Zero). You can make reservations for pousadas and land tours of Fernando de Noronha through Karitas Turismo Ltda.

Catamaran rides along the Rio Capibaribe pass Recife's grand houses, bridges, and mangrove swamps. There are two such excursions: the hour-long afternoon trip goes through the old rotating bridge and passes Recife Antigo and São José, the customs quay, the Santa Isabel Bridge, and the Rua da Aurora quays to the area near the Casa da Cultura. The two-hour-long night tour is aboard a slower—though more lively—vessel. The trip is like a party, with live music, drinks, and snacks. It passes the quays of São José Estelita (a set of restored warehouses) and then goes back by the Calanga Iate Clube, passing the ruins of the Casa de Banhos and running to the Rio Beberibe, where there's a beautiful view of Olinda. Boats leave from near the Praça do Marco Zero in Recife Antigo.

In Olinda, the guides with official ID badges in the Praça do Carmo can show you around. Under any other circumstances, though, don't hire sightseeing guides who approach you on the street. Hire one through the museum or sight you're visiting, a tour operator, the tourist board, your hotel, or a reputable travel agency—and no one else.

🖪 **ASS Turismo** ⊠ Av. Conselheiro Aguiar 3150, Loja 5, Boa Viagem ☎ 081/3465-8588. **Agência Luck** ⊠ Rua Jornalista Paulo Bittencourt 163, Casa A, Derby ☎ 081/3302-6222 🖴 081/3302-6201 ⊕ www.luckviagens.com.br. **Catamarã Tours** ☎ 081/3424-2845 or 081/3424-8930 ⊕ www.cataramatours.com.br. **Catamarã Tours** ☎ 081/3436-2220. **Karitas Turismo Ltda** ⊠ Rua Agenor Lopes 292, Boa Viagem ☎ 081/3466-4300 ⊕ www.karitas.com.br.

NATAL   Manary Ecotours, the only ecotourism operator in Natal, runs professional trips to diverse destinations such as Cariri, Dinosaur Valley, and Praia da Pipa. Ma-noa has a hotel pickup service, allowing for easy day trips to their aquatic park in Maracajaú. A number of companies run dune-buggy trips to Genipabu and other local beaches. Luck Natal Tour is one.

🖪 **Cariri Ecotours** ⊠ Av. Jaguarari 4990, Green Mall, Loja 4, Candelária ☎ 084/3604-0782 or 084/9928-0198 ⊕ www.caririecotours.com.br. **Luck Natal Tur** ⊠ Av. Praia de Ponta Negra 8884, Ponta Negra ☎ 084/3219-2966 ⊕ www.lucknataltur.com.br. **Ma-noa** ⊠ Av. Nascimento de Castro 1082, Lagoa Nova ☎ 084/3234-9321 ⊕ www.ma-noa.com.br. **Protour** ⊠ Av. Engenheiro Roberto Freire 8337, Ponta Negra ☎ 084/642-2829 ⊕ www.protour.com.br.

FORTALEZA   Recommended operators include Ernanitur, Lisatur Viagens e Turismo Ltda., Nettour Viagem e Turismo, and Beach Sun Serviços e Turismo Ltda. For trips to Flexeiras, Jericoacoara, or other beach areas outside Fortaleza, OceanView Tours and Travel is a solid choice.

🖪 **Beach Sun Serviços e Turismo Ltda** ⊠ Av. Santos Dumont 2727, Aldeota ☎🖴 085/3248-2288. **Ernanitur** ⊠ Av. Barão de Studart 1165, 1 andar, Aldeota ☎ 085/3244-9363

⊕ www.ernanitur.com.br. **Lisatur Viagens e Turismo Ltda** ✉ Av. Monsenhor Tabosa 1067, Praia Iracema ☎ 085/3219-5400. **OceanView Tours and Travel** ✉ Av. Monsenhor Tabosa 1165, Meireles ☎ 085/3219-1300 ⊕ www.oceanviewturismo.com.br.

VISITOR INFORMATION

RECIFE The state tourist board in Recife is Empetur. It has several booths and a 24-hour information hotline, which is the number at the Guarapes airport booth. In Olinda contact the Secretaria de Turismo.

🛈 **Empetur** ✉ Guararapes Airport, Praça Ministro Salgado Filho s/n, Imbiribeira ☎ 081/3462-4960 or 081/3428-8000 ⊕ www.empetur.com.br. **Secretaria de Turismo** ✉ Rua de São Bento 160, Varadouro, Olinda ☎ 081/3429-1988 🖷 081/3305-1148 ⊕ www.olinda.pe.gov.br.

NATAL SETUR is the state tourism board. Tourists can visit the main office or branches in Praia Shopping, Centro de Turismo, the bus station, or the airport. The main office is open 7–1 and 2–6 on weekdays; the other offices are open 8 AM–10 PM daily.

🛈 **SETUR** ✉ Rua Mossoró 359, Petrópolis ☎ 084/3232-2500 ⊕ www.setur.rn.gov.br ✉ Aeroporto Internacional Augusto Severo, BR 101, Parnamirim ☎ 084/3643-1811 ✉ Centro de Turismo, Rua Abedal de Figueiredo 980, Petrópolis ☎ 084/3211-6149 ✉ Praia Shopping, Av. Engenheiro Roberto Freire 8790, Ponta Negra ☎ 084/3232-7248 ✉ Terminal Rodoviário de Natal, Av Capitão Mor. Gouveia 1237, Cidade da Esperança ☎ 084/3232-7219.

FORTALEZA An English-language tourist information hotline, Disque Turismo, operates 24 hours a day. You can also get information through Ceará State's tourist board, SETUR, which has booths in several locations. The Cambeba booth is open weekdays 8–5; the Centro booth is open Monday–Saturday 8–6 and Sunday 8–noon; the booth in the João Tomé bus terminal is open daily 6 AM–9 PM. The airport booth is open daily 6 AM–11 PM. The municipal tourist board, Funcet, also has a booth open daily 8–noon and 2–6.

🛈 **Disque Turismo** ☎ 085/3252-1444. **Funcet** ✉ Rua Pereira Filgueiras 4, Centro ☎ 085/3252-1444. **SETUR** ✉ Centro Administrativo Virgílio Távora, Cambeba ☎ 085/3101-4688 ✉ Aeroporto Internacional Pinto Martins, Av. Senador Carlos Jereissati, Serrinha ☎ 085/3477-1667 ✉ Centro de Turismo, Rua Senador Pompeu 350, Centro ☎ 085/3101-5508 ✉ Terminal Rodoviário João Tomé, Av. Borges de Melo 1630, Fátima ☎ 085/3101-3397.

The Amazon

WORD OF MOUTH

"In Manaus, you must make a short boat trip to see the rendezvous of two mighty rivers: Negro, [with] its clear and dark waters, and Amazonas, with its turbid waters the color of earth. Their waters don't mix instantly, they flow together, forming colored eddies."

—Dilermando

"Without doubt, the most unique birthday I've ever had! We took a canoe to paddle into the flooded forests . . . where we saw three species of monkeys in their natural habitat. That afternoon, we went piranha fishing. Our prey must have known it was my birthday as I managed to catch one, but my husband didn't."

—quiCK

Updated by
Rhan Flatin

THE WORLD'S LARGEST TROPICAL FOREST seems an endless carpet of green that's sliced only by the curving contours of rivers. Its statistics are as impressive: the region covers more than 10 million square km (4 million square mi) and extends into eight other countries (French Guiana, Suriname, Guyana, Venezuela, Ecuador, Peru, Bolivia, and Colombia). It takes up roughly 40% of Brazil in the states of Acre, Rondônia, Amazonas, Roraima, Pará, Amapá, and Tocantins. The Amazon forest is home to 500,000 cataloged species of plants and a river that annually transports 15% of the world's available freshwater to the sea, yet it's inhabited by only 16 million people. That's less than the population of metropolitan São Paulo.

Life centers on the rivers, the largest of which is the Amazon itself. From its source in southern Peru, it runs 6,300 km (3,900 mi) to its Atlantic outflow. Of its hundreds of tributaries, 17 are more than 1,600 km (1,000 mi) long. The Amazon is so large it could hold the Congo, Nile, Orinoco, Mississippi, and Yangtze rivers with room to spare. In places it is so wide you can't see the opposite shore, earning it the appellation Rio Mar (River Sea). Although there has been increasing urbanization in the Amazon region, between one-third and one-half of the Amazon's residents live in rural settlements, many of which are along the riverbanks, where transportation, water, fish, and good soil for planting are readily available.

History

Spaniard Vicente Pinzón is credited with being the first to sail the Amazon, in 1500. But the most famous voyage was undertaken by Spanish conquistador Francisco de Orellano, who set out from Ecuador on a short mission to search for food in 1541. Instead of gold or a lost kingdom, however, Orellano ran into natives, heat, and disease. When he emerged from the jungle a year later, his crew told a tale of women warriors they called the Amazons (a nod to classical mythology), and the story lent the region its name.

Much later, Portuguese explorer Francisco Raposo claimed to have found the ruins of a lost civilization in the jungle. He wrote: "We entered fearfully through the gateways to find the ruins of a city. . . . We came upon a great plaza, a column of black stone, and on top of it the figure of a youth was carved over what seemed to be a great doorway." Whatever Raposo saw was never again found. The Amazon natives, primarily nomadic hunter-gatherers, did not leave behind remnants of kingdoms and cities as did those in Mexico and Peru.

Early Portuguese contacts with indigenous groups were relatively peaceful. But it wasn't long before diseases brought by the Europeans took their toll, and Portuguese attempts to enslave the *índios* (Indians—a politically correct term in Brazil) did the rest. From the time the Portuguese arrived in Brazil to the present day, the number of native people in Brazil (most of them in the Amazon) was reduced from 4.5 million to just 300,000.

In the late 19th century, rubber production transformed Belém and Manaus into cities. Rubber barons constructed mansions and monuments and

Even 10 days is a short time to explore the Amazon. Still, during a weeklong stay you can see some urban highlights and spend a little time on the river as well. The following itineraries start in Belém and end in Manaus, but it's fine to follow them in reverse order.

Numbers in the text correspond to numbers in the margin and on the Belém and Manaus maps.

10

If you have 7 days

Fly into 🗺 **Belém** ❶ – ⓲ 🏴 for two days of exploring the historic sites and natural reserves in and around the city. Then fly to 🗺 **Manaus** ㉔ – ㉟ for two days to see the meeting of the waters and to take a city tour that includes the **Teatro Amazonas** ㉝. Then head out for a day or two to one of the famed jungle lodges, or sign up for an eco-tour.

If you have 10 days

Spend two days in 🗺 **Belém** ❶ – ⓲ 🏴 exploring the city and its environs. On your third day travel by boat to 🗺 **Ilha do Marajó** for a two-day *fazenda* (ranch) stay. Return to Belém and fly to 🗺 **Manaus** ㉗ – �37 for two days to see the urban sights and the meeting of the waters. Spend your last few days at a jungle lodge outside Manaus, or go on an ecotour to see wildlife and villages.

If you have 15 days

After spending two days exploring 🗺 **Belém** ❶ – ⓲ 🏴 and two more on a fazenda on 🗺 **Ilha do Marajó,** hop a riverboat for the two-day journey to 🗺 **Santarém.** Spend a day strolling the city before heading to **Alter do Chão,** an hour away. Then fly into 🗺 **Manaus** ㉗ – �37 to spend a day or two sightseeing before heading to a jungle lodge or out on an ecotour or fishing expedition.

---

brought life's modern trappings into the jungle. In 1928 Henry Ford began to pour millions of dollars into vast rubber plantations. The array of explorers and opportunists drawn to the newly prosperous area included former U.S. president Theodore Roosevelt, in 1913. After much struggle and few results, Ford's rubber project was scrapped in the late 1940s.

Since the rubber era, huge reserves of gold and iron have been discovered in the Amazon. Land-settlement schemes and development projects, such as hydroelectric plants and major roadworks, have followed. In the process, vast portions of tropical forest have been indiscriminately cut; tribal lands have been encroached upon; and industrial by-products, such as mercury used in gold mining, have poisoned wildlife and people. The Brazilian government has established reserves and made some efforts to preserve the territory, but there is much more to be done.

And yet, 500 years after the first Europeans arrived, much of the Amazon has not been thoroughly explored by land. You still hear stories of lost cities and of unearthly creatures; and you can stand on a riverboat deck and be astounded by the vastness of the mighty Amazon River and hike through dense vegetation beneath 150-foot (35-meter) trees.

Exploring the Amazon

Although there are regular flights and some bus routes through the Amazon, many visitors opt for the area's primary mode of transportation—boat (⇨ The Amazon by Boat, *below*). Though much slower, boats offer a closer look at Amazon culture, nature, and the river system, and they go just about everywhere you'd want to go. A trip along the Amazon itself, especially the 1,602-km (993-mi) four- to five-day journey between Belém and Manaus, is a singular experience. Averaging more than 3 km (2 mi) in width, but reaching a size of as much as 48 km (30 mi) across in the rainy season, there are many spots where it's impossible to see either bank. At night the moon and stars are often the only sources of light, reinforcing the sense of being in true wilderness.

Visiting outlying areas in the Amazon usually results in unforgettable adventures, but tropical environments can be hostile, so prepare well and go with a companion if possible. It's a good idea to hire a guide or go with a tour company specializing in backcountry adventures. To join a tour or to choose a destination, contact one of the tour companies we suggest, or consult with a state-run tour agency. Paratur in Belém and SEC in Manaus can also be helpful. Before departure make sure someone knows exactly where you are going and when you are returning. Tell them you will contact them as soon as you have phone access. Before you set out, make all your transportation arrangements, gather all the necessary supplies, and do some research so you are knowledgeable about the health and safety precautions you need to take. A small cut can turn into a bad infection, and a painful encounter with a stingray's barb can result in a ruined vacation. The more remote your destination, the more seriously you should heed the travel advice and health precautions in this book. (⇨ For information on health, *see* Health *in* The Amazon Essentials, *below,* and Health *in* Smart Travel Tips A to Z. For information on emergency evacuation insurance, *see* Insurance *in* Smart Travel Tips A to Z.) Your adventure can be wonderful, but you have to prepare well.

When to Go

The dry season (low water) between Belém and Manaus runs roughly from mid-June into December, and it's often brutally hot. Shortly before the new year, rains come more often and the climate cools a bit. The average annual temperature is 80°F (27°C) with high humidity. The early morning and the evening are always cooler and are the best times for walking around. The rainy season (high water) runs from December to June. "High water" means flooded forests and better boat access to lakes and wetlands for wildlife spotting. It also means flooded river beaches. Fishing is prime during low water, when fish move from the forest back into rivers and lakes, making them more accessible. Keep in mind that even the driest month has an average rainfall of 2 inches (compared with up to 13 inches during the wet season), so some kind of raingear is always recommended. Depending on where you are in the Amazon, during the rainy season it may rain every day, or three out of every four days, whereas during the dry season it may rain only one out of four days or less.

The Rain Forest

This is why you visit the Amazon: to experience the largest tropical forest in the world and one of the wildest places on the planet. Plant-lovers can fawn over the more than 300,000 species; others can catch glimpses of tropical birds, the occasional mammal, and avoid the 2.5 million insect species. But the real appeal is just being here, awed by the complexity of nature, soothed by a symphony of strange sounds, and humbled by the more than 2 million square miles of untamed forest around you.

10

The River

The largest river in the world (by volume) and the second-longest, spanning more distance than the continental U.S., the Amazon River is also the earth's biggest freshwater ecosystem, and home to more fish than the Atlantic Ocean. Get at least one boat trip under your belt—whether it's for nighttime croc stalking, piranha fishing, or basic sightseeing.

Exotic Foods

Forget beef and poultry and dig into water-buffalo steak, duck in manioc sauce (*pato no tucupi*), fried piranha, and other river fish with exotic Indian names such as *tucunaré* and *pirarucú*. Amazonian fruits are truly unique: try *cupuaçu* (reminiscent of soursop) in desserts and candies, *guaraná* (small red fruit) in the soft drink of the same name, and *açaí* (small purple fruit) in soup and ice cream.

Handicrafts

Woodcrafted and woven items, bows, arrows, blowguns, and jewelry and headdresses of seeds and feathers are some traditional indigenous crafts. (Note: U.S. Customs prohibits the import of endangered animal parts.) In Belém you'll find intricately designed *marajoara* pottery. Vases and sculptures in Macapá are often made with locally mined manganese.

Packing

For remote travel in the Amazon, a small backpack is the most efficient way to carry your gear. Plan for drenching downpours by bringing sufficient plastic bags, especially for important items. Specific things to consider packing for an off-the-grid Amazon vacation are: water bottle, filter, and purification tablets, sunscreen, insect repellent, hat, a good medical kit, knife, lightweight gold-miner's hammock (*rede de garimpeiro*), mosquito netting, sheet, 3 yards of ¼-inch rope, tent (if you're planning to camp), rain poncho, light shorts, pants (important for warding off pests while hiking), jacket, flashlight, batteries, matches, earplugs, sunglasses, and a waterproof camera case (good old plastic bags work, too!) For more information on packing, *see* Packing *in* Smart Travel Tips A to Z.

The Amazon by Boat

Whatever the style, budget, or length of your Amazonian journey, there's a boat plying the river to suit your needs. Sleep in a hammock on the deck of a thatch-roof riverboat or in the air-conditioned suite of an up-scale tour operator's private ship. Keep in mind that wildlife viewing is not good on boats far from shore. Near shore, however, the birding can be excellent. Binoculars and a bird guide can help, and shorebirds, raptors, and parrots can be abundant. Common in many parts of the river system are *boto* (pink dolphins) and *tucuxi* (gray dolphins). Look for them as they surface for air. To see the most wildlife, plan your travels to allow time in the forest and streams.

ADVENTURE CRUISES
Adventure cruises combine the luxury of cruising with exploration. Their goal is to get you close to wildlife and local inhabitants without sacrificing comforts and amenities. Near daily excursions include wildlife viewing in smaller boats with naturalists, village visits with naturalists, and city tours. **G.A.P** (Great Adventure People; ✉ 19 Duncan St., Ste. 401, Toronto, ON ☎ 800/465–5600 or 416/260–0999 ⊕ www.gapadventures.com) makes these trips, which run from 9 to 16 days.

OCEANGOING SHIPS
Some cruise ships call at Manaus, Belém, and Santarém as part of their itineraries. Most trips take place October through May. They range in length from 10 to 29 days, and costs vary. Two major lines making such journeys are Princess Cruises and Royal Olympic Cruises.

TOURIST BOATS
Private groups can hire tourist boats that are more comfortable than standard riverboats. They generally travel close to the riverbank and have open upper decks from which you can observe the river and forest. The better tour operators have a regional English-speaking expert on board—usually an ecologist or botanist. You can either sleep out on the deck in a hammock or in a cabin, which usually has air-conditioning or a fan. Meals are generally provided.

SPEEDBOATS
You can take a speedboat to just about anywhere the rivers flow. Faster than most options, speedboats can be ideal for traveling between smaller towns, a morning of wildlife viewing, or visiting a place that doesn't have regular transportation, such as a secluded beach or waterfall. You design the itinerary, including departure and return times. Prices and availability vary with distance and locale. Contact tour agencies, talk with locals, or head down to the docks to find a boat willing to take you where you want to go. Work out the price, destination, and travel time before leaving. You may have to pay for the gas up front, but don't pay the rest until you arrive. For trips longer than an hour, bring water, snacks, and sunscreen.

MACAMAZON BOATS
Longer boat routes on the lower Amazon are covered by **MACAMAZON** (☎ 091/3222–5604 or 091/3228–0774). Regular departures run between Belém, Santarém, Macapá, Manaus, and several other destinations. The boats are not luxurious but are a step above regional boats. You can get a suite for two from Belém to Manaus with air-conditioning and bath for about R$800. *Camarote* (cabin) class gets you a tiny room for two with air-conditioning and a shared bath. *Rede* (hammock) class is the cheapest and most intimate way to travel, since you'll be hanging tight with the locals on the main decks. Hammocks are hung in two layers

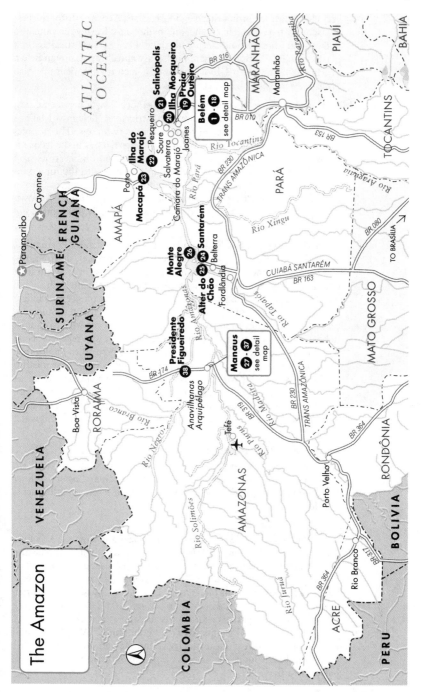

The Amazon

ATLANTIC OCEAN

Cayenne

Paramaribo

SURINAME

FRENCH GUIANA

GUYANA

VENEZUELA

Boa Vista

RORAIMA

Rio Branco

Rio Negro

COLOMBIA

PERU

Rio Solimões

Rio Juruá

ACRE

Rio Branco

BOLIVIA

BR 317

AMAZONAS

Rio Purus

Tefé

BR 364

Porto Velho

RONDÔNIA

BR 364

Rio Madeira

BR 319

TRANS AMAZÔNICA

BR 230

Anavilhanas Arquipélago

Manaus 27 - 37 see detail map

BR 174

Presidente Figueiredo 38

Rio Amazonas

Alter do Chão

Monte Alegre 25

Santarém 24

Belterra

Fordlândia

Rio Tapajós

CUIABÁ SANTARÉM BR 163

MATO GROSSO

PARÁ

Rio Xingu

TRANS AMAZÔNICA

BR 230

Rio Xingu

TO BRASÍLIA

BR 080

Rio Araguaia

TOCANTINS

BR 153

MARANHÃO

Maranhão

Rio Parnaíba

PIAUÍ

BAHIA

BR 010

BR 316

Belém 1 - 18 see detail map

Praia Outeiro 19

Ilha Mosqueiro 20

Salinópolis 21

Pesqueiro

Soure

Salvaterra

Ilha do Marajó 22

Câmara do Marajó

Joanes

Rio Pará

Rio Tocantins

Porto

AMAPÁ

Macapá 23

very close together, promoting neighborly chats. Arrive early for the best spots, away from the bar, engine, and bathrooms. Keep your valuables with you at all times and sleep with them. Conceal new sneakers in a plastic bag. In addition to a hammock (easy and cheap to buy in Belém or Manaus), bring two 4-foot lengths of ⅜-inch rope to tie it up. Also bring a sheet, since nights get chilly.

REGIONAL BOATS To travel to towns and villages or to meander slowly between cities, go by *barco regional* (regional boat). A trip from Belém to Manaus takes about four days; Belém to Santarém is two days. The double- or triple-deck boats carry freight and passengers. They make frequent stops at small towns, allowing for interaction and observation. You might be able to get a cabin with two bunks (around R$400 for a two-day trip), but expect it to be claustrophobic. Most passengers sleep in hammocks with little or no space between them. Bring your own hammock, sheet, and two 4-foot sections of rope. Travel lightly and inconspicuously.

Booths sell tickets at the docks, and even if you don't speak Portuguese, there are often signs alongside the booths that list prices, destinations, and departure times. If you plan to sleep in a hammock, arrive at least one hour early to get a good spot away from the engine, toilets, and bar. Keep valuables with you in your hammock while you sleep, including any new-looking clothing items (like sneakers), which you should conceal in a plastic bag. Sanitary conditions in bathrooms vary from boat to boat. Bring your own toilet paper, sunscreen, and insect repellent. Food is sometimes served, but the quality ranges from so-so to deplorable. Consider bringing your own water and a *marmita* (carry-out meal) if you'll be on the boat overnight. Many boats have a small store at the stern where you can buy drinks, snacks, and grilled *mixto quente* (ham-and-cheese) sandwiches. Fresh fruit and snacks are available at stops along the way. Be sure to peel or wash fruit thoroughly with bottled water before eating it.

About the Restaurants

Reservations and dressy attire are rarely needed in the Amazon (indeed, reservations are rarely taken). Tipping isn't customary except in finer restaurants. Call ahead on Monday night, when many establishments are closed.

About the Hotels

Amazonia is still a wild place, and many lodges and towns are remote. Don't expect to be pampered. Room prices tend to be reasonable and include breakfast, but services and amenities may cost quite a bit extra. Laundry service, for example, can be outrageously expensive. When checking in, ask about discounts (*descontos*). During the slow season and often in midweek, you can get a discount of around 20%. Cry a little, as the Brazilians say, and you may get a larger discount. Paying with cash may lower the price. Hotel rooms have air-conditioning, TVs, phones, and bathrooms unless we indicate otherwise, but showers don't always have hot water. Jungle lodges and smaller hotels in outlying areas often lack basic amenities.

WHAT IT COSTS In Reais					
	$$$$	**$$$**	**$$**	**$**	**¢**
RESTAURANTS	over R$60	R$45–R$60	R$30–R$45	R$15–R$30	under R$15
HOTELS	over R$500	R$375–R$500	R$250–R$375	R$125–R$250	under R$125

Restaurant prices are for a dinner entrée. Hotel prices are for two people in a standard double room in high season, excluding taxes.

BELÉM

The capital of Pará State, Belém is a river port of around 1.3 million people on the south bank of the Rio Guamá, 120 km (74 mi) from the Atlantic, and 2,933 km (1,760 mi) north of Rio de Janeiro. The Portuguese settled here in 1616, using it as a gateway to the interior and an outpost to protect the area from invasion by sea. Because of its ocean access, Belém became a major trade center. Like the upriver city of Manaus, it rode the ups and downs of the Amazon booms and busts. The first taste of prosperity was during the rubber era. Architects from Europe were brought in to build churches, civic palaces, theaters, and mansions, often using fine, imported materials. When Malaysia's rubber supplanted that of Brazil in the 1920s, wood and, later, minerals provided the impetus for growth.

Belém has expanded rapidly since the 1980s, pushed by the Tucuruvi hydroelectric dam (Brazil's second largest), the development of the Carajás mining region, and the construction of the ALBRAS/Alunorte bauxite and aluminum production facilities. Wood exports have risen, making Pará the largest wood-producing state in Brazil. As the forests are cut, pastures and cattle replace them, resulting in an increase in beef production. In 2000 the state government began construction of a bridge network connecting Belém to outlying cities. The resulting increase in commerce has spurred economic growth in the region, though there is still considerable poverty and high unemployment. In the city, high-rise apartments are replacing colonial structures. Fortunately, local governments have launched massive campaigns to preserve the city's rich heritage while promoting tourist-friendly policies. This effort has earned state and federal government funds to restore historical sites in the Belém area. Tourism is on the rise in the city and is becoming increasingly important for the city's economic well-being.

Exploring Belém

Belém is more than just a jumping-off point for the Amazon. It has several good museums and restaurants and lots of extraordinary architecture. Restored historic sites along the waterfront provide areas to walk, eat, and explore. Several distinctive buildings—some with Portuguese *azulejos* (tiles) and ornate iron gates—survive along the downtown streets and around the Praça Frei Caetano Brandão, in the Cidade Velha (Old City). East of here, in the Nazaré neighborhood, colorful colonial structures mingle with new ones housing trendy shops.

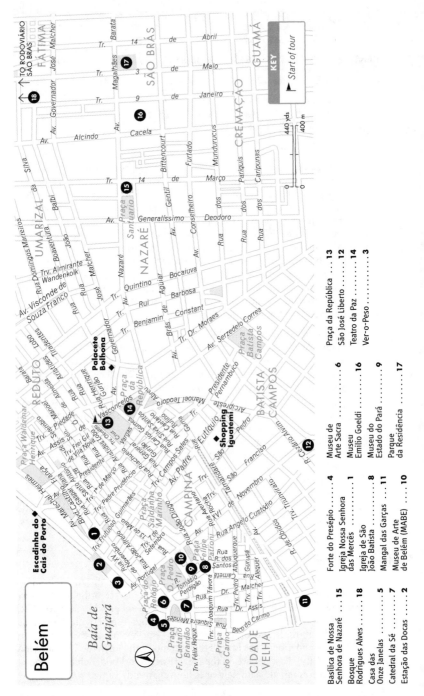

Belém

Baía de Guajará

KEY
▲ *Start of tour*

SAFETY In Belém watch out for pickpockets everywhere, but especially at Ver-o-Peso, on Avenida President Vargas, and in Comércio. Avoid walking alone at night or on poorly lighted streets, and don't wear jewelry, especially gold.

Cidade Velha

Cidade Velha (Old City) is the oldest residential part of Belém. Many of the houses are colonial, with clay walls and tile roofs. Three stories is the tallest they get, though 15-floor apartment buildings are invading from the north. Much of Cidade Velha is middle-income with a variety of hardware, auto parts, and fishing supply stores. On its northwestern edge, the Forte Presépio lies along the bank of the Rio Guamá.

What to See

❺ Casa das Onze Janelas. At the end of the 17th century, sugar baron Domingos da Costa Barcelar built the neoclassical House of Eleven Windows as his private mansion. Today Barcelar's mansion is a gallery for contemporary arts, including photography and visiting expositions. The view from the balcony is impressive. Take a walk through the courtyard and imagine scenes of the past. This is where the aristocracy took tea and watched over the docks as slaves unloaded ships from Europe and filled them with sugar and rum. ✉ *Praça Frei Caetano Brandão, Cidade Velha* ☎ *91/3219–1157* 💲 *R$2, free Tues.* ⏲ *Tues.–Fri. 10–6, weekends 10–8.*

❼ Catedral da Sé. In 1771 Bolognese architect Antônio José Landi, whose work can be seen throughout the city, completed the cathedral's construction on the foundations of an older church. Carrara marble adorns the rich interior, which is an interesting mix of baroque, colonial, and neoclassical styles. The high altar was a gift from Pope Pius IX. ✉ *Praça Frei Caetano Brandão, Cidade Velha* ☎ *91/3241–6282* 💲 *Free* ⏲ *Daily 8–noon and 2–6.*

★ ❷ Estação das Docas. Next to Ver-o-Peso market on the river, three former warehouses have been artfully converted into a commercial/tourist area. All have one wall of floor-to-ceiling glass that provides a full river view when dining or shopping. The first is a convention center with a cinema and art exhibits. The second has shops and kiosks selling crafts and snacks, and the third has a microbrewery and six upscale restaurants. The buildings are air-conditioned and connected by glass-covered walkways and contain photos and artifacts from the port's heyday. A stroll outside along the docks provides a grand view of the bay. Tourist boats arrive and depart at the dock—a good place to relax both day and night. ✉ *Boulevard Castilhos França s/n, Campina* ☎ *091/3212–5525* 💲 *Free* ⏲ *Noon–midnight or later.*

need a break? Need A Break? The many regional flavors at ice-cream shop **Cairu** include some unique to the Amazon, such as *taperebá, graviola,* and *cajá* (cashew fruit), as well as the more familiar *cocó* (coconut), mango, and chocolate. Juices, sandwiches, and soft drinks are also served. ✉ *Estação das Docas, Boulevard Castilhos França s/n, Comércio* ✉ *Conselheiro Furtado and Presidente Pernambuco* ✉ *Travessa 14 de Março and Rua João Balbi.*

★ ❹ **Forte do Presépio** (Fort of the Crèche). Founded January 12, 1616, this fort is considered Belém's birthplace. From here the Portuguese launched conquests of the Amazon and watched over the bay. The fort's role in the region's defense is evidenced by massive English- and Portuguese-made cannons pointing out over the water. They are poised atop fort walls that are 3 yards thick in places. Renovations completed in 2002 unearthed more than two dozen cannons, extensive military middens from the moat, and native Tupi artifacts. A small museum of prefort indigenous cultures is at the entrance. Just outside the fort, cobblestone walkways hug the breezy waterfront. ☒ *Praça Frei Caetano Brandão, Cidade Velha* 📞 *91/3219–1146* 💳 *R$2, free Tues.* ☉ *Tues.–Fri. 10–6, weekends 10–8.*

❼ **Igreja Nossa Senhora das Mercês** (Our Lady of Mercy Church). Another of Belém's baroque creations attributed to Antônio Landi, this church is notable for its pink color and convex facade. It's part of a complex that includes the Convento dos Mercedários, which has served both as a convent and a prison, though not simultaneously. ☒ *Gaspar Viana e Frutuosa Guimarães, Comércio* 💳 *Free* ☉ *Mon.–Sat. 8–1.*

❽ **Igreja de São João Batista** (St. John the Baptist Church). Prodigious architect Antônio Landi finished this small octagonal church in 1777. It was completely restored in the late 1990s and is considered the city's purest example of baroque architecture. ☒ *Rua João Diogo and Rodriguês Dos Santos, Cidade Velha* 💳 *Free* ☉ *Mon.–Sat. 6:30 AM–9 AM.*

★ ⓫ **Mangal das Garças.** City beautification efforts to increase tourism and encourage environmental conservation led to the creation of the Mangrove of the Egrets. A great place for a short stroll, it has an aviary, a tower with a view, a navigation museum, a boardwalk leading to a lookout over the Rio Guamá, a live butterfly exhibit, ponds with aquatic plants, food vendors, a gift shop, and a restaurant. ☒ *Passagem Carneiro da Rocha, Jurunas* 📞 *91/3242–5052* 💳 *R$4* ☉ *Weekdays 10–6.*

❿ **Museu de Arte de Belém (MABE).** Temporary exhibits on the bottom level of the Metropolitan Art Museum are free to view. On the second level staff members hand you brown furry slippers that you must wear over your shoes to protect the wooden floors. The permanent collection of furniture and paintings dates from the 18th century through the rubber boom. The museum is housed in the Palácio Antônio Lemos (circa 1883), a municipal palace built in the imperial Brazilian style with French influences. ☒ *Praça Dom Pedro II s/n, Cidade Velha* 📞 *091/ 3219–8228* 💳 *R$2, free Tues.* ☉ *Weekdays 10–6 PM.*

❻ **Museu de Arte Sacra.** A guided tour (call 48 hours in advance to reserve an English-speaking docent) begins in the early-18th-century baroque Igreja de Santo Alexandre (St. Alexander's Church), which is distinguished by intricate woodwork on its altar and pews. On the second half of the tour you see the museum's collection of religious sculptures and paintings. Temporary exhibitions, a gift shop, and a café are on the first floor. ☒ *Praça Frei Caetano Brandão, Cidade Velha* 📞 *091/3219–1155* 💳 *R$4, free Tues.* ☉ *Tues.–Fri. 1–6, weekends 9–1.*

TALES FROM THE MIST

THE IMMENSE AMAZON REGION is fertile ground not only for flora and fauna but also for legends, which are an integral part of local culture and are remarkably consistent throughout the region. Many are based on strange creatures that inhabit the rivers and jungle. One of the most widespread legends is that of the cobra grande (giant snake), which strikes fear into the hearts of many a river dweller. Popularized by the movie Anaconda (filmed near Manaus), the story involves sucuri (anaconda) snakes of epic proportions that terrorize. They're said to cause shipwrecks and to eat fleeing passengers whole.

Another extremely popular (and considerably less gruesome) legend is that of botos (dolphins) that take human form. Always dressed immaculately in white, they appear at parties and dance with the youngest, most beautiful girls. They lure the girls outside, where they seduce them, and then return to the water just before dawn. You can always tell a boto from its slightly fishy smell and the hole in the top of its head, which is covered by a hat.

Curupira appears as a nude and savage indigenous child, about six or seven years old, whose feet are turned backward. He is said to lure people into the jungle—causing them to become irreversibly lost. As the story goes, white men cut off his feet before killing him; a god sewed Curupira's feet on backward and returned him to the forest to exact revenge. Some people claim you can solicit Curupira's help for hunting and crop failures. As payment, you must bring him tobacco, matches, and a bottle of liquor—the latter of which he will down in one swig to seal the pact. If you ever tell anyone about the agreement, Curupira will hunt you down and stab you to death with his long, sharp fingernails.

Several tales explain the origins of important fruits and vegetables. Guaraná, for example, was the name of a young child beloved by all. As the story goes, he was killed by the jealous god Jurupari, who disguised himself as a snake. Lightning struck as the village gathered around Guaraná's body and wept. At that moment the lightning god, Tupã, ordered the villagers to bury the child's eyes. The guaraná fruit (which actually resembles eyes) sprouted from the burial spot.

In a legend explaining the origins of the açaí fruit (a rich, dark-purple fruit endemic to the Amazon), the chief of a starving tribe ordered all babies to be sacrificed to end the famine. The chief's daughter, Iaçá, had a beautiful baby. Before its sacrifice, she found the child holding a palm tree, and then he suddenly vanished. The tree then became full of açaí (which is Iaçá spelled backward), from which a wine was made that saved the tribe and ended the sacrifices. To this day, Amazonians call the cold soup made from the fruit vinho (wine).

The legend of the native water flower vitória régia begins with a beautiful girl who wished to become a star in the heavens. She trekked to the highest point in the land and tried in vain to touch the moon. Iaci—the god of the moon—was awed and enchanted by the girl's beauty. He knew that a mortal could never join the astral kingdom, so he decided to use his powers to immortalize the girl on earth instead. He transformed her into a stunning flower with an unmistakable, alluring scent. Realizing that he needed something fitting to help display this "star," he stretched a palm leaf and created a lily pad, and thus the vitória régia came to be.

⑨ Museu do Estado do Pará. Pará State Museum is in the sumptuous Palácio Lauro Sodré (circa 1771), an Antônio Landi creation with Venetian and Portuguese elements. Consistently outstanding visiting exhibits are on the first floor; the second floor contains the permanent collection of furniture and paintings. ✉ *Praça Dom Pedro II, Cidade Velha* ☎ *091/3219–1138* 💵 *R$4* ⊙ *Tues.–Fri. 1–6, weekends 9–1.*

⑫ São José Liberto Belém's old prison began as a monastery, became a brewery, then an armory, a nunnery, and eventually the final stop for many criminals. Today's museums and garden seem an attempt to redeem long years of tortuous conditions and bloody rebellions. Behind the enormously thick walls are a gem museum, a prison museum, and several shops. ✉ *Praça Amazonas, Jurunas* ☎ *91/3230–4451* 💵 *R$4* ⊙ *Tues.–Sat. 10–8, Sun. 3–8.*

★ ③ Ver-o-Peso. Its name literally meaning "see the weight" (a throwback to the time when the Portuguese weighed everything entering or leaving the region), this market is a hypnotic confusion of colors and voices. Vendors hawk tropical fruits, regional wares, and an assortment of tourist kitsch. Most interesting are the *mandingueiras,* women who claim they can solve any problem with "miracle" jungle roots and charms for the body and soul. They sell jars filled with animal eyes, tails, and even heads, as well as herbs, each with its own legendary power. The sex organs of the pink river dolphin are a supposedly unrivaled cure for romantic problems. In the fish market you get an up-close look at pirarucu, the Amazon's most colorful fish and the world's second-largest freshwater species. Look for bizarre armored catfish species, such as the *tamuatá* and the huge *piraíba*. Across the street is a small arched entrance to the municipal meat market. Duck in and glance at the French-style pink-and-green-painted ironwork, imported from Britain. Be sure to visit Ver-o-Peso before noon, when most vendors leave. It opens around 6 AM. Leave your jewelry at home and beware of pickpockets. ✉ *Av. Castilhos França s/n, Comércio.*

Nazaré

Just east of the Cidade Velha, Nazaré's mango tree–lined streets create the sensation of walking through tunnels. Among the historic buildings there's a tremendous variety of pastel colors and European styles. Many of the newer buildings house elegant shops.

A GOOD TOUR   Begin near the south end of the **Praça da República** ⑬ ▶ just across Avenida President Vargas from the Hilton. There you'll find the large pink **Teatro da Paz** ⑭. After leaving the theater, veer left onto Avenida President Vargas and then left again onto Avenida Nazaré. Just beyond Avenida Generalíssimo Deodoro is the **Basílica de Nossa Senhora de Nazaré** ⑮. Avenida Nazaré becomes Avenida Magalhães Barata at this point. Continue east three more blocks to the **Museu Emilio Goeldi** ⑯. After touring the museum, consider going east another three blocks to the **Parque da Residência** ⑰ for a relaxing break and lunch, or take a short (R$17) taxi ride northeast to the **Bosque Rodrigues Alves** ⑱, a chunk of jungle in the middle of town.

TIMING   It should take about 1½ hours to reach the Museu Emilio Goeldi. Plan to spend an hour or two here. If you need a break, the museum has a restaurant and a snack bar. Count on at least an hour at Bosque Rodrigues Alves.

WHAT TO SEE
🅕 **Basílica de Nossa Senhora de Nazaré.** It's hard to miss this opulent
Fodor'sChoice Roman-style basilica. Not only does it stand out visually, but there's an
★ enormous *samauma* tree (kapok variety) filled with screeching white-winged parakeets in the plaza out front. Built in 1908 on the site where a *caboclo* (rural, riverside dweller) named Placido is said to have seen a vision of the Virgin in the early 1700s. The basilica's ornate interior is constructed entirely of European marble and contains elaborate mosaics, detailed stained-glass windows, and intricate bronze doors. In the small, basement-level Museu do Círio, displays explain the Círio de Nazaré festival, which is held each October to honor the city's patron saint. ⊠ *Av. Nazaré s/n at Av. Generalisimo Deodoro, Nazaré* ☎ *091/4009–8400 basilica, 091/3226–2308 museum* ✉ *Free* ☉ *Daily 8–noon, 2–6.*

🅘 **Bosque Rodrigues Alves.** In 1883 this 40-acre plot of rain forest was designated an ecological reserve. Nowadays it has an aquarium and two amusement parks as well as natural caverns, a variety of animals (some in the wild), and mammoth trees. ⊠ *Av. Almirante Barroso, Marco* ☎ *091/ 3226–2308* ✉ *R$1* ☉ *Tues.–Sun. 8–5.*

★ 🅖 **Museu Emílio Goeldi.** Founded by a naturalist and a group of intellectuals in 1866, this complex contains one of the Amazon's most important research facilities. Its museum has an extensive collection of Indian artifacts, including the distinctive and beautiful pottery of the Marajó Indians, known as *marajoara*. A small forest has reflecting pools with giant *vitória régia* water lilies. But the true highlight is the collection of Amazon wildlife, including manatees, anacondas, macaws, sloths, and monkeys. ⊠ *Av. Magalhães Barata 376, Nazaré* ☎ *091/3249–1302 or 091/3249–1230* ✉ *Park R$2, park and museum R$4* ☉ *Tues.–Sun. 9–noon and 2–5:30.*

🅗 **Parque da Residência.** For decades this was the official residence of the governor of Pará. Now it provides office space for the Secretaria de Cultura (SECULT; Executive Secretary of Culture), as well as public space. Within the park are a 400-seat theater, an orchid conservatory, an ice-cream parlor, a restaurant, and shaded spots to relax and soak in the atmosphere. ⊠ *Av. Magalhães Barata 830, São Brás* ☎ *091/4009–8721* ✉ *Free* ☉ *Tues.–Sun. 9 AM–9 PM.*

 🅓 **Praça da República.** At this square you'll find a large statue that commemorates the proclamation of the Republic of Brazil, an amphitheater, and several French-style iron kiosks. On Sunday vendors, food booths, and musical groups create a festival-like atmosphere that attracts crowds of locals. ⊠ *Bounded by Av. Presidente Vargas, Trv. Osvaldo Cruz, and Av. Assis de Vasconcelos.*

🅔 **Teatro da Paz.** A complete renovation of this 1878 neoclassical theater was finished in 2001. Concert pianos were acquired to facilitate production of operas. Greek-style pillars line the front and sides; inside, note the imported details such as Italian marble pillars and French chandeliers. Classical music performances are also held in the theater, which seats more than 800 people. English-speaking guides are available to give 20-minute tours (included in admission price). ⊠ *Av. da Paz s/n, Praça da República, Campina* ☎ *091/4009–8758 or 091/4009–8759* ▨ *R$4* ☉ *Tours on the hour Tues.–Fri. 9–5, Sat. 9–1.*

Where to Eat

Brazilian

$–$$$$ ✕ **Boteca das Onze.** In the Casa das Onze Janelas (⇨ *above*), the Boteca das Onze has thick stone and mortar walls stylishly adorned with antique instruments. The full bar has a complete drink menu with one of the largest selections of wines in the city. The patio has a view of the garden and river. A house favorite is the seafood platter for two. ⊠ *Praça da Sé, Cidade Velha* ☎ *91/3224–8599/3241–8255* ⊕ *boteca@nautilus. com.br* ▭ *DC, MC, V* ☉ *No lunch Mon.*

$–$$ ✕ **Lá em Casa.** From inauspicious beginnings has emerged one of Belém's
Fodor'sChoice   most popular restaurants. Regional cuisine, prepared to exacting spec-
★   ifications, has earned Lá em Casa its good reputation. Consider trying Belém's premier dish, *pato no tucupi* (duck in a yellow manioc–herb sauce served with the mildly intoxicating *jambu* leaf). Crabs on the half-shell covered with *farofa* (finely ground manioc fried in margarine) is another good choice, as is *açaí* sorbet for dessert. Sitting on the patio fringed by tropical vines and bromeliads, you feel like you're dining in the middle of the forest. ⊠ *Av. Governador José Malcher 247, Nazaré* ☎ *091/223– 1212* ▭ *AE, DC, MC, V.*

$ ✕ **Garrote.** A traditional *churrascaria* (Brazilian barbecue restaurant), Garrote serves up as much grilled and roasted beef, pork, and other meat as you can eat for a reasonable fixed price. A salad buffet and dessert are also included. Service is excellent. ⊠ *Padre Eutíquio 1308, Batista Campos* ☎ *091/3225–2776* ▭ *DC, MC, V* ☉ *No dinner Sun.*

¢–$ ✕ **Palafita.** Excellent regional dishes with open-air dining over the river are why locals enjoy Palafita. Pirarucú fish balls and duck pastries are among the specialties. Palafita has music on weekend evenings and it's only a one-minute walk from the Forte do Precépio. ⊠ *Praça da Sé, Rua Siquiera Mendes 264, Cidade Velha* ☎ *091/3224–3618* ▭ *No credit cards* ☉ *Closed Mon.*

¢   ✕ **Casa do Caldo.** Eight soups (out of 36) are featured every night for family dining in the "House of Soup." One price covers unlimited soup, toast, and dessert porridge. Try the crab soup with cilantro and the cow's-foot soup. It's air-conditioned and casual, with superb service. ⊠ *Rua Diogo Moia 266, Umarizal* ☎ *091/3224–5744* ▭ *AE, DC, MC, V* ☉ *No lunch.*

¢   ✕ **Mixtura Paulista.** A convenient location near the Hilton and the Praça da Repúlica makes this pay-per-kilo restaurant a good choice for a quick lunch. The buffet table always has numerous main dishes and grilled meats, along with salads, beans, and rice. ⊠ *Rua Serzedelo Corrêa 15, Nazaré* ☎ *091/3222–4309* ☉ *No dinner.*

Italian

$–$$ ✕ **Dom Giuseppe.** From gnocchi to ravioli, flawless preparation of the basics distinguishes this Italian eatery from others. Everyone in town knows this, so reservations are a good idea—particularly on weekends. Don't leave without ordering a scrumptious *dolce Paula* (ice cream–and–brownie dessert). ✉ *Av. Conselheiro Furtado 1420, Batista Campos* ☎ *091/4008–0001* 🌐 *www.domguiseppe.com.br* 💳 *AE, DC, MC, V* ⏱ *No lunch Mon.–Sat.*

Japanese

¢–$ ✕ **Hatoba Restauranté.** This is the best sushi in Belém, which is no small potatoes, since the city has a large Japanese community (second only to that of São Paulo), and many Japanese restaurants. A bonus: Hotoba is in the Estação das Docas, so you can dine along the waterfront. ✉ *Estação das Docas, Campina* ☎ *091/3212–3143 or 091/3088–2900* 💳 *AE, DC, MC, V.*

Vegetarian

$ ✕ **Mãenatureza.** Lunches are strictly vegan at one of the few vegetarian restaurants in the city. Trained cooks work with soy products, vegetable protein, and whole grains to prepare the small buffet. It's not far from the Hilton. ✉ *Rua Manoel Barata 889, Comércio* ☎ *091/3212–8032* 🌐 *restaurantemaenatureza.com.br* 💳 *MC* ⏱ *Closed Sun. No dinner.*

Where to Stay

$$$ **Hilton International Belém.** The Hilton's reliability and amenities are topped only by its location right on the Praça da República. Although rooms have few decorations, bland color schemes, and simple furniture, they are well equipped and comfortable. Executive rooms have the nicest views as well as access to a lounge with a VCR, a meeting area, and complimentary food and drink. ✉ *Av. Presidente Vargas 882, Campina, 66017-000* ☎ *091/4006–7000, 800/891–4118 in U.S.* 📠 *091/3225–2942* 🌐 *www.hilton.com* 🛏 *361 rooms* 🛎 *Restaurant, pool, health club, hair salon, sauna, 2 bars, convention center* 💳 *AE, DC, MC, V.*

$ **Hotel Regente.** This hotel has excellent service and a prime location for a reasonable price. Stained-glass windows and soft leather couches welcome you in an attractive lobby. Rooms on the 12th floor are nicer and more modern than those on other floors, yet they cost the same. ✉ *Av. Governador José Malcher 485, Nazaré, 66035-100* ☎ *091/3181–5000* 📠 *091/3181–5005* 🌐 *www.hotelregente.com.br* 🛏 *196 rooms, 6 suites* 🛎 *Restaurant, pool, bar* 💳 *AE, DC, MC, V.*

$ **Itaoca Hotel.** It comes as no surprise that this small, reasonably priced hotel has the highest occupancy rate in town. Its rooms are extremely comfortable, well equipped, and modern, and most have a fantastic view of the dock area and river. ✉ *Av. Presidente Vargas 132, Campina, 66010-902* ☎📠 *091/4009–2400 or 091/4009–2402* ✉ *itaoca@canal13.com.br* 🛏 *32 rooms, 4 suites* 🛎 *Restaurant, in-room safes, cable TV, meeting room* 💳 *AE, DC, MC, V.*

¢ **Hotel Grão Pará.** The oldest hotel in town is also the best deal. Hotel Grão Pará has few amenities, but has the best price for a modern, clean room with the basics, and it's centrally located. ✉ *Av. Presidente Vargas 718, Campina, 66017–000* ☎ *091/3224–9600 or 091/3224–4100* 📠 *091/242–8073* 🛏 *150 rooms* 🛎 *Restaurant* 💳 *DC, MC, V* 🍽 *EP.*

★ ¢ 🏨 **Manacá Hotel.** This bright-red hotel with a slanted brown-tile roof looks like a cross between a Monopoly™ hotel piece and a pagoda. Cozy, artfully decorated common areas with soft lighting have more charm than those at larger places—for about a quarter of the price. Rooms are clean and simple, and it's a good choice if you can live without a pool or a bar. Make sure to call ahead, since it's often booked during the week. ⊠ *Trv. Quintino Bocaiuva 1645, Nazaré, 66033-620* 🕿 *091/3223–3335 or 091/3242–5665* 🛏 *16 rooms* ⚙ *Cable TV; no room phones* 🖃 *AE, DC, MC, V.*

Nightlife & the Arts

Nightlife

Umarizal is Belém's liveliest neighborhood at night, with a good selection of bars, clubs, and restaurants. Other nightlife hot spots are scattered around the city. For information about Brazilian music, *see* the Brazilian Music essay *in* Understanding Brazil.

BARS **Água Doce** (⊠ Rua Diogo Móia 283, Umarizal 🕿 091/3222–3383 ⊕ cachacariabelem.com.br) specializes in *cachaça* (Brazilian sugarcane liquor). Listed on its menu are 182 kinds of cachaça and 605 different drinks, along with appetizers and entrées as well. Softly lighted with lots of tables, this place gets busy on weekends. It's open Tuesday–Sunday. If you prefer your music in a relaxed environment, head to **Cosanostra Caffé** (⊠ Rua Benjamin Constant 1499, Nazaré 🕿 091/241–1068), which has live MPB (*música popular brasileira*) and jazz. Catering to locals and expatriate foreigners alike, it serves food from an extensive menu until late in the night. **Roxy Bar** (⊠ Av. Senador Lemos 231, Umarizal 🕿 091/224–4514) tops nearly everyone's list of hip spots at which to sip a drink and people-watch.

DANCE CLUBS The hot spots for dancing are open on Friday and Saturday nights and sometimes on Sundays; many are downtown. Mixed-age crowds frequent them no matter what the music. Prices vary depending on the show. Drinks are available but no food. All clubs except Signos have live music on occasion. Clubs open around 10 PM, though they don't get lively before 11 or midnight.

Signos (⊠ Governador José Malcher 247, Nazaré 🕿 091/3242–7702), underneath the Lá em Casa restaurant, has the fanciest decor of the clubs, with lots of mirrors and red booths. A DJ runs video clips of dance music on a huge screen. **Zeppelin Club** (⊠ Av. Senador Lemos 108, Umarizal 🕿 091/3241–1330) has two dance floors where techno is mixed with American and Brazilian pop and rock.

EVENING STROLLS Nights in Belém are comfortable for walking. There are several popular locations that are relatively safe, but catch a cab to your hotel if you stay late.

Estação das Docas (⊠ Boulevard Castilhos França s/n, Comércio) has a long, broad sidewalk that passes between the bay and numerous restaurants. **Praça Batista Campos** (⊠ Av. Padre Eutíquio s/n, Batista Campos) has sidewalks, benches, and coconut vendors. Nearby residents come here to jog, walk, and date. **Ver-O-Rio** (✉ Av. Marechal Hermes s/n, Umarizal) is on the edge of the bay. It has a small bridge and several small open-air restaurants.

The Arts

For information about cultural events, contact the state-run **Secretaria de Cultura** (SECULT; ✉ Av. Governador Magalhães Barata 830, São Brás ☎ 091/4009–8707 or 091/4009–8717), which prints a monthly listing of cultural events throughout the city.

Live music is played nightly at the **Estação das Docas** (✉ Boulevard Castilhos França s/n, Campina ☎ 091/3212–5525). Weekdays shows usually consist of acoustic singers and/or guitarists. On weekends rock, jazz, and MPB bands play on a suspended stage that moves back and forth on tracks about 8 meters (25 feet) above patrons of the microbrewery and surrounding restaurants. Outstanding theatrical productions in Portuguese are presented at the **Teatro Experimental Waldemar Henrique** (✉ Av. Presidente Vargas s/n, Praça da República, Campina ☎ 091/ 3222–4762). **Teatro da Paz** (✉ Av. da Paz s/n, Praça da República, Campina ☎ 091/4009–8758, 091/4009–8759, or 091/4009–8750) often hosts plays, philharmonic concerts, and dance recitals.

Sports & the Outdoors

Belém's two *futebol* (soccer) teams are Payssandú and Remo. Payssandú has been in the premier league for several years and is highly popular. Attending a Brazilian match is a memorable experience. Do not go alone and do not wear the other team's colors. Beware of pickpockets. For Remo games head to **Estádio Evandro Almeida** (✉ Av. Almirante Barroso s/n, Marco ☎ 091/3223–2847). Payssandú plays at **Estádio Leônidas de Castro** (✉ Av. Almirante Barroso s/n, Marco ☎ 091/3241–1726).

Shopping

Indigenous-style arts and crafts are popular souvenir items in Belém. Some of them, however, can create problems with customs when returning home. Import regulations of Australia, Canada, New Zealand, the United Kingdom, and the United States strictly prohibit bringing endangered species (dead or alive) into those countries, and the fines can be hefty. Nonendangered wildlife and plant parts are also illegal to import, though there are some exceptions. Wooden and woven items, for example, are usually not a problem. Avoid headdresses and necklaces of macaw feathers and caiman teeth, and go for the marajoara pottery and the tropical fruit preserves (pack them carefully). For more information on customs *see* Customs and Duties *in* Smart Travel Tips A to Z.

Shopping Areas & Malls

Belém's main shopping street is **Avenida Presidente Vargas,** particularly along the Praça da República. **Icoaraci,** a riverside town 18 km (11 mi) northeast of Belém, is a good place to buy marajoara pottery. **All Amazon pottery is soft and breaks readily. Be sure it is packed exceptionally well.** There are many boutiques and specialty shops in the neighborhood of **Nazaré.** To shop in air-conditioning, head for the upscale **Shopping Center Iguatemi**

(⊠ Trv. Padre Eutíquio 1078, Batista Campos), a mall in the truest sense of the word. There are a few well-stocked music stores, a food plaza on the third floor, a bookstore on the first floor that has maps, and two department stores—Y. Yamada and Visão—with a bit of everything.

Markets

Ver-o-Peso (⊠ Av. Castilhos França s/n, Campina) is one of the most popular markets in town. It sells fresh fruits, vegetables, fish, and meats. The city's largest concentration of vendors of medicinal plants and various concoctions (love potions, anyone?) is clustered under a canvas roof in the outdoor section. Look for beautifully woven hammocks. **Praça da República** (⊠ Bounded by Av. Presidente Vargas, Trv. Osvaldo Cruz, and Av. Assis de Vasconcelos) is busy only on Sundays, when *barracas* (small shops) pop up to sell paintings, snacks, artisanal items, and regional foods. You can watch the action from a park bench while sipping a cold coconut or eating a slice of *cupuaçú* cake. It's a local favorite for morning family strolls. A popular shopping district is **Comércio** (⊠ From Av. President Vargas take Senador Manoel Barata toward Cidade Velha). The streets are lined with shops selling hardware, fishing supplies, televisions, hammocks, and much more.

Specialty Shops

Artesanato Paruara (⊠ Rua Serzedelo Correa 15, Nazaré ☎ 091/3248–4555) specializes in oils, stones, and other "mystical" items. **Mercadão das Ervas** (⊠ Rua 28 de Setembro 130 ☎ 091/3212–3673) has dozens of kinds of medicinal plants, tinctures, syrups, oils, and soaps. A great souvenir shop, **Canto do Uirapurú** (⊠ Av. President Vargas 594, Campina) is well stocked with medicinal plant concoctions, T-shirts, hats, pottery, and more. **Casa Amazonia Artesanatos** (⊠ Av. President Vargas 512, Campina ☎ 091/3225–0150), though small, is packed with natural soaps, regional fruit preserves, pottery, and wood carvings. A short walk from Av. President Vargas, **Loja Jaguar** (⊠ Sen. Manoel Barata 298, Comércio ☎ 91/3224–9771) sells hammocks and *mosquiteiros* (mosquito nets). For photo needs visit **New Color** (⊠ Av. President Vargas 356, Campina ☎ 091/3212–2355), which is fast, friendly, and reliable. **São José Liberto** (⊠ Rua 16 de Novembro s/n, Jurunas ☉ Tues.–Sat. 10–8) is a combination museum (⇨ Cidade Velha in Exploring Belém, above) and high-priced jewelry and craft shops with Amazonian wares of gold, amethyst, and wood; pottery; and seeds and plant fibers.

SIDE TRIPS FROM BELÉM

If you're interested in beaches, fishing, forests, wildlife, or rural communities, there are some great spots to visit beyond the sidewalks of Belém. Buses and boats can take you to all of these spots and there's always a taxi driver willing to take you where you want to go.

Praia Outeiro

⓲ *30 km (19 mi) north of Belém; about 45 min by bus.*

The closest ocean beach to Belém is Salinas, a four-hour drive. River beaches like Outeiro and those at Ilha Mosqueiro are much closer. Depending on the season and time of day, river beaches are either expansive stretches or narrow strips of soft sand. Currents are rarely strong, and there's usually a large area of shallow water. Outeiro is generally crowded. The shoreline is eroded and dirty in places, but the swimming is good if you can handle muddy water. Restaurants line the beach with tables under trees. These are great places to have a cold drink, and snack on freshly boiled crabs, quail eggs, and salted shrimp. The bus ticket is a little over R$1. ⊠ *Buses depart from Rodoviário São Brás, Av. Almirante Barroso s/n, São Brás.*

Ilha Mosqueiro

20 *60 km (36 mi) from Belém; about 2 hrs by bus or car.*

Most Belém residents head for one of 18 beaches on Mosqueiro Island, along the Rio Pará. Mosqueiro is about an hour from the city by bus (ticket is a little over R$1). One of the most popular beaches, **Praia Farol**, is often crowded because it's close to **Vila**, the island's hub. At low tide you can walk to tiny, rocky Ilha do Amor (Love Island). In October and March the waves are high enough for river-surfing competitions. **Praia Morubira**, also close to Vila, has beautiful colonial houses and many restaurants and bars. The water is clear and the shore clean at **Praia Marahú**, but no bus from Belém travels here directly. You have to disembark in Vila and hop another bus. **Praia Paraíso** is lined with trees and has soft white sands and clear emerald waters. If you can't bear to leave at day's end, consider a stay at the Hotel Fazenda Paraíso. ⊠ *Buses depart from Rodoviário São Brás, Av. Almirante Barroso s/n, São Brás.*

Where to Stay

¢ 🏨 **Hotel Fazenda Paraíso.** Wood-and-brick chalets with red-tile roofs accommodate as many as five people. Similarly designed apartments, which house up to three people, are more economical for singles and couples. The pool is configured in the shape of a clover. Be sure to make reservations—the hotel is very popular on weekends. ⊠ *Beira-Mar, Praia do Paraíso, Ilha Mosqueiro, 66915-000* ☎ *091/3228–3950* ➪ *12 rooms, 10 chalets* ⚑ *Restaurant, pool, beach, boating, horseback riding* ☲ *AE, DC, MC, V.*

Salinópolis

21 *200 km (120 mi) east of Belém.*

Commonly known as **Salinas**, this old salt port on the Atlantic coast is loaded with beaches. It lies south of the mouth of the Amazon River, just three to four hours from Belém on good roads, making it accessible to weekend beachgoers. Tourist center **Praia Atalaia** is Salinas's largest and most popular beach. The 14-km (9-mi) white-sand beach is expansive; the highest dunes have nice views. Behind them is the black-water pond Lago Coca Cola, which sometimes dries up between September and January. Also visible are dunes encroaching on hotels and businesses, signs of poor coastal management. Atalaia has numerous restaurant–bars with simple, low-priced rooms for rent (R$25–R$50); expect no amenities, and bring your own towel and soap. The best places to eat and stay are in the middle of the beach, and some accept credit cards. Pampulha, David House, and Minha Deusa are good. They serve excellent seafood and other dishes at low prices (R$10–R$25). Beware of eating at other places. Shop around and choose a room with a secure window. A 10-minute walk from Atalaia is a quieter beach, **Praia Farol Velho,** which has few services. To get there, turn left at the entrance and walk around the point.

In the old section of downtown Salinas, known as **Centro,** life revolves around the Farol Velho (the old light tower). Just across from the tower on Rua João Pessoa is Mercado Marissol with an excellent selection of fruits, vegetables, drinks, and convenience items. In the same vicinity are a pharmacy, an ice-cream parlor, and a restaurant. The street changes dramatically at the beginning of the **Praia Maçarico.** The Maçarico strip, which sits back from the beach, is broad, clean, and dotted with benches and coco palms. On the strip are a couple of playgrounds, exercise stations, and some restaurants and hotels. The beach can get crowded. Maçarico is about a 10-minute walk downhill on João Pessoa toward the water. As you walk toward the beach, beware of the sidewalk on the left that occasionally drops off and has deep exposed gutters. **Praia Corvina,** near Maçarico, is a calmer spot. Upon entering Maçarico Beach, turn left and round the point to Corvina.

Buses run every couple of hours from the Belém *rodoviário* (bus terminal) and drop you off at the Salinas terminal. From there you can take a taxi about a mile to Centro and Maçarico Beach, or travel 20 minutes to Atalaia. A rickety old bus travels between the beaches every hour, from around 6:30 AM to 10 PM. It takes some work to get to Salinas's more secluded beaches. Praia Maria Baixinha and Praia Marieta, for example, require a boat, as do island beaches. (Inquire with your hotel.) Ecotours can be arranged to mangrove forests to see scarlet ibis and other species. Talk to your hotel manager or *see* Tours *in* The Amazon Essentials.

need a break?

The ice-cream parlor **Cairu** (⊠ Rua João Pessoa, Orla, near Praia Maçarico ☎ 091/423–2322) has the familiar chocolate and vanilla flavors, plus regional fruit flavors like *cupuaçu* (hint: try it with chocolate sauce). It's open until midnight and also serves sandwiches.

Where to Stay & Eat

$ ✕ **Tucuruvi.** Due to its solid reputation, many followers from Belém frequent this churrascaria. The unlimited quantities of grilled meats are accompanied by fish, chicken, and salads. ⊠ *Maçarico strip, Rua João Pessoa s/n* ☎ 091/3464-1077 ⊟ *AE, DC, MC, V.*

¢–$ ✕ **Restaurante São Miguel.** A steady stream of local families filters in and out of this establishment. The menu is lengthy and varied, with regional dishes, burgers, fries, and more. It's one of the few places that serves breakfast. ⊠ *Across from light tower, Rua João Pessoa 2465* ☎ *No phone* ⊟ *No credit cards.*

$ ✕▥ **Hotel Clube Privé do Atalaia.** Just off the beach, this place has more amenities than any other in town. Breezy, spacious public areas, a wet bar, and water slides help you keep cool. The restaurant ($–$$) specializes in shrimp and crab, but serves lots of fish and other dishes. ⊠ *Estrada do Atalaia 10* ☎ *091/3464–1210 or 091/3464–1241* ⊕ *www.privedoatalaia. com.br* ⮑ *141 rooms* ♻ *Restaurant, snack bar, pool tables, 5 pools, sauna, Ping-Pong, bar, video game room, shop* ⊟ *AE, MC, V.*

★ ¢ 🏨 **Hotel Salinópolis.** Right above Maçarico Beach, this hotel has the best location in town. You can look down the length of the beach from the pool. It's only a 10-minute walk from the light tower. ⊠ *Avenida Beira Mar 26, 68721-000* ☎ *091/3423–3000* ⮑ *35 rooms* ♻ *Restaurant, bar, pool, wading pool, lounge, shop* ⊟ *MC, V.*

¢ 🏨 **Pousada das Dunas.** Small, clean, and quiet, this place is excellent for those on a budget who don't want to rough it. The restaurant and bar open during the busy times. A four-bedroom house is available for rent next door. ⊠ *Estrada do Atalaia 40* ☎ *091/464–1002* ⮑ *13 rooms, 1 house* ⊟ *No credit cards.*

¢ 🏨 **Rango do Goiano.** Well situated on the Maçarico strip, this family-run place has compact but comfortable rooms. The restaurant (¢–$) has full meals as well as soups and salads. Try the crab soup. ⊠ *Rua João Pessoa 2165* ☎ *091/3423–3572, 091/3788–2054, or 091/3241–1099* ⮑ *5 rooms* ♻ *Restaurant, bar* ⊟ *MC.*

NIGHTLIFE During the week nightlife is almost nonexistent apart from a few folks gathered in a hotel bar or restaurant. On the weekends, though, and especially during holidays, things get lively. Atalaia restaurant-bars serve drinks and crank the music. Beach bar **Marujo's** (⊠ Praia Farol Velho) turns into a dance club at 10 PM on weekends.

SHOPPING The high-end boutique at **Hotel Clube Privé do Atalaia** (⊠ Estrada do Atalaia 10 ☎ 091/3464–1210) has sunscreen, hats, crafts, T-shirts, and Salinas memorabilia. Otherwise, ask hotel staff for directions to Shopping Maçarico or Russi Russi.

BETWEEN BELÉM & MANAUS

The smaller communities between the Amazon's two major cities give the best picture of pure Amazonian culture. Life tends to be even more intertwined with the river, and the center of activity is the dock area in village after village. Even a brief stop in one of these towns provides an interesting window into the region's day-to-day life.

Ilha do Marajó

㉒ *Soure is 82 km (49 mi) northwest of Belém.*

With an area of roughly 49,600 square km (18,900 square mi), Ilha do Marajó is reputedly the world's largest river island. Its relatively unspoiled environment and abundant wildlife make it one of the few accessible places in the Amazon that feel isolated. The Aruã tribes that once inhabited the island resisted invasion by the British and Dutch but were eventually conquered by the Portuguese through trickery. Ilha do Marajó's western half is dominated by dense forest and its eastern half by expansive plains, wetlands, and savannas. The island is ideal for raising cattle and water buffalo and has a half-million water buffalo and more than a million head of cattle; the human head count is about 250,000. According to local lore, the arrival of the water buffalo was an accident, the result of the wreck of a ship traveling from India to the Guianas. A day trip to a local ranch or a stay at Fazenda Carmo gives you a close-up look at the unique lifestyle of the island's people as well as the chance to view some of its animals, both domesticated and wild. You may see caiman, toco toucans, monkeys, and capybara, the world's largest rodent. Hiking is better in the dry season and boating in the rainy season.

NAVIGATING MARAJÓ On Ilha do Marajó one of the best ways to reach the beaches or to explore towns is to use a bike. Rates are around R$2 an hour. You can find motorcycles to rent as well, though you'll have to ask around, since they're not advertised. The locals usually know who has equipment for rent. Contact Pousada dos Guarás or Pousada Boto for more information.

Exploring Marajó

Marajó is a huge island, but most human activity is clustered on its eastern coast, due to proximity to Belém. The western side of the island is beachless and floods during the rainy season. On sleepy Ilha do Marajó, your greatest personal safety concern may be getting hit on the head by a falling mango.

Camará, one of the island's most important ports, is where many boats from Belém dock. With almost 20,000 people, **Soure** (20 mi north of Camará) is Ilha do Marajó's largest town. Its many palm and mango trees, simple but brightly painted houses, and shore full of fishing boats make it seem more Caribbean than Amazonian. **Salvaterra,** a quarter-mile boat ride south across the narrow Rio Paracauari, is smaller than Soure but equally charming. Enchanting **river beaches** are a short (and cheap) taxi ride from both Soure and Salvaterra.

Praia do Pesqueiro, 14 km (8 mi) north of Soure, is the island's most popular beach. When you stand on the white-sand expanse looking out at the watery horizon, the waves lapping at your feet, it's hard to believe you're not on the ocean. The beach has several thatch-roof restaurant–bars, making this an even more ideal place to spend an afternoon. You can travel here from Soure by taxi, by mototaxi (for one passenger), or by bike. Ask locals or hotel staff about bike rentals when you arrive in Soure.

The beach at **Caju Una,** a secluded fishing village, is breathtaking: a long strip of white sand with no vendors and few people. The village and its neighbor, Vila do Céu, are about a 45-minute drive (19 km/11 mi) north of Soure. Buses don't travel here, but you can hire a taxi (about R$45) or a mototaxi (about R$25) for an afternoon. A 20-minute, 4-km (2-mi) taxi ride northeast of Soure is **Praia do Araruna.** Rather than sandy stretches, it has a red-mangrove forest. In this eerie setting of twisted trees you almost expect Yoda to appear. More likely, it will be a flock of scarlet ibis. **Joanes,** 23 km (14 mi) southwest of Soure, was the island's first settlement. Poke around the ruins of a 16th-century Jesuit mission, bask on a beach, and have a meal in one of the seafood restaurants. A taxi from Soure costs about R$60.

Where to Stay & Eat

Local cuisine invariably involves the water buffalo, whether in the form of a succulent steak or in cheeses and desserts made with buffalo milk. There's also an array of local fish to try. Bring cash in small bills, as breaking large ones can be a challenge and credit cards are rarely accepted. In a pinch, beer vendors can usually make change. Marajó has few hotels, and they are all quite rustic. Those we've listed are the best on the island.

¢–$ ✕ **Anastacia Bar.** Good fish at a low price on the beach is the reason to come here, though Anastacia has beef and chicken as well. A plate of fish, rice, farofa, and salad can serve two. ⊠ *Praia Grande de Salvaterra s/n* ☎ *091/3765–1203.*

¢–$ ✕🖾 **Hotel Ilha do Marajó.** Clean rooms, solid creature comforts, and excellent facilities, including a lovely pool, make this hotel popular. During the rainy season (December–June) mosquitoes infiltrate rooms. The outdoor restaurant (¢–$) has good food and a view of the river. Saturday evening sometimes brings performances of *carimbo,* local music with African and native rhythms. Package deals, arranged at Belém travel agencies, include transport to and from the dock in Camará and day trips to fazendas and beaches. English-speaking guides are available. ⊠ *Trv. 2 No. 10, Soure 68870-000* ☎ *091/4006–3850* ⊕ *www.iaraturismo. com.br* ⤶ *32 rooms* ♻ *Restaurant, minibars, tennis court, pool, bar, recreation room, bicycles* ⊟ *V.*

$ 🖾 **Fazenda Carmo.** As a guest in this small antiques-filled farmhouse, you're privy to wonderful hospitality in a simple and rustic setting, and homestyle meals prepared with farm-fresh ingredients. Fazenda Carmo has fascinating activities like early-morning canoe trips in search of howler monkeys, horseback rides through wildlife-rich pastures, and muddy jeep rides to an archaeological site. Though loved by many, it lacks basic creature comforts, such as hot water, private bathrooms, and sometimes electricity. The farmhouse is in rough condition and the menu is repetitious. The fazenda can accommodate 8 to 10 people, and stays are part of a package that includes meals, an English-speaking guide, and transportation to and from Camará (a 90-minute trip via van and boat). The minimum stay is three days. An English-speaking guide costs extra. If you speak Portuguese, call the Fazenda directly and you may get a better price. ⊠ *Salvaterra* ♁ *Amazon Star Tours, Rua Henrique Gurjão 236, Belém 66053-360* ☎ *091/3212–6244 Amazon Star Tours, 091/ 3241–2202 or 091/3223–5696 Fazenda Carmo* ⤶ *8 rooms* ♻ *Lake; no a/c, no room phones, no room TVs* ⊟ *AE, MC, V* ⎮○⎮ *FAP.*

¢ 🖾 **Pousada & Camping Boto.** For a reasonable price you get lovely gardens, clean, modern (though small) rooms, friendly staff, and good food. The Boto is three minutes from the beach and is the only place in town with camping and hammock space. It rents motorcycles and bicycles—perfect for tooling around the island. ⊠ *Av. Alcindo Cacela, Salvaterra, 68870-000* ☎☎ *091/3765–1539* ⊕ *www.pousadaboto.com.br* ⤶ *15 rooms* ♻ *Restaurant, Internet, bicycles; no room phones* ⊟ *V* ⎮○⎮ *EP.*

¢ 🖾 **Pousada dos Guarás.** This intimate pousada has private bungalows. Consider the package that includes transportation to and from the docks and trips to Soure shops, local fazendas, and historic sites with a guide. Make arrangements with a travel agent in Belém. The restaurant has excellent food. Anastacia Bar is within a 15-minute walk along the beach. ⊠ *Av. Beira-Mar (Praia Grande), Salvaterra 66860-000* ☎ *091/3765–1133 or 091/3765–1149* 🖷 *091/4005–5656* ⊕ *www. pousadadosguaras.com.br* 🛏 *50 rooms* ♿ *Restaurant, minibars, pool, beach, horseback riding, bar* 🗖 *DC, MC, V.*

Nightlife

On Friday or Saturday night there are usually live music and dancing at **Badalué** (⊠ Trv. 14, Soure). The most popular music in the region is accordion-heavy *brega,* which translates as "tacky." The name is appropriate, but don't be surprised if it grows on you. A **carimbo group** performs at the Hotel Ilha do Marajó on Saturday and sometimes in Soure on Wednesday or Friday. Ask at your hotel or ask a taxi driver for details.

Shopping

There are a few stores that sell sundries along Travessa 17 and Rua 3 in Soure. For marajoara pottery and ceramic figurines, try **Arte Caboclo** (⊠ Trv. 5 between Ruas 8 and 9, Soure).You can even see how the ceramics are made in the workshop at the back of the store, which is open daily 8–6. For accurately re-created native pottery, ask anyone in Soure for **Carlos da ceramica** (Carlos of the ceramics). He'll show you how he makes items the native way. His work is the most authentic that we've seen. He usually has a few pieces for sale. **Soft marajoara pottery breaks easily. Pack it well.** For sandals, belts, and other leather goods, head to **Curtume Marajó** (⊠ Rua 1, Bairro Novo), a five-minute walk from downtown Soure and next to the slaughterhouse. The workers here can give you a tour of the tannery. The shop's hours are 7–11 and 1–5 Monday–Saturday. **Núcleo Operário Social Marilda Nunes** (⊠ Rua 3 between Trv. 18 and Trv. 19, Soure) has stalls with everything from marajoara pottery and woven items to T-shirts and liquor. In theory, the hours are daily 7–noon and 2:30–6; the reality may be something else entirely.

For more information on local events and shopping, stop in at SECTUR (the Secretary of Culture) in downtown Soure.

Macapá

➁ *330 km (198 mi) northwest of Belém.*

Macapá is on the north channel of the Amazon Delta and, like Belém, was built by the Portuguese as an outpost. Today it's the capital of and the largest city in the Amapá State, with 150,000 people. It's also one of only five metropolises in the world that sit on the equator. Macapá's main lure is as a base for trips to see an extraordinary phenomenon—the *pororoca* (riptide). From March to May, when the Amazon floods, the tide produces waves as high as 4 meters (15 feet); the final stage of this event sounds like thunder as waters sweep into the forest along the riverbanks. The trip to the pororoca takes nearly two days by boat and costs about R\$480 per person for a private cabin, meals, and an English-speaking guide.

Macapá's top man-made attraction is Brazil's largest fort, **Fortaleza de São José de Macapá.** Completed in 1782 after 18 grueling years, it is constructed of stones brought from Portugal as ship ballast. The well-preserved buildings house a visitor center, an art gallery, a meeting room, and a dance/music recital room. ✉ *Av. Cândido Mendes s/n* ☎ *096/3212–5118* 🎫 *Free* 🕐 *Tues.–Sun. 8–6.*

The **Marco Zero do Equador** is a modest monument to the equatorial line that passes through town. Although it consists of only a tall, concrete sundial and a stripe of red paint along the equator, there's a distinct thrill to straddling the line or hopping between hemispheres. The soccer stadium across the street uses the equator as its centerline. ✉ *Av. Equatorial 0288* ☎ *096/3241–1951* 🎫 *Free* 🕐 *Daily 9–noon and 2–8.*

Where to Stay & Eat

$–$$ ✕ **Cantinho Baiano.** To shake up the conservative cuisine scene here, the Salvador-born owner began cooking specialties from Bahia State. These dishes, especially the seafood *moqueca* (fried fish in vegetable, coconut milk, and dendê oil), are a highlight. The excellent river view, soft music, and colorfully clad waiters add to the ambience. ✉ *Av. Acelino de Leão 01* ☎ *096/3223–4153* 🟰 *DC, MC, V* 🕐 *No dinner Sun.*

¢–$ ✕ **Café Aymoré.** This is a local favorite for regional specialties such as *maniçoba* (stew with various cuts of pork—including feet and head—and cassava leaves) and *vatapá* (shrimp in flour and African palm oil). For those with more exotic tastes, it's the only restaurant in town with government consent to serve *tartaruga* (turtle), *jacaré* (caiman), and *capivara* (capybara). ✉ *Av. Iracema Carvão Nunes 92* ☎ *096/3223–2328* 🟰 *DC, MC, V* 🕐 *Closed Sun.*

$ 🏨 **Hotel Atalanta.** Garishly pink and supported by towering Roman columns, there's nothing else in town that looks like the Atalanta. Inside are stained-glass windows, small pink columns, and immaculate, comfortable guest rooms. The inconvenient location—10 blocks from the river in a residential neighborhood—is its only drawback. ✉ *Av. Coaracy Nunes 1148, 68900-010* ☎ *096/3223–1612* 📲 *33 rooms, 3 suites* ⚐ *Minibars, pool, gym, sauna* 🟰 *AE, DC, MC, V.*

$ 🏨 **Novotel Macapá.** Partially obscured by palm trees, this three-story, white, colonial-style hotel is on well-manicured grounds. The interior is slightly worn, and the guest rooms aren't very impressive, despite modern amenities. Instead, opt for one of the suites, which have balconies with exceptional river views. ✉ *Av. Francisco Azarias Neto 17, 68900-080* ☎ *096/3217–1350* 📠 *096/3217–1351* 📲 *74 rooms, 2 suites* ⚐ *In-room safes, minibars, tennis court, pool, bar* 🟰 *AE, DC, MC, V.*

¢ 🏨 **Frota Palace Hotel.** Clean and spacious, rooms here even have phones, which aren't easy to come by in this area. It's conveniently located in Centro, and the staff is friendly. ✉ *Rua Tiradentes 1104, 68906-420* ☎ *096/3223–3999* 📲 *33 rooms* ⚐ *Restaurant, bar* 🟰 *MC, V.*

Nightlife & the Arts

Macapá has a surprisingly active nightlife. If you like to bar-hop, head for the riverfront, where about 10 bars, some with music, are busy nearly every night. On weekends true night owls appreciate **Arena** (✉ Rua Hamilton Silva s/n), which doesn't open until midnight. Most weekends and even sometimes during the week there's a play, a Philharmonic concert, or a dance recital in the **Teatro das Bacabeiras** (⊠ Rua Cândido Mendes 368 ☎ 096/3212–5272). Tickets range from R$10 to R$20.

Shopping

Although Macapá has a free-trade zone, neither the prices nor the selection is anything special. The largest concentration of shops is on Rua Cândido Mendes and Rua São José. The **Núcleo Artesanal** (⊠ Av. Engenheiro Azarias Neto 2201 ☎ 096/3212–9156), an outstanding arts center, has two parts. The **Casa do Artesão** sells works by local craftspeople and artists—from tacky souvenirs to exquisite paintings and pottery—and is open 8–6 Monday–Sunday. Visa is accepted. The **Associação dos Povos Indígenas do Tumucumaque** (**APITU**) has textiles, baskets, and other objects made by Amapá natives. It is open Monday–Saturday 8–noon and 2–6 and Sunday 3–8.

Santarém

㉔ *836 km (518 mi) west of Belém, 766 km (475 mi) east of Manaus.*

Since its founding in 1661, Santarém has ridden the crest of many an economic wave. First wood, then rubber, and more recently minerals have lured thousands of would-be magnates hoping to carve their fortunes from the jungle. The most noteworthy of these may have been Henry Ford. Although he never actually came to Brazil, Ford left his mark on this country in the form of two rubber plantations southwest of Santarém—Fordlândia and Belterra. Today this a laid-back city of 242,000 has a new boom on the horizon—soybeans. As the highway BR 163 from Mato Grosso State improves (a federal government priority), it is becoming the fastest, cheapest route for hauling soybeans from Santarém to Atlantic seaports for international export. To meet the global demand for soybeans and to make enormous profits, Brazilian farmers are clearing vast tracts of forest south of town and all along the way to Mato Grosso. With this new boom, Santarém may change drastically in coming years.

Santarém-based trips can take you into a little-known part of the Amazon, with few foreign visitors, to places where the ecosystem is greatly different from those around Belém and Manaus. The area receives much less rain than either upstream or downstream, and has rocky hills, enormous wetlands, and the Amazon's largest clear-water tributary, the Rio Tapajós.

Perhaps the best place for walking is on the huge **riverfront sidewalk.** You can watch boat traffic and check out some of the shops along the way.

The city is at the confluence of the aquamarine Rio Tapajós and the muddy brown Amazon. Seeing the **meeting of the waters** is second only to witnessing the pororoca outside Macapá. It's best viewed from the **Praça Mirante do Tapajós,** on the hill in the center of town and just a few blocks from the waterfront.

To learn more about Santarém's culture and history, head for the **Centro Cultural João Fona** (João Fona Cultural Center). This small museum has a hodgepodge of ancient ceramics, indigenous art, and colonial-period paintings and a library for more in-depth studies. It also houses the

FORD'S IMPOSSIBLE DREAM

HENRY FORD SPENT MILLIONS *of dollars to create two utopian company towns and plantations to supply his Model T cars with rubber tires. In 1927 he chose an area 15 hours southwest of Santarém. A year later all the materials necessary to build a small town and its infrastructure were transported by boat from Michigan to the Amazon. Small Midwestern-style houses were built row after row. Seringueiros (rubber tappers) were recruited with promises of good wages, health care, and schools for their children. Fordlândia was born. Despite all the planning, the scheme failed. The region's climate, horticulture, and customs weren't taken into account. Malaria and parasites troubled the workers; erosion and disease plagued the trees.*

Convinced that he had learned valuable lessons from his mistakes, Ford refused to give up. In 1934 he established another community in Belterra, just 48 km (30 mi) outside Santarém. Although some rubber was extracted from the plantation, production fell far short of original estimates. World War II caused further disruptions as German boats cruised the Brazilian coast and prevented food and supplies from arriving. Advances in synthetic rubber struck the final blow. Today some rusted trucks and electric generators, a few industrial structures, and many empty bungalows are all that remain of Ford's impossible dream.

Secretary of Tourism. ⊠ *Praça Barão de Santarém* ☎ *093/3523–2434* ⊕ *centur@netsan.com.br* ☜ *Free* ☉ *Weekdays 8–5.*

Where to Stay & Eat

$–$$$ ✕ **Mascote.** Since 1934 this has been one of the most popular and famous restaurants in town. The indoor dining area is enchanting, but the palm-lined patio is well-lighted and inviting and has a good view of the river and the plaza. An extremely varied menu includes pizzas, sandwiches, steaks, and seafood. ⊠ *Praça do Pescador s/n* ☎ *093/3523–2844* ▤ *AE, DC, MC, V.*

$–$$ ✕ **Piracatú.** Just a five-minute taxi ride from downtown, Piracatú is the best fish house in town. You choose both the fish and how you want it prepared. The *surubim* (tiger catfish) soup is outstanding and easily serves two. ⊠ *Av. Mendoça Furtado 174, Prainha, just east of downtown* ☎ *093/3523–5110 or 093/3523–5098* ▤ *MC, V.*

¢–$ ✕ **Santo Antônio.** Fill up on *churrasco* (grilled meat) or one of the regional specialties at this restaurant behind a gas station. The fish is always fresh, and a single portion serves two. The tucunaré (peacock bass), served on a searing-hot marble platter, is incredible. ⊠ *Av. Tapajós 2061* ☎ *093/3523–5069* ▤ *No credit cards.*

¢ ✗ **Delícias Caseiras.** A constant stream of locals filters in to fill up at the buffet table of this restaurant whose name means, roughly, "homemade delectables." Salads aren't noteworthy, but the chicken *milanesa* (breaded and fried) and beef Stroganoff are very good. ✉ *Trv. 15 de Agosto 121, Centro* ☎ 093/3523–5525 ▤ *No credit cards* ⊘ *No dinner.*

¢ ✗ **Mistura Brasileira.** Excellent sandwiches and a self-service buffet keep the MB hopping. Try the beef fillet sandwich or the lasagna. ✉ *Av. Tapajós 23, Centro* ☎ 093/3522–4819 ▤ *No credit cards.*

¢ ⌂ **Amazon Park Hotel.** The only "luxury" hotel in town has a decent location (a short taxi ride from the center of town) and a gorgeous pool. Still, with little in the way of competition, it doesn't have much incentive to improve, as evidenced by the aging facilities and scantily furnished rooms. ✉ *Av. Mendonça Furtado 4120, 68040–050* ☎ 093/3522–3361 ⎙ 093/522–2631 ⊕ *www.amazonparkhotel.com.br* ⌫ *122 rooms* ⌂ *Restaurant, minibars, pool, bar* ▤ *AE, DC, MC, V.*

¢ ⌂ **Rio Dourado.** Reasonable rates get you simple but attractive accommodations, a convenient location, and friendly service. The hotel has a nice view of an open market area and a bit of the waterfront from the dining area on the second floor (where you have breakfast). ✉ *Rua Floriano Peixoto 799, 68005-080* ☎☎ 093/3522–4021 ⌫ *27 rooms* ⌂ *Airport shuttle* ▤ *AE, DC, MC* ⧖ *BP.*

Nightlife

Sunday afternoon can be sleepy in Santarém, but **Fun House!** (✉ Av. Presidente Vargas 1721, Santa Clara ☎ 093/3522–1787 or 093/9975–2087 ⊕ www.boitefunhouse.com.br) is where everyone goes to dance off their extra energy. On Friday **La Boom** (✉ Av. Cuiabá 694, Liberdade ☎ 093/ 9954–3920) is *the* place to dance. One of the best places in town to get a drink is **Mascotinho** (✉ Praça Manuel de Jesus Moraes s/n ☎ 093/ 3523–2844). It has passable food and is usually breezy since it's on the river. Friday and Saturday nights are filled with MPB. **Sygnus** (✉ Av. Borges Leal 2712, Santa Clara ☎ 093/3523–5122 or 093/3522–4119), with a mix of Brazilian and international music, is popular on Saturday night.

Shopping

One of three artisan shops grouped together, **Loja Muiraquitã** (✉ Rua Senador Lameira Bittencourt 131 ☎ 093/3522–7164) sells an incredible variety of regional items including native musical instruments, locally mined minerals, and wood carvings. A reliable photo shop in town is **Foto Society** (✉ Rui Barbosa 900, Centro ☎ 093/3522–1422). If you're looking for a one-stop convenience store downtown, head for **Center CR** (✉ Rua Galdino Veloso with Dos Mártires, Centro).

Sports & the Outdoors

Santarém, at the hub of two very different river systems and forests, has a lot of outdoor options. Secluded beaches for swimming, forest trails for hiking, boats for exploring backwater areas and wildlife watching—they're all here. An American who knows the area particularly well is Steven Alexander, who has been living down here for nearly 30 years. He leads ecotours on occasion, especially to a forest preserve he has created outside town called **Bosque Santa Lúcia.** It has several trails with tree identification tags, troops of monkeys, and lots of birds and insects. Contact **Amazon Tours** (⊠ Trv. Turiano Meira 1084, Santarém ☎ 093/ 3522–1928 ⊕ www.amazonriver.com) for information on Steven Alexander's ecotours, or check out his Web site.

Alter do Chão

★ ㉕ *About 30 km (about 20 mi) south of Santarém.*

The cruise down the Rio Tapajós to the village of Alter do Chão, on the Lago Verde (Green Lake), is one of the best excursions from Santarém. The area has been called "the Caribbean of the Amazon," and when you see its clear green waters and its white-sand beaches you understand why. Buses also make the hour-long journey from Santarém to Alter do Chão regularly. From the village it's a short canoe ride across a narrow channel to the beach. Note that from April to July, when the water is high, the beach shrinks considerably.

On weekends vendors and small restaurants set up on the beach. A hiking trail 100 meters beyond the vendors winds about one mile through scrub forest to **Serra Pelada** (Naked Hill). Wear good shoes and take water and a camera for the hike to the top. The trail can be slick and is eroded in places, but it's only a couple of hundred meters from the base to the top. **Lanche do Bené,** near the water, is a great stop for a cold drink under an Indian almond tree.

Where to Eat
Churrascaria e Pizzaria D'Italia has very good food at low prices. Try the grilled pirarucú or tambaqui. Two blocks up from the plaza on Rua Antônio Augustinho Lobato is **Restaurante Tribal.** Quiet, clean, and friendly, it has excellent homestyle grilled meat and grilled fish, and it's inexpensive.

Where to Stay & Eat
★ $–$$ ✕🏠 **Beloalter.** The white-sand beach is right outside the front door of this four-star establishment with an impressive range of room prices. Higher prices get you a better view or even a room in a treehouse! The restaurant (¢–$$) specializes in fish, but has a good variety of other dishes, too. ⊠ *Rua Pedro Texeira s/n,* ☎ *093/3527–1247 or 093/3527–1230* ⊕ *www. beloalter.com.br* ▤ *MC, V* ➦ *24 rooms* ⚭ *Restaurant, fans* ⑩ *EP.*

¢ 🏠 **Belas Praias Pousada.** Just up from the riverbank, Belas Praias is in a great location for those who want to be where the action is. Rooms are simple, modern, clean and have lots of wood. Request one with a view of the bay and beaches. ⊠ *On the edge of the plaza,* ☎ *093/3527–1365* ➦ *5 rooms* ⚭ *No room phones* ▤ *No credit cards* ⑩ *EP.*

Shopping
Shops ring the central plaza in the village of Alter do Chão. On the same street as Restaurante Tribal, close to the plaza, is **Araribá,** which has the best selection of authentic native artisanal items in town.

Monte Alegre

㉖ *90 km (60 mi) northeast of Santarém.*

Wedged on a hillside between fertile Amazon wetlands and *cerrado* (dry scrub forest), the Monte Alegre area has long been a preferred site for human habitation. In the hills behind the town, carbon dating of middens below cave paintings indicates a human presence as long as 11,000 years ago, making them some of the earliest known in the Americas. A small band of Irish and English settled here in the 1570s, about 40 years before the Portuguese arrived in Belém. The site later became a missionary outpost—called Gurupatuba—for area natives. In 1758 it was incorporated as a village.

Today Monte Alegre is a city of around 80,000 souls. Its economy relies mostly on ranching, farming, and fishing. The town obviously has a rich history, but it is not well organized for tourism. There's no town map, for example, and the streets are confusing. Also, visiting hours for the few historic sites change often or don't exist. You can thoroughly enjoy Monte Alegre, however, if you walk around and talk to the locals. They're very helpful and may go out of their way to assist you.

A GOOD WALK A short walking tour can give you a sense of the town. Begin at the Praça Fernando Guilhon in Cidade Alta (Upper City). The view over the Cidade Baixa (Lower City) and the Amazon River and wetlands is spectacular from here, especially at sunrise and sunset. Behind the praça is the Igreja de São Francisco (Church of St. Francis), which opens for mass at 6 AM and 7 PM. Descend the stairs at the overlook and walk down cobblestone Travessa do Matires toward the Cidade Baixa. In the commercial section you see Igreja Santa Lucia (Church of St. Lucia), with a small praça. Then head down to the river to watch the boat activity. Along the water you can get a *cafezinho* (small sweet coffee) and bakery item or fruit. Early or later is better since it's cooler.

Excursions

Thousands of **cave paintings** can bee seen in the hills behind town. Hire a cab or a mototaxi to take you to the closest ones, about an hour away. The only local guide who knows much about the cave paintings is **Nelsí Sadeck** (☎ 093/3533–1430 or 093/3533–1215), a civil engineer who assisted archaeologists in exploring the paintings and in the dig sites; he works independently as a guide. Nelsí speaks no English (though you can e-mail him in English), but whether you speak Portuguese or not, he's the best guide to go with. Contact him a few weeks in advance to hire him for a day of visiting the paintings (about R$200 for one or two people; R$250 for a group up to 10). He takes you out in a four-wheel-drive pickup. It's hot, dusty (or muddy), and bumpy; wear comfortable hiking clothes, sturdy shoes, and sunscreen, and take lots of water, a light lunch, snacks, and sunscreen. It's customary to tip the guide and driver. Plan to leave around 6:30 AM to be back by 3 PM.

Though he's not a naturalist, Nelsí can also set up wildlife outings for you. Bird-watching, especially, can be phenomenal in Monte Alegre, and there two habitats to choose from. The cerrado hills merit some time, but the wetlands are where you'll find the most. Go early, and you may see hoatzins, horned screamers, and chestnut-fronted macaws.

Where to Stay & Eat

¢ ✕ **Marisco.** Fish dishes are the specialties at this friendly restaurant. Try the *tucunaré escabeche* (peacock bass in a coconut-milk sauce with tomato, onion, garlic, cilantro, and other spices). Beef and chicken are also served. ⊠ *Rua 7 de Setembro* ☎ *093/9616–3990* ▭ *No credit cards.*

¢ ✕▦ **Panorama I.** In the Cidade Alta and a little out of the way, these small chalets are quiet and private. A 100-yard walk takes you to an impressive overlook. The restaurant (¢–$) is rated by locals as the best in town. ⊠ *Trv. Oriental 100* ☎ *093/533–1716* ➶ *4 chalets* ♨ *Restaurant, cable TV; no room phones* ▭ *No credit cards* ᵀᴼᶥ *EP.*

¢ ▦ **Hotel Panorama II.** Few hotels have a view as incredible as this one. Next to the plaza on top of the hill, the veranda looks out over the Lower City and the Amazon River. Rooms are clean and comfortable, but not especially attractive. Music at the bar next door can get noisy on weekends. Wander over for a cold drink and catch the sunset, or get the same view from the hotel's veranda. ⊠ *Praça Fernando Guilhon 500* ☎ *093/ 3533–1716* ➶ *6 rooms* ♨ *Cable TV; no room phones* ▭ *No credit cards* ᵀᴼᶥ *EP.*

MANAUS

Manaus, the capital of Amazonas State, is a hilly city of around 1.8 million people that lies 766 km (475 mi) west of Santarém and 1,602 km (993 mi) west of Belém on the banks of the Rio Negro 10 km (6 mi) upstream from its confluence with the Amazon. Manaus is the Amazon's most popular tourist destination, largely because of the 19 jungle lodges in the surrounding area. The city's principal attractions are its lavish, brightly colored houses and civic buildings—vestiges of an opulent time when the wealthy sent their laundry to be done in Europe and sent for old-world artisans and engineers to build their New World monuments.

Founded in 1669, Manaus took its name, which means "mother of the Gods," from the Manaó tribe. The city has long flirted with prosperity. Of all the Amazon cities and towns, Manaus is most identified with the rubber boom. In the late 19th and early 20th centuries it supplied 90% of the world's rubber. The industry was monopolized by rubber barons, whose number never exceeded 100 and who lived in the city, and spent enormous sums on ostentatious lifestyles. They dominated the region like feudal lords. Thousands of *seringueiros* (rubber tappers) were recruited to work on the rubber plantations, where they lived virtually as slaves. A few of the seringueiros were from indigenous tribes, but most were transplants from Brazil's crowded and depressed northeast. Eventually conflicts erupted between barons and indigenous workers over encroachment on tribal lands. Stories of cruelty abound. One baron is said to have killed more than 40,000 native people during his 20-year "reign." Another boasted of having slaughtered 300 Indians in a day.

The 25-year rubber era was brought to a close thanks to Englishman Henry A. Wickham, who took 70,000 rubber-tree seeds out of Brazil in 1876. (Transporting seeds across borders has since been outlawed.) The seeds were planted in Kew Gardens in England. The few that germinated were transplanted in Malaysia, where they flourished. Within

30 years Malaysian rubber ended the Brazilian monopoly. Although several schemes were launched to revitalize the Amazon rubber industry, and many seringueiros continued to work independently in the jungles, the high times were over. Manaus entered a depression that lasted until 1967, when the downtown area was made a free-trade zone. The economy was revitalized, and its population jumped from 200,000 to 900,000 in less than 20 years.

In the 1970s the industrial district was given exclusive federal free-trade-zone status to produce certain light-industry items. Companies moved in and began making motorcycles and electronics. In the mid-1990s the commercial district lost its free-trade-zone status. Hundreds lost their jobs and businesses crumbled, but the light-industrial sector held strong and even grew. Today it employs 80,000, has the largest motorcycle factory in South America, and makes 90% of Brazilian-made TVs.

Exploring Manaus

Manaus is a sprawling city with few true high-rises. Although many hotels and sights are in the city center (Centro), it's neither large nor attractive, and it's congested. It is also exotic and hilly and is on the edge of a river one and a half times larger than the Mississippi.

Centro

Manaus's downtown area has a lot going on. The floating docks are here, with tourist shops nearby. Open markets sell fish, meats, and all sorts of produce, while general stores ply machetes, hoes, hardtack, cassava flour, and boat motor parts to those pursuing a livelihood outside the city. Centro is also the most important historic section of the city. The Teatro Amazonas, the Customs House (Alfândega), and the Adolfo Lisboa Market are here, along with old churches, government buildings, and mansions. The result is a mix of neoclassic, Renaissance, colonial, and modern architecture.

A GOOD WALK Begin as early in the day as possible at the **Mercado Adolfo Lisboa** ㉗ ⊩. Exit at its south end and take the first right onto Rua M. de Santa Cruz. Just before it intersects with Avenida Eduardo Ribeiro, you see the **Alfândega** ㉘ on your left. Cross Avenida Eduardo Ribeiro. On your left will be the Hidroviária (Water Transport Terminal) for regional boats, and just beyond it lies the raised walkway to the international section. Be sure to look down at the Porto Flutuante, a floating dock made by the British. It's where many large ships anchor. Return to Avenida Eduardo Ribeiro and begin walking up the left side; almost immediately you see the Relógio Municipal (Municipal Clock). Just behind it is the **Catedral da Nossa Senhora da Conceição** ㉙. From here continue up Eduardo Ribeiro to Rua José Clemente. Cross Eduardo Ribeiro and you will see the **Teatro Amazonas** ㉝ on your left. Cross Rua 10 de Julho and you'll see **Igreja São Sebastião** ㉞ on the other side of Rua Tapajós.

TIMING Plan to spend two to three hours following the walk from start to finish.

WHAT TO SEE **Alfândega.** The Customs House was built by the British in 1902 with
㉘ bricks imported as ship ballast. It stands alongside the floating dock

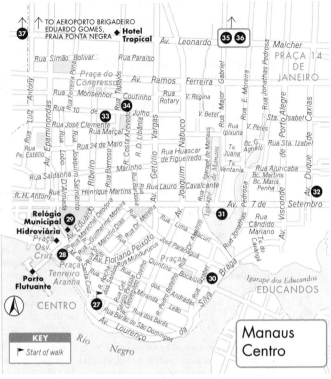

**Manaus
Centro**

that was built at the same time to accommodate the annual 10-meter (32-foot) rise and fall of the river. It's now home to the regional office of the Brazilian tax department, and the interior is of little interest. ⊠ *Rua Marquês de Santa Cruz s/n, Centro* ☎ *No phone* 🎫 *Free* ⊙ *Weekdays 10–3.*

㉙ Catedral da Nossa Senhora da Conceição. Built originally in 1695 by Carmelite missionaries, the Cathedral of Our Lady of Immaculate Conception (also called Igreja Matriz) burned down in 1850 and was reconstructed in 1878. It's a simple, predominantly neoclassical structure with a bright, colorful interior. ⊠ *Praça da Matriz, Centro* ☎ *91/ 3234–7821* 🎫 *Free* ⊙ *Usually Mon.–Sat. 9–5, but hours vary.*

㉞ Igreja São Sebastião. This neoclassical church (circa 1888), with its charcoal-gray color and medieval characteristics, seems foreboding. Its interior, however, is luminous and uplifting, with white Italian marble, stained-glass windows, and beautiful ceiling paintings. The church has a tower on only one side. No one is sure why this is so, but if you ask, you may get one of several explanations: the second tower wasn't built because of lack of funds; it was omitted as a symbolic gesture to the poor; or the ship with materials for its construction sank. As you stroll through the church plaza and the one in front of the Teatro Amazonas, note the black-and-white Portuguese granite patterns at your feet. They are said to represent Manaus's meeting of the waters. ⊠ *Praça São Sebastião, Centro* ☎ *092/3232–4572* ☎ *Free* ☉ *Usually Mon.–Sat. 9–5, but hours vary.*

★ ▶ **㉗ Mercado Adolfo Lisboa.** Vendors sell Amazon food products and handicrafts at this market. Built in 1882, it is a wrought-iron replica of the original Parisian Les Halles (now destroyed); the ironwork is said to have been designed by Gustave Eiffel himself. ⊠ *Rua dos Barés 6, Centro* ☎ *No phone* ☉ *Daily 6 AM–6 PM.*

㉜ Museu do Índio. The Indian Museum is maintained by Salesian Sisters, an order of nuns with eight missions in the upper Amazon. It displays handicrafts, weapons, ceramics, ritual masks, and clothing from the region's tribes. ⊠ *Rua Duque de Caxias 356, Centro* ☎ *092/3635–1922* ☎ *R$5* ☉ *Weekdays 8:30–11:30 and 2–4:30, Sat. 8:30–11:30.*

㉛ Palácio Rio Negro. The extravagant Rio Negro Palace was built at the end of the 19th century as the home of a German rubber baron. Later it was used as the official governor's residence. Today it houses some of the city's finest art exhibits and a cultural center. The Museu da Imagem e do Som, on the same property, has three daily screenings of art films and documentaries Tuesday through Friday and four screenings daily on weekends. Don't miss the cultural exhibits out back, which include a caboclo home, an indigenous home, and a cassava-processing house. ⊠ *Av. 7 de Setembro 1546, Centro* ☎ *No phone* ☎ *Free* ☉ *Weekdays 9–6.*

㉝ Teatro Amazonas. The city's lavish opera house was completed in 1896
Fodor'sChoice ★
after 15 years of construction. Its Italian Renaissance–style interior provides a clear idea of the wealth that marked the Amazon rubber boom. It has marble doorways, crystal chandeliers, handblown glass sconces from Italy, English wrought-iron banisters, and panels of French tiles. Italian frescoes depict Amazon legends. Operas and other events are presented regularly. Monday-evening performances are free and usually feature local artists of various musical genres. The Amazonas Philharmonic Orchestra plays Thursday night and can be seen and heard practicing in the theater weekdays 9–2. A variety of foreign entertainers, from José Carreras to the Spice Girls, have performed here. Half-hour tours are conducted daily 9–4. An annual opera festival takes place in April and May. ⊠ *Praça São Sebastião s/n, Centro* ☎ *092/3232–1768* ⊕ *www.teatroamazonas.com.br* ☎ *R$10* ☉ *Mon.–Sat. 9–4.*

㉚ Usina Chaminé. Transformed from a sewage treatment plant that never functioned, this art gallery displays exhibits and holds dance and theater performances. Its neo-Renaissance–style interior, with hardwood floors and massive wood beams, is another reason to visit. ⊠ *Av. Lourenço da Silva Braga, Centro* ☎ *092/3633–3026* ☎ *Free* ☉ *Tues.–Fri. 10–5, weekends 4–8.*

Elsewhere in Manaus

Most of the area surrounding downtown Manaus is not very attractive to visit. The few places of interest include the Natural History Museum and INPA's Bosque da Ciência in Aleixo. The Bosque and nearby Par-

THE VANISHING INDIANS

IN 1500, when the Portuguese arrived in Brazil, the Indian population was 4.5 million, with an estimated 1,400 tribes. From the beginning the Portuguese divided into two camps regarding the natives: the missionaries, who wanted to "tame" them and convert them to Catholicism, and the colonizers, who wished to enslave and exploit them. The missionaries lost, and when it became apparent that the Indians couldn't be enslaved, the infamous bandeirantes (assault forces) relentlessly persecuted the Indians to "liberate" tribal lands. Many Indians lost their lives defending their way of life, but the greatest killers were smallpox and influenza—European diseases against which they had no immunity. Slow but steady integration into Portuguese society caused the native population to dwindle.

Today, of Brazil's 328,000 remaining Indians, about 197,000 live in the Amazon. Each of the 220 societies has its own religious beliefs, social customs, and economic activities. The larger groups include the Manaó, Yanomami, Marajó, Juma, Caixana, Korubo, and Miranha. Each speaks one of the 170 distinct languages spoken by the indigenous peoples of Brazil; Tupi (with seven in-use derivations, including Tupi-Guarani) is the most widely spoken, followed by Macro Jê, Aruák, Karíb, and Arawá.

Throughout Brazil's history sporadic efforts were made to protect the Indians, but it was only in 1910 that the government established an official advocacy agency, the Service for the Protection of the Indians (SPI), to support Indian autonomy, ensure respect for traditional practices, and help indigenous peoples to acquire Brazilian citizenship. In 1930 the SPI was abolished due to corruption and lack of funds. It was replaced in 1967 by the current governmental advocacy group, FUNAI (Fundação Nacional do Indio, or the National Indian Foundation). Although it has been highly criticized, FUNAI helped to get the first (and, thus far, only) Indian elected into office: Mario Juruna, an Indian chief, served as federal deputy from 1983 to 1987. The foundation has also defended the rights of Indians to protect their lands (it allows only legitimate researchers to visit reservations), which are increasingly targeted for logging, rubber extraction, mining, ranching, or the building of industrial pipelines and hydroelectric plants.

The Indians have always respected and understood their environment; their plight and that of the rain forest are closely linked. Conservation efforts to preserve the rain forest have called attention to some of FUNAI's issues, but for the Brazilian government the issue is complicated: rain-forest conservation is often overshadowed by economic development. Further, the Indians still lack many basic human rights, and violence (such as the 1998 murder of prominent activist Francisco de Assis Araujó) still sporadically occurs as the Indians continue to defend their way of life against outsiders.

–Melisse Gelula and Althia Gamble

que Municipal do Mindu in Parque 10 are both forested and good for walks. A taxi will cost around R$30 one-way from downtown to these sites. The Mini-Zoo do CIGS is in São Jorge, and a taxi will cost about R$20. Ponta Negra along the Rio Negro has several restaurants and is super for evening strolls. Also, Hotel Tropical is situated on its upstream end. Taxis charge between R$40 and R$50 from downtown.

WHAT TO SEE ★ ㉟ **INPA–Bosque da Ciência.** Used as a research station for the INPA (Instituto Nacional de Pesquisa da Amazônia), this slice of tropical forest is home to a great diversity of flora and fauna. Some highlights include manatee tanks, caiman ponds, a museum, a botanical garden with an orchidarium, and nature trails. It's a great place for a walk in the shade. ✉ *Rua Otávio Cabral s/n, Aleixo* ☎ *092/3643–3192* *R$5* ⏲ *Tues.–Sun. 8–4.*

off the beaten path

MEETING OF THE WATERS – This natural phenomenon is one of the area's biggest tourist attractions. Here the Rio Solimões, a slow-moving muddy river, and the darker, fast-moving Rio Negro flow side by side for 4 mi (6 km) without mixing. If you run your foot in the water from the boat, you can feel the difference in temperature—the Solimões is warm and the Negro is cold. At the CEASA port you can rent a boat, or go with a tour company. It takes about an hour to go from CEASA to the Meeting of the Waters, spend some time there, and return. A taxi to CEASA from downtown is about R$30.

㊲ **Mini-Zoo do CIGS.** Dozens of animals native to the Amazon live at this 5-acre zoo. Pains have been taken to create natural habitats for some of the animals, but due to lack of funds, other animals are simply kept in cages. The Brazilian army operates a jungle-survival training school here, but it's not overrun with tanks and soldiers. ✉ *Estrada do São Jorge 750, São Jorge* ☎ *092/3625–2044 or 092/3625–5444* *R$3* ⏲ *Tues.–Sun. 8–4.*

㊱ **Museu de Ciências Naturais da Amazônia.** The Natural History Museum of the Amazon has preserved specimens of insects, turtles, and fish on display. This is a great place to get acquainted with fish, reptiles, and insects that you might later see in the Amazon jungle or river. ✉ *Estrada Belém s/n, Aleixo* ☎ *092/3644–2799* *R$10* ⏲ *Mon.–Sat. 9–noon and 2–5.*

Praia da Ponta Negra. Known as the Copacabana of the Amazon, this beach is next to the Hotel Tropical and has restaurants, bars, sports, and nightlife facilities (including an amphitheater).

Where to Eat

Brazilian

$$ Fodor'sChoice ★ **Churrascaria Búfalo.** Twelve waiters, each with a different cut of chicken, beef, or goat, scurry around this large, sparkling clean restaurant. As if the delectable meats weren't enough, tables are also stocked with side dishes, including manioc root, pickled vegetables, and caramelized bananas. ✉ *Rua Joaquim Nabuco 628-A, Centro* ☎ *092/3633–3773 or 092/3633–5091* 🌐 *www.churrascariabufalo.com.br* 💳 *AE, DC, MC, V.*

¢–$$ ✕**Chez Charufe.** On the banks of the Rio Negro, Chez Charufe is in a lovely location for breezy, open-air dining. Fish dishes as well as beef and chicken are all very good, and it's only a ten-minute walk from the Hotel Tropical. ⊠ *Ponta Negra, Tarumã* ☎ *091/3658–5580* ▭ *MC, V* ⊘ *No lunch.*

¢ ✕**Restaurante Aves Grill.** For a quick, cheap bite, you can't beat this pay-per-kilo restaurant. Most main courses contain some kind of bird, whether quail, turkey, duck, or chicken. Side dishes include lovely salads, fries, beans, and rice. ⊠ *Rua Henrique Martins 366, Centro* ☎ *092/3233–3809* ▭ *DC, MC, V* ⊘ *No dinner.*

Eclectic

★ $$ ✕**El Touro Loco.** Excellent regional dishes, unusual and tasty appetizers, pizza, pasta, sushi, salads—El Touro Loco has it all. It also has a fascinating rustic-European decor, and great service in an open-air setting. ⊠ *Av. Do Turismo 215, Tarumã* ☎ *92/3631–2557* ▭ *MC, V* ⊘ *No lunch.*

Italian

$–$$ ✕**Fiorentina.** The green awning and red-and-white-check tablecloths are hints that this restaurant serves authentic Italian cuisine. Pasta dishes are delicious, especially the lasagna *fiorentina* (with a marinara and ground-beef sauce). ⊠ *Praça da Polícia 44, Centro* ☎ *092/3215–2233* ⊕ *www.ristorantefiorentina.com.br* ▭ *AE, DC, MC, V.*

Japanese

$–$$$ ✕**Suzuran.** For more than 20 years this festive restaurant has served the town's best Japanese food. If you can't decide between raw fish and fried favorites, don't. The *suzuran teishoku* platter has sushi, sashimi, shrimp and vegetable tempura, and grilled fish. ⊠ *Rua Teresina 155, Adrianópolis* ☎ *092/3633–3570 or 092/3234–1693* ▭ *AE, DC, MC, V.*

Seafood

★ $–$$$$ ✕**Canto da Peixada.** When Pope John Paul II came to Manaus in 1981, this restaurant was chosen to host him. The dining areas aren't elegant, but the fish dishes are outstanding, and there are 43 types of salad. One platter feeds two. ⊠ *Rua Emilio Moreira 1677, Praça 14* ☎ *092/3234–1066* ▭ *AE* ⊘ *Closed Sun.*

Vegetarian

¢ ✕**Filosóphicus.** Whole grains, textured vegetable protein, gluten, and soy are used in the dishes at this buffet restaurant. It's on the second floor and tricky to find. From the street take the door between Belmiros and Marisa e Familia. ⊠ *Av. 7 de Setembro 752, 2nd floor, Centro* ☎ *092/3234–2224* ▭ *No credit cards* ⊘ *No dinner.*

Where to Stay

Manaus has several decent in-town hotels, but the jungle lodges outside town are where you should base yourself if you're interested in Amazon adventures. Most jungle lodges have naturalist guides, swimming, caiman "hunts" (the animals are blinded with flashlights, captured, photographed, and released), piranha fishing, and canoe trips. Many jungle lodges (and all of those that we list) are near the Rio Negro, where mosquitoes are less of a problem because they can't breed in its acidic black water. Unless otherwise noted, prices at jungle lodges are for two-day, one-night packages, which generally include transport to and from the lodge, meals (not drinks), and a variety of activities that depend on the length of your stay. These are essentially glorified camps that lack many amenities, so expect to rough it a bit. Air-conditioning, hot water, telephones, and televisions are rare amenities.

In-Town Hotels

$$$ ☷ **Hotel Tropical.** Nothing in the Amazon can match the majesty of this resort hotel. It's 20 km (12 mi) northwest of downtown and overlooks the Rio Negro, with a short path to the beach. In addition to a zoo, sports facilities, and two gorgeous pools, the Tropical has its own dock. The location is remote, far from Centro, but just a 20-minute cab ride from the airport. The restaurant is a reliable choice for dinners of regional and international fare. ⊠ *Av. Coronel Teixeira 1320, Ponta Negra, 69029–120* ☎ *092/3659–5000* 🖷 *092/3658–5026* ⊕ *www.tropicalhotel. com.br* ⟿ *588 rooms, 8 suites* ⟐ *2 restaurants, coffee shop, in-room safes, 4 tennis courts, 2 pools, gym, sauna, beach, dock, boating, basketball, bar, dance club, recreation room, shops, helipad, travel services* ▭ *AE, DC, MC, V* ⊨⊙∣ *EP.*

$ ☷ **St. Paul.** If you're planning an extended stay, this apartment hotel in Centro is a good deal at around R$1,700/month. Though plain, accommodations are immaculate and have living rooms and fully equipped kitchens. For stays of more than a week you may get a discount. ⊠ *Av. Ramos Ferreira 1115, Centro, 69010-120* ☎ *092/3622–2131* 🖷 *092/ 2101–3838* ⟿ *45 apartments* ⟐ *Kitchenettes, pool, gym, sauna* ▭ *AE, DC, MC, V* ⊨⊙∣ *EP.*

$ ☷ **Hotel Manaós.** Across from Teatro Amazonas and just up the street from the busy part of downtown, Hotel Manaós is in a great spot. Rooms are small but are clean and have nice woodwork. The staff are warm and friendly. ⊠ *Av. Eduardo Ribeiro 881, Centro 69010-001* ☎ *092/ 3633–5744/6148/5892* 🖷 *092/232–4443* ⊕ *www.hotelmanaos. brasilcomercial.com* ⟿ *39 rooms* ⟐ *Restaurant, bar* ▭ *AE, DC, MC, V* ⊨⊙∣ *EP.*

$ ☷ **Lider Hotel.** Although far from luxurious, this hotel is clean, comfortable, and conveniently located in Centro. It's a good base from which to branch out on city tours. ⊠ *Av. 7 de Setembro 827, Centro, 69005-140* ☎ *092/ 3621–9744* ⊕ *www.internext.com.br/liderhotel* ⟿ *60 rooms* ⟐ *Restaurant, bar* ▭ *AE, DC, MC, V* ⊨⊙∣ *EP.*

$ ☷ **Taj Mahal.** Much of the charming East Indian artwork of the original hotel disappeared in the last renovation, although you can still see some in the lobby. Albeit a bit unkempt, the Taj Mahal is a pleasant option, with a rooftop pool, a revolving restaurant with a view, and a convenient location. Request a room with a river view. ⊠ *Av. Getúlio Vargas 741, Centro, 69020-020* ☎ *092/3627–3737* 🖷 *092/3627–3737* ⊕ *www.grupotajmahal.com.br* ⟿ *144 rooms, 26 suites* ⟐ *Restaurant, pool, hair salon, massage, sauna, bar, meeting room* ▭ *AE, DC, MC, V* ⊨⊙∣ *EP.*

¢ ☷ **Central Hotel Manaus.** A good option if you're on a budget, this hotel has simple, clean rooms with standard amenities. It's near the market

CHICO MENDES: RUBBER TAPPER AND ENVIRONMENTAL PIONEER

BORN IN 1944 *in the northwestern state of Acre, Chico Mendes was the son of a seringueiro (rubber-tree tapper) who had moved across the country in the early 20th century to follow the rubber boom. Chico followed in his father's footsteps as a seringuero in Xapuri, close to the Bolivian border. In the 1960's rubber prices dropped dramatically, and tappers began to sell forests to cattle ranchers who cut them for pastures. In the '70s, to protect forests and the tappers' way of life, Mendes joined a group of non-violent activists who managed to prevent many ranch workers and loggers from clearing the rubber trees. On the local council of Xapuri, he promoted the creation of forest reserves for rubber and Brazil-nut production. He founded the Xapuri Rural Workers Union and the National Council of Rubber Tappers to educate tappers on forest issues.*

In 1987 Mendes was invited to Washington, D.C., to help convince the Inter-American Development Bank to rescind its financial support of a planned 1,200-km (750-mi) road to be constructed through the forest. That same year, Mendes was awarded the Global 500 environmental achievement award from the United Nations, making him an international celebrity.

In 1988 Mendes stopped rancher Darly Alves da Silva from extending his ranch into a reserve. On December 22, 1988, da Silva and son Darcy murdered Mendes outside his home. Upon his death, Chico Mendes made the front page of The New York Times *and numerous other publications worldwide. Subsequently, Brazil created the Chico Mendes Extractive Reserve near Xapuri, along with 20 other reserves covering more than 8 million acres.*

and the port, and is popular with businessmen on a tight budget. ⊠ *Rua Dr. Moreira 202, Centro, 69005-250* ☎ *092/3622–2600* 🖷 *092/ 3622–2609* ⊕ *www.hotelcentralmanaus.com.br* ➦ *50 rooms* ⚭ *Restaurant, minibars* ▤ *AE, DC, MC, V* ❝◯❞ *EP.*

Jungle Lodges

Though most tour companies will pick you up at the airport and drop you off following your adventure, airport pickup should not be assumed in all situations. It's often included in tour packages, but inquire while making arrangements. Local naturalist guides are often available at lodges. Though knowledgeable, they are neither biologists nor teachers. Do not expect accurate information and identification of species or interpretation of ecological relationships. The guides and companies in the Adventure & Learning Vacations chapter are those we recommend.

$$$$ 🏨 **Acajatuba Jungle Lodge.** Civilization seems hundreds of miles away at this thatch-hut lakeside lodge. Twenty individual screened cabins are elevated 1 meter (3 feet) aboveground and connected to the rest of the lodge by walkways. Lighting is provided by 12-volt batteries and kerosene lamps (generators would keep wildlife away), and there is no hot water, but what it lacks in luxury, it more than makes up for by putting you in the middle of the tropical forest. ⊠ *60 km (35 mi)/4 hours west of Manaus, Lago Acajatuba; boats to lodge leave from CEASA port near the meeting of the waters* ⅅ *Conj. Vila Municipal Rua 7 #87, Manaus 69057–750* ☏ *092/3642–0358 or 092/3642–0452* ⊕ *www.acajatuba.com.br* 🛏 *40 rooms* ⌂ *Bar; no a/c, no room phones, no room TVs* ▤ *V* ⅋ *FAP.*

4$ 🏨 **Amazon Ecopark.** For a very comfortable jungle experience, stay at this lodge with air-conditioned rooms, hot showers, and mosquito nets. You can visit monkeys in rehabilitation, hike with a naturalist guide on 6 mi (10 km) of trails through several habitat types with enormous trees, and relax in streams and small waterfalls. It's not far from Manaus. ⊠ *23 km (15 mi) northwest of Manaus; 30 minutes by boat from Hotel Tropical, Rio Tarumã,* ☏ *092/3622–2612* ⊕ *www.amazonecopark.com.br* 🛏 *60 rooms* ⌂ *Restaurant, bar, beach, massage, hiking, recreation room* ▤ *MC, V* ⅋ *MAP.*

$$$$ 🏨 **Amazon Lodge.** Rustic floating cabins with air-conditioning and baths make up this remote lodge. Monkey- and bird-watching is excellent. The English-speaking guides are knowledgeable and friendly. The minimum stay is two nights. ⊠ *74 km (50 mi) south of Manaus, Lago Juma; boats to lodge leave from CEASA port near meeting of the waters* ⅅ *Heliconia Amazônia Turismo Ltda., Rua José Clemente 500, Room 214, Manaus 69010-070* ☏ *092/3234–5915* 🖷 *092/3633–7094* ⊕ *www.naturesafaris.com.br* 🛏 *14 rooms* ⌂ *Restaurant, fishing, hiking; no room phones, no room TVs* ▤ *No credit cards* ⅋ *FAP.*

$$$$ 🏨 **Ariaú Amazon Towers.** The most famous of the Amazon jungle lodges, Ariaú is made up of four-story wooden towers on stilts and linked by catwalks. The effect is more dramatic when the river floods the ground below from December to June. The feeling of being integrated with nature is a bit lost here due to Ariaú's size, and contact with wildlife is rare, apart from brightly colored macaws and cute semiwild monkeys that visit and make mischief. Though Ariaú looks impressive and the food is excellent, we find the price a bit high, considering that many rooms have a mildew odor and small windows, and most rooms have fans instead of air conditioning. The exception are the tower suites, which have air-conditioning and most standard hotel amenities. One such suite is the Tarzan House, 100 feet up in the treetops. ⊠ *60 km (40 mi)/2 hours northwest of Manaus, Rio Ariaú; boats to lodge depart from Hotel Tropical* ⅅ *Rua Silva Ramos 41, Manaus 69010–180* ☏ *092/3622–5000* 🖷 *092/3233–5615* ⊕ *www.ariautowers.com.br* 🛏 *288 rooms, 19 suites* ⌂ *2 restaurants, 5 pools, dock, fishing, hiking, 4 bars, shops, Internet, helipad, auditorium, museum; no a/c in some rooms, no room TVs, no phones in some rooms* ▤ *AE, DC, MC, V* ⅋ *FAP.*

$$$$ 🏨 **Jungle Othon Palace.** It's quite a sight to cruise down the Rio Negro and see the neoclassical columns of this luxurious "flotel," built on a steel barge, looming on the horizon. Explore the region by day, and at night return to your air-conditioned cabin for a hot shower or to take a stroll on the observation deck. ⊠ *35 km (20 mi)/1 hour west of Manaus, Rio Negro; boats to lodge depart from Hotel Tropical* ⅅ *Rua Saldanha Marinho 700, Manaus 69010–040* ☏ *092/3633–6051 or 092/3633–6200* ⊕ *www.junglepalace.com.br* 🛏 *24 rooms* ⌂ *Restaurant, cable TV, pool, health club, bar, meeting room* ▤ *DC, MC, V* ⅋ *FAP.*

★ $$$$ ⬚ **Lago Salvador.** Although it's only a 15-minute ride from the Hotel Tropical, this lodge feels secluded. Four cabanas with three apartments each are on the shore of the lake from which the lodge takes its name. During the high-water season the lake flows over its shores to join the Rio Negro. Rooms are simple and comfortable. All of the small cabins have trails leading to them from the main house and restaurant, but your guide will probably use the most direct route—paddling a canoe across the lake—to get you there. ⊠ *15 km (10 mi)/15 minutes northwest of Manaus; boats to lodge leave from Hotel Tropical* ⬚ *Fontur, Hotel Tropical, Av. Coronel Teixeira 1320, Manaus 69029-120* ☎ *092/3658–3052 or 092/3658–3438* ⬚ *092/3658–3512* ⊕ *www.lagosalvador.com.br* ⬚ *12 cabins* ⬚ *Restaurant, room service, fans, boating, hiking* ⬚ *AE, MC, V* ⬚ *FAP.*

off the
beaten
path

MAMIRAUÁ SUSTAINABLE DEVELOPMENT RESERVE – The largest wildlife reserve in Brazil, Mamirauá is about 1,050 km (650 mi) west of Manaus on the Rio Solimões. The reserve is known for its abundant wildlife, including the endemic, and endangered, red-faced uakari monkey. Guided tours (from Uakari Lodge) take you through the *várzea* (flooded forest) in canoes during the rainy season (January–April) and on foot the rest of the year. Plan to get muddy if you're hiking. Frequent animal sightings include three species of monkeys, colorful birds, and pink river dolphins. Dry season is the best time to see caimans and fish.

Since Mamirauá encompasses several communities, cooperation and assistance of local inhabitants in the areas of research, ecotourism, maintenance, and fiscalization help make it successful as a sustainable development reserve.

To get to the reserve, you'll need to fly to Tefé (a one-hour flight from Manaus) and take Mamirauá's boat from there, but the effort is well worth it. ⊠ *Rio Solimões, near Tefé* ☎ *092/3233–9025* ⊕ *www.mamiraua.org.br.*

Nearly all visitors to Mamirauá stay at the nearby **UAKARI FLOATING LODGE,** – which has free transportation to and from the reserve. The lodge takes great pride in its efforts to exist in harmony with the local population and the environment—for instance, local guides are hired and most of the lodge uses solar power. Activities include river tours, fishing trips, and guided visits to a local village. Cabin-type rooms have few amenities but are clean, with large windows. Each has a small porch with a hammock. The minimum stay is three nights. Transport to and from the airport is included. ⊠ *30 minutes by boat from Tefé* ☎ *092/3233–9025* ⊕ *www. mamiraua.org.br* ⬚ *10 rooms* ⬚ *Restaurant, bar, library, tours, airport shuttle; no a/c, no room phones, no room TVs, no kids under 12* ⬚ *MC, V* ⬚ *FAP R$360 per person double occupancy, 4 days and 3 nights ($240 for 2 per night).*

CloseUp

ELUSIVE EL DORADO

THE SEARCH FOR EL DORADO (which means, in Spanish, "The Gilded Man") and his supposedly wealthy kingdom began with the arrival of the conquistadors to South America in the 1500s and continued into the 1900s. The suspected location of El Dorado (as the kingdom came to be called) changed depending on who was searching. The most captivating story placed it in Colombia, in a village where each year Chibcha natives rolled a chieftain in gold dust. The chieftain then paddled to the middle of sacred lake Gustavita and bathed. So powerful was the lure of finding riches there, that when conquistadors Gonzalo Pinzarro and Francisco de Orellana heard the story, they mounted an expedition of hundreds of men, horses, and dogs. They went east over the Andes, descended its steep slopes, and dropped into Amazon rain forest. Along the way they lost most of their men and animals. They never found El Dorado or any gold. Nor did Sir Walter Raleigh, Colonel Fawcett, or numerous others who searched. Many, like Fawcett, succumbed to illness or arrows and never returned.

Nightlife

Manaus em Tempo is a newspaper that lists nightlife events in Manaus; it's availabe at newsstands. *Boi bumbá* (ox legend) music and dance—native to the central Amazon region—tells stories with tightly choreographed steps and strong rhythms. The amphitheater at Praia da Ponta Negra holds regular boi-bumbá performances.

Alegro (⊠ Amazonas Shopping Av. Djalma 483, Nossa Senhora das Graças ☎ 092/3216–5099), open every night, is a nightclub and restaurant with a varied Italian-heavy menu. The club plays MPB, rock, and *sertanejo* (country music from Ceará).

Botequim (⊠ Rua Barroso 279, Centro ☎ 092/3232–1030), near the Teatro Amazonas, has a DJ spinning '70s and '80s music Thursday nights; Friday and Saturday live bands play a mix of MPB (*música popular brasileira,* or Brazilian pop music), samba, bossa nova, and other Brazilian styles. Four varieties of beer are made on site at microbrewery **Cervejaria Fellice** (⊠ Av. Rodrigo Otavio 3555 ☎ 092/3212–3400 or 092/3212–3401). It has food and live music as well.

Coração Blue (⊠ Km 6, Estrada da Ponta Negra 3701 ☎ 092/3658–4057) is an outdoor bar that has techno, *axé* (a Bahian rhythm), boi-bumbá, and dance music. Weeknights it's often the busiest place in town. A popular and somewhat highbrow dance club is the Hotel Tropical's **Studio Tropical** (⊠ Av. Coronel Teixeira 1320, Ponta Negra ☎ 092/3659–5000), which plays high-energy dance music for a well-dressed clientele. It's open Thursday through Saturday.

The Arts

Teatro Amazonas (⊠ Praça São Sebastião s/n, Centro ☎ 092/3232–1768) draws some of the biggest names in theater, opera, and classical music. Monday-evening performances are free. The Amazonas Philharmonic Orchestra plays every Thursday night. The Teatro holds an opera festival every year in April and May.

Sports & the Outdoors

Jet Skiing

Clube do Jet (⊠ Rua Praiana 13, access through Av. do Turismo, Ponta Negra ☎ 092/3657–5435) rents equipment for R$80 an hour or R$200 per day on the Rio Negro.

Jungle & River Excursions

Though Belém, Santarém, and other communities are great places for jungle and river excursions, they don't have nearly the selection or number of visitors that Manaus has. The most common excursion is a half- or full-day tourist-boat trip that travels 15 km (9 mi) east of Manaus to the point where the coffee-color water of the Rio Negro flows beside and gradually joins the coffee-with-cream-color water of the Rio Solimões. According to Brazilians, this is where the Amazon River begins. The waters flow alongside one another for 6 km (4 mi) before merging. Many of these meeting-of-the-waters treks include motorboat side trips along narrow streams or through bayous. Some also stop at the Parque Ecológico do Janauary, where you can see birds and a lake filled with the world's largest water lily, the *vitória régia*.

Nighttime boat trips into the forest explore flooded woodlands and narrow waterways. Some stop for trail hikes. Some companies take you by canoe on a caiman "hunt," where caimans are caught and released. Trips to the Rio Negro's upper reaches, where wildlife is a little wilder, are also offered. Such trips usually stop at river settlements to visit with local families. They may include jungle treks, fishing (they supply the gear and boat), and a trip to Anavilhanas, the world's largest freshwater archipelago. It contains some 400 islands with amazing Amazon flora, birds, and monkeys. To arrange any of these excursions, contact an area tour operator (⇨ Tours, *in* The Amazon Essentials, *below*).

Soccer

Manaus's professional soccer teams, Rio Negro and Nacional, play at **Estádio Vivaldo Lima** (⊠ Av. Constantino Nery, Flores ☎ 092/3236–3219). A taxi ride to the stadium and a ticket should each cost about R$25.

Shopping

Here, as in other parts of the Amazon, you can find lovely indigenous artisanal items made from animal parts. Macaws, for example, are killed in the wild for feathers to make souvenir items for tourists. As a result, there are no longer many macaws in the forests close to Manaus. Traveling home with items made from animal parts, certain types of wood, or plant fibers can result in big fines and even jail time, so beware.

Shopping Areas & Malls

The largest, most upscale mall is **Amazonas Shopping** (⊠ Av. Djalma Batista 482, Parque 10 ☎ 092/3642–3555), with 300 stores with 38 restaurants. **Studio 5 Festival Mall** (⊠ Av. Rodrigo Octavio 2555, Vila da Felicidade ☎ 092/3216–3517) is a large mall.

Specialty Shops

Ecoshop (⊠ Amazonas Shopping, Parque 10 ☎ 092/3234–8870) sells regional art and a variety of indigenous crafts. One of the best places to buy all kinds of things, from fresh fish to hammocks and souvenirs, is **Mercado Adolfo Lisboa** (⊠ Rua Dos Barés 46, Centro), down along the water. **Loja do Mamirauá,** near Teatro Amazonas, sells crafts made by inhabitants of the Mamirauá Reserve (⇨ *above*). **Museu do Índio** (⊠ Rua Duque de Caxias 296, Centro ☎ 092/3635–1927) has a gift shop that sells traditional crafts such as necklaces made from seeds and feathers and baskets.

SIDE TRIPS FROM MANAUS

Not far from Manaus you can explore black-water rivers, lakes, and beaches on the Rio Negro; muddy-water rivers and lakes on the Amazon River; and waterfalls and streams north of Manaus. You can also visit caboclo villages along the rivers. Perhaps your guide or boat driver will walk through the village with you to introduce you and show you around. Wildlife watching can be done anywhere, though it gets better the farther you get from the city.

Beaches

Praia da Lua is 23 km (14 mi) southwest of Manaus. Praia do Tupé is 34 km (20 mi) northwest of Manaus.

Crescent-shape **Praia da Lua** is on the Rio Negro, and is cleaner and less crowded than other beaches. **Praia do Tupé,** another Rio Negro beach, is popular with locals and tends to fill up on Sunday and holidays. Both beaches can only be reached by boat. Departures are from behind the mercado municipal every morning. A round-trip ticket is about R$10. You must bring your own food and drink.

Presidente Figueiredo

38 *107 km (64 mi) north of Manaus.*

One of the Amazon's best-kept secrets is a two-hour drive north of Manaus. The town of Presidente Figueiredo (founded 1981) has dozens of waterfalls—up to 32 meters (140 feet) in height—and caves with pre-historic paintings and pottery fragments. The area was stumbled on during the construction of the BR 174 highway, the only highway that takes you out of the state (to Roraima and on to Venezuela), and was ultimately discovered by explorers looking for minerals, who had based themselves in Presidente Figueiredo. The area is excellent for swimming in black-water streams and hiking through upland forest. The town has several hotels and restaurants, and there's a hydropower plant and reservoir and an archaeology museum in the area. The Centro de Proteção de Quelonias e Mamiferos Aquaticos (Center for the Protection of Turtles and Aquatic Mammals) is in Balbina, 82 km (51 mi) north of town.

THE AMAZON ESSENTIALS

Transportation

For more transportation information, *see* Smart Travel Tips A to Z, at the beginning of this book.

BY AIR

For major airline contact information, including Gol, TAM, and Varig, *see* Air Travel, *in* Smart Travel Tips A to Z.

BELÉM & SIDE TRIPS
All flights are served by Aeroporto Internacional Val-de-Cans, which is 11 km (7mi) northwest of the city. Varig and TAM sometimes offer direct flights to Miami. They also fly regularly to Rio, São Paulo, Brasília, and Manaus, as does GOL. TAF flies to the northeast of Brazil. Soure, Kovacs, and Renaissance airlines have charter flights to small regional airports, including rivers and grass strips. Prices vary, but a flight for four people to Marajó, for example, would be about R$1,000.

The easiest route from the airport is south on Avenida Julio Cesár and then west on Avenida Almirante Barroso. The 20-minute taxi ride from the airport to downtown Belém costs around R$30. There are also buses. Look for those labeled MAREX/PRES. VARGAS, for the Hilton and other hotels; MAREX/PRAÇA KENNEDY, for Paratur and the docks; or MAREX/VER-O-PESO, for Cidade Velha.

🛫 Airport **Aeroporto Internacional Val-de-Cans** ✉ Av. Julio Cesár s/n, Belém ☎ 091/3210-6000 or 091/3257-3780.

🛫 Local Airlines **Kovacs** ☎ 091/3233-1600. **Renaissance** ☎ 091/3233-1290. **Soure** ☎ 091/3233-4986. **TAF** ☎ 091/3210-6501 ⊕ www.voetaf.com.br.

BETWEEN BELÉM & MANAUS
Domestic carriers TAM, Varig, and Gol have flights to Santarém and Macapá. Aeroporto de Macapá is 4 km (2 mi) northwest of town. Take a taxi for the short, inexpensive ride. Santarém is easily accessible by air via Belém or Manaus. Aeroporto Maria José is 14 km (23 mi) west of town, and buses and taxis from the airport are plentiful.

🛫 Airport **Aeroporto Maria José** ✉ Rodovia Fernando Guilhon, Praça Eduardo Gomes s/n, Santarém ☎ 093/3523-1990.

MANAUS & SIDE TRIPS
Brigadeiro Eduardo Gomes Airport is 17 km (10 mi) north of downtown. Varig has a weekly direct flight to Miami. Most flights connect

454 < **The Amazon**

in São Paulo, where you can fly direct to Miami, New York, L.A., and Houston. Varig and TAM have regular flights to and from Santarém, Belém, Brasília, Rio, and São Paulo. Tavaj and Rico fly to Tefé.

The trip to Manaus Centro from the airport takes 25 minutes and costs about R$45 by taxi. A trip on one of the city buses, which depart regularly during the day and early evening, costs R$1.50.

🛈 Airport **Aeroporto Brigadeiro Eduardo Gomes** ✉ Av. Santos Dumont s/n, Manaus ☎ 092/3652-1210.

🛈 Local Airlines **Rico** ☎ 092/3652-1513. **Tavaj** ☎ 092/3652-1166.

BY BOAT

BELÉM & SIDE TRIPS
Most ships arrive and depart in the general dock area on the edge of downtown called the Escadinha. MACAMAZON and Bom Jesus have ships and standard riverboats to Macapá, Santarem, Manus, and other places. These boats dock at the Escadinha do Cais do Porto. Sightseeing boats leave from Estação das Docas, and from behind Hotel Beira Rio on Rua Bernardo Saião 20 minutes southeast of town near the Federal University.

🛈 **Bom Jesus** ✉ Av. Mendonça Junior 12, Macapá ☎ 096/3223-2342 or 091/3272-1423 in Belém. **MACAMAZON** ☎ 091/3222-5604 or 091/3228-0774.

BETWEEN BELÉM & MANAUS
Boats depart from the Escadinha do Cais do Porto in Belém. Arapari operates boats between Belém and Camará, on **Ilha do Marajó,** twice daily Monday through Saturday (R$25 round-trip). A ferry takes cars to Ilha do Marajó. Vans run from Camará to Soure and cost about R$12.

Although Macapá is very close to Ilha do Marajó's western side, most boats traveling to **Macapá,** including MACAMAZON and Bom Jesus, originate in Belém. Trips are 24 hours and you can get hammock space for around R$90, a *camarote* (cabin with bunks) for R$120, and a larger cabin with double bed (*cama de casal*) for R$200. Boats dock in the nearby port town of Santana, where taxis await. The fare to Macapá is R$20–R$50, depending on how many other passengers the driver can gather.

MACAMAZON makes the two-day trip from Macapá to **Santarém** and onward to Manaus. It also has trips from Belém to Santarém, which takes about 2½ days. Sleeping arrangements are the same as on the Belém–Macapá route. Taxis are always at the docks in Santarém. The cost to any of the nearby hotels in town is less than R$10.

🛈 **Arapari** ☎ 091/3242-1870 or 091/3241-4977. **Bom Jesus** ✉ Av. Mendonça Junior 12, Macapá ☎ 096/3223-2342 or 091/3272-1423 in Belém. **MACAMAZON** ☎ 091/3222-5604 or 091/3228-0774. **Vans (Camará to Soure)** ☎ 091/3741-1441.

MANAUS & SIDE TRIPS
If you're looking for a boat to another town, a lodge, or a beach, visit the Hidroviária Regional Terminal. At the ticket or tourist information booths you can get information about prices and departure times and days to all the locations. You can also walk down to Porto Flutuante via the bridge behind the terminal to take a look at the regional boats. Their destinations and departure times are listed on plaques.

To reach most Manaus-area beaches, catch a boat from Porto Flutuante. Sunday is the only day with regularly scheduled trips; boats transport great crowds for about R$10 per person. You can hire small craft to the beaches and other attractions, such as the meeting of the waters. Look for people wearing the green vests of the Associação dos Canoeiros Motorizados de Manaus near the Porto Flutuante or in the Escadinha area closer to the market in Belém. They can set you up with local boat trips at reasonable prices. You can also make arrangements through tour operators.

MACAMAZON boats run from Manaus to Santarém on Wednesday and Friday from the Porto São Raimundo (west of downtown) or the Porto Flutuante (about R$160).

🛈 **MACAMAZON** ☎ 091/3222-5604 or 091/3228-0774.

BY BUS

BELÉM & SIDE TRIPS
Rodoviário São Brás, the bus station in Belém, is east of Nazaré. Reservations for buses are rarely needed. Boa Esperança makes the 209-km (125-mi) journey to **Salinópolis** every couple of hours daily. Beira-Dão leaves every half hour on the 60-km (36-mi), two-hour journey to **Ilha Mosqueiro** for over R$1. Clearly marked buses to **Praia Outeiro** and the town of Icoaraci pass the bus station regularly and also costs a little over R$1. Belém's local bus service is safe (though you should keep an eye on your belongings) and comprehensive, but a little confusing. Ask a resident for guidance.

🛈 **Beira-Dão** ☎ 091/3226-1162. **Boa Esperança** ☎ 091/3266-0033. **Rodoviário São Brás** ✉ Av. Almirante Barroso s/n, São Brás, Belém ☎ 91/3246-7442.

BETWEEN BELÉM & MANAUS
In Soure buses to Camará pass by the riverside regularly. In Macapá there's an outdoor terminal on Rua Antônio Coelho de Carvalho, a block from the fort. Catch the bus labeled B. NOVO/UNIVERSIDADE to the Marco Zero, a 20-minute ride. Buses from Santarém to Alter do Chão depart from Praça Tiradentes in the city center or from Avenida Cuiabá (near the Amazon Park Hotel). They make the journey back and forth five or six times a day and hourly on Sunday.

MANAUS & SIDE TRIPS
The bus station in Manaus, Terminal Rodoviário Huascar Angelim, is 7 km (4 mi) north of the city center. The city bus system is extensive and easy to use. The fare is about R$1.50. Most of the useful buses run along Avenida Floriano Peixoto, including Bus 120, which goes to Ponta Negra and stops near the Hotel Tropical. The Fontur bus, which costs about R$14, travels between Centro and the Hotel Tropical several times a day. To get to Presidente Figueiredo, take the bus labeled ARUANÃ, which runs regularly from the terminal and costs around R$17.

🛈 **Terminal Rodoviário Huascar Angelim** ✉ Rua Recife 2784, Flores, Manaus ☎ 092/3642-5805.

BY CAR

BELÉM & SIDE TRIPS
In Belém rental cars cost between R$100 and R$180 a day. Several companies have offices at the airport and in town.

The BR 316 begins on the outskirts of Belém and runs eastward toward the coast and then south, connecting the city with Brazil's major northeastern hubs. To reach the beaches at Ilha Mosqueiro outside Belém, take BR 316 and then head north on PA 391. To reach Salinas Beach, take BR 316 to PA 324 and head north on PA 124.

Although Belém has the most traffic of any Amazon city and what seems like more than its fair share of one-way streets, in-town driving is relatively easy. Parking is only tricky in a few areas, such as Avenida Presidente Vargas and the Escadinha.

🚘 Rental Agencies **Avis** ⊠ Aeroporto Val de Cans, Belém ☎ 091/3257-2277 or 091/3257-2222.

BETWEEN BELÉM & MANAUS There aren't any car-rental companies on Ilha do Marajó, but you can rent a car in Belém (⇨ *above*) and transport it to the island on the ferry that leaves from Icoaraci. In Macapá you can rent from Locamais and in Santarém from Bill Car, though there are other companies. You can rent a car at the Manaus airport through Unidas Rent a Car.

Traffic and parking problems are nonexistent in the region between Belém and Manaus.

🚘 Rental Agencies **Bill Car** ⊠ Av. Mendoço Furtado, Santarém ☎ 093/3522-1705. **Locamais** ⊠ Av. Fab 2093, Macapá ☎ 096/223-0678.

MANAUS & SIDE TRIPS You can rent a car at the Manaus airport through Unidas Rent a Car.

From Manaus BR 174 runs north to Boa Vista, and BR 319 travels south to Porto Velho, which is south of Manaus in Rondônia State. To get to BR 319, you have to take a ferry across the Amazon. You can go about 100 km (63 mi) on paved road. Then it turns to dirt or mud. Even if you're after adventure, don't think about driving to Porto Velho. A four-wheel-drive vehicle takes you farther than 100 km (62 mi), but won't get you across the rivers and lakes that take over the road farther south.

Manaus has its share of traffic and parking problems, but is calmer than Belém.

🚘 Rental Agencies **Unidas Rent a Car** ⊠ Aeroporto Brigadeiro Eduardo Gomes, Av. Santos Dumont s/n, Manaus ☎ 092/3651-2558 or 092/3652-1347.

BY TAXI

There are plenty of taxis in Amazon cities, and they're easy to flag down. All have meters (except Marajó), and tips aren't necessary. Where meters don't exist, you have to bargain for the price. At odd hours call the taxi company. You can find them listed in the yellow pages, or call one of the companies below. Smaller towns also have mototaxis. They are much cheaper but only carry one passenger.

BELÉM & SIDE TRIPS 🚕 **Coopertáxi** ⊠ Belém ☎ 091/3257-1041 or 091/3257-1720. **Rádio Taxi** ⊠ Macapá ☎ 096/222-5200. **Soure Taxis** ⊠ Soure, Marajó ☎ 091/3741-1336. **Taxi Nazaré** ⊠ Belém ☎ 091/3242-7867.

BETWEEN BELÉM & MANAUS 🚕 **Rádio Táxi Piauí** ⊠ Santarém ☎ 093/3523-2725.

MANAUS 🚕 **Tucuxi** ⊠ Manaus ☎ 092/2123-9090. **Amazonas Rádio Táxi** ⊠ Manaus ☎ 092/3658-3333 or 092/3658-5888.

Contacts & Resources

BANKS & EXCHANGING SERVICES

ATMs are available at most bank branches in major cities. In smaller towns neither ATMs nor change are easy to come by: bring cash and lots of small bills.

Some banks accept only cards with Visa/Plus logos and others accept only cards with MasterCard/Cirrus logos. Banco24horas ATMs usually accept all cards, including American Express. *See* "Money Matters" *in* Smart Travel Tips A to Z for more information.

BELÉM & SIDE TRIPS In Belém the airport branch of the Banco do Brasil charges a hefty commission to cash traveler's checks. In town Banco Amazônia has the best rates; it's open weekdays 10–4. Casa Francesa Câmbio e Turismo is one of several exchange houses that offer comparable rates.

🏦 **Banco Amazônia** ✉ Av. Presidente Vargas 800, Comércio, Belém ☎ 091/4008-3388 or 091/4008-3399. **Banco do Brasil** ✉ Aeroporto Internacional Val-de-Cans, Av. Júlio César s/n, Belém ☎ 091/3242-3564. **Casa Francesa Câmbio e Turismo** ✉ Trv. Padre Prudêncio 40, Batista Campos, Belém ☎ 091/4006-6800.

BETWEEN BELÉM & MANAUS There are no exchange facilities on Ilha do Marajó. In Macapá, Banco do Brasil is open weekdays 11–2:30, but you'll probably get a better rate at Casa Francesa Câmbio e Turismo. In Santarém you can exchange money at Banco do Brasil, open weekdays 10–1.

🏦 **Banco do Brasil** ✉ Rua Independência 250, Macapá ☎ 096/223-2155 ✉ Av. Rui Barbosa 794, Santarém ☎ 093/3522-5657. **Casa Francesa Câmbio e Turismo** ✉ Rua Independência 232, Macapá ☎ 096/3224-1418.

MANAUS & SIDE TRIPS At the airport in Manaus you can exchange money at Banco do Brasil. In town, Cortez Câmbio has the best rates.

🏦 **Banco Amazônia** ✉ Aeroporto Brigadeiro Eduardo Gomes, Av. Santos Dumont s/n, Manaus ☎ 092/3652-1210. **Cortez Câmbio** ✉ Av. 7 de Setembro 1199, Centro, Manaus ☎ 092/3622-4222 ✉ Amazonas Shopping, Av. Djalma Batista 482, Parque 10, Manaus ☎ 092/3642-2525.

EMERGENCIES

🚑 Emergency Contacts **Ambulance** ☎ 192. **Fire** ☎ 193. **Police** ☎ 190.

BELÉM & SIDE TRIPS 🏥 Hospital **Hospital e Maternidade Dom Luiz I** ✉ Av. Generalíssimo Deodoro 868, Umarizal, Belém ☎ 091/3241-4144.

🏥 Late-Night Pharmacy **Big Ben** ✉ Av. Gentil Bittencourt 1548, Nazaré, Belém ☎ 091/3241-3000.

BETWEEN BELÉM & MANAUS 🏥 Hospitals **Hospital e Maternidade Sagrada Familia** ✉ Av. Presidente Vargas 1606, Santarém ☎ 093/3522-5157. **Pronto Socorro** ✉ Rua Milton Silva s/n, Macapá ☎ 096/212-6157 or 192. **Dotor Almir Gabriel** ✉ Rua 8 and Trv. 17, Ilha do Marajó, Soure ☎ 091/3765-1244.

🏥 Late-Night Pharmacies **Drogaria Droga Mil** ✉ Av. Magalhães Barata 674, Santarém ☎ 093/3523-1000. **Farmácia Globo** ✉ Rua Leopoldo Machado 1902, Macapá ☎ 096/621-1703. **Farmácia Salvador** ✉ Rua 2 s/n, Soure, Ilha do Marajó ☎ 091/3765-1165.

MANAUS & SIDE TRIPS 🏥 Hospital **Hospital e Pronto Socorro Municipal 28 de Agosto** ✉ Rua Recife s/n, Adrianópolis, Manaus ☎ 092/3236-0326.

🏥 Late-Night Pharmacies **Drogaria 24h** ✉ Boulevard Álvaro Maio 744, Centro, Manaus ☎ 092/3633-6040. **Drogaria Avenida** ✉ Av. Senador Alvaro Maia 744, Centro, Manaus ☎ 092/3627-4444.

INTERNET

In Belém, Speednet provides Internet service for R$3 an hour and is open all week 8 AM–9 PM. The Hilton charges R$6 per hour. In Santarém, Internet Cyber da Orla is open Monday through Saturday 9–6, at R$2 per hour. In Manaus, Cybercity is friendly and helpful, and charges R$3 per hour. Internext has 14 computers and charges R$3 per hour.

🚹 Internet Cafés **Cybercity** ✉ Av. Getúlio Vargas 188, Centro, Manaus ☎ 092/3234-8930. **Internext** ✉ Av. Eduardo Ribeiro, Rio Negro Center 220, 2nd floor, Centro, Manaus ☎ 092/3633-4409. **Internet Cyber da Orlá** ✉ 15 de Agosto, Centro, Santarém ☎ 093/3548-7720. **Speednet** ✉ Gama Abreu 152, Campina ☎ 091/3222-7506 or 091/8147-3937.

MAIL & SHIPPING

The central branch of the Belém *correio* (post office) is open weekdays 8–noon and 2–5. You can send faxes, and, as in all Brazilian post offices, SEDEX international courier service is available. On Ilha do Marajó, the Soure post office is on Rua 2 between Travessa 13 and Travessa 14. The Macapá central post office is open weekdays 9–noon and 2–5. You can mail a letter at the Santarém post office weekdays 8–4. The central Manaus post office is open weekdays 9–5 and on Saturday 9–1.

🚹 Post Offices **Belém post office** ✉ Av. Presidente Vargas 498, Campina ☎ 091/3212-1155. **Macapá post office** ✉ Av. Coroliano Jucá 125 ☎ 096/223-0196. **Manaus post office** ✉ Rua Marechal Deodoro 117, Centro ☎ 092/3622-2181. **Santarém post office** ✉ Praça da Bandeira 81 ☎ 093/3523-1178. **Soure post office** ✉ Rua 2 s/n ☎ 091/3741-1207.

TOUR OPTIONS

Whichever tour you choose, be sure your experience includes wildlife viewing with a guide, contact with locals, and regional foods and drinks. The most popular tours run from Manaus, since it is the best organized for tourism and has the best jungle lodges. It can feel clogged with tourists at times though, which can make the less-popular starting points of Santarém and Belém more appealing.

For adventure and culture tours, *see* Adventure & Learning Vacations (chapter 11).

BELÉM For excursions in Belém as well as help with plane and hotel reservations, contact Angel Turismo in the Hilton Hotel. Valeverde Turismo has a tour boat and office at the Estação das Docas. Amazon Star can do just about everything. Lusotur is a large company near the Praça da República that arranges city tours and ecotours.

🚹 **Amazon Star Tours** ✉ Rua Henrique Gurjão 236, Campina, Belém ☎ 091/3212-6244. **Angel Turismo** ✉ Hilton International Belém, Av. Presidente Vargas 882, Praça da República, Campina, Belém ☎ 091/3224-2111. **Lusotur** ✉ Av. Brás de Aguiar 471, Nazaré, Belém ☎ 091/3241-1011. **Valeverde Turismo** ✉ Boulevard Castilhos França s/n, Campina, Belém ☎ 091/3212-3388 or 091/3241-7333.

BETWEEN BELÉM & MANAUS Tour operators that arrange trips to Ilha do Marajó are based in Belém. Amapá Tours offers city and river tours and is the only company that arranges trips to see the pororoca. Near Santarém, boat trips on the Amazon and Arapiuns rivers, day trips to Alter do Chão, and city tours can be arranged by Santarém Tur. Amazon Tours, run by knowledgeable, friendly American Steven Alexander, conducts half-day trips to a patch of forest he owns that's a half hour's drive southeast of Santarém.

🖬 **Amapá Tours** ✉ Hotel Macapá, Av. Azarias Neto 17, Macapá ☎ 096/222-2553. **Amazon Tours** ✉ Trv. Turiano Meira 1084, Santarém ☎ 093/3522-6144 ⊕ www.amazonriver.com. **Santarém Tur** ✉ Rua Adriano Pimentel 44, Santarém ☎ 093/3522-4847 or 093/3522-5503 ⊕ www.santaremtur.com.br.

MANAUS & SIDE TRIPS In Manaus, Fontur arranges boat and city tours. Tarumã can help with hotel arrangements and transportation in the city or on the river. Amazon Explorers and Selvatur are two high-profile companies that arrange Manaus-area ecotours.

🖬 **Amazon Explorers** ✉ Av. Djalma Batista 21100 Tvlandia Mall, Vieralves, Manaus ☎ 092/3642-4777 or 092/3236-9484 ⊕ www.amazonexplorers.com.br. **Fontur** ✉ Hotel Tropical, Av. Coronel Teixeira 1320, Ponta Negra, Manaus ☎ 092/3658-3052 or 092/3658-3438. **Selvatur** ✉ Praça Adelberto Vale 17, Centro, Manaus ☎ 092/3622-2577 ⊕ www.selvatur.com.br. **Tarumã** ✉ Av. Eduardo Ribeiro 620, Centro, Manaus ☎ 092/3648-8347.

VISITOR INFORMATION

BELÉM BELEMTUR, the tourist board in Belém, is open weekdays 8–noon and 2–6.

🖬 **BELEMTUR** ✉ Av. Governador José Malcher 592, Nazaré ☎ 091/3242-0900 or 091/3242-0033.

BETWEEN BELÉM AND MANAUS Pará State's tourist board, PARATUR, is open weekdays 8–6. Both agencies are well organized and extremely helpful. On Ilha do Marajó contact the Secretaria Municipal de Turismo or ATURMA. For information in Macapá, contact the state tourism authority, DETUR. In Santarém contact SANTUR.

🖬 **ATURMA** ✉ Soure, Marajó ☎ 091/3228-1385. **DETUR** ✉ Rua Raimundo Álvares da Costa 18, Macapá ☎ 096/212-5335, 096/212-5336, or 096/212-5334 ⊕ www.macapa-ap.com.br. **PARATUR** ✉ Praça Maestro Waldemar Henrique s/n, Reduto, Belém ☎ 091/3212-0575 ⊕ www.paratur.pa.gov.br. **SANTUR** ✉ Rua Floriano Peixoto 777, Santarém ☎☎ 093/3523-2434. **Secretaria Municipal de Turismo Marajó** ✉ Rua 2 between Trv. 14 and Trv. 15, Soure ☎ 091/3741-1327.

MANAUS Amazonas State's helpful and trustworthy tourism authority in Manaus, Amazonastur is open weekdays 8–6. The Manaus tourism authority, Manaustur, is open weekdays 8–2. CAT (Centro de Atendimento ao Turista) in Manaus is an information center near the Teatro Amazonas with a desk in the airport and one in the Hidroviária. ATURMA is the official Marajó tourism organization.

🖬 **Amazonastur** ✉ Rua Saldanha Marinho 321, Centro ☎ 092/3233-1928 or 092/3233-1095 ⊕ www.amazonastur.com. **CAT** ✉ Av. Eduardo Ribeiro 666, Centro ☎ 092/3622-0767. **Secretaria de Estado da Cultura e Turismo** ✉ Av. 7 de Setembro 1546, Centro ☎ 092/3633-2850, 092/3633-3041, or 092/3633-1357 🖷 092/3233-9973 ⊕ www.culturamazonas.am.gov.br. **Secretária de Turismo Presidente Figueiredo** ✉ Rua Uatumã 321, Centro, Presidente Figueiredo ☎ 092/3324-1158 ⊕ www.amazonastravel.com.br.

Adventure & Learning Vacations

WORD OF MOUTH

"[When] we traveled the Amazon on a small boat, we met the indigenous people and ate the local food. It was rustic and wonderful. We arrived at Ariaú by boat, seeing the employees lined up and waving to welcome us. As we got closer, we saw that most of these 'employees' were monkeys . . . curious thieves who sat on our laps and tried to steal our beer!"

—swacm

"On the final boat approach to the lodge we saw amazing birds, pink and gray freshwater dolphins, monkeys, toucans, lizards, and frogs . . ."

—quiUK

Updated by
Rhan Flatin

WITH THE WORLD'S LARGEST TROPICAL ECOSYSTEM and more rivers, lakes, and ocean beaches than just about any other country, Brazil is ripe for adventure. The Amazon is one of the top places to get adventurous. Here you can fish for piranha from a riverboat or hike deep into the rainforest from a lodge accessible only by canoe. The Pantanal is a great place for watching wildlife, especially crocodiles and birds, and also has jungle lodges. The canyons and mountains of central and southern Brazil are great for camping, hiking, climbing, biking, and horseback riding. Then there are the endless east-coast beaches and the ocean, popular for boating, diving, and snorkeling. Brazil's influences from Africa, Europe, and its own indigenous groups, and its many volunteer opportunities with estimable non-profit organizations also make it a great place to delve into a culturally rich learning vacation.

For more information about planning an adventure or learning vacation, check out **South American Explorers Club** (✉ 126 Indian Creek Rd., Ithaca, NY 14850 ☎ 607/277–0488 or 800/274–0568 🖷 607/277–6122 🌐 www.saexplorers.org).

Choosing a Trip

Choosing a tour package carefully is always important, but it becomes even more critical when the focus is adventure or sports. You can rough it or opt for comfortable, sometimes even luxurious, accommodations. You can select "soft-adventure" trips that nearly anyone can handle, or go for hiking, biking, rafting, and climbing expeditions that require physical endurance and technical skill. Study multiple itineraries to find the trip that's right for you, and ask yourself and the tour companies these important questions:

- **What's my adventure quotient?** Adventure vacations commonly are split into "soft" and "hard" adventure. Hard adventure, such as strenuous treks (often at high altitudes), Class IV or V rafting, or ascents of some of the world's most challenging mountains, generally require excellent physical conditioning and previous experience. Most hiking, biking, canoeing/kayaking, and the like can be enjoyed by persons of all ages who are in good health and are accustomed to a reasonable amount of exercise. A little honesty goes a long way—recognize your own level of physical fitness and discuss it with the tour operator before signing on.

- **How remote is too remote?** Many trips described in this chapter might seem to be headed into uncharted territory, but tour operators carefully check each detail before an itinerary goes into a brochure. So while you won't be vying with busloads of tourists for photo ops, you'll probably run into at least a few like-minded travelers. Journeys into truly remote regions typically involve camping or the simplest of accommodations, but they reward with more abundant wildlife and locals who are less accustomed to the clicking of cameras. Ask yourself if it's the reality or the image of roughing it that appeals to you, and stick with the reality.

- **Do I want a company that is environmentally sound?** If so, ask hard questions of the tour operator. Does the company protect the fragile environments you'll be visiting? How? Are some of the company's profits designated for conservation efforts or put back into the communities visited? Does it encourage indigenous people to dress up (or dress down) so that your group can get great photos, or does it respect their cultures as they are? For ecotourism programs, ask for the credentials of the naturalist(s), and keep in mind that a string of degrees can be less important than familiarity with the area. A good operator will discuss its policies on its Web site, or at least have representatives with information at the ready via phone.

- **To group or not to group?** At its best, group travel connects you with like-minded people with whom to share the day's experiences. Is your like-minded group age-specific, singles, all-female? Or is it a mix? Or maybe group travel isn't your thing at all; most companies that do group trips can also customize a trip just for you. Many tour operators have trips designed for families, with itineraries that appeal both to kids and adults.

- **Is it a two-bit operation?** Gorgeous photos and well-written tour descriptions go a long way in selling a company's trips. But the "client consideration factor" is important, too. Does the operator provide useful information about health (suggested or required inoculations, tips for dealing with high altitudes)? A list of frequently asked questions and their answers? Tips for photography under destination-specific conditions? Recommended readings? Equipment needed for sports trips? Packing tips when baggage is restricted? Climate info? Visa requirements? A list of client referrals? The option of using your credit card? The more professional and trustworthy the company, the easier it will be to book and to find the information you need.

- **Are there hidden costs?** Make sure you know what is and isn't included in basic trip costs when comparing companies. International airfare is usually extra. Sometimes flights within the country you are visiting are additional. Is trip insurance included? How much does it cost and what situations are covered? Are airport transfers included? Visa fees? Departure taxes? All excursions? Gratuities? Equipment? Meals? Bottled water? Many factors affect the price, and the trip that looks cheapest in the brochure could well turn out to be the most expensive. Don't assume that roughing it will save you money, as prices rise when limited access and a lack of essential supplies on-site require costly special arrangements.

THE VACATIONS

To book these vacations, *see* Tour Operator Contacts, *at* the end of this chapter.

Amazon & Pantanal Trips
Season: Year-round
Locations: Throughout the Amazon and Pantanal
Cost: Beginning at about $1,400 for eight days from Manaus
Tour Operators: Ecotour Expeditions; Focus Tours; Heliconia; Latin American Escapes; Naturequest; Swallows and Amazons

Because the Amazon and its tributaries provide easy access to remote parts of the jungle, river transport often serves as the starting point for camping and lodge excursions. Many jungle lodges can also be reached by small planes using dirt or grass airstrips. Accommodations range from hammocks to comfortable rooms with private baths. Nature walks, canoe trips, piranha fishing, and visits to indigenous villages are typically part of rain-forest programs led by local guides. A few may even offer naturalist guides with training in biology. Numerous Amazon itineraries are available, so study several companies' offerings to choose an appropriate trip. Focus Tours has lodge visits and jungle camping in the Pantanal.

Most jungle adventures here begin with a boat trip up the Rio Negro, the main tributary of the Amazon. Naturequest has created a rustic jungle lodge and riverboat safari combination. With International Expeditions you explore the rain forest and watery byways from your base at remote Uakari Lodge's cluster of floating cabañas. Focus Tours' program focuses on the rain forest, rivers, and wildlife of the Alta Floresta region. Maxim Tours offers short stays at the comfortable Pousada dos Guanavenas or the more rustic Amazon Lodge. Swallows and Amazons has Over Look Lodge, with eight private bedrooms and shared baths.

Bird-Watching Tours
Seasons: Year-round

Locations: Amazon; Northeast; Pantanal; Southeast.

Cost: From $1,750 for seven days from Manaus.

Tour Operators: Field Guides; Focus Tours; Swallows and Amazons; Victor Emanuel Nature Tours.

Bird habitats in Brazil range from coastal rain forests to cloud forests to open plains. The Pantanal, a vast area of seasonally flooded grassland, has the hyacinth macaw, bare-faced curassow, epaulet oriole, and nacunda nighthawk, while the golden parakeet is but one of many exotic species inhabiting the Amazon. Brazilian avian life is so rich that Victor Emanuel Nature Tours runs five different programs here and Field Guides has seven.

When selecting a bird-watching tour, ask questions. What species might be seen? What are the guide's qualifications? Does the operator work to protect natural habitats? What equipment is used? (In addition to binoculars, this should include a spotting scope, a tape recorder to record and play back bird calls [a way of attracting birds], and a spotlight for night viewing.) Also, if you're interested in getting to know more than birds, look into natural-history tours. Bird tours can be very specific, leaving out other fascinating species, which can be frustrating for some.

Cruises
OCEAN CRUISES **Season:** October–April

Locations: Various (see below)

Cost: Varies according to type of ship, cabin category, and itinerary; prices usually about $225–$300 per day

Cruise Companies: Crystal Cruises; G.A.P Adventures; Holland America Line; Radisson Seven Seas Cruises; Royal Olympic Cruises; Seabourn Cruise Line; Silversea Cruises

Some Caribbean cruises or post-Antarctica-season cruises have ports of call in Brazil and a partial navigation of the Amazon River. Other ships have itineraries exclusively along the Atlantic and Pacific coasts of South America. You can opt for a circumnavigation of the continent (about 50 days) or choose one or more segments. Typical port calls in Brazil are Belém, Fortaleza, Salvador, and Rio de Janeiro.

RIVER CRUISES **Season:** Year-round

Locations: Río Negro; Anavilhanas Archipêlago; Amazon River; Lago Janauarí Ecological Park; Río Branco

Cost: From $395 for three days from Manaus

Tour Operators: Amazon Nature Tours; Crystal Cruises; Ecotour Expeditions; Heliconia; Latin American Escapes; Maxim Tours; Nature Expeditions International; Princess Cruises; Radisson Seven Seas; Royal Olympic Cruises; Seabourn Cruise Line; Silversea Cruises; Southwind Adventures; Swallows and Amazons; Travcoa

At five Congos or twelve Mississippis in volume, the Amazon is the world's largest river. From its source in the Peruvian Andes it snakes 6,600 km (4,102 mi) before emptying into the Atlantic, and its lower half lies in Brazil. The Amazon nourishes thousands of species of birds, mammals, and plants. Whatever your style of travel, there's a boat plying the river to suit your needs.

River journeys along the Amazon (on riverboats) typically begin in Manaus, though Belém and Santarém are plausible starting points as well. Some itineraries combine three or four cruising days with visits to Rio, others savor life on the river for the entire 7 to 15 days. You'll explore tributaries by small boats, take jungle walks, and visit indigenous villages. Accommodations range from hammocks on deck to luxurious wood-paneled cabins. With Swallows and Amazons you'll also do some beach and forest camping. A highlight of all trips is the "Meeting of the Waters," where the dark waters of the Rio Negro join the lighter waters of the Amazon. Cruise vessels, on the other hand, enter the Amazon via the Atlantic and work their way upriver. Though you'll travel in greater luxury, you'll stop in fewer places and have fewer opportunities to see wildlife up close and interact with locals.

Canoeing, Kayaking & Rafting
Season: Year-round
Location: Amazon
Cost: From $1,100 for eight days from Manaus
Tour Operator: Swallows and Amazons

Following a day's journey along the Rio Negro, you overnight in a small rain-forest lodge owned by Swallows and Amazons. The following day you set out by boat for Jau National Park for six days of canoeing, hiking, fishing, swimming, and visiting with the local river people. Accommodations are nil—you camp in the rain forest or on the beach each night.

You don't have to be an expert paddler to enjoy many of these adventures, but you should be a strong swimmer. Rivers are rated from Class I to Class V according to difficulty of navigation. Generally speaking, Class I to III rapids are suitable for beginners, while Class IV and V rapids are strictly for the experienced. Canoeing is a much gentler river experience.

Cultural Trips

Season: Year-round
Locations: Manaus; Olinda; Ouro Prêto; Pantanal; Paraty; Salvador; Santarém; Rio
Cost: From $1,390 for 14 days from Santarém
Tour Operators: Abercrombie and Kent; Amizade; Brazil Nuts; Focus Tours; Maxim Tours; Swallows and Amazons; Wilderness Travel

Immersing yourself in Brazilian culture could mean studying the archaeological remains of civilizations, learning about the lives and customs of indigenous peoples, trying your hand at local crafts or studying the language.

To learn about native Brazilian cultures, consider Swallows and Amazons' eight-day trip along the Rio Vaupes, during which you visit various indigenous groups—or choose the company's programs focusing on the Yanomami and Tucano people. You can help the organization's volunteers and Brazilian students by participating in various community-related projects. Maxim Tours lets you determine the number of days you'd like in the architectural and historical gems of Ouro Prêto, Olinda, and Salvador. To add a rewarding dimension to your trip, consider an Amizade work project in the Brazilian Amazon where you'll help construct a children's health clinic, or build a school in the Pantanal with Focus Tours. Amizade also has language-study trips.

Diving & Snorkeling Trips

Season: Year-round
Locations: Northeast coast; Amazon's Rio Negro
Cost: From $550 for 12 days (from Recife)
Tour Operators: G.A.P Adventures; Swallows and Amazons

Brazil has diverse aquatic environments to explore. The northeast, for example, is home to hundreds of miles of white-sand beaches and fascinating marine life, as well as a lively cultural scene. The Rio Negro is a freshwater Amazon tributary with many fish species. Many aquarium fish, including tetras and cardinals, come from the upper Rio Negro. In the dry season it also has white-sand beaches.

Fishing

Season: Year-round
Location: Amazon
Cost: From $2,650 for nine days from Manaus
Tour Operators: Augusto Albuquerque; Fishing International; G.A.P Adventures; Rod & Reel Adventures;, Santana; Yanna Ecofishing

With 2,500 species of fish identified (and possibly up to 5,000), the Amazon has more species than the Atlantic. Though pirapitinga, pirarucú, jacundá, matrichã, arapá, and many other exotic fish inhabit the Amazon, it is the legendary peacock bass (tucunaré) that anglers describe as the "ultimate adversary." Reaching around 27 pounds (12 kilograms), it goes for flies and lures, and rarely disappoints. A number of companies have packages to remote fishing sites. Some are boat-based and some are lodge-based. Accommodations, prices, and tour quality vary, so shop around.

Santana in Manaus has well-run tucunaré sportfishing tours that are popular with North Americans. Augusto Albuquerque runs a small operation setting up fishing tours for small groups to out-of-the-way places. Depending on the trip, your base will be a fishing camp, a five-star resort, or a comfortable live-aboard yacht. Fishing International will even take you by small plane to some very out-of-the-way places. Yanna Ecofishing has all the amenities of a typical upscale Amazon fishing company, including a luxury regional boat and small BassTracker fishing boats.

Hiking, Running & Trekking
Season: Year-round
Locations: Amazon basin; Pico da Neblina National Park
Cost: From $2,400 for 15 days from Manaus
Tour Operators: G.A.P Adventures; Swallows and Amazons

Brazil's varied terrain, natural beauty, and numerous parks and reserves make it a terrific place for trekkers and hikers. Camping is often part of the experience, although on some trips you stay at ranches, jungle lodges, or small hotels. Itineraries range from relatively easy hikes to serious trekking and even running.

For an up-close jungle experience, join Swallows and Amazons for 10 days of trekking and camping in Jau National Park, during which you walk an average of six hours a day through thick vegetation, then relax at night in a jungle camp. The company also runs two treks in Pico da Neblina National Park to the base of Mount Pico da Neblina. The 3,013-meter (9,885-foot) Neblina is known in English as the "Mountain of the Mists." G.A.P. Adventures runs longer (45 days or more) trekking tours that take you to the Pantanal, Iguaçú, and Rio on the Brazilian leg.

Horseback Riding
Season: Year-round
Locations: Highlands; Pantanal
Cost: From $1,075 for eight days from Campo Grande
Tour Operators: BikeHike Adventures; Hidden Trails

Observe the flora and fauna as you ride through the vast Pantanal with Hidden Trails on a "Wildlife Safari Ride" that includes picnics, camping, and ranch stays, plus sightseeing and a show in Rio. The company also has an eight-day "Southern Cross Fazenda Ride," where you journey along high plains at elevations reaching 1,676 meters (5,500 feet). Meet local ranchers and gauchos and, perhaps, participate in a local rodeo. BikeHike Adventures incorporates horseback riding into its multisport excursions (⇨ *below*).

Multisport Trips
Season: Year-round
Locations: Minas Gerais; Pico da Neblina National Park
Cost: From $1,695 for nine days from Belo Horizonte
Tour Operators: BikeHike Adventures; Swallows and Amazons

Innovative multisport itineraries combine biking, fishing, canoeing, hiking, horseback riding, kayaking, rafting, or trekking. BikeHike's nine-day adventure starts off with a three-day trek through the Cipó mountain range, followed by kayaking, horseback riding, and a 21-meter (70-foot) rappel down a waterfall. Nights are spent in farmhouses and camping. Swallows and Amazons' multisport trips include mountain biking, canyoning, snorkeling, and trekking in various locations.

Nature Tours
Season: Year-round
Locations: Amazon; Caraça National Park; Iguaçu Falls; Pantanal; Serra da Canastra National Park
Cost: From $265 for four days from Chapada Diamante
Tour Operators: Brazil Nuts; Ecotour Expeditions; ElderTreks; Focus Tours; G.A.P Adventures; International Expeditions; Latin American Escapes; Maxim Tours; Naturequest; Oceanic Society Expeditions; Southwind Adventures; Travcoa; Wilderness Travel; Zeghram Expeditions

Programs that provide insight into the importance and fragility of Brazil's ecological treasures take in the country's deserts, tropical forests, mountains, and rivers, as well as its impressive and diverse wildlife. Most Pantanal operators are based at Refúgio Caiman, which has comfortable lodgings and a staff of naturalists or local guides who lead excursions by truck, boat, on horseback, and on foot. Storks, tropical birds, anteaters, caimans, capybaras, and possibly jaguars are among the wildlife you might see. Some programs also spend time in Rio and at Iguaçu Falls. Zegrahm Expeditions' 17-day itinerary takes in several national parks.

Overland Safaris
Season: Year-round
Locations: Throughout Brazil
Cost: From $45 per day, depending on location, trip length, and mode of transport; prices don't include international airfare, food, or park entrance fees
Tour Operators: Exodus; Focus Tours; G.A.P Adventures; Tucan

An overland adventure is sure to take you far from the beaten path. Most programs visit between three and nine countries, and range from 20 to 171 days. Itineraries are typically composed of short segments, which you can combine into a longer trip if you wish. It's also a great way to immerse yourself in a number of cultures and landscapes.

Expect to travel by truck, bus, train, boat, or even custom-built expedition vehicles. Most of the time you'll be sleeping outdoors, and will be expected to help pitch tents, cook, and do other chores. The camaraderie that evolves often sparks lifelong friendships. Overland safaris attract an international mix of physically fit adventurers between 18 and 50.

Photo Safaris

Season: August
Locations: Iguaçu Falls; Pantanal; Atlantic Rainforest; Caraça Natural Park; Chapada National Park; Caratinga Biological Station
Cost: $3,999 for 21 days
Tour Operator: Focus Tours

Focus Tours custom designs photo tours for groups. It also has a package tour that takes you to six unique Brazilian habitats to shoot wildlife up close. Each destination has a number of endemic species and all are known as places with exceptional biodiversity. A maximum of six participants ensures that all have window seats in ground transportation. Highlights include the Pantanal, the largest freshwater wetlands on the planet, sparsely populated by humans but abundantly populated by animals. From small boats and other vehicles, you can photograph jabiru storks, caimans, capybaras, marsh deer, giant anteaters, and, with luck, the camera-shy jaguar. The price includes meals, accommodations, land transportation, and naturalist guide.

Research & Volunteer Trips

Season: July–February
Locations: Ararauna; Baía das Pedras; Baía Norte; Bananal Island; Barra Mansa; Emas; Nhumirim; Pantanal; Rio Negro
Cost: From $1,895 for 7 days from Pantanal
Tour Operators: Earthwatch; Focus Tours

Joining a research expedition team gives you more than great photos. By assisting scientists, you can make significant contributions toward a better understanding of Brazil's unique ecosystems. Flexibility, camping skills, and a sense of humor are important assets for these trips, which often require roughing it.

Earthwatch has three projects in Brazil. In and around a marine reserve with 53 mammal species, you'll work aboard a rigid-hull inflatable boat to determine the habits and habitat needs of *tucuxi* dolphins or other species, or you may patrol 74 mi of beaches looking for stranded marine mammals. The Amazon Turtles project helps identify and protect turtle nesting sites and explores the creatures' behavioral ecology and responses to environmental variables. In the Pantanal, the largest freshwater wetland on the planet, help a multinational team of scientists conduct a CRI (Conservation Research Initiative). Your role will be to assist in collecting data on vital links in the Pantanal food web, thus accelerating the conservation process.

TOUR OPERATOR CONTACTS

Below is contact information for all tour operators mentioned in this chapter. For international tour operators, we list both the tour operator and their North American representative, so you can contact whichever company is easier for you. Although the list below hardly exhausts the number of reputable companies, these are some of the best adventure tour operators in today's travel world.

Abercrombie & Kent ✉ *1520 Kensington Rd., Oak Brook, IL 60523 U.S.* ☏ *630/954–2944 or 800/323–7308* 🖷 *630/954–3324* ⊕ *www. abercrombiekent.com.*

Amazon Nature Tours ✉ *Box 128, Jamestown, RI 02835 U.S.* ☏ *401/423–3377 or 800/688–1822* 🖷 *401/423–9630* ⊕ *www.amazon-nature-tours.com.*

Amizade ✉ *Box 110107, Pittsburgh, PA 15232 U.S.* ☏ *412/441–6655 or 888/973–4443* 🖷 *412/648–1492* ⊕ *www.amizade.org.*

Augusto Albuquerque ✉ *Rua Rio Javarí 36 Vieralves, Manaus* ☏ *092/3635–6868.*

BikeHike Adventures ✉ *1807 Maritime Mews Suite 200, Vancouver, British Columbia V6H3W7 Canada* ☏ *604/731–2442 or 888/805–0061* 🖷 *604/677–5514* ⊕ *www.bikehike.com.*

Brazil Nuts ✉ *1854 Trade Center Way, Naples, FL 34109 U.S.* ☏ *239/593–9959, 239/593–0267, or 800/553–9959* ⊕ *www.brazilnuts.com.*

Crystal Cruises ✉ *2049 Century Park East, Los Angeles, CA 90067 U.S.* ☏ *800/446–6620* ⊕ *www.crystalcruises.com.*

Earthwatch ✉ *3 Clocktower Pl., Suite 100, Maynard, MA 01754 U.S.* ☏ *978/461–0081 or 800/776–0188* 🖷 *978/461–2332* ⊕ *www. earthwatch.org.*

Ecotour Expeditions ✉ *Box 128, Jamestown, RI 02835 U.S.* ☏ *401/423–3377 or 800/688–1822* 🖷 *401/423–9630* ⊕ *www.naturetours. com.*

ElderTreks ✉ *597 Markham St., Toronto, Ontario M6G 2L7, Canada* ☏ *416/588–5000 or 800/741–7956* 🖷 *416/588–9839* ⊕ *www.eldertreks. com.*

Exodus ✉ *9 Weir Rd., London SW12 OLT, England* ☏ *02086/730–859 or in the U.S. 800/228–8747* 🖷 *02086/730–779* ⊕ *www.exodus.co.uk.*

Field Guides ✉ *9433 Bee Cave Rd., Building 1, Suite 150, Austin, TX 78733 U.S.* ☏ *512/263–7295 or 800/728–4953* 🖷 *512/263–0117* ⊕ *www.fieldguides.com.*

Fishing International ✉ *Box 2132, Santa Rosa, CA 95405 U.S.* ☏ *707/542–4242 or 800/950–4242* 🖷 *707/526–3474* ⊕ *www. fishinginternational.com.*

Focus Tours ✉ *111 Malaga Rd., Santa Fe, NM 87505 U.S.* ☏ *505/989–7193* 🖷 *505/466–4689* ⊕ *www.focustours.com.*

G.A.P Adventures ✉ *19 Duncan St., Suite 401, Toronto, Ontario M5H 3H1 Canada* ☏ *416/260–0999 or 800/708–7761* 🖷 *416/260–1888* ⊕ *www.gapadventures.com.*

Heliconia Amazônia Turismo ✉ *Rua José Clemente 500, Room 214, Manaus, AM 69010-070 Brazil* ☏ *092/3234–5915* 🖷 *092/3633–7094* ⊕ *www.heliconia-amazon.com.*

Hidden Trails ✉ *202–380 West 1st Ave., Vancouver, BC V5Y 3T7 Canada* ☏ *604/323–1141 or 888/987–2457* 🖷 *604/323–1148* ⊕ *www. hiddentrails.com.*

Holland America Line ✉ *300 Elliott Ave. West, Seattle, WA 98119 U.S.* ☏ *877/724–5425* ⊕ *www.hollandamerica.com.*

International Expeditions ⊠ *One Environs Park, Helena, AL 35080 U.S.* ☎ *205/428–1700 or 800/633–4734* 🖷 *205/428–1714* ⊕ *www. internationalexpeditions.com.*

Latin American Escapes ⊠ *3209 Esplanade Suite 130, Chico, CA 95973 U.S.* ☎ *530/879–9292 or 800/510–5999* 🖷 *530/879–9290* ⊕ *www. latinamericanescapes.com.*

Maxim Tours ⊠ *268 Route 206, Flanders, NJ 07836 U.S.* ☎ *973/927–0760 or 800/655–0222* 🖷 *973/927–1417* ⊕ *www.maximtours.com.*

Nature Expeditions International ⊠ *7860 Peters Rd., Suite F-103, Plantation, FL 33324 U.S.* ☎ *954/693–8852 or 800/869–0639* 🖷 *954/ 693–8854* ⊕ *www.naturexp.com.*

Naturequest ⊠ *Box 185, 30872 S. Coast Hwy., Laguna Beach, CA 92651 U.S.* ☎ *949/499–9561 or 800/369–3033* 🖷 *949/499–0812* ⊠ *Box 22333 PMB128, Telluride, CO 81435 U.S.* ☎ *970/728–6743* 🖷 *970/728–7081* ⊕ *www.naturequesttours.com.*

Oceanic Society Expeditions ⊠ *Fort Mason Center Bldg. E, San Francisco, CA 94123 U.S.* ☎ *415/441–1106 or 800/326–7491* 🖷 *415/474–3395* ⊕ *www.oceanic-society.org.*

Princess Cruises ⊠ *24844 Ave. Rockefeller, Valencia, CA 91355 U.S.* ☎ *661/753–0000 or 800/774–6237* 🖷 *661/284–4745* ⊕ *www.princess. com.*

Radisson Seven Seas Cruises ⊠ *600 Corporate Dr., Suite 410, Fort Lauderdale, FL 33334 U.S.* ☎ *800/285–1835* ⊕ *www.rssc.com.*

Rod & Reel Adventures ⊠ *32617 Skyhawk Way, Eugene, OR 97405 U.S.* ☎ *541/349–0777 or 800/356–6982* 🖷 *541/338–0367* ⊕ *www. rodreeladventures.com.*

Royal Olympic Cruises ☎ *800/801–6086 in North America* ⊕ *www. royal-olympic-cruises.com.*

Santana ⊠ *Rua dos Andrades 106, Centro, Manaus* ☎ *092/3234–9814* 🖷 *092/3233–7127* ⊕ *www.santanaecologica.com.br.*

Seabourn Cruise Line ☎ *800/929–9391* ⊕ *www.seabourn.com.*

Silversea Cruises ⊠ *110 East Broward Blvd., Fort Lauderdale, FL 33301 U.S.* ☎ *800/722–9955* 🖷 *954/522–4499* ⊠ *77/79 Great Eastern St., London EC2A 3HU England* ☎ *0870/333–7030* 🖷 *0870/333–7040* ⊕ *www.silversea.com.*

Southwind Adventures ⊠ *Box 621057, Littleton, CO 80162 U.S.* ☎ *303/ 972–0701 or 800/377–9463* 🖷 *303/972–0708* ⊕ *www. southwindadventures.com.*

Swallows and Amazons ⊠ *Rua Quintino Bocaiuva 189, Suite 13, Manaus, AM 69005-110 Brazil* ☎🖷 *092/3622–1246* ⊕ *www. swallowsandamazonstours.com.*

Travcoa ⊠ *2424 SE Bristol Suite 30, Newport Beach, CA 92660 U.S.* ☎ *949/476–2800 or 800/992–2003, 800/563–0005 in Canada* 🖷 *949/ 476–2538* ⊕ *www.travcoa.com.*

Tucan ⊠ *217 Alison Rd., Randwick, NSW 2031 Australia* ☎ *02/ 9326–4557* 🖷 *02/9326–5993* ⊕ *www.tucantravel.com.*

Victor Emanuel Nature Tours ⊠ *2525 Wallingwood Dr., Suite 1003, Austin, TX 78746 U.S.* ☎ *512/328–5221 or 800/328–8368* 🖷 *512/328–2919* ⊕ *www.ventbird.com.*

Wilderness Travel ✉ *1102 9th St., Berkeley, CA 94710 U.S.* ☎ *510/588–2488 or 800/368–2794* 🖷 *510/558–2489* 🌐 *www.wildernesstravel.com.*

Yanna Ecofishing ☎ *092/3232–2522* 🖷 *092/3232–2397* 🌐 *www.yanna.com.br.*

Zegrahm Expeditions ✉ *192 Nickerson St., No. 200, Seattle, WA 98109 U.S.* ☎ *206/285–4000 or 800/628–8747* 🖷 *206/285–5037* 🌐 *www.zeco.com.*

UNDERSTANDING BRAZIL

BRAZIL AT A GLANCE

Politics & Government

Type of government: Federative republic
Capital: Brasília
Administrative divisions: 26 states, 1 federal district (Brasília)
Independence: September 7, 1822
Constitution: October 5, 1988
Legal system: Each state has its own judicial system; disputes between states and matters outside the jurisdiction of state courts are settled by federal courts
Suffrage: Voluntary between 16 and 18 years of age and over 70; compulsory over 18 and under 70 years of age
Legislature: Bicameral Congresso Nacional (National Congress), comprising the Federal Senate and the Chamber of Deputies. Senate has 81 members, representing each state and the federal district of Brasília. The Chamber of Deputies has 513 members, directly elected
Population: 182,032,604
Fertility rate: 2.05 children per woman
Language: Portuguese
Ethnic groups: White (includes Portuguese, German, Italian, Spanish, Polish) 55%, mixed white and African 38%, African 6%, other (includes Japanese, Arab, Amerindian) 1%
Life expectancy: Female 68, male 60
Literacy: Total population 83.3%; male 83.3%, female 83.2%
Religion: Catholic 73.8%, Protestant 15.4%, no religion 7.3%

Geography

Land area: 8,511,965 sq km (3,286,488 sq mi); slightly larger than the continental United States; occupies nearly 50% of South America
Coastline: 7,367 km (4,578 mi); bordered by the Altantic Ocean to the east
Border countries: Argentina 1,224 km, Bolivia 3,400 km, Colombia 1,643 km, French Guiana 673 km, Guyana 1,119 km, Paraguay 1,290 km, Peru 1,560 km, Suriname 597 km, Uruguay 985 km, Venezuela 2,200 km
Terrain: Highlands and some mountains in the south; Amazon Basin and flat and rolling lowlands in the north; cerrado in central Brazil, with savannah, woodland, and dry forest
Land use: Forests 58%, pasture 22%, crops 6%, other 14%
Natural resources: Bauxite, gold, iron ore, manganese, nickel, phosphates, platinum, tin, uranium, petroleum, hydropower, timber
Natural hazards: Droughts in northeast, floods and some frost in the south

Economy

Annual growth: 1.9%
Inflation: 7.7%
Unemployment: 6.4%
Per capita income: $7,250
GDP: $1.34 trillion
Services: 53%
Agriculture: 23%
Industry: 24%
Work force: 79 million (services 53%, agriculture 23%, industry 24%)
Currency: Real (plural: reais)
Exchange rate: R$2.92 per U.S. dollar
Debt: $232 billion
Major industries: Textiles, shoes, chemicals, cement, lumber, iron ore, tin, steel, aircraft, motor vehicles and parts, other machinery and equipment.
Agricultural products: Coffee, soybeans, wheat, rice, corn, sugarcane, cocoa, citrus; beef

Exports: $57.8 billion
Major export products: Manufactures, iron ore, soybeans, footwear, coffee, autos
Major export partners: U.S. 20.5%, Argentina 9.5%, Netherlands 7.1%, Japan 5.9%, Germany 4.7%, other European Union 27.1%

Imports: $57.7 billion
Major import products: Machinery and equipment, chemical products, oil, electricity, autos and auto parts
Import partners: U.S. 23.6%, Argentina 11.0%, Germany 10.4%, Japan 5.4%, other European Union 25.4%

Environment

Flora: 45,000 species (22% of world total)
Fauna: 524 mammal species (131 endemic), 517 amphibian species (294 endemic), 1,677 bird species (191 endemic), 468 reptile species (172 endemic), 3,000 freshwater fish species, 1.5 million insect species; Brazil ranks first in the world for numbers of species of primates, amphibians, and plants; third for bird species; and fourth for species of butterflies and reptiles

Endangered species: 395
Environmental issues: Deforestation in Amazon Basin and subsequent endangerment of plant and animal species; illegal wildlife trade; air and water pollution in Rio de Janeiro, São Paulo, and some other large cities; land degradation and water pollution due to mining activities; wetland degradation; oil spills

Fast Facts

• Brazil is the fifth-largest country in the world after Russia, Canada, the United States, and China

• Brazil is the second largest producer of gold.

• 60% of the world's precious stones are found in Brazil.

• Brazil has nearly 40 political parties.

HISTORICAL NOTES

Colonial Days

Brazil was officially "discovered" in 1500, when a fleet commanded by Portuguese diplomat Pedro Álvares Cabral, on its way to India, landed in Porto Seguro, between Salvador and Rio de Janeiro. (There is, however, strong evidence that other Portuguese adventurers preceded him. Duarte Pacheco Pereira, in his book *De Situ Orbis,* tells of being in Brazil in 1498, sent by King Manuel of Portugal.)

Brazil's first colonizers were met by the Tupinamba, one group in the vast array of the continent's native population. Lisbon's early goals were simple: monopolize the lucrative trade of *pau-brasil,* the red wood (valued for making dye) that gave the colony its name, and establish permanent settlements. There's evidence that the Indians and Portuguese initially worked together to harvest trees. Later, when it was necessary to head farther inland to find forested areas, the interest in establishing plantations on cleared lands increased and so did the need for laborers. The Portuguese tried to enslave the indigenous peoples, but many natives either fled far inland or died. (When Cabral arrived, the indigenous population was believed to have been more than 3 million; today the number is scarcely more than 200,000.) The Portuguese then turned to the African slave trade.

Although most settlers preferred the coastal areas, a few ventured into the hinterlands. Among them were Jesuit missionaries, determined men in search of Indian souls to "save," and the infamous *bandeirantes* (flag bearers), tough men in search of Indians to enslave. (Later they hunted escaped Indian and African slaves.)

For two centuries after Cabral's discovery, the Portuguese had to periodically deal with foreign powers that had designs on Brazil's resources. Although Portugal and Spain had the 1494 Treaty of Tordesillas—which set boundaries for each country in their newly discovered lands—the guidelines were vague. Further, England, France, and Holland didn't fully recognize the treaty, which was made by papal decree. Such competition made the Lusitanian foothold in the New World tenuous at times.

The new territory faced internal as well as external challenges. Initially, the Portuguese crown couldn't establish a strong central government in the subcontinent. It divided up the colony's territory into thirteen sections called "captaincies." The governors, or "captains," were low-ranking nobles and merchants who were granted authority over slices of land that, in some cases, were as big as their motherland. By 1549 it was evident that most captaincies were failing. Portugal's monarch dispatched a governor-general (who arrived with soldiers, priests, and craftspeople) to oversee them and to establish a capital (today's Salvador) in the central captaincy of Bahia.

At the end of the 17th century the news that fabulous veins of emeralds, diamonds, and gold had been found in Minas Gerais exploded in Lisbon. The region began to export 30,000 pounds of gold a year to Portugal. Bandeirantes and other fortune hunters descended, and boatloads of carpenters, stonemasons, sculptors, and painters came from Europe to build cities in the Brazilian wilderness.

In 1763 the capital was moved to Rio de Janeiro for a variety of political and administrative reasons. The country had successfully staved off invasions by other European nations, and it had roughly taken its current shape. It added cotton and tobacco to sugar, gold, and diamonds on its list of exports. As the interior opened, so did the opportunities for cattle ranching. Still, Portugal's policies tended toward stripping Brazil of its resources rather than developing a truly local economy. The arrival of the royal family, which was chased out of Portugal by Napoléon's armies in 1808, initiated major changes.

The Empire & the Republic

As soon as Dom João VI and his entourage arrived in Rio, he began transforming the city and its environs. Building projects were set in motion, universities as well as a bank and a mint were founded, and investments were made in the arts. The ports were opened to trade with other nations, and morale improved throughout the territory. With the fall of Napoléon, Dom João VI returned to Portugal, leaving his young son, Pedro I, behind to govern. But Pedro had ideas of his own: he proclaimed Brazil's independence on September 7, 1822, and established the Brazilian empire. Nine years later, following a period of internal unrest and costly foreign wars, the emperor stepped aside in favor of his five-year-old son, Pedro II. A series of regents ruled until 1840, when the second Pedro was 14 and Parliament decreed him "of age."

Pedro II's daughter, Princess Isabel, officially ended slavery in 1888. Soon after, disgruntled landowners united with the military to force the royal family back to Portugal. Brazil's first republican government was founded on November 15, 1889. A series of easily forgettable presidents, backed by strong coffee and rubber economies, brought about some industrial and urban development during what's known as the Old Republic. In 1930, after his running mate was assassinated, presidential candidate Getúlio Vargas seized power via military coup. In 1945 his dictatorship ended in another coup. He returned to the political scene with a populist platform and was elected president in 1951. However, halfway through his term, he was linked to the attempted assassination of a political rival; with the military calling for his resignation, he shot himself.

The next elected president, Juscelino Kubitschek, a visionary from Minas Gerais, decided to replace the capital of Rio de Janeiro with a grand, new, modern one that would be built in the middle of nowhere. True to the motto of his national development plan, "Fifty years in five," he opened the economy to foreign capital and offered credit to the business community. When Brasília was inaugurated in 1960, there wasn't a penny left in the coffers, but key sectors of the economy (such as the auto industry) were functioning at full steam. Still, turbulent times were ahead. Kubitschek's successor Jânio Quadros, an eccentric, spirited carouser, resigned after seven months in office. Vice-president João "Jango" Goulart, a Vargas man with leftist leanings, took office only to be overthrown by the military on March 31, 1964, after frustrated attempts to impose socialist reforms. Exiled in Uruguay, he died 13 years later.

Military Rule & Beyond

Humberto Castello Branco was the first of five generals (he was followed by Artur Costa e Silva, Emílio Médici, Ernesto Geisel, and João Figueiredo) to lead Brazil in 20 years of military rule that still haunt the nation. Surrounded by tanks and technocrats, the military brought about the "economic miracle" of the 1970s. It did not last. Their pharaonic projects—from hydroelectric and nuclear power plants to the conquest of the Amazon—never completely succeeded, and inflation soared. Power was to go peacefully back to civil hands in 1985.

All hopes were on the shoulders of Tancredo Neves, a 75-year-old democrat chosen to be president by an electoral college. But just before his investiture Neves was hospitalized for routine surgery; he died of a general infection days later. An astounded nation followed the drama on TV. Vice-president José Sarney, a former ally of the military regime, took office. By the end of his five-year term, inflation was completely out of hand. Sarney did, however, oversee the writing of a new constitution, promulgated in 1988, and Brazil's first free presidential elections in 30 years.

Fernando Collor de Mello, a debonair 40-year-old from the state of Alagoas, took office in March 1990. Dubbed "the maharajah hunter" (an allusion to his promises to rid the government of idle, highly paid civil servants), Mello immediately set about trying to control inflation (his first step was to block all savings accounts in Brazil). His extravagant economic plans only became clear two years later with the discovery of widespread corruption involving his friend and campaign manager Paulo César "P. C." Farias. After an impeachment process, Collor was ousted in December 1992, and Brazil's leadership fell to Vice-President Itamar Franco. With his Plano Real, Franco brought inflation under control.

In 1994 Franco was replaced by Fernando Henrique Cardoso, the former secretary of the treasury. Following the dictates of the International Monetary Fund, Cardoso brought about relative economic stability, but at the price of recession, cuts in health and educational programs, and a soaring national debt. His policy of selling state-owned industries—from banks to mines to phone companies—was riddled with irregular practices.

In October 1998, taking advantage of a constitutional amendment that he personally engineered allowing for reelection, Cardoso won a second term, running against Workers Party candidate Luis Inácio Lula da Silva. He based his campaign on propaganda that promised a return to economic growth and an end to unemployment. Cardoso managed to avoid draconian economic measures and a 35% currency devaluation until the day after the election. Then, new taxes and budget cuts were announced, recession settled in, and unemployment soared. In 1999 Cardoso's popularity was at a record low, causing nationwide calls for his resignation. He held on—ruling with more gusto than his military predecessors—by churning out endless "temporary" executive decrees, which bypassed normal legislative procedures. Before the first quarter of 2001 was over, Cardoso had signed 48,000 such decrees

in a seven-year period. The crowning reaction by Brazilians to what they saw as eight years of economic and political mismanagement came on October 27, 2002, with the landslide election of Lula da Silva over Cardoso's protégé, José Serra.

In Brasília, on January 1, 2003, the many acres between the Esplanada dos Ministérios and the Praça dos Três Poderes were jammed with a euphoric crowd—people carrying children and flags, street vendors peddling umbrellas and raincoats. Millions watched as Lula da Silva, a 57-year-old former steelworker, born in dire poverty, took office with pomp and circumstance as the nation's new president. Elected with 52.7 million votes, his campaign had consistently emphasized themes of hope, love, and peace. People believed in him, hoping he would be up to the huge task that lay ahead.

Lula met criticism in 2004 and early 2005 for rising inflation, for not spending as much as expected on social programs, for the lack of results in the programs that were begun, and for flying around in a fancy US$57 million jet. Most Brazilians, however, remained hopeful, if a little less starry-eyed than immediately following the election. But in 2005, Lula's government took a huge blow when 13 members of the Chamber of Deputies (Brazil's House of Representatives) were forced to resign following bribe accusations. One of them was the head of the Workers Party (essentially the Speaker of the House), and one of Lula's top aides. At this writing, polls indicate that Brazilians are divided on whether they believe Lula knew about the bribes. The 2006 presidential election should be an interesting one, to say the least.

–by José Fonseca

Born and raised in Minas Gerais, journalist José Fonseca left Brazil at the start of the military dictatorship, earned a master's degree from the University of Kansas, and then spent more than 10 years in Europe and West Africa before returning to Brazil. He is based in Porto Alegre.

CHRONOLOGY

1494 The Treaty of Tordesillas divides lands to be discovered in the New World between Spain and Portugal.

1500 On April 22 a Portuguese fleet commanded by 30-year-old Pedro Álvares Cabral lands on Brazil's easternmost point, near present-day Porto Seguro in the state of Bahia.

1502 On January 1 a Portuguese fleet commanded by Amerigo Vespucci first sights Guanabara Bay. Thinking it the mouth of a mighty river, he names it Rio de Janeiro (River of January).

1503 The name *Brasil* is used for the first time, taken from the Indian name of *pau-brasil* (brazilwood), valued for its red dye.

1532 The first Portuguese colony, called São Vicente, is established in the southern part of the land.

1549 A government seat is established in Salvador in the northeast to administer the colony as a whole and the unsuccessful system of 15 captaincies into which it had been divided in 1533. In the same year the first Africans are imported as slaves.

1554 A Jesuit mission is established at São Vicente, giving birth to the city of São Paulo.

1567 The Portuguese governor general establishes the city of Rio de Janeiro on Guanabara Bay.

1621 Dutch attacks on northeastern Brazil begin. These continue—with the Dutch gaining, holding, and then losing territory—for the next 30-odd years.

1654 The Dutch are completely ousted from the northeastern regions.

1695 Gold is discovered in Minas Gerais. Great inland colonial cities and churches are built with the sudden new wealth, and for the next century Brazilian gold enriches and supports the government of Portugal.

1720 Rio's landmark Glória church is built. Named Nossa Senhora da Glória do Outeiro (Our Lady of Glory on the Hill), the small baroque beauty stands on a low rise and looks out across Guanabara Bay.

1750 The Treaty of Madrid recognizes Portuguese rule in what is roughly today's Brazil.

1759 Jesuit priests are expelled from Brazil after 200 years of conflict with both colonial factors and the Portuguese government.

1763 With a shift away from wealth and power in the northeast, which had been based on sugar, to a newer center of influence in the southeast, based on gold, the capital is moved from Salvador to Rio de Janeiro.

1792 The Inconfidência Mineira, an independence movement based in Minas Gerais and spurred by repressive taxation policies, comes to an end when its leader, Tiradentes (Tooth Puller), is hanged in Rio de Janeiro.

1807　Portugal is conquered by Napoléon, and King João VI goes into exile in Brazil. With his court in Rio de Janeiro and with a new understanding of the colony from which he now directs all Portuguese affairs, he introduces reforms and permits Brazil to trade with other countries.

1814　Artist Aleijadinho dies, leaving behind a timeless treasure of religious art in the churches of his native state of Minas Gerais.

1821　King João returns to Portugal. His son, Dom Pedro, is named Prince Regent of Brazil.

1822　On September 7 Pedro I proclaims the Brazilian Empire and independence from Portugal, partly to establish his own position and partly to continue the reforms begun by his father. The United States recognizes the new nation in 1824; Portugal does so in 1825.

1824　Austrian-born Empress Dona Leopoldina, wife of Pedro I, begins a campaign to populate the southern Brazilian countryside with European farmers. For the next 30 years colonists from Germany, Italy, and elsewhere settle in this region.

1831　Hoping to regain the throne of Portugal for himself, Pedro I abdicates in favor of his son, Pedro II, who is only five. Until 1840 the country suffers through a period of unrest and rebellion under a regency of political leaders.

1840–89　The reign of Pedro II brings further reforms and economic stability. But territorial skirmishes with neighboring countries bring the military to prominence.

1850　The importation of African slaves comes to an end.

1855　The first Carnival celebration is held in Rio de Janeiro.

1871　All children of slaves are declared free.

1881　The Teatro Amazonas, modeled on the Paris Opera, opens in Manaus, capital of the Amazon.

1884　The first railway line takes passengers to the top of Corcovado, overlooking Rio de Janeiro.

1885　All slaves over the age of 60 are freed.

1888　On May 13 all remaining slaves (nearly a million people) are freed. Brazil begins to even more aggressively recruit agricultural laborers from Germany, Italy, Portugal, and Spain.

1889　A bloodless military coup overthrows Pedro II and sends him into exile in France. On November 15 the Republic of Brazil is founded.

1890–1910　Manaus and the Amazon region produce tremendous wealth in the rubber trade. The wealth of coffee growers shifts power from Rio de Janeiro to São Paulo.

1894　Prudente de Morais is elected as Brazil's first nonmilitary president.

1906　Alberto Santos-Dumont brings glory to Brazil with the first self-propelled, heavier-than-air plane flight.

1908   The first Japanese immigrants arrive in Brazil to work on coffee plantations.

1910   The government's first official Indian advocacy agency, the Service for the Protection of the Indians (SPI), is founded by adventurer Cândido Mariana da Silva Rondon, for whom the state of Rondônia was later named.

1912   The first cable car carries passengers to the top of Sugarloaf, at the mouth of Rio's Guanabara Bay.

1913   Rondon and former U.S. president Theodore Roosevelt mount the Rondon-Roosevelt Expedition into the Amazon.

1917   Ernesto dos Santos, known as Donga, records "Pelo Telefone" ("On the Telephone"), the first song designated a samba. It's the hit of the year and forever changes the music of Carnaval.

1923   The Copacabana Palace Hotel opens on Rio's famed beachfront.

1927   Henry Ford makes the first of two unsuccessful attempts to establish his own rubber plantation in Brazil.

1930   With the support of the military, Getúlio Vargas becomes president and assumes dictatorial powers, but he introduces many social reforms and is initially extremely popular.

1931   The monumental statue *Cristo Redentor* (*Christ the Redeemer*) is unveiled atop Corcovado, rising 30 meters (100 feet) above the 701-meter (2,300-foot) granite peak.

1938   Brazil is the first country in Latin America to send a national soccer team to the World Cup finals.

1942   Brazil declares war on Germany and sends 25,000 troops to fight in Italy.

1945   Getúlio Vargas is forced out of office by the military.

1950   Vargas becomes president again, this time elected by the people.

1951   In Rio during the early 1950s, Ipanema's dirt roads and beach cottages are replaced with fashionable, expensive apartments and shops.

1954   Again threatened by a military coup, Vargas commits suicide in the presidential palace.

1956   New president, Juscelino Kubitschek, promises to attract foreign investments, develop Brazilian industry, and construct a new capital city.

1958   With Pelé on the team, Brazil wins the World Cup.

1959   João Gilberto's first album, *Chega de Saudade* (*No More Sadness*), firmly establishes bossa nova as Brazil's most popular new music. The film *Orfeu Negro* (*Black Orpheus*) is released.

1960   On April 19, after four years of furious work, President Kubitschek inaugurates the new capital city of Brasília, designed by Oscar Niemeyer and Lúcio Costa.

1964 *Getz/Gilberto*, the album that includes "The Girl from Ipanema," becomes an instant classic around the world. A military coup ousts President João Goulart, and the generals begin a 20-year period of repression, runaway inflation, and national debt.

1967 Governmental Indian advocacy group, FUNAI (Fundação Nacional do Indio, or the National Indian Foundation), is established.

1970 Copacabana's beach is widened and the now-famous mosaic sidewalks designed by Roberto Burle Marx are installed on Avenida Atlântica.

1973 Singer-songwriter Chico Buarque releases "Cálice," a song whose title means "chalice" but sounds like "shut up" in Portuguese, turning it into a song of protest against governmental repression. From 1969 until 1972, just prior to the song's release, Buarque and fellow musician Caetano Veloso had been in exile.

1981–83 A period of deep recession leads to the downfall of the military government.

1984 Rio's Sambódromo, designed by Oscar Niemeyer, opens for Carnival.

1985 José Sarney becomes president. His Cruzado Plan fails to control inflation.

1988 A new constitution returns freedoms, ends censorship, and guarantees rights for Indians. In the same year Chico Mendes, a spokesman for the rain forest and its rubber tappers, is murdered.

1989 Luiz Ignácio da Silva, known as Lula, a trade-union leader, loses the presidential election to Fernando Collor de Mello. Chief Raoni of the Megkroniti tribe embarks on a worldwide tour with the rock musician Sting to garner support for Brazil's Indians and to raise environmental consciousness.

1990 Collor de Mello orders harsh fiscal constraints that only briefly stem the growth of inflation.

1992 The United Nations holds the Earth Summit in Rio de Janeiro. In December Collor de Mello, brought down by corruption scandals, resigns the presidency on the brink of impeachment.

1994 Fernando Henrique Cardoso is elected president. His Plano Real stabilizes the economy and curbs inflation.

1999 After a constitutional amendment, Cardoso is permitted to run for a second term and wins.

2002 After running for office three times, Lula (Luiz Ignácio da Silva) is voted president in a much-anticipated election. He vows to combat hunger and poverty in Brazil.

2005 Members of the Chamber of Deputies (House of Representatives) resign due to bribe accusations. Lula's popularity wanes, and faith in the new government is shaken. Lula maintains innocence and declares his intention to run for reelection in 2006.

BRAZILIAN MUSIC: THE HEARTBEAT OF A COUNTRY

Nothing in the world sounds like the music of Brazil. Whether you're listening to a rousing samba on a restaurant radio, a soothing bossa nova in a beachside café, or an uplifting Afro-Brazilian spiritist song on the street, you know instantly that you're hearing the country's beating heart. And even a short list of musical styles—which are as often linked to rhythms and dances as they are to tunes and lyrics—rolls off the tongue like an ancient chant: *axé, bossa nova, forró, frevo, maracatu, samba, tropicalismo.* Many of these are divided into subcategories, with varying types of lyrics, singing styles, arrangements, and instrumentation. Some also fall into the supercategory of *música popular brasileira* (MPB, or Brazilian popular music). All fill the ear with a seamless and enchanting blend of European, African, native Indian, and regional Brazilian sound.

History explains the eclecticism. The Portuguese colonists brought the Western tonal system and the music of the church with them to Brazil. When they arrived, they encountered the music of the native Indians, which was almost exclusively percussive. The African slaves added fresh, varied rhythms and a love for choral singing to the mix. In a country this large, it isn't surprising that different regions would develop their own styles as well. From the northeast alone come forró, which uses the accordion to its best and most rhythmic advantage; axé, a Bahian blend of samba and reggae; maracatu, a percussive beat derived from Afro-Brazilian religious traditions, and frevo, a fast-pace dance music, the last two most associated with Recife's Carnaval.

Although varied, Brazilian music is always characterized by complex rhythms and layers of textured sounds. Performers often embrace the use of violins, accordions, and flutes in their compositions. Some, such as Hermeto Pascoal and Naná

Vasconcelos, have innovative keyboard or percussion styles; others, such as Milton Nascimento, incorporate moving choral arrangements. Very often, musical groups have a percussionist armed with chimes, rattles, and shells, all used so subtly as to belie the word *noisemaker.* Most distinctive of all is the squeaking sound of the *cuíca,* and a solo on this samba instrument, made from a metal can, will always bring an audience to its feet.

Samba: The Spirit of Carnaval

The music for which Brazil is perhaps most famous is believed to have its roots in *lundu,* a Bantu rhythm reminiscent of a fandango yet characterized by a hip-swiveling style of dance, and *maxixe,* a mixture of polka as well as Latin and African rhythms. The earliest references to samba appear in the late 19th century, and one theory suggests the term comes from the Bantu word *semba,* meaning "gyrating movement." "Pelo Telefone" ("On the Telephone"), the first song actually designated a samba, was recorded in 1917. By the 1930s samba was being played in Rio de Janeiro's Carnaval parades, and by the 1960s it was the indisputable music of Carnaval. Today its many forms include the pure samba *de raiz* (literally, "roots samba") or *de morro* (literally, "of the hill"; figuratively, "of the poor neighborhood"), which is performed using only percussion instruments; the popular *pagode,* based on a small guitar-like instrument called a *cavaquinh;,* and the samba *canção* (the more familiar "samba song").

Samba evokes the spirit of Carnaval, regardless of when it's played. In cities such as Rio, Salvador, and São Paulo, entire neighborhoods are divided into *escolas de samba* (samba schools), which work all year on costumes, floats, dances, and music to prepare for the pre-Lenten festivities. Composers who might have remained unknown, such as Carlos Cachaça and the legendary Cartola, have become revered *sambistas* thanks to Carnaval and its escolas. Some schools also recruit well-known samba singers such as Martinho da Vila to perform what they hope will be the winning composition in the Carnaval competitions. Although today's Carnaval is big business, it manages to remain honest to this great country's soul. Costumed dancers still swirl, drums still thunder, and sweating faces still smile through it all. The opening line of one samba from Rio's Portela School says it all: "Samba may suffer, but it never dies."

The "New Music" of the '60s

Although Brazilian music has a long, rich history, it wasn't until the 1959 film *Black Orpheus* that it reached the outside world in a big way. The movie retells the Greek legend of Orpheus and Eurydice, only this time the tragic love story is set amid Rio de Janeiro's Carnaval. It's a great film, but what most people treasure is the beauty of its music, by Antônio Carlos Jobim (known affectionately as "Tom") and Luís Bonfá.

In the early 1960s things happened that caused the world to listen ever more closely to Brazilian music. Artists and intellectuals began gathering in the cafés and apartments of Rio's chic Zona Sul neighborhoods of Copacabana, Ipanema, and Leblon. From the mix of personalities and the air of creative freedom arose a sound never heard before. It came first from the voice and the guitar of a young songwriter named João Gilberto. He sang in an understated, breathy way, and when he recorded the song "Desafinado," he virtually stated a new philosophy of music. The title means "out of tune," and, indeed, a few listeners thought he was. Melodic lines went in unexpected directions and ended in surprising places, and under those melodies was a cool, intricate rhythm.

During this period Tom Jobim and his frequent collaborator, Vinicius de Moraes (former diplomat, lifelong poet and lyri-cist, and later singer), met daily at a corner café in Ipanema. And every day, while seated at their preferred table, they saw the same beautiful teenage girl pass along the street between the beach and her home. They felt compelled to pay tribute both to her beauty and to the way she made them feel; so they composed a song. Tom wrote the music, Vinicius the lyrics, and "The Girl from Ipanema" was born. Today that café is known as Garota de Ipanema, the song's title in Portuguese, and the street that it's on has been renamed in honor of Vinicius.

Already influenced by Miles Davis and the cool California jazz made popular by Chet Baker, Gerry Mulligan, and others, American jazz musicians began heading to Rio. The great saxophonist Stan Getz was among the first to arrive. He teamed up with Tom Jobim and João Gilberto to record an album. At the last minute it was decided that João's wife, who wasn't actually a singer, would perform both the Portuguese and English versions of "The Girl from Ipanema." Soon, Astrud Gilberto was a star, and the song became the quintessential bossa nova hit.

Loosely translated, the term *bossa nova* means "new thing," and its greatest songs are recorded time and again, presenting ever-new challenges to each generation of performers. The latest includes Bebel Gilberto, daughter of João Gilberto, who in 2000 released *Tanto Tempo* (*So Much Time*)—an album mixing electronic music and bossa that topped the charts in both Europe and the United States.

The politically turbulent late 1960s and '70s saw the development of the tropicalismo movement. Musicians and intellectuals like Caetano Veloso, Chico Buarque, Tom Zé, and Gilberto Gil began using such contemporary instruments as the electric guitar and keyboard in their works. They also combined rock-and-roll and avant-garde experimentation with samba and other traditional rhythms. Often the tunes were upbeat, though the lyrics, which were frequently written in double and triple entendres, were critical of social and political injustices.

Tropicalismo sparked such heated debate that an angry Veloso once harangued a São Paulo audience for being unwilling to accept anything new. Despite this controversy, the music gained a strong enough following that it brought about the attention and disapproval of the military regimes. Some of its performers were arrested; others had to live abroad for several years.

The tendency to mix traditional rhythms with electric instruments spawned *samba rock* and its major star Jorge Ben, aka Jorge Benjor, whose hit "Taj Mahal" was copycatted on Rod Stewart's "Do Ya Think I'm Sexy?" Jorge Ben and other groups, including the now-revered Mutantes, would later be considered the first Brazilian rock acts.

From the 1970s on, Jamaican reggae became part of the Brazilian mix. Gilberto Gil's recordings of classic Bob Marley songs, including "No Woman, No Cry," honor their source and yet have a richness all their own. The dreadlocked singer Carlinhos Brown and his group, Timbalada, as well as several other groups from the state of Bahia, blend reggae sounds with the traditional rhythms of northeastern Brazil. São Luís do Maranhão, nicknamed "reggae capital of the country," is in the state of Maranhão, in the northeast.

The two following decades witnessed the birth and consolidation of Brazilian rock and pop music. The process culminated in the early '90s with the rise of the MPopB generation, whose idol was the now-defunct Chico Science and his *mangue beat* band Nação Zumbi. MPopB mixes hip-hop, funk, rock, traditional rhythms, and electronic beats.

During the latter half of the 20th century, Brazilian musicians collaborated with or influenced several U.S. performers. Tom Jobim recorded two classic albums with Frank Sinatra and appeared again on Sina-

tra's *Duets* album. Wayne Shorter introduced Milton Nascimento to North America as a vocalist on his 1975 album, *Native Dancer*. Paul Simon found inspiration in the music of Bahia for his *Rhythm of the Saints* album. David Byrne has championed many Brazilian singers with his compilations of Brazilian music. And James Taylor has recorded and often performed with Nascimento. The song "Only a Dream in Rio" appears on albums by each man, and they made a memorable appearance together at the 2001 Rock in Rio music festival.

Brazilian Voices

One of the greatest strengths of Brazilian music is its number of extraordinary female vocalists. Although Carmen Miranda may always have a special place in many hearts, by general agreement the country's greatest woman singer was Elis Regina, who died in 1982 at the age of 37. Her pure voice, perfect diction, emotional performance, and wonderful melodic sense made her unique. Among her many great albums, those recorded with Tom Jobim and Milton Nascimento are considered the best. For samba, the recordings made by Clara Nunes, who also died at an early age, are *the* classics for most Brazilians.

Today singers such as Gal Costa, Maria Bethânia (Caetano Veloso's sister), Beth Carvalho, Elba Ramalho, Alcione, Marisa Monte, Daniela Mercury, Ivete Sangalo, and Adriana Calcanhoto fill concert halls at home and abroad. Far from the top charts, Virginia Rodrigues applies a voice of operatic quality to both beautiful ballads and impassioned songs in praise of the *orixás* (African spiritual deities), whereas Teresa Cristina's renditions of traditional sambas de raiz judiciously add her name to the ever-growing list of excellent Brazilian female voices.

Another characteristic of the country's singers is making their voices heard in forms of expression other than popular music. Several have written film scores. Milton Nascimento has composed a mass.

Chico Buarque and Vinicius de Moraes are highly regarded poets; Buarque is also a novelist and playwright. Caetano Veloso has written a lengthy memoir and meditation on music called *Verdade Tropical* (*Tropical Truth*). Gilberto Gil has held a seat on Salvador's city council and in early 2003 became minister of culture. Brazil's greatest artists are often more than mere pop stars, and the country acknowledges their efforts. Vinicius de Moraes isn't the only one with a street named in his honor. And though many Brazilians still refer to Rio's international airport as Galeão, after the death of Antônio Carlos Jobim, it was renamed for him.

A Few Notes of Your Own

The following anthologies provide good samplings of Brazilian singers, composers, and styles. If you like these, you can seek out CDs by individual artists.

Brasil: a Century of Song (Blue Jackel). This box set with a 48-page booklet and four CDs comprises the best of folk and traditional songs (Carmen Miranda, Pena Branca e Xavantinho), carnival music (Paulinho da Viola, Mangueira), bossa nova (João Gilberto, Toquinho e Vinícius), and MPB (Marisa Monte, Ivan Lins).

Brazil Classics 1: Beleza Tropical (Sire). The 18 tracks, compiled by David Byrne, include songs by Milton Nascimento, Caetano Veloso, Jorge Ben, Maria Bethânia, Gal Costa, and Chico Buarque.

Brazil Classics 2: O Samba (Sire). David Byrne compiled these 15 tracks that include sambas by Alcione, Clara Nunes, Beth Carvalho, Martinho da Vila, and others.

For updated info and complete discographies, you can refer to the **All Brazilian Music Guide** (⊕ www.allbrazilianmusic.com). Novelist and journalist Alan Ryan has written extensively about Brazilian music, literature, and culture for many newspapers and magazines. He lives in Rio de Janeiro.

–Alan Ryan

–Revised by Gabriela Dias

BOOKS & MOVIES

Books

On the nonfiction front, Joseph A. Page provides a fascinating, highly readable overview of Brazilian history and culture in his book *The Brazilians*. Along the same lines is Marshall C. Eakin's *Brazil: The Once and Future Country*. A short but good new history by Brazilian scholar Boris Fausto is *A Concise History of Brazil*. Social anthropologist Claude Lévi-Strauss discusses his research of Amazonian peoples in *Tristes Tropiques*, a book that's part travelogue, part scientific notebook—with many interesting observations and anecdotes.

Chris McGowan's *The Brazilian Sound: Samba, Bossa Nova, and the Popular Music of Brazil* provides an overview of the country's 20th-century music. Also recommended is *Bossa Nova: The Story of the Brazilian Music That Seduced the World*, by Ruy Castro. Christopher Idone's *Brazil: A Cook's Tour* has more than 100 color photos and 100 recipes. *Eat Smart in Brazil*, by Joan and David Peterson, is a good introduction to Brazilian food, with history, color photos, recipes, and a detailed glossary.

Fiction lovers should try John Grisham's captivating *The Testament*, in which a lawyer voyages to the Pantanal wetlands to search for a missionary who has inherited a fortune. Several Jorge Amado titles, which are usually set in his native Bahia, are available in English, including *Dona Flor and Her Two Husbands*; *Gabriela, Clove and Cinnamon*; and *The War of the Saints*.

Movies

City of God (2002), the story of adolescents living in the violent favelas of Rio, was nominated for an Academy Award for Best Foreign Film in 2003, though it didn't win. A film along the same lines is *Pixote* (1981), a chilling fictional account of street kids in São Paulo. In 1969, following the military takeover of the Brazilian government, Marxist revolutionaries kidnapped an American diplomat in protest. *Four Days in September* (1998) is an entertaining and well-executed film that tells the story of these young revolutionaries. *Central Station* (1998) is a heartwarming tale of the unlikely friendship between an orphaned street child and a middle-aged woman who is soured on life. *Bus 174* (2002) is a highly acclaimed documentary about a bus hijacking that took place Rio in 2000. *Black Orpheus* (1956) is one of the best known Brazilian films. It won an Academy Award in 1960 and is based on the Greek tragedy of Orpheus, set in a Rio favela around Carnaval. The 1999 update, *Orfeu*, brings the tale into modern times.

The lighter side of Brazilian culture is explored in movies such as *Bossa Nova* (2000), a romantic comedy set in Rio, and *Tieta de Agreste* (1996), the story of a successful businesswoman who returns to her home in a small village in the Northeast. The latter has some lovely shots of the northeastern landscape. For more views of the Brazilian countryside, see *Bye, Bye Brazil* (1979), which follows a group of traveling entertainers from the northeast to the Amazon jungle; *Me, You, Them* (2000), a story of woman in the Northeast who forms a series of unusual romantic relationships; and *Behind the Sun* (2001), a film that portrays two feuding families in the northeast of 1910. The acclaimed *Dona Flor and Her Two Husbands* (1978) follows a Bahian woman through joys and hardships. *The Boys from Brazil* (1990), not to be confused with the similarly named drama about hunting Nazis in Brazil, is a BBC documentary about Brazilian soccer.

BRAZILIAN PORTUGUESE VOCABULARY

Words and Phrases

	English	Portuguese	Pronunciation
Basics			
	Yes/no	Sim/Não	**see**ing/nown
	Please	Por favor	pohr fah-**vohr**
	May I?	Posso?	**poh**-sso
	Thank you (very much)	(Muito) obrigado	(**mooy**n-too) o-bree **gah**-doh
	You're welcome	De nada	day **nah**-dah
	Excuse me	Com licença	con lee-**ssehn**-ssah
	Pardon me/what did you say?	Desculpe/O que disse?	des-**kool**-peh/o.k. **dih**-say?
	Could you tell me?	Poderia me dizer?	po-day-**ree**-ah mee dee-**zehrr**?
	I'm sorry	Sinto muito	**seen**-too **mooy**n-too
	Good morning!	Bom dia!	bohn **dee**-ah
	Good afternoon!	Boa tarde!	**boh**-ah **tahr**-dee
	Good evening!	Boa noite!	**boh**-ah **noh**ee-tee
	Goodbye!	Adeus!/Até logo!	ah-**deh**oos/ah-**teh** **loh**-go
	Mr./Mrs.	Senhor/Senhora	sen-**yor**/sen-**yohr**-ah
	Miss	Senhorita	sen-yo-**ri**-tah
	Pleased to meet you	Muito prazer	**mooy**n-too prah-**zehr**
	How are you?	Como vai?	**koh**-mo **vah**-ee
	Very well, thank you	Muito bem, obri-gado	**mooy**n-too **beh**-in o-bree-**gah**-doh
	And you?	E o(a) Senhor(a)?	eh oh sen-**yor** (**yohr**-ah)
	Hello (on the telephone)	Alô	ah-**low**

Numbers

	English	Portuguese	Pronunciation
	1	um/uma	oom/**oom**-ah
	2	dois	**doh**ees
	3	três	**treh**ys
	4	quatro	**kwa**-troh

5	cinco	**seen**-koh
6	seis	**seh**ys
7	sete	**seh**-tee
8	oito	**oh**ee-too
9	nove	**noh**-vee
10	dez	**deh**-ees
11	onze	**ohn**-zee
12	doze	**doh**-zee
13	treze	**treh**-zee
14	quatorze	kwa-**tohr**-zee
15	quinze	**keen**-zee
16	dezesseis	deh-zeh-**seh**ys
17	dezessete	deh-zeh-**seh**-tee
18	dezoito	deh-**zoh**ee-toh
19	dezenove	deh-zeh-**noh**-vee
20	vinte	**veen**-tee
21	vinte e um	**veen**-tee eh **oom**
30	trinta	**treen**-tah
32	trinta e dois	**treen**-ta eh **doh**ees
40	quarenta	kwa-**rehn**-ta
43	quarenta e três	kwa-**rehn**-ta e **treh**ys
50	cinquenta	seen-**kwehn**-tah
54	cinquenta e quatro	seen-**kwehn**-tah e **kwa**-troh
60	sessenta	seh-**sehn**-tah
65	sessenta e cinco	seh-**sehn**-tah e **seen**-ko
70	setenta	seh-**tehn**-tah
76	setenta e seis	seh-**tehn**-ta e **seh**ys
80	oitenta	ohee-**tehn**-ta
87	oitenta e sete	ohee-**tehn**-ta e **seh**-tee
90	noventa	noh-**vehn**-ta
98	noventa e oito	noh-**vehn**-ta e **oh**ee-too
100	cem	**seh**-ing
101	cento e um	**sehn**-too e **oom**
200	duzentos	doo-**zehn**-tohss
500	quinhentos	key-**nyehn**-tohss

700	setecentos	seh-teh-**sehn**-tohss
900	novecentos	noh-veh-**sehn**-tohss
1,000	mil	meel
2,000	dois mil	**doh**ees meel
1,000,000	um milhão	oom mee-lee-**ahon**

Colors

black	preto	**preh**-toh
blue	azul	a-**zool**
brown	marrom	mah-**hohm**
green	verde	**vehr**-deh
pink	rosa	**roh**-zah
purple	roxo	**roh**-choh
orange	laranja	lah-**rahn**-jah
red	vermelho	vehr-**meh**-lyoh
white	branco	**brahn**-coh
yellow	amarelo	ah-mah-**reh**-loh

Days of the Week

Sunday	Domingo	doh-**meehn**-goh
Monday	Segunda-feira	seh-**goon**-dah **fey**-rah
Tuesday	Terça-feira	**tehr**-sah **fey**-rah
Wednesday	Quarta-feira	**kwahr**-tah **fey**-rah
Thursday	Quinta-feira	**keen**-tah **fey**-rah
Friday	Sexta-feira	**sehss**-tah **fey**-rah
Saturday	Sábado	**sah**-bah-doh

Months

January	Janeiro	jah-**ney**-roh
February	Fevereiro	feh-veh-**rey**-roh
March	Março	**mahr**-soh
April	Abril	ah-**breel**
May	Maio	**my**-oh
June	Junho	gy**oo**-nyoh
July	Julho	gy**oo**-lyoh
August	Agosto	ah-**ghost**-toh
September	Setembro	seh-**tehm**-broh
October	Outubro	owe-**too**-broh
November	Novembro	noh-**vehm**-broh
December	Dezembro	deh-**zehm**-broh

Useful Phrases

Do you speak English?	O Senhor fala inglês?	oh sen-**yor fah**-lah een-**glehs**?
I don't speak Portuguese.	Não falo português.	nown **fah**-loh pohr-too-**ghehs**
I don't understand (you)	Não lhe entendo	nown ly**eh** ehn-**tehn**-doh
I understand	Eu entendo	**eh**-oo ehn-**tehn**-doh
I don't know	Não sei	nown say
I am American/ British	Sou americano (americana)/ inglês/inglêsa	sow a-meh-ree-**cah**-noh (a-meh-ree-**cah**-nah/ een-**glehs** (een-**glah**-sa)
What's your name?	Como se chama?	**koh**-moh seh **shah**-mah
My name is . . .	Meu nome é . . .	mehw **noh**-meh eh
What time is it?	Que horas são?	keh **oh**-rahss **sa**-ohn
It is one, two, three . . . o'clock	É uma/São duas, três . . . hora/horas	eh **oom**-ah/**sa**-ohn **oo**mah, **doo**-ahss, **treh**ys **oh**-rah/**oh**-rahs
Yes, please/No, thank you	Sim por favor/ Não obrigado	seing pohr fah-**vohr**/ nown o-bree-**gah**-doh
How?	Como?	**koh**-moh
When?	Quando?	**kwahn**-doh
This/Next week	Esta/Próxima semana	**ehss**-tah/**proh**-see-mah seh-**mah**-nah
This/Next month	Este/Próximo mêz	**ehss**-teh/**proh**-see-moh mehz
This/Next year	Este/Próximo ano	**ehss**-teh/**proh**-see-moh **ah**-noh
Yesterday/today tomorrow	Ontem/hoje amanhã	**ohn**-tehn/**oh**-jeh/ ah-mah-**nyan**
This morning/ afternoon	Esta manhã/ tarde	**ehss**-tah mah-**nyan** / **tahr**-deh
Tonight	Hoje a noite	**oh**-jeh ah **noh**ee-tee
What?	O que?	oh **keh**
What is it?	O que é isso?	oh **keh** eh **ee**-soh
Why?	Por quê?	pohr-**keh**
Who?	Quem?	**keh**-in
Where is . . . ?	Onde é . . . ?	**ohn**-deh eh
the train station?	a estação de trem?	ah es-tah-**sah**-on deh train
the subway station?	a estação de metrô?	ah es-tah-**sah**-on deh meh-**tro**

the bus stop?	a parada do ônibus?	ah pah-**rah**-dah doh **oh**-nee-boos
the post office?	o correio?	oh coh-**hay**-yoh
the bank?	o banco?	oh **bahn**-koh
the hotel?	o hotel . . . ?	oh oh-**tell**
the cashier?	o caixa?	oh **kah**y-shah
the museum?	o museo . . . ?	oh moo-**zeh**-oh
the hospital?	o hospital?	oh ohss-pee-**tal**
the elevator?	o elevador?	oh eh-leh-vah-**dohr**
the bathroom?	o banheiro?	oh bahn-**yey**-roh
the beach?	a praia de . . . ?	ah **prah**y-yah deh
Here/there	Aqui/ali	ah-**kee**/ah-**lee**
Open/closed	Aberto/fechado	ah-**behr**-toh/feh-**shah**-doh
Left/right	Esquerda/direita	ehs-**kehr**-dah/dee-**ray**-tah
Straight ahead	Em frente	ehyn **frehn**-teh
Is it near/far?	É perto/longe?	eh **pehr**-toh/**lohn**-jeh
I'd like to buy . . .	Gostaria de comprar . . .	gohs-tah-**ree**-ah deh cohm-**prahr** . . .
a bathing suit	um maiô	oom mahy-**owe**
a dictionary	um dicionário	oom dee-seeoh-**nah**-reeoh
a hat	um chapéu	oom shah-**peh**oo
a magazine	uma revista	**oo**mah heh-**vees**-tah
a map	um mapa	oom **mah**-pah
a postcard	cartão postal	kahr-**town** pohs-**tahl**
sunglasses	óculos escuros	**ah**-koo-loss ehs-**koo**-rohs
suntan lotion	um óleo de bronzear	oom **oh**-lyoh deh brohn-zeh-**ahr**
a ticket	um bilhete	oom bee-ly**eh**-teh
cigarettes	cigarros	see-**gah**-hose
envelopes	envelopes	eyn-veh-**loh**-pehs
matches	fósforos	**fohs**-foh-rohss
paper	papel	pah-**pehl**
sandals	sandália	sahn-**dah**-leeah
soap	sabonete	sah-bow-**neh**-teh
How much is it?	Quanto custa?	**kwahn**-too **koos**-tah
It's expensive/cheap	Está caro/barato	ehss-**tah kah**-roh / bah-**rah**-toh
A little/a lot	Um pouco/muito	oom **pohw**-koh/**moo**yn-too
More/less	Mais/menos	**mah**-ees /**meh**-nohss

Enough/too much/too little	Suficiente/demais/muito pouco	soo-fee-see-**ehn**-teh/deh-**mah**-ees/**moo**yn-toh **pohw**-koh
Telephone	Telefone	teh-leh-**foh**-neh
Telegram	Telegrama	teh-leh-**grah**-mah
I am ill.	Estou doente.	ehss-**tow** doh-**ehn**-teh
Please call a doctor.	Por favor chame um médico.	pohr fah-**vohr shah**-meh oom **meh**-dee-koh
Help!	Socorro!	soh-**koh**-ho
Help me!	Me ajude!	mee ah-**jyew**-deh
Fire!	Incêndio!	een-**sehn**-deeoh
Caution!/Look out!/Be careful!	Cuidado!	kooy-**dah**-doh

On the Road

Avenue	Avenida	ah-veh-**nee**-dah
Highway	Estrada	ehss-**trah**-dah
Port	Porto	**pohr**-toh
Service station	Posto de gasolina	**pohs**-toh deh gah-zoh-**lee**-nah
Street	Rua	**who**-ah
Toll	Pedagio	peh-**dah**-jyoh
Waterfront promenade	Beiramar/orla	behy-rah-**mahrr**/**ohr**-lah
Wharf	Cais	**kah**-ees

In Town

Block	Quarteirão	kwahr-tehy-**rah**-on
Cathedral	Catedral	kah-teh-**drahl**
Church/temple	Igreja	ee-**greh**-jyah
City hall	Prefeitura	preh-fehy-**too**-rah
Door/gate	Porta/portão	**pohr**-tah/porh-**tah**-on
Entrance/exit	Entrada/saída	ehn-**trah**-dah/sah-**ee**-dah
Market	Mercado/feira	mehr-**kah**-doh/ **fey**-rah
Neighborhood	Bairro	**buy**-ho
Rustic bar	Lanchonete	lahn-shoh-**neh**-teh
Shop	Loja	**loh**-jyah
Square	Praça	**prah**-ssah

Dining Out

A bottle of . . .	Uma garrafa de . . .	**oo**mah gah-**hah**-fah deh
A cup of . . .	Uma xícara de . . .	**oo**mah **shee**-kah-rah deh
A glass of . . .	Um copo de . . .	oom **koh**-poh deh
Ashtray	Um cinzeiro	oom seen-**zehy**-roh
Bill/check	A conta	ah **kohn**-tah
Bread	Pão	**pah**-on
Breakfast	Café da manhã	kah-**feh** dah mah-**nyan**
Butter	A manteiga	ah mahn-**tehy**-gah
Cheers!	Saúde!	sah-**oo**-deh
Cocktail	Um aperitivo	oom ah-peh-ree-**tee**-voh
Dinner	O jantar	oh **jyahn**-tahr
Dish	Um prato	oom **prah**-toh
Enjoy!	Bom apetite!	bohm ah-peh-**tee**-teh
Fork	Um garfo	**gahr**-foh
Fruit	Fruta	**froo**-tah
Is the tip included?	A gorjeta esta incluída?	ah gohr-**jyeh**-tah ehss-**tah** een-clue-**ee**-dah
Juice	Um suco	oom **soo**-koh
Knife	Uma faca	**oo**mah **fah**-kah
Lunch	O almoço	oh ahl-**moh**-ssoh
Menu	Menu/ cardápio	me-**noo** / kahr-**dah**-peeoh
Mineral water	Água mineral	**ah**-gooah mee-neh-**rahl**
Napkin	Guardanapo	gooahr-dah-**nah**-poh
No smoking	Não fumante	nown foo-**mahn**-teh
Pepper	Pimenta	pee-**mehn**-tah
Please give me	Por favor me dê	pohr fah-**vohr** mee **deh**
Salt	Sal	sahl
Smoking	Fumante	foo-**mahn**-teh
Spoon	Uma colher	**oo**mah koh-ly**ehr**
Sugar	Açúcar	ah-**soo**-kahr
Waiter!	Garçon!	gahr-**sohn**
Water	Água	**ah**-gooah
Wine	Vinho	**vee**-nyoh

PRONOUNCING PLACE NAMES

Name	Pronunciation
Amazônia	ah-mah-**zoh**-knee-ah
Bahia	bah-**ee**-ah
Belém	beh-**lein**
Belo Horizonte	**beh**-loh ho-rih-**zon**-teh
Brasília	brah-**zee**-lee-ah
Fortaleza	for-tah-**leh**-zah
Manaus	mah-**nah**-oos
Minas Gerais	mee-**nahs** jyeh-**rah**-ees
Paraná	pah-rah-**nah**
Porto Alegre	pohr-**toh** ah-**leh**-greh
Recife	heh-**see**-fee
Rio de Janeiro	**hee**-oh day jah-**ne**-roh
Rio Grande do Sul	**hee**-oh **gran**-deh doh sool
Salvador	sahl-vah-**dohr**
Santa Catarina	sahn-**tah** kah-tah-**reeh**-nah
São Paulo	saohn **pow**-low

INDEX

PHOTO CREDITS:

Cover Photo (Dancers at Carnival in Rio de Janeiro): *ImageState-Pictor/PictureQuest*. F10, *Corbis*. F11 (left), *Blaine Harrington/age fotostock*. F11 (right), *Ken Ross/viestiphoto.com*. F12, *Giulio Andreini/Marka/age fotostock*. F13, *Bruno Perousse/age fotostock*. F14, *Jeffrey Dunn/viestiphoto.com*. F15, *Halaska/Mauritius/age fotostock*. F16, *Giulio Andreini/age fotostock*. F17 (left), *Giulio Andreini/Marka/age fotostock*. F17 (right), *Orange Stock/viestiphoto.com*. Color Section: Copacabana, Rio: *P. Narayan/age fotostock*. Buggies on the cliff at Morro Branco, near Fortaleza: *Stanislas Fautre/ASK Images/viestiphoto.com*. Recife: *Peter Adams/Agency Jon Arnold Images/age fotostock*. São Paulo: *Doug Scott/age fotostock*. Amazon River: *Juan Carlos Muñoz/age fotostock*. Christ the Redeemer statue at Corcovado, Rio: *Blaine Harrington/age fotostock*. Foods at a market in Rio: *Jeffrey Dunn/viestiphoto.com*. Brasilia: *Fotodiseño/age fotostock*. Ipanema, Rio: *kord.com/age fotostock*. Carnival in Rio: *Angelo Cavalli/Marka/age fotostock*. The Foz do Iguaçu cascades: *Jordi Camí/age fotostock*. Golden lion tamarin: *Roine Magnusson/age fotostock*. Spinning Brazilian samba: *John Wang/Photodisc*. Salvador: *P. Narayan/age fotostock*. Farmworkers playing music in the Pantanal: *F. Goifman/viestiphoto.com*. Toucan: *Kevin Schafer/age fotostock*. Carnival in Recife: *F. Rocha Perini/viestiphoto.com*. A favela outside Rio: *Bernard Martinez/viestiphoto.com*.

NOTES

ABOUT OUR WRITERS

Carolina Berard is a translator, writer, and a tourism guide accredited by Embratur, the national tourism office. She lived in Brasília for eight years and has also lived in Rio, São Paulo, Ponta Grossa, Curitiba, and in Spain. Carolina's articles have appeared in the on-line magazines *Brazzil* and *MultARTE Brazilian Culture.* For this book Carolina wrote the front-of-book sections, and updated Smart Travel Tips A to Z.

São Paulo resident Gabriela Dias is a Rio native and a freelance writer and editor for Brazilian books, magazines, and new media. The enthusiastic music fan and carioca lent her expertise to the São Paulo and Side Trips from São Paulo chapters for this edition.

Amazon updater Rhan Flatin is a naturalist, writer, and photographer. He has spent several years in the Amazon basin directing a college semester abroad program with the School for International Training and leading ecotours. Rhan and his Brazilian wife, Selma, live in Vermont.

Denise Oliveira is a native of Rio who spends her spare time writing and traveling around the world. Though she's seen breathtaking places far from home, Rio remains for her the most beautiful place in the world.

Born and bred in Brasília, Mariane Oliveira is an English translator and interpreter. Working as a freelance interpreter has given her the opportunity to travel extensively through Brazil and overseas. Mariane is also a music, movies, foreign affairs, and food enthusiast.

Jefferson Santos updated the Minas Gerais chapter for this and the previous edition of *Fodor's Brazil* and the Recife, Natal, and Fortaleza chapter for this edition. He is a journalist, DJ, and cultural promoter, and writes a weekly column about music and culture for newspaper *Estado de Minas.*

Longtime Fodor's writer Carlos Tornquist has a Ph.D. in soil science and works as an agricultural and environmental consultant based in Porto Alegre. He travels frequently and has seen much of the New World—from upper Wisconsin to the tip of Tierra del Fuego. Carlos updated The South and Bahia chapters for this edition.

Compulsive traveler, journalist, and Rio native Ana Lúcia do Vale updated the Side Trips from Rio de Janeiro chapter for this edition. Her career has included producing and directing Brazilian television shows as well as work with a news agency and seven years with Rio newspaper *O Dia,* for which she has covered international events like Cannes Film Festival.